PEARSON

Prealgebra with Elementary and Intermediate Algebra

Custom Edition for University of Maine at Augusta

Taken from:

Elementary & Intermediate Algebra, Third Edition
by George Woodbury

Prealgebra, Fourth Edition
by Jamie Blair, John Tobey, and Jeffrey Slater

Cover image courtesy of University of Maine at Augusta.

Taken from:

Elementary & Intermediate Algebra, Third Edition
by George Woodbury
Copyright © 2012 by Pearson Education, Inc.
Published by Addison-Wesley
Boston, Massachusetts 02116

Prealgebra, Fourth Edition
by Jamie Blair, John Tobey, and Jeffrey Slater
Copyright © 2010, 2006, 2002, 1999 by Pearson Education, Inc.
Published by Prentice Hall
Upper Saddle River, New Jersey 07458

This special edition published in cooperation with Pearson Learning Solutions.

All trademarks, service marks, registered trademarks, and registered service marks are the property of their respective owners and are used herein for identification purposes only.

Pearson Learning Solutions, 501 Boylston Street, Suite 900, Boston, MA 02116
A Pearson Education Company
www.pearsoned.com

Printed in the United States of America

3 4 5 6 7 8 9 10 0BRV 16 15 14

000200010270776425

CY

ISBN 10: 1-256-29656-2
ISBN 13: 978-1-256-29656-0

Contents

Prealgebra

Fourth Edition

by Jamie Blair, John Tobey, and Jeffrey Slater

CHAPTER

1

Should I buy or lease a car? What are the benefits of each? Which choice fits my needs? Does leasing a car or buying a car save me the most money?

Whole Numbers and Introduction to Algebra

1.1 UNDERSTANDING WHOLE NUMBERS

Student Learning Objectives

After studying this section, you will be able to:

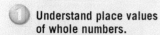 **Understand place values of whole numbers.**

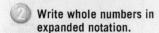 **Write whole numbers in expanded notation.**

③ Write word names for whole numbers.

④ Use inequality symbols with whole numbers.

⑤ Round whole numbers.

Often we learn a new concept in stages. First comes learning the new *terms* and basic assumptions. Then we have to master the *reasoning,* or logic, behind the new concept. This often goes hand in hand with learning a *method* for using the idea. Finally, we can move quickly with a *shortcut.*

For example, in the study of stock investments, before tackling the question "What is my profit from this stock transaction?" you must learn the meaning of such terms as *stock, profit, loss,* and *commission.* Next, you must understand how stocks work (reasoning/logic) so that you can learn the method for calculating your profit. After you master this concept, you can quickly answer many similar questions using shortcuts.

In this book, watch your understanding of mathematics grow through this same process. In the first chapter we review the whole numbers, emphasizing *concepts,* not shortcuts. Do not skip this review even if you feel you have mastered the material since understanding each stage of the concepts is crucial to learning algebra. With a little patience in looking at the terms, reasoning, and step-by-step methods, you'll find that your understanding of whole numbers has deepened, preparing you to learn algebra.

Understanding Place Values of Whole Numbers

We use a set of numbers called **whole numbers** to count a number of objects.

The whole numbers are as follows:
0, 1, 2, 3, 4, 5, 6, 7, 8, 9, 10, 11, 12, 13, 14, 15, 16, . . .

There is no largest whole number. The three dots . . . indicate that the set of whole numbers goes on forever. The numbers 0, 1, 2, 3, 4, 5, 6, 7, 8, and 9 are called **digits.** The *position* or *placement* of the digit in a number tells the *value* of the digit. For this reason, our number system is called a **place-value system.** For example, look at the following three numbers.

632   The "6" means 6 hundreds (600).
61   The "6" means 6 tens (60).
6   The "6" means 6 ones (6).

To illustrate the values of the digits in a number, we can use the following place-value chart. Consider the number 847,632, which is entered on the chart.

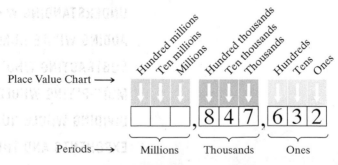

The digit 8 is in the hundred thousands place.
The digit 4 is in the ten thousands place.
The digit 7 is in the thousands place.
The digit 6 is in the hundreds place.
The digit 3 is in the tens place.
The digit 2 is in the ones place.

When we write very large numbers, we place a comma after every group of three digits, moving from right to left. These three-digit groups are called **periods.** It is usually agreed that four-digit numbers do not have a comma, but numbers with five or more digits do.

EXAMPLE 1 In the number 573,025:

(a) In what place is the digit 7?   **(b)** In what place is the digit 0?

Solution

(a) 5 7 3,025   **(b)** 573, 0 25

       ↑   ↑

   ten thousands   hundreds

Practice Problem 1 In the number 3,502,781:

(a) In what place is the digit 5?

(b) In what place is the digit 0?

NOTE TO STUDENT: Fully worked-out solutions to all of the Practice Problems can be found at the back of the text starting at page SP-1

 Writing Whole Numbers in Expanded Notation

We sometimes write numbers in **expanded notation** to emphasize place value. The number 47,632 can be written in expanded notation as follows:

40,000	+	7000	+	600	+	30	+	2
4 ten	+	7	+	6	+	3	+	2
thousands		thousands		hundreds		tens		ones

EXAMPLE 2 Write 1,340,765 in expanded notation.

Solution

We write 1 followed by a zero for each of the remaining digits.
↓

We write 1 ,340,765 as 1 ,000,000 + 3 00,000 + 4 0,000 + 7 00 + 6 0 + 5

                                We continue in this manner for each digit.

Since there is a zero in the thousands place, we do not write it as part of the sum.

Practice Problem 2 Write 2,507,235 in expanded notation.

EXAMPLE 3 Jon withdraws $493 from his account. He requests the minimum number of bills in one-, ten-, and hundred-dollar bills. Describe the quantity of each denomination of bills the teller must give Jon.

Solution If we write $493 in expanded notation, we can easily describe the denominations needed.

400	+	90	+	3
4		9		3
hundred-		ten-		one-
dollar		dollar		dollar
bills		bills		bills

Practice Problem 3 Christina withdraws $582 from her account. She requests the minimum number of bills in one-, ten-, and hundred-dollar bills. Describe the quantity of each denomination of bills the teller must give Christina.

Understanding the Concept

The Number Zero

Not all number systems have a zero. The Roman numeral system does not. In our place-value system the zero is necessary so that we can write a number such as 308. By putting a zero in the tens place, we indicate that there are zero tens. Without a zero symbol we would not be able to indicate this. For example, 38 has a different value than 308. The number 38 means three *tens* and eight ones, while 308 means three *hundreds* and eight ones. In this case, we use *zero* as a **placeholder.** It holds a position and shows that there is no other digit in that place.

 Writing Word Names for Whole Numbers

Sixteen, twenty-one, and *four hundred five* are **word names** for the numbers 16, 21, and 405. We use a hyphen between words when we write a two-digit number greater than twenty. To write a word name, start from the left. Name the number in each period, followed by the name of the period, and a comma. The last period name, "ones," is not used.

EXAMPLE 4   Write a word name for each number.

(a) 2135   **(b)** 300,460

Solution   Look at the place-value chart on page 2 if you need help identifying the period.

(a) 2135   The number begins with 2 in the *thousands* place. The word name is

two *thousand*, one hundred thirty-five.
↑
We use a hyphen here.

(b) 300,460   The number begins with 3 in the *hundred thousands* place.

Three *hundred thousand*, four hundred sixty
↑
We place a comma here to match the comma in the number.

Practice Problem 4   Write a word name for each number.

(a) 4006   **(b)** 1,220,032

NOTE TO STUDENT: *Fully worked-out solutions to all of the Practice Problems can be found at the back of the text starting at page SP-1*

CAUTION: We should not use the word *and* in the word names for whole numbers. Although we may hear the phrase "three hundred and two" for the number 302, it is not technically correct. As we will see later in the book, we use the word *and* for the decimal point when using decimal notation.

 Using Inequality Symbols with Whole Numbers

It is often helpful to draw pictures and graphs to help us visualize a mathematical concept. A **number line** is often used for whole numbers. The following number line has a point matched with zero and with each whole number. Each number is equally spaced, and the "→" arrow at the right end indicates that the numbers go on forever. The numbers on the line increase from left to right.

```
 +---+---+---+---+---+---+---+--->
 0   1   2   3   4   5   6   7
```

If one number lies to the *right* of a second number on the number line, it *is greater than* that number.

4 lies to the *right* of 2 on the number line because 4 *is greater than* 2.

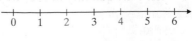
```
 +---+---+---+---+---+---+--->
 0   1   2   3   4   5   6
```

A number *is less than* a given number if it lies to the *left* of that number on the number line.

3 lies to the *left* of 5 on the number line because 3 *is less than* 5.

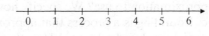

The symbol > means *is greater than,* and the symbol < means *is less than.* Thus we can write

$$4 > 2 \qquad\qquad 3 < 5$$

4 *is greater than* 2.   3 *is less than* 5.

The symbols < and > are called **inequality symbols.** The statements 4 > 2 and 2 < 4 are both correct. Note that the inequality symbol always points to the smaller number.

 Replace each question mark with the inequality symbol < or >.

(a) 1 ? 6   **(b)** 8 ? 7   **(c)** 4 ? 9   **(d)** 9 ? 4

Solution

(a) 1 < 6   **(b)** 8 > 7   **(c)** 4 < 9   **(d)** 9 > 4

1 is less than 6.   8 is greater than 7.   4 is less than 9.   9 is greater than 4.

 Replace each question mark with the inequality symbol < or >.

(a) 3 ? 2   **(b)** 6 ? 8   **(c)** 1 ? 7   **(d)** 7 ? 1

EXAMPLE 6 Rewrite using numbers and an inequality symbol.

(a) Five is less than eight.   **(b)** Nine is greater than four.

Solution

(a) Five *is less than* eight.   **(b)** Nine *is greater than* four.

5 < 8   9 > 4

Remember, the inequality symbol always points to the smaller number.

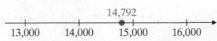 Rewrite using numbers and an inequality symbol.

(a) Seven is greater than two.   **(b)** Three is less than four.

⑤ Rounding Whole Numbers

We often approximate the values of numbers when it is not necessary to know the exact values. These approximations are easier to use and remember. For example, if our hotel bill was $82.00, we might say that we spent about $80. If a car cost $14,792, we would probably say that it cost approximately $15,000.

Why did we approximate the price of the car at $15,000 and not $14,000? To understand why, let's look at the number line.

14,792

13,000   14,000   15,000   16,000

The number 14,792 is closer to 15,000 than to 14,000, so we approximate the cost of the car at $15,000.

It would also be correct to approximate the cost at \$14,800 or \$14,790, since each of these values is close to 14,792 on the number line. How do we know which approximation to use? We specify how accurate we would like our approximation to be. **Rounding** is a process that approximates a number to a specific **round-off place** (ones, tens, hundreds, . . .). *Thus the value obtained when rounding depends on how accurate we would like our approximation to be.* To illustrate, we round the price of the car discussed above to the thousands and to the hundreds place.

14,792 rounded to the nearest *thousand* is 15,000.   The *round-off place* is thousands.

14,792 rounded to the nearest *hundred* is 14,800.   The *round-off place* is hundreds.

We can use the following set of rules instead of a number line to round whole numbers.

PROCEDURE TO ROUND A WHOLE NUMBER

1. Identify the round-off place digit.

2. If the digit to the *right* of the round-off place digit is:
   (a) *Less than 5,* do not change the round-off place digit.
   (b) *5 or more,* increase the round-off place digit by 1.

3. Replace all digits to the *right* of the round-off place digit with zeros.

EXAMPLE 7   Round 57,441 to the nearest thousand.

Solution   The round-off place digit is in the thousands place.

$$5 \,\textcircled{7}, 4\,4\,1$$

1. Identify the round-off place digit 7.
2. The digit to the right is less than 5.

Do not change the round-off place digit.

$$57,\mathbf{000}$$

3. Replace all digits to the right with zeros.

We have rounded 57,441 to the nearest thousand: **57,000.** This means that 57,441 is closer to 57,000 than to 58,000.

NOTE TO STUDENT: *Fully worked-out solutions to all of the Practice Problems can be found at the back of the text starting at page SP-1*

Practice Problem 7   Round 34,627 to the nearest hundred.

EXAMPLE 8   Round 4,254,423 to the nearest hundred thousand.

Solution   The round-off place digit is in the hundred thousands place.

$$4, \textcircled{2}\, 5\, 4, 4\, 2\, 3$$

1. Identify the round-off place digit 2.
2. The digit to the right is 5 or more.

Increase the round-off place digit by 1.

$$4,300,000$$

3. Replace all digits to the right with zeros.

We have rounded 4,254,423 to the nearest hundred thousand: **4,300,000.**

Practice Problem 8   Round 1,335,627 to the nearest ten thousand.

CAUTION: The round-off place digit either stays the same or increases by 1. It never decreases.

Verbal and Writing Skills

1. Write the word name for
   (a) 8002.
   (b) 802.
   (c) 82.
   (d) What is the place value of the digit 0 in the number eight hundred twenty?

2. Write in words.
   (a) 2 < 5
   (b) 5 > 2
   (c) What can you say about parts (a) and (b)?

3. In the number 9865:
   (a) In what place is the digit 8?
   (b) In what place is the digit 5?

4. In the number 23,981:
   (a) In what place is the digit 2?
   (b) In what place is the digit 9?

5. In the number 754,310:
   (a) In what place is the digit 4?
   (b) In what place is the digit 7?

6. In the number 913,728:
   (a) In what place is the digit 9?
   (b) In what place is the digit 1?

7. In the number 1,284,073:
   (a) In what place is the digit 1?
   (b) In what place is the digit 0?

8. In the number 3,098,269:
   (a) In what place is the digit 0?
   (b) In what place is the digit 8?

Write in expanded notation.

9. 5876

10. 7632

11. 4921

12. 3562

13. 867,301

14. 913,045

15. Damian withdraws $562 from his account. He requests the minimum number of bills in one-, ten-, and hundred-dollar bills. Describe the quantity of each denomination of bills the teller must give Damian.

16. Erin withdraws $274 from her account. She requests the minimum number of bills in one-, ten-, and hundred-dollar bills. Describe the quantity of each denomination of bills the teller must give Erin.

17. Describe the denominations of bills for $46:
   (a) Using only ten- and one-dollar bills.

   (b) Using tens, fives, and only 1 one-dollar bill.

18. Describe the denominations of bills for $96:
   (a) Using only ten- and one-dollar bills.

   (b) Using tens, fives, and only 1 one-dollar bill.

Write a word name for each number.

19. 6079

20. 4032

21. 86,491

22. 33,224

23. Fill in the check with the amount $672.

```
James Hunt                                          2824
4 Platt St.
Mapleville, RI  02839
                                    DATE_____ 20____
PAY to the
ORDER of  Hampton Apartments            $
_____ DOLLARS

Mason Bank
California

MEMO_____  _____
⑆580052⑆ 552022205⑈ 2824
```

24. Fill in the check with the amount $379.

```
Ellen Font                                          2520
22 Rose Place
Garden Grove, CA  92641
                                    DATE_____ 20____
PAY to the
ORDER of  Atlas Insurance               $
_____ DOLLARS

Mason Bank
California

MEMO_____  _____
⑆580052⑆ 552022205⑈ 2520
```

Replace each question mark with the inequality symbol < or >.

25. 5 ? 7

26. 2 ? 1

27. 6 ? 8

28. 9 ? 6

29. 13 ? 10

30. 10 ? 11

31. 9 ? 0

32. 0 ? 9

33. 2131 ? 1909

34. 3011 ? 3210

35. 52,647 ? 616,000

36. 101,351 ? 101,251

Rewrite using numbers and an inequality symbol.

37. Five is greater than two.

38. Seven is less than ten.

39. Two is less than five.

40. Six is greater than four.

Automobile Prices *The table lists the 2008 sticker prices on some popular vehicles. Use this table to answer exercises 41 and 42.*

Type of Automobile	2008 MSRP
2008 Ford Expedition XLT	$30,620
2008 Ford Supercab XLT	$27,595
2008 Dodge Charger SXT G	$25,685
2008 Dodge Caravan SXT K	$26,805

Source: www.dodge.com; www.fordvehicles.com

Replace the question mark with an inequality symbol to indicate the relationship between the prices of the vehicles.

41. Ford Expedition XLT ? Ford Supercab XLT

42. Dodge Caravan SXT K ? Dodge Charger SXT G

Round to the nearest ten.

43. 45

44. 85

45. 661

46. 123

Round to the nearest hundred.

47. 63,854

48. 12,799

49. 823,042

50. 701,529

Round to the nearest thousand.

51. 38,431

52. 56,312

53. 143,526

54. 312,544

Round to the nearest hundred thousand.

55. 5,254,423

56. 1,395,999

57. 9,007,601

58. 3,116,201

59. ***The Sun*** The diameter of the sun is approximately 865,000 miles. Round this figure to the nearest ten thousand.

60. ***Inches and Miles*** There are 3,484,800 inches in 55 miles. Round 3,484,800 to the nearest ten thousand.

One Step Further *Round to the nearest hundred.*

61. 16,962

62. 44,972

Very large numbers are used in some disciplines to measure quantities, such as distance in astronomy and the national debt in macroeconomics. We can extend the place-value chart to include these large numbers.

63. Write 5,311,192,809,000 using the word name.

64. Round 5,311,192,809,000 to the nearest million.

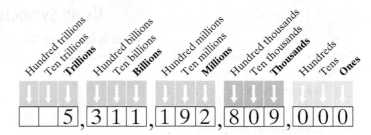

To Think About *Sometimes to get an approximation we must round to the nearest unit, such as a foot, yard, hour, or minute.*

65. *Train Travel Time* A train takes 3 hours and 50 minutes to reach its destination. Approximately how many hours does the trip take?

66. *Automobile Travel Time* An automobile trip takes 5 hours and 40 minutes. Approximately how many hours does the drive take?

67. *Fence Measurements* The Nguyens' backyard has a fence around it that measures 123 feet 5 inches. Approximately how many feet of fencing do the Nguyens have?

68. *Yardage Measurements* Jessica has 15 yards 4 inches of material. Approximately how many yards of material does Jessica have?

Quick Quiz 1.1

1. Write 6402 in expanded notation.

2. Replace each question mark with the appropriate symbol < or >.

   (a) 0 ? 10

   (b) 15 ? 10

3. Round 154,627 to

   (a) the nearest ten thousand

   (b) the nearest hundred

4. **Concept Check** Explain how to round 8937 to the nearest hundred.

Developing Your Study Skills

Finding a Study Partner

Attempt to make a friend in your class and become study partners. You may find that you enjoy sitting together and drawing support and encouragement from each other. You must not depend on a friend or fellow student to tutor you, do your work for you, or in any way be responsible for your learning. However, you will learn from each other as you seek to master the course. Studying with a friend and comparing notes, methods, and solutions can be very helpful. And it makes learning mathematics a lot more fun!

Exercises

1. Exchange phone numbers with someone in class so you can call each other whenever you are having difficulty with your studying.

2. Set up convenient times to study together on a regular basis, to do homework, and to review for exams.

Student Learning Objectives

After studying this section, you will be able to:

1. Use symbols and key words for expressing addition.

2. Use properties of addition to rewrite algebraic expressions.

3. Evaluate algebraic expressions involving addition.

4. Add whole numbers when carrying is needed.

5. Find the perimeters of geometric figures.

① Using Symbols and Key Words for Expressing Addition

What is *addition*? We perform **addition** when we group items together. Consider the following illustration involving the sale of bikes.

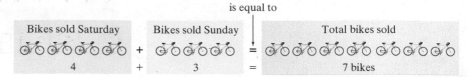

We see that the number 7 is the total of 4 and 3. That is, $4 + 3 = 7$ is an addition fact. The numbers being added are called **addends.** The result is called the **sum.**

$$\underset{\text{addend}}{4} \quad + \quad \underset{\text{addend}}{3} \quad = \quad \underset{\text{sum}}{7}$$

In mathematics we use symbols such as "+" in place of the words *sum* or *plus*. The English phrase "five plus two" written using symbols is "$5 + 2$." Writing English phrases using math symbols is like translating between languages such as Spanish and French.

There are several English phrases that describe the operation of addition. The following table gives some of them and their translated equivalents written using mathematical symbols.

English Phrase	Translation into Symbols
Six *more than* nine	$9 + 6$
The *sum of* some number and seven	$x + 7$
Four *increased by* two	$4 + 2$
Three *added* to a number	$n + 3$
One *plus* a number	$1 + x$

When we do not know the value of a number, we use a letter, such as x, to represent that number. A letter that represents a number is called a **variable.** Notice that the variables used in the table above are different. We can choose any letter as a variable. Thus we can represent "a number plus seven" by $x + 7, a + 7, n + 7, y + 7$, and so on. Combinations of variables and numbers such as $x + 7$ and $a + 7$ are called **algebraic expressions** or **variable expressions.**

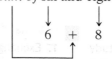 Translate each English phrase using numbers and symbols.

(a) The sum of six and eight   **(b)** A number increased by four

Solution

(a) The *sum of* six and eight   **(b)** A number *increased by* four

$$6 \; + \; 8 \qquad\qquad x \; + \; 4$$

Although we used the variable x to represent the unknown quantity in part (b), any letter could have been used.

NOTE TO STUDENT: Fully worked-out solutions to all of the Practice Problems can be found at the back of the text starting at page SP-1

 Translate each English phrase using numbers and symbols.

(a) Five added to some number   **(b)** Four more than five

Using Properties of Addition to Rewrite Algebraic Expressions

Most of us memorized some basic addition facts. Yet if we study these sums, we observe that there are only a few addition facts for each one-digit number that we must memorize. For example, we can easily see that when 0 items are added to any number of items, we end up with the same number of items: $5 + 0 = 5, 0 + 8 = 8$, and so on. This illustrates the **identity property of zero:** $a + 0 = a$ and $0 + a = a$.

EXAMPLE 2   Express 4 as the sum of two whole numbers. Write all possibilities. How many addition facts must we memorize? Why?

Solution   Starting with $4 + 0$, we write all the sums equal to 4 and observe any patterns.

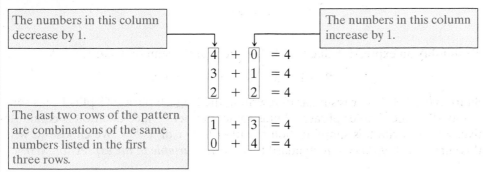

We need to learn only **two addition facts** for the number four: $3 + 1$ and $2 + 2$. The remaining facts are either a repeat of these or use the fact that when 0 is added to any number, the sum is that number.

Practice Problem 2   Express 8 as the sum of two whole numbers. Write all possibilities. How many addition facts must we memorize? Why?

In Example 2 we saw that the order in which we add numbers doesn't affect the sum. That is, $3 + 1 = 4$ and $1 + 3 = 4$. This is true for all numbers and leads us to a property called the **commutative property of addition.**

COMMUTATIVE PROPERTY OF ADDITION
$$a + b = b + a \qquad 4 + 9 = 9 + 4$$
$$13 = 13$$

Two numbers can be added in either order with the same result.

EXAMPLE 3   Use the commutative property of addition to rewrite each sum.

(a) $8 + 2$ **(b)** $7 + n$ **(c)** $x + 3$

Solution

(a) $8 + 2 = 2 + 8$ **(b)** $7 + n = n + 7$ **(c)** $x + 3 = 3 + x$

Notice that we applied the commutative property of addition to the expressions with variables n and x. That is because variables represent numbers, even though they are unknown numbers.

Practice Problem 3   Use the commutative property of addition to rewrite each sum.

(a) $x + 3$ **(b)** $9 + w$ **(c)** $4 + 0$

EXAMPLE 4   If $2566 + 159 = 2725$, then
$$159 + 2566 = ?$$

Solution

$159 + 2566 = 2725$ Why? The commutative property states that the order in which we add numbers doesn't affect the sum.

Practice Problem 4   If $x + y = 6075$, then
$$y + x = ?$$

NOTE TO STUDENT: Fully worked-out solutions to all of the Practice Problems can be found at the back of the text starting at page SP-1

To **simplify** an expression like $8 + 1 + x$, we find the sum of 8 and 1.

$$8 + 1 + x = 9 + x \ \text{ or } \ x + 9$$

Simplifying $8 + 1 + x$ is similar to rewriting the English phrase "8 plus 1 plus some number" as the simpler phrase "9 plus some number." Since addition is commutative, we can write this simplification as either $9 + x$ or $x + 9$. We choose to write this sum as $x + 9$, since it is standard to *write the variable in the expression first*.

EXAMPLE 5   Simplify. $3 + 2 + n$

Solution   To simplify, we find the sum of the known numbers.

$$3 + 2 + n = 5 + n$$
or
$$= n + 5$$

We cannot add the variable n and the number 5 because n represents an unknown quantity; we have no way of knowing what quantity to add to the number 5.

Practice Problem 5   Simplify. $6 + 3 + x$

Addition of more than two numbers may be performed in more than one manner. To add $5 + 2 + 1$ we can first add the 5 and 2, or we can add the 2 and 1 first. We indicate which sum we add first by using parentheses. *We perform the operation inside the parentheses first.*

$$5 + 2 + 1 = (5 + 2) + 1 = 7 + 1 = 8$$
$$5 + 2 + 1 = 5 + (2 + 1) = 5 + 3 = 8$$

In both cases the order of the numbers 5, 2, and 1 remains unchanged and the sums are the same. This illustrates the **associative property of addition.**

ASSOCIATIVE PROPERTY OF ADDITION

$$(a + b) + c = a + (b + c) \qquad (4 + 9) + 1 = 4 + (9 + 1)$$
$$13 + 1 = 4 + 10$$
$$14 = 14$$

When we add three or more numbers, the addition may be grouped in any way.

EXAMPLE 6 Use the associative property of addition to rewrite the sum and then simplify. $(x + 3) + 6$

Solution

$$(x + 3) + 6 = x + (3 + 6)$$ 　The associative property allows us to regroup.
$$= x + 9$$ 　　Simplify: $3 + 6 = 9$.

Practice Problem 6 Use the associative property of addition to rewrite the sum and then simplify. $(w + 1) + 4$

Sometimes we must use both the associative and commutative properties of addition to rewrite a sum and simplify. In other words, we can *change the order in which we add* (commutative property) and *regroup the addition* (associative property) to simplify an expression.

EXAMPLE 7 Use the associative and/or commutative property as necessary to simplify the expression. $5 + (n + 7)$

Solution

$$5 + (n + 7) = 5 + (7 + n)$$ 　The commutative property allows us to change the order of addition.

$$= (5 + 7) + n$$ 　Regroup the sum using the associative property.
$$= 12 + n$$ 　Simplify.
$$5 + (n + 7) = n + 12$$ 　Write $12 + n$ as $n + 12$.

Practice Problem 7 Use the associative and/or commutative property as necessary to simplify each expression.

(a) $(2 + x) + 8$ 　　　**(b)** $(4 + x + 3) + 1$

Understanding the Concept

Addition Facts Made Simple

There are many methods that can be used to add one-digit numbers. For example, if you can't remember that $7 + 8 = 15$ but can remember that $7 + 7 = 14$, just add 1 to 14 to get 15.

$$7 + 8 = 7 + (7 + 1)$$
$$= (7 + 7) + 1$$
$$= 14 + 1$$
$$= 15$$

Another quick way to add is to use the sum $5 + 5 = 10$, since it is easy to remember. Let's use this to add $7 + 5$.

$$7 + 5 = (2 + 5) + 5$$
$$= 2 + (5 + 5)$$
$$= 2 + 10$$
$$= 12$$

Exercises

1. Use the fact that $5 + 5 = 10$ to add $8 + 5$.
2. Use the fact that $6 + 6 = 12$ to add $6 + 8$.

Evaluating Algebraic Expressions Involving Addition

We have already learned that when we do not know the value of a number, we designate the number by a letter. We call this letter a *variable*. We use a variable to represent an unknown number until such time as its value can be determined. For example, if 6 is added to a number but we do not know the number, we could write

$$n + 6 \quad \text{where } n \text{ is the unknown number.}$$

If we were told that n has the value 9, we could *replace* n with 9 and then simplify.

$$\begin{array}{ll} n + 6 & \\ 9 + 6 & \text{Replace } n \text{ with 9.} \\ 15 & \text{Simplify by adding.} \end{array}$$

Thus $n + 6$ has the value 15 when n is replaced by 9. This is called evaluating the expression $n + 6$ if n is equal to 9.

> To **evaluate** an algebraic expression, we replace the variables in the expression with their corresponding values and simplify.

An algebraic expression has different values depending on the values we use to replace the variable.

EXAMPLE 8   Evaluate $x + y + 3$ for the given values of x and y.

(a) x is equal to 6 and y is equal to 1

(b) x is equal to 4 and y is equal to 2

Solution

(a) $\begin{array}{ll} x + y + 3 & \text{Replace } x \text{ with} \\ 6 + 1 + 3 & \text{6 and } y \text{ with 1.} \\ \quad 10 & \text{Simplify.} \end{array}$

When x is equal to 6 and y is equal to 1, $x + y + 3$ is equal to 10.

(b) $\begin{array}{ll} x + y + 3 & \text{Replace } x \text{ with} \\ 4 + 2 + 3 & \text{4 and } y \text{ with 2.} \\ \quad 9 & \text{Simplify.} \end{array}$

When x is equal to 4 and y is equal to 2, $x + y + 3$ is equal to 9.

Practice Problem 8   Evaluate $x + y + 6$ for the given values of x and y.

(a) x is equal to 9 and y is equal to 3   **(b)** x is equal to 1 and y is equal to 7

NOTE TO STUDENT: Fully worked-out solutions to all of the Practice Problems can be found at the back of the text starting at page SP-1

 Adding Whole Numbers When Carrying Is Needed

Of course, we are often required to add numbers that have more than a single digit. In such cases we must:

1. Arrange the numbers vertically, lining up the digits according to place value.
2. Add first the digits in the ones column, then the digits in the tens column, then those in the hundreds column, and so on, moving from *right to left*.

Sometimes the sum of a column is a multidigit number—that is, a number larger than 9. When this happens we evaluate the place values of the digits to find the sum.

EXAMPLE 9 Add. 68 + 25

Solution We arrange numbers vertically and add the digits in the ones column first, then the digits in the tens column.

$$
\begin{array}{l}
68 \longrightarrow 6 \text{ tens} \quad 8 \text{ ones} \\
+25 \longrightarrow 2 \text{ tens} \quad 5 \text{ ones} \\
\hline
\qquad\qquad 8 \text{ tens} \quad 13 \text{ ones} \longrightarrow
\end{array}
$$

We cannot have two digits in the ones column, so we must rename 13 as 1 ten and 3 ones.

8 tens + 1 ten + 3 ones ⟵

9 tens + 3 ones = 93

A shorter way to do this problem involves a process called "carrying." Instead of rewriting 13 ones as *1 ten and 3 ones* we would carry the *1 ten* to the tens column by placing a 1 above the 6 and writing the 3 in the ones column of the sum.

$$
\begin{array}{r}
\overset{1}{6}8 \\
+25 \\
\hline
3
\end{array}
$$
  8 ones + 5 ones = 13 ones

$$
\begin{array}{r}
\overset{1}{6}8 \\
+25 \\
\hline
93
\end{array}
$$
  Add 1 ten + 6 tens + 2 tens.

Practice Problem 9 Add. 247 + 38

Often you must *carry* several times, by bringing the left digit into the next column to the left.

EXAMPLE 10 A market research company surveyed 1870 people to determine the type of beverage they order most often at a restaurant. The results of the survey are shown in the table. Find the total number of people whose responses were iced tea, soda, or coffee.

Solution We add whenever we must find the "total" amount.

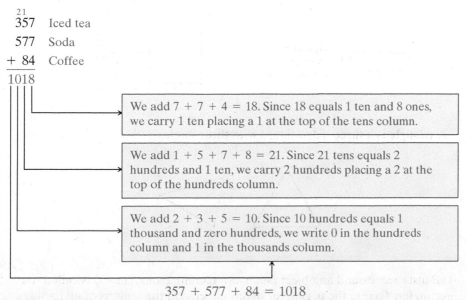

$$
\begin{array}{r}
\overset{21}{3}57 \quad \text{Iced tea} \\
577 \quad \text{Soda} \\
+\ 84 \quad \text{Coffee} \\
\hline
1018
\end{array}
$$

We add 7 + 7 + 4 = 18. Since 18 equals 1 ten and 8 ones, we carry 1 ten placing a 1 at the top of the tens column.

We add 1 + 5 + 7 + 8 = 21. Since 21 tens equals 2 hundreds and 1 ten, we carry 2 hundreds placing a 2 at the top of the hundreds column.

We add 2 + 3 + 5 = 10. Since 10 hundreds equals 1 thousand and zero hundreds, we write 0 in the hundreds column and 1 in the thousands column.

$$357 + 577 + 84 = 1018$$

Type of Beverage		Number of Responses
Soda		577
Orange juice		475
Coffee		84
Iced tea		357
Milk		286
Other		91

A total of 1018 people responded ice tea, soda, or coffee.

Practice Problem 10 Use the survey results from Example 10 to answer the following: Find the total number of people whose responses were milk, orange juice, or other.

 Finding the Perimeters of Geometric Figures

Geometry has a visual aspect that many students find helpful to their learning. Numbers and abstract quantities may be hard to visualize, but we can take pen in hand and draw a picture of a rectangle that represents a room with certain dimensions. We can easily visualize problems such as "what is the distance around the outside edges of the room (perimeter)?" In this section we study rectangles, squares, triangles, and other complex shapes that are made up of these figures.

A **rectangle** is a four-sided figure like the ones shown here.

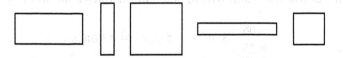

A rectangle has the following two properties:

1. Any two adjoining sides are perpendicular.
2. Opposite sides are equal.

When we say that any two adjoining sides are **perpendicular** we mean that any two sides that join at a corner form an angle that measures 90 degrees (called a **right angle**) and thus forms one of the following shapes.

When we say that opposite sides are equal we mean that the measure of a side is equal to the measure of the side across from it. When all sides of a rectangle are the same length, we call the rectangle a **square.**

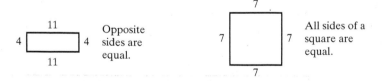

A **triangle** is a three-sided figure with three angles.

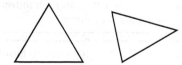

The distance around an object (such as a rectangle or triangle) is called the **perimeter.** To find the perimeter of an object, add the lengths of all its sides.

EXAMPLE 11 Find the perimeter of the triangle. (The abbreviation "ft" means feet).

Solution   We add the lengths of the sides to find the perimeter.

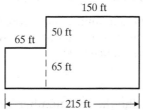

$5 \text{ ft} + 5 \text{ ft} + 7 \text{ ft} = 17 \text{ ft}$

The perimeter is 17 ft.

Practice Problem 11 Find the perimeter of the square.

15 ft

If you are unfamilar with the value, meaning, and abbreviations for the metric and U.S. units of measure, refer to Appendix A, which contains a brief summary of this information.

EXAMPLE 12 Find the perimeter of the shape consisting of a rectangle and a square.

150 ft

50 ft

65 ft

65 ft

215 ft

Solution   We want to find the distance around the figure. We look only at the *outside* edges since dashed lines indicate *inside* lengths.

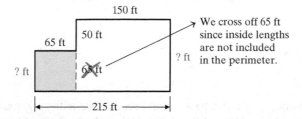

We cross off 65 ft since inside lengths are not included in the perimeter.

Now we must find the lengths of the unlabeled sides. The shaded figure is a square since the length and width have the same measure. Thus each side of the shaded figure has a measure of 65 ft.

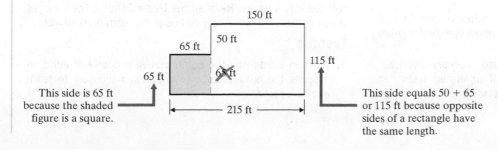

This side is 65 ft because the shaded figure is a square.

This side equals 50 + 65 or 115 ft because opposite sides of a rectangle have the same length.

Next, we add the length of the six sides to find the perimeter.

$$150 \text{ ft} + 115 \text{ ft} + 215 \text{ ft} + 65 \text{ ft} + 65 \text{ ft} + 50 \text{ ft} = 660 \text{ ft}$$

The perimeter is 660 ft.

NOTE TO STUDENT: *Fully worked-out solutions to all of the Practice Problems can be found at the back of the text starting at page SP-1*

Practice Problem 12 Find the perimeter of the shape consisting of a rectangle and a square.

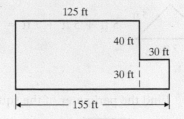

Understanding the Concept

Using Inductive Reasoning to Reach a Conclusion

When we reach a conclusion based on specific observations, we are using **inductive reasoning.** Much of our early learning is based on simple cases of inductive reasoning. If a child touches a hot stove or other appliance several times and each time he gets burned, he is likely to conclude, "If I touch something that is hot, I will get burned." This is inductive reasoning. The child has thought about several actions and their outcomes and has made a conclusion or generalization.

The following is an illustration of how we use inductive reasoning in mathematics.

Find the next number in the sequence 10, 13, 16, 19, 22, 25, 28, . . .

We observe a pattern that each number is 3 more than the preceding number: $10 + 3 = 13; 13 + 3 = 16$, and so on. Therefore, if we add 3 to 28, we conclude that the next number in the sequence is 31.

Exercise

1. For each of the following find the next number by identifying the pattern.
   (a) 8, 14, 20, 26, 32, 38, . . .
   (b) 17, 28, 39, 50, 61, . . .

For more practice, complete exercises 89–94 on page 22.

Developing Your Study Skills

Preparing to Learn Algebra

Many people have learned arithmetic by memorizing facts and properties without understanding why the facts are true or what the properties mean. Learning strictly by memorization can cause problems. For example:

- Many of the shortcuts in arithmetic do not work in algebra.
- Memorizing does not help one develop reasoning and logic skills, which are essential to understanding algebra concepts.
- Memorization can eventually cause *memory overload*. Trying to remember a collection of unrelated facts can cause you to become *anxious* and *discouraged*.

In this book you will see familiar arithmetic topics. Do not skip them, even if you feel that you have mastered them. The explanations will probably be different from those you have already seen because they emphasize the underlying concepts. If you don't understand a concept the first time, be patient and keep trying. Sometimes, by working through the material you will see why it works. Read all the Understanding the Concept boxes in the book since they will help you learn mathematics.

Exercise

1. Write in words why the commutative property of addition reduces the amount of memorization necessary to learn addition facts.

Verbal and Writing Skills *Write in words.*

1. $10 + x$

2. $n + 4$

3. Write in your *own words* the steps you must perform to find the answer to the following problem. Evaluate $x + 6$ if x is equal to 9.

4. Explain why the following statement is true. If $x + y + z = 105$, then $z + y + x = 105$.

State what property is represented in each mathematical statement.

5. $(2 + 3) + 4 = 2 + (3 + 4)$

6. $4 + (x + 3) = 4 + (3 + x)$

Translate using numbers and symbols.

7. A number plus two

8. Two added to a number

9. The sum of five and y

10. The sum of eight and x

11. Some number added to twelve

12. Twelve more than a number

13. A number increased by seven

14. A number plus four

Use the commutative property of addition to rewrite each sum.

15. $5 + a$

16. $y + 6$

17. $3 + x$

18. $5 + x$

19. If $3542 + 216 = 3758$, then $216 + 3542 = ?$

20. If $8791 + 156 = 8947$, then $156 + 8791 = ?$

21. If $5 + n = 12$, then $n + 5 = ?$

22. If $8 + x = 31$, then $x + 8 = ?$

Simplify.

23. $x + 4 + 2$

24. $a + 5 + 3$

25. $9 + 3 + n$

26. $7 + 1 + y$

27. $x + 0 + 2$

28. $x + 3 + 0$

Use the associative property of addition to rewrite each sum, then simplify.

29. $(x + 2) + 1$

30. $(x + 4) + 2$

31. $9 + (3 + n)$

32. $2 + (5 + x)$

33. $(n + 3) + 8$

34. $(a + 4) + 6$

Use the associative and/or commutative property as necessary to simplify each expression.

35. $(x + 4) + 11$

36. $(y + 1) + 4$

37. $(2 + n) + 5$

38. $(4 + x) + 5$

39. $8 + (1 + x)$

40. $5 + (3 + a)$

41. $(3 + n) + 6$

42. $4 + (n + 2)$

43. $(3 + a + 2) + 8$

44. $(6 + x + 4) + 4$

45. $(5 + x + 7) + 4$

46. $(2 + n + 8) + 5$

47. Evaluate $y + 7$ for the given values of y.
  (a) y is equal to 3
  (b) y is equal to 8

48. Evaluate $n + 8$ for the given values of n.
  (a) n is equal to 4
  (b) n is equal to 7

49. Evaluate $x + y$ if x is 6 and y is 13.

50. Evaluate $a + b$ if a is 6 and b is 9.

51. Evaluate $a + b + c$ if a is 9, b is 15, and c is 12.

52. Evaluate $x + y + z$ if x is 11, y is 18, and z is 15.

53. Evaluate $n + m + 13$ if n is 26 and m is 44.

54. Evaluate $x + y + 21$ if x is 32 and y is 44.

Yearly Bonus Pay *For exercises 55 and 56, use the table and the formula* **Bonus = x + y + 250** *to calculate the yearly bonus for MJ Industry employees.*

$$\text{Bonus} = x + y + 250$$

x represents the number of productivity units earned.

y represents the number of years of employment.

Employee Name	Employee Number	Years of Employment	Productivity Units Earned
Julio Sanchez	00315	15	150
Mary McCab	00316	12	180
Jamal March	00317	18	125
Leo J. Cornell	00318	10	175

55. Calculate the yearly bonus for
  (a) Mary McCab.
  (b) Leo J. Cornell.

56. Calculate the yearly bonus for
  (a) Julio Sanchez.
  (b) Jamal March.

Add. For more practice, refer to Appendix D.

57. $\begin{array}{r} 15 \\ + 23 \end{array}$

58. $\begin{array}{r} 71 \\ + 12 \end{array}$

59. $\begin{array}{r} 236 \\ + 43 \end{array}$

60. $\begin{array}{r} 331 \\ + 57 \end{array}$

61. $\begin{array}{r} 32 \\ 11 \\ 20 \\ + 7 \end{array}$

62. $\begin{array}{r} 33 \\ 11 \\ 6 \\ + 4 \end{array}$

63. $\begin{array}{r} 105 \\ 8 \\ 133 \\ + 98 \end{array}$

64. $\begin{array}{r} 308 \\ 7 \\ 245 \\ + 75 \end{array}$

65. $236 + 467 + 26$

66. $531 + 217 + 18$

67. $281 + 64 + 539$

68. $562 + 65 + 133$

69. $7287 + 732 + 423$

70. $3366 + 152 + 485$

71. $922{,}876 + 54 + 1287 + 5000$

72. $836{,}147 + 99 + 2413 + 4000$

73. $3107 + 9063 + 54 + 379{,}626$

74. $2902 + 9050 + 12 + 986{,}100$

Applications Exercises 75–78 *Answer each question.*

75. *Checking Account* Angelica's check register indicates the deposits and debits (checks written or ATM withdrawals) for a 1-month period.

Date	Deposits	Debits
12/3/09	$159	
12/9/09		$63
12/13/09	$241	
12/15/09		$121
12/22/09		$44

(a) What is the total of the deposits made to Angelica's checking account?

(b) What is the total of the debits made to Angelica's checking account?

76. *Checking Account* The bookkeeper for the Spaulding Appliance Company examined the following record from the company account for the month of March.

Date	Deposits	Debits
3/6/08	$3477	
3/9/08		$120
3/13/08		$3500
3/15/08	$4614	
3/22/08		$1388

(a) What is the total of the deposits in this time period?

(b) What is the total of the debits in this time period?

77. *Apartment Expenses* The rent on an apartment was $875 per month. To move in, Charles and Vincent were required to pay the first and last month's rent, a security deposit of $500, a connection fee with the utility company of $24, and a cable T.V. installation fee of $35. How much money did they need to move into the apartment?

78. *Car Expenses* Shawnee found that for a 6-month period, in addition to gasoline, she had the following car expenses: insurance, $562; repair to brakes, $276; and new tires, $142. If gasoline for her car cost $495 for this time period, what was the total amount she spent on her car?

Find the perimeter of each rectangle.

79.

13 in.

5 in.

80.

7 in.

1 in.

Find the perimeter of each square.

81.

3 ft

82.

8 ft

Find the perimeter of each triangle.

83.

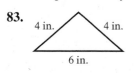

4 in.   4 in.

6 in.

84.

8 ft

3 ft

8 ft

Find the perimeters of the shapes made of rectangles and squares.

85.

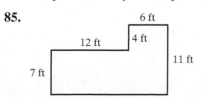

6 ft

4 ft

12 ft

11 ft

7 ft

86.

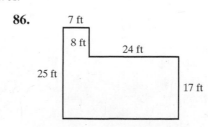

7 ft

8 ft

24 ft

25 ft

17 ft

87.

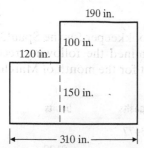

190 in.
100 in.
120 in.
150 in.
310 in.

88.

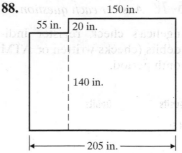

150 in.
55 in.   20 in.
140 in.
205 in.

To Think About *For each of the following, find the next number in the sequence by identifying the pattern.*

89. 1, 3, 5, 7, 9, 11, 13, . . .

90. 2, 4, 6, 8, 10, 12, . . .

91. 0, 5, 10, 15, 20, 25, . . .

92. 24, 31, 38, 45, 52, 59, 66, . . .

93. 7, 16, 25, 34, 43, . . .

94. 12, 25, 38, 51, 64, . . .

Quick Quiz 1.2

1. Use the associative and/or commutative property as necessary to simplify each expression.

  (a) $(4 + a) + 9$

  (b) $2 + (1 + x + 7)$

2. Evaluate $m + n + 13$ if m is 25 and n is 8.

3. Find the perimeter of the shape consisting of a rectangle and a square.

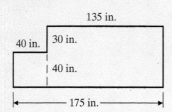

135 in.
40 in.   30 in.
40 in.
175 in.

4. Concept Check

$$\begin{array}{r} {}^{11}395 \\ +28 \\ \hline 423 \end{array}$$

  (a) When we carry, what is the value of the 1 that is placed above the 9?

  (b) When we carry, what is the value of the 1 that is placed above the 3?

Understanding Subtraction of Whole Numbers

What is **subtraction**? We do subtraction when we take objects away from a group. When we subtract we find "how many are left." The symbol used to indicate subtraction is called a **minus sign** "−." We illustrate below.

Three	take away	two	=	one left
↓	↓	↓		↓
3	−	2	=	1

$$3 - 2 = 1$$

There are three parts to a subtraction problem: **minuend, subtrahend,** and **difference.**

3	−	2	=	1
↓		↓		↓
minuend		subtrahend		difference

Subtraction is defined in terms of addition. Thus each subtraction sentence has a related addition sentence. For example, to find the value of $3 - 2$ we think of the number that when added to 2 gives 3.

$$3 - 2 = 1 \quad \text{Subtraction sentence}$$

$$3 = 1 + 2 \quad \text{Related addition sentence}$$

Therefore we can use related addition sentences to help with subtraction. To subtract $12 - 8 = ?$, we can think $12 = ? + 8$.

EXAMPLE 1 Subtract.

(a) $9 - 5$ **(b)** $7 - 2$ **(c)** $15 - 0$ **(d)** $15 - 15$

Solution

(a) $9 - 5 = 4$ **(b)** $7 - 2 = 5$ **(c)** $15 - 0 = 15$ **(d)** $15 - 15 = 0$

Practice Problem 1 Subtract.

(a) $5 - 2$ **(b)** $6 - 3$ **(c)** $18 - 0$ **(d)** $18 - 18$

Observe the pattern in the following subtraction problems: $6 - 0 = 6; 6 - 1 = 5; 6 - 2 = 4; 6 - 3 = 3$. Each time you subtract the next larger whole number, the result decreases by 1. We can use this subtraction pattern to subtract mentally.

EXAMPLE 2 $800 - 50 = 750$. Use this fact to find $800 - 53$.

Solution Since we know $800 - 50 = 750$, we can use subtraction patterns to find $800 - 53$.

Increase numbers in this column by 1.		Decrease numbers in this column by 1.

$$800 - 50 = 750$$
$$800 - 51 = 749$$
$$800 - 52 = 748$$
$$800 - 53 = 747$$

Practice Problem 2 $600 - 50 = 550$. Use this fact to find $600 - 54$.

Student Learning Objectives

After studying this section, you will be able to:

1 Understand subtraction of whole numbers.

2 Use symbols and key words for expressing subtraction.

3 Evaluate algebraic expressions involving subtraction.

4 Subtract whole numbers with two or more digits.

5 Solve applied problems involving subtraction of whole numbers.

NOTE TO STUDENT: Fully worked-out solutions to all of the Practice Problems can be found at the back of the text starting at page SP-1

Using Symbols and Key Words for Expressing Subtraction

There are several English phrases to describe the operation of subtraction. The following table presents some English phrases and their translated equivalents written using mathematical symbols.

English Phrase	Translation into Symbols
The *difference* of three and *x*	$3 - x$
Eight *minus* a number	$8 - n$
Two *subtracted from* seven	$7 - 2$
A number *decreased by* four	$n - 4$
Five *less than* nine	$9 - 5$

CAUTION: Math symbols are not always written in the same order as the words in the English phrase. Notice that when we translate the phrases "less than" or "subtracted from," the math symbols are not written in the same order as they are read in the statement.

EXAMPLE 3 Translate using numbers and symbols.

(a) The difference between five and *x*   **(b)** Four less than seven

Solution

(a) The *difference* between five and *x*   **(b)** Four *less than* seven

$$5 - x \qquad 7 - 4$$

Practice Problem 3 Translate using numbers and symbols.

(a) The difference of nine and *n*   **(b)** *x* minus three
(c) *x* subtracted from eight

CAUTION: Note that the symbol $<$ means "is less than" while the symbol $-$ means "less than." Therefore in Example 3b we use the minus symbol $-$, not the inequality symbol $<$.

When we use the phrase "less than" and "subtracted from," the order in which we write the numbers in the subtraction is *reversed*. It is important to write these numbers in the correct order because, in general, *subtraction is not commutative*. In other words, $30 - 20$ is not the same as $20 - 30$. To show this, let's see what happens when we change the order of the numbers in subtraction.

$\$30 - \$20$ You have \$30 in your checking account and write a check for \$20; your balance will be \$10.

$\$20 - \$30$ You have \$20 in your checking account and write a check for \$30; you will be overdrawn!

Obviously, the results are *not* the same. We summarize as follows.

> **SUBTRACTION IS NOT COMMUTATIVE**
>
> If *a* and *b* are not the same number, then
>
> $a - b$ does not equal $b - a$. $30 - 20$ does not equal $20 - 30$.

Evaluating Algebraic Expressions Involving Subtraction

Recall from Section 1.2 that to evaluate an expression we replace the variables in the expression with the given values and simplify.

EXAMPLE 4   Evaluate $7 - x$ for the given values of x.

(a) x is equal to 2
(b) x is equal to 4

Solution

(a) $7 - x$
  $7 - 2$ Replace x with 2.
    5 Simplify.
  When x is equal to 2, $7 - x$ is equal to 5.

(b) $7 - x$
  $7 - 4$ Replace x with 4.
    3 Simplify.
  When x is equal to 4, $7 - x$ is equal to 3.

Practice Problem 4   Evaluate $8 - n$ for the given values of n.

(a) n is equal to 3
(b) n is equal to 6

 Subtracting Whole Numbers with Two or More Digits

Often, we cannot subtract mentally, especially if the numbers being subtracted involve more than one digit. In this case we follow the same procedure as we did in addition, except we subtract digits instead of adding them. Therefore, we must:

1. Arrange the numbers vertically.
2. Subtract the digits in the ones column first, then the digits in the tens column, then those in the hundreds column, and so on, moving from *right to left*.

Many times, however, a digit in the lower number (subtrahend) is greater than the digit in the upper number (minuend) for a particular place value, as illustrated below.

$$
\begin{array}{r}
7\;\boxed{2} \\
-3\;\boxed{8}
\end{array} \quad 8 > 2
$$

When this happens we must *rename* 72 using place values so we can subtract.

EXAMPLE 5   Subtract. $72 - 38$

Solution

We cannot subtract 8 ones from 2 ones, so we rewrite 7 tens as "tens and ones."

$$
\begin{array}{r}
7\!\!\!\!/\,\boxed{2} \\
-\;3\boxed{8}
\end{array}
\qquad
\begin{array}{r}
\overset{6 \text{ tens}}{\cancel{7 \text{ tens}}} + \overset{10 \text{ ones}}{2} \text{ ones} \\
-3 \text{ tens} + 8 \text{ ones}
\end{array}
$$

7 tens   2 ones

6 tens   10 ones   2 ones

10 ones + 2 ones = 12 ones

$$
\begin{array}{r}
72 \\
-\;38 \\
\hline
34
\end{array}
\qquad
\begin{array}{r}
6 \text{ tens} + 12 \text{ ones} \\
-3 \text{ tens} + \;\;8 \text{ ones} \\
\hline
3 \text{ tens} + \;\;4 \text{ ones}
\end{array}
$$

12 ones − 8 ones = 4 ones; 6 tens − 3 tens = 3 tens

Thus $72 - 38 = 34$.

A shorter way to do this is called **borrowing.** Instead of rewriting *7 tens + 2 ones* as *6 tens + 12 ones*, we would borrow 1 ten from the 7 tens by crossing out the 7 and placing 6 above the 7. Then we would cross out the 2 and place 12 above the 2.

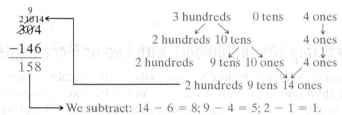

$$\begin{array}{r} {}^{6}{}^{12} \\ \cancel{72} \longrightarrow \quad \text{7 tens + 2 ones} \\ -38 \\ \hline 34 \longrightarrow \quad \text{We subtract: 12 ones} - \text{8 ones} = \text{4 ones.} \end{array}$$

6 tens + 12 ones

We subtract: 6 tens − 3 tens = 3 tens.

NOTE TO STUDENT: *Fully worked-out solutions to all of the Practice Problems can be found at the back of the text starting at page SP-1*

Practice Problem 5 Subtract. 93 − 46

Sometimes we cannot borrow from the digit directly to the left because this digit is 0. In this case we borrow from the next nonzero digit to the left of the 0, as illustrated in the next example.

EXAMPLE 6 Subtract. 304 − 146

Solution

304   We must borrow since we cannot subtract 6 ones from 4 ones.

− 146   We cannot borrow a ten since there are 0 tens, so we must borrow from 3 hundreds.

$$\begin{array}{r} {}^{9} \\ {}^{2}\,{}^{10}14 \\ \cancel{304} \\ -146 \\ \hline 158 \end{array}$$

3 hundreds	0 tens	4 ones
2 hundreds	10 tens	4 ones
2 hundreds	9 tens 10 ones	4 ones

2 hundreds 9 tens 14 ones

We subtract: 14 − 6 = 8; 9 − 4 = 5; 2 − 1 = 1.

Practice Problem 6 Subtract. 603 − 278

Understanding the Concept

Money and Borrowing

Converting money (changing $100 bills to $10 and $1 bills) illustrates the process of borrowing. To see this, let's look at the following:

A cashier in a gift shop must give a customer $11 change for a purchase. Since the cashier is out of small bills and has only 3 hundred-dollar bills in the register, she must ask another cashier to convert a hundred-dollar bill to tens and ones.

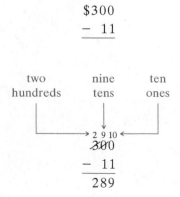

$300
− 11

| two hundreds | nine tens | ten ones |

$$\begin{array}{r} {}^{2}\,{}^{9}\,10 \\ \cancel{300} \\ -11 \\ \hline 289 \end{array}$$

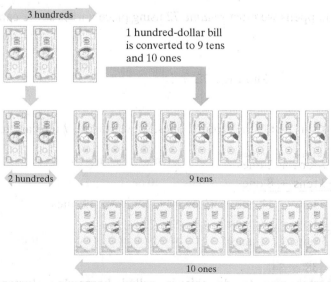

3 hundreds

1 hundred-dollar bill is converted to 9 tens and 10 ones

2 hundreds   9 tens

10 ones

The cashier now has 2 hundreds, 9 tens, and 10 ones and can give the customer $11 change.

Exercises

1. What happens when we must borrow from 0? That is, when subtracting 400 − 68, why must we change the middle 0 to 9, then borrow 1 from the first nonzero whole number to the left of it? Explain.

2. Explain why changing 1 ten-dollar bill to 10 one-dollar bills is similar to borrowing in subtraction.

We can check our subtraction problems using the related addition problems. For example, to check that 7 − 2 = 5, we verify that 7 = 5 + 2.

EXAMPLE 7 Subtract 7004 − 3675 and check your answer.

Solution

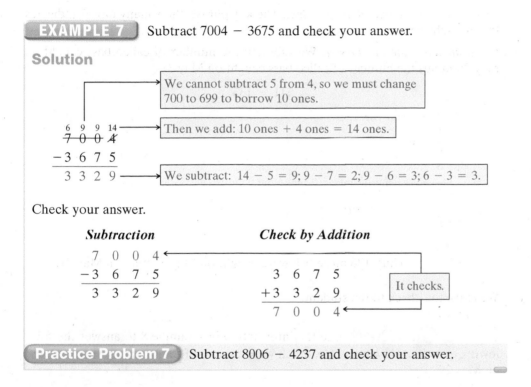

Check your answer.

	Subtraction					**Check by Addition**			
	7	0	0	4					
−	3	6	7	5		3	6	7	5
	3	3	2	9	+	3	3	2	9
						7	0	0	4

It checks.

Practice Problem 7 Subtract 8006 − 4237 and check your answer.

⑤ Solving Applied Problems Involving Subtraction of Whole Numbers

Key words and phrases found in applied problems often help determine which operations should be used for computations. Subtraction is often used in real-life problems when we are comparing more than one amount. Often we want to know *how much more* or *how much less* one amount is than another. Subtraction is also necessary when we want to know *how much is left* or when the problem uses the key words or phrases for subtraction, such as *difference, minus, subtracted from, decreased by,* or *less than.* When we solve applied problems it is a good idea to use the following three steps in the problem-solving process.

Step 1. *Understand the problem.* Draw pictures. Look for key words and phrases to help you determine what operations should be used.

Step 2. *Calculate and state the answer.* Perform all calculations and answer the question asked in the problem.

Step 3. *Check your answer.* You may use a different method to find the answer, or you may estimate to see if your answer is reasonable.

EXAMPLE 8 Fish counts of calico bass caught out of a local sportfishing wharf on the last three days of May are given in the table.

Number of Calico Bass Caught	
May 29	232
May 30	311
May 31	133

How many more calico bass were caught off the wharf on May 30 than on May 31?

Solution *Understand the problem.* The key phrase "how many more" indicates that we subtract.

Calculate and state the answer. We subtract: the number of calico bass caught on May 30 minus the number of calico bass caught on May 31.

$$311 - 133$$

$$
\begin{array}{r}
\overset{0\ 11}{3\cancel{1}\cancel{1}} \\
-1\ 3\ 3 \\
\hline
8
\end{array}
$$
→ We borrow 1 ten.

→ We cannot subtract 3 tens from 0 tens so we borrow again.

$$
\begin{array}{r}
\overset{2\ 10}{\underset{0\ 11}{3\cancel{1}\cancel{1}}} \\
-1\ 3\ 3 \\
\hline
1\ 7\ 8
\end{array}
$$
→ We borrow: write *3 hundreds* as *2 hundreds and 10 tens*.

Thus, 178 more fish were caught on May 30 than on May 31.

We leave the check to the student.

Practice Problem 8 Use the information in Example 8 to answer the following question. How many fewer fish were caught off the wharf on May 31 than on May 29?

NOTE TO STUDENT: Fully worked-out solutions to all of the Practice Problems can be found at the back of the text starting at page SP-1

EXAMPLE 9 Find the perimeter of the shape consisting of rectangles.

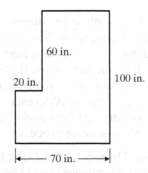

60 in.

20 in.

100 in.

70 in.

Solution　To find the perimeter we must find the distance around the figure. Therefore, we must find the measures of the unlabeled sides.

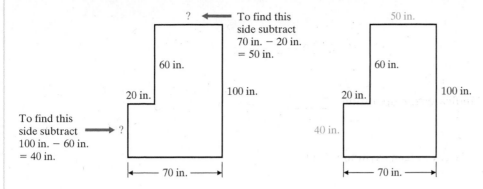

Next we add the lengths of the six sides.

$$50 \text{ in.} + 100 \text{ in.} + 70 \text{ in.} + 40 \text{ in.} + 20 \text{ in.} + 60 \text{ in.} = 340 \text{ in.}$$

The perimeter is 340 in.

Practice Problem 9　Find the perimeter of the shape consisting of rectangles.

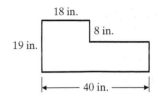

Developing Your Study Skills

Class Attendance and the Learning Cycle

Did you know that an important part of the learning process happens in the classroom? People learn by *reading, writing, listening, verbalizing,* and *seeing.* These activities are all part of the **learning cycle** and always occur in class.

- *Listening and seeing*: hearing and watching the instructor's lecture
- *Reading*: reading the information on the board and in handouts
- *Verbalizing*: asking questions and participating in class discussions
- *Writing*: taking notes and working problems assigned in class

The Learning Cycle

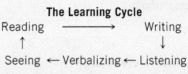

Attendance in class completes the entire learning cycle once. Completing assignments activates the entire learning cycle one more time:

- Reading class notes and the text
- Writing your homework
- Listening to other students and talking with them about your strategies

Keep in mind that you must pay attention and participate to learn. Just being there is not enough.

Verbal and Writing Skills

Write using words.

1. $6 - x$

2. $10 - 2$

Fill in the blank.

3. The key phrase "how many more" indicates the operation _____.

Answer true or false.

4. The English phrase "five less than x" written using symbols is $5 - x$.

Subtract.

5. $7 - 4$

6. $5 - 3$

7. $6 - 2$

8. $8 - 4$

9. $9 - 3$

10. $9 - 6$

11. $8 - 7$

12. $4 - 3$

13. $15 - 0$

14. $29 - 0$

15. $20 - 20$

16. $15 - 15$

17. If $700 - 600 = 100$, find $700 - 603$ using subtraction patterns.

18. If $900 - 800 = 100$, find $900 - 806$ using subtraction patterns.

19. If $300 - 200 = 100$, find $300 - 205$ using subtraction patterns.

20. If $800 - 700 = 100$, find $800 - 705$ using subtraction patterns.

Translate using symbols.

21. Nine minus two

22. Three decreased by a number

23. The difference of eight and y

24. The difference of three and a number

25. Ten subtracted from seventeen

26. Seven subtracted from a number

27. A number decreased by one

28. Eight minus two

29. Two less than some number

30. Nine less than twelve

Evaluate $9 - n$ for the given values of n.

31. If n is equal to 4

32. If n is equal to 6

33. If n is equal to 9

34. If n is equal to 1

Evaluate $x - 2$ for the given values of x.

35. If x is equal to 9

36. If x is equal to 5

37. If x is equal to 3

38. If x is equal to 9

Subtract and check. For more practice, refer to Appendix D.

39. $97 - 35$

40. $99 - 26$

41. $56 - 23$

42. $76 - 41$

43. $83 - 67$

44. $56 - 37$

45. $72 - 18$

46. $73 - 35$

47. $873 - 195$

48. $761 - 542$

49. $500 - 43$

50. $700 - 29$

51. $8912 - 3847$

52. $8721 - 654$

53. $5301 - 185$

54. $8801 - 4583$

55. $\begin{array}{r} 15,107 \\ -\ 6,428 \end{array}$

56. $\begin{array}{r} 29,002 \\ -\ 3,667 \end{array}$

57. $\begin{array}{r} 164,300 \\ -\ 58,923 \end{array}$

58. $\begin{array}{r} 796,020 \\ -\ 68,431 \end{array}$

Find the perimeter of each shape consisting of rectangles.

▲ **59.**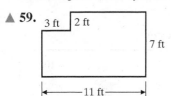

▲ **60.**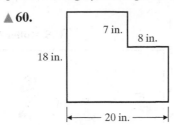

▲ **61.**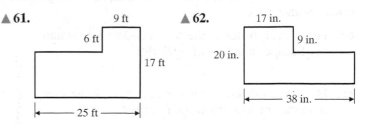

▲ **62.**

Applications

63. *Checking Account* Fill in the balances in Pedro's check register.

Check Number	Amount	Balance $1364
# 123	$238	
# 124	$137	
# 125	$ 69	
# 126	$ 98	
# 127	$369	

64. *Whale Population Decline* Although the International Whaling Commision has banned commercial whaling since 1987, several countries still hunt whales. As a result, the number of whales continues to decline, as shown in the following chart.

    (a) Which species has had the largest decline in population?

    (b) What is the decline in the total whale population?

Species	Approximate Population Years Earlier	Population in the World's Oceans 2000
Blue	275,000	5,000
Bowhead	60,000	8,500
Humpback	150,000	20,000

Source: Orange County Register

65. *Sun vs. Moon Diameter* The moon is about 400 times smaller than the sun.

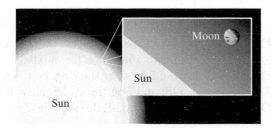

The diameter of the sun is approximately 865,000 miles, and the diameter of the moon is approximately 2160 miles. How many more miles is the diameter of the sun than that of the moon?

66. *Earth vs. Moon Diameter* If the moon were next to Earth it would be like a tennis ball next to a basketball.

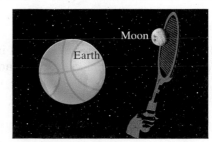

The approximate polar diameter of Earth (distance through Earth from North Pole to South Pole) is 7900 miles. The diameter of the moon is approximately 2160 miles. Find the difference in the diameters of Earth and the moon.

Roller Coasters *When a roller coaster descends at high speeds, the force exerted on a rider's body by the roller coaster becomes less than that of gravity, producing a sensation of weightlessness. Then when the roller coaster hits the bottom and either shoots up or turns sharply, a g-force is exerted on the rider's body for a fraction of a second. This g-force can be stronger than the one felt by astronauts during a space-shuttle launch.*

For exercises 67–70, refer to the bar graphs, which display the top speeds and maximum drops for some of the most popular roller coaster rides.

67. How much faster is the top speed of Superman the Escape than that of Goliath?

68. How much slower is the top speed of Ghostrider than that of Superman the Escape?

69. How much less is the maximum drop of Magnum XL-200 than that of Millennium Force?

70. How much greater is the maximum drop of Superman the Escape than that of Colossus?

To Think About

71. For what value(s) of x and y will $x - y = y - x$?

Translate using symbols, then evaluate.

72. Eight minus y, if y is equal to 3

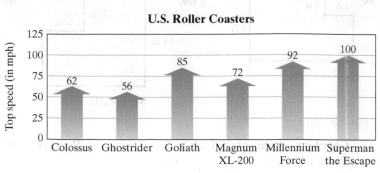

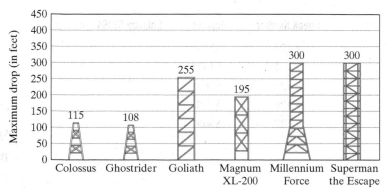

Source: www.ultimaterollercoaster.com

Cumulative Review *Replace each question mark with an inequality symbol.*

73. **[1.1.4]** 5,117,206 ? 13,842

74. **[1.1.4]** 2,386,702 ? 117,401

Add.

75. **[1.2.4]** *Hours Worked* Edward worked in the supermarket 120 hours in May, 135 in June, and 105 in July. How many hours did he work in the three-month period?

76. **[1.2.4]** *Pet Supply Purchases* Drew bought a dog for $430. He returned to the store the next day to purchase the following items for the dog: bed, $32; leash, $12; dog food, $28; and dog treats, $6. How much did Drew pay for the dog and all the supplies?

Quick Quiz 1.3

1. Translate the following using numbers and symbols.

  (a) Five subtracted from a number

  (b) A number decreased by 7

  (c) Eight less than a number

2. Subtract and check.

  (a) $14{,}062 - 7283$

  (b) $601{,}307 - 192{,}512$

3. Jose's salary was $2860 per month at his former job. His new job pays a salary of $3270 per month. How much more per month will Jose earn at his new job?

4. **Concept Check** Explain why when we subtract $800 - 35$, we change 8 to 7 in the borrowing process.

1.4 MULTIPLYING WHOLE NUMBER EXPRESSIONS

① Understanding Multiplication of Whole Numbers

Multiplication of whole numbers can be thought of as repeated addition. For example, suppose that a small parking lot has 4 rows of parking spaces with 8 spaces in each row. How many parking spaces are in the lot?

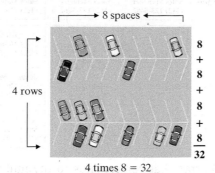

4 times 8 = 32

To get the total we add 8 four times, $8 + 8 + 8 + 8 = 32$, or we can use a shortcut: 4 rows of 8 is the same as 4 times 8, which equals 32. This is multiplication, a shortcut for repeated addition. When numbers are large, multiplication is easier than addition, but for smaller numbers, you can—if you are stuck—do a multiplication problem by working the equivalent addition problem.

The illustration of the parking lot is an example of an **array,** a rectangular figure that consists of rows and columns. Since the parking lot has 4 rows and 8 columns, it is a 4 by 8 array (always write the rows first). We can use dots, squares, or any figure to represent the elements of an array.

EXAMPLE 1 Draw two arrays that represent the multiplication 3 times 4.

Solution There are two arrays consisting of twelve items that represent the multiplication 3 times 4. One array has 4 rows and 3 columns, and the other one has 3 rows and 4 columns.

Practice Problem 1 Draw two arrays that represent the multiplication 5 times 3.

It is often helpful to use arrays for real-life multiplication problems.

EXAMPLE 2 L&M's Print Shop makes business cards in 3 colors: white, beige, and light blue. The shop has 4 types of print to choose from: boldface, italic, fine line, and Roman.

(a) Set up an array that describes all possible business cards that can be made.

(b) Determine how many different types of cards can be made.

Student Learning Objectives

After studying this section, you will be able to:

① Understand multiplication of whole numbers.

② Use symbols and key words for expressing multiplication.

③ Use multiplication properties to simplify numerical and algebraic expressions.

④ Multiply two several-digit numbers.

⑤ Solve applied problems involving multiplication of whole numbers.

NOTE TO STUDENT: Fully worked-out solutions to all of the Practice Problems can be found at the back of the text starting at page SP-1

Solution

(a) We set up a 4 by 3 array where *each row corresponds to a type of print* and *each column corresponds to a color*. Each item in the array represents one possible business card.

	White	Beige	Light blue
Boldface	**Jesse Willettes** **Sales Manager** **(312) 123-5462**	**Jesse Willettes** **Sales Manager** **(312) 123-5462**	**Jesse Willettes** **Sales Manager** **(312) 123-5462**
Italic	*Jesse Willettes* *Sales Manager* *(312) 123-5462*	*Jesse Willettes* *Sales Manager* *(312) 123-5462*	*Jesse Willettes* *Sales Manager* *(312) 123-5462*
Fine line	Jesse Willettes Sales Manager (312) 123-5462	Jesse Willettes Sales Manager (312) 123-5462	Jesse Willettes Sales Manager (312) 123-5462
Roman	Jesse Willettes Sales Manager (312) 123-5462	Jesse Willettes Sales Manager (312) 123-5462	Jesse Willettes Sales Manager (312) 123-5462

(b) We have a 4 by 3 array that corresponds to the multiplication 4 times 3, or 12 business cards.

Practice Problem 2 A manufacturer makes 3 different types of bikes; dirt, racer, and road. Each type comes in 5 different colors: red, blue, green, pink, and black.

(a) Set up an array that describes all possible bikes that can be made.

(b) Determine how many different bikes can be made.

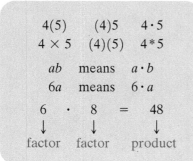

 Using Symbols and Key Words for Expressing Multiplication

In mathematics there are several ways of indicating multiplication. We write the multiplication problem *4 times 5* as illustrated in the margin.

If two variables a and b are multiplied, we indicate this by writing ab, with *no symbol between the a and b*. If a number is multiplied by a variable, we write the number first with *no symbol* between the number and the variable. Thus $6a$ indicates "six times a number."

The numbers or variables we multiply are called **factors.** The *result* of the multiplication is called the **product.**

EXAMPLE 3 Identify the product and the factors.

(a) $5(4) = 20$ **(b)** $3x = 12$

Solution

(a) 5 and 4 are the factors and 20 is the product.
(b) 3 and x are factors and 12 is the product.

Practice Problem 3 Identify the product and the factors in each equation.

(a) $9 \cdot 7 = 63$ **(b)** $xy = z$

The word *product* is also used to indicate the operation of multiplication. There are several other English phrases used to describe multiplication. The following table gives some English phrases and their translated equivalents written using mathematical symbols.

English Phrase	Translation into Symbols
The *product* of two and three	2(3) or 2·3
The *product* of x and y	xy
Six *times* a number	$6x$
Double a number	$2x$
Twice a number	$2x$
Triple a number	$3x$

 Translate using numbers and symbols.

(a) The product of four and a number   **(b)** Triple a number

Solution

(a) The product of four and a number   **(b)** Triple a number

$$4 \quad \cdot \quad n = 4n \qquad\qquad 3 \quad \cdot \quad n = 3n$$

 Practice Problem 4 Translate using numbers and symbols.

(a) Double a number   **(b)** Two times a number

Using Multiplication Properties to Simplify Numerical and Algebraic Expressions

Like addition, multiplication is **commutative.** By this we mean that the order in which we multiply factors does not change the product. We use an array to illustrate this fact.

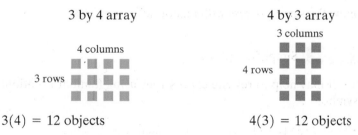

3 by 4 array

4 columns

3 rows

4 by 3 array

3 columns

4 rows

$3(4) = 12$ objects

$4(3) = 12$ objects

Both arrays represent multiplication of 3 and 4; $3(4) = 12$ and $4(3) = 12$, illustrating that multiplication is commutative.

Multiplication is also **associative,** meaning that we can regroup the factors when multiplying and the product does not change.

We state these properties as follows.

COMMUTATIVE PROPERTY OF MULTIPLICATION $ab = ba$

Changing the order of factors does not change the product.

$$5(6) = 6(5)$$
$$30 = 30$$

ASSOCIATIVE PROPERTY OF MULTIPLICATION $(ab)c = a(bc)$

Changing the grouping of factors does not change the product.

$$(7 \cdot 3) \cdot 2 = 7 \cdot (3 \cdot 2)$$
$$21(2) = 7(6)$$
$$42 = 42$$

In addition to these properties there are two other properties of multiplication. The **identity property of 1** states that when any number is multiplied by 1, the product is that number: $a \cdot 1 = a$; $2 \cdot 1 = 2$. The **multiplication property of 0** states that when any number is multiplied by 0, the product is 0: $a \cdot 0 = 0$; $2 \cdot 0 = 0$.

We list a few other facts that can help us with multiplication.

1. Multiplying by 2 is the same as doubling a number.
2. Multiplying by 5 is the same as repeatedly adding 5, which is easy since all the numbers end with 0 or 5: 5, 10, 15, 20, 25, ...
3. Multiplying any number by 10 can be done simply by attaching a 0 to the end of that number.

$$3(10) = 30 \qquad 4(10) = 40 \qquad 5(10) = 50$$

We can use these properties and facts to make multiplication of several numbers easier.

EXAMPLE 5 Multiply. $4 \cdot 2 \cdot 4 \cdot 5$

Solution

$= \quad 4 \cdot 2 \cdot 4 \cdot 5$ Use the commutative property to change the order of factors so that one factor is 10.

$= 4 \cdot 4 \cdot 2 \cdot 5$ $4 \cdot 4 = 16$; $2 \cdot 5 = 10$

$= \qquad 16 \cdot 10$ To multiply $16(10)$, write 16 and attach a zero at the end.

$= \qquad 160$

Practice Problem 5 Multiply.

(a) $2 \cdot 6 \cdot 0 \cdot 3$ **(b)** $2 \cdot 3 \cdot 1 \cdot 5$

We follow the same process with algebraic expressions.

EXAMPLE 6 Simplify. $2(3)(n \cdot 7)$

Solution It may help to rewrite expressions using familiar notation: the multiplication symbol $\cdot$.

$$\begin{aligned}
2(3)(n \cdot 7) &= 2 \cdot 3 \cdot (n \cdot 7) && \text{Rewrite using familiar notation.} \\
&= 6 \cdot (n \cdot 7) && \text{Multiply } 2 \cdot 3 = 6. \\
&= 6 \cdot (7 \cdot n) && \text{Change the order of factors.} \\
&= (6 \cdot 7) \cdot n && \text{Regroup.} \\
2(3)(n \cdot 7) &= 42n && \text{Multiply and write in standard notation: } 42 \cdot n = 42n.
\end{aligned}$$

Practice Problem 6 Simplify.

(a) $4(x \cdot 3)$ **(b)** $2(4)(n \cdot 5)$

Understanding the Concept

Memorizing of Multiplication Facts

If we think of multiplication as repeated addition, very little memorization is needed to learn the multiplication facts. Once we know the 2, 5, and 10 times tables, which are fairly easy to learn, we can get the rest using the methods that follow.

For example, from the 5 times table we can get the 4 and 6 times tables as follows. To find 4(7) we think

$$5(7) - 7 \text{ is the same as } 4(7)$$

$$(7 + 7 + 7 + 7 + 7) \qquad 7 + 7 + 7 + 7 = 28$$
$$35 - 7 = 28$$

$$5(7) \qquad + 7 \text{ is the same as } 6(7)$$

$$(7 + 7 + 7 + 7 + 7) + 7 \qquad 7 + 7 + 7 + 7 + 7 + 7 = 42$$
$$35 + 7 = 42$$

Similarly, from the 10 times table we can get the 9 times table, and from the 2 times table we can get the 3 times table.

Exercise

1. Use the techniques discussed to find each product.

(a) 3(7) **(b)** 4(8)

(c) 6(8) **(d)** 9(8)

Multiplying Two Several-Digit Numbers

The numbers 10, 100, 200, and 2000 have **trailing zeros** (zeros at the end). We can multiply these numbers fairly easily. For example, to find 3 times 300 we use repeated addition: 300 + 300 + 300 = 900. We see that to find 3(300) we need only *multiply the nonzero digits* (numbers that are not equal to zero) and attach the number of trailing zeros to the right side of the product.

EXAMPLE 7 Multiply. (547)(600)

Solution Since the number 600 has trailing zeros, we use the method stated above. We multiply the nonzero digits and attach the trailing zeros to the right side of the product.

$$
\begin{array}{r}
\overset{2\,4}{547} \\
\times \quad 600 \\
\hline
328200
\end{array}
$$
← Bring down the trailing zeros.

$6(7) = 42$; place the 2 here and carry the 4.

$6(4) = 24$. Then add the carried digit: $24 + 4 = 28$. Place the 8 here and carry the 2.

$6(5) = 30$. Then add the carried digit: $30 + 2 = 32$.

$$(547)(600) = 328{,}200$$

Practice Problem 7 Multiply. 436(700)

How can we multiply numbers with several digits when there are no trailing zeros? Consider the multiplication $2 \cdot 23$. Recall that in expanded notation $23 = 20 + 3$ or $3 + 20$. Thus $2 \cdot 23 = 2(3 + 20)$. We can use the expanded notation to see how to multiply large numbers using a *condensed form*.

Expanded Notation Process		Condensed Form

$2 \cdot 23 = 2 \cdot (3 + 20)$ To multiply $2 \cdot (3 + 20)$, we

$ = (3 + 20) + (3 + 20)$ can add $(3 + 20)$ twice.

$ = (3 + 3) + (20 + 20)$ We regroup.

$ = 2 \cdot 3 + 2 \cdot 20$ $3 + 3 = 2 \cdot 3;\ 20 + 20 = 2 \cdot 20$

$ = 6 + 40 = 46$

Condensed Form:

$$\begin{array}{r} 23 \\ \times\ 2 \\ \hline 46 \end{array} \quad \begin{array}{l} 2 \cdot 3 = 6 \\ 2 \cdot 20 = 40 \end{array}$$

We see that we can multiply $2 \cdot 23$ simply by calculating $2 \cdot 3$ and $2 \cdot 20$ using the condensed form.

EXAMPLE 8   Multiply. 857(43)

Solution   To multiply 857(43), we multiply 857(3 + 40) or 857(3) + 857(40) using the condensed form.

$$\begin{array}{r} 857 \\ \times\ 43 \\ \hline 2571 \\ 34280 \\ \hline 36{,}851 \end{array}$$

— Multiply: $3(857) = 2571$.

— To find the product $40(857) = 34{,}280$, we multiply $4(857)$ and add one trailing zero.

— Add.

The products 2571 and $34{,}280$ are called **partial products.**

NOTE TO STUDENT: Fully worked-out solutions to all of the Practice Problems can be found at the back of the text starting at page SP-1

Practice Problem 8   Multiply. 936(38)

EXAMPLE 9   Multiply. 3679(102)

Solution

$$\begin{array}{r} 3679 \\ \times\ 102 \\ \hline 7358 \\ 00000 \\ 367900 \\ \hline 375{,}258 \end{array}$$

Multiply: $2(3679)$.

Multiply: $0(3679)$, and attach 1 trailing zero.

Multiply: $100(3679)$, or $1(3679)$ and attach 2 trailing zeros.

Add.

$(3679)(102) = 375{,}258$

We can eliminate the trailing zeros in the partial products if we line up the partial products correctly.

$$\begin{array}{r} 3\ 6\ 7\ 9 \\ \times\ 1\ 0\ 2 \\ \hline 7\ 3\ 5\ 8 \\ 0\ 0\ 0 \\ 3\ 6\ 7\ 9 \\ \hline 375{,}2\ 5\ 8 \end{array}$$

Place the 8 under the 2.

Place the 0 under the 0.

Place the 9 under the 1.

Practice Problem 9   Multiply. 203(4651)

⑤ Solving Applied Problems Involving Multiplication of Whole Numbers

One of the most important steps in solving a word problem is determining what operation(s) we must perform to find the answer. Applied problems that require the multiplication operation often state key words such as *times* and *product*, deal with *arrays* (rows and columns), or represent situations involving *repeated addition*. When reading a word problem, look for this information so that you can easily determine that you must perform the multiplication operation to solve the problem.

Remember to use the following three steps in the problem-solving process.

Step 1. *Understand the problem.*

Step 2. *Calculate and state the answer.*

Step 3. *Check your answer.*

EXAMPLE 10 Jessica drove an average speed of 60 miles per hour for 7 hours (per hour means each hour). How far did she drive?

Solution *Understand the problem.* We draw a diagram and see that this is a situation that involves repeated addition, which indicates that we multiply.

⊢ 60 miles ⊣ ⊢ 60 miles ⊣ ⊢ 60 miles ⊣ and so on ...
↓ ↓ ↓
1 hour   1 hour   1 hour   ...

Calculate and state the answer.

$$
\begin{array}{rl}
60 & \text{Miles driven each hour} \\
\times\ 7 & \text{Number of hours driven} \\
\hline
420 & \text{Total miles driven}
\end{array}
$$

Check. From the diagram we can see that in 3 hours Jessica drove 180 miles (60 + 60 + 60). Thus in 6 hours she drove 360 miles (180 miles + 180 miles). Now, since she drove 60 miles the seventh hour we add 360 + 60 = 420 miles.

Practice Problem 10 Drew earns $9 per hour as a retail clerk. How much will he earn if he works 30 hours?

EXAMPLE 11 An apartment building is 4 stories high with 6 apartments on each floor. How many apartments are in the apartment building?

Solution *Understand the problem.* We draw a picture and see that this situation deals with an array and thus requires that we multiply.

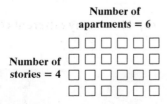

Calculate and state the answer. We have a 4 by 6 array. To find the total number of items in the array, we multiply 4 · 6 = 24. There are 24 apartments in the building.

Check. We can use repeated addition and add 6 four times: 6 + 6 + 6 + 6 = 24. We get the same result.

Practice Problem 11 Allen is building a brick wall. The wall will be 12 bricks high and 30 bricks long. How many bricks will Allen need to build the wall?

Verbal and Writing Skills

Translate the symbols into words.

1. (a) $4x$

   (b) ab

2. (a) $7y$

   (b) xy

Draw two arrays that represent each product.

3. 2 times 3

4. 4 times 2

State what property is represented in each mathematical statement.

5. $3(6 \cdot 5) = (3 \cdot 6)5$

6. $3(6 \cdot 5) = (6 \cdot 5) \cdot 3$

Fill in each box to complete each problem.

7. $3 \cdot 4(2y)$

$= 3 \cdot 4 \cdot \boxed{} \cdot y$

$= \boxed{} y$

8. $4 \cdot 5(3x)$

$= 4 \cdot 5 \cdot \boxed{} \cdot x$

$= \boxed{} x$

9. $(3a) \cdot 4 \cdot 2$

$= 3 \cdot \boxed{} \cdot 4 \cdot 2$

$= 3 \cdot 4 \cdot 2 \cdot \boxed{}$

$= \boxed{} a$

10. $(4y) \cdot 3 \cdot 2$

$= 4 \cdot \boxed{} \cdot 3 \cdot 2$

$= 4 \cdot 3 \cdot 2 \cdot \boxed{}$

$= \boxed{} y$

11. *Shirt and Tie* Anthony has 4 ties: brown, black, gray, and dark blue, and 3 shirts: white, pink, and blue.

   (a) Set up an array that shows all the possible outfits that Anthony can make.

   (b) How many different outfits are possible?

12. *Carpet and Window Blinds* Gerry has a choice of 4 carpet colors: beige, gray, blue, and light brown; and 3 colors of blinds: white, pale blue, and rose.

   (a) Set up an array that shows all the possible color combinations of carpet and blinds that Gerry can choose from.

   (b) How many different combinations are possible?

Ice Cream Toppings *The Ice Cream Palace has 8 flavors of ice cream: vanilla, French vanilla, chocolate, strawberry, coffee, pecan, chocolate chip, and mint chip. There are 5 toppings for the ice cream: fudge, cherry, candy sprinkle, caramel, and nut.*

13. How many different one-topping single scoop ice cream dishes can you order?

14. If the Ice Cream Palace increases the number of flavors to 10, how many different one-topping ice cream dishes can you order?

Identify the factors and the product in each equation.

15. $6(3) = 18$

16. $4(7) = 28$

17. $22x = 88$

18. $7a = 49$

Translate using numbers and symbols.

19. Seven times a number

20. A number times five

21. Triple a number

22. Double a number

23. The product of six and a number

24. The product of a and b

Use what you have learned about the properties of multiplication to answer each question.

25. If $x \cdot y = 0$ and $x = 6$, then $y = ?$

26. If $a \cdot b = 0$ and $a = 2$, then $b = ?$

27. If $x(y \cdot z) = 40$, then $(x \cdot y)z = ?$

28. If $b(a \cdot c) = 30$, then $(a \cdot b) \cdot c = ?$

Multiply. See Example 5.

29. $(3)(6)(2)(5)$

30. $(4)(5)(2)(2)$

31. $(2)(3)(8)(5)$

32. $(5)(4)(3)(2)$

33. $2 \cdot 4 \cdot 6 \cdot 0$

34. $9 \cdot 0 \cdot 3 \cdot 7$

35. $4 \cdot 2 \cdot 4 \cdot 5$

36. $3 \cdot 2 \cdot 4 \cdot 5$

Simplify.

37. $8(6b)$

38. $7(5b)$

39. $5(z \cdot 8)$

40. $4(x \cdot 6)$

41. $8(a \cdot 7)$

42. $3(a \cdot 6)$

43. $2(7 \cdot c)$

44. $5(8 \cdot x)$

45. $9(2)(x \cdot 5)$

46. $5(3)(2 \cdot z)$

47. $9(2)(0 \cdot y)$

48. $0(5)(z \cdot 9)$

49. $6(3)(1 \cdot b)$

50. $7(4)(x \cdot 1)$

51. $2 \cdot 3(5y)$

52. $6 \cdot 3(4y)$

53. $(6x)3 \cdot 7$

54. $(2a)5 \cdot 4$

55. $3(5y) \cdot 6$

56. $4(3a) \cdot 5$

Multiply. For more practice, refer to Appendix D.

57. $9(637)$

58. $8(926)$

59. $7(602)$

60. $6(405)$

61. $398(300)$

62. $578(500)$

63. $793(600)$

64. $871(300)$

65. $\begin{array}{r} 76 \\ \times\ 68 \\ \hline \end{array}$

66. $\begin{array}{r} 81 \\ \times\ 34 \\ \hline \end{array}$

67. $\begin{array}{r} 32 \\ \times\ 59 \\ \hline \end{array}$

68. $\begin{array}{r} 44 \\ \times\ 68 \\ \hline \end{array}$

69. $\begin{array}{r} 847 \\ \times\ 56 \\ \hline \end{array}$

70. $\begin{array}{r} 668 \\ \times\ 95 \\ \hline \end{array}$

71. $\begin{array}{r} 455 \\ \times\ 86 \\ \hline \end{array}$

72. $\begin{array}{r} 322 \\ \times\ 74 \\ \hline \end{array}$

73. $354(702)$

74. $632(201)$

75. $409(432)$

76. $(201)631$

77. $8324(922)$

78. $4456(578)$

79. $3006(837)$

80. $9002(563)$

81. $12,107(808)$

82. $23,109(605)$

83. $61,711(1000)$

84. $86,246(2000)$

Applications

85. *Total Weekly Pay* A restaurant cook earns $8 per hour and works 40 hours per week. Calculate the cook's total pay for the week.

86. *Airplane Travel Distance* An airplane travels for 6 hours at an average speed of 450 miles per hour. How far does it travel?

87. *Orange Trees in a Grove* An orange grove has 15 rows of trees with 25 trees in each row. How many orange trees are in the grove?

88. *Flowers in a Garden* John plants 6 rows of plants in his garden. Each row contains 12 small plants. How many plants does he have?

89. *Spelling Books Purchased* East Gate Academy purchased 327 spelling workbooks at $12 per book. What was the total cost of the workbooks?

90. *Yards Rushed* A football player averages 116 yards per game rushing. At this average, how many rushing yards will be gained in a 9-game season?

91. *Hotel Curtain Purchase* A five-story hotel has 40 rooms on each floor. The owners are purchasing 25 boxes of curtains at a discount. If there are 10 sets of curtains in each box, can the owners replace one set of curtains in every room of the hotel? Why or why not?

92. *Tiles Needed* Robert will be laying tile on sections of both floors of a two-story store. He has determined that each floor will require 50 rows of tile with 35 tiles in each row. Robert ordered 46 boxes of tiles at a discount. If there are 75 tiles in each box, will Robert have enough tiles to complete the job? Why or why not?

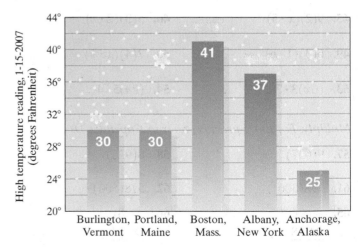

Temperatures in Various Cities Use the bar graph to answer exercises 93 and 94.

93. (a) What was the high temperature in Portland on January 15, 2007?

(b) If the high temperature reading in Honolulu, Hawaii, was two times the high temperature in Albany, New York, what was the high in Honolulu that day?

94. (a) What was the high temperature in Boston on January 15, 2007?

(b) On January 15, 2007, the high temperature reading in Buffalo, New York, was two times the high temperature in Burlington, Vermont. What was the high in Buffalo that day?

High temperature reading, 1-15-2007 (degrees Fahrenheit)

44°	
40°	41 (Boston, Mass.)
36°	37 (Albany, New York)
32°	
28°	30 (Burlington, Vermont) 30 (Portland, Maine)
24°	25 (Anchorage, Alaska)
20°	Burlington, Vermont Portland, Maine Boston, Mass. Albany, New York Anchorage, Alaska

Source: www.almanac.com

One Step Further *Simplify.*

95. $2a(4b)(5c)$

96. $(8x)(2y)(3z)$

97. $4(3a)(2b)(10c)$

98. $3(2x)(3y)(5z)$

99. $x(4y)7z$

100. $8a(5b)2c$

To Think About *Multiplication facts can be listed in a table such as shown here. For example, the product of 9 and 3 is placed where row 9 and column 3 meet.*

101. Fill in the multiplication table using the following step-by-step directions.

   (a) Use the multiplication property of zero to fill in the second row. Now, use the commutative property to fill in the second column.

   (b) Use the identity property of 1 to fill in the third row. Now, use the commutative property to fill in the third column.

   (c) Complete the 2 times table: $2 \cdot 1, 2 \cdot 2, 2 \cdot 3$, and so on. Place the products in the fourth row. Now, use the commutative property to place the products in the fourth column.

   (d) Complete the 5 times table: $5 \cdot 1, 5 \cdot 2, 5 \cdot 3$, and so on. Place the products in the seventh row. Now, use the commutative property to place the products in the seventh column.

   (e) How many multiplication facts are blank in the table?

   (f) Since the 0, 1, 2, and 5 times tables are fairly simple to learn, what does this process tell you about the amount of memorization necessary to learn all the multiplication facts?

	0	1	2	3	4	5	6	7	8	9
0										
1										
2										
3										
4										
5										
6										
7										
8										
9										

Cumulative Review

102. **[1.2.4]** Add. $426{,}862 + 2128$

103. **[1.3.4]** Subtract. $7000 - 142$

104. **[1.1.5]** Round to the nearest thousand. 826,540

105. **[1.1.5]** Round to the nearest ten thousand. 168,406,000

106. **[1.3.5]** *Electric Bill* Julio's electric bill for April was $97. If he planned a budget that included electricity expenses of $120 a month, how much less was the bill than the budget allotment?

107. **[1.3.5]** *Distance Traveled* Mary Ann is planning to drive 920 miles to her sister's house over a two-day period. If she stays at a hotel 455 miles from her house the first night, how far must she drive the second day?

Quick Quiz 1.4

1. Translate using numbers and symbols. The product of six and a number

2. Multiply. $(1610)(105)$

3. Simplify by multiplying. $3a(2b)(5)$

4. **Concept Check** Explain what to do with the zeros when you multiply 546×2000

1.5 DIVIDING WHOLE NUMBER EXPRESSIONS

Student Learning Objectives

After studying this section, you will be able to:

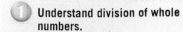 Understand division of whole numbers.

 Use symbols and key words for expressing division.

3 Master basic division facts.

4 Perform long division with whole numbers.

5 Solve applied problems involving division of whole numbers.

When is division necessary to solve real-life problems? How do I divide whole numbers? Both these questions are answered in this section. It is just as important to know when a situation requires division as it is to know how to divide. Even if we use a calculator, we must know when the situation requires us to divide.

1 Understanding Division of Whole Numbers

Suppose we wanted to display 12 roses in bouquets of 3. To determine the number of bouquets we can make, we count out 12 roses and repeatedly take out sets of 3.

$12 - 3 = 9$ 🌹	$9 - 3 = 6$ 🌹
1 bouquet	1 bouquet
$6 - 3 = 3$ 🌹	$3 - 3 = 0$ 🌹
1 bouquet	1 bouquet
4 bouquets can be made.	

By repeatedly subtracting 3, we found how many groups of 3 are in 12. In mathematics we express this as **division:**

$$12 \text{ divided by } 3 \text{ equals } 4.$$

The symbols used for division are $\overline{)}\ \ $, $\div$, $/$, $\rule{1cm}{0.4pt}$. We can write a division problem in any of the following ways:

$$3\overline{)12}^{\,4} \qquad 12 \div 3 = 4 \qquad 12/3 = 4 \qquad \frac{12}{3} = 4$$

3 divided into 12 equals 4   12 divided by 3 equals 4

EXAMPLE 1 Write the division statement that corresponds to the following situation. You need not carry out the division.

180 chairs in an auditorium are arranged so that there are 12 chairs in each row. How many rows of chairs are there?

Solution We draw an array with 12 columns.

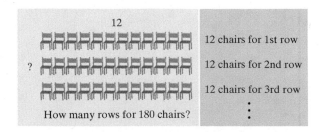

We want to know *how many groups of 12* are in 180. The division statement that corresponds to this situation is $180 \div 12$.

Practice Problem 1 Write the division statement that corresponds to the following situation. You need not carry out the division.

John has $150 to spend on paint that costs $15 per gallon. How many gallons of paint can John purchase?

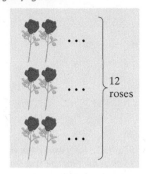

We also divide when we want to split an amount equally into a certain number of parts. For example, if we split the 12 roses into 3 equal groups, how many roses would be in each group? There would be 4 roses in each group.

The division statement that represents this situation is

12 divided by 3 equals 4 or 12 ÷ 3 = 4.

EXAMPLE 2 Write the division statement that corresponds to the following situation. You need not carry out the division.

120 students in a band are marching in 5 rows. How many students are in each row?

Solution We draw a picture. We want to *split 120 into 5 equal groups*.

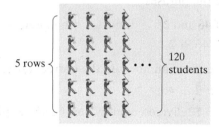

The division statement that corresponds to this situation is 120 ÷ 5.

Practice Problem 2 Write the division statement that corresponds to the following situation. You need not carry out the division.

Rita would like to donate $170 to 5 charities, giving each charity an equal amount of money. How much money will each charity receive?

 Using Symbols and Key Words for Expressing Division

When referring to division we sometimes use the words *quotient, divisor,* and *dividend* to identify the three parts in a division problem.

$$\overset{\text{quotient}}{\text{divisor}\overline{)\text{dividend}}}$$

There are also several phrases to describe division. The following table gives some English phrases and their mathematical equivalents.

English Phrase	Translation into Symbols
n divided by six	$n \div 6$
The *quotient* of seven and thirty-five	$7 \div 35$
The *quotient* of thirty-five and seven	$35 \div 7$
Fifteen items *divided equally* among five groups	$15 \div 5$
Fifteen items *shared equally* among five groups	$15 \div 5$

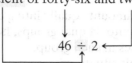

EXAMPLE 3   Translate using numbers and symbols.

(a) The quotient of forty-six and two   **(b)** The quotient of two and forty-six

Solution

(a) The quotient of forty-six and two   **(b)** The quotient of two and forty-six

$$46 \div 2$$ $$2 \div 46$$

Practice Problem 3   Translate using symbols.

(a) The quotient of twenty-six and three
(b) The quotient of three and twenty-six

NOTE TO STUDENT: Fully worked-out solutions to all of the Practice Problems can be found at the back of the text starting at page SP-1

Understanding the Concept

The Commutative Property and Division

Example 3 illustrates that the order in which we write the numbers in the division is different when we use the phrases

"the quotient of **46** and **2**"   and   "the quotient of **2** and **46**."
$$46 \div 2$$ $$2 \div 46$$

It is important to write these numbers in the correct order, as illustrated below.

The division statement: $2 \div 46$

The situation: $2 divided equally among 46 people

The division statement: $46 \div 2$

The situation: $46 divided equally between 2 people

We can see that these are **not** the same situations; thus in general, *division is not commutative:* $2 \div 46 \neq 46 \div 2$.

Exercise

1. Can you think of one case where $a \div b = b \div a$?

③ Mastering Basic Division Facts

By looking at rectangular arrays we can see how multiplication and division are related. Earlier we saw that the number of items in an array is equal to the *number of rows × the number of columns*. We can use this fact to find how many groups of 2 are in 6. That is, $6 \div 2 = ?$

The number of items in array	=	The number of rows	×	The number of columns
6	=	?	×	2

From the array we see that there are 3 rows, thus there are 3 groups of 2 in 6.

$$6 \div 2 = 3$$

These are called related sentences.

We see that the answer to the division $6 \div 2$ is that number which when multiplied by 2 yields 6. We can use this fact when we divide.

To find $6 \div 2 = ?$, think $6 = ? \times 2$.

EXAMPLE 4   Divide. $18 \div 3$

Solution

$$18 \div 3 = ? \qquad \text{Think, } 18 = ? \cdot 3.$$
$$18 \div 3 = 6 \qquad 18 = 6 \cdot 3$$

Practice Problem 4   Divide. $21 \div 7$

What about division by 0? Zero can be divided by any nonzero number, but division by zero is not possible. To see why, suppose that we could divide by zero. Then $7 \div 0 = some\ number$. Let us represent "some number" by $?$.

If $7 \div 0 = ?$

then $7 = 0 \times ?$ The related multiplication sentence.

Which would mean $7 = 0$ Since any number times 0 equals 0.

That is, we would obtain $7 = 0$, which we know is not true. Therefore, our assumption that $7 \div 0 = some\ number$ is wrong. Thus we conclude that we cannot divide by zero. We say division by 0 is **undefined.** It is helpful to remember the following basic concepts.

DIVISION PROBLEMS INVOLVING THE NUMBER 1 AND THE NUMBER 0

1. Any nonzero number divided by itself is 1 $\left(7 \div 7 = 1, \quad \dfrac{7}{7} = 1, \text{ and } \quad 7\overline{)7} \right)$.

2. Any number divided by 1 remains unchanged $\left(29 \div 1 = 29, \quad \dfrac{29}{1} = 29, \text{ and } \quad 1\overline{)29} \right)$.

3. Zero may be divided by any nonzero number; the result is always zero $\left(0 \div 4 = 0, \quad \dfrac{0}{4} = 0, \text{ and } \quad 4\overline{)0} \right)$.

4. Zero can never be the divisor in a division problem $\left(3 \div 0, \quad \dfrac{3}{0}, \text{ and } 0\overline{)3} \text{ are } \textbf{undefined.} \ 0 \div 0, \ \dfrac{0}{0}, \text{ and } \quad 0\overline{)0} \right.$ are impossible to determine. $\Big)$

EXAMPLE 5   Divide.

(a) $0 \div 9$ **(b)** $9 \div 0$ **(c)** $\dfrac{16}{16}$

Solution

(a) $0 \div 9 = 0$ 0 divided by any nonzero number is equal to 0.

(b) $9 \div 0$ Zero can never be the divisor in a division problem. $9 \div 0$ is undefined.

(c) $16 \div 16 = 1$ Any number divided by itself is 1.

Practice Problem 5   Divide.

(a) $3 \div 3$ **(b)** $3 \div 0$ **(c)** $\dfrac{0}{3}$

---

④ Performing Long Division with Whole Numbers

Suppose that we want to split 17 items equally between 2 people.

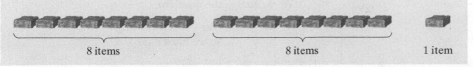

| 8 items | 8 items | 1 item |

Each person would get 8 items with 1 *left over*. We call this 1 the **remainder** (R) and write $17 \div 2 = 8\,R1$.

We use related multiplication sentences and the division symbol $\overline{)}$ when division involves large numbers, or remainders. For example,

$$2\overline{)17}^{\;?} \qquad 17 \div 2 = \;?$$

$$2\overline{)17}^{\;?} \qquad \text{Think: } 2 \cdot \;? \;= 17; \text{ two times what number is close to or equal to 17?}$$

$$2\overline{)17}^{\;8\,R} \qquad 2 \cdot 8 = 16, \text{ which is close to 17, so we have a remainder.}$$

$$\begin{array}{r} 8\,R1 \\ 2\overline{)17} \\ -16 \\ \hline 1 \end{array} \qquad \text{We subtract and get a remainder 1.}$$

Thus to divide, we *guess* the quotient and *check* by multiplying the quotient by the divisor. If the guess is too large or too small, we *adjust* it and continue the process until we get a remainder that is less than the divisor.

EXAMPLE 6   Divide and check your answer. $38 \div 6$

Solution   We *guess* that 6×6 is close to 38.

$$\begin{array}{r} 6 \\ 6\overline{)38} \\ -36 \\ \hline \end{array} \qquad \begin{array}{l}\text{Our guess, 6, is placed here.} \\ \\ 6 \times 6 = 36; \textit{ Check: 36 must be less than 38.}\end{array}$$

Since $36 < 38$, we do not need to *adjust* our guess to a smaller number.

$$\begin{array}{r} 6\,R2 \\ 6\overline{)38} \\ -36 \\ \hline 2 \end{array} \qquad \begin{array}{l}\text{We subtract: } 38 - 36 = 2. \\ \textit{Check: 2 must be less than 6. We write R2 in the quotient.}\end{array}$$

Since $2 < 6$, we do not need to *adjust* our guess to a larger number.

To verify that this is correct, we multiply the divisor by the quotient, then add the remainder:

$$\begin{array}{c} \text{Multiply } 6 \times 6 \;= 36 \\ \begin{array}{r} 6\,R2 \\ 6\overline{)38} \end{array} \quad\longleftarrow\quad \begin{array}{r} + \;2 \\ \hline 38 \end{array} \quad \text{Then add the remainder.} \\ 38 = 38 \;\checkmark \\ 38 \div 6 = 6\,R2 \end{array}$$

NOTE TO STUDENT: *Fully worked-out solutions to all of the Practice Problems can be found at the back of the text starting at page SP-1*

Practice Problem 6   Divide and check your answer. $43 \div 6$

Let's see what we do if our guess is either too large or too small.

EXAMPLE 7   Divide and check your answer. $293 \div 41$

Solution   *First guess* (too large):

$$\begin{array}{r} 8 \\ 41\overline{)293} \\ -328 \\ \hline \end{array} \qquad \begin{array}{l}\textit{Guess: } 41 \text{ times what number is close to 293? } 8 \\ \text{We write 8 in the quotient.} \\ \textit{Check: } 41(8) = 328; \text{ Our guess is too large} \\ \qquad\qquad\qquad\qquad\quad \text{so we must } \textit{adjust.}\end{array}$$

————— too large

Second guess (too small):

$$6$$
$$41\overline{)293}$$

too small $\qquad \begin{array}{c} -246 \\ \hline 47 \end{array}$

Guess: We try 6.

Check: $41(6) = 246; 246$ *is less than* 293,
but 47 is **not** less than 41.
Our guess is too small so we must *adjust*.

Third guess:

$$7 \text{ R6}$$
$$41\overline{)293}$$
$$\begin{array}{c} -287 \\ \hline 6 \end{array}$$

Guess: We try 7.

Check: $41(7) = 287; 287$ *is less than* 293, and 6 *is less than* 41. We *do not* need to *adjust* our guess, and 6 is the remainder. We write R6 in the quotient.

We verify that the answer is correct:

(divisor	·	quotient)	+	remainder	=	dividend
(41	·	7)	+	6	=	293

$$293 \div 41 = 7 \text{ R6}$$

Practice Problem 7 Divide and check your answer. $354 \div 36$

EXAMPLE 8 Divide and check your answer. $70\overline{)3672}$

Solution Accurate guesses can shorten the division process. If we consider only the *first digit of the divisor* and the *first two digits of the dividend,* it is easier to get accurate guesses.

First set of steps:

$$5$$
$$70\overline{)3672}$$
$$\begin{array}{c} -350 \\ \hline 17 \end{array}$$

Guess: We look at 7 and 36 to make our guess.
7 times what number is close to 36? 5

Check: $5(70) = 350.$
350 *is less than* 367, and
17 *is less than* 70. We *do not adjust* our guess.

Second set of steps: We bring down the next number in the dividend: 2. Then we continue the guess, check, and adjust process until there are no more numbers in the dividend to bring down.

$$52 \text{ R32}$$
$$70\overline{)3672}$$
$$\begin{array}{c} -350 \\ \hline 172 \\ -140 \\ \hline 32 \end{array}$$

Guess: We look at 7 and 17 to make our guess. We try 2.

Check: $2(70) = 140; 140$ *is less than* 172.

Check: 32 *is less than* 70.

32 is the remainder because there are no more numbers to bring down.

$$3672 \div 70 = 52 \text{ R32}$$

	(divisor	·	quotient)	+	remainder	=	dividend
Check:	(70	·	52)	+	32	=	3672.

Practice Problem 8 Divide and check your answer. $80\overline{)2611}$

NOTE TO STUDENT: Fully worked-out solutions to all of the Practice Problems can be found at the back of the text starting at page SP-1

EXAMPLE 9 Divide and check your answer. 33,897 ÷ 56

Solution *First set of steps:*

$$\begin{array}{r} 60 \\ 56\overline{)33897} \\ -336 \\ \hline 29 \end{array}$$

Guess: We look at 5 and 33 to make our guess. We try 6.
Check: 6(56) = 336; 336 *is less than* 338.

Check: 2 *is less than* 56.
We bring down the 9. Since 56 cannot be divided into 29, we write 0 in the quotient.

Second set of steps: We bring down the 7.

$$\begin{array}{r} 605 \text{ R}17 \\ 56\overline{)33897} \\ -336 \\ \hline 297 \\ -280 \\ \hline 17 \end{array}$$

Guess: We look at 5 and 29 to make our guess. We try 5.
Check: 5(56) = 280; 280 *is less than* 297, and 17 *is less than* 56.

17 is the remainder because there are no more numbers to bring down.

Practice Problem 9 Divide and check your answer. 14,911 ÷ 37

CAUTION: In Example 9 we placed a zero in the quotient because 56 did not divide into 29. You must remember to place a zero in the quotient when this happens, otherwise you will get the wrong answer. There is a big difference between 65 and 605, so be careful.

Solving Applied Problems Involving Division of Whole Numbers

As we have seen, there are various key words, phrases, and situations that indicate when we must perform the division operation. Knowing these can help us solve real-life applications.

EXAMPLE 10 Twenty-six students in Ellis High School entered their class project in a contest sponsored by the Falls City Baseball Association. The class won first place and received 250 tickets to the baseball play-offs. The teacher gave each student in the class an equal number of tickets, then donated the extra tickets to a local boys and girls club. How many tickets were donated to the boys and girls club?

Solution *Understand the problem.* Since we must split 250 equally among 26 students, we divide.

Calculate and state the answer.

$$\begin{array}{r} 9 \text{ R}16 \\ 26\overline{)250} \\ \underline{234} \\ 16 \end{array}$$

Since there are 16 tickets left over, 16 tickets are donated to the boys and girls club.

Check. (26 · 9) + 16 = 250.

Practice Problem 10 Twenty-two players on a recreational basketball team won second place in a tournament sponsored by Meris and Mann 3DMax Movie Theater. The team won 100 movie passes and divided these passes equally among players on the team. The extra passes were donated to a local children's home. How many passes were donated to the children's home?

Understanding the Concept

Conclusions and Inductive Reasoning

In Section 1.2 we saw how to use inductive reasoning to find the next number in a sequence. How accurate is inductive reasoning? Do we always come to the right conclusion? Conclusions arrived at by inductive reasoning are always tentative. They may require further investigation to avoid reaching the wrong conclusion. For example, inductive reasoning can result in more than one probable next number in a list as illustrated below.

> Identify 2 different patterns and find the next number for the following sequence: 1, 2, 4, . . .

Notice that $1 \cdot 2 = 2$ and $2 \cdot 2 = 4$. Using a pattern of multiplying the preceding number by 2, the next number is $4 \cdot 2 = 8$. For the second pattern we see that $1 + 1 = 2$ and $2 + 2 = 4$. Using a pattern of adding consecutive counting numbers, the next number is $4 + 3 = 7$.

To know for sure which answer is correct, we would need more information such as more numbers in the sequence to verify the pattern. You should always treat inductive reasoning conclusions as tentative, requiring further verification.

Exercise

1. Identify 2 different patterns and find the next number for the following sequence: 1, 1, 2, . . .

For more practice, complete exercises 55–62 on pages 53–54.

Developing Your Study Skills

Why Is Homework Necessary?

You learn mathematics by practicing, not by watching. Your instructor may make solving a mathematics problem look easy, but to learn the necessary skills you must practice them over and over again, just as your instructor once had to do. There is no other way. Learning mathematics is like learning how to play a musical instrument or to play a sport. *You must practice, not just observe, to do well.* Homework provides this practice. The amount of practice varies for each person. The more problems you do, the better you get.

Many students underestimate the amount of time each week that is required to learn math. In general, two to three hours per week per unit is a good rule of thumb. This means that for a three-unit class you should spend six to nine hours a week studying math. Spread this time throughout the week, not just in a few sittings. Your brain gets overworked just as your muscles do!

Exercise

1. Start keeping a log of the time that you spend studying math. If your performance is not up to your expectations, increase your study time.

Verbal and Writing Skills *Write the division statement that corresponds to each situation. You need not carry out the division.*

1. 220 paintings are arranged in rows so that 4 paintings are in each row. How many rows of paintings are there?

2. In the school gym, 320 chairs must be arranged in rows with 16 chairs in each row. How many rows of chairs are there?

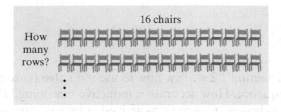

3. 225 tickets to the Dodgers' first game of the year will be distributed equally among *n* people.

4. A dinner bill totaling $*n* was split among 5 people.

5. For the division problem $15 \div 3$, which wording is correct? There may be more than one right answer.

   (a) 3 divided by 15   **(b)** 15 divided by 3
   (c) 3 divided into 15   **(d)** 15 divided into 3

6. For the division problem $18 \div 6$, which wording is correct? There may be more than one right answer.

   (a) 6 divided by 18   **(b)** 18 divided by 6
   (c) 6 divided into 18   **(d)** 18 divided into 6

Translate using numbers and symbols.

7. Twenty-seven divided by a number

8. Eight divided by a number

9. Forty-two dollars divided equally among six people

10. Sixty-three jelly beans divided equally among three children

11. The quotient of thirty-six and six

12. The quotient of forty-four and eleven

13. The quotient of three and thirty-six

14. The quotient of eleven and forty-four

Divide.

15. $42 \div 42$

16. $15 \div 15$

17. $\dfrac{0}{5}$

18. $\dfrac{0}{77}$

19. $17 \div 0$

20. $29 \div 0$

Divide and check your answer. Refer to Appendix D for more practice.

21. $58 \div 9$

22. $60 \div 9$

23. $7\overline{)2597}$

24. $5\overline{)3105}$

25. $3\overline{)1346}$

26. $6\overline{)4046}$

27. $\dfrac{1268}{30}$

28. $\dfrac{1863}{20}$

29. $30\overline{)632}$

30. $20\overline{)783}$

31. $19\overline{)5817}$

32. $32\overline{)6436}$

33. $\dfrac{1403}{29}$ **34.** $\dfrac{1301}{24}$ **35.** $1369 \div 19$ **36.** $1350 \div 16$

37. $18{,}985 \div 27$ **38.** $12{,}854 \div 42$ **39.** $11{,}571 \div 34$ **40.** $43{,}317 \div 117$

41. $113{,}317 \div 223$ **42.** $123{,}264 \div 136$ **43.** $70{,}141 \div 136$ **44.** $21{,}945 \div 29$

Applications

45. ***Computer Conference Tickets*** The 14 members of the Carver High School Chess Club team won first place in a tournament sponsored by the Carver Convention Center. The chess team won 60 tickets to the World-wide Computer Conference. The team decided to divide the tickets equally among all 14 team members and to donate the extra tickets to the PTA. How many tickets were donated to the PTA?

46. ***Entertainment Event Tickets*** The 21 members of the Laurel High School track team won first place in a tournament sponsored by the Laurel Recreation Center. The team won 75 tickets to the county fair. The team decided to divide the tickets equally among all 21 team members and to donate the extra tickets to the homeless shelter. How many tickets were donated to the shelter?

47. ***Restaurant Bill*** The bill for dinner, including tip, at Lido's Restaurant was $85. If 5 people split the bill evenly, how much did each person have to pay?

48. ***Banquet Ticket Price*** The members of the Elks Club are planning a banquet. The cost of the entire banquet will be $1071. If 63 members plan to attend, how much should the ticket price be to cover the cost of the banquet?

49. ***Travel Allowance*** JoAnn received a travel allowance of $1050 from her employer for food and lodging. If her business trip takes 6 days, how much money should she budget each day so that she will not go over her total travel allowance?

50. ***Cow Pasture Capacity*** A rancher plans to have 250 square feet of pasture for each cow on his field. If the area of the field is 156,250 square feet, how many cows should the rancher allow on the field?

51. ***Photographing Deer*** A photographer sets a telephoto lens so that she can be twice as far away from her subject as she would with a regular lens. She is taking pictures of deer that are 124 feet from her camera. How far from the deer would the photographer have to be to get the same shot with a regular lens?

52. ***Cross-Stitch Pattern*** Janice is making a cross-stitch pattern on 14-count material. This means that there are 14 squares to the inch. If Janice's pattern is 98 squares across, how many inches wide will it be?

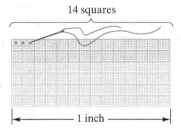

14 squares

1 inch

53. How many 41-cent stamps can be bought with 1300 cents?

54. A young toy-car collector has 218 miniature cars. He bought carrying cases to store these cars. Each carrying case holds 15 cars. He plans to give his younger brother any cars that won't fill up a case.

    (a) How many cases can he fill completely?

    (b) How many cars will he give to his brother?

To Think About *For each of the following, find the next number in the sequence by identifying the pattern.*

55. 5, 15, 45, 135, . . .

56. 4, 16, 64, 256, . . .

57. 3, 4, 7, 12, 19, 28, 39, . . .

58. 0, 2, 6, 12, 20, . . .

59. 7, 9, 10, 12, 13, 15, 16, . . .

60. 1, 6, 8, 13, 15, 20, . . .

Identify two patterns and find the next number for each of the following.

61. 0, 1, 4, . . .

62. 1, 4, 8, . . .

Complete each of the following.

63. (a) $(32 \div 4) \div 2$
(b) $32 \div (4 \div 2)$
(c) What can you say about division and the associative property?

64. (a) $(48 \div 6) \div 2$
(b) $48 \div (6 \div 2)$
(c) What can you say about division and the associative property?

Cumulative Review

65. **[1.2.1]** Translate into symbols. Seven plus x equals eleven.

66. **[1.3.4]** Subtract. $1060 - 114$

67. **[1.4.4]** Multiply. $4031 (202)$

68. **[1.1.5]** Round 556,432 to the nearest thousand.

69. **[1.3.5]** *Distance Traveled* Leo wanted to make a 1389-mile trip in 3 days to visit his aunt. He drove 430 miles the first day and 495 miles the second day. How far does Leo have to drive the third day to reach his destination?

70. **[1.3.5]** *Truck Purchase Price* The total cost of the truck Ranak purchased, including tax and license, is $29,599. If the dealer gave Ranak $6200 for his car as a trade-in and Ranak put $5500 down, what is the balance owed on the truck?

Quick Quiz 1.5

1. Translate using numbers and symbols.
   (a) the quotient of fourteen and seven
   (b) the quotient of seven and fourteen

2. Divide. $15,916 \div 39$

3. A school district receives a grant for $5,484,000 to be distributed equally among its three junior colleges. How much does each college receive?

4. Concept Check

$$13\overline{\smash{)}2645}$$
with quotient digit 2, 26 subtracted, remainder 04

Explain the next 2 steps for this division problem.

1.6 EXPONENTS AND THE ORDER OF OPERATIONS

 Writing Whole Numbers and Variables in Exponent Form

Recall that in the multiplication problem $3 \cdot 3 \cdot 3 \cdot 3 \cdot 3 = 243$ the number 3 is called a **factor.** We can write the repeated multiplication $3 \cdot 3 \cdot 3 \cdot 3 \cdot 3$ using a shorter notation, 3^5, because there are five factors of 3 in the repeated multiplication. We say that 3^5 is written in **exponent form.** 3^5 is read "three to the fifth power."

Student Learning Objectives

After studying this section, you will be able to:

1. Write whole numbers and variables in exponent form.

2. Evaluate numerical and algebraic expressions in exponent form.

3. Use symbols and key words for expressing exponents.

4. Follow the order of operations.

EXPONENT FORM

The small number 5 is called an **exponent.** Whole number exponents, except zero, tell us how many factors are in the repeated multiplication. The number 3 is called the **base.** The base is the number that is multiplied.

$$3 \cdot 3 \cdot 3 \cdot 3 \cdot 3 = 3^5 \longrightarrow \text{The exponent is 5.}$$

3 appears as a factor 5 times.   The base is 3.

We do not multiply the base 3 by the exponent 5. The 5 just tells us how many 3's are in the repeated multiplication.

If a whole number or variable does not have an exponent visible, the exponent is understood to be 1.

$$9 = 9^1 \quad \text{and} \quad x = x^1$$

EXAMPLE 1 Write in exponent form.

(a) $2 \cdot 2 \cdot 2 \cdot 2 \cdot 2 \cdot 2$ **(b)** $4 \cdot 4 \cdot 4 \cdot x \cdot x$ **(c)** 7 **(d)** $y \cdot y \cdot y \cdot 3 \cdot 3 \cdot 3 \cdot 3$

Solution

(a) $2 \cdot 2 \cdot 2 \cdot 2 \cdot 2 \cdot 2 = 2^6$ **(b)** $4 \cdot 4 \cdot 4 \cdot x \cdot x = 4^3 \cdot x^2$ or $4^3 x^2$

(c) $7 = 7^1$ **(d)** $y \cdot y \cdot y \cdot 3 \cdot 3 \cdot 3 \cdot 3 = y^3 \cdot 3^4$, or $3^4 y^3$

Note, it is standard to write the number before the variable in a term. Thus $y^3 3^4$ is written $3^4 y^3$.

Practice Problem 1 Write in exponent form.

(a) n **(b)** $6 \cdot 6 \cdot y \cdot y \cdot y \cdot y$
(c) $5 \cdot 5 \cdot 5 \cdot 5 \cdot 5 \cdot 5 \cdot 5 \cdot 5$ **(d)** $x \cdot x \cdot 8 \cdot 8 \cdot 8$

EXAMPLE 2 Write as a repeated multiplication.

(a) n^3 **(b)** 6^5

Solution

(a) $n^3 = n \cdot n \cdot n$ **(b)** $6^5 = 6 \cdot 6 \cdot 6 \cdot 6 \cdot 6$

Practice Problem 2 Write as a repeated multiplication.

(a) x^6 **(b)** 1^7

Evaluating Numerical and Algebraic Expressions in Exponent Form

To *evaluate,* or find the *value* of, an expression in exponent form, we first write the expression as repeated multiplication, then multiply the factors.

EXAMPLE 3 Evaluate each expression.

(a) 3^3 **(b)** 1^9 **(c)** 2^4

Solution

(a) $3^3 = 3 \cdot 3 \cdot 3 = 27$

(b) $1^9 = 1$

We do not need to write out this multiplication because repeated multiplication of 1 will always equal 1.

(c) $2^4 = 2 \cdot 2 \cdot 2 \cdot 2 = 16$

Practice Problem 3 Evaluate each expression.

(a) 4^3 **(b)** 8^1 **(c)** 10^2

NOTE TO STUDENT: Fully worked-out solutions to all of the Practice Problems can be found at the back of the text starting at page SP-1

Sometimes we are asked to express an answer in *exponent form* and other times to *find the value of (evaluate)* an expression. Therefore, it is important that you read the question carefully and express the answer in the correct form.

Write $5 \cdot 5 \cdot 5$ in *exponent* form: $5 \cdot 5 \cdot 5 = 5^3$.

Evaluate 5^3: $5^3 = 5 \cdot 5 \cdot 5 = 125$.

Large numbers are often expressed using a number in exponent form that has a base of 10: 10^1, 10^2, 10^3, 10^4 and so on. Let's look for a pattern to find an easy way to evaluate an expression when the base is 10.

$$10^1 = 1\,0 \qquad\qquad 10^3 = (10)(10)(10) = 1\,000$$
$$10^2 = (10)(10) = 1\,00 \qquad 10^4 = (10)(10)(10)(10) = 1\,0,000$$

Notice that when the exponent is 1 there is 1 trailing zero; when the exponent is 2 there are 2 trailing zeros; when it is 3 there are 3 trailing zeros; and so on. Thus to calculate a power of 10, we write 1 and attach the number of trailing zeros named by the exponent.

EXAMPLE 4 Evaluate 10^7.

Solution

Write 1.

10,000,000

The exponent is 7; attach 7 trailing zeros.

$10^7 = 10,000,000$

Practice Problem 4 Find the value of 10^5.

To evaluate the expression x^2 when *x is equal to 4,* we replace the variable x with the number 4 and find the value of 4^2: $4^2 = 4 \cdot 4 = 16$. We can write the statement "*x is equal to 4*" using math symbols "$x = 4$."

EXAMPLE 5   Evaluate x^3 for $x = 3$.

Solution

$$x^3 \rightarrow (3)^3 \qquad \text{Replace } x \text{ with 3.}$$

$$3 \cdot 3 \cdot 3 = 27 \qquad \text{Write as repeated multiplication, then multiply.}$$

When $x = 3$, x^3 is equal to 27.

Practice Problem 5   Evaluate y^2 for $y = 8$.

 ## Using Symbols and Key Words for Expressing Exponents

How do you say 10^2 or 5^3? We can say "10 raised to the power 2," or "5 raised to the power 3," but the following phrases are more commonly used.

If the value of the exponent is 2, we say the base is **squared.**

6^2 is read "six squared."

If the value of the exponent is 3, we say the base is **cubed.**

6^3 is read "six cubed."

If the value of the exponent is *greater than* 3, we say that the base is raised to the **(exponent)th power.**

6^5 is read "six to the fifth power."

EXAMPLE 6   Translate using symbols.

(a) Five cubed   **(b)** Seven squared   **(c)** y to the eighth power

Solution

(a) Five cubed $= 5^3$ **(b)** Seven squared $= 7^2$ **(c)** y to the eighth power $= y^8$

Practice Problem 6   Translate using symbols.

(a) Four to the sixth power   **(b)** x cubed   **(c)** Ten squared

 ## Following the Order of Operations

It is often necessary to perform more than one operation to solve a problem. For example, if you bought one pair of socks for $3 and 4 undershirts for $5 each, you would multiply first and then add to find the total cost. In other words, the order in which we performed the operations (order of operations) was multiply first, then add. However, the order of operations may not be as clear when dealing with a math statement. When we see the problem written as $3 + 4(5)$ understanding what to do can be tricky. Do we add, then multiply, or do we multiply before adding? Let's work this calculation both ways.

Add First	Multiply First
$3 + 4(5) = 7(5) = 35$ Wrong!	$3 + 4(5) = 3 + 20 = 23$ Correct

Since $3 + 4(5)$ can be written $3 + (5 + 5 + 5 + 5) = 3 + 20$, 23 is correct. Thus we see that the order of operations makes a difference. The following rule tells which operations to do first: the correct **order of operations.** We call this a *list of priorities.*

ORDER OF OPERATIONS

Follow this order of operations.

Do first   **1.** Perform operations inside *parentheses*.

           2. Simplify any expression with *exponents*.

           3. *Multiply* or *divide* from left to right.

Do last   **4.** *Add* or *subtract* from left to right.

parentheses → exponents → multiply or divide → add or subtract

Now, following the order of operations, we can clearly see that to find $3 + 4(5)$, we multiply and then add. You will find it easier to follow the order of operations if you keep your work neat and organized, perform one operation at a time, and follow the sequence *identify, calculate, replace*.

1. *Identify* the operation that has the highest priority.
2. *Calculate* this operation.
3. *Replace* the operation with your result.

EXAMPLE 7 Evaluate. $2^3 - 6 + 4$

Solution

$2^3 - 6 + 4 = 8 - 6 + 4$ *Identify*: The highest priority is **exponents.**
                                            Calculate: $2 \cdot 2 \cdot 2 = 8$. *Replace*: 2^3 with 8.

           $= 8 - 6 + 4$ *Identify*: **Subtraction** has the highest priority.
                                              Calculate: $8 - 6 = 2$. *Replace*: $8 - 6$ with 2.

                $= 2 + 4$ *Identify*: **Addition** is last. *Calculate*: $2 + 4 = 6$.

$2^3 - 6 + 4 = 6$ *Replace*: $2 + 4$ with 6.

Note that addition and subtraction have equal priority. We do the operations as they appear, reading from *left* to *right*. In Example 7 the subtraction appears first, so we subtract before we add.

Practice Problem 7 Evaluate. $3^2 + 2 - 5$

NOTE TO STUDENT: *Fully worked-out solutions to all of the Practice Problems can be found at the back of the text starting at page SP-1*

EXAMPLE 8 Evaluate. $2 \cdot 3^2$

Solution

$2 \cdot 3^2 = 2 \cdot 9$ *Identify*: The highest priority is **exponents.** *Calculate*: $3 \cdot 3 = 9$.
                                Replace: 3^2 with 9.

        $= 2 \cdot 9$ *Identify*: **Multiplication** is last. *Calculate*: $2 \cdot 9 = 18$.
                              Replace: $2 \cdot 9$ with 18.

$2 \cdot 3^2 = 18$

CAUTION: $2 \cdot 3^2$ *does not equal* 6^2! We must follow the rules for the order of operations and simplify the exponent 3^2 before we multiply; otherwise, we will get the wrong answer.

Practice Problem 8 Evaluate. $4 \cdot 2^3$

EXAMPLE 9   Evaluate. $4 + 3(6 - 2^2) - 7$

Solution   We always perform the calculations inside the parentheses first. Once inside the parentheses, we proceed using the order of operations.

$4 + 3(6 - 2^2) - 7$ Within the parentheses, **exponents** have the highest priority: $2^2 = 4$.

$= 4 + 3(6 - 4) - 7$ We must finish all operations inside the

$= 4 + 3(2) - 7$ parentheses, so we **subtract:** $6 - 4 = 2$.

$= 4 + 6 - 7$ The highest priority is **multiplication:** $3 \cdot 2 = 6$.

$= 10 - 7$ **Add** first: $4 + 6 = 10$.

$= 3$ **Subtract** last: $10 - 7 = 3$.

$4 + 3(6 - 2^2) - 7 = 3$

Practice Problem 9   Evaluate. $2 + 7(10 - 3 \cdot 2) - 4$

As we stated earlier, it is easier to follow the order of operations if we keep our work neat and organized, perform one operation at a time, and follow the sequence: **identify, calculate, replace.**

EXAMPLE 10   Evaluate. $\dfrac{(6 + 6 \div 3)}{(5 - 1)}$

Solution   We rewrite the problem as division and then follow the order of operations.

$(6 + 6 \div 3) \quad \div \quad (5 - 1)$ We perform operations inside parentheses first.

$(6 + 2) \quad \div \quad 4$ $6 \div 3 = 2; \quad 5 - 1 = 4$.

$8 \quad \div \quad 4 = 2$ Divide.

Practice Problem 10   Evaluate.

$$\frac{(4 + 8 \div 2)}{(7 - 3)}$$

Developing Your Study Skills

Reviewing for an Exam

Reviewing for an exam enables you to connect concepts you learned over several classes. Your review activities should cover all the components of the learning cycle.

The Learning Cycle

Reading $\longrightarrow$ Writing

$\uparrow$ $\downarrow$

Seeing $\leftarrow$ Verbalizing $\leftarrow$ Listening

1. Reread your textbook. Make 3-by-5 study cards as follows.
   - Write the name of the new term or rule on the front of the card. Then write the definition of the term or the rule on the back.
   - Write sample examples on the front of the card and the solutions on the back.
   - Periodically use these cards as flash cards and quiz yourself, or study with a classmate.

2. Reread your notes. Study returned homework and quizzes and redo problems you got wrong.

3. Read the Chapter Organizer and solve some of the review problems at the end of the chapter. Check your answers and redo problems you got wrong.

4. After you finish the exercises in Section 1.6, complete the How Am I Doing? Sections 1.1–1.6. Complete this as if it were the real exam. Do not refer to notes or to the text while completing the exercises. Then check your answers. The problems you missed are the type of problems that you should get help with and review before the exam.

5. Start reviewing several days before the exam so that you have time to get help if you need it.

It is not a good idea to complete all six steps at one time. For best results, complete each step at a separate sitting and start the process early so that you are done at least three days before the exam.

Exercise

1. Can you think of other ways of preparing for an exam that include activities in the learning cycle?

Verbal and Writing Skills

1. Write in words the question being asked by the equation $n^2 = 16$.

2. Write in words the question being asked by the equation $x^3 = 27$.

Write each product in exponent form.

3. $2 \cdot 2 \cdot 2$

4. $4 \cdot 4$

5. $a \cdot a \cdot a \cdot a \cdot a$

6. $z \cdot z$

7. 4

8. y

9. $3 \cdot 3 \cdot 3 \cdot 3$

10. $9 \cdot 9 \cdot 9$

Write each product in exponent form.

11. $5 \cdot 5 \cdot a \cdot a \cdot a$

12. $3 \cdot 3 \cdot x \cdot x \cdot x$

13. $2 \cdot 2 \cdot z \cdot z \cdot z \cdot z \cdot z$

14. $3 \cdot 3 \cdot y \cdot y \cdot y \cdot y$

15. $5 \cdot 5 \cdot 5 \cdot y \cdot y \cdot x \cdot x$

16. $7 \cdot 7 \cdot x \cdot y \cdot y$

17. $n \cdot n \cdot n \cdot n \cdot n \cdot 9 \cdot 9$

18. $x \cdot x \cdot x \cdot x \cdot x \cdot 7 \cdot 7$

Write as a repeated multiplication.

19. (a) 7^3 (b) y^5

20. (a) 7^6 (b) x^2

Evaluate.

21. 2^3

22. 3^3

23. 5^2

24. 6^2

25. 1^6

26. 1^{11}

27. 7^2

28. 3^2

29. 4^4

30. 9^3

31. 10^1

32. 5^1

33. 5^3

34. 2^4

35. 10^6

36. 10^4

37. x^2 for $x = 5$

38. y^3 for $y = 3$

39. a^4 for $a = 1$

40. b^{14} for $b = 1$

Translate using numbers and exponents.

41. Seven to the third power

42. Three cubed

43. Nine squared

44. Four to the seventh power

Evaluate.

45. $3 \cdot 4 - 7$

46. $3 \cdot 5 - 2$

47. $7^2 + 5 - 3$

48. $6^3 + 4 - 8$

49. $5 \cdot 3^2$

50. $4 \cdot 2^2$

51. $2 \cdot 2^2$

52. $4 \cdot 4^2$

53. $5^2 - 7 + 3$

54. $4^3 - 8 + 7$

55. $9 + 2 \cdot 2$

56. $5 + 3 \cdot 9$

57. $9 + (6 + 2^2)$

58. $8 + (7 + 4^3)$

59. $40 \div 5 \times 2 + 3^2$

60. $6^2 \div 6 \times 2 + 1$

61. $2 \times 15 \div 5 + 10$

62. $3 \times 12 \div 4 + 2$

63. $2^2 + 8 \div 4$

64. $3^3 + 6 \div 3$

65. $\dfrac{(8 + 4 \div 2)}{(5 - 3)}$

66. $\dfrac{(5 + 15 \div 5)}{(9 - 5)}$ **67.** $\dfrac{(3 + 1)}{(12 \div 6 \times 2)}$ **68.** $\dfrac{(16 - 4)}{(36 \div 6 \times 2)}$

69. $7 + 5(3 \cdot 4 + 7) - 2$ **70.** $3 + 4(5 \cdot 2 + 8) - 3$ **71.** $59 - 4(1 + 5 \cdot 2) + 4$

72. $88 - 3(2 + 6 \cdot 4) + 6$ **73.** $6 + 2(4 \cdot 5 + 9) - 11$ **74.** $2 + 12(3 \cdot 2 + 1) - 10$

One Step Further

75. $32 \cdot 6 - 4(4^3 - 5 \cdot 2^2) + 3$ **76.** $63 \cdot 4 - 5(3^2 + 4 \cdot 2^3) + 5$

77. $12 \cdot 5 - 3(3^3 - 2 \cdot 3^2) + 1$ **78.** $42 \cdot 5 - 3(5^2 + 2 \cdot 4^2) + 3$

To Think About

79. Fred wanted to evaluate $3 \cdot 2 + 4$. He multiplied 3 times 6 to get 18. What is wrong with his reasoning? What is the correct answer?

80. Sara wanted to evaluate $2 \cdot 4^2$. She squared 8 to get 64. What is wrong with her reasoning? What is the correct answer?

81. Multiply: $21 \cdot 10^1$; $21 \cdot 10^2$; $21 \cdot 10^3$; $21 \cdot 10^4$. Do you see a pattern that might suggest a quick way to multiply a number by a power of 10? Explain.

82. Multiply: $10^1 \cdot 10^2$; $10^1 \cdot 10^3$; $10^1 \cdot 10^4$. Do you see a pattern that might suggest a quick way to multiply 10 by a power of 10? Explain.

Cumulative Review

83. **[1.2.4]** Add. $4079 + 2762$ **84.** **[1.3.4]** Subtract. $8900 - 477$

85. **[1.4.4]** Multiply. $(387)(196)$ **86.** **[1.4.2]** Translate using symbols. The product of two and some number.

Quick Quiz 1.6

1. Write the product in exponent form.
   (a) $9 \cdot 9 \cdot 9 \cdot x \cdot x$ **(b)** $5 \cdot 5 \cdot 5 \cdot 5 \cdot 5$

2. Evaluate.
   (a) 2^4 **(b)** 1^5

3. Evaluate. $2^2 + 2(10 \div 2) - 11$

4. **Concept Check** Explain in what order you would do the steps to evaluate $50 + 3 \times 5^2 \div 25$.

In this section we will see how to translate some new types of phrases into symbols. We will also use the skills we learned in previous sections to simplify and evaluate algebraic expressions.

Using Symbols and Key Words for Expressing Algebraic Expressions

When we translate phrases into numbers and symbols we must take care to preserve the order of operations indicated by the phrase. When a phrase contains key words for more than one operation, the phrases *sum of* or *difference of* indicate that these operations must be placed within parentheses so that they are completed first. We illustrate below.

Three *times* the *difference of* five and two
↓   ↓   ↓   ↓
3   ·   (5 − 2)

The phrase *difference of* indicates that we must place 5 − 2 within parentheses.

Three times five minus two
↓   ↓   ↓   ↓   ↓
3   ·   5   −   2

We must include parentheses when we see the phrases *sum of* or *difference of* or we will get the wrong answer: $3 \cdot (5 - 2) = 3 \cdot 3 = 9$ but $3 \cdot 5 - 2 = 15 - 2 = 13$.

EXAMPLE 1   Translate using numbers and symbols.

(a) Two times x plus seven   **(b)** Two times the sum of x and seven

Solution

(a) Two times x plus seven
↓   ↓   ↓   ↓   ↓
2   ·   x   +   7
$2x + 7$

(b) Two times the sum of x and seven
↓   ↓   ↓   ↓
2   ·   (x + 7)
$2(x + 7)$

The key phrase *sum of* indicates that $x + 7$ is placed within parentheses.

Practice Problem 1   Translate using numbers and symbols.

(a) Five times y plus three   **(b)** Three times the sum of m and two

Evaluating Algebraic Expressions Involving Multiplication and Division

We evaluate variable expressions involving multiplication and division just as we did expressions involving addition and subtraction. For example, to evaluate $2n$ if n is equal to 5, we replace the variable in the expression with 5 and then simplify: $2n \rightarrow 2(5) = 10$.

EXAMPLE 2   Evaluate $\dfrac{(2a + 3)}{7}$ for $a = 9$.

Solution

$$\frac{(2a + 3)}{7} = \frac{(2 \cdot 9 + 3)}{7}$$ We replace a with 9.

$$= \frac{(18 + 3)}{7}$$ We multiply first.

$$= \frac{21}{7}$$ Next, we complete operations within the parentheses.

$$= 3$$ We divide.

Practice Problem 2

$$\text{Evaluate } \frac{(5y - 4)}{3} \text{ for } y = 2.$$

EXAMPLE 3 Evaluate.

(a) $3x + 3y + 6$ for $x = 3$ and $y = 5$ **(b)** $\dfrac{(x^2 - 2)}{y}$ for $x = 4$ and $y = 2$

Solution We replace each variable with the indicated value and then follow the order of operations to simplify.

(a) $3x + 3y + 6$
$\quad = 3 \cdot 3 + 3 \cdot 5 + 6$ We replace x with 3 and y with 5.
$\quad = 9 + 15 + 6$ We multiply first.
$\quad = 30$ We add last.

(b) $\dfrac{(x^2 - 2)}{y}$
$\quad = \dfrac{(4^2 - 2)}{2}$ We replace x with 4 and y with 2.

$\quad = \dfrac{14}{2}$ We square 4 first then subtract:
$\qquad\qquad 4^2 = 16, \ 16 - 2 = 14.$

$\quad = 7$ We divide last: $14 \div 2 = 7$.

Practice Problem 3 Evaluate.

(a) $5m - 2n + 1$ for $m = 7$ and $n = 3$ **(b)** $\dfrac{(a^3 - 2)}{b}$ for $a = 2$ and $b = 3$

NOTE TO STUDENT: Fully worked-out solutions to all of the Practice Problems can be found at the back of the text starting at page SP-1

③ Using the Distributive Property to Simplify Numerical and Algebraic Expressions

A property that is often used to simplify and multiply is the **distributive property.** This property states that we can distribute multiplication over addition or subtraction. The following example will help you understand what we mean by this.

"4 *times* $(n + 7)$" is written $4(n + 7)$.   We can find this product using repeated addition.

$4(n + 7) = (n + 7) + (n + 7) + (n + 7) + (n + 7)$ We write $4(n + 7)$ as
$\quad\quad = (n + n + n + n) + (7 + 7 + 7 + 7)$ repeated addition.

$\qquad\qquad\quad \downarrow \qquad\qquad\qquad \downarrow$ We change the order of addition and group the
$\qquad\qquad 4n \qquad + \qquad 4 \cdot 7$ n's and 7's together.

$4(n + 7) = 4n + 28$ We have 4 n's plus 4 7's.

A shorter way to do this is to **distribute** the 4 by multiplying each number or variable inside the parentheses by 4.

$$4(n + 7) = 4(n + 7) = 4 \cdot n + 4 \cdot 7 = 4n + 28$$

We can state the distributive property as follows.

DISTRIBUTIVE PROPERTY

If a, b, and c are numbers or variables, then

$$a(b + c) = ab + ac \quad \text{and} \quad a(b - c) = ab - ac$$

We distribute a over addition and subtraction by multiplying every number or variable inside the parentheses by a. Then we simplify the result.

EXAMPLE 4 Use the distributive property to simplify. $3(x - 2)$

Solution

$$3(x - 2) = 3(x - 2) = 3 \cdot x - 3 \cdot 2$$

Multiply 3 times x.

Multiply 3 times 2.

$$3(x - 2) = 3x - 6$$

Simplify.

Practice Problem 4 Use the distributive property to simplify.

(a) $2(x - 5)$ **(b)** $4(y + 3)$

CAUTION: We must only use the distributive property if the numbers or variables inside the parentheses are separated by a $+$ or $-$ sign. We *do not use the distributive property* when the numbers or variables inside the parentheses are *separated by multiplication or division symbols*. Thus, we can use the distributive property in Example 4 because in the expression $3(x - 2)$ the x and the 2 are separated by a $-$ sign. We *cannot use the distributive property* for the expression $3(2x)$ because the 2 and the x are not separated by a $+$ or $-$ sign. Thus $3(x - 2) = 3x - 6$ while $3(2x) = 3 \cdot 2 \cdot x = 6x$.

EXAMPLE 5 Simplify. $2(y + 1) + 4$

Solution First we use the distributive property and then we simplify.

$$2(y + 1) + 4 = 2 \cdot y + 2 \cdot 1 + 4$$ We use the distributive property
$$= 2y + 2 + 4$$ to multiply $2(y + 1)$.
$$= 2y + 6$$ We simplify: $2 + 4 = 6$.

Practice Problem 5 Simplify. $7(y + 3) + 2$

Developing Your Study Skills

Getting the Most from Your Study Time

Did you know that there are many things you can do to increase your learning when you study? If you use the following strategies, you can improve the way you study and learn more while studying less.

1. Read the material and review your class notes on the same day as your class meets.

2. Do homework in more than one sitting so that you are fresh for the later problems, which are usually the hardest.

3. Check your answer only **after** you complete a problem. Put an * beside any problem that you get wrong or don't know how to start.

4. Follow up wrong answers. Check your work for errors or look in the book for a similar problem. Compare your solution with the book's and, if necessary, rework the problem using the book's solution as a guide. Use this process to solve the

problems you didn't know how to start. If you still can't solve a problem, reread the section or ask for help.

5. Revisit * problems. After finishing the assignment, work another problem that is like each * problem. In this text, an even-numbered problem is similar to the preceding odd-numbered problem.

6. Review or rewrite your notes at the end of each week. Work a few problems in the sections covered since the last test. Review past tests periodically, especially if you are having difficulty or having trouble remembering earlier material.

It is important that you realize that completing your homework assignment and studying your homework are separate activities. Activity 4 describes the process of *completing your homework*, whereas activity 5 describes the process of *studying your homework*. For best results, these two activities should be done at different times.

Verbal and Writing Skills

State what property is represented in each mathematical statement.

1. $5(3 + 4) = 5 \cdot 3 + 5 \cdot 4$

2. $5(6 - 4) = 5 \cdot 6 - 5 \cdot 4$

Are the following true or false? Explain your answers.

3. (a) $8(3y) = 8 \cdot 3 \cdot 8 \cdot y$

  (b) $8(3 + y) = 8 \cdot 3 + 8 \cdot y$

4. (a) $4(2x) = 4 \cdot 2 \cdot 4 \cdot x$

  (b) $4(2 + x) = 4 \cdot 2 + 4 \cdot x$

Fill in each box with the correct number or variable.

5. $2(x + 1) = 2 \cdot \boxed{} + 2 \cdot \boxed{}$

6. $3(y + 2) = 3 \cdot \boxed{} + 3 \cdot \boxed{}$

7. $6(y - 3) = 6 \cdot \boxed{} - 6 \cdot \boxed{}$

8. $8(x - 1) = 8 \cdot \boxed{} - 8 \cdot \boxed{}$

Translate using numbers and symbols.

9. Six times y plus two

10. Four times x plus three

11. Seven times four minus one

12. Eleven times five minus two

13. Four times the sum of three and nine

14. Nine times the sum of four and six

15. Triple the sum of y and six

16. Double the sum of x and one

17. Eight times the difference of four and y

18. Five times the difference of six and x

Mixed Practice Exercises 19–24

Translate using numbers and symbols, then simplify.

19. (a) Four times two plus seven
  (b) Four times the sum of two and seven

20. (a) Eight times six plus one
  (b) Eight times the sum of six and one

21. (a) Four times three minus one
  (b) Four times the difference of three and one

22. (a) Two times seven minus one
  (b) Two times the difference of seven and one

23. (a) Twelve times one plus three
  (b) Twelve times the sum of one and three

24. (a) Nine times four plus one
  (b) Nine times the sum of four and one

Evaluate for the given values.

25. $4a + 5b$ for $a = 2$ and $b = 6$

26. $3m + 2n$ for $m = 4$ and $n = 5$

27. $8x - 6y$ for $x = 9$ and $y = 2$

28. $9x - 2y$ for $x = 8$ and $y = 5$

29. $\dfrac{(x + 4)}{3}$ for $x = 11$

30. $\dfrac{(y + 7)}{5}$ for $y = 13$

31. $\dfrac{(a^2 - 4)}{b}$ for $a = 5$ and $b = 3$

32. $\dfrac{(m^2 - 6)}{n}$ for $m = 6$ and $n = 3$

33. $\dfrac{(x^3 + 4)}{y}$ for $x = 2$ and $y = 2$

34. $\dfrac{(x^3 + 9)}{y}$ for $x = 3$ and $y = 6$

35. $\dfrac{(a^2 + 6)}{b}$ for $a = 2$ and $b = 5$

36. $\dfrac{(n^2 + 5)}{m}$ for $n = 3$ and $m = 7$

37. $\dfrac{(y-2)}{2}$ for $y=16$

38. $\dfrac{(y-3)}{3}$ for $y=18$

39. $4m+3n$ for $m=2$ and $n=7$

40. $5x+4y$ for $x=4$ and $y=6$

41. $\dfrac{(x^2-5)}{y}$ for $x=5$ and $y=4$

42. $\dfrac{(x^2-3)}{y}$ for $x=6$ and $y=11$

Use the distributive property to simplify.

43. $4(x+1)$

44. $2(x+1)$

45. $3(n-5)$

46. $6(n-4)$

47. $3(x-6)$

48. $4(x-3)$

49. $4(x+4)$

50. $5(x+9)$

51. $2(x+6)+5$

52. $4(x+2)+6$

53. $2(y+1)+5$

54. $7(y+1)+3$

55. $4(x+3)+6$

56. $3(x+2)+5$

57. $9(y+1)-3$

58. $5(y+1)-2$

59. $3(x+1)-1$

60. $6(x+1)-3$

One Step Further

Evaluate for the given values.

61. yx^2-3 for $y=6$ and $x=2$

62. ab^2+4 for $a=5$ and $b=3$

63. $\dfrac{(a^2-3)+2^3}{b}$ for $a=5$ and $b=2$

64. $\dfrac{(a^3-4)-3^2}{b}$ for $a=3$ and $b=7$

To Think About

65. (a) Add $(x+2)$ four times.

(b) Multiply $4(x+2)$ using the distributive property.

(c) What do you notice about the answers in **(a)** and **(b)**?

66. (a) Add $(x+4)$ three times.

(b) Multiply $3(x+4)$ using the distributive property.

(c) What do you notice about the answers in **(a)** and **(b)**?

Cumulative Review

67. [1.4.3] Simplify. $8(2)(x\cdot 4)$

68. [1.2.3] Evaluate $4+x$ if x is 2.

69. [1.2.3] Evaluate $x+y+4$ if x is 1 and y is 3.

70. [1.3.4] Subtract. $2001-463$

Quick Quiz 1.7

1. Translate using numbers and symbols. Double the sum of n and five

2. Use the distributive property to simplify. $6(y+1)+3$

3. Evaluate.
 (a) $3x+2y$ if $x=3$ and $y=4$
 (b) $\dfrac{(x^2-2)}{y}$ if $x=4$ and $y=7$

4. Concept Check Simplify $5(x+1)$, then evaluate $5(x+1)$ for $x=2$. Compare results and state the difference in the process to simplify and to evaluate.

1 Combining Like Terms

In algebra we often deal with terms such as $4y$ or $7x$. What do we mean by *terms*?

A **term** is a number, a variable, or a product of a number and one or more variables. Terms are separated from other terms in an expression by a + sign or a − sign. Often a term has a number factor and a variable factor. The number factor is called the **coefficient.**

$$7x$$
numerical part of term ←⎦ ⎣→ variable part of term

A term that has no variable is called a **constant term,** and a term that has a variable is called a **variable term.**

$$9 + 3n + 4x$$
constant term variable terms

What do the expressions $3n$ and $4x$ mean? $3n$ is the term that represents the sum $n + n + n$, and $4x$ is the term that represents the sum $x + x + x + x$. As we saw earlier, $3n$ and $4x$ also indicate multiplication: 3 times n and 4 times x.

$n + n + n$ We count three n's added. $x + x + x + x$ We count four x's added.
↓   ↓
$3n$ $4x$

EXAMPLE 1 Write a term that represents each of the following.

(a) Two y's   **(b)** $a + a + a + a$
(c) Seven   **(d)** One x

Solution

(a) Two y's = $2y$ **(b)** $a + a + a + a = 4a$
(c) Seven = 7 **(d)** One $x = 1x$ or x

Practice Problem 1 Write a term that represents each of the following.

(a) Four n's   **(b)** $y + y + y$
(c) Eight   **(d)** One y

We see many examples of adding and subtracting quantities that are like quantities, as shown in the following example.

$$3 \text{ feet} + 7 \text{ feet} = 10 \text{ feet} \qquad 7 \text{ trucks} - 2 \text{ trucks} = 5 \text{ trucks}$$

However, we cannot combine things that are not the same:

$$7 \text{ trucks} - 4 \text{ feet} \qquad \text{(cannot be done!)}$$

Similarly, in algebra we cannot combine terms that are not like terms. **Like terms** are terms that have *identical variable parts.* For example, in the expression $8x + 6b + 2x$, the terms $8x$ and $2x$ are called like terms since they have the same variable parts. They are both counting x's.

Student Learning Objectives

After studying this section, you will be able to:

1. Combine like terms.

2. Translate English statements into equations.

3. Solve equations using basic arithmetic facts.

4. Translate and solve equations.

NOTE TO STUDENT: Fully worked-out solutions to all of the Practice Problems can be found at the back of the text starting at page SP-1

Expression	*Like Terms*
$8x + 6b + 2x$	$8x \qquad 2x$

The variable parts are the same.

There are no like terms for $6b$, since none of the terms have exactly the same variable part as $6b$.

EXAMPLE 2   Identify the like terms. $7ab + 4a + 2ab + 3y$

Solution

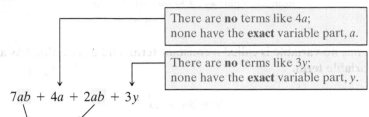

There are **no** terms like $4a$; none have the **exact** variable part, a.

There are **no** terms like $3y$; none have the **exact** variable part, y.

$7ab + 4a + 2ab + 3y$

$7ab$ and $2ab$ are like terms; the variable parts, ab, are the same.

Practice Problem 2   Identify the like terms. $2mn + 5y + 4mn + 6n$

The numerical part of a term is called the **coefficient** of a term. The coefficient tells you how many you have of whatever variable follows. To combine like terms, we either add or subtract the coefficients of like terms.

> **COMBINING LIKE TERMS**
>
> To combine like terms, add or subtract the numerical coefficients of like terms. The variable parts stay the same.
>
> $$6x + 4x = 10x \qquad 8y - 2y = 6y$$

EXAMPLE 3   Identify like terms, then combine like terms.

(a) $3x + 7y + 2x$ **(b)** $9m - m - 8$ **(c)** $4xy + 8y + 2xy$

Solution

There are **no** terms like $7y$; none have the **exact** variable part.

(a) $3x + 7y + 2x = (3x + 2x) + 7y$ We identify and group like terms.

$ = (3 + 2)x + 7y$ "Three x's plus two x's" can be restated as $(3 + 2)x$'s; "three plus two x's."

$3x + 7y + 2x = 5x + 7y$ $(3 + 2)x = 5x$

(b) $9m - m - 8 = 9m - 1m - 8$ Write the numerical coefficient 1.

$ = 9\,m - 1\,m - 8$ Think: "nine m's minus one m equals 8 m's."

$9m - m - 8 = 8\,m - 8$

Note that the term m does not have a visible numerical coefficient. We can write "1" as the numerical coefficient since $1m = 1 \cdot m = m$.

(c) $4xy + 8y + 2xy = (4xy + 2xy) + 8y$　　We identify and group like terms.

$\qquad\qquad\quad = (4 + 2)xy + 8y$　　　Add the numerical coefficients of like terms.

$4xy + 8y + 2xy = 6xy + 8y$

We write $8y$ as a separate term. We cannot combine it with $6xy$ since the variable parts are not the same.

> **Practice Problem 3**　Identify like terms, then combine like terms.
>
> **(a)** $2ab + 4a + 3ab$　　　　　　**(b)** $4y + 5x + y + x$
>
> **(c)** $7x + 3y + 3z$

 EXAMPLE 4　Write the perimeter of the rectangular figure as an algebraic expression and simplify.

$$4a + 7b$$
$$\boxed{}\ 2a + 3b$$

Solution　Since the figure is a rectangle, opposites sides are equal.

$$4a + 7b$$
$$2a + 3b\ \boxed{}\ 2a + 3b$$
$$4a + 7b$$

We add all sides to find the perimeter:

$(2a + 3b) + (4a + 7b) + (2a + 3b) + (4a + 7b)$　　We must combine like terms.

$= (2a + 2a + 4a + 4a) + (3b + 3b + 7b + 7b)$　　We use the associative and commutative properties to change the order of addition and regroup.

$= 12a + 20b$　　　　　　　　　　　　　　　We combine like terms.

The algebraic expression for the perimeter is $12a + 20b$.

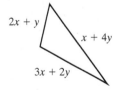

 Practice Problem 4　Write the perimeter of the triangular figure in the margin as an algebraic expression and simplify.

② Translating English Statements into Equations

Two expressions separated by an equals sign is called an **equation.** When we use an equals sign ($=$), we are indicating that two expressions are equal in value.

$$2 + 6 = 8$$

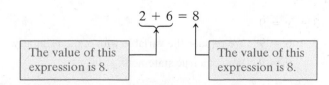

Some English phrases for the symbol $=$ are

is　　　　is the same as　　　　equals　　　　is equal to　　　　the result is

EXAMPLE 5 Translate each English sentence into an equation.

(a) Three subtracted from what number is equal to ten?

(b) Five times what number is the same as thirty-five?

(c) Kari's savings decreased by $100 equals $500.

Solution

(a) Three subtracted from what number is equal to ten?

$$n - 3 = 10$$

(b) Five times what number *is the same as* thirty-five?

$$5 \cdot n = 35$$
$$5n = 35$$

(c) We let x represent Kari's savings, the unknown value.

Kari's savings decreased by $100 *equals* $500.

$$x - \$100 = \$500$$
$$x - \$100 = \$500$$

NOTE TO STUDENT: *Fully worked-out solutions to all of the Practice Problems can be found at the back of the text starting at page SP-1*

Practice Problem 5 Translate each English sentence into an equation.

(a) Four times what number is the same as seven?

(b) Three subtracted from what number is equal to nine?

(c) The number of baseball cards in a collection plus 20 new cards equals 75 cards.

3 Solving Equations Using Basic Arithmetic Facts

Suppose we ask the question "Three plus what number is equal to nine?" The answer to this question is 6, since *three plus six is equal to nine.* The number 6 is called the **solution** to the equation $3 + x = 9$ and is written $x = 6$: "the value of x is 6." In other words, an *equation* is like a *question,* and the *solution* is the *answer* to this question.

English Phrase	**Math Symbols**
Question	*Equation*
Three plus what number is equal to nine?	$3 + x = 9$
Answer to the Question	*Solution*
Three plus *six* is equal to nine.	$x = 6$

The solution to an equation must make the equation a true statement. For example, if 6 is a solution to $3 + x = 9$, we must get a true statement when we evaluate the equation for $x = 6$.

$$3 + x = 9$$
$$3 + 6 = 9 \quad \text{We replace the variable with 6, then simplify.}$$
$$9 = 9 \quad \text{We get a true statement.}$$

> To *solve* an *equation* we must find a value for the variable in the equation that makes the equation a true statement.

EXAMPLE 6   Is 2 a solution to $6 - x = 9$?

Solution   If 2 is a solution to $6 - x = 9$, when we replace x with the value $x = 2$ we will get a true statement.

$$6 - x = 9 \quad \text{“Six minus what number equals nine?”}$$
$$6 - 2 \overset{?}{=} 9 \quad \text{Replace the variable with 2 and simplify.}$$
$$4 \overset{?}{=} 9 \quad \text{This is a false statement.}$$

Since $4 = 9$ is *not* a true statement, 2 is *not* a solution to $6 - x = 9$.

Practice Problem 6   Is 5 a solution to $x + 8 = 11$?

NOTE TO STUDENT: Fully worked-out solutions to all of the Practice Problems can be found at the back of the text starting at page SP-1

EXAMPLE 7   Solve the equation $3 + n = 10$ and check your answer.

Solution   To solve the equation $3 + n = 10$, we answer this question:

"Three plus what number is equal to ten?"

Using addition facts we see that the *answer, or solution,* is 7.
     To check the solution, we replace n with the value $n = 7$ and verify that we get a true statement.

Check: $3 + n = 10$ Write the equation.
             $3 + 7 \overset{?}{=} 10$ Replace the variable with 7 and simplify.
             $10 = 10 \ \checkmark$ Verify that we get a true statement.

Since we get a true statement, the solution to $3 + n = 10$ is 7 and is written $n = 7$.

Practice Problem 7   Solve the equation $4 + n = 9$ and check your answer.

EXAMPLE 8   Solve the equation $9n = 45$ and check your answer.

Solution   To solve the equation $9n = 45$, we answer this question:

"Nine times what number equals forty-five?"

The answer or solution is 5 and is written $n = 5$.
     To check the answer, we replace n with the value $n = 5$ and verify that we get a true statement.

Check: $9n = 45$
                 $9(5) \overset{?}{=} 45$ Replace the variable with 5 and simplify.
                 $45 = 45 \ \checkmark$ Verify that this is a true statement.

Thus the solution to $9n = 45$ is 5 and is written $n = 5$.

Practice Problem 8   Solve the equation $6x = 48$ and check your answer.

EXAMPLE 9 Solve the equation $\dfrac{6}{x} = 3$ and check your answer.

Solution $\dfrac{6}{x} = 3$ "Six divided by what number equals 3?"

Using division facts, we see that the answer or solution is 2 and is written $x = 2$.

Check:

$$\frac{6}{x} = 3 \rightarrow \frac{6}{2} \stackrel{?}{=} 3 \qquad \text{Replace the variable with 2 and simplify.}$$
$$3 = 3 \quad \checkmark \qquad \text{Verify that this is a true statement.}$$

Thus $x = 2$ is the solution.

Practice Problem 9 Solve the equation $\frac{x}{4} = 2$ and check your answer.

Sometimes, we must first use the associative and commutative properties to simplify an equation and then find the solution.

EXAMPLE 10 Simplify using the associative and commutative properties and then find the solution to the equation $(5 + n) + 1 = 9$.

Solution First we simplify.

$$(5 + n) + 1 = 9$$
$$(n + 5) + 1 = 9 \qquad \text{Commutative property}$$
$$n + (5 + 1) = 9 \qquad \text{Associative property}$$
$$n + 6 = 9 \qquad \text{Simplify.}$$

Next we solve $n + 6 = 9$.

$$n + 6 = 9 \qquad \text{"What number plus 6 is equal to 9?"}$$
$$n = 3$$

We leave the check to the student.

The solution to the equation is 3 and is written $n = 3$.

Practice Problem 10 Simplify using the associative and commutative properties and then find the solution to the equation $(3 + x) + 1 = 7$.

We may need to combine like terms before we solve an equation.

EXAMPLE 11 Simplify by combining like terms and then find the solution to the equation $n + 5n = 18$.

Solution

$$n + 5n = 18 \qquad \text{Write the equation.}$$
$$1n + 5n = 18 \qquad \text{Write } n \text{ as } 1n.$$
$$(1 + 5)n = 18 \qquad \text{Add numerical coefficients of like terms.}$$
$$6n = 18 \qquad \text{Think: "Six times what number equals eighteen?" 3.}$$
$$n = 3$$

Practice Problem 11 Simplify by combining like terms and then find the solution to the equation $n + 3n = 20$.

NOTE TO STUDENT: Fully worked-out solutions to all of the Practice Problems can be found at the back of the text starting at page SP-1

④ Translating and Solving Equations

In many real-life applications we must translate an English statement into an equation and then solve the equation.

EXAMPLE 12 Translate, then solve. Double what number is equal to eighteen?

Solution   Double what number is equal to eighteen?

$$2 \quad \cdot \quad n \quad = \quad 18 \qquad \text{Translate.}$$
$$n = 9 \qquad\qquad \text{Use multiplication facts to find } n.$$

Practice Problem12 Translate, then solve. What number times five is equal to twenty?

◯ Understanding the Concept

Evaluate or Solve?

Do you know the difference between evaluating the expression $8x$ when x is 3 and solving the equation $8x = 16$?

- *Evaluate an expression.* We replace the variable in the expression with the given number and then perform the calculation(s).
  Evaluate $8x$ when x is 3. $8 \cdot 3 = 24$
- *Solve an equation.* We find the value of the variable that makes the equation a true statement—that is, the solution to the equation.
  Solve: $8x = 16$. $x = 2$

We can illustrate this idea with the following situations.

1. Evaluating
   (a) *Fact.* You are given directions to the Lido Movie Theater.
   (b) *Evaluate.* You follow these directions to the movie theater.
2. Solving
   (a) *Fact.* You know the address of the theater.
   (b) *Solve.* You must find the directions yourself.

In summary, an equation has an equals sign, and an expression does not. We find the solutions to equations, and we evaluate expressions as directed.

Exercise

1. Can you think of other real-life situations that illustrate the difference between evaluating and solving?

Developing Your Study Skills

Improving Your Test-Taking Skills

Step 1 *Write key facts on your test.* As soon as you get your test, find a blank area to write down any important strategies, formulas, or key facts.

An ideal place to write these facts is on the blank back page of the test. If there are no blank pages or areas on the test, be sure to ask the instructor if you can have a *blank* piece of paper for this purpose. Having this information easily accessible should lessen your anxiety and help you focus on the type of problem-solving techniques you need.

Step 2 *Scan the test and work problems that are easy first.* Quickly glance at each question on the test, placing an * beside the ones you feel confident you can complete. Then complete these problems first. This will help build your confidence.

Step 3 *Keep track of the time as you complete the rest of the test.* Determine how much time is left so you can plan the strategy for the rest of the test. This plan should include determining how many minutes you should spend on each of the remaining unanswered questions so that you can finish the test in the time that is left. For example, if there are 10 questions remaining on the test and 30 minutes left, you should try to spend no more than 3 minutes on each of the remaining questions.

Step 4 *Complete the rest of the problems on the test.* Complete the remaining problems on the test, starting with the ones you feel most confident about. If you get stuck on a problem, stop working on it and move on to another one. Do not spend too much time trying to complete one problem; leave it and move on!

Step 5 *Relax periodically.* If you start to feel anxious at any time during the test, take a few moments to relax. Close your eyes, place yourself in a comfortable position in your chair, breathe deeply, and take a moment to think about something pleasant. Next, think positive thoughts such as "I will answer the question to the best of my ability and will not worry about what I have forgotten or do not understand. Instead I will show that I can master what I do understand."

You may think that taking a few minutes away from the test to relax is wasting time. This is not true. You will perform better if you are relaxed.

Step 6 *Revisit the problems you are not sure of or did not complete.* Try to rework the problems that you struggled with earlier. You may recall how to complete these problems once you have completed the majority of the test.

Step 7 *Review the entire test to check for careless errors.* Take whatever time is left to review all your work. Check for careless errors and be sure that you have followed all directions properly.

Verbal and Writing Skills

Translate the mathematical symbols using words.

1. $7x$

2. $5x$

3. $8x = 40$

4. $5x = 30$

5. Can we add $2x + 3y$? Why or why not?

6. Can we add $6x + 3xy$? Why or why not?

Fill in the blanks.

7. In the expression $6x + 5$, $6x$ is called a _____ term and 5 is called a _____ term.

8. When two expressions are separated by an equals sign, we call it an _____.

9. The numerical part of $8x$ is __ and is called the _____ of the term.

10. The numerical part of x is __ and is called the _____ of the term.

11. Rewrite y with a coefficient: ___.

12. In the expression $12x + 9x$, $12x$ and $9x$ are called ____ terms.

Fill in each box to complete each problem.

13. $7x + 3\boxed{} = 10x$

14. $10x - 2\boxed{} = 8x$

15. $3xy + \boxed{} = 7xy$

16. $\boxed{} + 4ab = 6ab$

17. $3x + 5xy + \boxed{} = 7x + 5xy$

18. $9a + 2ab + \boxed{} = 9a + 4ab$

Write a term that represents each expression.

19. Three x's

20. Six y's

21. $a + a + a + a$

22. $x + x + x + x + x$

Identify like terms.

23. $5x + 3y + 2x + 8m + 7y$

24. $6m + 4b + 7m + 3x + 4b$

25. $2mn + 3y + 4mn + 6$

26. $6x + 3xy + 9 + 2xy$

Combine like terms.

27. $7x + 2x$

28. $12x + 4x$

29. $9y - y$

30. $7m - m$

31. $3x + 2x + 6x$

32. $5a + 3a + 7a$

33. $8x + 4a + 3x + 2a$

34. $9y + 2b + 2y + 4b$

35. $6xy + 4b + 3xy$

36. $3ab + 5x + 9ab$

37. $6xy + 3x + 9 + 9xy$

38. $5mn + 6m + 1 + 2mn$

39. $12ab - 5ab + 9$

40. $12xy - 3xy + 3$

41. $14xy + 4 + 3xy + 6$

42. $13ab + 6 + 4ab + 2$

Write the perimeter of each rectangular figure as an algebraic expression, then simplify.

▲ **43.**

$4x + 7y$

$5x$

▲ **44.**

$6a + 5b$

$2b$

▲ **45.**

$8a + 2b$

$6a + 5b$

▲ **46.**

$9x + 7y$

$3x + 4y$

Write the perimeter of each triangle as an algebraic expression, then simplify.

▲ **47.**

$6y$ $5x + 2y$

x

▲ **48.**

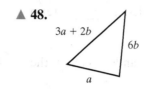

$3a + 2b$

$6b$

a

Translate to an equation. **Do not solve** *the equation.*

49. Five plus what number equals sixteen?

50. When twenty-four is added to a number, the result is fifty.

51. What number times three equals thirty-six?

52. What number times two is equal to forty?

53. If a number is subtracted from forty-five, the result is six.

54. If a number is subtracted from twelve, the result is two.

55. Twenty-five divided by what number is equal to five?

56. Twenty-two divided by what number is equal to eleven?

57. Let *J* represent James' age. James' age plus 12 years equals 25.

58. Let *S* represent Sherie's checking account balance. Sherie's checking account balance plus $14 equals $56.

59. Let *C* represent Chuong's monthly salary. Chuong's monthly salary decreased by $50 equals $1480.

60. Let *P* represent the price of the ticket. The price of the ticket decreased by $5 equals $16.

Answer yes or no.

61. Is 4 a solution to the equation $9 - x = 3$?

62. Is 3 a solution to the equation $5 - x = 3$?

63. Is 15 a solution to the equation $x + 4 = 19$?

64. Is 20 a solution to the equation $x + 6 = 26$?

Solve and check your answer.

65. $x + 5 = 9$

66. $x + 4 = 10$

67. $11 - n = 3$

68. $13 - n = 10$

69. $x - 6 = 0$

70. $x - 2 = 0$

71. $2 + x = 13$

72. $21 + x = 25$

73. $25 - x = 20$

74. $44 - n = 42$

75. $8x = 16$

76. $7y = 14$

77. $4y = 12$ **78.** $9x = 63$ **79.** $8x = 56$ **80.** $10y = 30$

81. $\dfrac{15}{y} = 1$ **82.** $\dfrac{12}{x} = 1$ **83.** $\dfrac{14}{x} = 2$ **84.** $\dfrac{20}{x} = 2$

Simplify using the associative and/or commutative property, then find the solution. Check your answer.

85. $(x + 1) + 3 = 7$ **86.** $(x + 6) + 5 = 13$ **87.** $2 + (7 + y) = 10$

88. $(3 + x) + 2 = 7$ **89.** $3 + (n + 5) = 10$ **90.** $2 + (8 + x) = 12$

Simplify by combining like terms, then find the solution. Check your answer.

91. $3n + n = 12$ **92.** $6n + n = 21$ **93.** $7x - 2x - x = 4$ **94.** $3y + y + 2y = 12$

Mixed Practice Exercises 95–102

Solve.

95. $5x = 20$ **96.** $\dfrac{30}{x} = 15$ **97.** $16 - x = 1$ **98.** $38 - n = 34$

99. $1 + (4 + a) = 15$ **100.** $(6 + x) + 1 = 10$ **101.** $8x - 5x - x = 10$ **102.** $4y + y + 2y = 14$

For the following English sentences,

    (a) *Translate into an equation.*   **(b)** *Solve the equation.*

103. Four plus what number equals eight?   **104.** Three added to what number equals nine?

105. Three times what number is equal to nine?   **106.** Four times what number is equal to twelve?

One Step Further

▲ **107.** Find the missing side of the following triangle if the perimeter is 170 feet.

▲ **108.** Find the missing side of the following triangle if the perimeter is 110 yards.

Simplify by combining like terms.

109. $6 + (2x^2 + 5) + (7 + 3x^2) + x^2$ **110.** $(2 + 8x^2) + 9 + (4x^2 + 6) + x^2$

Simplify.

111. **(a)** $2x + 3x + 5y$
    (b) $(2x)(5y)$

112. **(a)** $5x + 4x + 6y$
    (b) $(5x)(6y)$

113. **(a)** $5a + 6y + 2a$
    (b) $(5a)(6y)$

114. **(a)** $6a + 7y + 3a$
    (b) $(6a)(7y)$

To Think About

Running Speeds Compared Use the bar graph to answer exercises 115 and 116.

115. (a) How fast can a domestic cat run if it is as fast as a grizzly bear?
   (b) The speed of a lion is two times the speed of an elephant. How fast is the elephant?

116. (a) Which animal is faster, a zebra or a Cape hunting dog?
   (b) The speed of a cheetah is two times the speed of a rabbit. How fast is the rabbit?

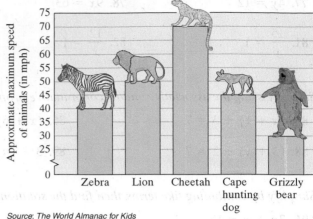

Source: The World Almanac for Kids

Cumulative Review

Match each operation described by the phrase in the right column with the appropriate operation listed in the left column. Place the correct letter in the blank space.

(a) Addition

(b) Subtraction

(c) Multiplication

(d) Division

117. [1.5.2] __ Split equally between

118. [1.4.2] __ Find the number of items in an array

119. [1.2.1] __ Find the total

120. [1.3.2] __ How much less

Quick Quiz 1.8

1. Combine like terms.

$2ab + 4a + 1 + ab$

2. Solve each equation and check your answer.

   (a) $\dfrac{10}{a} = 2$

   (b) $4 + (x + 7) = 12$

   (c) $8y + y = 72$

3. Translate into an equation and solve.

   (a) The product of three and what number is equal to eighteen?

   (b) Let D represent Dave's age. Dave's age increased by seven is equal to twenty-one.

4. Concept Check Explain the difference in the process you must use to complete (a) and (b).

   (a) Combine like terms. $3x + x + 2x$

   (b) Solve. $3x + x + 2x = 12$

Developing Your Study Skills

Positive Thinking

Some people convince themselves that they cannot learn mathematics. If you are concerned that you may have difficulty in this course, it is time to reprogram your thinking. Replace those negative thoughts with positive ones such as

> "I can learn mathematics if I work at it. I will give this math class my best shot."

You will be pleasantly surprised at the difference this positive attitude makes!

Now, some might wonder how a change in attitude can make a difference. Well, the approach and features in this book can be the keys to your success. Here are a few features that you should pay special attention to:

- Developing Your Study Skills boxes offer tips on how to study. If you know how to study, learning will be far easier.
- Understanding the Concept boxes help you understand what you are doing and why you are doing it. These explanations and other descriptions relate the concepts to other topics such as algebra and applications.
- Exercises develop the fundamentals on which the concepts are built. Many students do not learn because they miss certain building blocks. For example, how can someone learn long division if he or she doesn't know multiplication facts?

If you take this advice to heart, you'll be off to a good start. Keep up the good work.

Exercises

1. Name a few things that you plan to do in this class to help you be successful.
2. Write in words two positive thoughts about mathematics and/or your ability to complete this course.

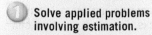
 ## Solving Applied Problems Involving Estimation

Often, it is not necessary to know the exact sum or difference; in this case we can estimate. Estimating is also helpful when it is necessary to do mental calculations. There are many ways to estimate, but in this book we use the following rule to make estimations.

> To estimate a sum or difference, round each number to the same round-off place and then find the sum or difference.

EXAMPLE 1 Some sample sale prices for 2008 Ford motor vehicles are listed below.

(a) Estimate the difference in the price between a Mustang V6 Premium Coupe and a Ford Focus S Coupe by rounding each price to the nearest thousand.

(b) Calculate the exact difference in cost. Is your estimate reasonable?

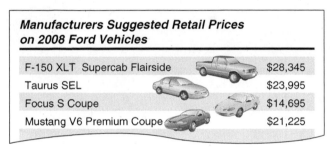

Manufacturers Suggested Retail Prices on 2008 Ford Vehicles

F-150 XLT Supercab Flairside	$28,345
Taurus SEL	$23,995
Focus S Coupe	$14,695
Mustang V6 Premium Coupe	$21,225

Source: www.fordvehicles.com

Solution *Understand the problem.* The information we need to solve the problem is listed in the table.

(a) *Calculate and state the answer.* To estimate, we round each number to the thousands place.

	Exact Value		Rounded Value
The price of the Mustang V6 Premium Coupe:	21,225	→	21,000
The price of the Focus S Coupe:	14,695	→	15,000

We subtract the *rounded figures* to *estimate* the difference in the cost of the two vehicles.

$$21,000 - 15,000 = 6000$$

The estimated difference in price is $6000.

(b) We subtract the *original figures* to find the *exact* difference in the cost of the two vehicles.

$$\$21,225 - \$14,695 = \$6530$$

The exact difference in price is $6530.

The estimated difference in price, $6000, is close to the exact difference, $6530, so our estimate is reasonable. Note that if you round each number to the nearest hundred instead of to the nearest thousand your estimate will not be wrong, just a little closer to the exact amount. When we estimate we want to make calculations with numbers that are easy to work with. In this case, it is easier to subtract numbers rounded to the thousands place than to the hundreds place; that is, subtracting $21{,}000 - 15{,}000$ is easier than subtracting $21{,}200 - 14{,}700$.

 Practice Problem 1 Use the sale prices listed in Example 1 to answer the following.

(a) Estimate the difference in price between an F-150 XLT and a Taurus SEL.

(b) Calculate the exact difference in cost. Is your estimate reasonable?

NOTE TO STUDENT: Fully worked-out solutions to all of the Practice Problems can be found at the back of the text starting at page SP-1

② Solving Applied Problems Involving Charts and Diagrams

How much material do I need to fence my yard? How much gasoline will I need for my trip? How much profit did my business make? One important use of mathematics is to answer these types of questions. In this section we combine problem-solving skills with the mathematical operations of addition, subtraction, multiplication, and division to solve everyday problems. We follow the three-step problem-solving process discussed earlier in the chapter when solving applied problems. We restate the three steps for your review.

Step 1. *Understand the problem.* Read the problem and organize the information. Use pictures and charts to help you see facts more clearly.

Step 2. *Calculate and state the answer.* Use arithmetic and algebra to find the answer.

Step 3. *Check the answer.* Use estimation and other techniques to test your answer.

EXAMPLE 2 The three owners of the Pizza Palace redecorated their business. The items purchased are listed on the invoice in the margin. If the cost of these purchases excluding tax was divided equally among the owners, how much did each owner pay?

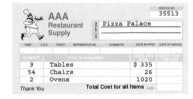

Solution *Understand the problem.* Read the problem carefully and study the invoice. Then fill in the invoice.

Calculate and state the answer. Multiply to get the total cost per item. Then place these amounts on the invoice.

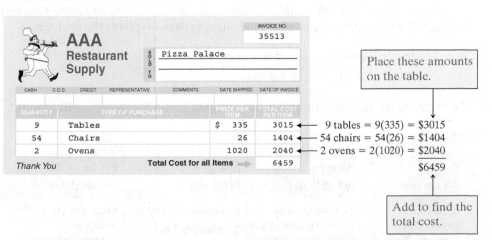

9 tables = 9(335) = $3015
54 chairs = 54(26) = $1404
2 ovens = 2(1020) = $2040
                      $6459

Place these amounts on the table.

Add to find the total cost.

Now, divide the total cost by 3 to find the amount that each owner paid: $6459 \div 3 = 2153$. Each owner paid \$2153.

Check your answer. We estimate and compare the estimate with our calculated answer.

Round:	Number of Items	Price per Item	Find Total Cost
	$9 \rightarrow 10$	$\$335 \rightarrow \$\ 300$	$10 \cdot 300 = \$3000$
	$54 \rightarrow 50$	$\$26 \rightarrow \$\ \ 30$	$50 \cdot 30 = 1500$
	$2 \rightarrow 2$	$\$1020 \rightarrow \$1000$	$2 \cdot 1000 = \underline{2000}$
			$\$6500$

Divide the estimated total by 3: $3\overline{)6500}$ $\qquad$ $2166 \text{ R2} \approx \$2167$

Our estimate of $2167 per owner is close to our exact calculation of $2153. Thus our *exact answer is reasonable.*

Practice Problem 2 The two owners of a Chinese restaurant redecorated their place of business. The items purchased are listed on the invoice in the margin. If the cost of these purchases was divided equally between the owners, excluding tax, how much did each owner pay?

 Using the Mathematics Blueprint for Problem Solving

To solve a word problem that contains many facts and requires several steps, it is helpful to *organize* the information and then *plan* the process that you will use. This is very similar to what we do when we use a daily planner or date book to *organize* and *plan* our days. A Mathematics Blueprint for Problem Solving will be used to organize the information in a word problem and plan the method to solve it. From the blueprint we will be able to see clearly the three steps for solving problems in real-life situations: understand the problem; calculate and state the answer; and then check the answer.

EXAMPLE 3 A frequent-flyer program offered by many major airlines to first-class passengers awards 3 frequent-flyer mileage points for every 2 miles flown. When customers accumulate a certain number of frequent-flyer points, they can cash them in for free air travel, ticket upgrades, or other awards. How many frequent-flyer points would a customer accumulate after flying 3500 miles in first class?

Solution *Understand the problem.* Sometimes, drawing charts or pictures can help us understand the problem as well as plan our approach to solving the problem.

2 miles + 2 miles $\cdots$ = 3500 miles   How many groups of 2's are in 3500?
3 points + 3 points $\cdots$ = ? points

We organize the information and make our plan in the Mathematics Blueprint.

Mathematics Blueprint for Problem Solving

Gather the Facts	What Am I Asked to Do?	How Do I Proceed?	Key Points to Remember
A customer is awarded 3 frequent-flyer points for every 2 miles flown.	Determine how many frequent-flyer points a customer earns after flying 3500 miles.	1. *Divide* 3500 by 2. 2. *Multiply* 3 times the number obtained in step 1.	Frequent-flyer points are determined by the number of miles flown.

Calculate and state the answer.

Step 1. We divide to find how many groups of 2 are in 3500.

$$3500 \div 2 = 1750$$

Step 2. We multiply 1750 times 3 to find the total points earned.

$$1750 \cdot 3 = 5250 \text{ points}$$

The customer would earn 5250 points.

Check. If the customer earned 4 points (instead of 3) for every 2 miles traveled, we could just double the mileage to find the points earned.

> 2 miles earns 4 points (double 2).
> 3500 miles earns 7000 points (double 3500).

Since the customer earned a little less than 4 points, the total should be less than 7000. It is: 5250 < 7000. The customer also earned more points than miles traveled (3 points for every 2 miles), so the total points should be more than the total miles traveled. It is: 5250 > 3500. *Our answer is reasonable.*

Practice Problem 3 Use the information in Example 3 to determine how many frequent-flyer points a customer would accumulate if she flew 4500 miles.

NOTE TO STUDENT: Fully worked-out solutions to all of the Practice Problems can be found at the back of the text starting at page SP-1

EXAMPLE 4 Koursh was offered two different jobs: a 40-hour-a-week store management position that pays $12 per hour and an executive secretary position paying a monthly salary of $2600. Which job pays more per year?

Solution *Understand the problem.* We organize the information in the Mathematics Blueprint.

Mathematics Blueprint for Problem Solving

Gather the Facts	What Am I Asked to Do?	How Do I Proceed?	Key Points to Remember
The store management position pays $12 per hour for 40 hours. The secretary's position pays $2600 per month.	Determine which job pays a higher salary per year.	1. Calculate the manager's weekly pay. 2. Multiply the result of step 1 by 52 weeks to find yearly pay. 3. Multiply the secretary's pay by 12 months to find yearly pay. 4. Compare both salaries.	I must find *yearly* pay: 12 months = 1 year 52 weeks = 1 year

Calculate and state the answer. From the information organized in the blueprint, we can write out a process to find the answer.

$12 × 40 = $480	Pay for 1 week (management)
$480 × 52 = $24,960	Pay for 1 year (management)
$2600 × 12 = $31,200	Pay for 1 year (secretary)

The yearly pay is $24,960 for the management position and $31,200 for the secretary's position. The *secretary's position* pays more per year.

Check the answer. We estimate the manager's pay per year by rounding $12 per hour to $10 and 52 weeks to 50 weeks.

$$\$10 \times 40 \text{ hr} = \$400 \text{ per week};   \$400 \times 50 \text{ weeks} = \$20,000 \text{ per year}$$

We estimate the secretary's pay per year by rounding 12 months per year to 10.

$$\$10 \times \$2600 = \$26,000 \text{ per year}$$

Since $26,000 > $20,000, the secretary position pays more. ✓

> **Practice Problem 4** Emily is a salesperson for A&E Appliance. For the last two years she has averaged about 7 sales per week, and she is paid solely on commission—$55 per sale. The store manager has decided to offer all salespersons the options of accepting a salary of $1770 per month or remaining on commission. If Emily continues to maintain her past sales record, which option will earn her more money per year?

Developing Your Study Skills

The Day Before the Exam

If you have been following the advice in the other Developing Your Study Skills boxes, you should be almost ready for the exam. If you have not read these boxes, reading them now will provide valuable advice.

The day before the exam is not a good time to start reviewing. Use this day to skim your chapter review, homework, quizzes, and other review material. On this day you can fine-tune what you already know and review what you are unsure of. Starting your review early reduces anxiety so that you can think clearly during the test. Often, low test scores are related to high anxiety. Plan ahead so that you can relax on the day of the exam.

A few days before the exam, complete the How Am I Doing? test at the end of the chapter. Take this test as if it were the real exam. Do not refer to notes or to the text while completing the test. Grade the test. The problems you missed on this test are the type of problems that you should get help with and review the day before the exam.

Applications

Estimate each of the following.

1. Supplies Purchased Emma purchased supplies to paint her kitchen, family room, and dining room. The following store receipt indicates the supplies she purchased.

7/17/2009
Sale Transaction

Satin enamel paint, 5 gal.	$81
Paint brushes	36
Drop cloths, 2	22
Paint roller and tray	14

Total
Tax
Total Sale

THANK YOU

(a) Excluding tax, *estimate* how much money Emma spent by rounding each amount to the nearest ten.

(b) Find the total money spent.

(c) Is your *estimate* reasonable?

2. Supplies Purchased Julio Arias bought schoolbooks and school supplies. The following store receipt indicates his purchases.

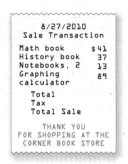

8/27/2010
Sale Transaction

Math book	$41
History book	37
Notebooks, 2	13
Graphing calculator	89

Total
Tax
Total Sale

THANK YOU
FOR SHOPPING AT THE
CORNER BOOK STORE

(a) Excluding tax, *estimate* how much money Julio spent by rounding each amount to the nearest ten.

(b) Find the total money spent.

(c) Is your *estimate* reasonable?

3. Mileage on Vehicle The Arismendi family took a scenic drive across the country. From Phoenix, Arizona, they drove east 597 miles the first day, 512 miles the second day, 389 miles the third day, and 310 miles the fourth day. Round each amount to the nearest hundred and then *estimate* how many more miles the Arismendi family drove the first two days than the last two days.

4. Mileage on Vehicle Jay drove his Toyota Tundra truck 14,200 miles the first year he owned it, 15,980 the second year, 8,100 the third year, and 14,950 the fourth year. Round each amount to the nearest thousand and then *estimate* how many more miles Jay drove his truck the first two years than the second two years.

5. Restaurant Remodeling The 5 owners of Mei's Restaurant remodeled their business. They bought 7 tables, 20 chairs, and 2 crystal light fixtures. The cost of these purchases was divided equally among the owners. Excluding tax, how much did each owner pay?

6. Appliances Purchased Last weekend, May's Appliance Store sold 10 washing machines, 5 dryers, and 20 dishwashers to a private college. The college will divide the expense for upgrades equally among the 200 students in the college apartments by charging each student a one-time assessment fee. How much will the assessment fee be for each student?

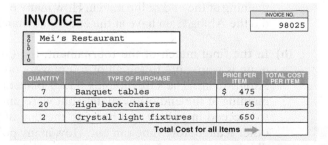

INVOICE

INVOICE NO. 98025

SOLD TO: Mei's Restaurant

QUANTITY	TYPE OF PURCHASE	PRICE PER ITEM	TOTAL COST PER ITEM
7	Banquet tables	$ 475	
20	High back chairs	65	
2	Crystal light fixtures	650	
	Total Cost for all Items ➡		

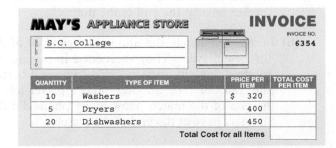

MAY'S APPLIANCE STORE   **INVOICE**

INVOICE NO. 6354

SOLD TO: S.C. College

QUANTITY	TYPE OF ITEM	PRICE PER ITEM	TOTAL COST PER ITEM
10	Washers	$ 320	
5	Dryers	400	
20	Dishwashers	450	
	Total Cost for all Items ➡		

Solve each problem involving charts and diagrams.

7. ***Entertainment Event Tickets*** Dave and his family went to the Middletown Amusement Park. They purchased 2 adult tickets, 4 child tickets, and 1 senior citizen ticket. How much did they spend on the tickets?

Middletown Ticket Prices
Adult – $ 13
Child – $ 5 (under 12 years)
Senior citizen – $ 7 (over 55 years)

8. ***Entertainment Event Tickets*** Janice and her friends went to an outdoor jazz concert. They purchased 4 adult, 6 student, and 2 child tickets. How much money did they spend on concert tickets?

Outdoor Jazz Concert Ticket Prices
Adult – $ 17
Child – $ 8 (under 12 years)
Student discount – $ 9 (college ID required)

▲ 9. ***Fencing Needed*** John Tulson wants to put a fence around the back and sides of his property (see the diagram). How many feet of fence must he purchase?

▲ 10. ***Ceiling Molding Needed*** Rosa would like to put molding along the edge of the ceiling in her kitchen (see the diagram). How many feet of molding will she need?

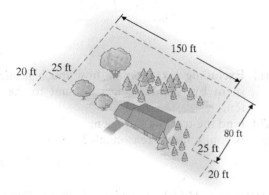

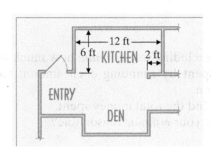

Paintball *In many paintball tournaments there are 100 points possible in each match of a round of play. There are 7 players on each team and when a player is tagged with a paintball they are out of the match. The team with the higher point total at the end of each round of play moves on to the next round. Use the chart below to answer exercises 11 and 12.*

Point Chart	
Tagging the opposing team players with paintballs	3 points/player
Pulling the flag of the opposing team	22 points
Hanging the flag of the opposing team	50 points
Players left in the game at the end of play	1 point/player

11. **(a)** The Torches tagged 6 of the Shooters' players, and succeeded in pulling and hanging the Shooters' flag. The Torches had 5 players remaining at the end of the match. How many points did the Torches have at the end of the match?

(b) In another match, the Shooters tagged all of the Torches' players. They succeeded in pulling the Torches' flag but were not able to hang it before time ran out. The Shooters had 1 player left at the end of the match. How many points did the Shooters have at the end of the match?

12. **(a)** In the second half of the tournament the Alpha team was able to tag 5 players on the Greyhounds' team and succeeded in pulling and hanging the Greyhounds' flag. The Alphas had 3 players remaining at the end of the match. How many points did the Alpha team have at the end of the match?

(b) In the final match of the tournament, the Greyhounds were able to tag all of the players on the Alpha team. The Greyhounds had 5 players remaining at the end of the match, but were unable to succeed in pulling and hanging the flag of the other team before time ran out. How many points did the Greyhounds receive in this match?

13. *Hourly/Overtime Wages* A restaurant cook earns $8 per hour for the first 40 hours worked and $12 per hour for overtime (hours worked in addition to the 40 hours a week). Last week the cook worked 52 hours. Calculate the cook's total pay for that week.

(a) Fill in the Mathematics Blueprint for Problem Solving.
(b) Calculate and state the answer.

Mathematics Blueprint for Problem Solving

Gather the Facts	What Am I Asked to Do?	How Do I Proceed?	Key Points to Remember

14. *Apartment Expenses* Four roommates share equally the following expenses for their apartment: $920 for rent, $96 for utilities, and $56 for the telephone. How much is each roommate's monthly share?

(a) Fill in the Mathematics Blueprint for Problem Solving.
(b) Calculate and state the answer.

Mathematics Blueprint for Problem Solving

Gather the Facts	What Am I Asked to Do?	How Do I Proceed?	Key Points to Remember

15. *Business Profit* T. B. Etron's Company made $68,542 last year. The expenses for that year were $14,372.

(a) How much profit did the company make?
(b) If the two owners divided the profits equally, how much money did each owner receive?

16. *PTA Raffle* The R. L. Saunders High School PTA sold $2568 in raffle tickets. The expenses for the prizes were $1062.

(a) How much profit did the PTA make?
(b) If the profits were divided equally among three clubs, how much money did each club receive?

17. *Fishing Trip Expenses* Carlos and three of his friends will equally share the expenses for a 2-day fishing trip they plan to take this summer. The boat rental will be $450 per day, and they estimate that the gasoline will cost $50 per day. If the total cost of food and bait for the entire 2-day trip is $200, what will be each person's share of the total expenses?

18. *Comparing Earning* Sara's current job as a computer technician at ComTec pays a salary of $2200 per month. BLM Accountants offered her a programmer's position that pays $14 per hour for a 40-hour week. Which job pays more per year?

19. *Bus Pass vs. Daily Rate* Round-trip bus fare is $2. Justin rides the bus 5 days a week to work and 2 nights a week to school. He can buy a pass at school that allows 6 months of unlimited bus rides for $400. If Justin only rides the bus round-trip to work and school, is it cheaper for Justin to buy the pass or to pay each time he rides the bus?

20. *Salary vs. Commission* Myra sells new memberships for a Total Flex Fitness Center chain. She is paid only on commission—$35 for each new membership. For the last three years she has signed up an average of 11 new members per week. She has been offered an alternative pay option—a salary of $1800 per month. Which pay option pays more per year?

21. *Inheritance Proceeds* Glenda has inherited $6000, which will be distributed in two equal payments. She will receive the first half of the inheritance now and the remainder of the inheritance in 6 months. Glenda plans to invest the first payment in a certificate of deposit (CD) at her bank. She will distribute the second payment equally among her three children.

(a) How much will Glenda invest in a CD?

(b) How much will each child receive?

22. *Stamp Collection* Lester donated one-half of the 2500 stamps in his collection to the local senior citizen group. He distributed the remaining stamps in his collection equally among his five grandchildren.

(a) How many stamps did Lester donate to the senior citizen group?

(b) How many stamps from Lester's collection did each grandchild receive?

Grocery Store Purchases Al's Grocery Store gave customers the following incentive to shop at the store.

23. Jesse made three purchases at Al's Grocery Store during the month of June: $30, $240, and $170.

(a) How many points did Jesse earn during the month of June?

(b) How many discount dollars did Jesse earn?

Earn free groceries during the month of June. Earn 5 points for every $50 spent during the month of June, plus an additional 25 points for any single purchase over $200.

Cash in your points!

10 points earn you a $1 discount in July.

24. Marsha made three purchases at Al's Grocery Store during the month of June: $230, $140, and $180.

(a) How many points did Marsha earn during the month of June?

(b) How many discount dollars did Marsha earn?

Promotional Points The L&M Clothing chain offered customers the following incentive to use their L&M charge card.

25. Alyssa made two purchases at L&M Clothing during the month of January: $170 and $260.

(a) How many points did Alyssa earn during the month of January?

(b) How many discount dollars did Alyssa earn?

January's Promotion

Earn points every time you use your *L & M* charge card.

Earn 10 points for every $50 charged during the month of January plus an additional 50 points for any single purchase over $200.

Cash in your points!

25 points earn you a $5 discount in February.

26. Ian made three purchases at L&M Clothing during the month of January: $80, $160, and $220.

(a) How many points did Ian earn during the month of January?

(b) How many discount dollars did Ian earn?

To Think About

27. *Credit Card Debt Repayment* A $5000 debt on a credit card will take 32 years to repay if only the minimum monthly payment is made. This debt will cost the borrower about $7800 in interest. The borrower could be out of debt in 3 years by paying $175 per month. Find the amount of interest paid at the end of 3 years.

Writing numbers in exponent form can often help us identify a pattern in a sequence of numbers. For example, the sequence 1, 8, 27, 64, 125, ... can be written as 1^3, 2^3, 3^3, 4^3, 5^3, . . . and we see that the next number would be 6^3 or 216.

Identify a pattern and then find the next number in the following sequences.

28. 4, 16, 36, 64, 100, . . .

29. 9, 25, 49, 81, 121, . . .

Find the next two figures that would appear in the sequence.

30. 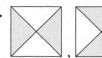 , , , ,   **31.** , , ,

Cumulative Review

32. **[1.4.3]** Multiply. $4 \cdot 3 \cdot 2 \cdot 5$ **33.** **[1.8.3]** Solve. $6x = 30$ **34.** **[1.8.3]** Solve. $x + 9 = 12$

Quick Quiz 1.9

1. The Belmont High Service Club organized a charity jazz festival. Tickets to the festival were $20 for adults, $15 for students, and $7 for children under 12 years old. The service club sold 350 adult tickets, 200 student tickets, and 47 children tickets.

   (a) Find the total income from the sale of tickets.

   (b) If the expenses for the festival were $3400, how much profit did the Club make for the charity event?

2. **Dairy Cows** A dairy cow produces an average of 7 gallons of milk a day. If a farmer has a herd of 35 cows, how much milk will they produce in 1 day? In 1 week?

3. Luis is opening his new accounting office and must order furniture for the front office. He found a sale at a local store that is offering free delivery and no sales tax. Luis must order 2 filing cabinets, 1 desk, 1 office chair, 2 bookcases, 6 guest chairs, 2 end tables, and 1 coffee table. The prices are listed in the table below. Round each price to the nearest hundred and then *estimate* the total price of the furniture.

Filing Cabinet	$467	Guest Chair	$197
Desk	$765	End Table	$317
Office Chair	$255	Coffee Table	$421
Bookcase	$299		

4. **Concept Check** At the end of January, Sahara had $200 left in her vacation savings account and $1000 in her household savings account. Each month for the next six months, Sahara plans to put $100 in her vacation account and $200 in her household account. In addition, she plans to split her $900 tax return equally between both accounts. Explain how to determine if Sahara will have enough money in her vacation account at the end of six months to take a $1500 vacation.

Find the next two figures that would appear in the sequence.

35.

36.

Cumulative Review

32. [1.4.3] Multiply $4 \cdot 3 \cdot 2 \cdot 5$.

33. [1.8.3] Solve $6x = 30$.

34. [1.8.3] Solve $x + 9 = 12$.

CHAPTER

2

Whether you are planning to save for a vacation, new car, or other expenses, you must make decisions about how to spend money. Sometimes the costs are higher than you thought they would be, and you must adjust your spending habits to save money for these extra expenses.

Integers

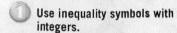

A dive $20\frac{1}{4}$ feet below the surface can be written "$-20\frac{1}{4}$ feet."

 Using Inequality Symbols with Integers

In this section we enlarge the set of whole numbers to include numbers that are less than 0. These numbers are called **negative numbers.** We use the symbol "$-$" to indicate that the sign of a number is negative, and the symbol "$+$" to indicate that the sign is positive. Thus, we write the number *negative six* in symbols as -6. For **positive numbers** we usually do not write the plus sign. That is, we write $+6$ as 6.

We say	negative six	positive six
We write	-6	$+6$ or 6

We often encounter real-life applications that require us to consider numbers that are less than 0. For example, a weather report states that the Fahrenheit temperature is 20 degrees below 0. How can we write this temperature? We can use negative numbers. Thus the temperature reading of 20 degrees below 0 is written $-20°$. Here are some other examples of negative numbers.

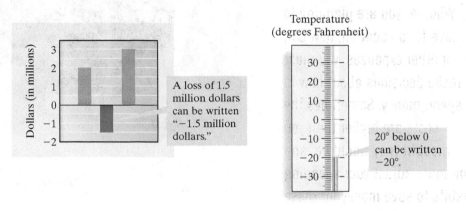

A loss of 1.5 million dollars can be written "-1.5 million dollars."

Temperature (degrees Fahrenheit)

20° below 0 can be written $-20°$.

We can also picture negative numbers using a **number line.** Positive numbers are to the right of 0 on the number line. Negative numbers are to the left of 0 on the number line. Note that the number 0 is neither positive nor negative.

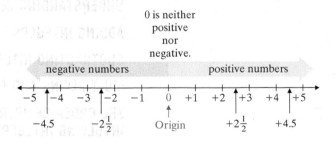

0 is neither positive nor negative.

negative numbers   positive numbers

-4.5 $-2\frac{1}{2}$ Origin $+2\frac{1}{2}$ $+4.5$

The positive numbers, negative numbers, and 0 are called **signed numbers.** In later chapters we will study signed numbers such as fractions and decimals. In this chapter we will study the set of signed numbers called **integers.** The integers are $\ldots, -3, -2, -1, 0, 1, 2, \ldots$.

Numbers decrease in value as we move from right to left on the number line. Therefore, 1 is less than 3 $(1 < 3)$ since 1 lies to the left of 3 on the number line, and -5 is less than -2 $(-5 < -2)$ since -5 lies to the left of -2 on the number line.

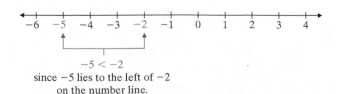

$-5 < -2$
since -5 lies to the left of -2
on the number line.

EXAMPLE 1   Graph −5, −3, 1, and 5 on a number line.

Solution   We draw a dot in the correct location on the number line.

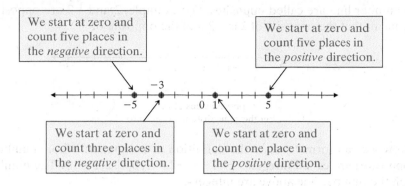

Practice Problem 1   Graph −4, −2, 2, and 4 on a number line.

EXAMPLE 2   Replace each ? with the inequality symbol < or >.

(a) −3 ? −1   **(b)** 4 ? −5   **(c)** −10 ? −345

Solution

(a) −3 < −1   −3 lies to the left of −1 on the number line.

(b) 4 > −5   Positive numbers are always greater than negative numbers.
                         This reads: "4 is greater than −5" or "−5 is less than 4."

(c) −10 > −345   The inequality symbol always points to the smaller number.

Practice Problem 2   Replace each ? with the inequality symbol < or >.

(a) −5 ? 2   **(b)** −3 ? −6   **(c)** −53 ? −218

In everyday situations we use the concept of positive and negative numbers to represent many different things. We can use "+" to represent an increase, a rise, or whenever something goes up, and "−" to represent a decrease, a decline, or whenever something goes down. For example, when you use a checking account you can associate a deposit with "+" since your balance goes *up* and a check written with "−" since your balance goes *down*.

EXAMPLE 3   Fill in each blank with the appropriate symbol, + or −, to describe either an increase or a decrease.

(a) A discount of $5: _____ $5
(b) The temperature rises 10°F: _____ 10°F

Solution

(a) A discount of $5 results in the price decreasing: −$5
(b) The temperature rises 10°F: +10°F

Practice Problem 3   Fill in each blank with the appropriate symbol, + or −, to describe either an increase or a decrease.

(a) A property tax increase of $130: _____ $130
(b) A dive of 7 ft below the surface of the sea: _____ 7 ft

Finding the Opposite of Numbers

Numbers that are the same distance from zero but lie on the opposite sides of zero on the number line are called **opposites.** For example, 2 and −2 are opposites. By this we mean that the opposite of 2 is −2 and the opposite of −2 is 2.

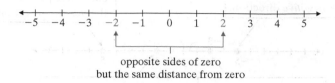

opposite sides of zero
but the same distance from zero

Now we can formally state the definition of an integer: Whole numbers and their opposites are called **integers:** $\{\ldots -3, -2, -1, 0, 1, 2, 3 \ldots\}$. The numbers labeled on the number line above are integers.

EXAMPLE 4 Label −5 and the *opposite* of −5 on a number line.

Solution   We first label −5.

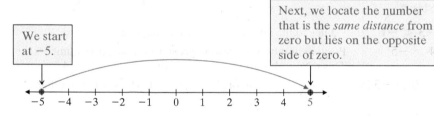

We start at −5.

Next, we locate the number that is the *same distance* from zero but lies on the opposite side of zero.

Thus the opposite of −5 is 5.

Practice Problem 4   Label −3 and the *opposite* of −3 on a number line.

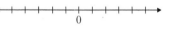

Another way to find the opposite of a number is to *change the sign* of the number. In Example 4 we can find the opposite of −5 by changing −5 to +5.

EXAMPLE 5   State the opposite of each number.

(a) 6   **(b)** −9

Solution   To find the opposite of a number, we change the sign of the number.

(a) The opposite of 6 is −6.   **(b)** The opposite of −9 is 9.

Practice Problem 5   State the opposite of each number.

(a) −6   **(b)** −1   **(c)** 12   **(d)** 1

NOTE TO STUDENT: Fully worked-out solutions to all of the Practice Problems can be found at the back of the text starting at page SP-1

So far we have used the symbol "−" to indicate the operation *subtraction* and to write a *negative number.* We also use the "−" symbol to indicate *"the opposite of."*

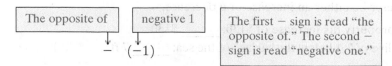

The opposite of   negative 1

$-\ (-1)$

The first − sign is read "the opposite of." The second − sign is read "negative one."

The interpretation of the symbol depends on the context in which it is used.

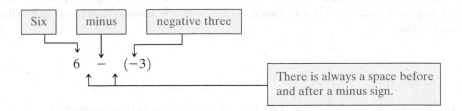

There is always a space before and after a minus sign.

EXAMPLE 6   Simplify. $-(-(-12))$

Solution

$-(-(-12))$ The opposite of negative 12 is positive 12.

$= -(12)$ The opposite of positive 12 is negative 12.

$= -12$

Practice Problem 6   Simplify. $-(-(-(-1)))$

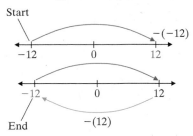

The opposite of negative 12

Start

$-(-12)$

The opposite of 12

EXAMPLE 7   Evaluate $-(-x)$ for $x = -9$.

Solution   To avoid errors involving negative signs, we can place parentheses around the variables and their replacements.

$-(-x)$

$= -(-(x))$ Place parentheses around x.

$= -(-(-9))$ Replace x with -9.

$= -(9)$ The opposite of -9 is 9: $-(-9) = 9$.

$= -9$ The opposite of 9 is -9.

Practice Problem 7   Evaluate $-(-(-a))$ for $a = 6$.

NOTE TO STUDENT: *Fully worked-out solutions to all of the Practice Problems can be found at the back of the text starting at page SP-1*

 Finding the Absolute Value of Numbers

Suppose that we want to find the distance from 0 to -4 and from 0 to $+4$. We can use the number line to measure this distance just as we use a ruler to measure feet or inches.

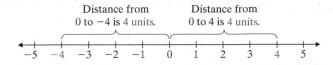

Distance from 0 to -4 is 4 units.   Distance from 0 to 4 is 4 units.

Both distances are the same; 4 and -4 are both 4 units from 0. As you can see, it is sometimes convenient to talk about just the numerical part of the number (the 4 of -4) and disregard the sign. The following definition gives us a way to do this.

The **absolute value** of a number is the distance between that number and 0 on the number line.

We place the symbols "| |" around the number to indicate that we want the absolute value of that number. We write $|-4| = 4$ and $|4| = 4$. The absolute value is never negative because it is a distance, and distance is always measured in positive or zero units.

> **PROCEDURE TO FIND THE ABSOLUTE VALUE OF A NUMBER**
> 1. If a number is *positive* or *zero*, the absolute value is that number.
>
> $$|7| = 7$$
> $$|0| = 0$$
>
> 2. If a number is *negative*, make the number positive to find the absolute value.
>
> $$|-7| = 7$$

EXAMPLE 8 Simplify each absolute value expression.

(a) $|-9|$ **(b)** $|3|$

Solution

(a) $|-9| = 9$ The absolute value of a negative number is positive.
(b) $|3| = 3$ The absolute value of a positive number is positive.

Practice Problem 8 Simplify each absolute value expression.

(a) $|-67|$ **(b)** $|8|$

NOTE TO STUDENT: Fully worked-out solutions to all of the Practice Problems can be found at the back of the text starting at page SP-1

EXAMPLE 9 Replace the ? with the symbol $<$, $>$, or $=$. $|-15|$? $|6|$

Solution $|-15|$? $|6|$
                   ↓   ↓

                 15   ?   6   We find the absolute values.
                 15   >   6   We write the appropriate inequality symbol, $>$.
               $|-15|$ > $|6|$ -15 has a larger absolute value than 6.

Distance from zero is 15.   Distance from zero is 6.

$$-15 \; -10 \; -5 \quad 0 \quad 5\,6 \quad 10 \quad 15$$

Note that when we say -15 has a larger absolute value, we mean that -15 is a greater distance from 0 than 6 is.

Practice Problem 9 Replace the ? with the symbol $<$, $>$, or $=$. $|-12|$? $|2|$

EXAMPLE 10 Simplify. $-|-7|$

Solution   We must find the opposite of the absolute value of -7.

            $-|-7|$ First we find the absolute value of -7: $|-7| = 7$.
          $= -(7)$ Then we take the opposite of 7: $-(7) = -7$.
          $= -7$

Practice Problem 10 Simplify. $-|-1|$

Reading Line Graphs

We can use a line graph to display information much the same way that we use a bar graph. On a line graph we use dots instead of bars to record data. Then we connect the dots with straight lines. The vertical number line on a graph is sometimes extended to include negative numbers.

EXAMPLE 11 The line graph below indicates the low temperatures for selected cities on January 25, 2007.

(a) In which city was the temperature colder, Syracuse or Burlington?

(b) Which cities recorded a positive temperature for the day, and which cities recorded a negative temperature?

Solution On the graph negative numbers are located below zero and positive numbers above zero.

(a) The low temperature was 3°F in Syracuse and −8°F in Burlington. It was colder in Burlington.
Note that the dot representing Burlington's temperature is lower on the line graph than the dot representing Syracuse's temperature.

(b) The positive temperatures appear as dots above 0 and negative temperatures below 0.

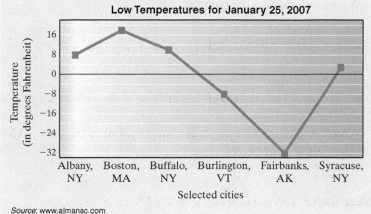

Cities with positive temperatures: Albany, Boston, Buffalo, and Syracuse
Cities with negative temperatures: Burlington and Fairbanks

Practice Problem 11 Use the line graph in Example 11 to answer the following.

(a) In which city was the temperature colder, Fairbanks or Buffalo?

(b) Name the city that recorded the highest temperature and the city that recorded the lowest temperature.

Verbal and Writing Skills *Write in words.*

1. $-(-1)$

2. $-|-4|$

Translate into numbers and symbols.

3. Negative four minus two

4. Five minus negative one

Fill in the blanks.

5. -9 is a _____ number, and 9 is a _____ number.

6. Numbers that are the same distance from zero but lie on opposite sides of zero on the number line are called _____.

Graph each number on the number line.

7. $-6, -4, 3,$ and 4

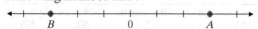

8. $-7, -2, 2,$ and 5

9. $-3, -1, 1,$ and 3

10. $-5, -4, 4,$ and 5

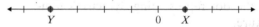

11. Which dot, A or B, represents a larger number on the following number line?

12. Which dot, X or Y, represents a larger number on the following number line?

Replace each ? with the inequality symbol $<$ or $>$.

13. $-9 \; ? \; 4$ **14.** $-7 \; ? \; 4$ **15.** $4 \; ? \; -3$ **16.** $6 \; ? \; -4$

17. $-5 \; ? \; 5$ **18.** $-6 \; ? \; 6$ **19.** $-9 \; ? \; -5$ **20.** $-6 \; ? \; -2$

21. $-8 \; ? \; -6$ **22.** $-41 \; ? \; -6$ **23.** $-298 \; ? \; -350$ **24.** $-765 \; ? \; -990$

Fill in the blanks with the appropriate symbol, $+$ or $-$, to describe either an increase or a decrease.

25. _____ A loss of $100

26. _____ A plane descends 1000 ft.

27. _____ A raise of $100

28. _____ The temperature rises 10°F

29. _____ A discount of $10

30. _____ A profit of $220

31. _____ A plane ascends 1000 ft.

32. _____ A tax decrease of $150

33. Label -1 and the *opposite* of -1 on the number line.

34. Label 5 and the *opposite* of 5 on the number line.

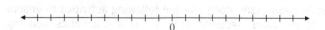

Fill in the blanks.

35. The opposite of -3 is ____.

36. The opposite of -8 is ____.

37. The opposite of 16 is _____.

38. The opposite of 19 is _____.

Simplify.

39. $-(-4)$ **40.** $-(-9)$ **41.** $-(8)$ **42.** $-(1)$

Label the following on the number line.

43. $-(-(-7))$

44. $-(-(-8))$

Simplify.

45. $-(-(13))$

46. $-(-(30))$

47. $-(-(-(-1)))$

48. $-(-(-(-2)))$

Evaluate.

49. $-(-a)$ for $a = 6$

50. $-(-y)$ for $y = 13$

51. $-(-(-x))$ for $x = -1$

52. $-(-(-n))$ for $n = -6$

53. $-(-(-(-y)))$ for $y = -2$

54. $-(-(-(-x)))$ for $x = -5$

Simplify each absolute value expression.

55. $|8|$

56. $|6|$

57. $|-5|$

58. $|-7|$

59. $|-16|$

60. $|-19|$

61. $|0|$

62. $|42|$

Replace each ? with the symbol $<$, $>$, or $=$.

63. $|-3| \ ? \ |1|$

64. $|-9| \ ? \ |5|$

65. $|8| \ ? \ |-8|$

66. $|6| \ ? \ |-6|$

67. $|16| \ ? \ |-9|$

68. $|19| \ ? \ |-13|$

69. $|-35| \ ? \ |-8|$

70. $|-71| \ ? \ |-6|$

Simplify.

71. $-|-3|$

72. $-|-10|$

73. $-|14|$

74. $-|17|$

Applications

75. ***Charted Temperatures*** The line graph indicates the low temperature in selected cities during a week in January.

   (a) In which city was the temperature colder, Fargo or Albany?

   (b) Which cities recorded a positive temperature for the day, and which cities recorded a negative temperature?

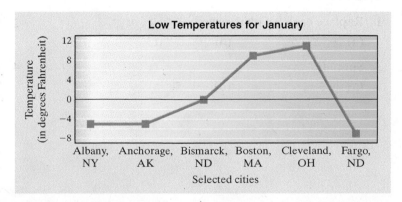

76. Use the line graph in exercise 75 to answer the following.

   (a) In which city was the temperature colder, Anchorage or Bismarck?

   (b) Name the cities that recorded the highest and lowest temperatures.

One Step Further *Simplify each statement, then replace the ? with the symbol <, >, or =.*

77. $-|-16|$? -16

78. $|-12|$? $-(-12)$

79. $|-9|$? $-|-9|$

80. $-(-(-1))$? $|-1|$

Simplify each statement, then perform the operation indicated.

81. $-(-6) + |-5|$

82. $-(-4) + |-9|$

83. $-(-|8|) - |-1|$

84. $-(-|5|) - |-2|$

To Think About

85. Which of the two numbers has the larger absolute value, -33 or 20?

86. Which of the two numbers has the larger absolute value, -43 or 40?

87. Which of the two numbers has the larger absolute value, 129 or -112?

88. Which of the two numbers has the larger absolute value, 231 or -98?

State whether each statement is true or false.

89. If $x > y$, then x must be a positive number.

90. The numbers $-2, -1, 0, 1,$ and 2 are called integers.

Fill in the blank.

91. If m is a negative number, then $-m$ is a _____ number.

92. There are two numbers that are 3 units from 1 on the number line. One of these numbers is 4 and the other number is _____

Cumulative Review *Perform the operation indicated.*

93. **[1.3.4]** $5009 - 258$

94. **[1.2.4]** $5699 + 351$

95. **[1.4.4]** $(256)(91)$

96. **[1.5.4]** $456 \div 3$

97. **[1.9.3]** *Budgeting* For a trip to Hawaii, Wanda has a vacation budget of $2600. The cost of airfare is $480, and lodging is $1200. If the travel agent estimates that Wanda will spend $350 on food, how much will Wanda have left in the budget to spend during the vacation?

98. **[1.9.3]** *Financing a Purchase* Tran Troung is buying new appliances for her home. She ordered a stove for $780, a washer for $520, a dryer for $450, and a refrigerator for $1150. The tax for the entire purchase is $203, and the delivery charge is $45. If Tran puts $800 down on the purchase, how much does she have to finance?

Quick Quiz 2.1

1. Replace each ? with the symbol $<, >,$ or $=$.
   (a) -5 ? -6
   (b) $|-11|$? $|13|$

2. Simplify. $-(-(-7))$

3. Simplify.
   (a) $|-3|$
   (b) $-|-5|$

4. **Concept Check** Rearrange numbers in order from smallest to largest: $-1, -6, -4, -10, 0$

2.2 ADDING INTEGERS

① Adding Integers with the Same Sign

We often associate the $+$ and $-$ symbols with positive and negative situations. We can find the sum of integers by considering the outcome of these situations as illustrated below.

A price decrease of $10 followed by a price decrease of $20 results in a decrease of $30.

$$(-\$10) \quad + \quad (-\$20) \quad = \quad (-\$30)$$

In the same sense, an *increase* followed by an *increase* results in an *increase,* or a positive outcome.

EXAMPLE 1

(a) Fill in the blank. A loss of $1000 followed by a loss of $1000 results in a _____.

(b) Write the math symbols that represent the situation described in **(a)**.

Solution

(a) A loss of $1000 followed by a loss of $1000 results in a loss of $2000.

(b) A loss of $1000 followed by a loss of $1000 results in a loss of $2000.

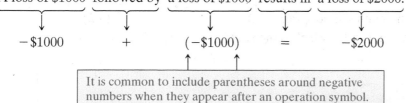

$$-\$1000 \quad + \quad (-\$1000) \quad = \quad -\$2000$$

> It is common to include parentheses around negative numbers when they appear after an operation symbol.

Practice Problem 1

(a) Fill in the blank. A decrease in altitude of 100 feet followed by a decrease in altitude of 100 feet results in a _____.

(b) Write the math symbols that represent the situation described in (a).

Since integers are often used to indicate *direction* and *distance*, we can also use the number line to find the sum of numbers such as $-1 + (-2)$. A move to the *right* on the number line is a move in the *positive* direction, and a move to the *left* on the number line is a move in the *negative* direction. The direction we move on the number line is indicated by the sign of the number.

> We see that
> $-1 + (-2) = -3.$

> We start at 0 and move 1 unit in the negative direction, followed by another 2 units in the negative direction.

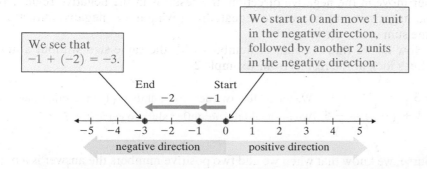

EXAMPLE 2

(a) Begin at 0 on the number line and move 3 units to the left followed by another 2 units to the left.

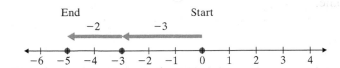

(b) Is the end result in the positive or the negative region?
(c) Write the math symbols that represent the situation.
(d) Use the number line to find the sum.

Solution

(a)

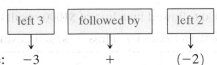

(b) From the illustration we see that the end result is in the negative region since we began at 0 and moved 3 units in the negative direction (left), followed by another 2 units in the negative direction.

left 3	followed by	left 2

(c) The math symbols are: -3 $+$ (-2)
(d) We end at -5, which is the sum.

$$-3 + (-2) = -5$$

Practice Problem 2

(a) Begin at 0 on the number line and move 4 units to the left followed by another 1 unit to the left.

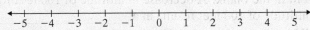

(b) Is the end result in the positive or the negative region?
(c) Write the math symbols that represent the situation.
(d) Use the number line to find the sum.

NOTE TO STUDENT: *Fully worked-out solutions to all of the Practice Problems can be found at the back of the text starting at page SP-1*

Example 2 shows that if we make a move in the negative direction followed by another move in the negative direction, the result is in the negative region. When we add negative numbers, we are repeatedly moving in the negative direction and thus the sum is a negative number.

How do we find the sum of numbers with the same sign without a number line? Let's look at the results from Example 2.

$-3 + (-2) = -$ We are adding two negative numbers, and the sum is negative.
$-3 + (-2) = -5$ We must add the absolute values to get 5: $2 + 3 = 5$.

Of course, we know that when we add two positive numbers the answer is a positive number.

We state the formal rule.

RULE FOR ADDING TWO OR MORE NUMBERS WITH THE SAME SIGN

To add numbers with the *same* sign:

1. Use the common sign in the answer.
2. Add the absolute values of the numbers.

If all the numbers are positive, the sum is positive.
If all the numbers are negative, the sum is negative.

EXAMPLE 3   Add. $-1 + (-3)$

Solution   We are adding two numbers with the same sign, so we keep the common sign (negative sign) and add the absolute values.

$-1 + (-3) = -$ The answer is *negative* since the common sign is negative.
$-1 + (-3) = -4$ Add. $1 + 3 = 4$

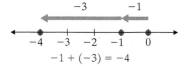

$-1 + (-3) = -4$

Practice Problem 3   Add. $-2 + (-4)$

Adding Integers with Different Signs

So far we have seen how to add numbers with the *same sign*. We use a similar approach to see how we add numbers that have *different signs*. Addition of numbers with *different signs* often involves situations such as a decrease followed by an increase or a quantity that rises and then falls.

If we wish, we can also use a vertical number line instead of a horizontal number line to illustrate these types of situations. If we move *up*, we are moving in the positive direction. If we move *down*, we are moving in the negative direction.

EXAMPLE 4   One night the temperature on Long Island, New York, dropped to $-25°F$. At dawn the temperature had risen $10°F$.

(a) Write the math symbols that represent the situation.

(b) Use the thermometer to determine if the temperature at dawn was positive or negative.

(c) Find the sum.

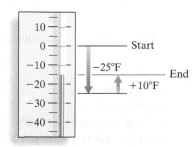

Solution

    down 25   followed by   up 10
     ↓   ↓   ↓
(a) $-25°F$ $+$ $(+10°F)$

(b) From the chart we see that the temperature reading was negative since it went down $(-)$ more degrees than it went up $(+)$.

(c) The final temperature is $-15°F$, which is the sum: $-25°F + 10°F = -15°F$.

Practice Problem 4   Last night the temperature in Boston, Massachusetts, dropped to $-15°F$. At dawn it had risen $30°F$.

(a) Write the math symbols that represent the situation.

(b) Use the thermometer to determine if the temperature at dawn was positive or negative.

(c) Find the sum.

Example 4 involves addition of integers with *different signs*. How do we perform this addition without using a chart? Let's look at the results from Example 4.

$$-25 + (+10) = -$$ The sign of the sum is *negative* since we move a larger distance in the *negative* direction.

$$-25 + (+10) = -15$$ We must subtract $25 - 10$ to get the result, 15.

We see that to find the sum, we actually find the *difference* between 25 and 10. Also notice that if we do not account for the *sign*, the larger number is 25. The sign of 25 is *negative*, and the answer is also *negative*. This suggests the addition rule for two numbers with different signs.

RULE FOR ADDING TWO NUMBERS WITH DIFFERENT SIGNS

To add two numbers with *different* signs:

1. Use the *sign* of the number with the larger absolute value in the answer.

2. Subtract the absolute values of the numbers.

In other words, we keep the sign of the larger absolute value and subtract.

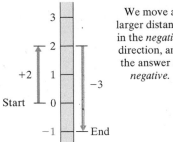

We move a larger distance in the *negative* direction, and the answer is *negative*.

EXAMPLE 5   Add.

(a) $2 + (-3)$ **(b)** $-2 + 3$

Solution   We are adding numbers with *different* signs, so we keep the sign of the larger absolute value and subtract.

(a) $2 + (-3) = -$ The answer is *negative* since -3 is negative and has the larger absolute value.

$\quad 2 + (-3) = -1$ Subtract: $3 - 2 = 1$.

(b) $-2 + 3 = +$ The answer is *positive* since 3 is positive and has the larger absolute value.

$\quad -2 + 3 = +1$ Subtract: $3 - 2 = 1$.

We move a larger distance in the *positive* direction, and the answer is *positive*.

Practice Problem 5   Add.   **(a)** $-4 + 7$ **(b)** $4 + (-7)$

We summarize the rules for adding numbers as follows.

Adding numbers with the *same sign:* Keep the common sign and add the absolute values.

Adding numbers with *different signs:* Keep the sign of the larger absolute value and subtract the absolute values.

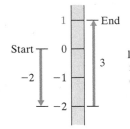

EXAMPLE 6   Add.

(a) $8 + (-5)$ **(b)** $-8 + (-5)$

Solution

(a) $8 + (-5)$ We have *different* signs.

$\quad 8 + (-5) = +$ 8 is larger than 5, so the answer is *positive*.

$\quad 8 + (-5) = +3$ or 3   Subtract: $8 - 5 = 3$.

(b) $-8 + (-5)$ We have the *same* sign.

$\quad -8 + (-5) =$ Keep the common sign.

$\quad -8 + (-5) = -13$ Add: $8 + 5 = 13$.

Practice Problem 6 Add.

(a) $-3 + 8$

(b) $-3 + (-8)$

Recall from Section 2.1 that the numbers 3 and -3 are called opposites. Let's look at the number line in the margin and see what happens when we add the opposites $3 + (-3)$. When we add opposites the sum is 0 because we move the same distance in the positive direction as we move in the negative direction. This fact is referred to as the **additive inverse property,** and thus 3 and -3 are also called **additive inverses.**

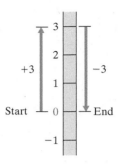

ADDITIVE INVERSE PROPERTY

For any number a,

$$a + (-a) = 0 \quad \text{and} \quad (-a) + a = 0$$

The sum of any number and its opposite is 0.

EXAMPLE 7

(a) Add. $1298 + (-1298)$

(b) Find x. $x + 21 = 0$

Solution

(a) Since 1298 and -1298 are additive inverses, their sum is 0.
$1298 + (-1298) = 0$

(b) The sum of additive inverses is 0. Thus if $x + 21 = 0$, then $x = -21$ since $-21 + 21 = 0$.

Practice Problem 7

(a) Add. $3544 + (-3544)$

(b) Find y. $-13 + y = 0$

NOTE TO STUDENT: Fully worked-out solutions to all of the Practice Problems can be found at the back of the text starting at page SP-1

If there are three or more numbers to add, it may be easier to add positive numbers and negative numbers separately and then combine the results. We can do this because, just like with whole numbers, addition of integers is commutative and associative.

EXAMPLE 8 Add. $-3 + 9 + (-4) + 12$

Solution

$$-3 + 9 + (-4) + 12 = [(-3) + (-4)] + (9 + 12)$$

Change the order of addition and regroup.

$$= -7 + (9 + 12)$$

Add the negative numbers: $-3 + (-4) = -7$.

$$= -7 + 21$$

Add the positive numbers: $9 + 12 = 21$.

$$= 14$$

Add the result: $-7 + 21 = 14$.

Practice Problem 8 Add. $-8 + 6 + (-2) + 5$

Evaluating Algebraic Expressions Involving Addition of Integers

We evaluate expressions involving integers just as we did expressions involving whole numbers. We replace the variables with the given numbers and perform the operations indicated.

EXAMPLE 9 Evaluate.

(a) $-7 + a + b$ for $a = -3$ and $b = 9$

(b) $-x + y + (-13)$ for $x = -2$ and $y = -6$

Solution   We place parentheses around the variables, and then replace each variable with the appropriate values.

(a)

$$-7 + (a) + (b)$$
$$= -7 + (-3) + (9)$$
$$= \underbrace{-10} + 9$$
$$= -1$$

(b)

$$-(x) + (y) + (-13)$$
$$= -(-2) + (-6) + (-13)$$
$$= 2 + \underbrace{(-19)}$$
$$= -17$$

NOTE TO STUDENT: *Fully worked-out solutions to all of the Practice Problems can be found at the back of the text starting at page SP-1*

Practice Problem 9 Evaluate.

(a) $-3 + x + y$ for $x = -5$ and $y = -11$

(b) $-x + 8 + y$ for $x = -2$ and $y = -15$

 ### Solving Applied Problems Involving Addition of Integers

EXAMPLE 10 Information on Micro Firm Computer Sales' profit and loss situation is given on the graph. What was the company's overall profit or loss at the end of the third quarter?

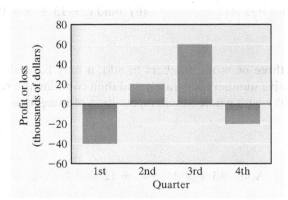

Solution

1st quarter loss	+	2nd quarter profit	+	3rd quarter profit	=	net profit
$-\$40,000$	+	$\$20,000$	+	$\$60,000$	=	$\$40,000$

$$-40,000 + (20,000 + 60,000) = -40,000 + 80,000 = 40,000$$

At the end of the third quarter the company had a net profit of $40,000.

Practice Problem 10 What was Micro Firm Computer Sales' overall profit or loss at the end of the second quarter?

Developing Your Study Skills

When to Use a Calculator

A calculator is an important tool and therefore we benefit by learning how to use it. You may be thinking, "Why learn math if I can use a calculator?" Well, often it is not practical or convenient to use a calculator. Many times we must perform calculations unexpectedly and do not have a calculator available, as in the following situations.

- You receive change for a purchase made. Is the change correct?
- You are shopping and notice that an item you'd like to buy is marked down 30 percent. You must calculate the reduced price to determine if you can afford to buy the item.
- You have lunch with four friends and the bill is on one check. How much do you owe for your lunch?

These are just a few of the many situations that require you to use your knowledge of mathematics. Besides, even if you had a calculator in the situations above, you would still need to know how to go about solving the problem. Should you add, subtract, multiply, or divide? The calculator does only what you tell it to do; it does not plan the approach! Learning how to do mathematics develops problem-solving skills, and the calculator assists us in solving problems.

Exercises

Do the following exercises without and then with a calculator. Which way is faster, with or without a calculator?

1. Add. $-2 + (-3) + (-1)$
2. Combine like terms. $4xy + 2x + 3xy$
3. If you didn't know the rules for combining like terms, could you have done exercise 2 with a calculator?

Calculator

 ### Adding Negative Numbers

There are a few different ways to enter negative numbers in a calculator. Usually, either a $\boxed{+/-}$ or the $\boxed{(-)}$ key is used. You should read the manual for directions. To find $(-119) + 85$, enter 119 $\boxed{+/-}$ $\boxed{+}$ 85 $\boxed{=}$

The display should read $\boxed{-34}$.

Verbal and Writing Skills

1. Explain in your own words why a negative number added to a negative number is a negative number.

2. Write an application about temperatures to describe the addition of two negative numbers.

Fill in the blanks.

3. To add two numbers with different signs, we keep the sign of the _____ _____ _____ and _____.

4. The sum of two positive numbers is a _____ number. The sum of two negative numbers is a _____ number.

Fill in the box with + or −, then write the rule for adding integers that you used.

5. (a) $-2 + (-3) = \boxed{}5$ Rule:

(b) $2 + (-3) = \boxed{}1$ Rule:

(c) $-2 + 3 = \boxed{}1$ Rule:

6. (a) $-4 + (-6) = \boxed{}10$ Rule:

(b) $4 + (-6) = \boxed{}2$ Rule:

(c) $-4 + 6 = \boxed{}2$ Rule:

7. (a) Begin at 0 on the number line and move 2 units to the left followed by another 2 units to the left.

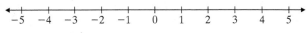

(b) Is the end result in the positive or negative region?
(c) Write the math symbols that represent the situation.
(d) Use the number line to find the sum.

8. (a) Begin at 0 on the number line and move 1 unit to the left followed by another 2 units to the left.

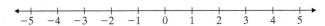

(b) Is the end result in the positive or negative region?
(c) Write the math symbols that represent the situation.
(d) Use the number line to find the sum.

9. (a) Begin at 0 on the number line and move 3 units to the right followed by another 2 units right.

(b) Is the end result in the positive or negative region?
(c) Write the math symbols that represent the situation.
(d) Use the number line to find the sum.

10. (a) Begin at 0 on the number line and move 1 unit to the right followed by another 4 units right.

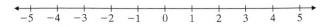

(b) Is the end result in the positive or negative region?
(c) Write the math symbols that represent the situation.
(d) Use the number line to find the sum.

11. Fill in the blanks.
    (a) A decrease of 10°F followed by a decrease of 5°F results in a _____.
    (b) Write the math symbols that represent the situation described in (a). _____

12. Fill in the blanks.
    (a) A discount of $4 followed by a discount of $2 results in _____.
    (b) Write the math symbols that represent the situation described in (a). _____

13. Fill in the blanks.
    (a) A profit of $100 followed by a profit of $50 results in a _____.
    (b) Write the math symbols that represent the situation described in (a). _____

14. Fill in the blanks.
    (a) An increase of 120 units followed by an increase of 50 units results in a(n) _____.
    (b) Write the math symbols that represent the situation described in (a). _____

Add by using the rules for addition of integers.

15. (a) $-11 + (-13)$
    (b) $11 + 13$

16. (a) $-15 + (-19)$
    (b) $15 + 19$

17. (a) $-29 + (-39)$
    (b) $29 + 39$

18. (a) $-24 + (-44)$
    (b) $24 + 44$

19. (a) $-53 + (-18)$
    (b) $53 + 18$

20. (a) $-30 + (-10)$
    (b) $30 + 10$

Applications

21. **Temperature Fluctuations** During the early morning hours on a ski slope in Colorado the temperature dropped to $-3°F$. At dawn it had risen $10°F$.
    (a) Write the math symbols that represent the situation.
    (b) Use the chart to determine if the temperature at dawn was positive or negative.
    (c) Find the sum.

22. **Temperature Fluctuations** At midnight in Trenton, New Jersey, the temperature dropped to $-4°F$. At dawn it had risen $2°F$.
    (a) Write the math symbols that represent the situation.
    (b) Use the chart to determine if the temperature at dawn was positive or negative.
    (c) Find the sum.

23. (a) Write the math symbols that represent the situation: move a marker up 2 units followed by a move down 4 units.
    (b) Use the chart to determine if the marker is in the positive or negative region.
    (c) Use the chart to find the sum.

24. (a) Write the math symbols that represent the situation: move a marker up 3 units followed by a move down 6 units.
    (b) Use the chart to determine if the marker is in the positive or negative region.
    (c) Use the chart to find the sum.

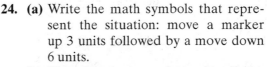

Express the outcome of each situation as an integer.

25. A 300-foot increase in altitude followed by a 400-foot decrease in altitude

26. Diving 10 feet downward followed by rising 2 feet

27. A loss of $400 followed by a profit of $500

28. An increase of 10 pounds in weight followed by a decrease of 5 pounds

Add by using the rules for addition of integers.

29. (a) $6 + (-8)$
(b) $-6 + 8$

30. (a) $4 + (-9)$
(b) $-4 + 9$

31. (a) $5 + (-1)$
(b) $-5 + 1$

32. (a) $8 + (-3)$
(b) $-8 + 3$

33. (a) $22 + (-16)$
(b) $-22 + 16$

34. (a) $15 + (-24)$
(b) $-15 + 24$

35. (a) $3 + (-1)$
(b) $-3 + (-1)$
(c) $-3 + 1$

36. (a) $5 + (-9)$
(b) $-5 + (-9)$
(c) $-5 + 9$

37. (a) $-9 + (-11)$
(b) $9 + (-11)$
(c) $-9 + 11$

38. (a) $-12 + (-3)$
(b) $12 + (-3)$
(c) $-12 + 3$

39. $2 + (-2)$

40. $3 + (-3)$

41. $-9 + 9$

42. $-5 + 5$

43. $-360 + 360$

44. $-120 + 120$

45. $452 + (-452)$

46. $786 + (-786)$

Find x.

47. $x + 19 = 0$

48. $x + 23 = 0$

49. $-12 + x = 0$

50. $-21 + x = 0$

Mixed Practice Exercises 51–70 *Add by using the rules for addition of integers.*

51. $12 + (-11)$

52. $14 + (-13)$

53. $-10 + 4$

54. $-8 + 5$

55. $-7 + 14$

56. $-4 + 9$

57. $22 + (-10)$

58. $34 + (-14)$

59. $-33 + (-5)$

60. $-42 + (-12)$

61. $-27 + (-12)$

62. $-43 + (-23)$

63. $-15 + 15$

64. $-92 + 92$

65. $-12 + 16$

66. $-11 + 15$

67. $6 + (-8)$

68. $5 + (-7)$

69. $15 + (-15)$

70. $13 + (-13)$

Add by using the rules for addition of integers.

71. $6 + (-9) + 1 + (-3)$

72. $4 + (-7) + 2 + (-5)$

73. $-21 + 16 + (-33)$

74. $-31 + 19 + (-25)$

75. $57 + (-29) + (-34) + 23$

76. $25 + (-17) + (-28) + 64$

77. $-15 + 7 + (-10) + 3$

78. $-12 + 4 + (-8) + 5$

79. Evaluate $y + 5$ for each of the following.
   (a) $y = -2$ **(b)** $y = -7$

80. Evaluate $x + 5$ for each of the following.
   (a) $x = -1$ **(b)** $x = -8$

81. Evaluate $a + (-8)$ for each of the following.
   (a) $a = 4$ **(b)** $a = -5$

82. Evaluate $x + (-6)$ for each of the following.
   (a) $x = 3$ **(b)** $x = -9$

83. Evaluate $-2 + x + y$ for each of the following.
   (a) $x = -6$ and $y = 4$
   (b) $x = 5$ and $y = -9$

84. Evaluate $-9 + a + b$ for each of the following.
   (a) $a = 7$ and $b = -3$
   (b) $a = -1$ and $b = 4$

85. Evaluate $-x + y + 6$ for $x = -3$ and $y = -1$.

86. Evaluate $-x + y + 4$ for $x = -2$ and $y = -5$.

87. Evaluate $-a + b + (-1)$ for $a = -3$ and $b = -5$.

88. Evaluate $-a + b + (-6)$ for $a = -5$ and $b = -1$.

Applications

Profit and Loss *The quarterly profit or loss in 2009 for Citron Foods is indicated on the graph. Use the graph to answer exercises 89 and 90.*

89. What was the company's overall profit or loss at the end of the second quarter?

90. What was the company's overall profit or loss at the end of the fourth quarter?

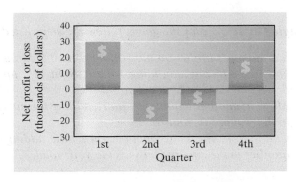

Solve each applied problem.

91. ***Checking Account*** While balancing her checkbook, Jessica discovered that her balance was $-\$121$. She hurried to the bank, hoping to prevent a bounced check, and deposited $\$200$. What was the balance in her checking account after the deposit? (Assume there was no penalty from the bank.)

92. ***Checking Account*** Allison found that she had made an arithmetic mistake in her checkbook and the actual balance was $-\$97$. She quickly went to the bank and made a deposit of $\$150$. What was the balance in her checking account after the deposit? (Assume there was no penalty from the bank.)

93. ***Submarine*** A submarine is 75 feet below sea level. It dives to a point 150 feet lower. Represent this distance below sea level as an integer.

94. ***Temperature*** The temperature at 3 P.M. was 2 degrees below zero. By midnight the temperature dropped another 8 degrees. Represent this temperature as an integer.

One Step Further *Evaluate.*

95. $3 + x + y + (-1) + z$ for $x = -1$, $y = 9$, and $z = -5$

96. $-2 + a + b + 6 + c$ for $a = 8$, $b = -4$, and $c = 4$

Add.

97. $-33 + 24 + (-38) + 19 + (-3)$

98. $9 + (-42) + (-88) + 10 + (-13)$

99. $12 + (-45) + (-9) + 5 + (-19)$

100. $2 + (-72) + (-41) + 11 + (-33)$

To Think About *Place the number in the box that makes each statement true.*

101. $-2 + \boxed{} = -5$

102. $-6 + \boxed{} = -7$

103. $3 + \boxed{} = -1$

104. $4 + \boxed{} = -3$

105. What number can be added to -11 to obtain -10?

106. What number can be added to -33 to obtain -30?

107. If $x + y + 30 = 0$, what does the sum $x + y$ equal? Find possible values of x and y for this equation.

108. If $22 + x + y = 0$, what does the sum $x + y$ equal? Find possible values of x and y for this equation.

Triangle Game *To play the game, follow the steps listed below.*

1. *Start at any number on the bottom row of the triangle and move to any adjoining square, right, left, up, or down and then add the two numbers.*
2. *Move to another adjoining square, adding the number in that square to your total.*
3. *Continue in the same manner, each time adding the number in the square you select to your total.*

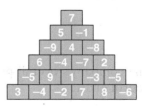

The goal is to reach the square at the top with the fewest number of squares selected while keeping the sum within the following guidelines.

109. At **no** time may the sum of the numbers be less than -6 or greater than or equal to 6.

110. At **no** time may the sum of the numbers be less than -5 or greater than or equal to 5.

Cumulative Review *Simplify.*

111. **[1.8.1]** $4x + 6x$

112. **[1.4.3]** $2(3x)$

113. **[1.8.1]** $8x - 3x$

114. **[1.7.3]** $3(x - 4)$

115. **[1.9.3]** *Distance Traveled* Vu Nguyen drives his car 150 miles from Phoenix to Tucson, Arizona, to visit a friend. Vu then proceeds from Tucson 110 miles to Sierra Vista for a one-week stay. He returns home to Phoenix from Sierra Vista driving the same route through Tucson. Vu had 23,566 miles on his odometer before he began his trip. If he did not drive any additional miles during his stay, what is the reading on the odometer at the end of the trip?

116. **[2.2.1]** *Boarding and Exiting a Bus* At the beginning of the day, 12 people boarded an empty bus on Route 33A. At the first stop, 4 people exited the bus and 8 people boarded. At the second stop, no one exited and 11 people boarded. At the third stop, 7 people exited and 15 boarded. Represent the number of people exiting with negative numbers and the number of people boarding with positive numbers. Then determine how many people were on the bus after the third stop.

Quick Quiz 2.2

1. Perform the operation indicated.

    (a) $-6 + (-4)$

    (b) $-6 + 4$

    (c) $-9 + 5 + (-3) + 6$

2. Evaluate $-a + b + 3$ for $a = -1$ and $b = -7$.

3. The profit or loss statement for Raskin Consulting, Inc. in 2006 showed a loss the first quarter of $3000, a loss the second quarter of $2500, a profit the third quarter of $8000, and a loss the fourth quarter of $3500. What was the company's overall profit or loss at the end of the fourth quarter?

4. **Concept Check** Without completing the calculations, explain how you can determine whether the answer is a positive or negative number.

Evaluate $132 + x + y + z$ for $x = -1$, $y = -3$, and $z = -2$.

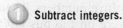
 Subtracting Integers

How do we subtract integers? What is the value of $-4 - 2$? Before we define a rule for subtracting integers, let's look at a few subtraction problems that we can do mentally.

Suppose that you have $20 in the bank and you write a check for $30. The bank will not be able to pay the $30 because you are *short $10*. If the bank cashed the check, your balance would represent a debt of $10, or $-\$10$. Thus we can see that $\$20 - \$30 = -\$10$.

Now, what do you think the value of $6 - 7$ is? We can think of this as a situation in which we have 6 items and want to take away 7 items. We are *short 1 item*, or -1. Thus $6 - 7 = -1$.

EXAMPLE 1 Subtract.

(a) $\$15 - \$20$ **(b)** $3 - 4$

Solution

(a) $\$15 - \$20 = -\$5$ If we have $15 and want to spend $20, we are short $5, or $-\$5$.

(b) $3 - 4 = -1$ If we have 3 items and try to take away 4 items, we are short 1 item, or -1.

Practice Problem 1 Subtract.

(a) $\$10 - \$20$ **(b)** $5 - 7$

It is not always possible to subtract mentally, so we must find an efficient way to do more complicated subtraction problems. *We can rewrite a subtraction problem as a related addition problem and then use the rules for adding integers we learned in Section 2.2.* To illustrate, we write an addition problem that gives the same result as the subtraction problem in Example 1a. Look for a pattern.

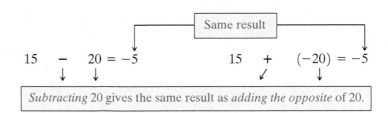

Same result

$15 \quad - \quad 20 = -5 \qquad\qquad 15 \quad + \quad (-20) = -5$

Subtracting 20 gives the same result as *adding the opposite* of 20.

We see that $15 - 20$ is equivalent to $15 + (-20)$. They give the same result, -5. That is, subtracting 20 gives the same result as adding the opposite of 20. We see it is reasonable to generalize that subtracting is equivalent to adding the opposite.

EXAMPLE 2 Rewrite each subtraction as addition of the opposite.

(a) $40 - 10 = 30$ **(b)** $6 - 2 = 4$ **(c)** $25 - 5 = 20$

Solution

Subtraction	*Addition of the Opposite*
(a) $40 - 10 = 30$	$40 + (-10) = 30$
(b) $6 - 2 = 4$	$6 + (-2) = 4$
(c) $25 - 5 = 20$	$25 + (-5) = 20$

NOTE TO STUDENT: *Fully worked-out solutions to all of the Practice Problems can be found at the back of the text starting at page SP-1*

Practice Problem 2 Rewrite each subtraction as addition of the opposite.

(a) $20 - 10 = 10$ **(b)** $5 - 2 = 3$ **(c)** $20 - 5 = 15$

We now state the rule for subtraction.

RULE FOR SUBTRACTING TWO NUMBERS

$$a - b = a + (-b)$$

To subtract b, add its *opposite*, $-b$.

To subtract, add the opposite of the second number to the first.

CAUTION: The *first* number does not change. Be sure to only change the *second* number.

EXAMPLE 3 Subtract.

(a) $-8 - 3$ **(b)** $-6 - (-4)$

Solution We replace the *second* number by its opposite and then add using the rules for addition.

(a) -8 $-$ 3

$\quad\quad -8$ $+$ (-3) $= -11$

Change subtraction to addition.	Write the opposite of the second number.	Add using the rule for adding numbers with the *same sign*.

$$-8 - 3 = -8 + (-3) = -11$$

(b) -6 $-$ (-4)

$\quad\quad -6$ $+$ 4 $= -2$

Change subtraction to addition.	Write the opposite of the second number.	Add using the rule for adding numbers with *different signs*.

$$-6 - (-4) = -6 + 4 = -2$$

Practice Problem 3 Subtract.

(a) $-5 - 4$ **(b)** $-9 - (-5)$

At this point you should be able to do simple subtraction problems quickly.

Remember that in performing subtraction of two numbers:

1. The first number does not change.
2. The subtraction sign is changed to addition.
3. We write the opposite of the second number.
4. We find the result of this addition problem.

When you see $7 - 10$, you should think: "$7 + (-10)$." Try to think of each subtraction problem as a problem of *adding the opposite*.

If you see $-3 - 19$, think $-3 + (-19)$.

If you see $8 - (-2)$, think $8 + 2$.

EXAMPLE 4 Subtract.

(a) $8 - 9$ **(b)** $-3 - 16$

(c) $5 - (-4)$ **(d)** $-4 - (-4)$

Solution

(a) $8 - 9 = 8 + (-9) = -1$ **(b)** $-3 - 16 = -3 + (-16) = -19$

(c) $5 - (-4) = 5 + 4 = 9$ **(d)** $-4 - (-4) = -4 + 4 = 0$

Practice Problem 4 Subtract.

(a) $7 - 10$ **(b)** $-4 - 15$ **(c)** $8 - (-3)$ **(d)** $-5 - (-1)$

 Performing Several Integer Operations

Subtraction of integers is not commutative or associative, but addition is. Thus if we first rewrite *all* subtraction as addition of the opposite, we can perform the addition in any order.

EXAMPLE 5 Perform the necessary operations. $4 - 7 - 5 - 3$

Solution

$$4 - 7 - 5 - 3$$
$$= 4 + (-7) + (-5) + (-3) \quad \text{First, write all subtraction as addition of the opposite.}$$
$$= 4 + (-15) \quad \text{Then add all } \textit{like signs:}$$
$$(-7) + (-5) + (-3) = -15.$$
$$= -11 \quad \text{Next, add } \textit{unlike signs}: 4 + (-15) = -11.$$

Practice Problem 5 Perform the necessary operations. $6 - 9 - 2 - 8$

 Understanding the Concept

Another Approach to Subtracting Several Integers

In Example 5, would you obtain the same answer if you first added $4 + (-7) = -3$ and then added the remaining numbers working from left to right? Let's try this approach.

$$4 - 7 - 5 - 3 = 4 + (-7) - 5 - 3$$
$$= -3 - 5 - 3$$
$$= -3 + (-5) - 3$$
$$= -8 - 3$$
$$= -8 + (-3)$$
$$= -11$$

Although this approach requires more calculations, it yields the same answer. This illustrates how using the associative and commutative properties of addition can simplify the process.

Exercise

1. Subtract. $2 - 6 - 8 - 11$

   (a) Change all subtraction to addition of the opposite, then perform the operations.

   (b) Complete the subtraction problem working from left to right.

   (c) Which method do you prefer?

EXAMPLE 6   Perform the necessary operations. $-9 - (-3) + (-4)$

Solution

$$-9 - (-3) + (-4) = -9 + 3 + (-4)$$ Write subtraction as addition of the opposite.

$$= -13 + 3$$ Add like signs: $-9 + (-4) = -13$.

$$= -10$$ Add unlike signs: $-13 + 3 = -10$.

Practice Problem 6   Perform the necessary operations.

$$-3 - (-5) + (-11)$$

NOTE TO STUDENT: Fully worked-out solutions to all of the Practice Problems can be found at the back of the text starting at page SP-1

EXAMPLE 7   Evaluate $-x - y - 4$ for $x = -3$ and $y = -1$.

Solution

$$-(x) - (y) - 4$$ Place parentheses around variables.

$$= -(-3) - (-1) - 4$$ Replace x with -3 and y with -1.

$$= 3 - (-1) - 4$$ Simplify: $-(-3) = 3$.

$$= 3 + 1 + (-4)$$ Change each subtraction to addition of the opposite.

$$= 4 + (-4)$$ Add: $3 + 1 = 4$.

$$= 0$$ Add opposites.

Practice Problem 7   Evaluate $-a - b - 2$ for $a = -4$ and $b = 7$.

---

③ Solving Applied Problems Involving Subtraction of Integers

When we subtract $3000 - (-50)$, we obtain a result of 3050, which is larger than 3000. Why is the result larger than 3000 if we are subtracting a number from 3000? Because we are subtracting a negative number. We illustrate this idea next.

    Suppose that we want to find the difference in altitude between the two mountains shown below. We subtract the *lower* altitude from the *higher* altitude. The difference in altitude between the two mountains is 3000 feet − 1000 feet = 2000 feet.

$3000\,\text{ft} - 1000\,\text{ft} = 2000\,\text{ft}$

Subtract a positive number, and the result is *less than* 3000.

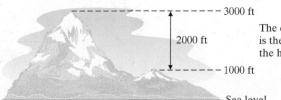

3000 ft

2000 ft

1000 ft

The difference in altitude is the distance between the highest points.

Sea level

Land that is below sea level is considered to have a negative altitude. A valley that is 50 feet below sea level is said to have an altitude of −50 feet. The difference in altitude between the mountain and the valley is found by subtracting 3000 feet − (−50) feet.

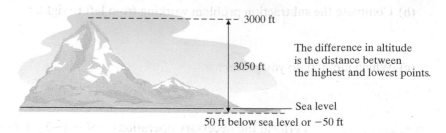

3000 ft

The difference in altitude is the distance between the highest and lowest points.

3050 ft

Sea level

50 ft below sea level or −50 ft

$$3000 \text{ ft} - (-50 \text{ ft}) = 3050 \text{ ft}$$

Subtract a negative number, and the result is *more than* 3000.

EXAMPLE 8   A portion of the Dead Sea is 1286 feet below sea level. What is the difference in altitude between Mount Carmel in Israel, which has an altitude of 1791 feet, and the Dead Sea?

Solution

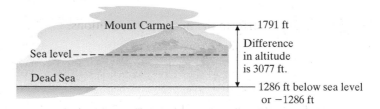

Mount Carmel ————— 1791 ft

Difference in altitude is 3077 ft.

Sea level ——————————

Dead Sea

1286 ft below sea level or −1286 ft

We want to find the difference, so we must subtract.

higher altitude	minus	lower altitude	
↓	↓	↓	
1791 ft	−	(−1286 ft)	
= 1791 ft	+	1286 ft	= 3077 ft

The difference in altitude is 3077 ft.

Practice Problem 8   Find the difference in altitude between a mountain 3800 feet high and a desert valley 895 feet below sea level.

EXAMPLE 9   The melting points in degrees Celsius of four chemical elements are listed on the bar graph. What is the difference between the melting point of sulfur and the melting point of mercury?

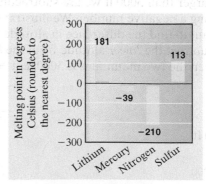

Solution   We subtract the lower melting point from the higher melting point.

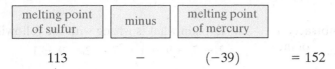

melting point of sulfur	minus	melting point of mercury		
113	−	(−39)	=	152

The difference is 152°C.

Practice Problem 9   Refer to the bar graph in Example 9 to answer the following. What is the difference between the melting point of lithium and the melting point of nitrogen?

NOTE TO STUDENT: Fully worked-out solutions to all of the Practice Problems can be found at the back of the text starting at page SP-1

Developing Your Study Skills

Previewing New Material

Does the pace of the lecture seem too fast for you? Do you miss parts of the instructor's explanation? Previewing the new material can help you with these problems as well as enhance the amount of learning that happens while you are *listening* to the lecture.

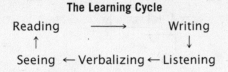

The Learning Cycle

Reading ⟶ Writing

Seeing ← Verbalizing ← Listening

Part of your study time each day should consist of looking ahead to those sections in your text that are to be covered the following day. You do not necessarily have to learn the material on your own. Survey the concepts, terminology, diagrams, and examples, so that you are familiar with the new ideas when the instructor presents them.

To help yourself in class:

1. Take note of concepts that appear confusing or difficult as you read.
2. Listen carefully for your instructor's explanation of material that gave you difficulty.
3. Be prepared to ask questions.

Previewing new material enables you to see what is coming and prepares you to learn.

Verbal and Writing Skills

1. To subtract two numbers, we change the subtraction sign to _____ and take the _____ of the second number. Then we _____.

2. Explain what is wrong with the following problem.
$$2 - 7 - 9 - 1 = 7 - 2 - 9 - 1$$

3. When we subtract $25 - (-10)$, we get a number that is larger than 25. Explain why. You can use an illustration in your explanation.

4. Write an application about money where you subtract two integers and get a negative answer.

Fill in each box with the correct number.

5. To subtract -3, we add $\boxed{}$.

6. To subtract -9, we add $\boxed{}$.

7. To subtract 5, we add $\boxed{}$.

8. To subtract 7, we add $\boxed{}$.

9.
$$-7 - 6$$
$$= -7 + \boxed{}$$
$$= \boxed{}$$

10.
$$-5 - 2$$
$$= -5 + \boxed{}$$
$$= \boxed{}$$

11.
$$4 - 9$$
$$= 4 + \boxed{}$$
$$= \boxed{}$$

12.
$$3 - 8$$
$$= 3 + \boxed{}$$
$$= \boxed{}$$

13.
$$6 - (-3)$$
$$= 6 \,\boxed{}\, 3$$
$$= \boxed{}$$

14.
$$8 - (-2)$$
$$= 8 \,\boxed{}\, 2$$
$$= \boxed{}$$

15.
$$9 - (-5)$$
$$= 9 \,\boxed{}\, 5$$
$$= \boxed{}$$

16.
$$7 - (-2)$$
$$= 7 \,\boxed{}\, 2$$
$$= \boxed{}$$

Rewrite each subtraction as addition of the opposite.

17.

Subtraction	Addition of the Opposite
(a) $7 - 4 = 3$	
(b) $15 - 7 = 8$	
(c) $10 - 8 = 2$	

18.

Subtraction	Addition of the Opposite
(a) $5 - 3 = 2$	
(b) $12 - 6 = 6$	
(c) $7 - 1 = 6$	

Subtract.

19. $\$20 - \$35$

20. $\$4 - \$6$

21. $\$6 - \$7$

22. $\$4 - \$3$

23. $-6 - 4$

24. $-8 - 3$

25. $-5 - 4$

26. $-4 - 3$

27. $5 - (-2)$

28. $8 - (-4)$

29. $5 - (-9)$

30. $6 - (-7)$

31. $-8 - (-6)$

32. $-6 - (-3)$

33. $-8 - (-8)$

34. $-7 - (-7)$

35. $2 - 7$

36. $8 - 11$

37. $3 - 7$

38. $7 - 9$

39. $50 - 70$

40. $70 - 80$

41. $-85 - (-20)$

42. $-77 - (-11)$

Perform the necessary operations.

43. $12 - 9 - 5 - 8$

44. $5 - 2 - 6 - 10$

45. $2 - 1 - 9 - 7$

46. $9 - 3 - 7 - 25$

47. $9 - 10 - 2 + 3$

48. $8 - 11 - 4 + 7$

49. $-8 - (-3) + (-10)$

50. $-5 - (-2) + (-7)$

51. $-7 - (-2) - (-5)$

52. $-5 - (-9) - (-4)$

53. $-3 - (-8) + (-6)$

54. $-7 - (-2) + (-9)$

Mixed Practice Exercises 55–68. *Perform the necessary operations.*

55. $7 - 21$

56. $9 - 13$

57. $-9 - (-9)$

58. $-6 - (-6)$

59. $-13 - 18$

60. $-18 - 56$

61. $50 - (-1)$

62. $39 - (-1)$

63. $8 - 1 - 9 - 5$

64. $3 - 7 - 5 - 16$

65. $7 + 8 - 6 - 11$

66. $6 + 4 - 8 - 22$

67. $9 - 10 - 2 + 3$

68. $-6 - 3 + (-7) - 2$

Evaluate.

69. $a - 9$ for $a = -8$

70. $x - 12$ for $x = -9$

71. $x - 11$ for $x = -3$

72. $x - 10$ for $x = -2$

73. $14 - m$ for $m = -5$

74. $19 - y$ for $y = -6$

75. $21 - y + x$ for $y = -1$ and $x = 2$

76. $14 - y + x$ for $y = -2$ and $x = 3$

77. $-8 - x - y$ for $x = -4$ and $y = 2$

78. $-7 - x - y$ for $x = -3$ and $y = 4$

79. $-1 - x + y$ for $x = -6$ and $y = -5$

80. $-2 - x + y$ for $x = -5$ and $y = -3$

Applications

81. *Altitude* Find the difference in altitude between a mountain that has an altitude of 3556 feet and a desert valley that is 150 feet below sea level.

82. *Altitude* Find the difference in altitude between a mountain that has an altitude of 5889 feet and a desert valley that is 175 feet below sea level.

83. *Calculating Distance* How far above the floor of the basement is the roof of the office building shown in the figure?

84. *Temperature Readings* On a particular day the temperature in a city was recorded.

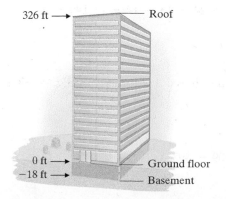

326 ft → Roof

0 ft →
−18 ft → Ground floor
Basement

4 A.M.   10 A.M.   4 P.M.   10 P.M.

(a) What was the difference between the temperatures at 10 A.M. and 10 P.M.?

(b) What was the difference between the temperatures at 4 P.M. and 4 A.M.?

High and Low Temperatures *The following chart displays the hottest and coldest spots for selected days in a recent winter. Use this chart to answer exercises 85 and 86.*

85. (a) Where was the temperature the highest during the five days listed on the chart?

   (b) What was the difference in temperature between the record high and the record low on day 3?

86. (a) Where was the temperature the lowest during the five days listed on the chart?

   (b) What was the difference in temperature between the record high and the record low on day 5?

	Record High		Record Low	
Day 1	Gila Bend, Arizona	72°F	Presque Isle, Maine	−18°F
2	Lajitas, Texas	79°F	Ely, Minnesota	−8°F
3	Indio, California	77°F	Devil's Lake, North Dakota	−9°F
4	Brownsville, Texas	88°F	Bodie State Park, California	−13°F
5	Del Rio, Texas	84°F	Presque Isle, Maine	−9°F

Golf Scores *The following double bar graph indicates the scores for Sandra and Tran at selected holes at a National Pro-Am Tournament.*

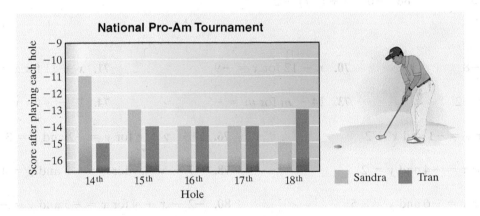

87. What was the point difference between Sandra's and Tran's scores after the fourteenth hole?

88. What was the point difference between Sandra's and Tran's scores after the fifteenth hole?

89. If the lowest score after the eighteenth hole determines the winner, who won the National Pro-Am Tournament?

One Step Further *Perform the operations indicated.*

90. $-22 + 18 - 34 - 11 + (-16) - 2$

91. $-31 + 24 - 13 - 12 + (-14) - 3$

Evaluate.

92. $9 - x - y + z + 4$ for $x = -11, y = -2, z = -8$

93. $7 - a - b + c + 2$ for $a = -13, b = -4, c = -9$

Calculate.

94. $-345 - 768$

95. $-3009 - 893$

96. $632 - (-1346)$

97. $-2001 - (-987)$

To Think About *For Exercises 98 and 99, (a) translate, and (b) solve.*

98. The sum of negative three and six is equal to what number?

99. Eight subtracted from negative one is equal to what number?

100. Is −1 a solution to $x - 4 = 6$?

101. Is −4 a solution to $x - 3 = -7$?

Fill in each box with the correct number.

102. $-1 - \boxed{} = -2$

103. $-2 - \boxed{} = -4$

For each of the following, find the next number in the sequence by identifying the pattern.

104. −8, −3, 2, 7, 12, ...

105. −6, −3, 0, 3, 6, ...

106. 2, −8, −18, −28, −38, ...

107. 4, −1, −6, −11, −16, ...

Cumulative Review *Simplify.*

108. **[1.6.4]** $2 + 3(5)$

109. **[1.6.4]** $12 - 3(4 - 1)$

110. **[1.6.4]** $3^2 + 4(2) - 5$

111. **[1.6.4]** $3 + [3 + 2(8 - 6)]$

112. **[1.5.4]** *Educational Supplies* L. R. William Elementary School must order 550 pencils for students to use on their standardized tests. If the pencils are packaged in boxes of 12, how many boxes should the school order?

113. **[1.5.4]** *Word Problems* A word processor can type 85 words per minute. At this rate, how long will it take to type 8670 words?

Quick Quiz 2.3

1. Perform the indicated operation.
   (a) $-9 - 15$ **(b)** $-6 - (-8)$

2. Perform the necessary operations.
   $-8 + 6 - (-5) - 10$

3. Find the difference in altitude between a mountain 6300 feet high and a desert valley that is 419 feet below sea level.

4. **Concept Check** Is the following problem completed correctly? Why or why not?
$$-6 - (-3) + (-7)$$
$$= -6 - (-10)$$
$$= -6 + 10$$
$$= 4$$

Student Learning Objectives

After studying this section, you will be able to:

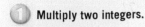 Multiply two integers.

Multiply two or more integers.

Use exponents with integers as bases.

Divide integers.

We are familiar with multiplying and dividing whole numbers. In this section we learn how to multiply and divide integers.

Before we begin our discussion, we must introduce some new vocabulary words. The set of whole numbers is made up of **odd numbers** and **even numbers.** The number 0 is the first even number. To find each consecutive even number, we add 2 to the previous number. Thus, the first four even numbers are 0, 2, 4, and 6. Whole numbers that are not even are odd. Thus, 1, 3, 5, and 7 are the first four odd numbers.

1 Multiplying Two Integers

Recall the different ways we can indicate multiplication. You should be able to identify and use all of them.

$$-3 \times 3 \qquad -3 \cdot 3 \qquad 3(-3) \qquad (-3)(-3)$$

How do we determine whether a product is positive or negative? We follow a set of rules for multiplying integers. Before we state these rules, let's look at some situations involving multiplication of integers.

Since multiplication represents repeated addition, we can express some situations involving addition as multiplication problems.

Situation 1: Your business has a profit of $1000 a month for 3 months. *Math symbols that represent Situation 1:*

$$\$1000 + \$1000 + \$1000 = \$3000 \quad \text{or} \quad (3)(\$1000) = \$3000$$

Situation 2: Your business suffers a loss of $1000 a month for 3 months. *Math symbols that represent Situation 2:*

$$-\$1000 + (-\$1000) + (-\$1000) = -\$3000 \quad \text{or} \quad (3)(-\$1000) = -\$3000$$

EXAMPLE 1 Find the product by writing as repeated addition. $2(-3)$

Solution $2(-3) = -3 + (-3) = -6$

Therefore, $2(-3) = -6$.

Practice Problem 1 Find the product by writing as repeated addition. $3(-1)$

NOTE TO STUDENT: *Fully worked-out solutions to all of the Practice Problems can be found at the back of the text starting at page SP-1*

Since it is not always practical to use repeated addition, we need a rule for multiplying integers. Let's look at the following pattern to help us understand the rule.

This column decreases by 1. ⟶ ⟵ This column decreases by 2.

$$\left.\begin{array}{l} 3 \cdot 2 = 6 \\ 2 \cdot 2 = 4 \\ 1 \cdot 2 = 2 \end{array}\right\} \quad [+]\cdot[+] = [+] \quad \text{Positive product}$$

$$0 \cdot 2 = 0$$

$$\left.\begin{array}{l} -1 \cdot 2 = -2 \\ -2 \cdot 2 = -4 \\ -3 \cdot 2 = -6 \end{array}\right\} \quad [-]\cdot[+] = [-] \quad \text{Negative product}$$

Since multiplication is commutative, we know that $-3 \cdot 2 = 2 \cdot (-3)$. Thus

Negative product

$$2 \cdot (-3) = -6 \qquad [+]\cdot[-] = [-]$$

We see that whenever one number is positive and the other number is negative, the product is negative.

Now how do we multiply two *negative* numbers? Consider the following pattern.

This column decreases by 1.⌐   ⌐This column increases by 5.

$$3(-5) = -15$$
$$2(-5) = -10$$
$$1(-5) = -5$$
$$0(-5) = 0$$
$$-1(-5) = 5$$
$$-2(-5) = 10$$
$$-3(-5) = 15 \quad [-] \cdot [-] = [+]$$

This seems to suggest that a *negative* number times a *negative* number gives a *positive* result, and this is the case. Let's summarize the results and look for a pattern.

The number of negative signs, 0, is **even.** → $[+] \cdot [+] = [+]$
   The product is **positive.** ↗

The number of negative signs, 1, is **odd.** → $[-] \cdot [+] = [-]$
   The product is **negative.** ↗

The number of negative signs, 1, is **odd.** → $[+] \cdot [-] = [-]$
   The product is **negative.** ↗

The number of negative signs, 2, is **even.** → $[-] \cdot [-] = [+]$
   The product is **positive.** ↗

We notice that when there is an *even* number of negative signs, the answer is *positive* and when there is an *odd* number of negative signs, the answer is *negative*. Why is this true? Because every pair of negative signs yields a positive result.

$$[-] \cdot [-] \quad = \quad [+] \quad \text{Even number}$$
one pair of   =   positive   of negative signs.
negative numbers   result

$$[-] \cdot [-] \quad \cdot \quad [-] \cdot [-] \quad \cdot \quad [-] \quad = \quad [-] \quad \text{Odd number}$$
positive   ×   positive   ×   negative   =   negative   of negative
result   result   number   result   signs.

The pattern is summarized in the following procedure.

PROCEDURE TO DETERMINE THE SIGN OF A PRODUCT

For all nonzero numbers:

The product will be *positive* if there is an *even* number of negative signs.
The product will be *negative* if there is an *odd* number of negative signs.

When we multiply integers, we first determine the sign of the product and then multiply absolute values.

EXAMPLE 2   Multiply.

(a) $6(7)$ **(b)** $6(-7)$ **(c)** $-6(7)$ **(d)** $-6(-7)$

Solution

(a) $6(7) = +42$ The number of negative signs, 0, is *even* so the answer is *positive*.
                          We multiply absolute values: $6 \cdot 7 = 42$.

(b) $6(-7) = -$ The number of negative signs, 1, is *odd* so the answer is *negative*.
       $= -42$ We multiply absolute values: $6 \cdot 7 = 42$.

(c) $-6(7) = -$ The number of negative signs, 1, is *odd* so the answer is *negative*.

$= -42$ We multiply absolute values: $6 \cdot 7 = 42$.

(d) $-6(-7) = +$ The number of negative signs, 2, is *even* so the answer is *positive*.

$= +42$ We multiply absolute values: $6 \cdot 7 = 42$.

Practice Problem 2   Multiply.

(a) $3(8)$ **(b)** $3(-8)$ **(c)** $-3(8)$ **(d)** $-3(-8)$

NOTE TO STUDENT: *Fully worked-out solutions to all of the Practice Problems can be found at the back of the text starting at page SP-1*

Multiplying Two or More Integers

Recall that multiplication is commutative and associative, so we can either multiply integers in the order they appear, or we can multiply any pair of numbers first and then multiply the result by another number. Then we continue until all of the factors have been multiplied.

EXAMPLE 3   Multiply. $(-3)(-1)(-2)$

Solution

$(-3)(-1)\,(-2) = 3\,(-2)$ First we multiply $(-3)(-1) = 3$.

$= -6$ Then we multiply $3(-2) = -6$.

Practice Problem 3   Multiply. $(-2)(-1)(-4)$

We can simplify the multiplication process if *before* we multiply we count the *total* number of negative signs to determine the sign of the product. Then we multiply absolute values last.

$(-2)(-1) = +2$ We multiply two negative numbers and the answer is positive.

$(-2)(-1)(-1) = -2$ We multiply three negative numbers and the answer is negative.

$(-2)(-1)(-1)(-1) = +2$ We multiply four negative numbers and the answer is positive.

EXAMPLE 4   Multiply. $(-3)(2)(-1)(4)(-3)$

Solution

$(-3)(2)(-1)(4)(-3)$ The answer is *negative* since there are 3 negative signs and 3 is an *odd* number.

$= -[3(2)(1)(4)(3)]$ Multiply the absolute values.

$= -72$

Practice Problem 4   Multiply. $(-3)(2)(-1)(-4)(-3)$

Using Exponents with Integers as Bases

In Chapter 1 we saw that we can use exponents to abbreviate repeated multiplication.

$$\underset{\text{repeated multiplication}}{(-3) \cdot (-3) \cdot (-3)} = \underset{\substack{\text{exponent} \\ \text{form}}}{(-3)^3}$$

Therefore, we can find the sign of a negative number raised to a power in the same way that we find the sign of a product.

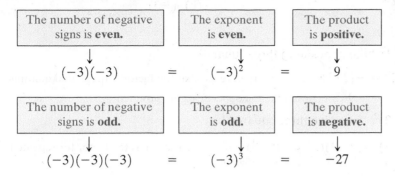

We see that the sign of the result depends on whether the exponent is odd or even. This can be generalized as follows.

> Suppose that a number is written in exponent form and the *base* is *negative*. The result is *positive* if the exponent is *even*. The result is *negative* if the exponent is *odd*.

EXAMPLE 5   Evaluate. $(-4)^3$

Solution

$$(-4)^3 = (-4)(-4)(-4) = -64 \quad \text{The answer is negative since the exponent 3 is odd.}$$

Practice Problem 5   Evaluate. $(-4)^4$

NOTE TO STUDENT: Fully worked-out solutions to all of the Practice Problems can be found at the back of the text starting at page SP-1

EXAMPLE 6   Evaluate.

(a) $(-1)^2$ **(b)** $(-1)^3$ **(c)** $(-1)^{31}$

Solution

(a) $(-1)^2 = 1$ The answer is positive since the exponent 2 is even.
(b) $(-1)^3 = -1$ The answer is negative since the exponent 3 is odd.
(c) $(-1)^{31} = -1$ The answer is negative since the exponent 31 is odd.

Practice Problem 6   Evaluate.

(a) $(-2)^3$ **(b)** $(-2)^6$ **(c)** $(-2)^7$

We must be sure to use parentheses around the base when the base is a negative number. For example, $(-2)^4$ is *not* the same as -2^4. The base of a number in exponent form does not include the negative sign unless we use parentheses.

$(-2)^4$ means "-2 raised to the fourth power," since -2 is the base.

-2^4 means "the opposite of 2 raised to the fourth power," since 2 is the base.

$$(-2)^4 \quad = \quad (-2)(-2)(-2)(-2) = 16$$
$\quad\quad\uparrow \quad\quad\quad\quad\quad \uparrow$
The base is -2.   We use the -2 as the factor for repeated multiplication.

$$-2^4 \quad = \quad -(2 \cdot 2 \cdot 2 \cdot 2) = -(16) = -16$$
$\quad\uparrow \quad\quad\quad\quad \uparrow$
The base is 2.   We use 2 as the factor for repeated multiplication and take the opposite of the product.

EXAMPLE 7   Evaluate.

(a) -3^2 (b) $(-3)^2$

Solution

(a) -3^2, "the opposite of three squared"

$-3^2 = -(3 \cdot 3)$ The base is 3; we use 3 as the factor for repeated multiplication.

$ = -9$ We take the opposite of the product.

(b) $(-3)^2$, "negative three squared"

$(-3)^2 = (-3)(-3)$ The base is -3; we use -3 as the factor for repeated multiplication.

$ = 9$

Practice Problem 7   Evaluate.

(a) -5^2 (b) $(-5)^2$

NOTE TO STUDENT: *Fully worked-out solutions to all of the Practice Problems can be found at the back of the text starting at page SP-1*

CAUTION: Pay special attention to parentheses when evaluating a number in exponent form. If the exponent is *hanging* on to the *parentheses* $(\ )^2$, the sign is included in the multiplication: $(-10)^2 = (-10)(-10) = 100$. If the exponent is *hanging* on to the *base* $-b^2$, the sign is not included in the multiplication: -4^2 means the opposite of $4^2 = -16$.

 Dividing Integers

What about division? Any division statement can be rewritten as a related multiplication statement. Therefore, the sign rules for division are very much like those for multiplication.

Division problem	$-20 \div (-4) = n$	
Related multiplication problem	$-20 = n(-4)$	Since $5(-4) = -20$, n must be positive.
Therefore,	$-20 \div (-4) = 5$	The number of negative signs is even and the result is positive.
Division problem	$-20 \div 4 = n$	
Related multiplication problem	$-20 = n(4)$	Since $(-5)(4) = -20$, n must be negative.
Therefore,	$-20 \div 4 = -5.$	The number of negative signs is odd and the result is negative.

Similarly, $20 \div (-4) = -5$ because $20 = (-5)(-4)$. As we can see, the sign rules for division are the same as those for multiplication. We will state them together.

RULE FOR MULTIPLYING OR DIVIDING NUMBERS

To multiply or divide nonzero numbers: First determine the sign of the answer as follows.

The answer will be *positive* if the problem has an *even* number of negative signs.

The answer will be *negative* if the problem has an *odd* number of negative signs.

Next multiply or divide the absolute values of the numbers.

EXAMPLE 8   Divide.

(a) $36 \div 6$ **(b)** $36 \div (-6)$ **(c)** $-36 \div 6$ **(d)** $-36 \div (-6)$

Solution

(a) $36 \div 6 = 6$ **(b)** $36 \div (-6) = -6$

(c) $-36 \div 6 = -6$ **(d)** $-36 \div (-6) = 6$

Practice Problem 8   Divide.

(a) $42 \div 7$ **(b)** $42 \div (-7)$ **(c)** $-42 \div 7$ **(d)** $-42 \div (-7)$

EXAMPLE 9   Perform each operation indicated.

(a) $56 \div (-8)$ **(b)** $9(-5)$ **(c)** $-20(-3)$ **(d)** $\dfrac{-72}{-8}$

Solution

(a) $56 \div (-8) = -7$ **(b)** $9(-5) = -45$

(c) $-20(-3) = 60$ **(d)** $\dfrac{-72}{-8} = -72 \div (-8) = 9$

Practice Problem 9   Perform each operation indicated.

(a) $49 \div (-7)$ **(b)** $4(-9)$ **(c)** $-30(-4)$ **(d)** $\dfrac{-54}{-9}$

EXAMPLE 10   Evaluate.

(a) $\dfrac{m}{-n}$ for $m = -16$ and $n = -2$ **(b)** x^4 for $x = -2$

Solution   We place parentheses around the variables and then we replace each variable with the given value.

(a) $\dfrac{(m)}{-(n)} = \dfrac{(-16)}{-(-2)}$ We replace m with -16 and n with -2.

$= \dfrac{-16}{2}$ $-(-2) = 2$: The opposite of negative 2 is 2.

$= -8$ $-16 \div 2 = -8$

(b) $(x)^4 = (-2)^4$ We replace x with -2. The answer is positive since the

$= 16$ exponent is even. $2 \cdot 2 \cdot 2 \cdot 2 = 16$

Practice Problem 10   Evaluate.

(a) $\dfrac{-x}{y}$ for $x = -22$ and $y = 11$ **(b)** a^3 for $a = -3$

Verbal and Writing Skills

1. Why is the following statement false? Two negatives always gives us a positive result.

2. Explain why $-3^2 \neq 9$.

3. If you multiply 4 negative numbers, the product will be a _____ number.

4. If you multiply 7 negative numbers the product will be a _____ number.

5. The quotient of a positive number and a _____ number is negative.

6. The quotient of a negative number and a _____ number is positive.

Find the product by writing as repeated addition.

7. $3(-4)$

8. $4(-1)$

9. $4(-6)$

10. $2(-5)$

11. $2(-3)$

12. $3(-2)$

Fill in each box with the correct number.

13. (a) $3 \cdot \boxed{} = 9$

    (b) $3 \cdot \boxed{} = -9$

    (c) $-3 \cdot \boxed{} = -9$

    (d) $-3 \cdot \boxed{} = 9$

14. (a) $5 \cdot \boxed{} = 25$

    (b) $5 \cdot \boxed{} = -25$

    (c) $-5 \cdot \boxed{} = -25$

    (d) $-5 \cdot \boxed{} = 25$

15. (a) $\dfrac{12}{\boxed{}} = 3$

    (b) $\dfrac{-12}{\boxed{}} = 3$

    (c) $\dfrac{12}{\boxed{}} = -3$

    (d) $\dfrac{-12}{\boxed{}} = -3$

16. (a) $\dfrac{18}{\boxed{}} = 9$

    (b) $\dfrac{-18}{\boxed{}} = 9$

    (c) $\dfrac{18}{\boxed{}} = -9$

    (d) $\dfrac{-18}{\boxed{}} = -9$

Multiply.

17. (a) $9(2)$
    (b) $9(-2)$
    (c) $-9(2)$
    (d) $-9(-2)$

18. (a) $11(7)$
    (b) $11(-7)$
    (c) $-11(7)$
    (d) $-11(-7)$

19. (a) $5(2)$
    (b) $-5(-2)$
    (c) $-5(2)$
    (d) $5(-2)$

20. (a) $1(8)$
    (b) $-1(-8)$
    (c) $-1(8)$
    (d) $1(-8)$

21. $-2(-9)$

22. $-5(-4)$

23. $-1(-6)$

24. $-4(-3)$

25. $8(-7)$

26. $2(-11)$

27. $-5(9)$

28. $-7(3)$

To Think About Exercises 29–32 *Determine the sign of each product without multiplying the integers.*

29. Is the product of $(-1)(3)(-236)(42)(-16)(-90)$ a positive or negative number?

30. Is the product of $(-2)(-96)(-69)(-72)(-6)(68)$ a positive or negative number?

31. Is the product of $(-943)(-721)(-816)(-96)(-51)$ a positive or negative number?

32. Is the product of $(-66)(-918)(-818)(-22)$ a positive or negative number?

Multiply.

33. $4(-5)(-2)$

34. $2(-4)(-6)$

35. $(-3)(-2)(-3)(-4)$

36. $(-5)(-3)(-2)(-2)$

37. $2(-1)(5)(-7)$

38. $9(-1)(2)(-3)$

39. $(-2)(-1)(4)(-5)$

40. $(-1)(-3)(2)(-4)$

41. $(-5)(4)(-3)(2)(-1)$

42. $(-4)(5)(-2)(1)(-4)$

To Think About Exercises 43–48 *Determine the sign of each of the following without multiplying the integers.*

43. Is the value of $(-2)^{13}$ a positive or negative number?

44. Is the value of $(-8)^{12}$ a positive or negative number?

45. Is the value of $(-96)^{52}$ a positive or negative number?

46. Is the value of $(-81)^{51}$ a positive or negative number?

47. Is the value of -96^{52} a positive or negative number?

48. Is the value of -81^{51} a positive or negative number?

Evaluate.

49. $(-10)^2$

50. $(-7)^2$

51. $(-5)^3$

52. $(-7)^3$

53. (a) $(-4)^2$
(b) $(-4)^3$

54. (a) $(-2)^2$
(b) $(-2)^3$

55. (a) $(-1)^{13}$
(b) $(-1)^{24}$

56. (a) $(-1)^{29}$
(b) $(-1)^{16}$

57. (a) -4^2
(b) $(-4)^2$

58. (a) -6^2
(b) $(-6)^2$

59. (a) -2^3
(b) $(-2)^3$

60. (a) -5^3
(b) $(-5)^3$

61. (a) $(-4)^3$
(b) -4^3

62. (a) $(-8)^2$
(b) -8^2

63. (a) $(-9)^2$
(b) -9^2

64. (a) $(-1)^{11}$
(b) -1^{11}

Divide.

65. (a) $35 \div 7$
(b) $35 \div (-7)$
(c) $-35 \div 7$
(d) $-35 \div (-7)$

66. (a) $50 \div 5$
(b) $50 \div (-5)$
(c) $-50 \div 5$
(d) $-50 \div (-5)$

67. (a) $40 \div 8$
(b) $40 \div (-8)$
(c) $-40 \div 8$
(d) $-40 \div (-8)$

68. (a) $20 \div 4$
(b) $20 \div (-4)$
(c) $-20 \div 4$
(d) $-20 \div (-4)$

69. $30 \div (-5)$

70. $12 \div (-2)$

71. $\dfrac{-45}{5}$

72. $\dfrac{-24}{6}$

73. $-16 \div (-2)$

74. $-12 \div (-3)$

75. $\dfrac{-49}{-7}$

76. $\dfrac{-70}{-10}$

Mixed Practice *Perform each operation indicated.*

77. (a) $22 \div (-2)$
(b) $22(-2)$

78. (a) $18 \div (-3)$
(b) $18(-3)$

79. (a) $-4 \div (-2)$
(b) $-4(-2)$

80. (a) $-8 \div (-4)$
(b) $-8(-4)$

81. (a) $-15 \div 3$
(b) $-15(3)$

82. (a) $-12 \div 3$
(b) $-12(3)$

83. (a) $14 \div (-7)$
(b) $-14(7)$

84. (a) $9 \div (-3)$
(b) $-9(3)$

85. Evaluate x^2 for $x = -1$.

86. Evaluate x^3 for $x = -2$.

87. Evaluate $\dfrac{-x}{y}$ for $x = -42$ and $y = -7$.

88. Evaluate $\dfrac{-a}{b}$ for $a = -12$ and $b = -4$.

89. Evaluate $\dfrac{-m}{-n}$ for $m = -20$ and $n = 2$.

90. Evaluate $\dfrac{-x}{-y}$ for $x = -15$ and $y = 5$.

One Step Further

91. Evaluate.
(a) $-y^3$ for $y = -2$
(b) $-y^4$ for $y = -2$

92. Evaluate.
(a) $-a^8$ for $a = -1$
(b) $-a^{10}$ for $a = -1$

Applications

Distance Traveled The following formula is used to calculate the distance an object has traveled at a given rate and time. Use this formula to answer exercises 93 and 94.

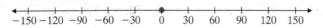

$$\text{distance} = \text{rate} \times \text{time}$$

93. The velocity (rate) of a projectile is −30 meters per second on a number line. The negative sign on the velocity indicates that it is moving to the left. At time $t = 0$ the projectile is at the zero mark on the number line. Find where it will be on the number line at $t = 3$ seconds.

94. Find where the projectile in exercise 93 will be on the number line at $t = 4$ seconds.

95. *Discounted Sporting Goods* Baker Sporting Goods marked $2 off the price of each baseball glove in stock. If there are 350 gloves in stock, write the total reduction in price of all gloves as an integer.

96. *Temperature Fluctuations* As a cold front passed through Minnesota, the temperature dropped 3°F each hour for 4 hours. Express the total drop in temperature as an integer.

To Think About

97. Is 8 a solution to the equation $\dfrac{x}{2} = -12$?

98. Is −10 a solution to the equation $\dfrac{x}{-5} = 2$?

Determine the value of x.

99. $\dfrac{x}{-3} = 8$

100. $\dfrac{x}{2} = -10$

Cumulative Review *Simplify.*

101. [1.6.4] $2^2 + 3(5) - 1$ **102.** [1.6.4] $8 + 2(9 \div 3)$

103. [1.6.4] $2^3 + (4 \div 2 + 6)$ **104.** [1.6.4] $3^2 + (6 \div 2 + 8)$

105. [1.5.5] *Speed of Sound* Kristina heard a train 3261 feet away approaching the station. How long did it take the sound of the train to reach Kristina's ear, if sound travels at a speed of approximately 1087 feet per second?

106. [1.4.5] *Manufacturing* R. L. MacDonald Manufacturing schedules two 8-hour shifts per day, 5 days a week, and manufactures 42 radios per hour. How many radios can be manufactured in 5 days?

Quick Quiz 2.4

1. Perform the indicated operations.

   (a) $4(-3)$ **(b)** $-45 \div 5$ **(c)** $\dfrac{-48}{-8}$

2. Multiply. $(-2)(-6)(-1)(3)$

3. Evaluate.

   (a) x^5 for $x = -1$

   (b) $\dfrac{-a}{b}$ for $a = 10$ and $b = -2$

4. **Concept Check** When we evaluate $(-x)(y)$ for $x = -6$ and $y = 2$, we obtain a positive number. Is this true? Why or why not?

2.5 THE ORDER OF OPERATIONS AND APPLICATIONS INVOLVING INTEGERS

When there is more than one operation in a problem, we must follow the order of operations presented in Chapter 1. We use additional grouping symbols when more than one set are required in a problem. We start with parentheses, then use brackets [ ], then braces { }.

> Do first.
> Do last.
>
> 1. Perform operations inside grouping symbols such as parentheses and brackets.
> 2. Simplify any expressions with exponents.
> 3. Multiply or divide from left to right.
> 4. Add or subtract from left to right.

Student Learning Objectives

After studying this section, you will be able to:

 Follow the order of operations with integers.

 Solve applied problems involving more than one operation.

We perform one operation at a time and follow the sequence: *identify, calculate, replace*. We identify the highest priority, do this calculation, and then replace the operation with the calculated amount.

We must be careful when working with integers, paying special attention to the signs of the numbers.

 Following the Order of Operations with Integers

EXAMPLE 1 Simplify. $12 - 30 \div 5(-3)^2 - 2$

Solution

$12 - 30 \div 5\,(-3)^2 - 2$ *Identify:* The highest priority is exponents. *Calculate:* $(-3)^2 = 9$. *Replace:* $(-3)^2$ with 9.

$= 12 - \underline{30 \div 5}(9) - 2$ *Identify:* The highest priority is division. *Calculate:* $30 \div 5 = 6$. *Replace:* $30 \div 5$ with 6.

$= 12 - 6(9) - 2$ *Identify:* The highest priority is multiplication. *Calculate:* $6 \cdot 9 = 54$. *Replace:* $6 \cdot 9$ with 54.

$= 12 - 54 - 2$ We subtract last, changing all subtraction to addition of the opposite.

$= 12 + (-54) + (-2)$ We add: $12 + (-54) + (-2) = -44$.

$= -44$

Practice Problem 1 Simplify. $-6 + 20 \div 2(-2)^2 - 5$

EXAMPLE 2 Simplify. $\dfrac{[-15 + 5(-3)]}{(13 - 18)}$

Solution We perform operations inside parentheses and brackets first.

$\dfrac{[-15 + 5(-3)]}{(13 - 18)} = \dfrac{[-15 + (-15)]}{(13 - 18)}$ We multiply: $5(-3) = -15$.

$= \dfrac{-30}{(13 - 18)}$ We add: $-15 + (-15) = -30$.

$= \dfrac{-30}{-5}$ We subtract: $13 - 18 = -5$.

$= 6$ We divide last: $-30 \div (-5) = 6$.

NOTE TO STUDENT: *Fully worked-out solutions to all of the Practice Problems can be found at the back of the text starting at page SP-1*

Practice Problem 2 Simplify.

$$\frac{[-10 + 4(-2)]}{(11 - 20)}$$

EXAMPLE 3 Simplify. $-24 \div \{-3 \cdot [4 \div (-2)]\}$

Solution   We perform operations within the innermost grouping symbols first.

$$-24 \div \{-3[4 \div (-2)]\} \qquad \text{We divide: } 4 \div (-2) = -2.$$
$$= -24 \div \{-3(-2)\} \qquad \text{We complete operations inside the bracket:}$$
$$\qquad\qquad\qquad\qquad -3(-2) = 6.$$
$$= -24 \div 6 \qquad\qquad \text{Now we divide: } -24 \div 6 = -4.$$
$$= -4$$

Practice Problem 3 Simplify. $-18 \div \{3[12 \div (-2)]\}$

2 Solving Applied Problems Involving More Than One Operation

Since real-life applications often require that we perform more than one operation, we must take care to follow the order of operations when solving these problems.

EXAMPLE 4   Ions are atoms or groups of atoms with positive or negative electrical charges. An oxide ion has an electrical charge of -2, while a magnesium ion has a charge of $+2$. Find the total charge of 8 oxide and 3 magnesium ions.

Solution   We summarize the information.

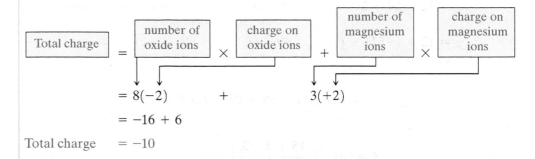

$$= 8(-2) \qquad\qquad + \qquad\qquad 3(+2)$$
$$= -16 + 6$$
$$\text{Total charge} = -10$$

Practice Problem 4   Using the information from Example 4, find the total charge of 9 oxide and 4 magnesium ions.

Developing Your Study Skills

Time Management

Planning and organizing your schedule is an efficient, low-stress way to juggle school, work, family, and social activities. It allows you to set realistic goals and priorities. You will also be less likely to forget assignments or appointments. A time management schedule provides you with a road map to achieving your goals.

1. Make a list of your daily activities.
2. Make a list of exam and assignment due dates.
3. Place this information in a weekly planner.

4. Plan your study time for each day. Since exam and assignment schedules vary, these activities may vary from day to day.
5. Leave space to insert last-minute things that come up or specific questions that you want to ask during class.
6. Review the planner periodically during the day so that you don't forget a task and can adjust for unexpected changes.

Think of your time management plan as a contract with yourself. You will find that by adhering to the contract, your grades will improve and you will have more free time.

Mon.	Tues.
7–9 A.M. Jogging and breakfast ————————————→	
9 A.M. Preview math lecture material.	Prepare test review questions.
10 A.M. Math class ————————————————————→	
	*Homework due
11 A.M. English class, questions for final draft of paper	————————————————————→
	*Term paper due
12 P.M. Lunch ——————————————————————————→	
1 P.M. Review math class notes and begin homework	Do practice test—math.
2:30–5:30 P.M. Work ————————————————————→	
5:30–8 P.M. Dinner and social time ——————————→	
8–10 P.M. Finish math homework, review term paper	Review math and read history.

PRACTICE   WATCH   DOWNLOAD   READ   REVIEW

Verbal and Writing Skills

1. Is $2 + 3(-1) = 5(-1) = -5$? Why or why not?

2. Is $3 + 4(-2) = 7(-2) = -14$?

3. Is $-2^2 + 8 = -4 + 8 = 4$?

4. Is $-2^4 - 5 = 16 - 5 = 11$?

Simplify.

5. $-2 + 3 \cdot 4$

6. $-6 + (10)2$

7. $1 + 7(2 - 6)$

8. $3 + 3(2 - 5)$

9. $-3 + 6(8 - 5)$

10. $-1 + 4(7 - 2)$

11. $12 - 5(2 - 6)$

12. $15 - 3(5 - 7)$

13. $5(-3)(4 - 7) + 9$

14. $6(-2)(3 - 9) + 4$

15. $-3(6 \div 3) + 7$

16. $-7(8 \div 2) + 6$

17. $3(-2)(9 - 5) - 10$

18. $5(-3)(5 - 2) - 3$

19. $-24 \div 12 - 8$

20. $-36 \div 12 - 10$

21. $(-3)^2 + 5(-9)$

22. $(-2)^2 + 4(-7)$

23. $(-3)^3 - 7(8)$

24. $(-2)^3 - 6(2)$

25. $(-2)^3 + 2(-8)$

26. $(-3)^3 + 6(-4)$

27. $36 \div (-6) + (-6)$

28. $16 \div (-4) + (-4)$

29. $12 - 20 \div 4(-4)^2 + 9$

30. $-15 - 50 \div 10(-3)^2 + 2$

31. $8 - 2(5 - 2^2) + 6$

32. $7 - 3(11 - 3^2) + 1$

Simplify.

33. $\dfrac{(-50 \div 2 + 3)}{(20 - 9)}$

34. $\dfrac{(-45 \div 5 + 1)}{[2 - (-2)]}$

35. $\dfrac{[3^2 + 4(-6)]}{[-3 + (-2)]}$

36. $\dfrac{[2^2 + 6(-3)]}{[-2 + (-5)]}$

37. $\dfrac{[-12 - 3(-2)]}{(15 - 17)}$

38. $\dfrac{[-10 - 4(-1)]}{(13 - 19)}$

39. $-16 \div \{-4 \cdot [8 \div (-2)]\}$

40. $20 \div \{4 \cdot [15 \div (-3)]\}$

41. $-60 \div \{5 \cdot [-2 \cdot (-12 \div 4)]\}$

42. $-36 \div \{2 \cdot [-3 \cdot (-9 \div 3)]\}$

Applications

43. *Altitude of a Plane* A plane flying at an altitude of 35,000 feet descends 2000 feet three times before ascending 1000 feet. What is the current altitude of the plane?

44. *Temperature Fluctuations* During a storm in Anchorage, Alaska, the temperature was 8°F at noon. Then it dropped 2°F each hour for the next 4 hours, followed by an additional drop of 5°F the fifth hour. What was the temperature at 5 P.M.?

Ion Charges Ions are atoms or groups of atoms with positive or negative electrical charges. The charges of some ions are given below. Use these values to find the total charge in exercises 45–48.

Aluminum +3	Chloride −1
Phosphate −3	Silver +1

45. 14 phosphate and 9 silver

46. 11 chloride and 2 aluminum

47. 7 aluminum, 5 chloride, and 4 silver

48. 15 silver, 9 phosphate, and 8 chloride

Baseball Some baseball fans play a game called Fantasy Baseball. A fan can create a team made up of real baseball players and receive points based on their players' statistics (stats) for that day. Fans' fantasy teams compete against each other, and the team that accumulates the most points at the end of the season wins. The total points for each player are calculated based on the point value indicated in the chart. **Note that a strikeout receives points as an out and as a strikeout.**

Stat	Point Value	Stat	Point Value
Single	5	Walk	3
Double	10	Strikeout	−1
Triple	15	Out	−1
Home run	20	Stolen base	5
RBI*	5	Caught stealing	−5

*RBI: Runs Batted In

49. Sammy Sosa is a player on Megan's team and had the following stats in a game: 1 double, 1 RBI, 1 walk, 1 strikeout, and 2 outs. Calculate the total points Slammin' Sammy received for Megan's team that night.

50. How many combined points does Megan's team receive for her first and second basemen's stats shown below?
First baseman: 1 single, 2 triples, 2 RBIs, 2 strikeouts, 2 outs, and caught stealing once
Second baseman: 4 outs, 1 walk, 1 stolen base, and 2 strikeouts

51. Vladimir Guerrero is a player on Ian's team and had the following stats in a game: 1 home run, 1 RBI, 2 walks, 2 strikeouts, and 2 outs. Calculate the total points Vladimir Guerrero received for Ian's team that night.

52. How many combined points does Ian's team receive for his catcher and third baseman's stats shown below?
Catcher: 1 home run, 2 doubles, 1 walk, 2 strikeouts, 3 RBIs, 2 outs, and caught stealing once.
Third baseman: 5 outs and 2 strikeouts

One Step Further

53. $\dfrac{[(30 - 15 \div 3) + (-5)]}{(5 - 10)}$

54. $\dfrac{[(32 - 16 \div 4) + (-6)]}{(7 - 9)}$

55. $[(3 + 24) \div (-3)] \cdot [2 + (-3)^2]$

56. $[(-2 + 14) \div (-6)] \cdot [3 + (-2)^3]$

To Think About *Find the value of x.*

57. $3 + x - 2(-4) = 7 - (-13)$

58. $-2 + x + 3(-4) = -6 + (-4)$

Cumulative Review *Simplify.*

59. [1.7.3] $2(x + 3)$

60. [1.7.3] $3(a + 2)$

61. [1.7.3] $4(x - 2)$

62. [1.7.3] $7(x - 1)$

Quick Quiz 2.5

1. Perform the indicated operations.
$15 - 20 \div 5(-2)^2 + 3$

2. Perform the indicated operations. $\dfrac{(16 \div 8 - 4)}{(3 - 5)}$

3. Last winter in the northeast the temperature was 4 degrees Fahrenheit at midnight. It dropped 5 degrees every hour for 5 hours and then rose 8 degrees every hour after that. What was the temperature at noon?

4. **Concept Check** Explain in what order to do the operations to obtain the answer to the problem. $3^2 + 5(2 - 4)$

2.6 SIMPLIFYING AND EVALUATING ALGEBRAIC EXPRESSIONS

① Combining Like Terms with Integer Coefficients

Simplifying algebraic expressions with integers differs from doing so with whole numbers only in that we must consider the sign of the number when simplifying.

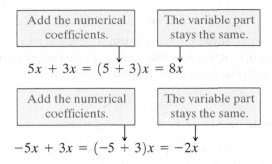

| Add the numerical coefficients. | The variable part stays the same. |

$$5x + 3x = (5 + 3)x = 8x$$

| Add the numerical coefficients. | The variable part stays the same. |

$$-5x + 3x = (-5 + 3)x = -2x$$

Student Learning Objectives

After studying this section, you will be able to:

① Combine like terms with integer coefficients.

② Evaluate algebraic expressions with integers.

③ Use the distributive property with integers.

④ Solve applied problems with integers.

EXAMPLE 1 Simplify by combining like terms. $-4x + 7y + 2x$

Solution

$$
\begin{aligned}
-4x + 7y + 2x &= -4x + 2x + 7y && \text{Rearrange terms.} \\
&= (-4 + 2)x + 7y && \text{Add numerical coefficients of like terms.} \\
&= -2x + 7y && -2x \text{ and } 7y \text{ are not like terms.}
\end{aligned}
$$

Practice Problem 1 Simplify by combining like terms. $-6y + 8x + 4y$

In Example 1 we were able to rearrange terms because addition is commutative. Since subtraction is *not commutative,* we must first change all subtraction statements to additions of the opposite and then rearrange the terms.

EXAMPLE 2 Simplify. $3x + 5y - x$

Solution

$$
\begin{aligned}
3x + 5y - x &= 3x + 5y + (-x) && \text{First we change subtraction to addition of the opposite.} \\
&= 3x + (-1x) + 5y && \text{Now we rearrange terms. Note that } -x = -1x. \\
&= 2x + 5y && \text{We add like terms: } [3 + (-1)]x = 2x.
\end{aligned}
$$

Practice Problem 2 Simplify. $7a + 4b - a$

The next example illustrates the similarity between the process of combining like terms and performing operations with integers.

EXAMPLE 3 Perform each operation indicated.

(a) $2 - 3 + 6$ **(b)** $2x - 3x + 6x$

Solution

(a) $2 - 3 + 6$

$$
\begin{aligned}
&= 2 + (-3) + 6 \\
&= -1 + 6 \\
&= 5
\end{aligned}
$$

(b) $2x - 3x + 6x$

$$
\begin{aligned}
&= 2x + (-3x) + 6x \\
&= -1x + 6x \\
&= 5x
\end{aligned}
$$

NOTE TO STUDENT: *Fully worked-out solutions to all of the Practice Problems can be found at the back of the text starting at page SP-1*

Practice Problem 3   Perform each operation indicated.

(a) $4 - 6 + 8$ **(b)** $4x - 6x + 8x$

In Example 3b we rewrote subtraction as the addition of the opposite. That is, we wrote

$$2x - 3x \quad \text{as} \quad 2x + (-3x).$$

When we write our final answer, it is sometimes necessary to reverse this process, and *write addition of the opposite as subtraction*. For example, consider the expression $-4b + 6a$. This expression can be written as follows.

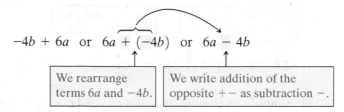

$$-4b + 6a \quad \text{or} \quad 6a + (-4b) \quad \text{or} \quad 6a - 4b$$

We rearrange terms $6a$ and $-4b$.	We write addition of the opposite $+ -$ as subtraction $-$.

The expression $6a + (-4b)$ is not considered simplified since it can be written using fewer symbols. Therefore, we usually simplify: $6a + (-4b)$ to $6a - 4b$.

EXAMPLE 4   Simplify. $3a + 8b - 9a + 3ab - 10b$

Solution

$3a + 8b - 9a + 3ab - 10b$

$= 3a + 8b + (-9a) + 3ab + (-10b)$ Change subtraction to addition of the opposite.

$= 3a + (-9a) + 8b + (-10b) + 3ab$ Rearrange terms to group like terms.

$= [3 + (-9)]a + [8 + (-10)]b + 3ab$ Add coefficients of like terms.

$= -6a + (-2b) + 3ab$

$= -6a - 2b + 3ab$ Rewrite addition of the opposite as subtraction so that the answer is simplified.

Practice Problem 4   Simplify. $2x + 8y - 5x + 4xy - 12y$

Evaluating Algebraic Expressions with Integers

To evaluate expressions we replace the variables with the given numbers and then perform the indicated operations following the order of operations.

EXAMPLE 5   Evaluate. $\dfrac{(x^2 - y)}{4}$ for $x = -1$ and $y = -3$

Solution

$\dfrac{[(x)^2 - (y)]}{4} = \dfrac{[(-1)^2 - (-3)]}{4}$ Place parentheses around each variable. Replace x with -1 and y with -3.

$= \dfrac{[1 - (-3)]}{4}$ Calculate $(-1)^2 = 1$.

$= \dfrac{(1 + 3)}{4}$ Write subtraction as addition of the opposite.

$= \dfrac{4}{4} = 1$ Simplify.

Practice Problem 5 Evaluate.

$$\frac{(a^3 + b)}{2} \text{ for } a = -2 \text{ and } b = -4$$

NOTE TO STUDENT: Fully worked-out solutions to all of the Practice Problems can be found at the back of the text starting at page SP-1

③ Using the Distributive Property with Integers

Recall that to multiply $3(x + 1)$ we use the distributive property to "distribute" the 3. That is, we multiply every number or variable inside the parentheses by 3, and then we simplify the result. We proceed the same way when working with integers.

We distribute 3.   We distribute -3.

$$3(x + 1) = 3x + 3 \qquad -3(x + 1) = -3x + (-3)$$
$$= -3x - 3$$

EXAMPLE 6 Simplify. $-2(y - 4)$

Solution

$$-2(y - 4) = -2y - (-2)(4) \qquad \text{Distribute the } -2 \text{ over subtraction.}$$
$$= -2y - (-8) \qquad \text{Multiply: } (-2)(4) = -8.$$
$$-2(y - 4) = -2y + 8 \qquad \text{Rewrite subtraction as addition of the opposite.}$$

Practice Problem 6 Simplify. $-8(m - 1)$

④ Solving Applied Problems with Integers

EXAMPLE 7 To find the speed of a free-falling skydiver, we use the formula given below.

speed of skydiver		initial velocity		time since start of free fall
↓		↓		↓
s	$=$	v	$-$	$32t$

Find the speed of a skydiver at time $t = 5$ seconds if her initial downward velocity (v) is -7 feet per second.

Solution We evaluate the formula for the values given: $v = -7$ and $t = 5$.

$$s = v - 32t$$
$$= -7 - 32(5)$$
$$= -7 - 160$$
$$= -167$$

A negative speed means that the object is moving in a downward direction. Therefore, the skydiver is falling 167 feet per second.

Practice Problem 7 Use the formula in Example 7 to find the speed of the skydiver at $t = 4$ seconds if her initial downward velocity (v) is -5 feet per second.

Verbal and Writing Skills

1. Is $-2x + 5x = -10x^2$? Why or why not?

2. Is $7x + 6y = 13xy$? Why or why not?

Fill in each box.

3. $-6x + \left(-3\boxed{}\right) = -9x$

4. $-4x + \left(-2\boxed{}\right) = -6x$

5. $5y + \boxed{}xy - 2y + 7xy = 3y + 10xy$

6. $8a + \boxed{}ab - 4a + 7ab = 4a + 11ab$

7. To simplify $9x + (-3y)$, we write $9x \boxed{} 3y$.

8. To simplify $4x + (-7y)$, we write $4x \boxed{} 7y$.

9. $-6(y - 1) = -6 \cdot \boxed{} - (-6) \cdot \boxed{} = -6y \boxed{} 6$

10. $-3(x - 2) = -3 \cdot \boxed{} - (-3) \cdot \boxed{} = -3x \boxed{} 6$

Simplify by combining like terms.

11. $-8x + 3x$

12. $-6x + 2x$

13. $4x + (-3x)$

14. $6y + (-5y)$

15. $-5x - 7x$

16. $-5a - 8a$

17. $-7a - (-2a)$

18. $-9b - (-3b)$

19. $14y + (-7y)$

20. $6x + (-2x)$

21. $-7x + (-6x)$

22. $-6y + (-8y)$

Write in simplest form.

23. $7a + (-9b)$

24. $2x + (-6y)$

25. $-5m + (-8n)$

26. $-3a + (-9b)$

27. $2x + (-y)$

28. $11x + (-y)$

29. $-2a - (-3b)$

30. $-12m - (-6n)$

Perform the operations indicated.

31. (a) $2 - 7 + 3$
(b) $2x - 7x + 3x$

32. (a) $4 - 9 + 2$
(b) $4x - 9x + 2x$

33. (a) $3 - 8 + 4$
(b) $3x - 8x + 4x$

34. (a) $6 - 10 + 3$
(b) $6x - 10x + 3x$

35. (a) $2 - 6 + 1$
(b) $2x - 6x + 1x$

36. (a) $3 - 8 + 1$
(b) $3x - 8x + 1x$

Simplify by combining like terms.

37. $-8y + 4x + 2y$

38. $-7x + 2y + 5x$

39. $6x + 4y + (-8x)$

40. $9a + 4b + (-11a)$

41. $9x + 3y + (-5x)$

42. $10y + 2x + (-4y)$

43. $-8x - 4x - y$

44. $-7a - 2a + b$

45. $3x + 8y - 10x - 2y$

46. $6x + 3y - 9x - 2y$

47. $4x + 2y - 6x - 7$

48. $8x + 4y - 11x - 9$

49. $4 + 3ab - 2 - 9ab$

50. $7 + 5xy + 9 - 8xy$

51. $5x + 7xy - 9x - xy$

52. $5y + 8xy - 11y - xy$

53. $7a - 2ab - 2 - 7ab + 3a$

54. $3x - 4xy - 7 - 9xy + 2x$

55. $3a + 2x - 5a + 7ax - x$

56. $5y + 4x - 8y + 3xy - x$

57. $6a + 7b - 9a + 5ab - 11b$

58. $-2y + 5x - 4y + 9xy + 3x$

59. $4x + 8y - 7x + 6xy - 10y$

60. $2a + 7b - 4a + 3ab - 12b$

Evaluate.

61. $x + 3y$ for $x = -3$ and $y = -2$

62. $a + 3b$ for $a = -1$ and $b = -3$

63. $m - 6n$ for $m = 6$ and $n = -3$

64. $x - 3y$ for $x = 4$ and $y = -1$

65. $a \cdot b - 6$ for $a = -1$ and $b = 5$

66. $m \cdot n - 8$ for $m = -5$ and $n = 2$

67. $\dfrac{(x + y)}{5}$ for $x = -9$ and $y = 4$

68. $\dfrac{(m + n)}{3}$ for $m = -10$ and $n = 7$

69. $9t^2$ for $t = -3$

70. $7a^2$ for $a = -2$

71. $8x - x^2$ for $x = -5$

72. $9m - m^2$ for $m = -3$

73. $\dfrac{(x^2 - x)}{2}$ for $x = -4$

74. $\dfrac{(t^2 - t)}{3}$ for $t = -3$

75. $\dfrac{(a - b^2)}{-3}$ for $a = 13$ and $b = 2$

76. $\dfrac{(x - y^2)}{-5}$ for $x = 30$ and $y = 5$

77. $\dfrac{(m^2 + 2n)}{-8}$ for $m = 6$ and $n = -2$

78. $\dfrac{(a^2 + 4b)}{-3}$ for $a = 5$ and $b = -4$

Simplify.

79. $-3(y + 1)$

80. $-5(x + 1)$

81. $-9(y - 1)$

82. $-8(a - 1)$

83. $-2(m - 3)$

84. $-3(x - 9)$

85. $-1(x + 5)$

86. $-1(a + 4)$

87. $6(-2 + y)$

88. $5(-3 + x)$

89. $2(-4 + a)$

90. $7(-1 + x)$

Applications

Skydiving *To find the speed of a free-falling skydiver, we use the formula* $s = v - 32t$, *where s is the speed of the skydiver, v is the initial velocity, and t is the time since the start of the free fall.*

91. Find the speed of a skydiver at time $t = 4$ seconds if his initial downward velocity (v) is -8 feet per second.

92. Find the speed of the skydiver at time $t = 3$ seconds if his initial downward velocity (v) is -7 feet per second.

Objects Rising and Descending *A projectile is fired straight up with an initial velocity of 72 feet per second. It is known that the subsequent velocity of the projectile is given by the formula* $v = 72 - 32t$, *where t represents time in seconds. If* $v > 0$, *the object is rising, and if* $v < 0$, *it is descending.*

93. At which of the following times is the object descending: $t = 1, 2$, and/or 3 seconds?

Velocity $= 72 - 32t$

Velocity > 0 ↑ Object is rising

Velocity < 0 ↓ Object is descending

Temperature Conversion *In the metric system temperature is measured on the Celsius scale. To convert Fahrenheit temperature to Celsius, we can use the formula*

$$C = \frac{(5F - 160)}{9}$$

where F is the number of Fahrenheit degrees and C is the number of Celsius degrees.

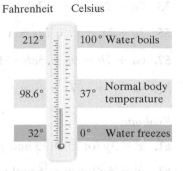

94. When the temperature is 5°F, what is the Celsius reading?

95. When the temperature is 14°F, what is the Celsius reading?

To Think About *Answer yes or no.*

96. Is 0 a solution to $\dfrac{x^3}{2} = 0$?

97. Is 7 a solution to $\dfrac{x^2}{7} = 13$?

Cumulative Review

▲ **98. [1.2.5]** *Geometry* Find the perimeter of a rectangle with a length of 6 feet and a width of 3 feet.

▲ **99. [1.2.5]** *Geometry* Find the perimeter of a square with a side of 7 inches.

100. [1.9.3] *Speed of Light* Light travels at a speed of 5,580,000 miles in 30 seconds. How far does it travel in 1 second? 1 minute? (60 seconds = 1 minute)

101. [1.9.3] *Heartbeat* The average heart beats 73 times per minute. How many times will the heart beat in 1 hour? 1 day? (60 minutes = 1 hour)

Quick Quiz 2.6

1. Simplify by combining like terms.
$-5x + 9y + 2 - 2y - 6x$

2. Simplify.
  (a) $-3(a - 1)$
  (b) $-8(x + 7)$

3. Use the formula $s = v - 32t$ to find the speed (s) of a free-falling skydiver at $t = 3$ seconds if his initial downward velocity (v) is -10 feet per second.

4. Concept Check State 2 other ways we can write $-3b + 7$.

Suppose that you decide to redecorate or remodel your home. Do you know how to determine how much the entire project will cost? After you have studied the topics in this chapter, you will have an opportunity to consider this situation.

Introduction to Equations and Algebraic Expressions

Student Learning Objectives

After studying this section, you will be able to:

1. Use the additive inverse property.

2. Solve equations using the addition principle of equality.

3. Solve applied problems involving angles.

NOTE TO STUDENT: *Fully worked-out solutions to all of the Practice Problems can be found at the back of the text starting at page SP-1*

1 Using the Additive Inverse Property

Recall from Chapter 2 that the numbers 2 and -2 are called **opposites** and their sum is equal to zero. This fact is often referred to as the **additive inverse property:** $a + (-a) = 0$ and $-a + a = 0$. We will use this property to help us solve equations involving addition and subtraction.

EXAMPLE 1 Fill in the box with the number that gives the desired result.
$$x + 8 + \square = x + 0 = x$$

Solution

$$x + 8 + \boxed{} = x + 0 = x$$

We want the sum of $8 + \square$ to equal 0.

$$x + 8 + (-8) = x + 0 = x$$

$$8 + (-8) = 0$$

Thus, $x + 8 + (-8) = x + 0 = x$.

Practice Problem 1 Fill in the box with the number that gives the desired result. $y - 6 + \square = y + 0 = y$

2 Solving Equations Using the Addition Principle of Equality

We observe in our everyday world that if we add the same amount to two equal values, the results are equal. We illustrate this below.

We place 5 pounds on both sides of a seesaw

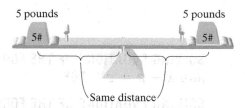

We would expect the seesaw to balance.

We add a 2-pound weight to the center of each 5-pound weight simultaneously.

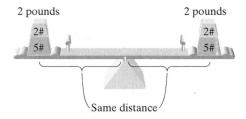

The seesaw should still balance.

In mathematics, a similar principle is observed. That is, we can add the same number to both sides of an equation without changing the solution. We state this principle of equality.

ADDITION PRINCIPLE OF EQUALITY

If the same number is added to both sides of an equation, the results on both sides are equal in value.

We can restate this principle in symbols this way. For any numbers a, b, and c,

$$\text{If } a = b, \text{ then } a + c = b + c$$

To illustrate the addition principle, let's see what happens when we solve the equation $x - 2 = 7$ using basic arithmetic facts (as we did in Chapter 1). Then, let's solve the same equation by the addition principle of equality.

Solve using basic arithmetic facts.

$$x - 2 = 7 \quad \text{What number minus 2 equals 7?}$$
$$9 - 2 = 7 \quad \text{Nine minus 2 equals 7.}$$

Thus $x = 9$.

Solve using the addition principle.

$$x - 2 = 7$$
$$x - 2 + 2 = 7 + 2 \quad \text{We add the opposite of } -2 \text{ to both sides of the equation.}$$
$$x + 0 = 9 \quad \text{We simplify: } -2 + 2 = 0.$$
$$x = 9 \quad \text{The solution is the same.}$$

We see that adding 2 to both sides of the equation did not change the solution. In other words, using the addition principle of equality gives the same result.

You will find it easier to use the addition principle of equality to solve more complex equations. The goal when using this principle is to *add the same number to both sides of the equation so that when we simplify, x is left alone.* That is, we'll use it to get a simpler equation of the form $x = $ *some number* or *some number* $= x$.

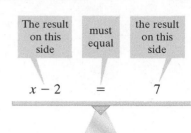

The result on this side | must equal | the result on this side

$x - 2 \quad = \quad 7$

The seesaw is balanced.

$x - 2 + 2 \quad = \quad 7 + 2$

We add the same number to both sides and the seesaw is still balanced.

EXAMPLE 2 Solve. $x - 22 = -14$

Solution We want an equation of the form $x = $ *some number*. Therefore, we want to get x alone on one side of the equation.

$$x - 22 = -14$$
$$x - 22 + 22 = -14 + 22 \quad \text{Add the opposite of } -22 \text{ to both sides of the equation.}$$
$$x + 0 = 8 \quad x - 22 + 22 = x + 0 \text{ and } -14 + 22 = 8$$
$$x = 8 \quad \text{The solution is 8.}$$

How do we know what number to add to both sides of the equation to get x alone? We think, "What can we add to both sides so that $x - 22$ becomes simply x?" We add the *opposite* of -22, or $+22$, to both sides.

Practice Problem 2 Solve. $x - 19 = -31$

$x - 22 \quad = \quad -14$

The seesaw is balanced.

$x - 22 + 22 \quad = \quad -14 + 22$

Add 22 to both sides and the seesaw is still balanced.

EXAMPLE 3 Solve and check your solution. $75 = 83 + x$

Solution The variable x is on the right side of the equation; therefore we want an equation of the form *some number* $= x$.

$$75 = 83 + x$$
$$75 + (-83) = 83 + (-83) + x \quad \text{Add the opposite of 83 to both sides}$$
$$-8 = 0 + x \quad \text{since } 83 + (-83) = 0.$$
$$-8 = x$$

Check: To check our answer, we replace x with -8 and verify we get a true statement.

$$75 = 83 + x$$
$$75 \stackrel{?}{=} 83 + (-8)$$
$$75 = 75 \; \checkmark$$

Practice Problem 3 Solve and check your solution. $92 = 46 + x$

$75 \quad = \quad 83 + x$

$75 + (-83) \quad = 83 + (-83) + x$

Add -83 to both sides and the seesaw is still balanced.

Sometimes problems require that we write many steps. Writing too many steps can make the problem seem more complicated than it really is. We can eliminate some steps if, when adding a number to both sides of the equation, we place the addition *below* the terms rather than *beside* the terms. We can rewrite Example 3 using this format.

$$75 = \quad 83 + x$$
$$\underline{+ \; -83 \quad -83} \qquad \text{Add } -83 \text{ below the terms on both sides.}$$
$$-8 = \quad 0 + x$$

Try this with a few problems. You may find it easier and decide to use this format.

EXAMPLE 4   Solve and check your solution. $3x - 2x - 4 = 9$

Solution   The variable x appears *more than once* on the left side of the equation. This means we'll need to complete an extra step, combining like terms, so that x appears only once in the equation.

$$3x - 2x - 4 = 9$$
$$x - 4 = 9 \qquad \text{We combine like terms: } 3x - 2x = 1x \text{ or } x.$$
$$\underline{+ \qquad 4 \quad 4} \qquad \text{Think: "Add the opposite of } -4 \text{ to both sides of the equation."}$$
$$x + 0 = 13$$
$$x = 13$$

$$\begin{aligned} \text{Check:} \qquad 3x - 2x - 4 &= 9 \\ 3(13) - 2(13) - 4 &\overset{?}{=} 9 \\ 39 - 26 - 4 &\overset{?}{=} 9 \\ 9 &= 9 \; \checkmark \end{aligned}$$

NOTE TO STUDENT: *Fully worked-out solutions to all of the Practice Problems can be found at the back of the text starting at page SP-1*

Practice Problem 4   Solve and check your solution. $5x - 4x - 3 = 11$

There are three facts to remember when solving the equations we've studied so far.

1. First, if necessary, we must simplify each side of the equation by combining like terms or completing any addition and subtraction.
2. Next, we use the addition principle of equality to get the variable alone on one side of the equation, i.e., in the form $x = some\ number$ or $some\ number = x$.
3. An equation is like a balanced scale. Whatever we do to one side of the equation, we must do to the other side of the equation to maintain the balance.

EXAMPLE 5   Solve and check your solution. $2 - 6 = y - 7 + 12$

Solution   First, we must simplify each side of the equation separately by completing the addition and subtraction.

$$2 - 6 = y - 7 + 12$$
$$-4 = y + 5 \qquad \text{Simplify: } 2 - 6 = -4; -7 + 12 = 5.$$

Then we add -5 to both sides of the equation to get y alone on the right side: *some number = y.*

$$-4 = y + 5 \qquad \text{Think: "Add the opposite of 5 to both sides of the equation."}$$
$$\underline{+ \; -5 \qquad - 5} \qquad \text{Add } -5 \text{ to both sides.}$$
$$-9 = y \qquad \text{We usually do not write the step } -9 = y + 0.$$

$$\begin{aligned} \text{Check:} \quad 2 - 6 &= y - 7 + 12 \\ 2 - 6 &\overset{?}{=} -9 - 7 + 12 \\ -4 &= -4 \; \checkmark \end{aligned}$$

Practice Problem 5   Solve. $5 - 8 = y - 2 + 19$

Solving Applied Problems Involving Angles

In this section we will find the measure of an angle by finding the solution to an equation. Before we begin our discussion on this topic, we introduce terms and definitions.

In geometry a **line** ⟷ extends indefinitely, but a portion of a line, called a **line segment** •——•, has a beginning and an end. A **ray** •—→ starts at a point and extends indefinitely in one direction. An **angle** is formed whenever two rays meet at the same endpoint. The point at which they meet is called the **vertex** of the angle.

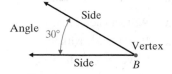

One way to name the angle in the figure above is $\angle B$.

The *amount of opening* of an angle can be measured. Angles are commonly measured in degrees. In the sketch above, the angle measures 30 degrees or 30°. The symbol ° indicates degrees. If you fix one side of an angle and keep moving the other side, the angle measure will get larger and larger until eventually you have gone around in one complete revolution.

One complete revolution is 360°.

One-half of a revolution is 180°.

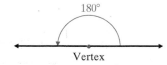

Two angles that have a sum of 180° are called **supplementary angles.** Two angles that share a common side are called **adjacent angles.** Adjacent angles formed by two intersecting lines are supplementary (they add up to 180°).

When a problem involves geometric shapes, we can draw pictures to help us visualize the situation and thus better *understand the problem.* Next, we *gather the facts.* In algebra, we often use these facts to find an equation that represents the situation. The following process will help you solve these types of problems.

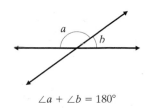

$\angle a + \angle b = 180°$

1. Use the facts stated to *draw a picture.*
2. Write an *equation.*
3. *Replace variables* in the equation with the appropriate known values.
4. *Solve* the equation and answer the question.

We use this process to work Examples 6 and 7.

▲ **EXAMPLE 6** $\angle a$ and $\angle b$ are supplementary angles. Find the measure of $\angle a$ if the measure of $\angle b$ is 36°.

Solution   We *draw a picture.*

Since $\angle a$ and $\angle b$ are supplementary angles, we know that their sum is 180°. We use this information to *write an equation.*

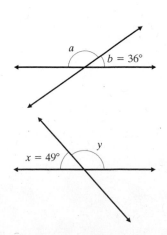

$\angle a + \angle b =$	$180°$	Write an equation.
$\angle a + 36° =$	$180°$	Replace $\angle b$ with 36°.
$+\quad -36°\qquad -36°$		Solve the equation.
$\angle a =$	$144°$	The measure of $\angle a$ is 144°.

▲ **Practice Problem 6** $\angle x$ and $\angle y$ are supplementary angles. Find the measure of $\angle y$ if the measure of $\angle x$ is 49°.

▲ **EXAMPLE 7**

(a) Translate into symbols. Angle y measures 40° more than angle x.

(b) Find the measure of $\angle x$ if the measure of $\angle y$ is 95°.

Solution

(a) Angle y measures 40° more than angle x.

$$\angle y \qquad = \qquad 40° \quad + \quad \angle x$$

(b)

$\angle y =$	$40° + \angle x$	Write an equation.
$95° =$	$40° + \angle x$	Replace $\angle y$ with 95°.
$+\,{-40°}$	$-40°$	Solve the equation.
$55° =$	$\angle x$	The measure of $\angle x$ is 55°.

NOTE TO STUDENT: Fully worked-out solutions to all of the Practice Problems can be found at the back of the text starting at page SP-1

▲ **Practice Problem 7**

(a) Translate into symbols. Angle a measures 20° less than angle b.

(b) Find the measure of $\angle b$ if the measure of $\angle a$ is 80°.

EXAMPLE 8 Find x and the measure of $\angle b$ for the following pair of supplementary angles.

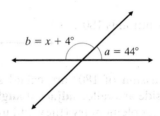

$$b = x + 4° \qquad a = 44°$$

Solution We know that $\angle a$ and $\angle b$ are supplementary angles and therefore their sum is 180°. We write the equation as follows.

$\angle a + \angle b = 180°$	Write an equation.
$44° + (x + 4°) = 180°$	Replace $\angle a$ with 44° and $\angle b$ with $x + 4°$.
$48° + x = 180°$	Simplify: $44° + 4° + x = 48° + x$.
$+\quad\quad\quad -48° \quad\quad\quad -48°$	Solve the equation.
$x = 132°$	

Since $\angle b = x + 4°$ we must substitute 132° for x to find the measure of $\angle b$.

$$\angle b = x + 4°$$
$$\angle b = 132° + 4° = 136°$$

Therefore $x = 132°$ and $\angle b = 136°$.

Practice Problem 8 Refer to Example 8 and find x and the measure of $\angle b$ if the measure of $\angle a$ is 55°.

Verbal and Writing Skills *Fill in the blanks.*

1. The sum of two opposite numbers is equal to _____.

2. The sum of two supplementary angles is equal to _____.

3. To solve $x - 6 = 3$, we _____ 6 to both sides of the equation.

4. To solve $x + 6 = 2$, we _____ 6 to both sides of the equation.

Fill in each □ with the number that gives the desired result.

5. $3 + \square = 0$

6. $6 + \square = 0$

7. $-9 + \square = 0$

8. $-1 + \square = 0$

9. $17 + \square = 0$

10. $43 + \square = 0$

11. $-28 + \square = 0$

12. $-13 + \square = 0$

13. $x + 5 + \square = x$

14. $y + 8 + \square = y$

15. $m - 2 + \square = m$

16. $a - 6 + \square = a$

Fill in each □ with the correct number to solve the equation.

17.
$$
\begin{array}{r}
x + 12 = 16 \\
+ \quad \square \quad \square \\
\hline
x + \square = \square \\
x = \square
\end{array}
$$

18.
$$
\begin{array}{r}
x + 9 = 21 \\
+ \quad \square \quad \square \\
\hline
x + \square = \square \\
x = \square
\end{array}
$$

19.
$$
\begin{array}{r}
y - 16 = 32 \\
+ \quad \square \quad \square \\
\hline
y + \square = \square \\
y = \square
\end{array}
$$

20.
$$
\begin{array}{r}
y - 18 = 25 \\
+ \quad \square \quad \square \\
\hline
y + \square = \square \\
y = \square
\end{array}
$$

Solve and check your solution.

21. (a) $x - 8 = 22$
    (b) $x + 8 = 22$

22. (a) $a - 4 = 29$
    (b) $a + 4 = 29$

23. (a) $x + 2 = -11$
    (b) $x - 2 = -11$

24. (a) $y + 2 = -10$
    (b) $y - 2 = -10$

25. (a) $-18 = x + 2$
    (b) $-18 = x - 2$

26. (a) $-19 = y - 1$
    (b) $-19 = y + 1$

Solve and check your solution.

27. $y - 10 = 5$

28. $m - 21 = 9$

29. $n - 43 = -74$

30. $y - 81 = -12$

31. $y + 30 = -50$

32. $x + 1 = -15$

33. $38 + x = 4$

34. $10 + x = 12$

35. $1 = x - 13$

36. $5 = x - 7$

37. $20 = y + 11$

38. $46 = a + 14$

39. $-13 = x + 1$

40. $-5 = x + 7$

Simplify and then solve. Check your solution.

41. $4x - 3x - 3 = 8$

42. $3x - 2x - 5 = 7$

43. $5y - 4y + 1 = -5$

44. $3y - 2y + 3 = 1$

45. $5 = 2y - y + 1$

46. $6 = 2y - y + 4$

Simplify each side of the equation, then solve the equation. Check your solution.

47. $-23 + 8 + x = -2 + 13$

48. $-33 + 9 + x = -1 + 7$

49. $4 - 9 = a - 1 + 14$

50. $3 - 8 = m - 4 + 7$

51. $-45 + 9 + m = -6 + 18$

52. $-27 + 7 + n = -5 + 8$

53. $-1 + 11 + x = -5 + 9$

54. $-3 + 9 + a = -4 + 7$

55. $3(7 - 11) = y - 5$

56. $5(8 - 13) = x - 1$

Find the measure of the unknown angle for each pair of supplementary angles.

▲ **57.** Find the measure of $\angle a$ if the measure of $\angle b = 86°$.

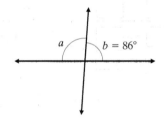

▲ **58.** Find the measure of $\angle x$ if the measure of $\angle y = 22°$.

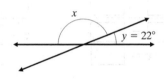

▲ **59.** Find the measure of $\angle x$ if the measure of $\angle y = 112°$.

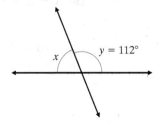

▲ **60.** Find the measure of $\angle a$ if the measure of $\angle b = 101°$.

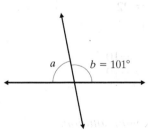

▲ **61.** Find the measure of $\angle x$ if the measure of $\angle y$ is $43°$.

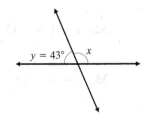

▲ **62.** Find the measure of $\angle m$ if the measure of $\angle n$ is $66°$.

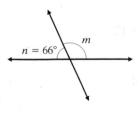

Translate each of the following statements into symbols. Then find the unknown angle.

▲ **63. (a)** Translate into symbols. Angle x measures $70°$ more than angle y.
(b) Find the measure of $\angle y$ if $\angle x = 125°$.

▲ **64. (a)** Translate into symbols. Angle a measures $50°$ more than angle b.
(b) Find the measure of $\angle b$ if $\angle a = 115°$.

▲ **65.** **(a)** Translate into symbols. Angle a measures 40° less than angle b.
(b) Find the measure of $\angle b$ if the measure of $\angle a$ is 50°.

▲ **66.** **(a)** Translate into symbols. Angle x measures 80° less than angle y.
(b) Find the measure of $\angle y$ if the measure of $\angle x$ is 40°.

Find x and the measure of $\angle b$ for the following pairs of supplementary angles.

▲ **67.**

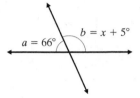

▲ **68.**

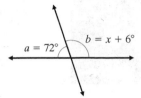

69. Refer to exercise 67. Find x and the measure of $\angle b$ if the measure of $\angle a$ is 52°.

70. Refer to exercise 68. Find x and the measure of $\angle b$ if the measure of $\angle a$ is 65°.

One Step Further *Simplify each side of each equation, then solve the equation.*

71. $2^2 + (5 - 9) = x + 3^3$

72. $4^2 + (3 - 7) = y + 2^3$

73. $5x + 1 - 2x = 4x - 2$

74. $8x + 6 - 5x = 2x - 3$

To Think About

▲ **75.** Find the measures of $\angle c$, $\angle d$, and $\angle f$.

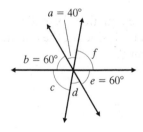

▲ **76.** Find the measure of $\angle b$, $\angle e$, and $\angle f$.

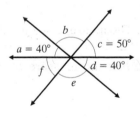

Cumulative Review *Translate into symbols.*

77. **[1.4.2]** Seven times a number.

78. **[1.4.2]** The product of three and a number.

79. **[1.8.4]** Eight times what number equals forty?

80. **[1.8.4]** Double what number equals thirty?

81. **[2.2.2]** *Temperature Fluctuations* If the low temperature on Tuesday was −8°F and the temperature rose 21°F during the day, what was the high temperature?

82. **[2.2.2]** *Temperature Fluctuations* If the low temperature on Monday was −4°F and the temperature rose 15°F during the day, what was the high temperature?

Fantasy Basketball *Fantasy basketball is a game that many sports fans participate in. A fan can create a team made up of real basketball players and receive points based on their players' statistics (stats) for that day. Fans compete against other fantasy teams, and the team that accumulates the most points at the end of the season wins. The total points for each player are calculated based on the point values in the following chart.*

Statistic	Fantasy Point Value	Statistic	Fantasy Point Value
Field goal	2	Steal	2
Rebound	1	Block	2
Missed shot	−1	Turnover	−1

83. **[2.6.4]** How many fantasy points did a player on Delroy's fantasy team, the Lasers, earn based on the following stats: 15 field goals, 8 rebounds, 6 missed shots, 5 steals, 5 blocks, and 2 turnovers?

84. **[2.6.4]** How many fantasy points did a player on Joe's fantasy team, River Run, earn based on the following stats: 12 field goals, 14 rebounds, 8 missed shots, 3 steals, 7 blocks, and 4 turnovers?

Quick Quiz 3.1

1. Solve each equation and check your solution.
   (a) $x + 12 = -15$
   (b) $y - 7 = -20$

2. Solve each equation and check your solution.
   (a) $6x - 5x + 2 = 10 - 15$
   (b) $-8 + 10 = 6 - 9 + y$

3. (a) Translate into symbols. The measure of $\angle a$ is 35° less than the measure of $\angle b$.
   (b) Find the measure of $\angle b$ if the measure of $\angle a$ is 75°.

4. **Concept Check** To solve the equation $-9 + x = -15$, Damien subtracted 9 from both sides of the equation. Is this correct, why or why not?

① Solving Equations Using the Division Principle of Equality

Recall from Chapter 1 that any number divided by itself is equal to 1. For example, $2 \div 2 = \frac{2}{2} = 1$ and $-3 \div (-3) = \frac{-3}{-3} = 1$. We will use this division fact when we solve equations.

Student Learning Objectives

After studying this section, you will be able to:

① Solve equations using the division principle of equality.

② Translate English statements into equations.

③ Solve applied problems involving numbers and finance.

EXAMPLE 1 Fill in the box with the number that gives the desired result.

$$\frac{-5x}{\square} = 1 \cdot x = x$$

Solution

$$\frac{-5x}{\square} = 1 \cdot x = x$$

We want the quotient of $\frac{-5}{\square}$ to equal 1.

$$\frac{-5x}{-5} = 1 \cdot x = x$$

$$\frac{-5}{-5} = 1$$

Practice Problem 1 Fill in the box with the number that gives the desired result.

$$\frac{-9x}{\square} = 1 \cdot x = x$$

NOTE TO STUDENT: Fully worked-out solutions to all of the Practice Problems can be found at the back of the text starting at page SP-1

Now let's see how we can use this division fact to help us solve equations. To solve an equation like $2x = 30$, we can think: "What can we do to the left side of the equation so that $2x$ becomes simply x?" We can divide by 2 since *dividing* $2 \cdot x$ by 2 *undoes* the *multiplication* by 2. Remember, whatever we do to one side of the equation, we must do to the other side of the equation.

$$2x = 30$$
$$\frac{2x}{2} = \frac{30}{2} \qquad \text{We divide both sides by 2.}$$
$$1 \cdot x = 15 \qquad 2 \div 2 = 1; \quad 30 \div 2 = 15$$
$$x = 15$$

To see why we must divide by 2 on *both sides* of the equation, let's return to our example of a balanced seesaw. If we cut the weight on each side in half (i.e., divide each side by 2) the seesaw should still balance.

In mathematics, a similar principle is observed. We now state this principle of equality.

> ## DIVISION PRINCIPLE OF EQUALITY
>
> If both sides of an equation are divided by the same nonzero number, the results on both sides are equal in value.
>
> We can restate it in symbols this way. For any numbers a, b, c, with c not equal to 0,
>
> $$\text{If } a = b, \text{ then } \frac{a}{c} = \frac{b}{c}.$$

It should be noted that, as stated in Chapter 1, division is defined in terms of multiplication. For example $\frac{10}{2} = 5$ because $10 = 5 \cdot 2$. In a similar manner, the division principle of equality is a form of the multiplication principle that we will learn about in Chapter 5 when we study fractions.

EXAMPLE 2 Solve and check your solution. $7x = -147$

Solution We want to make $7x = -147$ into a simpler equation, $x = some$ *number*.

$7x = -147$ The variable, x, is *multiplied* by 7.

$\dfrac{7x}{7} = \dfrac{-147}{7}$ Dividing both sides by 7 undoes the *multiplication* by 7.

$x = -21$ $\dfrac{7x}{7} = 1 \cdot x = x$ and $-147 \div 7 = -21$

Check: $7x = -147$

$7(-21) \overset{?}{=} -147; \quad -147 = -147$ ✓

NOTE TO STUDENT: Fully worked-out solutions to all of the Practice Problems can be found at the back of the text starting at page SP-1

Practice Problem 2 Solve and check your solution. $5m = -155$.

Remember, it is best to first simplify each side of the equation, if necessary, before any other steps are taken.

EXAMPLE 3 Solve. $3(x \cdot 5) = \dfrac{450}{5}$

Solution First, we simplify the equation.

$3(x \cdot 5) = \dfrac{450}{5}$

$3(x \cdot 5) = 90$ Divide: $450 \div 5 = 90$.

$3(5x) = 90$ Change the order of the factors.

$(3 \cdot 5)x = 90$ Regroup the factors.

$15x = 90$ Simplify.

$\dfrac{15x}{15} = \dfrac{90}{15}$ Dividing both sides by 15 undoes the multiplication by 15.

$x = 6$

We leave the check to the student.

Practice Problem 3 Solve.

$$8(n \cdot 5) = \frac{320}{2}$$

EXAMPLE 4   Solve. $-50 + 10 = 6y - 4y$

Solution   We always simplify each side of the equation first.

$$-50 + 10 = 6y - 4y$$
$$-40 = 6y - 4y \quad \text{Simplify the left side of the equation: } -50 + 10 = -40.$$
$$-40 = 2y \quad \text{Simplify the right side of the equation: } 6y - 4y = 2y.$$
$$\frac{-40}{2} = \frac{2y}{2} \quad \text{Divide both sides of the equation by 2.}$$
$$-20 = y \quad -40 \div 2 = -20; 2 \div 2 = 1; 1 \cdot y = y$$

We leave the check to the student.

Practice Problem 4   Solve. $30 + (-12) = 7y - 5y$

 Translating English Statements into Equations

When we translate a statement into an equation, we must first *define the variables* that we are going to use. This helps us distinguish between the different things that are being compared. For example, consider the statement

> Kathy makes three times as many sales as Mark does.

We are comparing Kathy's sales to Mark's, so we can let the variable K represent the number of sales Kathy makes and M represent the number of sales Mark makes. Since Kathy makes three times as many sales as Mark, we have $K = 3M$. Keep in mind that we can use any letters; it is usually easiest to use the first letter of the word we are considering.

▲ **EXAMPLE 5**   Translate the statement into an equation. The measure of angle s (S) is two times the measure of angle y (Y).

Solution   We are representing the measure of angle s with the letter S and the measure of angle y with the letter Y. Now we translate.

The measure of angle s is two times the measure of angle y.
$$S = 2 \cdot Y$$

The equation that represents the statement is $S = 2Y$.

▲ **Practice Problem 5**   Translate the statement into an equation. The measure of angle a (A) is four times the measure of angle b (B).

EXAMPLE 6   Translate the statement into an equation. There are five times as many dimes (D) as pennies (P) in a coin collection.

Solution   This statement is phrased a little differently than others we have translated. Therefore, it is helpful to write a sentence that *compares* the two quantities.

> There are more dimes (D) than pennies (P).

There are 5 times as many dimes as pennies.

Think of a simple comparison of pennies and dimes, such as the case when there is only 1 penny.

If there is 1 penny in the collection, then there are 5 dimes.

five times as many dimes

Now we can rephrase the statement and translate into an equation.

The number of dimes is five times the number of pennies.

$$D = 5 \cdot P$$

The equation that represents the statement is $D = 5P$.

Practice Problem 6   Translate the statement into an equation. Sara (S) ran twice as many laps as Dave (D).

3 Solving Applied Problems Involving Numbers and Finance

EXAMPLE 7   The number of peanuts (P) is triple the number of cashews (C).

(a) Translate the statement into an equation.

(b) Find the number of cashews if there are 27 peanuts.

Solution P represents the number of peanuts, and C represents the number of cashews.

(a) The number of peanuts (P) is triple the number of cashews (C).

The word *triple* means *three times*.

The number of peanuts is triple the number of cashews.

$$P = 3 \cdot C$$

(b) Find the number of cashews if there are 27 peanuts.

$$P = 3C \quad \text{We use the equation from part (a).}$$
$$27 = 3C \quad \text{We replace } P \text{ with 27.}$$
$$\frac{27}{3} = \frac{3C}{3} \quad \text{We divide both sides by 3.}$$
$$9 = C \quad \text{There are 9 cashews.}$$

Practice Problem 7   The number of cars (C) is twice the number of trucks (T).

(a) Translate the statement into an equation.

(b) Find the number of trucks if there are 150 cars on the road.

NOTE TO STUDENT: *Fully worked-out solutions to all of the Practice Problems can be found at the back of the text starting at page SP-1*

EXAMPLE 8   Lena purchased x shares of stock at $35 per share. She sold all the stock for $56 per share and made a profit of $546. How many shares of stock did Lena purchase?

Solution   *Understand the problem.* We use a Mathematics Blueprint for Problem Solving to organize the information.

Mathematics Blueprint for Problem Solving

Gather the Facts	What Am I Asked to Do?	How Do I Proceed?	Key Points to Remember
Let x = the number of shares of stock purchased. Lena paid $35 for each share. She sold each share for $56.	Find the number of shares of stock purchased.	Let $35x$ = the purchase price and $56x$ = the sale price. Find the profit: profit = sale price − purchase price	Profit is how much money is made.

Solve and state the answer.

$$\text{profit} = \text{sale price} - \text{purchase price}$$

$$546 = 56x - 35x \quad \text{We must simplify the equation.}$$
$$546 = 21x \quad \text{We combine like terms: } 56x - 35x = 21x.$$
$$\frac{546}{21} = \frac{21x}{21} \quad \text{We divide both sides by 21.}$$
$$26 = x \quad \text{Lena purchased 26 shares of stock.}$$

Check: We can estimate to see if our answer is reasonable. We round so that each number has 1 nonzero digit.

$$546 \rightarrow 500; \quad 56 \rightarrow 60; \quad 35 \rightarrow 40$$

Now we estimate the value of x.

$$500 = 60x - 40x$$
$$500 = 20x$$
$$\frac{500}{20} = x$$
$$25 = x \quad \text{Our answer is reasonable.} \checkmark$$

Practice Problem 8   Ian purchased x shares of stock at $25 per share. He sold all the stock for $45 per share and made a profit of $200. How many shares of stock did Ian purchase?

Developing Your Study Skills

Seeking Assistance

Getting the right kind of help at the right time can be a key factor to being successful in mathematics. When you have attended class on a regular basis, taken careful notes, methodically read your textbook, and diligently done your homework—in other words, when you have made every effort possible to learn the mathematics—you may still find that you are having difficulty. If this is the case, then you need to seek help.

Exercise

1. Make an appointment with your instructor to find out what help is available to you. The instructor, tutoring services, a mathematics lab, videotapes, and computer software may be among the resources you can draw on.

Verbal and Writing Skills

Fill in the blanks.

1. To solve the equation $-22x = 66$, we undo the multiplication by _____ both sides of the equation by ___.

2. To solve the equation $-16x = 64$, we undo the multiplication by _____ both sides of the equation by ___.

Fill in each □ with the number that gives the desired result.

3. $\dfrac{5x}{\square} = x$

4. $\dfrac{8x}{\square} = x$

5. $\dfrac{-2x}{\square} = x$

6. $\dfrac{-3x}{\square} = x$

7. $\dfrac{6 \cdot x}{\square} = x$

8. $\dfrac{2 \cdot x}{\square} = x$

9. $\dfrac{-1 \cdot x}{\square} = x$

10. $\dfrac{-9 \cdot x}{\square} = x$

Solve and check your solution.

11. $3x = 36$

12. $5x = 65$

13. $10x = 40$

14. $9x = 99$

15. $6y = -18$

16. $2a = -32$

17. $5m = -35$

18. $6y = -42$

19. $-3y = 15$

20. $-4x = 12$

21. $-7a = 49$

22. $-5y = 20$

23. $48 = 6x$

24. $20 = 2y$

25. $72 = 9x$

26. $56 = 14y$

27. $8x = 104$

28. $9y = 135$

29. $-19x = -76$

30. $-22y = -132$

31. $2(3x) = 54$

32. $4(2x) = 64$

33. $5(4x) = 40$

34. $2(2x) = 16$

35. $5(x \cdot 2) = \dfrac{40}{2}$

36. $3(x \cdot 5) = \dfrac{60}{2}$

37. $4(x \cdot 2) = \dfrac{96}{3}$

38. $6(x \cdot 5) = \dfrac{120}{2}$

Simplify each side of the equation, then solve. Check your solution.

39. $-26 - 18 = 11a$

40. $-44 - 16 = 6y$

41. $-4 - 4 = 8y$

42. $-3 - 3 = 6x$

43. $5x - 2x = 24$

44. $5x - 3x = 30$

45. $65 = 15x - 10x$

46. $81 = 15x - 6x$

Mixed Practice *Solve and check your solution.*

47. $-15y = 165$

48. $-14x = 168$

49. $-4x = 3 - 23$

50. $-3a = 4 - 13$

51. $12x - 4x = 56$

52. $15x - 10x = 95$

53. $55 = 5a$

54. $44 = 4y$

55. $(3x) \cdot 2 = \dfrac{36}{3}$

56. $(8x) \cdot 3 = \dfrac{48}{2}$

57. $9x + 3x = -120$

58. $7x + 3x = -90$

Applications

▲ **59. *Dimensions of a Building*** The length (L) of a building is three times the width (W). Translate the statement into an equation.

60. *Comparing Weights* The weight of a steel beam (B) is three times the weight of a steel pole (P). Translate the statement into an equation.

61. *Discount Price* The original price (R) of a ring is double the sale price (S). Translate the statement into an equation.

▲ **62.** The width (W) of a yard is triple the length (L). Translate the statement to an equation.

63. *Cost of Race Boat* The cost of a new race boat (R) is double the cost of an older model boat (B).

   (a) Translate the statement into an equation.

   (b) Find the cost of the older model if the new race boat costs $124,000.

▲ **64. *Dimensions of Wood*** The length of the larger piece of wood (L) is double the length of the smaller piece of wood (S).

   (a) Translate the statement into an equation.

   (b) Find the length of the smaller piece of wood if the larger piece of wood is 86 inches.

65. *Tickets Sold* There were three times as many children's tickets (C) sold as adult tickets (A).

   (a) Translate the statement into an equation.

   (b) Find the number of adult tickets sold if there were 300 children's tickets sold.

66. *Red vs. White Roses* There are four times as many red roses (R) in the garden as white roses (W).

   (a) Translate the statement into an equation.

   (b) Find the number of white roses if there are 64 red roses.

67. *Soccer Goals* The total number of soccer goals attempted (A) by a team is double the number of goals scored (S).

   (a) Translate the statement into an equation.

   (b) If the team attempted to score 42 times, find the number of goals scored.

68. *Coin Collection* There are four times as many nickels (N) in a coin collection as quarters (Q).

   (a) Translate the statement into an equation.

   (b) Find the number of quarters if there are 48 nickels in the collection.

69. *Stock Investment* Vu Nguyen purchased x shares of Baron Electric stock at $30 per share. He sold all the stock for $42 per share and made a profit of $360. How many shares of stock did Vu purchase?

70. *Stock Investment* Leslie purchased x shares of stock at $75 per share. She sold all the stock for $85 per share and made a profit of $800. How many shares of stock did Leslie purchase?

One Step Further

71. *Distance Traveled* On Monday Leah drove x miles on her road trip to visit her parents. On Tuesday she drove twice the number of miles she drove on Monday. If Leah drove a total of 360 miles on her two-day trip, how many miles did she drive on Monday?

72. *Hourly Rate* Mercelita charges $$x$ per hour as a consultant. She worked on a consulting job for 8 hours on Monday, 6 hours on Tuesday, and 9 hours on Wednesday. If her total earnings for the three days were $1035, what is the hourly rate she charges?

To Think About *Solve.*

73. (a) $13x = 26$

   (b) $-13x = 26$

   (c) $x + 13 = 26$

   (d) $x - 13 = 26$

74. (a) $9y = 72$

   (b) $-9y = 72$

   (c) $y + 9 = 72$

   (d) $y - 9 = 72$

75. (a) $13x = -26$

   (b) $-13x = -26$

   (c) $x + 13 = -26$

   (d) $x - 13 = -26$

76. (a) $9y = -72$

   (b) $-9y = -72$

   (c) $y + 9 = -72$

   (d) $y - 9 = -72$

Find x for each pair of supplementary angles. Then find the degree measure of each angle.

▲ **77.**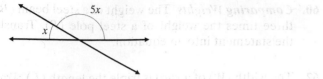

▲ **78.**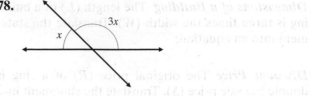

▲ **79.**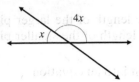

▲ **80.**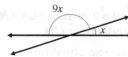

Find x for each pair of supplementary angles.

▲ **81.**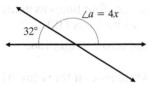

▲ **82.**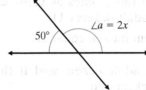

Cumulative Review

▲ **83.** **[1.2.5]** Find the perimeter of a rectangle with a length of 6 ft and a width of 4 ft.

▲ **84.** **[1.2.5]** Find the perimeter of a square with a side of 3 in.

85. **[1.7.2]** Evaluate. $2xy$ for $x = 7$ and $y = 9$

▲ **86.** **[1.7.2]** Evaluate. $L \cdot W \cdot H$ for $L = 2, W = 3,$ and $H = 5$

Quick Quiz 3.2

1. Solve each equation and check your solution.
   (a) $7x - 10x = 18 + 45$
   (b) $-8 + 20 = 3(2x)$

2. Translate this statement into an equation. Mindy (M) has five times as many quarters as Sara (S).

3. The number of blue marbles (B) is twice the number of red marbles (R).
   (a) Translate the statement into an equation.
   (b) Find the number of red marbles if there are 10 blue marbles.

4. **Concept Check** Explain in words the steps that are needed to solve $4x + 3(2x) = -20$.

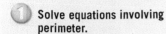
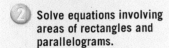

In this section we will work with the perimeter, area, and volume of various shapes. You will need to be familiar with the abbreviations used for units of measure in order to understand the material. For your review, Appendix B includes this information.

1 Solving Equations Involving Perimeter

Earlier we learned that to find the perimeter of a rectangle we find the sum of the lengths of all four sides: $P = L + L + W + W$. We can rewrite this formula as $P = 2L + 2W$. A square is the special case of a rectangle where all sides are equal. We find the perimeter using the formula $P = s + s + s + s$, or $P = 4s$.

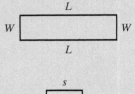

PERIMETER

The perimeter (P) of a rectangle is twice the length (L) plus twice the width (W).

$$P = 2L + 2W$$

The perimeter (P) of a square is four times the length of a side (s).

$$P = 4s$$

Recall that we use a four-step process to solve problems involving geometry.

1. Use the facts stated to *draw a picture*.
2. Write an *equation* or *formula*.
3. *Replace variables* with the appropriate known values.
4. *Solve* the equation and answer the question.

▲ **EXAMPLE 1** Find the perimeter of a rectangle with $L = 8$ feet and $W = 6$ feet.

Solution We use the four-step process.

$L = 8$ ft

$W = 6$ ft

Step 1: Draw a picture.

$P = 2L + 2W$ *Step 2:* Write the formula.

$= 2(8\text{ ft}) + 2(6\text{ ft})$ *Step 3:* Replace L with 8 ft and W with 6 ft.

$= 16\text{ ft} + 12\text{ ft}$ *Step 4:* Simplify.

$P = 28\text{ ft}$ The perimeter is 28 feet.

▲ **Practice Problem 1** Find the perimeter of a square with sides 11 yards in length.

It is important that you understand that formulas are the beginning equations we need in working these problems. Once we write the formula, we replace the variables with known values and solve.

Sometimes we must solve an equation to find the unknown side of a geometric shape.

▲ **EXAMPLE 2**   The length of a rectangle is three times the width. If the perimeter of the rectangle is 24 feet, find the width.

$L = 3W$

W

Solution   Since we are given the picture, we start with step 2 of the four-step process.

$P = 2L + 2W$	First, we write the formula for perimeter.
$24 = 2(3W) + 2W$	Next, we replace P with 24 and L with the given value $3W$.
$24 = 6W + 2W$	Then, we multiply: $2(3W) = 6W$.
$24 = 8W$	We combine like terms.
$\dfrac{24}{8} = \dfrac{8W}{8}$	Now we can divide each side by 8.
$3 = W$	The width of the rectangle is 3 feet.

▲ **Practice Problem 2**   The length of a rectangle is twice the width. If the perimeter of the rectangle is 30 feet, find the width.

$L = 2W$

W

Solving Equations Involving Areas of Rectangles and Parallelograms

Arrays can be used to illustrate the area of a rectangular region. In Chapter 1 we learned that to find the number of items in an array we multiply the number of rows times the number of columns. Thus, the number of items in a 3 by 5 array is 3×5, or 15.

5

3 ★ ★ ★ ★ ★ $3 \times 5 = 15$

If each object in a 3×5 array is a square with sides of length 1 foot, then the number of squares needed to fill the region is 3 times 5, or 15. Thus the **area** of the rectangular array is 15 square feet. We can check this by counting the number of squares in the array.

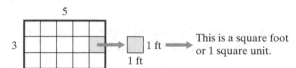

This is a square foot or 1 square unit.

There are 3×5 or 15 squares in the array.
Area = 15 square feet

▲ **EXAMPLE 3**   What is the area of the rug pictured in the margin?

Solution   Think of an array with 3 rows and 9 columns.

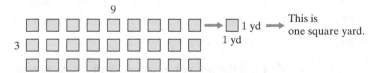

This is one square yard.

Just as we multiplied the number of rows times the number of columns to find the number of items in an array, we *multiply* the *length* times the *width* to find the area of the rug. The area is 3 yards × 9 yards = 27 square yards. Note, this means that there are 27 squares in the above illustration.

▲ **Practice Problem 3**   What is the area of the flower garden pictured in the margin?

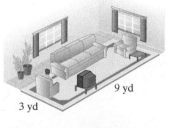

9 yd

3 yd

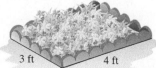

3 ft   4 ft

As we saw in Example 3, the area of a rectangle is the product of the length and the width, $A = L \cdot W$, where A represents the value of the area, L the value of the length, and W the value of the width.

Since the length and width of a square are equal, we can use the formula $A = s \cdot s$ or $A = s^2$ to find the area of a square.

$A = L \cdot W$ L $A = s^2$ s

W s

Parallelograms are figures that are related to rectangles. Actually, they are in the same "family," the **quadrilaterals** (four-sided figures).

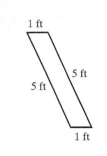

1 ft
5 ft
5 ft
1 ft

> A **parallelogram** is a four-sided figure in which both pairs of opposite sides are parallel.

Parallel lines are straight lines that are always the same distance apart. The opposite sides of a parallelogram are equal in length. The figures in the margin are parallelograms. Notice that adjoining sides need not be perpendicular.

To find the area of a parallelogram, we multiply the base times the height. Any side can be considered the base. The height is the length of a line segment perpendicular to the base. When we write the formula for area, we denote the length of the **base** as b and the **height** as h.

The formulas for area are summarized as follows.

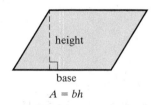

height

base
$A = bh$

> The area of a *rectangle* is the length times the width. $A = LW$
>
> The area of a *square* is the length of one side squared. $A = s^2$
>
> The area of a *parallelogram* is the base times the height. $A = bh$

How do we write the *units* when we multiply to find area? We perform calculations with units in the same way as with variables.

▲ **EXAMPLE 4**   Find the area of a rectangle with a length of 3 feet and a width of 2 feet.

Solution   Follow the four-step process. *Step 1:* Draw a picture (shown at right). Now we complete steps 2–4.

3 ft

2 ft

$A = L \cdot W$ *Step 2:* Write the formula.

$= 3 \text{ ft} \cdot 2 \text{ ft}$ *Step 3:* Replace L and W with the given values.

$= (3 \cdot 2)(\text{ft} \cdot \text{ft})$ *Step 4:* Simplify. Multiply the units: ft *times* ft $= \text{ft}^2$.

$= 6 \text{ ft}^2$ This is read "six square feet."

NOTE TO STUDENT: *Fully worked-out solutions to all of the Practice Problems can be found at the back of the text starting at page SP-1*

▲ **Practice Problem 4**   Find the area of a square with a side of 6 feet.

The units for area can be expressed two ways:

1. Using exponents: ft^2, yd^2, in.^2, and so on.
     ↓   ↓   ↓

2. Using abbreviations: sq ft,   sq yd,   sq in.
     (square feet)   (square yards)   (square inches)

▲ **EXAMPLE 5** Find the height of a parallelogram with base = 8 meters and area = 24 m².

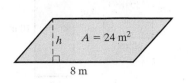

Solution First we draw a picture (see margin).

$A = bh$	Next, we write the formula.
$24 = 8h$	Then we replace A and b with the values given.
$\dfrac{24}{8} = \dfrac{8h}{8}$	Now, we solve the equation for h by dividing by 8 on both sides of the equation.
$3 = h$	The height is 3 meters.

▲ **Practice Problem 5** Find the base of a parallelogram with area = 117 ft² and height = 9 ft.

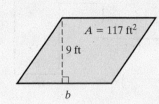

When we calculate area or perimeter or solve any problem that deals with geometric figures and formulas, it is important that we know the type of figure and the correct formula associated with the problem.

▲ **EXAMPLE 6** Find the area of the following shape made of rectangles.

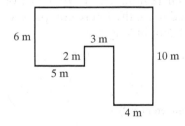

Solution Divide the figure into three rectangles and then find the area of each rectangle separately. Next, add these three areas together to find the area of the figure.

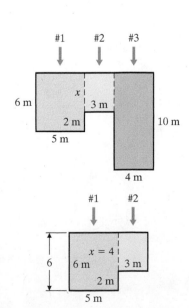

Area of rectangle #1:

$A = L \cdot W$

$\quad = 5 \text{ m} \cdot 6 \text{ m}$

$\quad = 30 \text{ m}^2$ The area of rectangle #1 is 30 m².

To find the area of rectangle #2 we must find the *width* of the rectangle. We indicate this width with the variable x in the figure in the margin. Since the width of rectangle #1 is 6 m, we know that $x + 2 = 6$. Solving this equation we have $x = 4$, and thus the width of rectangle #2 equals 4*m*.

Area of rectangle #2:

$A = L \cdot W$

$\quad = 3 \text{ m} \cdot 4 \text{ m}$

$\quad = 12 \text{ m}^2$ The area of rectangle #2 is 12 m².

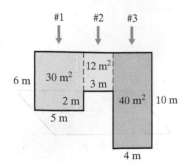

Next we find the area of rectangle #3.

Area of rectangle #3:

$A = L \cdot W$

$= 4 \text{ m} \cdot 10 \text{ m}$

$= 40 \text{ m}^2$ The area of rectangle #3 is 40 m².

We add the three areas to find the area of the figure.

$30 \text{ m}^2 + 12 \text{ m}^2 + 40 \text{ m}^2 = 82 \text{ m}^2$ The area of the shape is 82 m².

▲ **Practice Problem 6**   Find the area of the following shape made of rectangles and squares.

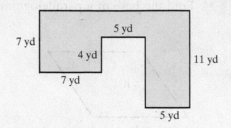

③ Solving Equations Involving Volume

How much water can a pool hold? How much air is inside a box? These are questions of *volume*. We use volume to measure the space enclosed by a geometric figure that has three dimensions. We call the three dimensions length (L), width (W), and height (H).

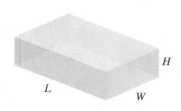

Recall that the area of a rectangular region is the number of unit squares needed to fill the rectangular region. The **volume** (V) of a rectangular solid is the number of unit cubes needed to fill the figure completely. A unit cube is a rectangular solid with all the edges 1 unit in length.

Unit cube

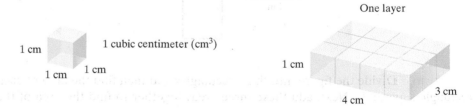

Unit cubes in a rectangular solid with two layers

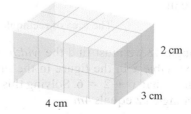

The one-layer rectangular solid can be viewed as a 3 by 4 array (3 rows of cubes with 4 cubes in each row). There are 3(4) or 12 cubes in the layer. In the two-layer solid, there are 3(4)(2) cubes or 24 cubes. Therefore, the volume of the third figure is 3 cm · 4 cm · 2 cm or 24 cubic centimeters (cm³).

As you can see, to find the number of cubes in the solid figure, we can either count the cubes needed to fill the figure or multiply the length times the width times the height.

$V = LWH$

VOLUME

The volume of a rectangular solid is the product of the length times the width times the height.

$$V = LWH$$

▲ **EXAMPLE 7**   Find the unknown side of the rectangular solid.

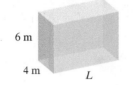

6 m

4 m

L

$V = 216 \text{ m}^3$

Solution   We complete the four-step process. The picture is drawn for us, so we first write the formula. Then we replace the appropriate variables with the values given. Finally, we solve the equation to find the unknown.

$V = L \cdot W \cdot H$ Write the formula.

$216 = L \cdot 4 \cdot 6$ Replace the variables with the values given.

$216 = 24L$ Simplify.

$\dfrac{216}{24} = \dfrac{24L}{24}$ Solve for L.

$9 = L$ The length of the box is 9 m.

▲ **Practice Problem 7**   Find the unknown side of the rectangular solid.

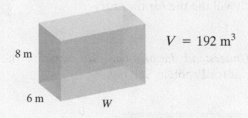

8 m

6 m W

$V = 192 \text{ m}^3$

We summarize all the formulas in this section for your reference.

TABLE OF FORMULAS

Perimeter

The perimeter of a rectangle is twice the length plus twice the width.

$P = 2L + 2W$

L

W

The perimeter of a square is four times the length of a side.

$P = 4s$

s

s s

s

Area

The area of a rectangle is the length times the width.	$A = LW$	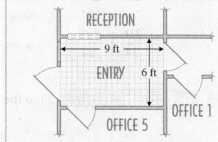
The area of a square is the length of one side squared.	$A = s^2$	
The area of a parallelogram is the base times the height.	$A = bh$	

Volume

The volume of a rectangular solid is the length times the width times the height.	$V = LWH$

④ Solving Applied Geometry Problems

 EXAMPLE 8 The blueprints for an office building show that the length of the entryway is 9 feet and the width is 6 feet. The tile for the entryway costs $16 per square yard.

(a) How many square yards of tile must be purchased for the entryway?

(b) How much will the tile for the entryway cost?

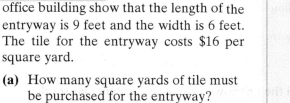

Solution *Understand the problem.* We organize the information in a Mathematics Blueprint for Problem Solving.

Mathematics Blueprint for Problem Solving

Gather the Facts	What Am I Asked to Do?	How Do I Proceed?	Key Points to Remember
The dimensions of the entryway are: $L = 9$ ft $W = 6$ ft The tile costs $16 per square yard.	(a) Find the area to determine the number of square yards of tile that must be purchased. (b) Find the cost of the tile for the entryway.	1. Draw a 6-foot by 9-foot rectangle. 2. Convert feet to yards. 3. Find the area of the entryway. 4. Multiply the area times $16 to find the cost of the tile.	Change feet to yards since we are asked to find square yards. There are 3 feet in 1 yard. Area = Length × Width

Solve and state the answer.

(a) To find the number of square yards of tile needed, we proceed as follows.

1. We draw a rectangle and label the sides.
2. We convert feet to yards, since the tile is sold in square yards.

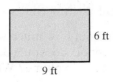

$$9 \text{ ft} = 3 \text{ ft} + 3 \text{ ft} + 3 \text{ ft} \qquad\qquad 6 \text{ ft} = 3 \text{ ft} + 3 \text{ ft}$$
$$= 3 \times 3 \text{ ft} \qquad\qquad\qquad\quad = 2 \times 3 \text{ ft}$$
$$= 3 \times 1 \text{ yd} \qquad\qquad\qquad = 2 \times 1 \text{ yd}$$
$$= 3 \text{ yd} \qquad\qquad\qquad\quad = 2 \text{ yd}$$

3. We relabel the figure and find the area in square yards.

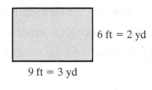

$$A = L \times W$$
$$= 3 \text{ yd} \times 2 \text{ yd}$$
$$= 3 \times 2 \times \text{yd} \times \text{yd}$$
$$= 6 \text{ yd}^2$$

    6 yd^2 of tile must be purchased.

(b) The tile sells for $16 per square yard and 6 square yards must be purchased: $16 \times 6 = \$96$. The tile will cost $96.

Check: Use your calculator to verify that these calculations are correct.

▲ **Practice Problem 8**   Jesse is purchasing carpet for his living room. The room is 12 feet long and 15 feet wide and the carpet costs $11 per square yard.

(a) How many square yards of carpet must be purchased for the living room?

(b) How much will the carpet cost for the living room?

Developing Your Study Skills

Reading the Text

Homework time each day should begin with a careful reading of the assigned section(s) in your textbook. Your instructor has spent much time and effort selecting a text that will help you become successful in this mathematics class. You should take advantage of this important resource.

    Reading a mathematics textbook is unlike reading the books you use in literature and history. Mathematics texts are technical books that provide you with exercises to practice on. Using a mathematics text successfully requires that you read each word slowly and carefully. The following tips will help you use a mathematics text more effectively.

- Read your textbook with paper and a pencil in hand.

- Underline new definitions or concepts and write them in your notebook on a separate sheet labeled "Important Facts."

- Whenever you encounter unfamiliar terms, look them up and note their definitions on your "Important Facts" notebook pages.

- When you come to an example, work through it step by step. Be sure to read each word and to follow directions carefully.

- Be sure that you understand what you are reading. Make a note of any things that you do not understand and ask your instructor about them.

- Do not hurry through the material. Learning mathematics takes time.

Verbal and Writing Skills

1. To find out how much water is needed to fill a rectangular pool, do you need to find the perimeter, the area, or the volume? Why?

2. To determine how much brick you need to trim the edge of the pool, do you need to find the perimeter, the area, or the volume? Why?

3. Fill in each blank with the correct formula.

   (a) Perimeter of a rectangle: _____.

   (b) Perimeter of a square: _____.

   (c) Volume of a rectangular solid: _____.

   (d) Area of a rectangle: _____.

   (e) Area of a square: _____.

   (f) Area of a parallelogram: _____.

4. Write the four-step process for solving problems involving geometry.

   Step 1. _____.

   Step 2. _____.

   Step 3. _____.

   Step 4. _____.

▲ *For each of the following:* **(a)** *State the appropriate formula for perimeter.* **(b)** *Find the perimeter.*

5. A rectangle with $L = 2$ feet and $W = 7$ feet

   (a) _____   (b) _____

6. A rectangle with $L = 18$ feet and $W = 25$ feet

   (a) _____   (b) _____

7. A square with sides of length 11 feet

   (a) _____   (b) _____

8. A square with sides of length 38 inches

   (a) _____   (b) _____

9. A square with sides of length 54 yards

   (a) _____   (b) _____

10. A square with sides of length 28 centimeters

    (a) _____   (b) _____

▲ *For each of the following:* **(a)** *State the appropriate formula for perimeter.* **(b)** *Find the unknown side.*

11. A square has a perimeter of 40 feet. Find the length of each side of the square.

    (a) _____   (b) _____

12. A square has a perimeter of 84 inches. Find the length of each side of the square.

    (a) _____   (b) _____

13. The length of a rectangle is four times the width. If the perimeter of the rectangle is 30 feet, find the width.

    (a) _____   (b) _____

$L = 4W$

W $P = 30$ ft

14. The length of a rectangle is twice the width. If the perimeter of the rectangle is 48 yards, find the width.

    (a) _____   (b) _____

$L = 2W$

W $P = 48$ yd

▲ *Find the length and width of each rectangle.*

15. Perimeter = 66 ft. The length is ten times the width.

W

$L = 10W$

16. Perimeter = 36 in. The length is eight times the width.

W

$L = 8W$

17. **(a)** How many squares with 1-inch sides can be placed in a space that is 50 square inches?
(b) What is the area of the rectangle?

18. **(a)** How many squares with 1-foot sides can be placed in a space that is 22 square feet?
(b) What is the area of the rectangle?

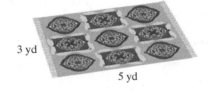

19. *Floor Tiles* Squares tiles with sides 1 foot in length are placed in a space that has an area of 50 square feet. How many of the 1-foot squares are needed to fill the space?

20. *Linoleum Floor Tiles* How many squares of linoleum floor tiles with sides 1 foot in length would be needed to cover a floor space that has an area of 60 square feet?

▲ *For each of the following:* **(a)** *State the appropriate formula for area.* **(b)** *Find the area.*

21. A driveway

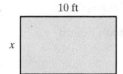

18 ft   22 ft

(a) _____   **(b)** _____

22. An Oriental rug

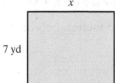

3 yd

5 yd

(a) _____   **(b)** _____

23. A square with sides of 10 inches
(a) _____   **(b)** _____

24. A square with sides of 10 meters
(a) _____   **(b)** _____

25. A parallelogram with a base of 12 feet and a height of 9 feet
(a) _____   **(b)** _____

26. A parallelogram with a base of 92 inches and a height of 74 inches
(a) _____   **(b)** _____

▲ *Find the unknown side of each rectangle*

27.

10 ft

x $A = 60 \text{ ft}^2$

28.

x

7 yd $A = 56 \text{ yd}^2$

▲ *Find the unknown measure for each parallelogram.*

29.

8 m

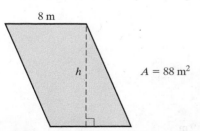

h $A = 88 \text{ m}^2$

30.

b

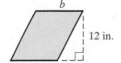

12 in. $A = 132 \text{ in.}^2$

▲ *Find the area of each shape made of rectangles.*

31.

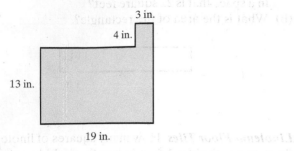

32.

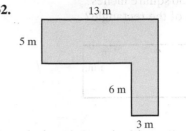

33.

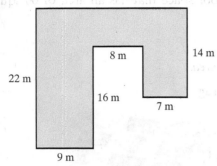

34.

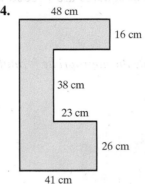

▲ *Solve each applied problem.*

35. (a) How many cubes with 1-inch sides can be placed in a rectangular solid of length = 4 inches, width = 5 inches, and height = 2 inches?
(b) What is the volume of the rectangular solid?

36. (a) How many cubes with 1-centimeter sides can be placed in a rectangular solid of length = 5 centimeters, width = 2 centimeters, and height = 3 centimeters?
(b) What is the volume of the rectangular solid?

37. *Water in a Fish Tank* A fish tank is 3 feet wide, 4 feet long, and 3 feet high. How much water can be placed in the tank?

38. *Airspace in a Room* The ceiling height of a room is 8 feet. The width of the floor is 10 feet, and the length is 15 feet. How much airspace is in the room?

▲ *For each of the following rectangular solids: (a) State the appropriate formula for volume. (b) Find the volume.*

39. Length = 11 inches, width = 5 inches, height = 15 inches

(a) _____   **(b)** _____

40. Length = 13 feet, width = 7 feet, height = 10 feet

(a) _____   **(b)** _____

41. Length = 27 yards, width = 10 yards, height = 16 yards

(a) _____   **(b)** _____

42. Length = 120 meters, width = 32 meters, height = 37 meters

(a) _____   **(b)** _____

▲ *Find the unknown side of each rectangular solid.*

43. $V = 300 \text{ cm}^3$

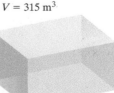

44. $V = 315 \text{ m}^3$

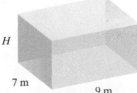

▲ **Mixed Practice** *Find the perimeter of each shape.*

45. A square with sides of length 7 inches

46. A rectangle with $L = 12$ feet and $W = 7$ feet

▲ *Find the area of each shape.*

47. A parallelogram with a base of 17 meters and a height of 8 meters

48. A square with sides of 9 inches

▲ *Find the volume of each solid.*

49. A rectangular solid with $L = 15$ yards, $W = 7$ yards, and $H = 2$ yards

50. A rectangular solid with $L = 8$ feet, $W = 5$ feet, and $H = 6$ feet

▲ *Find the unknown side of each shape.*

51.

6 ft

x ▢ $A = 30$ ft^2

52.

x

5 in. ▢ $A = 40$ in.^{2}

53. $V = 200$ m^3

8 m

5 m

L

54. $V = 64$ ft^3

4 ft

4 ft L

▲ **Applications**

55. *A Piece of Marble* Damien has a 2-foot-square piece of marble.

   (a) State the dimensions of the marble on the figure below in inches (1 ft = 12 in.).

2 ft = _____

▢ 2 ft = _____

   (b) State the area of the marble in square inches.

56. *A Card Table* Marcy has a 3-foot-square card table.

   (a) State the dimensions of the table on the figure below in inches (1 ft = 12 in.).

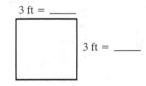

3 ft = _____

3 ft = _____

   (b) State the area of the table in square inches.

57. *A Vegetable Garden* A rectangular vegetable garden has a length of 12 feet and a width of 9 feet.

   (a) State the dimensions of the garden in yards (3 feet = 1 yard).

   (b) State the area of the garden in square yards.

58. *An Entryway* A rectangular entryway has a length of 12 feet and a width of 6 feet.

   (a) State the dimensions of the entryway in yards (3 feet = 1 yard).

   (b) State the area of the entryway in square yards.

59. *Carpeting a Patio* Carmen is purchasing outdoor carpet for her patio enclosure, which is 12 *feet* long and 9 *feet* wide. The carpet she plans to purchase is priced at $8 per *square yard*.

   (a) How many *square yards* of carpet must she purchase?

   (b) How much will the outdoor carpet for Carmen's patio cost?

60. *Carpeting an Office* The blueprints for a warehouse show that the length of the main office is 15 *feet* and the width is 12 *feet*. The carpet for the office costs $11 per *square yard*.

   (a) How many *square yards* of carpet must be purchased for the office?

   (b) How much will the office carpet cost?

61. *Linoleum Flooring* Shannon has a one-story house with a family room that has a length of 21 *feet* and width of 15 *feet*. The linoleum floor she will purchase for the family room costs $16 per *square yard*.

    (a) How many *square yards* of linoleum must Shannon purchase for her family room?

    (b) How much will the family room linoleum cost?

62. *Ceramic Tile Picture* Jamel is making a picture out of ceramic tile for a wall in the Teen Center. The Teen Center wants the picture to fit exactly in a space with $L = 24$ *inches* and $W = 36$ *inches*. Jamel charges $30 per *square foot* to make ceramic designs.

    (a) How many *square feet* will the picture be? (12 in. = 1 ft)

    (b) How much will it cost the Teen Center to have Jamel make the picture?

One Step Further

▲ **63. *Fertilizer Cost*** A 1-pound container of rose fertilizer sells for $3. Each 1-pound container will fertilize 100 *square feet*. If the length of the rose garden is 5 *yards* and the width is 4 *yards*, how much will it cost to fertilize the entire rose garden?

▲ **64. *Chest Lining*** One roll of felt material at the fabric store sells for $12 and can cover 10 *square feet* of area. Daisy wishes to place felt on the base of the interior of a large wooden chest. The base measures 2 *yards* by 1 *yard*. How much will it cost Daisy to purchase the felt for the chest?

To Think About

Painting a Room *The walls of Anita's family room are illustrated below. All of the walls are 8 feet high, and the rear and front walls are each 22 feet long. Each of the side walls is 16 feet long. The French door is 3 feet wide and 7 feet high, while the sliding door is 6 feet wide and 7 feet high. The window on the first side wall is 4 feet by 3 feet; the window on the second side wall is 2 feet by 4 feet.*

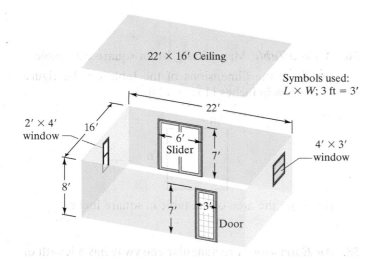

Paint Store Price List

Type	Price	Coverage
One-coat	$18 per gal $5 per qt	1 gal per 400 ft^2 1 qt per 100 ft^2
Primer	$12 per gal $3 per qt	1 gal per 300 ft^2 1 qt per 75 ft^2

▲ *Use the figure and table to answer exercises 65 and 66.*

65. Anita's landlord will paint her family room. He has agreed to let Anita purchase the paint so that she can choose the brand and color she wants. The landlord will reimburse Anita only for the cost of the paint used. Anita must buy only as much paint as she needs since the extra paint cannot be returned. Describe the quantity of paint that Anita should purchase if the landlord will put 1 coat of paint on all of the walls and the ceiling of the family room.

66. Refer to exercise 65. If the landlord will put 1 coat of primer on the walls and ceiling of the family room, describe the quantity of primer that Anita must purchase.

▲ *Find the area of the shaded region.*

67.

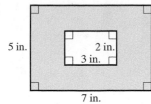

68. Find the area of the region that is *not* shaded.

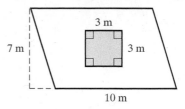

69. Find the next figure that would appear in the sequence.

70. Find the next two figures that would appear in the sequence.

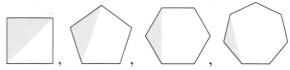

Cumulative Review

71. **[2.6.3]** Simplify. $-7(x - 2)$

72. **[2.6.1]** Combine like terms. $-7x + 3x - 2y$

73. **[1.4.3]** Simplify. $(2)(3x)(5)$

74. **[1.6.1]** Write in exponent form. $3 \cdot 3 \cdot 3 \cdot 3$

Quick Quiz 3.3

1. The width of a rectangle is double the length. If the perimeter of the rectangle is 72 feet, find the length.

2. Find the area of the following shape made of rectangles.

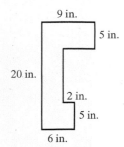

3. A storage facility claims the volume of its smallest rental unit is 200 cubic feet. If its length and width both measure 5 feet, what is the height of the unit?

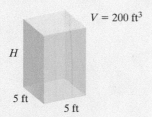

4. **Concept Check** Hanna purchased a redwood box at the garden store and filled it with sand.

(a) To determine how much sand is needed to fill the box, do you find the area, perimeter, or volume?

(b) State the formula you must use.

(c) The volume of the box is 200 ft^3, the height is 5 in., and length of the box is double the height. Explain in words how you would find the width of the box.

67. Find the area of the shaded region.

68. Find the area of the region that is not shaded.

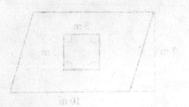

69. Find the next figure that would appear in the sequence.

70. Find the next two figures that would appear in the sequence.

Cumulative Review

71. [2.6.3] Simplify $9(2x - 2)$

72. [2.6.1] Combine like terms. $-2x + 3x + 2y$

73. [1.4.3] Simplify $(2)(2y)(5)$

74. [1.6.1] Write in exponent form. $5 \cdot 2 \cdot 5 \cdot 5$

Chapter 3.5

1. The width of a rectangle is double the length. If the perimeter of the rectangle is 72 ft, find the length.

2. Find the area of the following shape made of two triangles.

3. A store rents a facility, defines the volume of its warehouse rental unit as 18,000 cubic feet. If its length and width both measure 3 feet, what is the height of the unit?

4. Concept Check: Maria purchased a redwood box at a hardware store and filled it with sand.

(a) To determine how much sand is needed to fill the box, do you find the area, perimeter, or volume?

(b) What are the units she must use.

(c) The volume of the box is 200 ft^3, the height is 5 ft, and length of the box is double the height. Explain in words how you would find the width of the box.

Roxanne and Jason are planning to enclose a small area of their backyard with a fence for their new puppy. Will the measure they choose for the length and width of the space affect the size of the area enclosed? Is there a relationship between the length, width, and area of an enclosed space?

Fractions, Ratio, and Proportion

4.1 FACTORING WHOLE NUMBERS

Student Learning Objectives

After studying this section, you will be able to:

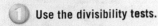 Use the divisibility tests.

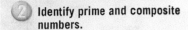 Identify prime and composite numbers.

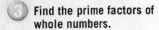 Find the prime factors of whole numbers.

The set of whole numbers includes many special types of numbers, such as *prime numbers* and *composite numbers*. In this section you will learn the difference between prime and composite numbers and see how to write a whole number as a product of prime factors.

Using the Divisibility Tests

A number x is said to be **divisible** by a number y if y divides x exactly, without a remainder (a remainder equal to 0). We say "25 is divisible by 5" because there is *no remainder* when we divide 25 by 5 ($25 \div 5 = 5$). We say that "26 is *not* divisible by 5" because there is a *remainder* when we divide 26 by 5: $26 \div 5 = 5$ R1.

Some students find the following rules helpful when deciding if a number is divisible by 2, 3, and/or 5.

DIVISIBILITY TESTS

1. A number is divisible by 2 if it is even. This means that the last digit is 0, 2, 4, 6, or 8.

2. A number is divisible by 3 if the sum of its digits is divisible by 3.

3. A number is divisible by 5 if its last digit is 0 or 5.

EXAMPLE 1 Determine if the number is divisible by 2, 3, and/or 5.

(a) 234   (b) 910   (c) 711   (d) 38,910

Solution

(a) 234	2 and 3	Divisible by 2 because 234 is even and by 3 since $2 + 3 + 4 = 9$ and 9 is divisible by 3.
(b) 910	5 and 2	Divisible by 5 because the last digit is 0 and by 2 since 910 is even.
(c) 711	3	Divisible by 3 because the sum of the digits is divisible by 3.
(d) 38,910	2, 3, 5	Divisible by 2 because 38,910 is even, by 3 since the sum of the digits is divisible by 3, and by 5 since the last digit is 0.

NOTE TO STUDENT: *Fully worked-out solutions to all of the Practice Problems can be found at the back of the text starting at page SP-1*

Practice Problem 1 Determine if the number is divisible by 2, 3, and/or 5.

(a) 975   (b) 122   (c) 420   (d) 11,121

Identifying Prime and Composite Numbers

A **prime number** is a whole number greater than 1 that is divisible only by itself and 1.

The number 5 is *prime* since it is divisible only by the numbers 5 and 1. The number 6 is *not prime* since it is divisible by 2 and 3, in addition to 6 and 1.

A **composite number** is a whole number greater than 1 that can be divided by whole numbers other than itself and 1.

Any whole number (except 0 and 1) that is not prime is composite. The numbers 0 and 1 are neither prime nor composite numbers.

The number 10 is *composite* since it is divisible by 2 and 5 as well as by 10 and 1.

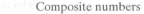

Composite numbers

0, 1   2,   3   4   5   6

Neither   Prime numbers
prime nor composite

EXAMPLE 2 State whether each number is prime, composite, or neither.

1, 4, 7, 11, 14, 15, 17, 22, 27, 31, 120

Solution   1 is neither prime nor composite.
4, 14, 15, 22, 27, and 120 are composite.
7, 11, 17, and 31 are prime.

Practice Problem 2 State whether each number is prime, composite, or neither.   0, 3, 9, 13, 16, 19, 23, 32, 37, 41, 50

The first few prime numbers are 2, 3, 5, 7, 11, 13, 17, 19, 23, 29, ...

3 Finding the Prime Factors of Whole Numbers

Factors are numbers that are multiplied together. In the product $4 \cdot 6 = 24$, 4 and 6 are called factors of 24.

$24 = 4 \cdot 6$ These factors are *not* prime numbers.

factor factor

Prime factors are factors that are prime. To write a number as a product of prime factors, we must break the multiplication down until each factor is prime. Thus, 24 written as a product of prime factors is

$24 = 4 \cdot 6$

$24 = 2 \cdot 2 \cdot 2 \cdot 3$ These factors are prime numbers.

EXAMPLE 3 Express as a product of prime factors.

(a) 9   **(b)** 20

Solution

(a) $9 = 3 \cdot 3$ or 3^2

(b) $20 = 2 \cdot 2 \cdot 5$ or $2^2 \cdot 5$ $20 = 4 \cdot 5$ is *not correct* because 4 is not a prime number.

Note that when a number has duplicate factors such as $20 = 2 \cdot 2 \cdot 5$, we often express the factors in terms of *powers of prime factors:* $2^2 \cdot 5$.

Practice Problem 3 Express as a product of prime factors.

(a) 14   **(b)** 27

When you divide two whole numbers and get a remainder of 0, both the divisor and the quotient are factors. Thus *we can divide to find prime factors*. We use the division $15 \div 3 = 5$ to find the prime factors of 15.

Division Problem	Related Multiplication
$\begin{array}{r} 5 \rightarrow \text{quotient} \\ 3\overline{)15} \\ \uparrow \\ \text{divisor} \end{array}$	$\begin{array}{c} 3 \cdot 5 = 15 \\ \uparrow \uparrow \\ \text{Divisor and quotient are factors.} \end{array}$

The following process uses repeated division to find prime factors. We often refer to this method as using a **division ladder** to find prime factors.

PROCEDURE TO FIND PRIME FACTORS USING A DIVISION LADDER

1. Determine if the original number is divisible by a *prime number*. If so, divide and find the quotient.

2. Divide the quotient by *prime numbers* until the final quotient is a prime number.

3. Write the divisors and the *final quotient* as a product of prime factors.

EXAMPLE 4   Express 28 as a product of prime factors.

Solution   Since 28 is even, it is divisible by the prime number 2. We start the division ladder by dividing 28 by 2.

Step 1 $\begin{array}{r} 14 \\ 2\overline{)28} \end{array}$ The quotient 14 is *not* a prime number.

We must continue to divide until the quotient is a prime number.

Step 2 $\begin{array}{r} 7 \\ 2\overline{)14} \end{array}$ The quotient 7 is a prime number.

This quotient is a prime number. Thus all the factors are prime. We are finished dividing. This process is simplified if we write the divisions as follows, placing step 1 on the bottom and moving up the ladder as we divide.

$$\begin{array}{r} 7 \\ \textbf{Step 2}\ 2\overline{)14} \\ \uparrow \textbf{Step 1}\ 2\overline{)28} \end{array}$$

Now we write all the divisors and the quotient as a product of prime factors.

$$28 = 2 \cdot 2 \cdot 7 \quad \text{or} \quad 2^2 \cdot 7$$

Practice Problem 4   Express 50 as a product of prime factors.

NOTE TO STUDENT: Fully worked-out solutions to all of the Practice Problems can be found at the back of the text starting at page SP-1

CAUTION: It is important to note that all the divisors and the final quotient must be prime numbers to ensure that all factors are prime.

EXAMPLE 5   Express 60 as a product of prime factors and check your answer.

Solution   We must divide by prime numbers to ensure that all factors are prime. Since 60 is even, we know that we can divide 60 by 2. (*Note:* 0 is an even number.)

$$
\begin{array}{ll}
& \underline{5} \quad \text{5 is prime, so we are finished dividing.} \\
\textbf{Step 3} & 3\overline{)15} \\
\textbf{Step 2} & 2\overline{)30} \\
\textbf{Step 1} & 2\overline{)60} \quad \text{We start by dividing by 2.}
\end{array}
$$

$60 = 2 \cdot 2 \cdot 3 \cdot 5$ or $2^2 \cdot 3 \cdot 5$

We can check our answer by multiplying the prime factors.

Check: $60 \stackrel{?}{=} 2^2 \cdot 3 \cdot 5$

                 $60 \stackrel{?}{=} 4 \cdot 15$

                 $60 = 60$ ✓   The answer checks.

Practice Problem 5   Express 96 as a product of prime factors and check your answer.

Understanding the Concept

The Various Division Ladders

In Example 5, if we had started the division process with either 3 or 5 instead of 2, the result would have been the same. In fact, it does not matter what prime number is used to start the division—the results will be equivalent. Why? To illustrate, let's compare the following results.

$$
\begin{array}{lll}
& \underline{5} & \underline{2} & \underline{2} \\
\textbf{Step 3} \quad 3\overline{)15} & \quad 5\overline{)10} & \quad 2\overline{)4} \\
\textbf{Step 2} \quad 2\overline{)30} & \quad 2\overline{)20} & \quad 3\overline{)12} \\
\textbf{Step 1} \quad 2\overline{)60} & \quad 3\overline{)60} & \quad 5\overline{)60} \\
\end{array}
$$

$$
\begin{array}{lll}
60 = 2 \cdot 2 \cdot 3 \cdot 5 & \quad 60 = 3 \cdot 2 \cdot 5 \cdot 2 & \quad 60 = 5 \cdot 3 \cdot 2 \cdot 2 \\
& \quad 60 = 2^2 \cdot 3 \cdot 5 &
\end{array}
$$

EXAMPLE 6   Express 210 as a product of prime factors.

Solution   From the divisibility rules we know that 210 is divisible by 2, 3, and 5. We can start with 5.

$$
\begin{array}{ll}
& \underline{7} \quad \text{7 is prime, so we are finished dividing.} \\
\textbf{Step 3} & 2\overline{)14} \\
\textbf{Step 2} & 3\overline{)42} \\
\textbf{Step 1} & 5\overline{)210} \\
& 210 = 5 \cdot 3 \cdot 2 \cdot 7 = 2 \cdot 3 \cdot 5 \cdot 7
\end{array}
$$

Note that we wrote all factors in ascending order since this is standard notation.

Practice Problem 6   Express 315 as a product of prime factors.

We can also use a **factor tree** to find prime factors. This method uses the related multiplication instead of division to find the factors. Let's see how we would have factored the number 210 from Example 6 using a factor tree.

Division → Related Multiplication   **Factor Tree**

$$\frac{42}{5)210} \quad \rightarrow \quad 210 = 5 \cdot 42$$

$$\frac{14}{3)42} \quad \rightarrow \quad 42 = 3 \cdot 14$$

$$\frac{7}{2)14} \quad \rightarrow \quad 14 = 2 \cdot 7$$

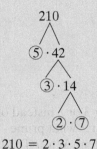

We write 210 as a product of circled numbers: $210 = 2 \cdot 3 \cdot 5 \cdot 7$

PROCEDURE TO BUILD A FACTOR TREE TO FIND PRIME FACTORS

$$210$$
$$\overset{\frown}{5} \cdot 42$$
$$\overset{\frown}{3} \cdot 14$$
$$\overset{\frown}{2} \cdot 7$$
$$210 = 2 \cdot 3 \cdot 5 \cdot 7$$

1. Write the number to be factored as a product of any two numbers other than 1 and itself.
2. In this product, circle any prime factor(s).
3. Write all factors that are *not prime* as products.
4. *Circle* any prime factor(s).
5. Repeat steps 3 and 4 until *all factors* are prime.
6. Write the numbers that are circled as a product of prime numbers.

Note that when we use the factor tree we can break the number into a product of any two numbers. These numbers do not need to be prime. However, we must continue to factor each number in the tree until we get all prime numbers.

EXAMPLE 7 Use a factor tree to express 48 as a product of prime factors.

Solution

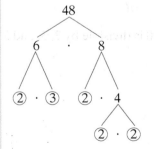

$$48 = 2 \cdot 3 \cdot 2 \cdot 2 \cdot 2 \text{ or } 2^4 \cdot 3$$

1. Write 48 as the product of any two factors other than 1 and itself.
2. We *do not* circle 6 or 8 since neither is prime. We must write both 6 and 8 as products: $6 = 2 \cdot 3$ and $8 = 2 \cdot 4$.
3. *Circle* the prime numbers 2 and 3. Since 4 is *not prime* we must write it as a product: $4 = 2 \cdot 2$.
4. *Circle* both factors of 4 since they are both prime.
5. Write 48 as a product of the prime factors, i.e., the numbers that are circled: $48 = 2 \cdot 3 \cdot 2 \cdot 2 \cdot 2$.

Practice Problem 7 Use a factor tree to express 36 as a product of prime factors.

NOTE TO STUDENT: *Fully worked-out solutions to all of the Practice Problems can be found at the back of the text starting at page SP-1*

Verbal and Writing Skills *Fill in the blanks.*

1. A number is divisible by _____ if it is even.

2. A number is divisible by _____ if the sum of the digits is divisible by 3.

3. A number is divisible by 5 if the last digit is _____ or _____.

4. A number is divisible by 10 if the last digit is _____.

5. Explain why you must divide by prime numbers when you use a division ladder to find prime factors.

6. Write in words the difference between a composite number and a prime number.

7. Is 165 divisible by 2? Why or why not?

8. Is 175 divisible by 2? Why or why not?

9. Is 232 divisible by 3? Why or why not?

10. Is 156 divisible by 3? Why or why not?

Determine if each number is divisible by 2, 3, and/or 5.

11. 102

12. 732

13. 705

14. 955

15. 330

16. 540

17. 22,971

18. 700,550

State whether each number is prime, composite, or neither.

19. 0, 9, 1, 17, 40, 8, 15, 22

20. 1, 32, 7, 12, 50, 6, 13, 41

21. Write 8 as a product of the following.
  (a) Any two factors
  (b) Prime factors

22. Write 20 as a product of the following.
  (a) Any two factors
  (b) Prime factors

Fill in the missing factors so that the number is expressed as a product of prime factors.

23. $28 = 2 \cdot \square \cdot 7 = 2^{\square} \cdot 7$

24. $27 = 3 \cdot 3 \cdot \square = 3^{\square}$

25. $75 = 3 \cdot \square \cdot 5 = 3 \cdot 5^{\square}$

26. $45 = 3 \cdot \square \cdot 5 = 3^{\square} \cdot 5$

For each of the following: **(a)** *Fill in the division ladder to complete each problem.* **(b)** *State the prime factors.*

27. (a)   **(b)** _____

28. (a)   **(b)** _____

$$3\overline{)15}$$
$$\square\overline{)30}$$
$$3\overline{)90}$$

For each of the following: **(a)** *Fill in the factor tree to complete each problem.* **(b)** *Express the original number as a product of the prime factors.*

29. (a)   **(b)** _____

30. (a) 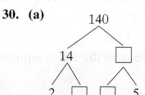   **(b)** _____

Use a factor tree or division ladder to express each number as a product of prime factors.

31. 15   **32.** 4   **33.** 20

34. 18   **35.** 24   **36.** 32

37. 70   **38.** 42   **39.** 64

40. 56   **41.** 80   **42.** 36

43. 75   **44.** 81   **45.** 45

46. 55   **47.** 99   **48.** 63

49. 300   **50.** 200   **51.** 110

52. 155   **53.** 136   **54.** 126

55. 90   **56.** 175   **57.** 225

One Step Further   *The calculator can be a useful tool for finding prime factors when 2, 3, and/or 5 are not factors. You can quickly check for factors by dividing by the prime numbers 7, 11, 13, 17, 19 or higher if needed. Use your calculator to help you express each number as a product of prime factors.*

 58. 91   **59.** 1309   **60.** 561   **61.** 2737

62. We can also use a calculator to check that the prime factors in an answer are correct. Use your calculator to multiply the prime factors in exercises 58–61, and verify that your answers are correct.

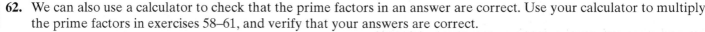

To Think About

63. Write a five-digit number that is divisible by the number 3 and the number 5.

64. Write a six-digit number that is divisible by the number 2 and the number 3.

When we square a whole number or fraction, the number we obtain is called a **perfect square.** *For example, 9 is a perfect square since when we square the number 3 we obtain 9. In exercises 65–74 we will look at a relationship that exists between the sequence of perfect squares and the sequence of positive odd numbers. This relationship was investigated in the thirteenth century by an Italian mathematician named Leonardo of Pisa, also known as Fibonacci.*

65. List the first 6 odd numbers.

66. Complete the green table as follows. In the third row, write the first 3 odd numbers, in the fourth row, write the first 4 odd numbers, and so on.

67. In the blue boxes, write the sum of the odd numbers.

68. In the orange boxes, write each sum in exponent form.

69. Describe the pattern observed with the set of numbers in the blue boxes.

70. Describe the pattern observed with the set of numbers in the orange boxes.

						Write the sum	Write in exponent form
1						1	1^2
1	3					4	2^2

71. Based on the observations made in exercises 69 and 70, fill in the last four black boxes.

72. Write each of the following sums in exponent form.

The sum of the first 2 positive odd numbers equals: $\boxed{}^2$

The sum of the first 3 positive odd numbers equals: $\boxed{}^2$

The sum of the first 4 positive odd numbers equals: $\boxed{}^2$

The sum of the first 5 positive odd numbers equals: $\boxed{}^2$

The sum of the first 6 positive odd numbers equals: $\boxed{}^2$

73. Observe the pattern above and complete the following.

The sum of the first 12 positive odd numbers equals: $\boxed{}^2$

The sum of the first 20 positive odd numbers equals: $\boxed{}^2$

74. Without actually adding the first 30 positive odd numbers, describe how you could find the sum.

Cumulative Review *Simplify.*

75. [3.4.2] $(2x^2)(5x^3y)$

76. [3.4.3] $7y^2 + 2y^2$

77. [2.6.1] $5x + 3x + 2$

78. [3.4.2] $(5x)(3x)(2)$

▲ *Find the measure of the unknown angle in each pair of supplementary angles.*

79. [3.1.3] Find the measure of $\angle a$ if the measure of $\angle b = 81°$.

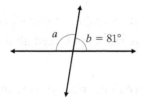

80. [3.1.3] Find the measure of $\angle x$ if the measure of $\angle y$ is 62°.

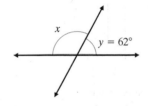

Quick Quiz 4.1

1. Determine if 504 is divisible by 2, 3, and/or 5.

2. Is the number 57 prime, composite, or neither?

3. Express 315 as the product of prime factors.

4. Concept Check Delroy is having a hard time factoring the number 318.

  (a) Explain in words how Delroy can determine one factor of 318.

  (b) State this factor.

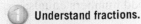

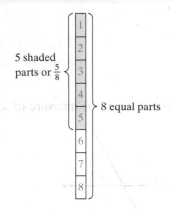

5 shaded parts or $\frac{5}{8}$

8 equal parts

3 pieces eaten

4 pieces in one pizza

1 Understanding Fractions

Whole numbers are used to describe whole objects or entire quantities. However, often we have to represent parts of whole quantities. In mathematics, **fractions** are a set of numbers used to describe parts of whole quantities. The *whole* can be an object (a pizza), or, just as often, the whole can be a set of things (pieces of pizza) that we choose to consider as a whole unit.

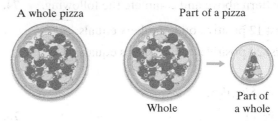

A whole pizza   Part of a pizza

Whole   Part of a whole

The vertical bar in the margin is divided into eight equal parts. The five shaded parts represent *part* of the whole bar and are represented by the fraction 5/8 or $\frac{5}{8}$.

In the fraction $\frac{5}{8}$ the number 5 is called the **numerator** and the number 8 is called the **denominator.**

$\frac{5}{8}$ → The *numerator* specifies how many of these parts are being considered.

$\ \ $ → The *denominator* specifies the total number of equal parts.

> The *denominator* of a fraction shows the number of equal parts in the whole.
>
> The *numerator* shows the number of parts being talked about or being used.

When you say "$\frac{3}{4}$ of a pizza has been eaten," what you are indicating is that if the pizza was cut into four equal pieces, then three of the four pieces have been eaten.

Remember that the *numerator* is always the *top number* and the *denominator* is always the *bottom number*.

EXAMPLE 1   Use a fraction to represent the shaded part of each object.

(a)    (b) 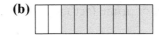   (c)

Solution

(a) One out of four parts is shaded, or $\frac{1}{4}$.

(b) Seven out of nine parts are shaded, or $\frac{7}{9}$.

(c) Three out of three parts are shaded, or $\frac{3}{3} = 1$.

Practice Problem 1   Use a fraction to represent the shaded part of each object.

(a) 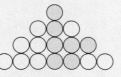   (b) 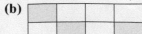   (c)

Note that in Example 1c when 3 out of 3 parts are shaded we have 1 whole amount. This illustrates a division fact, which states that any nonzero number divided by itself is 1.

What does it mean when a fraction has a 0 in the numerator, or when there is a 0 in the denominator? Let's look at the following situations to see how to answer these questions.

If $20 is divided equally among 5 people, each person receives $4.

$$20 \div 5 = 4 \quad \text{or} \quad \frac{20}{5} = 4$$

If $0 is divided equally among 5 people, each person receives $0.

$$0 \div 5 = 0 \quad \text{or} \quad \frac{0}{5} = 0$$

If $20 is divided among 0 people? — This cannot be done.

$$20 \div 0 \quad \text{and} \quad \frac{20}{0} \text{ are undefined.}$$

We summarize as follows.

DIVISION PROBLEMS INVOLVING THE NUMBERS ONE AND ZERO

1. Any nonzero number divided by itself is 1.

$$3 \div 3 = \frac{3}{3} = 1$$

2. Zero can never be the divisor in a division problem.

$$5 \div 0 = \frac{5}{0} \quad \text{We say division by 0 is } \textbf{undefined.}$$

3. Zero may be divided by any number except zero; the result is always zero.

$$0 \div 4 = \frac{0}{4} = 0 \quad \text{In other words, } \textit{any fraction with 0 in the numerator}$$
$$\textit{and a nonzero denominator equals 0.}$$

EXAMPLE 2   Divide, if possible.

(a) $\dfrac{x}{x}, x \neq 0$ **(b)** $\dfrac{23}{0}$ **(c)** $\dfrac{0}{23}$

Solution

(a) $\dfrac{x}{x} = 1$

(b) $\dfrac{23}{0}$ Division by 0 is undefined.

(c) $\dfrac{0}{23} = 0$ Any fraction with 0 in the numerator and a nonzero denominator equals 0.

Practice Problem 2   Divide, if possible.

(a) $y \div y, y \neq 0$ **(b)** $0 \div 18$ **(c)** $\dfrac{0}{65}$ **(d)** $\dfrac{65}{0}$

NOTE TO STUDENT: *Fully worked-out solutions to all of the Practice Problems can be found at the back of the text starting at page SP-1*

Circle graphs are especially helpful for showing the relationship of parts to a whole. The circle represents the whole, and the pie-shaped pieces represent parts of the whole.

EXAMPLE 3   The approximate number of inches of rain that falls during selected periods of one year in Seattle, Washington, is shown by the circle graph.

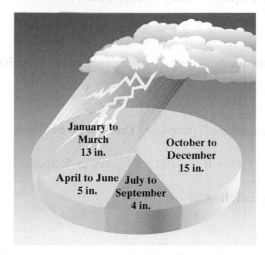

(a) What fractional part of the total yearly rainfall occurs from October to December?

(b) What fractional part of the total yearly rainfall does *not* occur from July to September?

Solution   First we must find the total rainfall for 1 year.

$$13 \text{ in.} + 15 \text{ in.} + 4 \text{ in.} + 5 \text{ in.} = 37 \text{ in.}$$

(a) From October to December there were 15 inches of rain out of a total of 37 inches.

$$\frac{15}{37} \quad \text{Fractional part of rainfall that does occur.}$$

(b) From July to September there were 4 inches of rain out of a total of 37 inches.

$$37 \text{ in.} - 4 \text{ in.} = 33 \text{ in.} \quad \text{Rainfall that does } not \text{ occur from July to September.}$$

$$\frac{33}{37} \quad \text{Fractional part of rainfall that does } not \text{ occur.}$$

NOTE TO STUDENT: *Fully worked-out solutions to all of the Practice Problems can be found at the back of the text starting at page SP-1*

Practice Problem 3   Use the circle graph in Example 3 to answer the following.

(a) What fractional part of the total yearly rainfall occurs from January to March?

(b) What fractional part of the total yearly rainfall does *not* occur from April to June?

Identifying Proper Fractions, Improper Fractions, and Mixed Numbers

We have names for different kinds of fractions. A **proper fraction** is used to describe a quantity *less than 1*. If the numerator is *less* than the denominator, the fraction is a proper fraction. The fraction $\frac{3}{4}$ is a proper fraction.

An **improper fraction** is used to describe a quantity *greater* than or equal to 1. If the numerator is *greater than or equal to* the denominator, the fraction is an improper fraction. The fraction $\frac{7}{4}$ is an improper fraction because the numerator is larger than the denominator. Since $\frac{4}{4}$ describes a quantity equal to 1, it is also an improper fraction.

A **mixed number** is the sum of a whole number greater than zero and a proper fraction, and is used to describe a quantity greater than 1. An improper fraction can also be written as a mixed number.

The following chart will help you visualize the different fractions and their names.

Value	Illustration	Math Symbol	Name
Less than 1		$\frac{3}{4}$	proper fraction
Equal to 1		$\frac{4}{4}$	improper fraction
Greater than 1		$\frac{7}{4}$	improper fraction or
		$1\frac{3}{4}$	mixed number

The last figure can be represented by 1 whole added to $\frac{3}{4}$ of a whole, or $1 + \frac{3}{4}$. This is written $1\frac{3}{4}$ (we do not write the addition symbol) and is a mixed number. Thus the improper fraction $\frac{7}{4}$ is equivalent to the mixed number $1\frac{3}{4}$.

EXAMPLE 4 Identify each as a proper fraction, an improper fraction, or a mixed number.

(a) $\frac{9}{8}$ **(b)** $\frac{8}{9}$ **(c)** $7\frac{3}{4}$ **(d)** $\frac{3}{3}$

Solution

(a) $\frac{9}{8}$ Improper fraction   The numerator is larger than the denominator.

(b) $\frac{8}{9}$ Proper fraction   The numerator is less than the denominator.

(c) $7\frac{3}{4}$ Mixed number   A whole number is added to a proper fraction.

(d) $\frac{3}{3}$ Improper fraction   The numerator is equal to the denominator.

Practice Problem 4 Identify each as a proper fraction, an improper fraction, or a mixed number.

(a) $\frac{6}{5}$ **(b)** $\frac{x}{x}, x \neq 0$ **(c)** $6\frac{2}{9}$ **(d)** $\frac{1}{2}$

③ Changing Improper Fractions to Mixed Numbers

We can see the relationship between an improper fraction and a mixed number by drawing pictures. For example, the fraction $\frac{13}{5}$ is represented by the shaded boxes below. Note that each box is divided into 5 pieces. Thus 13 pieces, each of which is $\frac{1}{5}$ of a box, are shaded. We see that $\frac{13}{5} = 2\frac{3}{5}$ since 2 whole boxes and $\frac{3}{5}$ of another box are shaded.

$$\frac{13}{5} = 2\frac{3}{5}$$

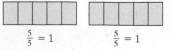

$\frac{5}{5} = 1$ $\frac{5}{5} = 1$ $\frac{3}{5}$

Since $\frac{13}{5} = 13 \div 5$, we can divide to change an improper fraction to a mixed number.

$$\frac{13}{5} = 13 \div 5 = \begin{array}{r} 2 \text{ R3} \\ 5\overline{)13} \\ \underline{10} \\ 3 \end{array} = 2\frac{3}{5}$$

We summarize this procedure as follows.

PROCEDURE TO CHANGE AN IMPROPER FRACTION TO A MIXED NUMBER

1. Divide the numerator by the denominator.

2. The quotient is the whole number part of the mixed number.

3. The remainder from the division will be the numerator of the fraction. The denominator of the fraction remains unchanged.

A mixed number is in the following form: quotient $\dfrac{\text{remainder}}{\text{denominator}}$.

EXAMPLE 5 Write $\dfrac{19}{7}$ as a mixed number.

Solution   The answer is in the form quotient $\dfrac{\text{remainder}}{\text{denominator}}$.

$$\frac{19}{7} \rightarrow \begin{array}{r} 2 \\ 7\overline{)19} \\ \underline{14} \\ 5 \end{array} \qquad 2\frac{5}{7} \begin{array}{l} \text{Remainder} \\ \text{Denominator from original fraction} \end{array}$$

NOTE TO STUDENT: Fully worked-out solutions to all of the Practice Problems can be found at the back of the text starting at page SP-1

Practice Problem 5   Write $\dfrac{23}{6}$ as a mixed number.

---

4 Changing Mixed Numbers to Improper Fractions

We often change mixed numbers to improper fractions since improper fractions are usually easier to work with. To illustrate the method used to change a mixed number to an improper fraction, we can draw a picture. For example, suppose that we want to write $2\frac{1}{4}$ as an improper fraction. We can illustrate the quantity $2\frac{1}{4}$ as two whole boxes that are divided into fourths plus $\frac{1}{4}$ of a third box. Now if we count the shaded pieces, we see that we have $\frac{9}{4}$.

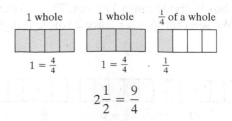

We can perform the same procedure using the following method.

PROCEDURE TO CHANGE A MIXED NUMBER TO AN IMPROPER FRACTION

1. Multiply the whole number by the denominator of the fraction.

2. Add this product to the numerator. The result is the numerator of the improper fraction. The denominator does not change.

$$\text{Improper fraction:} \quad \frac{(\text{denominator} \cdot \text{whole number}) + \text{numerator}}{\text{denominator}}$$

EXAMPLE 6 Change $6\frac{1}{2}$ to an improper fraction.

Solution

$$\text{Improper fraction:} \quad \frac{(\text{denominator} \cdot \text{whole number}) + \text{numerator}}{\text{denominator}}$$

Multiply the whole number by the denominator.	Add the numerator to the product.

$$6\frac{1}{2} = \frac{(2 \cdot 6) + 1}{2} = \frac{12 + 1}{2} = \frac{13}{2}$$

The denominator does not change.

We can also write the process as follows.

$$6 \quad {}^{+1}\!\!\diagup \frac{}{2}$$

$$6\frac{1}{2} = \frac{2 \text{ times } 6 \text{ plus } 1}{2} = \frac{13}{2}$$

Practice Problem 6 Change $8\frac{2}{3}$ to an improper fraction.

Developing Your Study Skills

Problems with Accuracy

Strive for accuracy. Mistakes are often made because of accidental errors rather than a lack of understanding. Such mistakes are frustrating. A simple arithmetic or sign error can lead to an incorrect answer. These six steps will help you cut down on errors.

1. Work carefully and take your time. Do not rush through a problem just to get it done.

2. Concentrate on the problem. Sometimes problems become mechanical, and your mind begins to wander. You become careless and make a mistake. Concentrating on the problem will help you avoid this.

3. Check your problem. Be sure that you copied it correctly from the book.

4. Check each step of the problem for sign errors as well as computation errors. Does your answer make sense?

5. Make a mental note of the types of errors you make most often. Becoming aware of where you make errors will help you avoid making them again.

6. Keep practicing new skills. Remember the old saying that "practice makes perfect." Many errors are due simply to a lack of practice.

Verbal and Writing Skills   *Fill in the blanks and boxes.*

1. Fractions are a set of numbers used to describe _____ of a whole quantity. In the fraction $\frac{2}{3}$, the 2 is called the _____ and the 3 is called the _____.

2. When you say $\frac{3}{7}$ of a cake has been eaten, you are indicating that if the cake were cut into ____ equal pieces, then ____ of these pieces were eaten.

3. To change the mixed number $6\frac{2}{3}$ to an improper fraction, we multiply ____ × ____, and then add ____ to the product. We write the improper fraction as $\frac{\square}{\square}$.

4. To change the improper fraction $\frac{31}{4}$ to a mixed number, we divide _____ by ____ and get a quotient of ____. We write the mixed number as ____$\frac{\square}{\square}$.

Use a fraction to represent the shaded area in each figure.

5.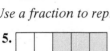

6.

7.

8.

Divide, if possible. Assume all variables in the denominators are nonzero.

9. $\dfrac{7}{0}$

10. $\dfrac{4}{0}$

11. $\dfrac{0}{z}$

12. $\dfrac{0}{a}$

13. $\dfrac{44}{44}$

14. $\dfrac{a}{a}$

15. $\dfrac{0}{9}$

16. $\dfrac{0}{6}$

17. $\dfrac{8}{0}$

18. $\dfrac{6}{0}$

19. $\dfrac{y}{y}$

20. $\dfrac{97}{97}$

Applications

21. *Baseball* A baseball player had 5 base hits in 12 times at bat. Write the fractional part of the times at bat that describes the number of times the player had a base hit.

22. *Archery* An archer hit the target 3 times out of 11 shots. Write the fractional part of the total shots that describes the number of times the archer hit the target.

23. *Men vs. Women* There are 57 women and 37 men in the hospital cafeteria. What fractional part of the customers in the hospital cafeteria consists of men?

24. *Male vs. Female* There are 83 men and 67 women working for a small corporation. What fractional part of the employees consists of men?

25. *Dance Production Class* There are 26 dancers in the dance production class at a high school. Nine of the dancers are juniors. Write the fraction that describes the dancers who are *not* juniors.

26. *Salad Bar Choices* At a salad bar, there are 29 different items to choose from. Eleven of the choices contain pasta. Write the fraction that describes the choices that do *not* contain pasta.

27. *Baseball* The city baseball team won 21 of the 32 games they played. What fractional part of the games did the team lose?

28. *Manufacturing Defects* Lois inspected 137 computer chips and found that 11 were defective. What fractional part of the chips were *not* defective?

Payroll Deductions The deductions from Arnold's paycheck are shown on the circle graph. Use this circle graph to answer exercises 29–32.

29. What fractional part of the deductions is for state or federal income tax?

30. What fractional part of the deductions is for insurance or Social Security?

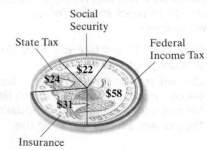

31. What fractional part of the deductions is *not* for insurance?

32. What fractional part of the deductions is *not* for state tax?

Identify each as a proper fraction, an improper fraction, or a mixed number.

33. $\dfrac{11}{9}$　　　　**34.** $4\dfrac{1}{2}$　　　　**35.** $\dfrac{8}{8}$　　　　**36.** $\dfrac{9}{7}$

37. $\dfrac{5}{6}$　　　　**38.** $\dfrac{z}{z}, z \neq 0$　　　**39.** $7\dfrac{1}{9}$　　　　**40.** $\dfrac{3}{7}$

Change each improper fraction to a mixed number or a whole number.

41. $\dfrac{15}{8}$　　　　**42.** $\dfrac{19}{4}$　　　　**43.** $\dfrac{48}{5}$　　　　**44.** $\dfrac{92}{7}$

45. $\dfrac{41}{2}$　　　　**46.** $\dfrac{25}{3}$　　　　**47.** $\dfrac{32}{5}$　　　　**48.** $\dfrac{79}{7}$

49. $\dfrac{47}{5}$　　　　**50.** $\dfrac{54}{7}$　　　　**51.** $\dfrac{33}{33}$　　　　**52.** $\dfrac{89}{89}$

Change each mixed number to an improper fraction.

53. $8\dfrac{3}{7}$　　　　**54.** $6\dfrac{2}{3}$　　　　**55.** $24\dfrac{1}{4}$　　　　**56.** $10\dfrac{1}{9}$

57. $15\dfrac{2}{3}$　　　**58.** $13\dfrac{3}{5}$　　　**59.** $33\dfrac{1}{3}$　　　**60.** $41\dfrac{1}{2}$

61. $8\dfrac{9}{10}$　　　**62.** $3\dfrac{1}{50}$　　　**63.** $8\dfrac{7}{15}$　　　**64.** $5\dfrac{19}{20}$

Cumulative Review　*Simplify.*

65. [2.4.1] $(-5)(-8)$

66. [2.4.1] $(-7)(9)$

67. [4.1.3] Express 63 as a product of prime factors.

68. [4.1.3] Express 54 as a product of prime factors.

Quick Quiz 4.2

1. Divide, if possible. $\dfrac{0}{9}$

2. Change $4\dfrac{3}{5}$ to an improper fraction.

3. The local humane society has 8 cats, 5 dogs, and 2 rabbits that need homes. What fractional part of these pets are cats?

4. Concept Check Explain in words how you change the mixed number $2\dfrac{3}{4}$ to an improper fraction.

Student Learning Objectives

After studying this section, you will be able to:

① Find equivalent fractions.

② Reduce fractions to lowest terms.

③ Simplify fractions containing variables.

④ Solve applied problems involving fractions.

① Finding Equivalent Fractions

There are many fractions that name the same quantity. For example, in the following illustration the two pieces of wood are the same length.

One piece of wood cut into 2 equal parts
One piece of wood cut into 4 equal parts

As you can see, 1 of 2 pieces of wood represents the same quantity as 2 of 4 pieces of wood. We say that $\frac{1}{2} = \frac{2}{4}$ and call these fractions **equivalent fractions.**

There are many other fractions that represent the same value as $\frac{1}{2}$ and thus are equivalent to $\frac{1}{2}$.

$$\frac{1}{2} = \frac{2}{4} = \frac{4}{8} = \frac{8}{16} \text{ are equivalent fractions}$$

Equivalent fractions *look different* but have the *same value* because they represent the same quantity. Now, how can we find an equivalent fraction without using a picture or diagram? Observe the following pattern.

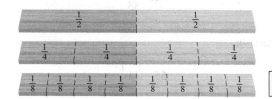

$$\frac{1}{2} = \frac{1 \cdot 2}{2 \cdot 2} = \frac{2}{4} \qquad \frac{1 \cdot 4}{2 \cdot 4} = \frac{4}{8}$$

Equivalent fractions represent the same value.

We see that when we multiply the numerator and denominator of $\frac{1}{2}$ by the same nonzero number we get an equivalent fraction. Why is this true? Recall that the identity property of 1 states that if we multiply a number by 1, the value of that number does not change. Since $1 = \frac{1}{1} = \frac{2}{2} = \frac{3}{3}$, we have the following.

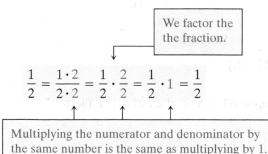

We factor the the fraction.

$$\frac{1}{2} = \frac{1 \cdot 2}{2 \cdot 2} = \frac{1}{2} \cdot \frac{2}{2} = \frac{1}{2} \cdot 1 = \frac{1}{2}$$

Multiplying the numerator and denominator by the same number is the same as multiplying by 1.

We see that when we multiply the numerator and denominator of a fraction by the same nonzero number we are actually *multiplying by a form of 1,* and therefore we do not change the value of the fraction. Now we can state a procedure to find an equivalent fraction.

PROCEDURE TO FIND EQUIVALENT FRACTIONS

To find an equivalent fraction, we multiply *both* the numerator and denominator by the *same* nonzero number.

$$\frac{a}{b} = \frac{a \cdot c}{b \cdot c} \qquad \text{where } b \text{ and } c \text{ are not 0}$$

When there is a variable in the denominator, we will assume that the variable does not equal zero, since division by zero is not defined.

EXAMPLE 1

(a) Multiply the numerator and denominator of $\frac{3}{4}$ by 2 to find an equivalent fraction.

(b) Multiply the numerator and denominator of $\frac{3}{4}$ by $3x$ to find an equivalent fraction.

Solution

(a) $\dfrac{3}{4} = \dfrac{3 \cdot 2}{4 \cdot 2} = \dfrac{6}{8}$ **(b)** $\dfrac{3}{4} = \dfrac{3 \cdot 3x}{4 \cdot 3x} = \dfrac{9x}{12x}$

Practice Problem 1

(a) Multiply the numerator and denominator of $\frac{4}{7}$ by 3 to find an equivalent fraction.

(b) Multiply the numerator and denominator of $\frac{4}{7}$ by $5x$ to find an equivalent fraction.

NOTE TO STUDENT: Fully worked-out solutions to all of the Practice Problems can be found at the back of the text starting at page SP-1

EXAMPLE 2   Write $\frac{3}{4}$ as an equivalent fraction with a denominator of $16x$.

Solution

$$\frac{3}{4} = \frac{\square}{16x}$$

$$\frac{3 \cdot ?}{4 \cdot ?} = \frac{\square}{16x} \quad \text{4 times what number equals } 16x? \quad 4x$$

Since we must multiply the denominator by $4x$ to obtain $16x$, we must also multiply the numerator by $4x$.

$$\frac{3 \cdot 4x}{4 \cdot 4x} = \frac{12x}{16x}$$

Practice Problem 2   Write $\frac{2}{9}$ as an equivalent fraction with a denominator of $36x$.

Reducing Fractions to Lowest Terms

A fraction is considered to be **reduced to lowest terms** (or written in simplest form) if the numerator and denominator have no common factors other than 1.

reduced   not reduced

↓   ↓

$\dfrac{2}{3} = \dfrac{2 \cdot 1}{3 \cdot 1}$ $\dfrac{4}{6} = \dfrac{2 \cdot 2}{3 \cdot 2}$

no common factor   common factor
other than 1   of 2

As we saw earlier, when we multiply a fraction by any form of 1 such as $\frac{2}{2}$, or $\frac{3}{3}$, or $\frac{4}{4}$, and so on, we obtain an equivalent fraction. However, this equivalent fraction is *not reduced*. We reverse this process to reduce a fraction.

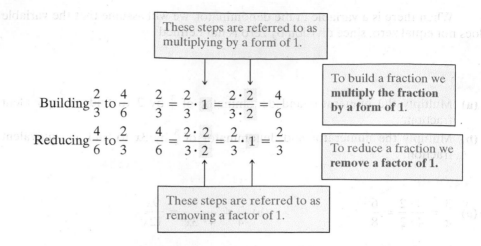

$$\text{Building } \frac{2}{3} \text{ to } \frac{4}{6} \qquad \frac{2}{3} = \frac{2}{3} \cdot 1 = \frac{2 \cdot 2}{3 \cdot 2} = \frac{4}{6}$$

$$\text{Reducing } \frac{4}{6} \text{ to } \frac{2}{3} \qquad \frac{4}{6} = \frac{2 \cdot 2}{3 \cdot 2} = \frac{2}{3} \cdot 1 = \frac{2}{3}$$

As you can see, reducing fractions requires that you recognize common factors of the numerator and denominator. One way to do this is to write the numerator and denominator each as a product of prime factors. Then use slashes / to indicate that you are rewriting common factors as the equivalent fraction $\frac{1}{1}$ so that you can remove a factor of 1.

$$\frac{4}{6} = \frac{2 \cdot \overset{1}{\cancel{2}}}{3 \cdot \underset{1}{\cancel{2}}} = \frac{2}{3} \qquad \text{Slashes indicate that we are rewriting } \frac{2}{2} \text{ as } \frac{1}{1}.$$

$$\text{Since } \frac{1}{1} = 1, \text{ we have } \frac{2}{3} \cdot 1 = \frac{2}{3}.$$

PROCEDURE TO REDUCE A FRACTION TO LOWEST TERMS

1. Write the numerator and denominator of the fraction each as a product of prime factors. For example, $\frac{4}{6} = \frac{2 \cdot 2}{3 \cdot 2}$.

2. Any factor that appears in both the numerator and denominator is a common factor. Rewrite the common factors as the equivalent fraction $\frac{1}{1}$ and multiply.

$$\frac{2 \cdot 2}{3 \cdot 2} = \frac{2 \cdot \overset{1}{\cancel{2}}}{3 \cdot \underset{1}{\cancel{2}}} = \frac{2}{3}$$

Note that you could reduce $\frac{4}{6}$ by dividing the numerator and denominator by 2. This method *does not work* as well as the one presented when variables are involved.

It is important that you reduce fractions using the method of removing factors of 1 in order to prepare for algebra.

The direction *simplify* or *reduce* means to reduce to lowest terms.

EXAMPLE 3   Simplify. $\dfrac{15}{35}$

Solution   Since the last digit of both 15 and 35 is 5, we know that both numbers are divisible by 5.

$$\frac{15}{35} = \frac{3 \cdot 5}{7 \cdot 5} \qquad \text{First, write the numerator and denominator as products of prime numbers.}$$

$$= \frac{3 \cdot \overset{1}{\cancel{5}}}{7 \cdot \underset{1}{\cancel{5}}} \qquad \text{Then, rewrite } \frac{5}{5} \text{ as the equivalent fraction } \frac{1}{1}.$$

$$= \frac{3 \cdot 1}{7 \cdot 1} = \frac{3}{7}$$

Practice Problem 3 Simplify.

$$\frac{18}{54}$$

NOTE TO STUDENT: *Fully worked-out solutions to all of the Practice Problems can be found at the back of the text starting at page SP-1*

We can reduce a fraction with a negative number in either the numerator or the denominator by writing the negative sign in *front* of the fraction. The value of the fraction will not change, as illustrated below.

$$\frac{-15}{5} = -15 \div 5 = -3 \qquad \frac{15}{-5} = 15 \div (-5) = -3$$

$$-\frac{15}{5} = -(15 \div 5) = -(3) = -3$$

When we reduce a fraction, we write the negative sign in front of the fraction. We do not include it as part of the prime factors.

EXAMPLE 4 Simplify. $\dfrac{-72}{48}$

Solution If we recognize that the numerator and denominator have common factors that are *not* prime, we can use these factors to reduce the fraction.

$$\frac{-72}{48} = -\frac{72}{48} \qquad \text{Write the negative sign in front of the fraction.}$$

$$= -\frac{\overset{1}{\cancel{8}} \cdot 9}{\underset{1}{\cancel{8}} \cdot 6} \qquad \text{8 is a common factor of 72 and 48.}$$

$$= -\frac{3 \cdot \overset{1}{\cancel{3}}}{2 \cdot \underset{1}{\cancel{3}}} \qquad \text{Write the remaining factors as products of primes.}$$

$$= -\frac{3}{2} \qquad \text{Simplify.}$$

Practice Problem 4 Simplify.

$$\frac{60}{-36}$$

CAUTION: In Example 4 we used common factors (not prime factors) when we reduced the fraction: $\frac{-72}{48} = -\frac{\cancel{8} \cdot 9}{\cancel{8} \cdot 6}$. When we use common factors to reduce fractions, it is important that we rewrite any remaining factors as products of primes: $-\frac{9}{6} = -\frac{\cancel{3} \cdot 3}{\cancel{3} \cdot 2}$. This will ensure that the fraction is reduced to lowest terms.

 Simplifying Fractions Containing Variables

We use the same process to simplify fractions containing variables. That is, we rewrite common factors in the numerator and denominator as the equivalent fraction $\frac{1}{1}$ and simplify.

EXAMPLE 5 Simplify. $\dfrac{150n^2}{200n}$

Solution Since 25 is a common factor of the numerator and denominator, we can write each as a product of 25 times some prime numbers.

$$\frac{150n^2}{200n} = \frac{25 \cdot 3 \cdot 2 \cdot n \cdot n}{25 \cdot 2 \cdot 2 \cdot 2 \cdot n}$$

Write all other factors as products of prime numbers to ensure that the fraction is reduced to lowest terms.

$$= \frac{\overset{1}{\cancel{25}} \cdot 3 \cdot \overset{1}{\cancel{2}} \cdot n \cdot \overset{1}{\cancel{n}}}{\underset{1}{\cancel{25}} \cdot 2 \cdot \underset{1}{\cancel{2}} \cdot 2 \cdot \underset{1}{\cancel{n}}}$$

$$= \frac{3 \cdot n}{2 \cdot 2}$$

$$\frac{150n^2}{200n} = \frac{3n}{4}$$

Note that we could have also used $50n$ as a common factor in both the numerator and denominator of $\dfrac{150n^2}{200n}$.

Practice Problem 5 Simplify.

$$\frac{80x^2}{140x}$$

CAUTION: Students sometimes apply slashes incorrectly as follows.

$$\frac{\cancel{x} + 4}{\cancel{x}} = 4 \quad \text{THIS IS WRONG!}$$

$$\frac{3 + 4}{3} = \frac{7}{3} \quad \text{THIS IS RIGHT!} \qquad \frac{\cancel{x} \cdot 4}{\cancel{x}} = \frac{4}{1} = 4 \quad \text{THIS IS RIGHT!}$$

We may not use slashes with addition or subtraction signs. We may use slashes only if we are multiplying factors.

4 **Solving Applied Problems Involving Fractions**

EXAMPLE 6 The yearly sales report in the margin shows the number and type of real estate sales made by Tri-Star Realty.

(a) What fractional part of the total sales were single-family homes?

(b) What fractional part of the total sales were *not* condominiums?

Solution

(a) *Understand the problem.* We use the information on the chart to find the total sales. Then we write the fraction and simplify.

Solve and state the answer.

End of the Year Sales Report

Type of Sale	Total Sales
Condominium	14
Town home	21
Single-family home	45

Condominium sales	+	Town home sales	+	Single-family home sales	=	Total sales
14	+	21	+	45	=	80

$$\frac{\text{single-family home sales}}{\text{total sales}} = \frac{45}{80} = \frac{9 \cdot \overset{1}{\cancel{5}}}{16 \cdot \underset{1}{\cancel{5}}} = \frac{9}{16} \quad \text{of the sales were single-family homes.}$$

Note that we should always reduce fractions to lowest terms.

(b) *Understand the problem.* We refer to the chart and determine how many sales were *not* condominiums. Then we write the fraction and simplify.

Solve and state the answer.

Type of Sale	Total Sales
~~Condominium~~	~~14~~
Town home	21
Single-family home	45

We want the total sales that are *not* condominiums.

We find the sum: $21 + 45 = 66$.

$$\frac{\text{sales that were not condominiums}}{\text{total sales}} = \frac{66}{80} = \frac{33 \cdot \overset{1}{\cancel{2}}}{40 \cdot \underset{1}{\cancel{2}}} = \frac{33}{40}$$

of the sales were *not* condominiums.

Check:

(a) The fraction $\frac{9}{16}$ is a little more than $\frac{8}{16}$, which equals $\frac{1}{2}$. This means that approximately one-half of the total yearly sales were single-family homes. Since 45 sales is a little more than one-half of the total sales of 80, our answer is reasonable.

(b) The fraction $\frac{33}{40}$ represents a number close to the whole amount $\frac{40}{40}$. This means that most of the sales were *not* condominiums. Since 66 of the 80 sales were *not* condominiums, it is true that most of the sales were *not* condominiums, and our answer is reasonable.

Practice Problem 6   Refer to Example 6 to answer the following. Write each fraction in simplest form.

(a) What fractional part of the sales were town homes?

(b) What fractional part of the sales were not single-family homes?

NOTE TO STUDENT: Fully worked-out solutions to all of the Practice Problems can be found at the back of the text starting at page SP-1

Developing Your Study Skills

Taking Notes in Class

During a lecture you are *listening, seeing, reading,* and *writing* all at the same time. Although an important part of mathematics studying is taking notes, you must also focus on what the instructor is saying so you can follow the logic.

The Learning Cycle

Reading $\longrightarrow$ Writing

$\uparrow$ $\qquad\qquad\qquad$ $\downarrow$

Seeing $\leftarrow$ Verbalizing $\leftarrow$ Listening

1. Preview the lesson before class so that the important concepts will be more familiar and you will have a better idea of what to write down.

2. Ask the teacher if you can record the lecture.

3. Write down only the important ideas and examples as the instructor lectures, making sure that you're also listening so you can follow the reasoning.

4. Include helpful hints and references to the text that your instructor gives. You will be amazed how easily you forget these if you don't write them down.

5. Review your notes, clarifying whatever appears vague, on the *same day* sometime after class, so that you will be able to recall material from the lecture that you did not include in your notes.

You may find that you learn more by *seeing* and *listening* than by the other modes of learning. You may prefer to take fewer notes, focusing more on what the instructor is saying. This is fine as long as you write a brief outline during class of the instructor's lecture. Then immediately after class, you should add the details.

Verbal and Writing Skills *Fill in the blanks.*

1. To build an equivalent fraction, we _____ the numerator and denominator by the _____ number.

2. State three ways that we can write the fraction *negative two-thirds*.

Fill in each box so that the fractions are equivalent.

3. $\dfrac{3 \cdot \boxed{}}{7 \cdot 2} = \dfrac{\boxed{}}{14}$

4. $\dfrac{2 \cdot \boxed{}}{9 \cdot 4} = \dfrac{\boxed{}}{36}$

5. $\dfrac{7 \cdot \boxed{}}{5x \cdot 3} = \dfrac{\boxed{}}{15x}$

6. $\dfrac{5 \cdot \boxed{}}{8x \cdot 3} = \dfrac{\boxed{}}{24x}$

7. $\dfrac{7 \cdot \boxed{}}{8 \cdot \boxed{}} = \dfrac{7y}{8y}$

8. $\dfrac{3 \cdot \boxed{}}{4 \cdot \boxed{}} = \dfrac{3x}{4x}$

9. $\dfrac{2 \cdot \boxed{}}{9 \cdot \boxed{}} = \dfrac{\boxed{}}{9y}$

10. $\dfrac{4 \cdot \boxed{}}{11 \cdot \boxed{}} = \dfrac{\boxed{}}{11y}$

Multiply the numerator and denominator of each given fraction by the following numbers to find two different equivalent fractions: **(a)** 4 *and* **(b)** 5x. *Assume* $x \neq 0$.

11. $\dfrac{7}{9}$

12. $\dfrac{6}{7}$

13. $\dfrac{4}{11}$

14. $\dfrac{9}{13}$

Find an equivalent fraction with the given denominator.

15. $\dfrac{3}{8} = \dfrac{?}{32}$

16. $\dfrac{10}{15} = \dfrac{?}{60}$

17. $\dfrac{5}{6} = \dfrac{?}{30}$

18. $\dfrac{7}{8} = \dfrac{?}{40}$

19. $\dfrac{9}{13} = \dfrac{?}{39}$

20. $\dfrac{8}{11} = \dfrac{?}{44}$

21. $\dfrac{35}{40} = \dfrac{?}{80}$

22. $\dfrac{45}{50} = \dfrac{?}{100}$

23. $\dfrac{8}{9} = \dfrac{?}{9y}$

24. $\dfrac{7}{13} = \dfrac{?}{13n}$

25. $\dfrac{3}{7} = \dfrac{?}{28y}$

26. $\dfrac{3}{12} = \dfrac{?}{60y}$

27. $\dfrac{3}{6} = \dfrac{?}{18a}$

28. $\dfrac{4}{9} = \dfrac{?}{81x}$

29. $\dfrac{5}{7} = \dfrac{?}{21x}$

30. $\dfrac{7}{8} = \dfrac{?}{16x}$

Simplify.

31. $\dfrac{20}{25}$

32. $\dfrac{14}{21}$

33. $\dfrac{12}{16}$

34. $\dfrac{24}{30}$

35. $\dfrac{30}{36}$

36. $\dfrac{12}{32}$

37. $\dfrac{16}{28}$

38. $\dfrac{18}{27}$

39. $\dfrac{24}{36}$

40. $\dfrac{32}{64}$

41. $\dfrac{30}{85}$

42. $\dfrac{33}{55}$

43. $\dfrac{48}{56}$

44. $\dfrac{63}{81}$

45. $\dfrac{36}{72}$

46. $\dfrac{46}{23}$

47. $\dfrac{49}{35}$

48. $\dfrac{81}{72}$

49. $\dfrac{75}{60}$

50. $\dfrac{62}{54}$

Simplify.

51. **(a)** $\dfrac{-12}{18}$ **(b)** $\dfrac{12}{-18}$ **(c)** $-\dfrac{12}{18}$

52. **(a)** $\dfrac{-15}{25}$ **(b)** $\dfrac{15}{-25}$ **(c)** $-\dfrac{15}{25}$

53. $\dfrac{-15}{30}$ **54.** $\dfrac{-35}{40}$ **55.** $\dfrac{-42}{48}$ **56.** $\dfrac{-60}{70}$

57. $\dfrac{30}{-42}$ **58.** $\dfrac{25}{-60}$ **59.** $-\dfrac{16}{18}$ **60.** $-\dfrac{14}{18}$

Simplify. Since division by zero is undefined, assume that any variable in a denominator is nonzero.

61. $\dfrac{21a}{24a}$ **62.** $\dfrac{25n}{55n}$ **63.** $\dfrac{20y}{35y}$ **64.** $\dfrac{14x}{21x}$

65. $\dfrac{24xy}{42x}$ **66.** $\dfrac{20nx}{45n}$ **67.** $\dfrac{12y}{14xy}$ **68.** $\dfrac{12x}{18nx}$

69. $\dfrac{27x^2}{45x}$ **70.** $\dfrac{28x^2}{49x}$ **71.** $\dfrac{20y}{24y^2}$ **72.** $\dfrac{21y}{24y^2}$

73. $\dfrac{36n^2}{-42n}$ **74.** $\dfrac{64y^2}{-72y}$ **75.** $\dfrac{-35x}{45x^2}$ **76.** $\dfrac{-20y}{30y^2}$

Applications *Solve. Write each fraction in simplest form.*

77. **Incorrect Test Answers** Shawn answered 22 questions correctly on a test of 36 questions. What fractional part of the questions did he answer *incorrectly*?

78. **Floor Tiles** During an earthquake 18 of the 81 floor tiles in Hamza's family room were cracked. What fractional part of the tiles in the family room were *not* cracked?

Correct/Incorrect Test Answers *The chart shows the number of questions Alexsandra answered correctly on a three-part English test. Use this chart to answer exercises 79 and 80.*

79. What fractional part of the questions did Alexsandra answer correctly?

80. What fractional part of the questions did Alexsandra answer incorrectly?

English Test Results

	Number of Correct Answers	Number of Questions
Part 1	22	36
Part 2	15	20
Part 3	20	25

Shark Attacks *Use the bar graph to answer exercises 81–83. Use the divisibility tests to write each fraction in simplest form.*

The highest number of recorded unprovoked shark attacks on humans worldwide occurred in the year 2000. Over half of the attacks happened on offshore reefs or banks.

81. What fractional part of the total number of shark attacks happened in 2006?

82. What fractional part of the total number of shark attacks happened in 2000?

83. What fractional part of the total number of shark attacks happened in 2005 or 2006?

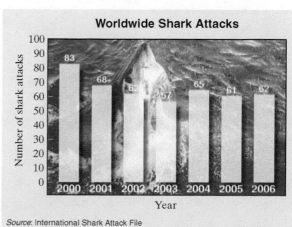

Source: International Shark Attack File

One Step Further *Simplify. Assume that any variable in a denominator is nonzero.*

84. $\dfrac{25x^2y^2z^4}{135x^3y}$

85. $\dfrac{40a^2b^2c^4}{88ab}$

86. $\dfrac{156ab^3}{144bc^4}$

87. $\dfrac{256xy^3}{300yz^5}$

To Think About

▲ **88.** *Garden Dimensions* Sean's rectangular garden is 84 inches by 48 inches. If he increases the length from 84 inches to 168 inches, what will the width have to be in order for the garden to have the same area?

▲ **89.** *Garden Enlargement* A rectangular garden has a length of 90 inches and a width of 80 inches. If the length is increased from 90 inches to 120 inches, what will the width have to be in order for the garden to have the same area?

Cumulative Review *Simplify.*

90. [3.4.1] $x^4 \cdot x^3 \cdot x^3$

91. [3.4.1] $2^4 \cdot 2^6$

92. [3.4.2] $(-3a)(2a^4)$

93. [3.2.3] *Peanuts and Cashews* The number of peanuts (P) in a mix is double the number of cashews (C).

(a) Translate the statement into an equation.

(b) If there are 34 peanuts in the mix, how many cashews are in the mix?

▲ **94.** [3.3.4] *Comparing Room Sizes* Which has the greater area, a rectangular room that is 13 feet by 16 feet or a square room that is 15 feet on each side? Which has the greater perimeter?

Quick Quiz 4.3

1. Find an equivalent fraction with the given denominator. $\dfrac{3}{7} = \dfrac{?}{56}$

2. Simplify. $\dfrac{-24}{36}$

3. Simplify. $\dfrac{33a^2}{44a}$

4. **Concept Check** Can the fraction $\frac{105}{231}$ be reduced? Why or why not?

Using the Quotient Rule for Exponents

Frequently, we must divide variable expressions such as in $x^6 \div x^4$. We can rewrite the expression as the fraction $\dfrac{x^6}{x^4}$ and simplify using repeated multiplication.

$$\frac{x^6}{x^4} = \frac{x \cdot x \cdot x \cdot x \cdot x \cdot x}{x \cdot x \cdot x \cdot x} = \frac{\overset{1}{\cancel{x}} \cdot \overset{1}{\cancel{x}} \cdot \overset{1}{\cancel{x}} \cdot \overset{1}{\cancel{x}} \cdot x \cdot x}{\underset{1}{\cancel{x}} \cdot \underset{1}{\cancel{x}} \cdot \underset{1}{\cancel{x}} \cdot \underset{1}{\cancel{x}}} = \frac{x^2}{1} = x^2$$

When exponents are large, this process can be time consuming. Let's examine some divisions and look for a pattern to discover a division rule. Notice in the previous division that there are 6 factors in the numerator and 4 factors in the denominator. After we simplify, we have $6 - 4 = 2$ factors left in the numerator. Thus we can write

$$\frac{x^6}{x^4} = \frac{\overbrace{\cancel{x} \cdot \cancel{x} \cdot \cancel{x} \cdot \cancel{x} \cdot x \cdot x}^{6 \text{ factors}}}{\underbrace{\cancel{x} \cdot \cancel{x} \cdot \cancel{x} \cdot \cancel{x}}_{4 \text{ factors}}} = x^2 \quad 6 - 4 = 2 \text{ factors left in the } \textit{numerator.}$$

Let's consider another division problem.

$$\frac{2^3}{2^4} = \frac{2 \cdot 2 \cdot 2}{2 \cdot 2 \cdot 2 \cdot 2} = \frac{\overbrace{\cancel{2} \cdot \cancel{2} \cdot \cancel{2}}^{3 \text{ factors}}}{\underbrace{\cancel{2} \cdot \cancel{2} \cdot \cancel{2} \cdot 2}_{4 \text{ factors}}} = \frac{1}{2^1} \quad 4 - 3 = 1 \text{ factor left in the } \textit{denominator.}$$

We see that we *subtract exponents* to divide these expressions.
    Let's summarize the results.

$\dfrac{x^6}{x^4} = x^2$ Since there are more factors in the *numerator*, after we simplify we have $6 - 4 = 2$ factors left in the *numerator*.

$\dfrac{2^3}{2^4} = \dfrac{1}{2}$ Since there are more factors in the *denominator*, after we simplify we have $4 - 3 = 1$ factor left in the *denominator*.

THE QUOTIENT RULE

If the bases in the numerator and denominator of a fractional expression are the same and a and b are positive integers, then

$\dfrac{x^a}{x^b} = x^{a-b}$ Use this form if the *larger exponent* is in the *numerator* and $x \neq 0$.

$\dfrac{x^a}{x^b} = \dfrac{1}{x^{b-a}}$ Use this form if the *larger exponent* is in the *denominator* and $x \neq 0$.

Since division by zero is undefined, in all problems in this book we assume that the denominator of any variable expression is not zero.

EXAMPLE 1 Simplify. Leave your answer in exponent form.

(a) $\dfrac{n^9}{n^6}$ (b) $\dfrac{5^8}{5^9}$ (c) $\dfrac{2^7}{3^4}$

Solution

(a) $\dfrac{n^9}{n^6} = n^{9-6}$ There are more factors in the numerator.
The leftover factors are in the numerator.

$\dfrac{n^9}{n^6} = \dfrac{n^3}{1} = n^3 \longleftarrow$

(b) $\dfrac{5^8}{5^9} = \dfrac{1}{5^{9-8}}$ There are more factors in the denominator.

$\dfrac{5^8}{5^9} = \dfrac{1}{5^1}$ or $\dfrac{1}{5}$ The leftover factor is in the denominator.

(c) $\dfrac{2^7}{3^4}$ We cannot divide using the rule for exponents. The bases are not the same.

Practice Problem 1 Simplify. Leave your answer in exponent form.

(a) $\dfrac{4^{11}}{4^7}$ (b) $\dfrac{6^9}{8^{14}}$ (c) $\dfrac{y^5}{y^9}$

NOTE TO STUDENT: *Fully worked-out solutions to all of the Practice Problems can be found at the back of the text starting at page SP-1*

TO THINK ABOUT: When Can We Use the Quotient Rule? Write the numerator and denominator of $\dfrac{2^7}{3^4}$ using repeated multiplication. Do you see why we cannot use the rule for exponents to simplify?

Let's see what happens when the expressions in the numerator and denominator are equal. For example, consider $\dfrac{5^2}{5^2}$. Since any number divided by itself is equal to 1, we know that we can rewrite 1 as $\dfrac{5^2}{5^2}$. Now, using the rules of exponents we have

$$1 = \dfrac{5^2}{5^2} = 5^0 \quad 5^{2-2} = 5^0 \quad \text{Thus, } 1 = 5^0$$

We can generalize that any number (except 0) can be raised to the zero power. The result is 1.

For any nonzero number a, $a^0 = 1$. The expression 0^0 is not defined.

EXAMPLE 2 Simplify. $\dfrac{16x^6 y^0}{20x^8}$

Solution

$$\dfrac{16x^6 y^0}{20x^8} = \dfrac{\overset{1}{\cancel{4}} \cdot 2 \cdot 2 \cdot x^6 y^0}{\underset{1}{\cancel{4}} \cdot 5 \cdot x^8} \quad \text{We factor 16 and 20.}$$

$$= \dfrac{2 \cdot 2 \cdot 1}{5 \cdot x^{8-6}} \quad \dfrac{x^6}{x^8} = \dfrac{1}{x^{8-6}}; \quad y^0 = 1$$

$$= \dfrac{4}{5x^2} \quad \text{The leftover } x \text{ factors are in the denominator.}$$

Practice Problem 2 Simplify.

$$\dfrac{25y^5 x^0}{45y^8}$$

Understanding the Concept

Do I Add, Subtract, Multiply, or Divide Coefficients and Exponents?

What can we do if we forget algebraic rules? Do we add, subtract, or multiply exponents? If we start with a simple problem and then *think* about what it is we are actually trying to do, we can often determine the rules by observing our calculations.

1. $6x^5 + 3x^5 = ?$

We have six x^5's and add three more x^5's; we have nine x^5's.

$6x^5 + 3x^5 = 9x^5$

In this case, we *add* coefficients and the variable stays the same.

2. $(6x^2)(3x^4) = ?$

$$6 \cdot x \cdot x \cdot 3 \cdot x \cdot x \cdot x \cdot x = 6 \cdot 3 \cdot x \cdot x \cdot x \cdot x \cdot x \cdot x$$
$$= 18 \cdot x^6$$
$$(6x^2)(3x^4) = 18x^6$$

In this case, we *multiply* coefficients and then *add* exponents of like bases.

3. $\dfrac{6x^2}{3x} = ?$ $\qquad \dfrac{6x^2}{3x} = \dfrac{2 \cdot 3 \cdot x \cdot x}{3 \cdot x} = 2x$

In this case, we *divide* coefficients and then *subtract* exponents of like bases.

Raising a Power to a Power

If we have $(x^3)^4$, we say that we are *raising a power to a power*. A problem such as $(x^3)^4$ can done by first writing $(x^3)^4$ as a product and then simplifying.

$(x^3)^4$ means $x^3 \cdot x^3 \cdot x^3 \cdot x^3$ By definition of raising a value to the fourth power

$\quad = x^{3+3+3+3}$ Use the product rule of exponents.

$\quad = x^{12}$ Add exponents $3 + 3 + 3 + 3$ to simplify.

EXAMPLE 3 Write $(2^4)^2$ as a product and then simplify. Leave your answer in exponent form.

Solution $(2^4)^2$ means $2^4 \cdot 2^4 = 2^{4+4} = 2^8$

Practice Problem 3 Write $(4^2)^3$ as a product and then simplify. Leave your answer in exponent form.

Since repeated addition can be written as multiplication, we can simplify the calculations in Example 3 as follows.

$\quad (2^4)^2 = 2^{4 \cdot 2} = 2^8$ We multiply exponents since $4 + 4 = 4 \cdot 2$.

This leads to the following rule.

> ### RAISING A POWER TO A POWER OR A PRODUCT TO A POWER
>
> To raise a power to a power, keep the same base and multiply the exponents.
>
> $$(x^a)^b = x^{ab}$$
>
> To raise a product to a power, raise each factor to that power.
>
> $$(xy)^b = x^b y^b$$

EXAMPLE 4   Use the rules for raising a power to a power or a product to a power to simplify. Leave your answer in exponent form.

(a) $(3^3)^3$ (b) $(x^2)^0$ (c) $(4x^4)^5$

Solution

(a) $(3^3)^3 = 3^{(3)(3)} = 3^9$ We multiply exponents.

The base does not change when raising a power to a power.

(b) $(x^2)^0 = x^{(2)(0)} = x^0 = 1$

(c) $(4x^4)^5 = (4^1 \cdot x^4)^5$ We write 4 as 4^1.

$\qquad = 4^{(1)(5)} \cdot x^{(4)(5)}$ We raise each factor to the power 5.

$\qquad = 4^5 \cdot x^{20}$ We multiply exponents.

$\qquad = 4^5 x^{20}$

NOTE TO STUDENT: Fully worked-out solutions to all of the Practice Problems can be found at the back of the text starting at page SP-1

Practice Problem 4   Use the rules for raising a power to a power or a product to a power to simplify. Leave your answer in exponent form.

(a) $(3^3)^4$ (b) $(n^0)^7$ (c) $(3y^4)^6$

Now we introduce a similar rule involving quotients that is very useful.

ADDITIONAL POWER RULE

If a fraction in parentheses is raised to a power, the parentheses indicate that the numerator and denominator are *each* raised to that power.

$$\left(\frac{x}{y}\right)^a = \frac{x^a}{y^a} \quad \text{if } y \neq 0$$

EXAMPLE 5   Simplify. $\left(\dfrac{2}{x}\right)^3$

Solution   We must remember to raise both the numerator and the denominator to the power.

$$\left(\frac{2}{x}\right)^3 = \left(\frac{2^1}{x^1}\right)^3 = \frac{2^{(1)(3)}}{x^{(1)(3)}} = \frac{2^3}{x^3} = \frac{8}{x^3}$$

Practice Problem 5   Simplify.

$$\left(\frac{x}{3}\right)^3$$

Developing Your Study Skills

Success in Mathematics

The Learning Cycle

Reading $\longrightarrow$ Writing

$\uparrow \qquad\qquad \downarrow$

Seeing $\leftarrow$ Verbalizing $\leftarrow$ Listening

Mathematics is a building process, mastered one step at a time. The foundation of this process is composed of a few basic requirements. Those who are successful in mathematics realize the absolute necessity of building a study of

mathematics on the firm foundation of these six minimum requirements.

1. Attend class every day.
2. Read the textbook.
3. Take notes in class.
4. Do assigned homework every day.
5. Get help immediately when needed.
6. Review regularly.

Verbal and Writing Skills *State the rule for simplifying each of the following, then simplify.*

1. (a) $15x^3 + 5x^3$

   (b) $(15x^3)(5x^3)$

   (c) $\dfrac{15x^3}{5x}$

2. (a) $14x^2 + 6x^2$

   (b) $(14x^2)(6x^2)$

   (c) $\dfrac{14x^2}{6x}$

Simplify. In this exercise set, assume that all variables in any denominator are nonzero. Leave your answers in exponent form.

3. $\dfrac{7^4}{7^3}$

4. $\dfrac{5^9}{5^8}$

5. $\dfrac{a^8}{a^3}$

6. $\dfrac{x^7}{x^4}$

7. $\dfrac{5^8}{5^9}$

8. $\dfrac{2^3}{2^7}$

9. $\dfrac{3}{3^6}$

10. $\dfrac{8}{8^4}$

11. $\dfrac{z^4}{y^8}$

12. $\dfrac{z^6}{x^8}$

13. $\dfrac{9^3}{8^8}$

14. $\dfrac{6^6}{7^8}$

15. $\dfrac{z^8}{z^8}$

16. $\dfrac{a^5}{a^5}$

17. $\dfrac{y^3 z^4}{y^5 z^7}$

18. $\dfrac{a^3 b^5}{a^7 b^7}$

19. $\dfrac{m^9 3^6}{m^7 3^7}$

20. $\dfrac{5^6 r^3}{5^2 r^6}$

21. $\dfrac{a^5 7^4}{a^3 7^7}$

22. $\dfrac{p^3 z^9}{p^9 z^2}$

23. $\dfrac{b^9 9^9}{b^7 9^{11} 3^0}$

24. $\dfrac{7^7 r^2 s^0}{7^2 r^6}$

25. $\dfrac{4^6 a b^0}{4^9 a^4 b}$

26. $\dfrac{6^3 x y^0}{6^9 x^6 y}$

Simplify.

27. $\dfrac{20 y^4}{35 y}$

28. $\dfrac{24 x^5}{36 x}$

29. $\dfrac{9 a^4}{27 a^3}$

30. $\dfrac{7 m^5}{21 m^4}$

31. $\dfrac{56 x^9 y^0}{64 x^3}$

32. $\dfrac{32 y^7}{48 y^5 z^0}$

33. $\dfrac{12 x^4 y^2}{15 x y^3}$

34. $\dfrac{20 a^5 b^3}{30 a b^5}$

To Think About Exercises 35–38 *Multiply and write in exponent form.*

35. (a) $z^2 \cdot z^2 \cdot z^2$
    (b) $(z^2)^3$

36. (a) $a^3 \cdot a^3 \cdot a^3$
    (b) $(a^3)^3$

37. (a) $x^4 \cdot x^4$
    (b) $(x^4)^2$

38. (a) $y^6 \cdot y^6$
    (b) $(y^6)^2$

Simplify. Leave your answer in exponent form.

39. $(z^2)^4$

40. $(x^7)^4$

41. $(3^5)^4$

42. $(2^3)^2$

43. $(b^1)^6$

44. $(x^3)^1$

45. $(x^0)^4$

46. $(5^5)^0$

47. $(y^3)^3$

48. $(6^2)^3$

49. $(2^4)^5$

50. $(x^3)^9$

51. $(x^2)^0$

52. $(y^0)^4$

53. $(6^3)^9$

54. $(8^2)^3$

55. $(x^2)^2$

56. $(b^3)^3$

57. $(y^2)^6$

58. $(x^3)^4$

59. $(4x^2)^3$

60. $(5b^4)^6$

61. $(3a^4)^8$

62. $(3y^3)^7$

63. $(2^2x^5)^3$

64. $(3^4y^6)^2$

65. $(8^3n^4)^6$

66. $(6^5b^4)^4$

Simplify.

67. $\left(\dfrac{4}{x}\right)^2$

68. $\left(\dfrac{3}{y}\right)^3$

69. $\left(\dfrac{a}{b}\right)^7$

70. $\left(\dfrac{b}{a}\right)^7$

71. $\left(\dfrac{3}{x}\right)^3$

72. $\left(\dfrac{4}{y}\right)^2$

73. $\left(\dfrac{m}{n}\right)^4$

74. $\left(\dfrac{x}{y}\right)^7$

75. $\left(\dfrac{x}{6}\right)^2$

76. $\left(\dfrac{y}{5}\right)^3$

77. $\left(\dfrac{3}{7}\right)^2$

78. $\left(\dfrac{1}{2}\right)^3$

One Step Further *Simplify.*

79. $\dfrac{25x^2y^3z^4}{135x^7y}$

80. $\dfrac{40a^9b^2c^4}{88a^3b}$

81. $\dfrac{156a^0b^8}{144b^6c^9}$

82. $\dfrac{256x^0y^{15}}{300y^9z^8}$

83. $\left(\dfrac{2y}{5x}\right)^2$

84. $\left(\dfrac{5x}{3y}\right)^2$

85. $\left(\dfrac{3a^2}{2b^3}\right)^3$

86. $\left(\dfrac{4a^3}{3b^5}\right)^3$

Mixed Problems *Simplify.*

87. **(a)** $15x^3 + 5x^3$
(b) $(15x^3)(5x^3)$
(c) $(x^3)^3$
(d) $\dfrac{15x^3}{5x^5}$

88. **(a)** $24x^5 + 6x^5$
(b) $(24x^5)(6x^5)$
(c) $(x^5)^5$
(d) $\dfrac{24x^5}{6x^3}$

89. **(a)** $3x^3 + 9x^3$
(b) $(3x^3)(9x^3)$
(c) $(3x^3)^3$
(d) $\dfrac{3x^3}{9x^4}$

90. **(a)** $7x^6 + 14x^6$
(b) $(7x^6)(14x^6)$
(c) $(7x^6)^2$
(d) $\dfrac{7x^6}{14x^2}$

91. (a) $12x^4 + 3x^4$
  (b) $(12x^4)(3x^4)$
  (c) $(2x^4)^4$
  (d) $\dfrac{2x^4}{3x}$

92. (a) $14x^3 + 3x^3$
  (b) $(14x^3)(3x^3)$
  (c) $(4x^3)^3$
  (d) $\dfrac{4x}{3x^4}$

93. (a) $5y^2 + 15y^2$
  (b) $(5y^2)(15y^2)$
  (c) $(5y^2)^2$
  (d) $\dfrac{5y^2}{15y^7}$

94. (a) $8a^5 + 16a^5$
  (b) $(8a^5)(16a^5)$
  (c) $(8a^5)^5$
  (d) $\dfrac{8a^5}{16a}$

To Think About

95. Find the next row in the triangular pattern below.

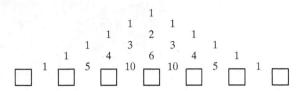

Cumulative Review *Solve.*

96. **[3.2.1]** $3x = 42$

97. **[3.2.1]** $48 = 16x$

98. **[3.2.1]** $(18 - 4) = 7x$

99. **[3.2.1]** $13x = 130$

▲ **100.** **[3.4.4]** Write the area of the rectangle as an algebraic expression and then simplify. $(A = LW)$

$3x + 3$

$2x^2$

101. **[1.9.3]** *College Expenses* Kristina has a $45,000 trust fund for her college expenses. She plans to attend college for 9 months a year, for 4 years, to earn a B.A. During her first two years the on-campus room and board will be $620 per month. For her last two years Kristina will live off campus, and she estimates that her rent will be $350 and food expenses $250 per month for the entire 18 months. Tuition and books will cost $7500 per year. How much should Kristina plan to borrow on a student loan to cover the college expenses that will exceed the amount in her trust fund?

Quick Quiz 4.4

1. Simplify. $\dfrac{a^5b}{a^3b^2}$

2. Simplify. $(7x^3)^2$

3. Simplify. $\left(\dfrac{y}{2}\right)^4$

4. **Concept Check** Explain in words the steps you would need to follow to simplify the expression $\left(\dfrac{6x^2}{3}\right)^3$.

Student Learning Objectives

After studying this section, you will be able to:

 1 Write two quantities with the same units as a ratio.

2 Write two quantities with different units as a unit rate.

3 Solve applied problems involving rates.

1 Writing Two Quantities with the Same Units as a Ratio

A **ratio** is a comparison of two quantities that have the same units. For example, if we compare the 5-foot width of a garden to the 22-foot width of a backyard, the ratio of the lengths would be 5 to 22.

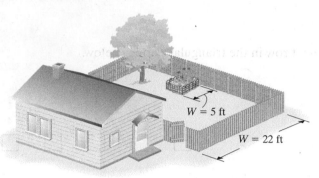

$W = 5$ ft

$W = 22$ ft

We can express a ratio in three ways.

In words:	the ratio of 5 to 22
Using a colon:	$5:22$
Using a fraction:	$\dfrac{5}{22}$

Each of the ways of expressing a ratio is read "5 to 22."

Although a ratio can be written in different forms, it is a fraction and therefore should always be simplified (reduced to lowest terms). However, improper fractions *are not* changed to mixed numbers.

EXAMPLE 1 Write each ratio in simplest form. Express your answer as a fraction.

(a) The ratio of 20 dollars to 35 dollars　　　　**(b)** $14:21$

Solution

(a) 20 dollars to 35 dollars $= \dfrac{20 \text{ dollars}}{35 \text{ dollars}} = \dfrac{\cancel{5} \cdot 4}{\cancel{5} \cdot 7} = \dfrac{4}{7}$

We treat units in the same way we do numbers and variables, for example, $\dfrac{3}{3} = 1, \dfrac{a}{a} = 1,$ and $\dfrac{\text{dollars}}{\text{dollars}} = 1.$

(b) $14:21 = \dfrac{14}{21} = \dfrac{\cancel{7} \cdot 2}{\cancel{7} \cdot 3} = \dfrac{2}{3}$

NOTE TO STUDENT: Fully worked-out solutions to all of the Practice Problems can be found at the back of the text starting at page SP-1

Practice Problem 1 Write each ratio in simplest form. Express your answer as a fraction.

(a) The ratio of 28 feet to 49 feet　　　　**(b)** $27:81$

It is important that you read ratio problems carefully since the *order of quantities* is important, as shown in the next example.

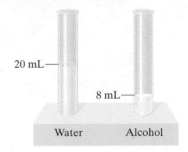

EXAMPLE 2 A mixture consists of 20 milliliters (mL) of water and 8 milliliters of alcohol. Write each ratio as a fraction and reduce to lowest terms.

(a) The ratio of alcohol to water   **(b)** The ratio of water to alcohol

Solution

(a) $\dfrac{\text{alcohol}}{\text{water}} \Rightarrow \dfrac{8 \ \cancel{mL}}{20 \ \cancel{mL}} = \dfrac{\cancel{4} \cdot 2}{\cancel{4} \cdot 5} = \dfrac{2}{5}$ **(b)** $\dfrac{\text{water}}{\text{alcohol}} \Rightarrow \dfrac{20 \ \cancel{mL}}{8 \ \cancel{mL}} = \dfrac{\cancel{4} \cdot 5}{\cancel{4} \cdot 2} = \dfrac{5}{2}$

Practice Problem 2 15 women and 21 men are enrolled in a physical science class. Write each ratio as a fraction and reduce to lowest terms.

(a) The ratio of men to women   **(b)** The ratio of women to men

EXAMPLE 3 Some regions of Alaska receive less annual snowfall than mainland areas of the United States. For example, Barrow, Alaska, located near the Arctic Ocean, receives only 29 inches annually on average, while Chicago's Midway Airport receives an annual average of 46 inches. What is the ratio of the annual average snowfall in Barrow, Alaska, to the annual average snowfall at Midway Airport in Chicago?

Solution

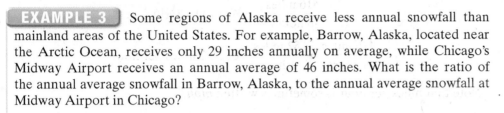

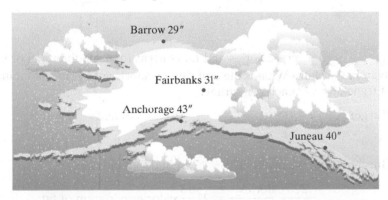

Practice Problem 3 Refer to Example 3 to complete the following problem. Write the ratio of the annual average snowfall at Midway Airport, Chicago, to the annual average snowfall in Barrow, Alaska.

 ## Writing Two Quantities with Different Units as a Unit Rate

A **rate** is a comparison of two quantities with *different* units. Usually, to avoid misunderstanding, we include the units when we write a rate. For example, we write $44 earned in 4 hours as the following rate.

$$\$44 \text{ earned in 4 hours: } \frac{\$44}{4 \text{ hours}} = \frac{\$11}{1 \text{ hour}} \quad \text{We include units in a rate.}$$

Since the denominator is 1, we can write our rate as "*$11 for each hour*" or "*$11 per hour.*" When the denominator is 1, we have the rate for a single unit, which is the **unit rate.** Since the key words *per* and *for each* mean that we divide, to find a unit rate we divide.

Rate: $\dfrac{45 \text{ students}}{2 \text{ teachers}}$ We have different units in a rate.

Unit rate: $\dfrac{126 \text{ trees}}{3 \text{ acres}} = \dfrac{42 \text{ trees}}{1 \text{ acre}}$ or 42 trees per acre

We divide $126 \div 3 = 42$ to find the unit rate.

EXAMPLE 4 Bertha drove her car 416 miles in 8 hours. Find the unit rate in miles per hour.

Solution

$$\frac{416 \text{ miles}}{8 \text{ hours}} \qquad \text{We divide: } 8\overline{)416}.^{52}$$

$$\frac{416 \text{ miles}}{8 \text{ hours}} = \frac{52 \text{ miles}}{1 \text{ hour}} \quad \text{or} \quad 52 \text{ miles per hour}$$

Note that miles per hour is sometimes written *mph*.

Practice Problem 4 Iris travels 90 miles on 5 gallons of gas. Find the unit rate in miles per gallon.

NOTE TO STUDENT: Fully worked-out solutions to all of the Practice Problems can be found at the back of the text starting at page SP-1

EXAMPLE 5 The calories and fat content for 1 medium bag of french fries are given in the chart. What is the unit rate in calories per grams of fat in 1 medium bag of french fries at each restaurant?

(a) Burger King   **(b)** McDonald's

Solution

(a) Burger King: We divide $370 \div 17$ to find the unit rate.

$$\frac{370 \text{ calories}}{17 \text{ grams of fat}} = 21\frac{13}{17} \text{ calories per gram of fat}$$

(b) McDonald's: We divide $440 \div 22$ to find the unit rate.

$$\frac{440 \text{ calories}}{22 \text{ grams of fat}} = 20 \text{ calories per gram of fat}$$

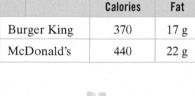

	Calories	Fat
Burger King	370	17 g
McDonald's	440	22 g

Practice Problem 5 C & R construction can dispose of 400 pounds of trash for $26 at the local dump. What is the unit rate in pounds per dollar?

3 Solving Applied Problems Involving Rates

We work with **unit rates** in many areas, such as sports, business, budgeting, and science. Sometimes we want to find the number of boards needed to panel each wall of a room, or we may need to find the number of people needed to complete a task. Often we want to find the best buy for the dollar. These are all applications of unit rates.

EXAMPLE 6 University of Chicago tornado researcher Tetsuya Theodore Fujita cataloged 31,054 tornados in the United States during the 70 years 1916–1985 and found that $\frac{7}{10}$ of the tornados occurred in the spring and early summer.

Write as a unit rate: the average number of tornados per year that occurred in the month of May. Round your answer to the nearest whole number.

Source: "U.S. Tornados Part 1", T. Fujita, University of Chicago

Solution $\dfrac{6859 \text{ tornados in May}}{70 \text{ years}}$

We divide to find the unit rate.

$$\dfrac{97\frac{69}{70}}{70)\overline{6859}} \text{ or approximately } 98 \text{ tornados per year in May}$$

Note that we rounded $97\frac{69}{70}$ to 98 because the fraction $\frac{69}{70}$ is close to 1.

Practice Problem 6 Refer to Example 6. Write as a unit rate: the average number of tornados per year that occur in the month of June. Round your answer to the nearest whole number.

EXAMPLE 7 Sunshine Preschool has a staffing policy requiring that for every 60 children, there are 3 preschool teachers, and for every 24 children, there are 2 aides.

(a) How many children per teacher does the preschool have?

(b) How many children per aide does the preschool have?

(c) If there are 60 students at the preschool, how many aides must there be to satisfy the staffing policy?

Solution

(a) Children per teacher:

$$\dfrac{\text{children}}{\text{teacher}} \Rightarrow \dfrac{60 \text{ children}}{3 \text{ teachers}} = \dfrac{20 \text{ children}}{1 \text{ teacher}} \text{ or } 20 \text{ children per teacher}$$

(b) Children per aide:

$$\dfrac{\text{children}}{\text{aide}} \Rightarrow \dfrac{24 \text{ children}}{2 \text{ aides}} = \dfrac{12 \text{ children}}{1 \text{ aide}} \text{ or } 12 \text{ children per aide}$$

(c) Since every 12 children require 1 aide, we divide $60 \div 12$ to find how many aides are needed for 60 children.

$$60 \div 12 = 5 \text{ aides for 60 children}$$

Practice Problem 7   Autumn Home, a private nursing home, has a medical staffing policy requiring that for every 40 patients there are 2 registered nurses (RNs), and for every 30 patients there are 2 nurse's aides.

(a) How many patients per RN does Autumn Home have?

(b) How many patients per aide does Autumn Home have?

(c) If there are 60 patients at Autumn Home, how many aides must there be to satisfy the staffing policy?

We often ask ourselves questions like, "Which package is the better buy, the pack of 3 or the pack of 7?" "Is it cheaper to buy the 12-ounce box or the 16-ounce box?" We find the *unit price* (price per item) to answer these types of questions.

EXAMPLE 8   The Computer Warehouse is having a sale on black print cartridges. A package of 6 sells for $96, and the same brand in a package of 8 sells for $136.

(a) Find each unit price.

(b) Which is the better buy?

Solution

(a) $\dfrac{\$96}{6} = \$16$ per cartridge; $\dfrac{\$136}{8} = \$17$ per cartridge

(b) The package of 6 cartridges is the better buy.

Practice Problem 8   The Linen Factory is having a sale on their designer hand towels. The Hazelette Collection is on sale at 6 for $78, and the Springview Collection is on sale at 9 for $108.

(a) Find each unit price.

(b) Which is the better buy?

NOTE TO STUDENT: Fully worked-out solutions to all of the Practice Problems can be found at the back of the text starting at page SP-1

Developing Your Study Skills

Positive Thinking

Some people convince themselves that they cannot learn mathematics. If you are concerned that you may have difficulty in this course, it is time to reprogram your thinking. Replace those negative thoughts with positive ones such as

"I can learn mathematics if I work at it. I will give this math class my best shot."

You will be pleasantly surprised at the difference this positive attitude makes!

Now, some might wonder how a change in attitude can make a difference. Well, the approach and features in this book can be the keys to your success. Here are a few features that you should pay special attention to:

• Developing Your Study Skills boxes offer tips on how to study. If you know how to study, learning will be far easier.

• Understanding the Concept boxes help you understand what you are doing and why you are doing it. These explanations and other descriptions relate the concepts to other topics such as algebra and applications.

• Exercises develop the fundamentals on which the concepts are built. Many students do not learn because they miss certain building blocks. For example, how can someone learn long division if he or she doesn't know multiplication facts?

If you take this advice to heart, you'll be off to a good start. Keep up the good work.

Exercises

1. Name a few things that you plan to do in this class to help you be successful.

2. Write in words two positive thoughts about mathematics and/or your ability to complete this course.

Verbal and Writing Skills

1. Explain the difference between a ratio and a rate.

2. Explain the difference between a rate and a unit rate.

Write each ratio as a fraction in simplest form.

3. 25 to 45

4. 12 to 32

5. 35 : 10

6. 46 : 14

7. 54 : 70

8. 30 : 45

9. 34 minutes to 12 minutes

10. 24 dollars to 16 dollars

11. 14 gallons to 35 gallons

12. 25 feet to 45 feet

13. 17 hours to 41 hours

14. 3 inches to 11 inches

15. $121 to $423

16. $85 to $151

Applications *Write each ratio as a fraction and simplify.*

17. *Solution Mixture* A mixture contains 35 milliliters of water and 15 milliliters of chlorine.

   (a) State the ratio of chlorine to water.

   (b) State the ratio of water to chlorine.

18. *Field Trip* The marine science field trip consisted of 40 juniors and 22 seniors.

   (a) State the ratio of seniors to juniors.

   (b) State the ratio of juniors to seniors.

19. *Basketball* The Willow Brook recreational basketball team had a season record of 29 wins and 13 losses.

   (a) State the ratio of wins to losses.

   (b) State the ratio of losses to wins.

20. *Men vs. Women* A choir consists of 17 men and 11 women.

   (a) State the ratio of men to women.

   (b) State the ratio of women to men.

Fatty Acids Write as a ratio and simplify.

21. The number of grams of trans-fatty acids in a serving of corn flakes cereal to the number of grams in a serving of margarine

22. The number of grams of trans-fatty acids in a serving of white bread to the number of grams in a serving of potato chips

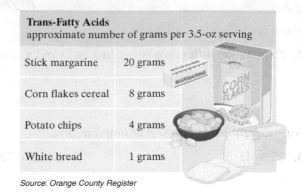

Trans-Fatty Acids
approximate number of grams per 3.5-oz serving

Stick margarine	20 grams
Corn flakes cereal	8 grams
Potato chips	4 grams
White bread	1 grams

Source: Orange County Register

Suspension Bridge Use the following information to answer exercises 23 and 24. The world's longest suspension bridge is Japan's Akashi Kaikyo Bridge. The bridge is 6532 feet long and links Kobe and Awaji Island.

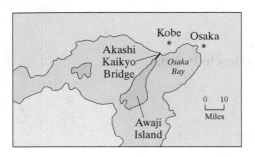

10 Longest Suspension Bridges

Akashi Kaikyo, Japan	6532 ft
Great Belt East, Denmark	5328 ft
Runyang South, China	4888 ft
Humber River, England	4625 ft
Jiangyin, China	4543 ft
Tsing Ma, China	4517 ft
Verrazano Narrows, New York City	4258 ft
Golden Gate, San Francisco	4200 ft
Yangluo, China	4200 ft
Hoga Kusten, Sweden	3970 ft

Source: www.tkk.fi

Write as a ratio and simplify.

23. The length of the shortest of the 10 suspension bridges to the length of the longest suspension bridge

24. The length of the Golden Gate Bridge to the length of the Great Belt East Bridge

What is the unit rate in calories per gram of fat?

25. 410 calories for 19 grams of fat

26. 205 calories for 7 grams of fat

What is the unit rate in miles per gallon?

27. Traveling 300 miles on 15 gallons of gas

28. Traveling 405 miles on 18 gallons of gas

What is the unit rate in dollars per hour?

29. Earning $304 in 38 hours

30. Earning $455 in 35 hours

What is the unit rate in miles per hour (mph)?

31. Traveling 320 miles in 6 hours

32. Traveling 410 miles in 7 hours

Applications

33. **Gas Mileage** A car travels 616 miles on 28 gallons of gas. Find how many miles the car can be driven on one gallon of gas.

34. **Walking Speed** Michelle and Debi walk for 75 minutes. They average 6525 steps in that time. How many steps per minute do they take on average?

35. **Book Club** Marci joined a book club that charges $108 for 9 books. What is the cost per book?

36. **CD Club** Delroy joined a CD club that charges $189 for 21 CDs. How much per CD did Delroy pay?

37. **Student-Teacher Ratio** The J. D. Robertson Academy of Arts school has a staffing policy requiring that for every 90 students there are 5 instructors, and for every 30 students there are 2 tutors.

(a) How many students per instructor does the academy have?

(b) How many students per tutor does the academy have?

(c) How many tutors are needed to satisfy the staffing policy if there are 90 students in the academy?

38. **Agent-Client Ratio** The All Point Insurance Group requires each office to have 4 insurance agents for every 620 clients and 5 clerical staff members for every 310 clients.

(a) How many clients per agent does the group have?

(b) How many clients per clerical staff member does the group have?

(c) How many clerical staff members would be required for an office that has 930 clients?

39. **Comparison Shopping** The Crystal Shop has their Gold Lace crystal wine glasses on sale. A box of 8 glasses is $96, and a box of 6 is $78.

(a) Find each unit price.

(b) Which is the better buy?

40. **Comparison Shopping** The tanning salon has a special on their tanning sessions: 12 sessions for $96 or 15 sessions for $135.

(a) Find each unit price.

(b) Which is the better deal?

41. **Comparison Shopping** The music shop sells used CDs 4 for $32 or 6 for $48.

(a) Find each unit price.

(b) Which is the better deal?

42. **Comparison Shopping** Computer World is having a sale on printer paper: 4 reams of paper for $12 or 7 reams of paper for $21.

(a) Find each unit price.

(b) Which is the better deal?

Sales Statistics Johnson and Brothers Suits recorded the sales shown in the bar graph for the third quarter of the year. Use the graph to answer exercises 43 and 44.

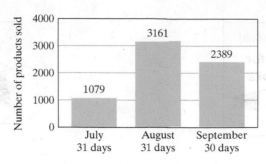

43. Write as a unit rate: the average number of sales per day in the month of August. Round your answer to the nearest whole number.

44. Write as a unit rate: the average number of sales per day in the month of July. Round your answer to the nearest whole number.

Cumulative Review *Solve and check your answer.*

45. **[3.1.2]** $x - 12 = 25$

46. **[3.1.2]** $x + 15 = 40$

47. **[3.1.2]** $5x - 4x + 6 = 14$

48. **[3.1.2]** $-2 - 5 + a = 15$

49. **[2.3.3]** *High/Low Temperature* The record high temperature for a city in the Midwest was 101°F, and the record low recorded was −8°F. Find the difference in temperature between the record high and low.

50. **[2.2.4]** *Football* On the first play of a college football game, the home team lost 4 yards. On the second play, a pass resulted in a gain of 8 yards. If there was a penalty against the home team on the third play resulting in a loss of 5 yards, determine the net gain (or loss) of the home team after the third play.

Quick Quiz 4.5

1. Sara and Mark ran for president of their elementary school. Mark received 45 of the votes while Sara received 75 of the votes. Write the ratio and simplify: the number of votes Mark received to the number of votes Sara received.

2. Reza cooked 30 hot dogs in 12 minutes. How many hot dogs did he cook per minute?

3. Chocolate Delite is having a sale on its sugar free chocolate bars: $72 for 36 bars or $60 for 18 bars. Which is the better buy?

4. **Concept Check** A large furniture store determined they needed to have 8 sales people in the store for every 160 customers. Explain how to determine how many sales people per customer the store has.

4.6 PROPORTIONS AND APPLICATIONS

Writing Proportions

Recall that the fractions $\frac{4}{8}$ and $\frac{1}{2}$ are equivalent fractions: $\frac{4}{8} = \frac{1}{2}$. If these fractions represent ratios or rates, we say that they are *proportional.* In other words, a **proportion** states that two ratios or two rates are equal. For example, $\frac{4}{8} = \frac{1}{2}$ is a proportion and $\frac{2 \text{ trees}}{7 \text{ feet}} = \frac{4 \text{ trees}}{14 \text{ feet}}$ is also a proportion. The proportion $\frac{4}{8} = \frac{1}{2}$ is read "four *is to* eight as one *is to* two."

Student Learning Objectives

After studying this section, you will be able to:

1 Write proportions.

2 Determine if statements are proportions.

3 Find the missing number in proportions.

4 Solve applied problems involving proportions.

> A **proportion** states that two ratios or two rates are equal.
>
> If $\dfrac{a}{b}$ and $\dfrac{c}{d}$ are two equal ratios, then $\dfrac{a}{b} = \dfrac{c}{d}$ is a proportion.

When we write a proportion we must be sure that the units are in the appropriate position. One way to write a proportion is for the numerators to have the same units and the denominators to have the same units. In other words, we write each fraction as we would a rate or a ratio. In this book we write proportions in this manner.

EXAMPLE 1 Translate the statement into a proportion. 2 waiters is to 6 tables as 8 waiters is to 24 tables.

Solution   2 waiters is to 6 tables as 8 waiters is to 24 tables

$$\frac{2 \text{ waiters}}{6 \text{ tables}} = \frac{8 \text{ waiters}}{24 \text{ tables}}$$

Practice Problem 1 Translate the statement into a proportion. 3 nails is to 6 feet as 9 nails is to 18 feet.

EXAMPLE 2 Translate the statement into a proportion. If 6 pounds of flour cost \$2, then 18 pounds will cost \$6.

Solution   We can restate as follows: 6 pounds is to \$2 as 18 pounds is to \$6.

$$\frac{6 \text{ pounds}}{2 \text{ dollars}} = \frac{18 \text{ pounds}}{6 \text{ dollars}}$$ We write pounds in the numerator. We write dollars in the denominator.

Practice Problem 2 Translate the statement into a proportion. If it takes 4 hours to drive 144 miles, it will take 6 hours to drive 216 miles.

 Determining If Statements Are Proportions

A proportion states that two ratios or two rates are equal. Since ratios and rates are fractions, a proportion is a statement that 2 fractions are equal. Therefore, to determine if a statement is a proportion we must verify that the fractions in the proportion are equal.

How can we *check* to see if two fractions are equal? We use the **equality test for fractions,** which states that if two fractions are equal, their cross products are equal. By **cross product** we mean the denominator of one fraction times the numerator of the other fraction.

EQUALITY TEST FOR FRACTIONS

For any two fractions where $b \neq 0, d \neq 0$,

$$\frac{a}{b} = \frac{c}{d} \text{ if and only if } d \cdot a = b \cdot c$$

In other words, two fractions are equal if the cross products are equal.

If two fractions are unequal (we use the symbol $\neq$), their cross products are unequal.

EXAMPLE 3 Use the equality test for fractions to see if the fractions are equal.

(a) $\dfrac{2}{11} \stackrel{?}{=} \dfrac{18}{99}$

(b) $\dfrac{3}{16} \stackrel{?}{=} \dfrac{12}{62}$

Solution We form the cross products to determine if the fractions are equal.

Products are equal. Products are *not* equal.

(a) | $99 \cdot 2 = 198$ | $11 \cdot 18 = 198$ |

(b) | $62 \cdot 3 = 186$ | $16 \cdot 12 = 192$ |

$$\frac{2}{11} \diagdown\!\!\!\diagup \frac{18}{99} \qquad\qquad \frac{3}{16} \diagdown\!\!\!\diagup \frac{12}{62}$$

Since $198 = 198$, we know that $\dfrac{2}{11} = \dfrac{18}{99}$.

Since $186 \neq 192$, we know that $\dfrac{3}{16} \neq \dfrac{12}{62}$.

Practice Problem 3 Use the equality test for fractions to see if the fractions are equal.

(a) $\dfrac{4}{22} \stackrel{?}{=} \dfrac{12}{87}$

(b) $\dfrac{84}{108} \stackrel{?}{=} \dfrac{7}{9}$

NOTE TO STUDENT: Fully worked-out solutions to all of the Practice Problems can be found at the back of the text starting at page SP-1

Since a proportion is just a statement that two fractions are equal, we can use the equality test for fractions to determine if a statement is a proportion.

DETERMINING IF A STATEMENT IS A PROPORTION

To determine if a statement is a proportion, we use the equality test for fractions, which states that two fractions are equal if their cross products are equal.

EXAMPLE 4   Determine if the statement is a proportion.

(a) $\dfrac{16 \text{ points}}{35 \text{ games}} \overset{?}{=} \dfrac{48 \text{ points}}{125 \text{ games}}$

(b) $\dfrac{22}{29} \overset{?}{=} \dfrac{88}{116}$

Solution   We check $\dfrac{16}{35} \overset{?}{=} \dfrac{48}{125}$ by forming the two cross products.

(a) $125 \cdot 16 = 2000$ $\quad \dfrac{16}{35} \overset{?}{=} \dfrac{48}{125} \quad$ $35 \cdot 48 = 1680$

The two cross products are *not* equal.

Thus $\dfrac{16 \text{ points}}{35 \text{ games}} \neq \dfrac{48 \text{ points}}{125 \text{ games}}$. This is not a proportion.

(b) We form the two cross products.

$116 \cdot 22 = 2552$ $\quad \dfrac{22}{29} \overset{?}{=} \dfrac{88}{116} \quad$ $29 \cdot 88 = 2552$

The two cross products are equal. Thus $\dfrac{22}{29} = \dfrac{88}{116}$. This is a proportion.

Practice Problem 4   Determine if the statement is a proportion.

(a) $\dfrac{14 \text{ opals}}{45 \text{ diamonds}} \overset{?}{=} \dfrac{42 \text{ opals}}{135 \text{ diamonds}}$

(b) $\dfrac{32}{72} \overset{?}{=} \dfrac{128}{144}$

③ Finding the Missing Number in Proportions

Sometimes one of the quantities in a proportion is unknown. We can find this unknown quantity by finding the cross products and solving the resulting equation.

PROCEDURE TO SOLVE FOR A MISSING NUMBER IN A PROPORTION

1. Find the cross products and form an equation.

$$\frac{x}{21} = \frac{2}{7}$$
$$7 \cdot x = 21 \cdot 2$$

2. Solve the equation by dividing on both sides so that the variable stands alone.

$$\frac{7x}{7} = \frac{42}{7}$$

3. Simplify the result.

$$x = 6$$

4. Check your answer.

$$\frac{6}{21} \overset{?}{=} \frac{2}{7}$$
$$6 \cdot 7 \overset{?}{=} 21 \cdot 2$$
$$42 = 42 \quad \checkmark$$

EXAMPLE 5 Find the value of n in $\frac{n}{24} = \frac{15}{60}$.

Solution

$$\frac{n}{24} = \frac{15}{60}$$

$$60 \cdot n = 24 \cdot 15 \quad \text{Find the cross products and form an equation.}$$

$$60n = 360 \quad \text{Simplify.}$$

$$\frac{60 \cdot n}{60} = \frac{360}{60} \quad \text{Divide by 60 on both sides of the equation.}$$

$$n = 6 \quad \text{Divide: } 60 \div 60 = 1; 360 \div 60 = 6$$

Check whether the proportion is true.

$$\frac{6}{24} \stackrel{?}{=} \frac{15}{60}$$

$$60 \cdot 6 \stackrel{?}{=} 24 \cdot 15 \quad \text{We check cross products.}$$

$$360 = 360 \quad \checkmark$$

Practice Problem 5 Find the value of n in

$$\frac{n}{18} = \frac{28}{72}.$$

NOTE TO STUDENT: Fully worked-out solutions to all of the Practice Problems can be found at the back of the text starting at page SP-1

Understanding the Concept

Reducing a Proportion

Can we reduce a proportion before we solve for the missing number in the proportion? Yes. If you can see that the ratio or rate without the variable can be reduced, you may reduce it, and the answer will still be correct. Let's look at the proportion in Example 5 and observe what happens when we reduce the ratio $\frac{15}{60}$.

$$\frac{n}{24} = \frac{15}{60} \quad \text{We see that we can reduce } \frac{15}{60}.$$

$$\frac{n}{24} = \frac{1}{4} \quad \text{Reduce: } \frac{15}{60} = \frac{\cancel{3} \cdot \cancel{5}}{\cancel{3} \cdot 4 \cdot \cancel{5}} = \frac{1}{4}.$$

$$4 \cdot n = 24 \cdot 1 \quad \text{Cross products.}$$

$$4n = 24 \quad \text{This step is easier when we reduce. Do you see why?}$$

$$\frac{4n}{4} = \frac{24}{4} \quad \text{Divide by 4 on both sides.}$$

$$n = 6 \quad \text{We see that the answer is the same.}$$

Exercise

1. Why can we reduce a ratio or rate and still get the correct answer when we solve a proportion?

 Solving Applied Problems Involving Proportions

When a situation involves a ratio or rate, we can use a proportion to find the solution. Let's examine a variety of applied problems that can be solved with proportions.

EXAMPLE 6 Johanna owns two rectangular plots of land that have the same dimensions. She subdivides one into 5 equal parcels and the other into 7 equal parcels. For the same price you can buy either 3 of the 5 parcels or 4 of the 7 parcels. Do the two parcels for sale yield the same amount of land?

Solution We must determine if 3 out of 5 parcels is equivalent to 4 out of 7 parcels. We have 3 of the 5 parcels → $\frac{3}{5}$; 4 of the 7 parcels → $\frac{4}{7}$.

We use the equality test for fractions to determine if we have a proportion.

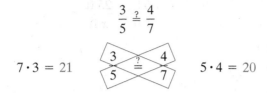

$$\frac{3}{5} \overset{?}{=} \frac{4}{7}$$

$$7 \cdot 3 = 21 \qquad \frac{3}{5} \overset{?}{=} \frac{4}{7} \qquad 5 \cdot 4 = 20$$

The cross products are *not* equal. Thus $\frac{3}{5} \neq \frac{4}{7}$ and this is *not* a proportion. The two parcels do not yield the same amount of land.

Practice Problem 6 Brett owns two square plots of land that have the same dimensions. He subdivides one into 8 equal parcels and the other into 11 equal parcels. For the same price you can buy either 7 of the 8 parcels or 10 of the 11 parcels. Do the two parcels yield the same amount of land?

You can solve many problems using proportions. To solve the problem in Example 6 we had to determine if the statement was a proportion. Often we can write a proportion that has a missing number to solve a problem, as you will see in the next example.

EXAMPLE 7 Kim Nguyen is planning a company party for 120 people. The delicatessen told her that 3 quarts of potato salad will serve 24 people. How many quarts of potato salad should Kim order for the party?

Solution We write the statement in words that represents the proportion, and then set up the proportion. We let n represent the number of quarts of potato salad Kim must order.

3 quarts of potato salad is to 24 people as n quarts of potato salad is to 120 people.

$$\frac{3 \text{ quarts}}{24 \text{ people}} = \frac{n \text{ quarts}}{120 \text{ people}}$$

We must solve for n.

$$\frac{3}{24} = \frac{n}{120}$$

$$\frac{1}{8} = \frac{n}{120} \qquad \text{We see that the fraction } \frac{3}{24} \text{ can be reduced to } \frac{1}{8}.$$

$$120 \cdot 1 = 8n \qquad \text{We form the cross product.}$$

$$\frac{120 \cdot 1}{8} = \frac{8n}{8} \qquad \text{We divide both sides by 8 to solve for } n.$$

$$15 = n \qquad \text{We simplify.}$$

Kim must order 15 quarts of potato salad for the party.

Practice Problem 7 Mary Lou's Catering has a policy that when planning a buffet there should be 18 desserts for every 15 people who will be attending the buffet. How many desserts should the catering company plan to serve at a buffet if 180 people are expected to attend?

▲ **EXAMPLE 8** Estelle has a fence in her yard around her vegetable garden. The garden is 6 feet wide and 7 feet long. The yard's dimensions are proportional to the garden's. What is the length of the yard if the width is 25 feet?

Solution First, we set up the proportion, letting the letter x represent the length of the yard.

$$\frac{\text{width of garden}}{\text{length of garden}} = \frac{\text{width of yard}}{\text{length of yard}}$$

$$\frac{6 \text{ ft}}{7 \text{ ft}} \stackrel{?}{=} \frac{25 \text{ ft}}{x \text{ ft}}$$

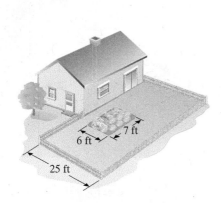

Now we solve for x.

$$\frac{6}{7} = \frac{25}{x}$$

$6x = 7 \times 25$ We form the cross product.

$6x = 175$ We simplify.

$$\frac{6x}{6} = \frac{175}{6}$$

$x = 29\dfrac{1}{6}$ We change $\frac{175}{6}$ to the mixed number $29\frac{1}{6}$.

The length of the yard is $29\frac{1}{6}$ feet.

▲ **Practice Problem 8** Refer to Example 8 to answer the following. If the width of the yard is 20 feet, what must the length of the yard be for the dimensions of the yard to be proportional to those of the garden?

EXAMPLE 9 Two partners, Cleo and Julie, invest money in their small business at the ratio 3 to 5, with Cleo investing the smaller amount. If Cleo invested $6000, how much did Julie invest?

Solution The ratio *3 to 5* represents Cleo's investment *to* Julie's investment.

$$\frac{3}{5} = \frac{\text{Cleo's investment of } \$6000}{\text{Julie's investment of } \$x}$$

$$\frac{3}{5} = \frac{6000}{x}$$

$3x = 30,000$

$$\frac{3x}{3} = \frac{30,000}{3}$$

$x = 10,000$

Julie invested $10,000 in their business.

Practice Problem 9 Refer to Example 9 to answer the following. Cleo and Julie also split the profits from the partnership in the same ratio, 3 to 5. If Cleo receives $2400 for her share of the profit, how much does Julie receive in profits?

NOTE TO STUDENT: Fully worked-out solutions to all of the Practice Problems can be found at the back of the text starting at page SP-1

PRACTICE   WATCH   DOWNLOAD   READ   REVIEW

Verbal and Writing Skills

1. Why should we be able to see that $\frac{55}{55} = \frac{621}{621}$ without doing any calculations?

2. Why should we be able to see that $\frac{1}{8} < \frac{8}{9}$ without doing any calculations?

Translate each statement into a proportion.

3. 2 is to 7 as 24 is to 84.

4. 6 is to 11 as 30 is to 55.

5. 12 goals is to 7 games as 24 goals is to 14 games.

6. 16 doctors is to 5 nurses as 48 doctors is to 15 nurses.

7. 3 is to 8 as 18 is to 48.

8. 2 is to 9 as 8 is to 36.

Translate each statement into a proportion.

9. **Fat Content** If 14 crackers contain 6 grams of fat, then 70 crackers contain 30 grams of fat.

10. **Reading Maps** If 3 inches on a map represent 270 miles, 6 inches represent 540 miles.

11. **Pulley Rotations** If a pulley can complete $3\frac{1}{2}$ rotations in 2 minutes, it should complete 14 rotations in 8 minutes.

12. **Fabric Needed** If it takes $2\frac{1}{4}$ yards of material to make 1 skirt, it will take 9 yards to make 4 skirts.

13. **Basketball** If Matt averages 4 baskets out of 7 free throws attempted in a basketball game, he should make 12 out of 21 free throws.

14. **Basketball** If Sal averages 2 baskets out of 5 free throws attempted in a basketball game, he should make 12 out of 30 free throws.

Use the equality test for fractions to determine if the fractions are equal.

15. $\dfrac{5}{8} \overset{?}{=} \dfrac{30}{45}$

16. $\dfrac{4}{7} \overset{?}{=} \dfrac{28}{49}$

17. $\dfrac{6}{11} \overset{?}{=} \dfrac{42}{77}$

18. $\dfrac{11}{16} \overset{?}{=} \dfrac{33}{36}$

Determine if each statement is a proportion.

19. $\dfrac{2}{7} \overset{?}{=} \dfrac{8}{28}$

20. $\dfrac{5}{8} \overset{?}{=} \dfrac{25}{40}$

21. $\dfrac{14}{19} \overset{?}{=} \dfrac{26}{29}$

22. $\dfrac{15}{37} \overset{?}{=} \dfrac{19}{39}$

23. $\dfrac{2 \text{ American dollars}}{11 \text{ Euros}} \overset{?}{=} \dfrac{65 \text{ American dollars}}{135 \text{ Euros}}$

24. $\dfrac{6 \text{ defective parts}}{109 \text{ parts produced}} \overset{?}{=} \dfrac{20 \text{ defective parts}}{401 \text{ parts produced}}$

Find the value of x in each proportion. Check your answer.

25. $\dfrac{x}{8} = \dfrac{5}{2}$

26. $\dfrac{x}{10} = \dfrac{6}{5}$

27. $\dfrac{12}{x} = \dfrac{2}{5}$

28. $\dfrac{4}{x} = \dfrac{2}{7}$

29. $\dfrac{12}{18} = \dfrac{x}{21}$

30. $\dfrac{12}{18} = \dfrac{x}{3}$

31. $\dfrac{15}{6} = \dfrac{10}{x}$

32. $\dfrac{25}{10} = \dfrac{20}{x}$

Find the value of n.

33. $\dfrac{80 \text{ gallons}}{24 \text{ acres}} = \dfrac{20 \text{ gallons}}{n \text{ acres}}$

34. $\dfrac{70 \text{ women}}{25 \text{ men}} = \dfrac{14 \text{ women}}{n \text{ men}}$

35. $\dfrac{n \text{ grams}}{15 \text{ liters}} = \dfrac{12 \text{ grams}}{45 \text{ liters}}$

36. $\dfrac{n \text{ miles}}{15 \text{ gallons}} = \dfrac{16 \text{ miles}}{3 \text{ gallons}}$

Applications

37. *Typing Speed* Mark can type 400 words in 5 minutes, and John can type 675 words in 9 minutes. Do they type at the same rate?

38. *Soccer Goals* Amy scored 4 goals in 7 soccer games, and Sara scored 6 goals in 9 soccer games. Do they score at the same rate?

39. *Size Comparison* Two cakes for a banquet are the same size. One cake is cut into 30 pieces and the other is cut into 25 pieces. Is 18 out of 30 slices of cake the same amount as 15 out of 25 slices of cake?

▲ **40.** *Land Parcels* Lester owns two large farms with square plots of the same dimensions. He subdivides one farm into 3 equal parcels and the other into 4 equal parcels. For the same price you can buy either 2 of 3 parcels or 3 of 4 parcels. Do the parcels yield the same amount of land?

▲ **41. *Parcels of Land*** Jason owns two square plots of land that have the same dimensions. He subdivides one into 4 equal parcels and the other into 5 equal parcels. For the same price you can buy either 3 of the 4 parcels or 4 of the 5 parcels. Do the two parcels yield the same amount of land?

42. *Pizza Slices* Two pizzas are the same size. One pizza is cut into 8 slices, while the other pizza is cut into 12 slices. Is 6 out of 8 slices of pizza the same amount as 9 out of 12 slices?

43. *Calories* If 2 servings of cereal contain 126 calories, then how many calories are there in 5 servings of cereal?

44. *Medicine Dosage* If a 200-pound man can have 1000 milligrams of a medicine a day, how much can a 120-pound woman have?

45. *Calories* A 1-ounce serving of Deluxe Mixed Nuts contains 170 calories. How many calories are there in a 40-ounce jar?

46. *Baseball* A baseball player gets 20 hits out of 50 times at bat. How many hits must she get in her next 150 times at bat to keep her batting average the same?

47. *Snickers Candy* In 1999 the Snickers candy bar was the most popular candy bar, with sales reaching $120 million. In one day, 16 million are made. At this rate how many Snickers bars are made in 7 days? (*Source:* Orange County Register)

48. *M&M Candy* Over 300 million M&Ms were produced each day in the United States in 1999. The process to make one M&M takes 4 hours from the initial mix to printing an M on every shell. If 1 bag of M&Ms contains approximately 60 M&Ms, how many processing hours does it take for 1 bag of M&Ms? (*Source:* Orange County Register)

49. *Scale Drawing* In a scale drawing, a 210-foot-tall building is drawn 3 inches high. If another building is drawn 5 inches high, how tall is that building?

50. *Ice Cream* If 100 grams of ice cream contain 15 grams of fat, how much fat is in 260 grams of ice cream?

51. *Weight on Pluto* If a 120-pound person weighs approximately 8 pounds on Pluto, how much does a 150-pound person weigh on Pluto?

52. *Reading Maps* On a tour guide map of Ohio, 2 inches on the map represent 260 miles. How many miles do 3 inches represent?

53. *Shares of Stock* In a stock split, each person received 8 shares for each 5 shares that he or she held. If a person had 850 shares of stock in the company, how many shares did she receive in the stock split?

54. *Bicycle Speed* If Wendy pedals her bicycle at 84 revolutions per minute, she travels at 14 miles per hour. How fast does she go if she pedals at 96 revolutions per minute?

55. *Stereo Speaker* A 100-watt stereo system needs copper speaker wire that is 30 millimeters thick to handle the output of sound clearly. How thick would the speaker wire need to be if you had a 140-watt stereo and you wanted the same ratio of watts to millimeters?

56. *Weed Killer* A bottle of spurge and oxalis killer for your lawn states that you need to use 2 tablespoons to treat 300 square feet of lawn. How many tablespoons will you need to use to treat 1500 square feet of lawn?

▲ **57.** *Pool Fence Dimension* Julio wants to put a fence around his rectangular pool, which is 12 feet wide and 18 feet long. If the size of the yard will only allow for a fence that is 30 feet long and Julio wants the dimensions of the enclosed area to be proportional to those of the pool, how wide should the fence be?

▲ **58.** *Patio Enlargement* Devon has a small concrete patio 5 feet wide and 7 feet long in his yard. He wants to enlarge the patio, keeping the dimensions of the new patio proportional to those of the old patio. If he has room to increase the length to 21 feet, how wide should the patio be?

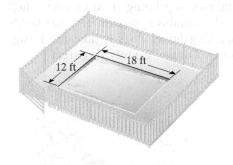

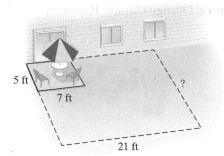

Profit and Loss *Use the following information to answer exercises 59 and 60.*

Two partners, John Ling and Kelvey Marks, each invest money in their business at a ratio of 6 to 7, with Kelvey investing the larger amount.

59. If John invested $2400, how much did Kelvey invest?

60. If the profits from the partnership are distributed to John and Kelvey based on the ratio of their investment, how much profit will John receive if Kelvey receives $798 in profits?

One Step Further

Write as a proportion.

61. $\frac{1}{3}$ is to $\frac{1}{8}$ as $\frac{1}{4}$ is to $\frac{3}{32}$.

62. $\frac{1}{5}$ is to $\frac{1}{9}$ as $\frac{1}{6}$ is to $\frac{5}{54}$.

Mixed Problems

Payroll Deductions *Renée Sharp received a promotion from file clerk to receptionist at Elen Insurance Group. She earns a monthly salary of $1950 in her new position as a receptionist instead of a weekly salary of $325 as a file clerk. Assume that Renée's deductions as a receptionist remain proportional to her deductions as a file clerk as you answer exercises 63–68.*

Weekly paycheck

Employee		Position		ELEN	
Renee Sharp		File Clerk		ELEN INSURANCE GROUP	

Total Gross Pay	Federal Withholding	State Withholding	Retirement	Insurance	Net Pay
$ 325	$ 40	$ 22	$ 32	$ 16	$ 215

Monthly paycheck

Employee		Position		ELEN	
Renee Sharp		Receptionist		ELEN INSURANCE GROUP	

Total Gross Pay	Federal Withholding	State Withholding	Retirement	Insurance	Net Pay
$ 1950					

Determine the following information about her new position as a receptionist.

63. Find the federal withholding.

64. Find the state withholding.

65. Find the retirement deduction.

66. Find the insurance deduction.

67. Find Renée's take-home pay.

68. When Renée worked as a file clerk, she placed $20 a week in her savings account. How much should Renée place in her savings account each month so that her monthly savings contribution is proportional to the amount she saved as a clerk?

To Think About

▲ **69.** ***Box Dimensions*** A box has dimensions of $L = 2$ inches, $W = 3$ inches, and $H = 5$ inches. If you increase the length of this box to 6 inches, what do the width and height have to be so that the dimensions of the new box are proportional to the dimensions of the original box?

▲ **70.** ***Picture Frames*** Helena is making three frames for her living room wall. She wants three different-sized frames with dimensions that are proportional. If the smallest frame is 5 inches wide by 7 inches high, and the largest frame is 21 inches high, what must the width of the largest frame be? What must the dimensions of the medium-sized frame be? Assume the dimensions of all the frames are whole numbers.

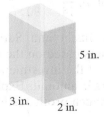

5 in.

3 in.   2 in.

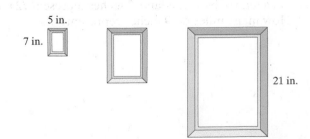

5 in.

7 in.

21 in.

Photo Enlargement *Use the following information to answer exercises 71 and 72.*

35 mm is a size of film in common use today. On a metric ruler the image (less the border) on the negative measures 24 mm by 36 mm. The usual pictures (without borders) offered to the consumer at photo labs are 3 in. by 5 in. and 4 in. by 6 in.

71. (a) If the 36-mm side of the image on the negative is enlarged to 6 in., will the 24-mm side of the image on the negative be enlarged to 4 in.? Why or why not?

    (b) If the 24-mm side of the image on the negative is enlarged to 3 in., will the 36-mm side of the image on the negative be enlarged to 5 in.? Why or why not?

72. (a) If the 36-mm side of the image on the negative is enlarged to 12 in., will the 24-mm side of the image on the negative be enlarged to 8 in.? Why or why not?

    (b) If the 36-mm side of the image on the negative is enlarged to 5 in., will the 24-mm side of the image on the negative be enlarged to 3 in.? Why or why not?

73. (a) Fill in the boxes with the **sum** of the two numbers that are marked in the following sequence.

    (b) Observe the pattern in 73(a), then explain how to find the next number in the sequence.

    (c) Find the next 3 numbers in the sequence.

1, 1, 2, 3, 5, 8, 13, 21, 34,...

Cumulative Review *Translate each sentence using mathematical symbols.*

74. [1.8.3] Two times a number added to six is equal to twenty-eight.

75. [1.8.3] Twenty divided by a number is equal to five.

76. [1.8.3] Eight subtracted from some number is equal to nine.

77. [1.8.3] Four plus three times some number is equal to nineteen.

Exam Grading Scale *To discourage guessing on the multiple-choice final exam, a history professor chose the following grading scale.*

78. Find the final exam score for Victor if he left 5 questions blank, got 50 correct, and got 10 incorrect.

79. What score would Victor have earned if he had guessed incorrectly instead of leaving the 5 questions blank?

Response	Point Value
Blank	-1
Correct	$+5$
Incorrect	-3

Quick Quiz 4.6

1. Determine if $\dfrac{18}{30} = \dfrac{34}{56}$ is a proportion.

2. Find the value of n. $\dfrac{12}{15} = \dfrac{n}{90}$

3. On a map of New England, 2 inches represent 72 miles. How many miles do 9 inches represent?

4. Concept Check Justin and Sara share the profits from their business based on the ratio of their investment. The ratio of the investment is 5 to 7, with Sara investing the larger amount. Explain how you would determine how much profit Justin will receive if Sara gets $840.

Whether you want a new stove, a flat screen TV, or just a weekend getaway, finding the additional funds to pay for these items can be a challenge. Do you think you could find extra money in your budget?

Operations on Fractional Expressions

Multiplying Fractions

Let's look at multiplication with fractions. We begin with an illustration representing the fraction $\frac{1}{3}$.

One whole divided into 3 parts with each part equal to the fraction $\frac{1}{3}$ (1 out of 3 parts)

Let's see what it means to have one-half of $\frac{1}{3}$. Imagine cutting each of the 3 pieces in the figure above in half. Instead of 3 parts, we would then have 6 parts.

One whole divided into 6 parts with each part equal to the fraction $\frac{1}{6}$ (1 out of 6 parts)

This is one-half of $\frac{1}{3}$.

From the illustration above, we see that one-half of $\frac{1}{3}$ is $\frac{1}{6}$. To find *one-half* of $\frac{1}{3}$, *we multiply* $\frac{1}{2} \cdot \frac{1}{3} = \frac{1}{6}$. We state the rule for multiplying fractions.

> **RULE FOR MULTIPLYING FRACTIONS**
>
> To multiply fractions, we multiply numerator times numerator and denominator times denominator.
>
> In general, for all numbers a, b, c, and d, with $b \neq 0$, and $d \neq 0$,
>
> $$\frac{a}{b} \cdot \frac{c}{d} = \frac{a \cdot c}{b \cdot d} \qquad \frac{2}{3} \cdot \frac{1}{7} = \frac{2 \cdot 1}{3 \cdot 7} = \frac{2}{21}$$

We often use multiplication of fractions to describe *taking a fractional part of something*. The word *of* indicates that we perform the operation multiplication.

EXAMPLE 1 Find $\frac{3}{7}$ of $\frac{2}{9}$.

Solution

$$\frac{3}{7} \text{ of } \frac{2}{9} = \frac{3}{7} \cdot \frac{2}{9} = \frac{3 \cdot 2}{7 \cdot 9} = \frac{3 \cdot 2}{7 \cdot 3 \cdot 3} = \frac{\overset{1}{\cancel{3}} \cdot 2}{7 \cdot \underset{1}{\cancel{3}} \cdot 3} = \frac{2}{21}$$

Practice Problem 1 Find $\frac{5}{8}$ of $\frac{2}{3}$.

NOTE TO STUDENT: Fully worked-out solutions to all of the Practice Problems can be found at the back of the text starting at page SP-1

In Example 1 we removed the common factor 3. This process is often referred to as removing a factor of 1, or **factoring out common factors.**

Factoring out common factors.

$$\frac{3 \cdot 2}{7 \cdot 3 \cdot 3} = \frac{\overset{1}{\cancel{3}}}{\underset{1}{\cancel{3}}} \cdot \frac{2}{7 \cdot 3} \qquad \text{We factor the fraction and write } \frac{3}{3} \text{ as } \frac{1}{1}.$$

We often skip this step and *factor out the common factor* by placing slashes on common factors as we did in Example 1.

We should always factor out common factors before we multiply the numerators and denominators; otherwise, we must simplify the product. This is a lot of extra work! Let's see what would happen if in Example 1 we multiplied the numbers in the numerator and denominator before we factored out common factors.

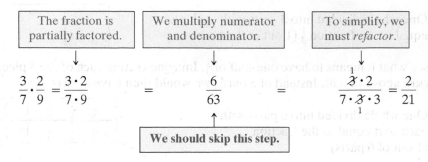

When multiplying fractions, always try to simplify before performing the multiplication in the numerator and the denominator of the fraction. This will ensure that the product will be in lowest terms.

EXAMPLE 2   Find. $\dfrac{9}{20} \cdot \dfrac{5}{21}$

Solution

$$\frac{9}{20} \cdot \frac{5}{21} = \frac{9 \cdot 5}{20 \cdot 21} = \frac{3 \cdot 3 \cdot 5}{2 \cdot 2 \cdot 5 \cdot 3 \cdot 7} = \frac{3 \cdot \cancel{3} \cdot \cancel{5}}{2 \cdot 2 \cdot \cancel{5} \cdot \cancel{3} \cdot 7} = \frac{3}{28}$$

Practice Problem 2   Find.

$$\frac{8}{15} \cdot \frac{12}{14}$$

EXAMPLE 3   Find. $\dfrac{-2}{18} \cdot \dfrac{9}{11}$

Solution   When multiplying positive and negative fractions, we determine the sign of the product and then multiply and simplify.

$$\frac{-2}{18} \cdot \frac{9}{11} = (-)$$ The product is negative since there is 1 negative sign and 1 is an odd number.

$$= -\frac{2 \cdot 9}{18 \cdot 11}$$

$$= -\frac{2 \cdot 9}{2 \cdot 9 \cdot 11}$$ Factor.

$$= -\frac{\cancel{2} \cdot \cancel{9}}{\cancel{2} \cdot \cancel{9} \cdot 11}$$ Factor out common factors and simplify.

$$= -\frac{1}{11}$$

Practice Problem 3   Find.

$$\frac{-12}{24} \cdot \frac{-2}{13}$$

CAUTION: If you do not write the steps showing the 1 above the slashes, you *must remember* that the factor 1 is part of the multiplication. For example, in Example 3

$$-\frac{\cancel{2}\cdot\cancel{9}}{\cancel{2}\cdot\cancel{9}\cdot 11} = -\frac{1}{11} \text{ not } -\frac{0}{11}.$$

When multiplying a fraction by a whole number expression, it is helpful to write the expression with a denominator of 1. We can do this since $\frac{6}{1} = 6$, and $\frac{x}{1} = x$, and so on.

EXAMPLE 4   Multiply. $12x^3 \cdot \dfrac{5x^2}{4}$

Solution

$$\frac{12x^3}{1} \cdot \frac{5x^2}{4} = \frac{4\cdot 3\cdot x^3 \cdot 5\cdot x^2}{1\cdot 4} = \frac{\cancel{4}\cdot 3\cdot 5\cdot x^3\cdot x^2}{1\cdot \cancel{4}} = \frac{3\cdot 5\cdot x^{3+2}}{1} = 15x^5$$

Practice Problem 4   Multiply.

$$\frac{3x^6}{7}\cdot(14x^2)$$

To find the area of a triangle we use the formula $A = \frac{1}{2}bh$, where b is the base of the triangle and h is the height. The height of any triangle is the distance of a line drawn from a vertex perpendicular to the opposite side or extension of the opposite side.

height

base

EXAMPLE 5   Find the area of a triangle with $b = 12$ in. and $h = 7$ in.

Solution   We evaluate the formula with the given values.

$$A = \frac{1}{2}bh$$

$$= \frac{1}{2}\cdot 12 \text{ in.} \cdot 7 \text{ in.} \qquad \text{We replace } b \text{ with 12 in. and } h \text{ with 7 in.}$$

$$= \frac{1\cdot 12 \text{ in.} \cdot 7 \text{ in.}}{2\cdot 1\cdot 1} \qquad \text{We multiply: } \frac{1}{2}\cdot\frac{12 \text{ in.}}{1}\cdot\frac{7 \text{ in.}}{1}.$$

$$= \frac{1\cdot 12\cdot 7 \text{ in.} \cdot \text{in.}}{2} \qquad \text{We factor: } 12 = 2\cdot 6. \text{ Then we simplify.}$$

$$A = 42 \text{ in.}^2 \qquad \frac{\cancel{2}\cdot 6\cdot 7}{\cancel{2}} = 6\cdot 7 = 42; \text{ in.}\cdot\text{in.} = \text{in.}^2$$

Practice Problem 5   Find the area of a triangle with $b = 20$ cm and $h = 9$ cm.

NOTE TO STUDENT: Fully worked-out solutions to all of the Practice Problems can be found at the back of the text starting at page SP-1

 Dividing Fractions

Before we discuss division with fractions, we introduce *reciprocal fractions*. The fractions $\frac{2}{3}$ and $\frac{3}{2}$ are called *reciprocals*, and $\frac{x}{a}$ and $\frac{a}{x}$ are also reciprocals. Let's see what happens when we multiply reciprocal fractions.

$$\frac{2}{3}\cdot\frac{3}{2} = \frac{2\cdot 3}{3\cdot 2} = \frac{\cancel{2}\cdot\cancel{3}}{\cancel{2}\cdot\cancel{3}} = 1 \qquad \frac{x}{a}\cdot\frac{a}{x} = \frac{x\cdot a}{a\cdot x} = \frac{\cancel{x}\cdot\cancel{a}}{\cancel{x}\cdot\cancel{a}} = 1$$

Notice that both products are equal to 1. If the product of two numbers is 1, we say that these two numbers are **reciprocals** of each other.

To find the reciprocal of a nonzero fraction, we *interchange* the numerator and denominator. This is often referred to as **inverting the fraction.**

EXAMPLE 6 Find the reciprocal.

(a) $\dfrac{-7}{8}$

(b) 6

Solution To find the reciprocal, we invert the fraction.

(a) $\dfrac{-7}{8} \rightarrow \dfrac{8}{-7} = -\dfrac{8}{7}$

$\underbrace{\qquad\qquad}_{\text{invert}}$

(b) $6 = \dfrac{6}{1} \rightarrow \dfrac{1}{6} = \dfrac{1}{6}$

$\underbrace{\qquad\qquad}_{\text{invert}}$

Practice Problem 6 Find the reciprocal.

(a) $\dfrac{a}{-y}$

(b) 4

Now let's see how we use reciprocals when we divide fractions. Consider this problem.

A total of $\frac{3}{4}$ pound of peanuts is to be placed in $\frac{1}{4}$-pound bags. How many $\frac{1}{4}$-pound bags will there be?

We must find how many $\frac{1}{4}$'s are in $\frac{3}{4}$. This is the division situation $\frac{3}{4} \div \frac{1}{4}$. To illustrate, we draw a picture.

How many bags?

$$\frac{3}{4} \div \frac{1}{4}$$

Notice that there are three $\frac{1}{4}$'s in $\frac{3}{4}$. Thus, $\frac{3}{4} \div \frac{1}{4} = 3$. Therefore, we can fill three $\frac{1}{4}$-pound bags.

Now, how can we find $\frac{3}{4} \div \frac{1}{4} = 3$ without drawing a diagram? Notice that if we *find the reciprocal of (invert) the second fraction* and then *multiply,* we get 3.

$$\boxed{\text{Invert the second fraction and multiply.}}$$
$$\downarrow$$
$$\frac{3}{4} \div \frac{1}{4} = \frac{3}{4} \cdot \frac{4}{1} = \frac{3 \cdot \cancel{4}}{\cancel{4} \cdot 1} = \frac{3}{1} = 3$$

Thus dividing $\frac{3}{4}$ by $\frac{1}{4}$ is the same as multiplying $\frac{3}{4}$ by the reciprocal of $\frac{1}{4}$.

RULE FOR DIVIDING FRACTIONS

To divide two fractions, we find the reciprocal of (invert) the second fraction and *multiply.*

$$\frac{a}{b} \div \frac{c}{d} = \frac{a}{b} \cdot \frac{d}{c} \quad \text{(when } b, c, \text{ and } d \text{ are not 0)}$$

EXAMPLE 7 Divide. $\dfrac{-4}{11} \div \left(\dfrac{-3}{5}\right)$

Solution   There are 2 negative signs in the division. The number 2 is even, so the answer is positive.

$$\dfrac{-4}{11} \div \left(\dfrac{-3}{5}\right) = \dfrac{-4}{11} \cdot \left(\dfrac{5}{-3}\right) \qquad \text{Invert the second fraction and multiply.}$$

$$= \dfrac{4 \cdot 5}{11 \cdot 3} = \dfrac{20}{33} \qquad \text{The product of two negative numbers is positive.}$$

Practice Problem 7 Divide.

$$\dfrac{-7}{8} \div \dfrac{5}{13}$$

Understanding the Concept

Reciprocals and Division

Why do we invert the second fraction and multiply when we divide? Let's write the fraction $\frac{8}{2}$ as both a division problem and a multiplication problem and see what happens.

$$\text{Division problem: } \dfrac{8}{2} = 8 \div 2 = 4 \quad \text{We divide by 2.}$$

$$\text{Multiplication problem: } \dfrac{8}{2} = 8 \cdot \dfrac{1}{2} = 4 \quad \text{We invert 2 and multiply.}$$

Thus we see that whether we *divide* 8 by *2* or *multiply* 8 by $\frac{1}{2}$ (the reciprocal of 2), we get the same result.

Since we cannot divide by zero, we will assume that all variables in denominators are nonzero.

EXAMPLE 8 Divide. $\dfrac{7x^4}{20} \div \left(\dfrac{-14x^2}{45}\right)$

Solution

$$\dfrac{7x^4}{20} \div \left(\dfrac{-14x^2}{45}\right) = \dfrac{7x^4}{20} \cdot \left(\dfrac{45}{-14x^2}\right) \qquad \text{Invert the second fraction and multiply.}$$

$$= - \qquad\qquad \text{The product is negative since there is 1 negative sign and 1 is an odd number.}$$

$$= -\dfrac{\cancel{7} \cdot \cancel{5} \cdot 3 \cdot 3 \cdot x^4}{2 \cdot 2 \cdot \cancel{5} \cdot 2 \cdot \cancel{7} \cdot x^2} \qquad \text{Factor and simplify.}$$

$$= -\dfrac{9x^2}{8} \qquad\qquad \dfrac{x^4}{x^2} = x^{4-2} = x^2.$$

Practice Problem 8 Divide.

$$\dfrac{9x^6}{21} \div \left(\dfrac{-42x^4}{18}\right)$$

CAUTION: To obtain the right answer, it is important that you *invert the second fraction,* not the first.

EXAMPLE 9 Divide. $16x^5 \div \dfrac{8x^2}{11}$

Solution

$$16x^5 \div \frac{8x^2}{11} = \frac{16x^5}{1} \cdot \frac{11}{8x^2} = \frac{2 \cdot \cancel{8} \cdot 11 \cdot x^5}{1 \cdot \cancel{8} \cdot x^2}$$

$$= 22x^3 \qquad \text{Simplify: } \frac{2 \cdot 11}{1} = 22 \text{ and } \frac{x^5}{x^2} = x^{5-2} = x^3.$$

NOTE TO STUDENT: *Fully worked-out solutions to all of the Practice Problems can be found at the back of the text starting at page SP-1*

Practice Problem 9 Divide.

$$28x^5 \div \frac{4x}{19}$$

Solving Applied Problems Involving Fractions

One of the most important steps in solving a real-life application is determining what operation to use. We often ask ourselves, "Should I multiply or divide?" The multiplication and division situations for fractions are similar to those for whole numbers and are stated below for your review. Drawing pictures and making charts can also help you determine whether to multiply or divide.

MULTIPLICATION SITUATIONS

We multiply in situations that require repeated addition or taking a fractional part *of* something.

1. *Repeated addition.* A recipe requires $\frac{1}{4}$ cup of flour for each serving. How many cups of flour are needed to make 3 servings?

1 serving	+	1 serving	+	1 serving	=	3 servings
↓		↓		↓		
$\frac{1}{4}$	+	$\frac{1}{4}$	+	$\frac{1}{4}$	=	$3 \cdot \frac{1}{4} = \frac{3}{4}$ cup of flour

We add $\frac{1}{4}$ cup 3 times, or $3 \cdot \frac{1}{4}$.

2. *Taking a fractional part of something.* A recipe requires $\frac{3}{4}$ cup of flour. How much flour is needed to make $\frac{1}{2}$ of the recipe?

We want to find $\dfrac{1}{2}$ of $\dfrac{3}{4}$ or $\dfrac{1}{2} \cdot \dfrac{3}{4} = \dfrac{3}{8}$ cup of flour.

DIVISION SITUATIONS

We divide when we want to split an amount into a certain number of equal parts or to find how many groups of a certain size are in a given amount.

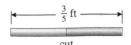
$\frac{3}{5}$ ft

cut

1. *Split an amount into equal parts.* A pipe $\frac{3}{5}$ foot long must be cut into 2 equal parts. How long is each part?

$$\frac{3}{5} \div 2 = \frac{3}{5} \cdot \frac{1}{2} = \frac{3}{10} \qquad \text{Each part is } \frac{3}{10} \text{ foot long.}$$

2. *Find how many groups of a certain size are in a given amount.* A scarf requires $\frac{4}{5}$ yards of material. How many scarves can be made from 8 yards of material? We must find how many $\frac{4}{5}$-yard segments are in 8 yards.

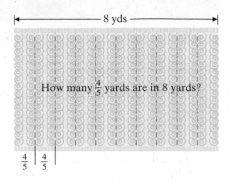

How many $\frac{4}{5}$ yards are in 8 yards?

$$8 \div \frac{4}{5} = 8 \cdot \frac{5}{4} = \frac{2 \cdot 4 \cdot 5}{4} = 10 \quad \text{10 scarves can be made.}$$

When we solve applied problems, we must decide whether we have a division situation or a multiplication situation so we know which operation to use.

EXAMPLE 10 Samuel Jensen has $\frac{9}{40}$ of his income withheld for taxes and retirement. What amount is withheld each week if he earns $1440 per week?

Solution The key phrase is "$\frac{9}{40}$ *of* his income." The word *of* often indicates multiplication.

$\frac{9}{40}$ of *income* is withheld for taxes and retirement

$$\frac{9}{40} \cdot \$1440 = \frac{9}{40} \cdot \frac{\$1440}{1} = \$324$$

$324 is withheld for taxes and retirement each week.

Practice Problem 10 Nancy Levine places $\frac{2}{13}$ of her income in a savings account each week. How much money does she place in her savings account if her income is $1703 per week?

▲ **EXAMPLE 11** Harry must install 44 feet of baseboard along the edge of the floor of a library. After placing a nail at the corner, he must place a nail in the baseboard every $\frac{2}{3}$ foot. How many more nails will he need?

Solution We draw a picture.

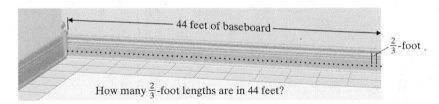

44 feet of baseboard

$\frac{2}{3}$-foot

How many $\frac{2}{3}$-foot lengths are in 44 feet?

Since we need to find out how many $\frac{2}{3}$-foot lengths are in 44 feet, we divide.

$$44 \div \frac{2}{3} = 44 \cdot \frac{3}{2} = \frac{44 \cdot 3}{2} = \frac{2 \cdot 22 \cdot 3}{2} = 66$$

He will need 66 more nails.

Practice Problem 11 Alice must place $\frac{3}{4}$ pound of sugar in 2 equal-size containers. How much sugar should Alice place in each container?

NOTE TO STUDENT: Fully worked-out solutions to all of the Practice Problems can be found at the back of the text starting at page SP-1

In this exercise set, assume that all variables in any denominator are nonzero.

Verbal and Writing Skills

1. Explain how to multiply fractions.

2. Explain how to divide fractions.

3. To split $\frac{1}{4}$ into 6 equal parts, do we multiply or divide? Why?

4. To find out how much money we have if we inherit $\frac{1}{4}$ of $6000, do we multiply or divide? Why?

5. Write an application that requires multiplication of $\frac{1}{3}$ and 90.

6. Write an application that requires division of 27 and $\frac{3}{4}$.

Fill in each box to complete each problem.

7. $\frac{1}{2} \cdot \frac{3}{7} = \frac{3}{\boxed{}}$

8. $\frac{5}{9} \cdot \frac{2}{3} = \frac{10}{\boxed{}}$

9. $\frac{1}{4} \div \frac{3}{7} = \frac{1}{4} \cdot \frac{\boxed{}}{\boxed{}} = \frac{7}{12}$

10. $\frac{1}{8} \div \frac{5}{3} = \frac{1}{8} \cdot \frac{\boxed{}}{\boxed{}} = \frac{3}{40}$

11. $\frac{1}{2} \cdot \frac{\boxed{}}{\boxed{}} = \frac{5}{12}$

12. $\frac{2}{9} \cdot \frac{\boxed{}}{\boxed{}} = \frac{10}{27}$

13. $\frac{5}{7} \div \frac{4}{3} = \frac{5}{7}\boxed{}\frac{\boxed{}}{\boxed{}} = \frac{15}{28}$

14. $\frac{4}{9} \div \frac{3}{7} = \frac{4}{9}\boxed{}\frac{\boxed{}}{\boxed{}} = \frac{28}{27}$

Find the following.

15. $\frac{1}{4}$ of $\frac{1}{3}$

16. $\frac{1}{5}$ of $\frac{1}{7}$

17. $\frac{5}{21}$ of $\frac{7}{8}$

18. $\frac{2}{16}$ of $\frac{8}{9}$

Multiply. Be sure your answer is simplified.

19. $\frac{7}{12} \cdot \frac{8}{28}$

20. $\frac{6}{21} \cdot \frac{9}{18}$

21. $\frac{3}{20} \cdot \frac{8}{9}$

22. $\frac{4}{35} \cdot \frac{5}{24}$

23. $\frac{-3}{8} \cdot \left(\frac{14}{-6}\right)$

24. $\frac{-5}{2} \cdot \left(\frac{2}{-30}\right)$

25. $\frac{16}{11} \cdot \left(\frac{-18}{36}\right)$

26. $\frac{4}{3} \cdot \left(\frac{-45}{18}\right)$

27. $\frac{-2}{21} \cdot \left(\frac{-14}{18}\right)$

28. $\frac{-8}{20} \cdot \left(\frac{-25}{32}\right)$

29. $-14 \cdot \frac{1}{28}$

30. $-13 \cdot \frac{2}{26}$

31. $\frac{6}{35} \cdot 5$

32. $\frac{2}{21} \cdot 15$

33. $\frac{2x}{3} \cdot \frac{3x}{5}$

34. $\dfrac{4x}{5} \cdot \dfrac{5x}{3}$

35. $\dfrac{6x^4}{7} \cdot 28x$

36. $\dfrac{6x^5}{15} \cdot 30x^7$

37. $8x^2 \cdot \dfrac{3x^3}{2}$

38. $9x^3 \cdot \dfrac{2x^4}{3}$

Mixed Practice Exercises 39–46 *Multiply. Be sure your answer is simplified.*

39. $\dfrac{2}{10} \cdot \dfrac{6}{8}$

40. $\dfrac{3}{21} \cdot \dfrac{7}{9}$

41. $\dfrac{6x}{25} \cdot \dfrac{15}{12x^2}$

42. $\dfrac{4x}{35} \cdot \dfrac{7}{6x^2}$

43. $\dfrac{-3y^3}{20} \cdot \dfrac{12}{21y^2}$

44. $\dfrac{15y^3}{26} \cdot \left(\dfrac{-13}{10y}\right)$

45. $\dfrac{3x^2}{15} \cdot \dfrac{18x^3}{20}$

46. $\dfrac{5x^4}{6} \cdot \dfrac{2x^2}{25}$

▲ *Find the area of each triangle with the given base and height.*

47. $b = 12$ m and $h = 8$ m

48. $b = 19$ in. and $h = 26$ in.

49. $b = 21$ in. and $h = 40$ in.

50. $b = 8$ cm and $h = 11$ cm

Find the reciprocal.

51. $\dfrac{1}{3}$

52. $\dfrac{1}{9}$

53. 5

54. 9

55. $\dfrac{2}{-5}$

56. $\dfrac{7}{-8}$

57. $\dfrac{-x}{y}$

58. $\dfrac{-a}{b}$

Divide. Be sure your answer is simplified.

59. $\dfrac{6}{14} \div \dfrac{3}{8}$

60. $\dfrac{8}{12} \div \dfrac{5}{6}$

61. $\dfrac{7}{24} \div \dfrac{9}{16}$

62. $\dfrac{9}{28} \div \dfrac{4}{7}$

63. $\dfrac{-1}{12} \div \dfrac{3}{4}$

64. $\dfrac{-1}{15} \div \dfrac{2}{3}$

65. $\dfrac{-7}{24} \div \left(\dfrac{7}{-8}\right)$

66. $\dfrac{-9}{28} \div \left(\dfrac{4}{-7}\right)$

67. $\dfrac{8x^6}{15} \div \dfrac{16x^2}{5}$

68. $\dfrac{6y^4}{20} \div \dfrac{36y^2}{10}$

69. $\dfrac{7x^4}{12} \div \dfrac{-28}{36x^2}$

70. $\dfrac{3x^4}{45} \div \dfrac{-27}{45x^5}$

71. $14 \div \dfrac{2}{7}$

72. $18 \div \dfrac{2}{3}$

73. $\dfrac{7}{22} \div 14$

74. $\dfrac{8}{26} \div 16$

75. $21x^4 \div \dfrac{7x}{3}$

76. $15x^3 \div \dfrac{5x^2}{8}$

77. $22x^3 \div \dfrac{11}{6x^5}$

78. $18x^4 \div \dfrac{9}{5x^6}$

Mixed Practice *Perform the operation indicated.*

79. (a) $\dfrac{1}{15} \cdot \dfrac{25}{21}$

   (b) $\dfrac{1}{15} \div \dfrac{25}{21}$

80. (a) $\dfrac{1}{6} \cdot \dfrac{24}{15}$

   (b) $\dfrac{1}{6} \div \dfrac{24}{15}$

81. (a) $\dfrac{2x^2}{3} \div \dfrac{12}{21x^5}$

   (b) $\dfrac{2x^2}{3} \cdot \dfrac{12}{21x^5}$

82. (a) $\dfrac{3x^3}{7} \div \dfrac{21}{25x^4}$

   (b) $\dfrac{3x^3}{7} \cdot \dfrac{21}{25x^4}$

83. $\dfrac{5x^7}{-27} \cdot \dfrac{-9}{20x^4}$

84. $\dfrac{7x^4}{-6} \cdot \dfrac{-30}{21x^2}$

85. $\dfrac{12x^6}{35} \div \dfrac{-16}{25x^2}$

86. $\dfrac{32x^3}{-15} \div \dfrac{28}{35x^4}$

Applications

87. *Payroll Deductions* Lilly Smith has $\frac{2}{15}$ of her weekly income withheld for taxes. What amount is withheld each week if she earns \$1350 per week?

88. *Savings Plan* Elliott has $\frac{3}{16}$ of his weekly income placed in a savings account. What amount is placed in his savings account if he earns \$1600 per week?

▲ **89. *Pipe Length*** Babette must cut pipes into lengths of $\frac{3}{4}$ foot. How many pipes can she make from a pipe that is 12 feet long?

90. *Satin Material* Beth has a piece of satin 12 feet long. How many $\frac{2}{3}$-foot pieces of satin can she cut from the material?

91. *Miles Run* Julie runs 32 laps for her daily workout. If each lap is $\frac{1}{4}$ mile, how many miles does Julie run in her 32-lap workout?

92. *Propeller Revolutions* The propeller on the Ipswich River Cruise Boat turns 320 revolutions per minute. How fast would it turn at $\frac{3}{4}$ of that speed?

93. *Factory Vats* In the Westerfield Factory, products are made in vats that have the capacity to hold 120 quarts. If each bottle of a product contains $\frac{3}{4}$ quart, how many bottles can be made from each vat?

94. *Land Parcels* Dunday Building Company purchased 56 acres of land. The company subdivided the land into $\frac{2}{5}$-acre parcels. How many $\frac{2}{5}$-acre parcels does the company have?

One Step Further

95. $\dfrac{5}{14} \div \dfrac{2}{21} \div \left(\dfrac{15}{-3}\right)$

96. $\dfrac{8}{21} \div \left(\dfrac{4}{-7}\right) \div \dfrac{4}{3}$

97. After building a house the homeowners discover the land is sinking $\frac{2}{3}$ inch every year. How many years will it take the house to sink 4 inches?

98. On a recent history test, you answered $\frac{3}{5}$ of the questions and left the rest blank. Of the ones you answered, you got $\frac{2}{3}$ right. What fractional part of the questions did you answer correctly on the test?

99. *Pizza Party* James is planning a party at which he intends to serve pizza. If James estimates that each guest will eat $\frac{3}{8}$ of a pizza, how many pizzas should he order if 17 people will attend the party?

100. *Students' Home States* The records at a private college with 9600 students indicate that $\frac{1}{6}$ of these students are from California and $\frac{1}{5}$ are from Texas. How many students attending the college are not from Texas or California?

To Think About   *Find the value of the variable in each of the following.*

101. $\dfrac{3}{4} \cdot \dfrac{x}{27} = \dfrac{4}{9}$

102. $\dfrac{1}{2} \div \dfrac{3}{x} = \dfrac{8}{3}$

103. $\dfrac{2}{7}, \dfrac{4}{7}, \dfrac{x}{7}, \dfrac{8}{7}, \dfrac{10}{7}, \dfrac{y}{7}, \cdots$

104. $\dfrac{1}{5}, \dfrac{2}{5}, \dfrac{4}{5}, \dfrac{x}{5}, \dfrac{16}{5}, \dfrac{32}{5}, \dfrac{y}{5}, \cdots$

105. $\dfrac{1}{2}, \dfrac{2}{6}, \dfrac{4}{18}, \dfrac{x}{54}, \dfrac{16}{y}, \dfrac{32}{486}, \cdots$

106. $\dfrac{1}{3}, \dfrac{3}{6}, \dfrac{9}{x}, \dfrac{27}{24}, \dfrac{y}{48}, \dfrac{243}{96}, \cdots$

Cumulative Review   *Find an equivalent fraction with the given denominator.*

107. **[4.3.1]** $\dfrac{2}{3} = \dfrac{?}{15}$

108. **[4.3.1]** $\dfrac{3}{4} = \dfrac{?}{20}$

Express as a product of prime factors.

109. **[4.1.3]** 120

110. **[4.1.3]** 145

Quick Quiz 5.1   Perform the operation indicated.

1. Find $\dfrac{3}{14}$ of $\dfrac{14}{27}$.

2. $\dfrac{-2x^2}{5} \cdot \dfrac{15x^4}{8}$

3. $\dfrac{5x^5}{8} \div \dfrac{x^3}{20}$

4. **Concept Check** Explain how you would divide $\dfrac{-16x^2}{3}$ by $8x$.

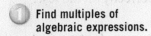
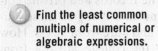
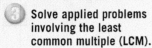
 Finding Multiples of Algebraic Expressions

To generate a list of **multiples** of a number, we multiply that number by 1, and then by 2, and then by 3, and so on. For example, we can list some multiples of 4 by multiplying 4 by $1, 2, 3, \ldots, 8$.

$$4 \cdot 1 \quad 4 \cdot 2 \quad 4 \cdot 3 \quad 4 \cdot 4 \quad 4 \cdot 5 \quad 4 \cdot 6 \quad 4 \cdot 7 \quad 4 \cdot 8 \ldots$$

Multiples of 4: $\quad 4, \quad 8, \quad 12, \quad 16, \quad 20, \quad 24, \quad 28, \quad 32, \ldots$

EXAMPLE 1

(a) List the first six multiples of $8x$ and the first six multiples of $12x$.

(b) Which of these multiples are common to both lists?

Solution

(a)
$$8x \cdot 1 \quad 8x \cdot 2 \quad 8x \cdot 3 \quad 8x \cdot 4 \quad 8x \cdot 5 \quad 8x \cdot 6$$

Multiples of $8x$: $\quad 8x, \quad 16x, \quad 24x, \quad 32x, \quad 40x, \quad 48x$

$$12x \cdot 1 \quad 12x \cdot 2 \quad 12x \cdot 3 \quad 12x \cdot 4 \quad 12x \cdot 5 \quad 12x \cdot 6$$

Multiples of $12x$: $\quad 12x, \quad 24x, \quad 36x, \quad 48x, \quad 60x, \quad 72x$

(b) The multiples common to both lists are $24x$ and $48x$.

Practice Problem 1

(a) List the first five multiples of $12x$ and the first five multiples of $20x$.

(b) Which of these multiples are common to both lists?

NOTE TO STUDENT: *Fully worked-out solutions to all of the Practice Problems can be found at the back of the text starting at page SP-1*

 Finding the Least Common Multiple of Numerical or Algebraic Expressions

An expression that is a multiple of two different expressions is called a *common multiple* of those two expressions. Therefore, in Example 1, we call $24x$ and $48x$ common multiples of $8x$ and $12x$. The number $24x$ is the *smaller of these common multiples* and is called the **least common multiple,** or **LCM,** of $8x$ and $12x$.

EXAMPLE 2 Find the LCM of 10 and 15.

Solution First, we list some multiples of 10: 10, 20, 30, 40, 50, 60.

Next, we list some multiples of 15: 15, 30, 45, 60.

We see that both 30 and 60 are common multiples. Since 30 is the smaller of these common multiples, we call 30 the least common multiple (LCM).

Practice Problem 2 Find the LCM of 4 and 5.

Suppose that we must find the LCM of 14, 32, 78, and 210. Listing the multiples of each number to find the LCM would be time consuming. A quicker, more efficient way to find LCMs uses prime factorizations. With this method we **build the LCM** using the prime factors of each number. In Example 2 we listed some multiples for 10 and 15 to find the LCM, 30. Now let's see how to find the LCM of 10 and 15 using prime factors.

$$\text{factors of 10}$$
$$\downarrow \quad \downarrow$$
$$10 = 2 \cdot 5 \qquad \text{LCM} \rightarrow 30 = 2 \cdot 3 \cdot 5$$
$$15 = 3 \cdot 5 \qquad\qquad\qquad \uparrow \ \uparrow$$
$$\text{factors of 15}$$

Notice that the LCM has all the factors of 10 and all the factors of 15 in its prime factorization. Thus the LCM of 10 and 15 must satisfy at least two requirements.

First, the LCM must have all factors of 10 in its prime factorization: a 2 and a 5.

Second, the LCM must have all factors of 15 in its prime factorization: a 3 and a 5.

> To build the LCM, we write a prime factorization that satisfies the first require-ment and then *add to this factorization* to satisfy the second requirement.

We build the LCM of 10 and 15 as follows.

1. The LCM must have a 2 and a 5 as factors. $\boxed{\text{LCM} = 2 \cdot 5 \cdot ?}$

2. The LCM must have a 3 and a 5 as factors. $\boxed{\text{LCM} = 2 \cdot 5 \cdot 3}$

        5 is already a factor, so we just multiply by a 3.

Now, we multiply the factors to find the LCM, 30: $2 \cdot 5 \cdot 3 = 30$.

Notice that when we built the LCM we were also constrained by a third requirement.

3. The LCM must contain the *minimum* number of factors necessary to satisfy the first two requirements.

Without this third requirement, we cannot create the *smallest* common multiple (LCM). For example, in the above illustration, to satisfy the second requirement—the LCM must have a 3 and a 5 in its prime factorization—we only inserted a 3 to the existing prime factorization, not a 3 and a 5. There was a 5 in the factorization already, so we did not need to insert another one. *If we insert an extra 5, we build a multiple of 10 and 15 that is not the smallest common multiple.*

$2 \cdot 5 \cdot 3 = 30$ $2 \cdot 5 \cdot 3 \cdot 5 = 150$

| This factorization includes the *minimum number of factors needed.* | This factorization includes an *extra 5.* |

Although both 30 and 150 are common multiples of 10 and 15, the smallest common multiple, or LCM, is 30.

> **PROCEDURE TO FIND THE LCM**
>
> 1. Factor each number into a product of prime factors.
> 2. List the requirements for the factorization of the LCM.
> 3. Build the LCM using the minimum number of factors.

EXAMPLE 3   Find the LCM of 18, 42, and 45.

Solution

| Factor each number | → | List requirements for factorization of LCM | → | Build the LCM |

$18 = 2 \cdot 3 \cdot 3$ → must have a 2 and a pair of 3's → $\boxed{LCM = 2 \cdot 3 \cdot 3 \cdot ?}$

$42 = 2 \cdot 3 \cdot 7$ → must have a 2, a 3, and a 7 → $\boxed{LCM = 2 \cdot 3 \cdot 3 \cdot 7 \cdot ?}$

2 and 3 are already factors, so we just multiply by a 7.

$45 = 3 \cdot 3 \cdot 5$ → must have a pair of 3's and a 5 → $\boxed{LCM = 2 \cdot 3 \cdot 3 \cdot 7 \cdot 5}$

A pair of 3's already exists, so we just multiply by a 5.

The LCM of 18, 42, and 45 is $2 \cdot 3 \cdot 3 \cdot 7 \cdot 5 = 630$.

Practice Problem 3   Find the LCM of 28, 36, and 70.

EXAMPLE 4   Find the LCM of $2x$, x^2, and $6x$.

Solution

| Factor each expression | → | List requirements for factorization of LCM | → | Build the LCM |

$2x = 2 \cdot x$ → must have a 2 and an x → $\boxed{LCM = 2 \cdot x \cdot ?}$

$x^2 = x \cdot x$ → must have a pair of x's → $\boxed{LCM = 2 \cdot x \cdot x \cdot ?}$

One x is already a factor, so we just multiply by another x.

$6x = 2 \cdot 3 \cdot x$ → must have a 2, a 3, and an x → $\boxed{LCM = 2 \cdot x \cdot x \cdot 3}$

A 2 and an x are already factors, so we just multiply by a 3.

The LCM of $2x$, x^2, and $6x$ is $2 \cdot x \cdot x \cdot 3 = 6x^2$.

NOTE TO STUDENT: Fully worked-out solutions to all of the Practice Problems can be found at the back of the text starting at page SP-1

Practice Problem 4   Find the LCM of $4x$, x^2, and $10x$.

3 Solving Applied Problems Involving the Least Common Multiple (LCM)

EXAMPLE 5   Shannon and Marsha are swimming laps from the dock on one side of a lake to a marker and back. Shannon can swim a lap in 12 minutes and Marsha can swim the same distance in 10 minutes. If Shannon and Marsha start swimming at the same time, in how many minutes will they meet to begin their next lap together?

Solution   *Understand the problem.* We organize the facts on a chart and then fill in the Mathematics Blueprint for Problem Solving.

Time	End of 1st Lap	End of 2nd Lap	...	
Shannon	12 min	24 min	...	← These are multiples of 12.
Marsha	10 min	20 min	...	← These are multiples of 10.

Mathematics Blueprint for Problem Solving

Gather the Facts	What Am I Asked to Do?	How Do I Proceed?	Key Points to Remember
See the chart.	Find how many minutes it takes for them to begin another lap together.	Find the LCM of 12 and 10, which is how long before they begin a new lap together.	The LCM is the smallest common multiple.

Solve and state the answer.
We must factor 12 and 10 and find the LCM.

$$12 = 2 \cdot 2 \cdot 3 \quad \text{LCM} = 2 \cdot 2 \cdot 3 \cdot 5 = 60$$
$$10 = 2 \cdot 5$$

Time	End of 1st Lap	End of 2nd Lap	...
Shannon	12 min	24 min	60 min
Marsha	10 min	20 min	60 min

Shannon and Marsha will begin another lap together 60 minutes after they start swimming.

Practice Problem 5 Refer to Example 5 to complete this problem. Shannon can swim a lap in 15 minutes and Marsha can swim a lap in 18 minutes. In how many minutes will they meet to begin their next lap together?

EXAMPLE 6 Sonia and Leo are tour guides at a castle. Sonia gives a 40-minute tour of the interior of the castle, and Leo gives a 30-minute tour of the castle grounds. There is a 10-minute break after each tour. If tours start at 8 A.M., what is the next time that both tours will start at the same time?

Solution *Understand the problem.* We make a chart to help us develop a plan to solve the problem.

Tours	Number of Minutes after 8 A.M. Tours Start
Interior tours start every 50 minutes (40 min + 10-min break).	50, 100, ...
Grounds tours start every 40 minutes (30 min + 10-min break).	40, 80, ...

Mathematics Blueprint for Problem Solving

Gather the Facts	What Am I Asked to Do?	How Do I Proceed?	Key Points to Remember
See the chart.	Determine the next time when both tours start at the same time.	To find the *next* time that both tours start at the same time, we must find the LCM of 50 and 40.	60 min = 1 hr Once we have the LCM in minutes, we change the LCM to hours and minutes to find the common start time.

Solve and state the answer.

First we factor 40 and 50 and find the LCM.

$$40 = 2 \cdot 2 \cdot 2 \cdot 5 \quad \text{LCM} = 2 \cdot 2 \cdot 2 \cdot 5 \cdot 5 = 200$$
$$50 = 2 \cdot 5 \cdot 5$$

Tours	Number of Minutes after 8 A.M. Tours Start
Interior tours start every 50 minutes	$50, 100, \ldots, 200$
Grounds tours start every 40 minutes	$40, 80, \ldots, 200$

Both tours will start at the same time 200 minutes after 8 A.M.

Next, we change minutes to hours and minutes. Since we need to know how many 60's are in 200, we divide.

200 minutes ÷ 60 minutes per hour = 3 hours and 20 minutes after 8 A.M.

8 A.M. + 3 hours and 20 minutes = 11:20 A.M.

At 11:20 A.M. both tours will start at the same time.

NOTE TO STUDENT: *Fully worked-out solutions to all of the Practice Problems can be found at the back of the text starting at page SP-1*

Practice Problem 6   Refer to Example 6 to complete this problem. Leo's tour of the grounds is reduced to 25 minutes. Determine the next time that both tours will start at the same time.

Developing Your Study Skills

Class Attendance and the Learning Cycle

Did you know that an important part of the learning process happens in the classroom? People learn by *reading, writing, listening, verbalizing,* and *seeing.* These activities are all part of the **learning cycle** and always occur in class.

- *Listening and seeing:* hearing and watching the instructor's lecture
- *Reading:* reading the information on the board and in handouts
- *Verbalizing:* asking questions and participating in class discussions
- *Writing:* taking notes and working problems assigned in class

The Learning Cycle

Reading ⟶ Writing

↑ ↓

Seeing ← Verbalizing ← Listening

Attendance in class completes the entire learning cycle once. Completing assignments activates the entire learning cycle one more time:

- Reading class notes and the text
- Writing your homework
- Listening to other students and talking with them about your strategies

Keep in mind that you must pay attention and participate to learn. Just being there is not enough.

Verbal and Writing Skills

1. Explain why 12 is a multiple of 3 and not a multiple of 5.

2. Explain the relationship between a multiple and an LCM.

3. (a) List the first four multiples of 6 and the first four multiples of 8.
   (b) Which of these multiples are common to both lists?

4. (a) List the first five multiples of 4 and the first five multiples of 5.
   (b) Which of these multiples are common to both lists?

5. (a) List the first five multiples of 2 and the first five multiples of 5.
   (b) Which of these multiples are common to both lists?

6. (a) List the first six multiples of 4 and the first six multiples of 6.
   (b) Which of these multiples are common to both lists?

7. (a) List the first four multiples of $12x$ and the first four multiples of $18x$.
   (b) Which of these multiples are common to both lists?

8. (a) List the first four multiples of $15x$ and the first four multiples of $5x$.
   (b) Which of these multiples are common to both lists?

There are two factors missing in the LCM for the numbers listed. State the two missing factors.

9. $525 = 3 \cdot 5 \cdot 5 \cdot 7$
   $90 = 2 \cdot 3 \cdot 3 \cdot 5$
   $28 = 2 \cdot 2 \cdot 7$
   $\boxed{LCM = 2 \cdot 3 \cdot 5 \cdot 5 \cdot 7 \cdot ? \cdot ?}$

10. $220 = 2 \cdot 2 \cdot 5 \cdot 11$
    $189 = 3 \cdot 3 \cdot 3 \cdot 7$
    $385 = 5 \cdot 7 \cdot 11$
    $\boxed{LCM = 2 \cdot 2 \cdot 3 \cdot 3 \cdot 7 \cdot 11 \cdot ? \cdot ?}$

11. $10x^2 = 2 \cdot 5 \cdot x \cdot x$
    $18x = 2 \cdot 3 \cdot 3 \cdot x$
    $49x = 7 \cdot 7 \cdot x$
    $\boxed{LCM = 2 \cdot 3 \cdot 3 \cdot 5 \cdot 7 \cdot x \cdot ? \cdot ?}$

12. $15y^2 = 3 \cdot 5 \cdot y \cdot y$
    $25y = 5 \cdot 5 \cdot y$
    $9y^2 = 3 \cdot 3 \cdot y \cdot y$
    $\boxed{LCM = 3 \cdot 3 \cdot 5 \cdot y \cdot ? \cdot ?}$

Find the LCM of each group of numbers or expressions.

13. 5 and 15

14. 11 and 22

15. 8 and 28

16. 18 and 30

17. 15 and 20

18. 12 and 20

19. 40 and 60

20. 30 and 45

21. 5, 8, and 12

22. 6, 14, and 26

23. 7, 14, and 20

24. 8, 12, and 42

25. $4x$ and $18x$

26. $8x$ and $26x$

27. $21a$ and $81a$

28. $15a$ and $35a$

29. $18x$ and $45x^2$

30. $15x$ and $63x^2$

31. $22x^2$ and $4x^3$

32. $9x^2$ and $3x^3$

33. $12x^2, 5x, 3x^3$

34. $15x, 3x^3, 10x^2$

35. $12x, 14,$ and $4x^2$

36. $14x, 36,$ and $7x^2$

Applications

37. *Running Laps* Jessica and Luis are running laps around a field. Luis runs 1 lap every 4 minutes, while Jessica runs 1 lap every 6 minutes. If Luis and Jessica begin their run at the same time and location on the field, in how many minutes will they meet to begin their next lap together?

38. *Power Walking* Olga will power walk around the track field, and Annette will jog around the same field. Annette can complete 1 lap every 8 minutes, while Olga takes 12 minutes to complete a lap. If Annette and Olga begin their workout at the same time and location on the track, in how many minutes will they meet to begin their next lap together?

39. *Bottle Labeling* One machine takes 6 minutes to place labels on each bottle of juice in a carton. A second machine takes 8 minutes to place labels on each bottle of juice in a carton. If both machines start labeling at the same time, in how many minutes will each machine begin labeling a carton of juice at the same time again?

40. *Bike Assembly* Tuan and Sal work at a bike store. Sal puts together the 21-speed bikes and Tuan the dirt bikes. Sal takes 80 minutes to put together a 21-speed bike, and Tuan takes 60 minutes to put together a dirt bike. If they both start putting bikes together at 1 P.M., at what time will they both start on a new bike at the same time again?

41. *Track and Field Event* An elementary school track and field competition is held on two different fields. Each event on the first field is 20 minutes long, while each event on the second field is 30 minutes long. There are 15-minute breaks between events on both of the fields. If the competition on both fields starts at 8 A.M., determine the next time that both fields will start their track events at the same time.

42. *History Museum Shows* A history museum offers two shows, a 30-minute presentation that overviews all the displays in the museum and a 20-minute film on dinosaurs. There is a 10-minute break after each show. If the shows start at 10 A.M., what is the next time that both shows will start at the same time?

One Step Further *Find the LCM of each group of expressions.*

43. $2x^3, 8xy^2,$ and $10x^2y$

44. $4y^2, 2xy,$ and $9x^3y$

45. $2z^2, 5xyz,$ and $15xy$

46. $3x, 9xy^2,$ and $18xyz$

Cumulative Review

47. [4.2.3] Change $\dfrac{19}{2}$ to a mixed number.

48. [4.2.4] Change $4\dfrac{2}{5}$ to an improper fraction.

49. [2.5.1] Evaluate. $2 + 6(-1) \div 3$

50. [2.5.1] Evaluate. $12 - 5 \cdot 2^2 \div 4$

Quick Quiz 5.2 Find the least common multiple (LCM) of each group of numbers or expressions.

1. 9, 15

2. $12x, 4x^3, 9x^2$

3. 3, 18, 30

4. Concept Check Is $= 3 \times 5 \times 5 \times 7 \times x \times x$ the correct factorization for the LCM of $63x^2$ and $75x^3$? Why or why not?

Adding and Subtracting Fractional Expressions with a Common Denominator

What does it mean to add or subtract fractions? Well, the idea is similar to counting like items or adding and subtracting like terms. For example, if we have 3 CDs and we get 2 more, we end up with 5 CDs: $3 + 2 = 5$. Similarly, we can add $3x + 2x = 5x$ because $3x$ and $2x$ are like terms. In the case of fractions, instead of adding like items or terms, we add *like parts* of a whole. By this we mean fractions with the same denominators: $\frac{3}{6} + \frac{2}{6} = \frac{5}{6}$. This is because when the denominators of fractions are the same, we are comparing *like parts* of a whole. The following situation and illustration can help us understand this idea.

Suppose that a large piece of wood is cut into 6 equal-size parts and we have 3 of these parts and then acquire 2 more. We add to find the total number of parts of wood we have.

Situation	You have **3** out of 6	followed by	an additional **2** out of 6.	You end up with **5** out of 6.
Math symbols	$\frac{3}{6}$	$+$	$\frac{2}{6}$	$=$ $\frac{5}{6}$
Picture		$+$		$=$

When fractions have the *same denominator,* we say that these fractions have a **common denominator.** From the previous illustration, we observe that to add fractions that have a common denominator, we add the numerators and write the sum over the common denominator. A similar rule is followed for subtraction, except that the numerators are subtracted.

> **PROCEDURE TO ADD OR SUBTRACT FRACTIONAL EXPRESSIONS WITH COMMON DENOMINATORS**
>
> 1. The fractions added or subtracted must have a common denominator (denominators that are the same).
> 2. Add or subtract the numerators only.
> 3. The denominator stays the same.

EXAMPLE 1 Subtract. $\dfrac{7}{15} - \dfrac{3}{15}$

Solution

$$\frac{7}{15} - \frac{3}{15} = \frac{7-3}{15} \quad \text{Subtract numerators.}$$
$$\text{The denominator stays the same.}$$
$$= \frac{4}{15}$$

Practice Problem 1 Add.

$$\frac{3}{13} + \frac{7}{13}$$

Student Learning Objectives

After studying this section, you will be able to:

 Add and subtract fractional expressions with a common denominator.

 Add and subtract fractional expressions with different denominators.

NOTE TO STUDENT: Fully worked-out solutions to all of the Practice Problems can be found at the back of the text starting at page SP-1

CAUTION: It is important to remember that to add or subtract fractions, the *denominators* must be the *same* (common denominators) and *stay* the *same*. *We do not add or subtract the denominators—only the numerators.*

EXAMPLE 2 Add. $\dfrac{-11}{20} + \left(\dfrac{-13}{20}\right)$

Solution

$$\dfrac{-11}{20} + \left(\dfrac{-13}{20}\right) = \dfrac{-11 + (-13)}{20} \qquad \text{Add numerators.}$$

$$\phantom{\dfrac{-11}{20} + \left(\dfrac{-13}{20}\right)} = \dfrac{-24}{20} \qquad \text{The denominator stays the same.}$$

$$\phantom{\dfrac{-11}{20} + \left(\dfrac{-13}{20}\right)} = \dfrac{\cancel{4}(-6)}{\cancel{4}(5)} \qquad \text{Factor and simplify.}$$

$$\phantom{\dfrac{-11}{20} + \left(\dfrac{-13}{20}\right)} = -\dfrac{6}{5}$$

Although the answer may also be written as the mixed number $-1\frac{1}{5}$, we generally leave it as an improper fraction. In either case, the answer must be reduced to lowest terms.

Practice Problem 2 Add.

$$\dfrac{-7}{6} + \left(\dfrac{-21}{6}\right)$$

EXAMPLE 3 Perform the operation indicated.

(a) $\dfrac{6}{y} - \dfrac{2}{y}$

(b) $\dfrac{x}{5} + \dfrac{4}{5}$

Solution

(a) $\dfrac{6}{y} - \dfrac{2}{y} = \dfrac{6-2}{y} = \dfrac{4}{y}$

(b) $\dfrac{x}{5} + \dfrac{4}{5} = \dfrac{x+4}{5}$

The answer to part (b), $\dfrac{x+4}{5}$, is simplified. We cannot add x and 4. They are not like terms.

Practice Problem 3 Perform the operation indicated.

(a) $\dfrac{8}{x} - \dfrac{3}{x}$

(b) $\dfrac{y}{9} + \dfrac{5}{9}$

Adding and Subtracting Fractional Expressions with Different Denominators

As we stated earlier, we can add and subtract fractions if the fractions have common denominators (denominators that are the same). Now, what do we do when the denominators are not the same? The following example will help us determine the answer to this question.

Suppose that we have 2 equal-size blocks of molding clay. One block of clay is cut into 2 equal-size parts and another is cut into 3 equal-size parts. If we take 1 of the 2 parts, then 1 of the 3 parts, we must add to find the total amount of clay we have.

We have 1 out of 2 parts.

We have 1 out of 3 parts.

$\frac{1}{2} + \frac{1}{3} = ?$

How much molding clay do we have?

$\frac{1}{2}$ $\frac{1}{3}$

Since we are adding pieces of molding clay that came from blocks that were cut into a different number of parts, **we are not adding like parts of a whole.** The total amount of clay could be determined more easily if each block of clay had been cut into 6 equal-size parts.

$\frac{1}{2}$ or $\frac{3}{6}$ $\frac{1}{3}$ or $\frac{2}{6}$

$$\frac{1}{2} + \frac{1}{3} = ?$$
$$\downarrow \quad \downarrow \quad \downarrow$$
$$\frac{3}{6} + \frac{2}{6} = \frac{5}{6}$$

As we can see, cutting the blocks of clay into the same number of pieces makes it possible to work with fractions that have a common denominator. We know how to add and subtract these fractions. *We use a similar idea to add and subtract fractions with different denominators.*

PROCEDURE TO ADD OR SUBTRACT FRACTIONAL EXPRESSIONS WITH DIFFERENT DENOMINATORS

1. Find the least common denominator (LCD).

2. Write equivalent fractions that have the LCD as the denominator.

3. Add or subtract the fractions with common denominators.

4. Simplify the answer if necessary.

How do we find a *least common denominator?* Let's look at the fractions $\frac{1}{2}$ and $\frac{1}{3}$ from the earlier illustration. Notice that the least common denominator, 6, is also the least common multiple of 2 and 3. In fact, the **least common denominator** of two fractions is the least common multiple (LCM) of the two denominators. Since we are working with denominators, we call the LCM the least common denominator, or LCD.

EXAMPLE 4   Find the least common denominator (LCD) of the fractions.

(a) $\frac{1}{5}, \frac{1}{3}$

(b) $\frac{1}{12}, \frac{5}{18}$

Solution

(a) $\frac{1}{5}, \frac{1}{3}$

The LCD of $\frac{1}{5}$ and $\frac{1}{3}$ is 15.

(b) We find the LCD of $\dfrac{1}{12}$ and $\dfrac{5}{18}$.

$$12 = 2 \cdot 2 \cdot 3$$
$$18 = 2 \cdot 3 \cdot 3$$
$$\text{LCD} = 2 \cdot 2 \cdot 3 \cdot 3 = 36$$

The LCD of $\dfrac{1}{12}$ and $\dfrac{5}{18}$ is 36.

NOTE TO STUDENT: Fully worked-out solutions to all of the Practice Problems can be found at the back of the text starting at page SP-1

Practice Problem 4 Find the least common denominator of the fractions.

(a) $\dfrac{1}{4}, \dfrac{1}{5}$

(b) $\dfrac{1}{12}, \dfrac{3}{28}$

How do we write equivalent fractions that have the LCD as the denominator? In Chapter 4 we learned that to find equivalent fractions we multiply the numerator and denominator by the same nonzero number. Therefore, we must determine the value of the nonzero number that when multiplied by the denominator yields the LCD.

EXAMPLE 5 Write the equivalent fraction for $\dfrac{1}{5}$ that has 40 as the denominator.

$$\frac{1}{5} = \frac{?}{40}$$

Solution

$\dfrac{1}{5} = \dfrac{?}{40}$ What number multiplied by the denominator, 5, yields 40? It is 8, since $5(8) = 40$.

$\dfrac{1 \cdot 8}{5 \cdot 8} = \dfrac{8}{40}$ We multiply the numerator and denominator of $\dfrac{1}{5}$ by 8.

$\dfrac{1}{5} = \dfrac{8}{40}$

Practice Problem 5 Write the equivalent fractions that have 10 as the denominator.

(a) $\dfrac{3}{5} = \dfrac{?}{10}$

(b) $\dfrac{1}{2} = \dfrac{?}{10}$

Once we find the LCD and write equivalent fractions with the LCD as the denominator, we simply add or subtract the fractions with the common denominators. We summarize the process.

1. Find the LCD.
2. Write equivalent fractions.
3. Add or subtract fractions.
4. Simplify if necessary.

EXAMPLE 6 Perform the operation indicated.

(a) $\dfrac{-5}{7} + \dfrac{3}{4}$

(b) $\dfrac{11}{12} - \dfrac{3}{20}$

Solution

(a) $\dfrac{-5}{7} + \dfrac{3}{4}$ **Step 1** Find the LCD of $\dfrac{-5}{7}$ and $\dfrac{3}{4}$.

$$\boxed{\text{LCD} = 28}$$

Step 2 Write equivalent fractions.

$$\dfrac{-5 \cdot 4}{7 \cdot 4} = \boxed{\dfrac{-20}{28}} \qquad \dfrac{3 \cdot 7}{4 \cdot 7} = \boxed{\dfrac{21}{28}}$$

Step 3 Add fractions with common denominators.

$$\dfrac{-5}{7} + \dfrac{3}{4} = \boxed{\dfrac{-20}{28} + \dfrac{21}{28}} = \dfrac{1}{28}$$

(b) $\dfrac{11}{12} - \dfrac{3}{20}$ **Step 1** Find the LCD of $\dfrac{11}{12}$ and $\dfrac{3}{20}$.

$$\text{LCD} = \overbrace{2 \cdot 2 \cdot 3}^{12} \cdot 5 = 60$$
$$\underbrace{\qquad \longrightarrow 20 \longleftarrow \qquad}$$
$$\boxed{\text{LCD} = 60}$$

Step 2 Write equivalent fractions.

$$\dfrac{11}{12} = \dfrac{11 \cdot 5}{12 \cdot 5} = \boxed{\dfrac{55}{60}} \qquad \dfrac{3}{20} = \dfrac{3 \cdot 3}{20 \cdot 3} = \boxed{\dfrac{9}{60}}$$

Step 3 Subtract fractions with common denominators.

$$\dfrac{11}{12} - \dfrac{3}{20} = \boxed{\dfrac{55}{60} - \dfrac{9}{60}} = \dfrac{46}{60}$$

Step 4 Simplify.

$$\dfrac{46}{60} = \dfrac{\cancel{2} \cdot 23}{\cancel{2} \cdot 2 \cdot 3 \cdot 5} = \dfrac{23}{30}$$

$$\dfrac{11}{12} - \dfrac{3}{20} = \dfrac{23}{30}$$

Practice Problem 6 Perform the operation indicated.

(a) $\dfrac{-3}{8} + \dfrac{7}{9}$

(b) $\dfrac{13}{30} - \dfrac{2}{15}$

NOTE TO STUDENT: Fully worked-out solutions to all of the Practice Problems can be found at the back of the text starting at page SP-1

EXAMPLE 7 Perform the operation indicated.

(a) $\dfrac{6}{x} + \dfrac{5}{3x}$

(b) $\dfrac{4}{y} - \dfrac{2}{x}$

Solution

(a) $\dfrac{6}{x} + \dfrac{5}{3x}$

Step 1 Find the LCD of $\dfrac{6}{x}$ and $\dfrac{5}{3x}$.

$$\boxed{\text{LCD} = 3x}$$

Step 2 Write equivalent fractions.

$$\frac{6}{x} = \frac{6 \cdot 3}{x \cdot 3} = \boxed{\frac{18}{3x}} \qquad \frac{5}{3x} = \boxed{\frac{5}{3x}}$$

Step 3 Add fractions with common denominators.

$$\frac{6}{x} + \frac{5}{3x} = \boxed{\frac{18}{3x} + \frac{5}{3x}} = \frac{18 + 5}{3x} = \frac{23}{3x}$$

We did not need to write $\frac{5}{3x}$ as an equivalent fraction with the common denominator since its denominator, $3x$, is the LCD.

(b) $\dfrac{4}{y} - \dfrac{2}{x}$

Step 1 Find the LCD of $\dfrac{4}{y}$ and $\dfrac{2}{x}$.

$$\boxed{\text{LCD} = xy}$$

Step 2 Write equivalent fractions.

$$\frac{4}{y} = \frac{4 \cdot x}{y \cdot x} = \boxed{\frac{4x}{xy}} \qquad \frac{2}{x} = \frac{2 \cdot y}{x \cdot y} = \boxed{\frac{2y}{xy}}$$

Step 3 Subtract fractions with common denominators.

$$\frac{4}{y} - \frac{2}{x} = \boxed{\frac{4x}{xy} - \frac{2y}{xy}} = \frac{4x - 2y}{xy}$$

We cannot subtract $4x - 2y$ since $4x$ and $2y$ are not like terms. Therefore, we leave the numerator as the expression $4x - 2y$.

CAUTION: We may not use slashes to divide out *part* of an addition or subtraction problem. We may use slashes only if we are multiplying factors.

$\dfrac{4\cancel{x} - 2\cancel{y}}{\cancel{x}\,\cancel{y}} = 4 - 2 = 2$ This is wrong!

$\dfrac{(4\cancel{x})(2\cancel{y})}{\cancel{x}\,\cancel{y}} = 8$ This is correct.

$\dfrac{4x - 2y}{xy}$ This expression *cannot* be simplified any further since we are *subtracting* $4x$ and $2y$.

$\dfrac{(4x)(2y)}{xy} = 8$ This expression *can* be simplified since we are *multiplying* $4x$ and $2y$.

Practice Problem 7 Perform the operation indicated.

(a) $\dfrac{8}{x} + \dfrac{2}{5x}$

(b) $\dfrac{7}{y} - \dfrac{4}{x}$

EXAMPLE 8 Add. $\dfrac{7x}{16} + \dfrac{3x}{32}$

Solution

$\dfrac{7x}{16} + \dfrac{3x}{32}$ **Step 1** Find the LCD of $\dfrac{7x}{16}$ and $\dfrac{3x}{32}$.

$$\boxed{\text{LCD} = 32}$$

Step 2 Write equivalent fractions.

$$\dfrac{7x \cdot 2}{16 \cdot 2} = \boxed{\dfrac{14x}{32}} \qquad \dfrac{3x}{32} = \boxed{\dfrac{3x}{32}}$$

Step 3 Add fractions with common denominators.

$$\dfrac{7x}{16} + \dfrac{3x}{32} = \boxed{\dfrac{14x}{32} + \dfrac{3x}{32}} = \dfrac{14x + 3x}{32} = \dfrac{17x}{32}$$

Practice Problem 8 Add.

$$\dfrac{8x}{15} + \dfrac{9x}{24}$$

When solving applied problems, we must determine what operation to use. As we saw in Chapter 1, problems that involve subtraction often use the phrases "how much more," or "how much is left." Those that require addition often state "how many," or "find the total." Identifying these key phrases in an applied problem will help you solve the problem.

EXAMPLE 9 Leila finished $\frac{1}{8}$ of her English term paper before spring break and $\frac{1}{2}$ of the paper during spring break. How much more did she complete during the break than before the break?

Solution *Understand the problem.* The phrase "how much more" indicates that we subtract.

Solve and state the answer.

Completed during break	minus	Completed before break
$\dfrac{1}{2}$	$-$	$\dfrac{1}{8}$

1. The LCD is 8.

2. Write equivalent fractions. $\dfrac{1}{2} = \dfrac{1 \cdot 4}{2 \cdot 4} = \boxed{\dfrac{4}{8}} \qquad \dfrac{1}{8} = \boxed{\dfrac{1}{8}}$

3. Subtract. $\dfrac{1}{2} - \dfrac{1}{8} = \boxed{\dfrac{4}{8} - \dfrac{1}{8}} = \dfrac{3}{8}$

Leila finished $\frac{3}{8}$ more of the term paper *during* the break than *before* the break.

Check: Double-check your calculations on a separate piece of paper.

Practice Problem 9 Jesse painted $\frac{1}{4}$ of his home on Monday and $\frac{1}{6}$ of his home on Tuesday. How much more did he complete on Monday than on Tuesday?

EXAMPLE 10 Ranak bought $\frac{3}{4}$ pound of sliced turkey and $\frac{5}{8}$ pound of sliced ham at the delicatessen. How many pounds of deli meat did she buy?

Solution *Understand the problem.* Since we want to find *how many* pounds she purchased, we must add $\frac{3}{4}$ and $\frac{5}{8}$.

To add $\frac{3}{4} + \frac{5}{8}$ we must first find the least common denominator, which is 8.

$$\frac{3}{4} = \frac{3 \cdot 2}{4 \cdot 2} = \frac{6}{8} \qquad \text{We write } \frac{3}{4} \text{ as the equivalent fraction } \frac{6}{8}.$$

$$\frac{6}{8} + \frac{5}{8} = \frac{11}{8} \text{ or } 1\frac{3}{8} \text{ pounds} \qquad \text{We add and then change } \frac{11}{8} \text{ to the mixed number } 1\frac{3}{8}.$$

Ranak bought $1\frac{3}{8}$ pounds of deli meat.

Practice Problem 10 Lester jogged $\frac{2}{3}$ mile on Monday and $\frac{4}{5}$ mile on Tuesday. How many miles did he jog in the two-day period?

NOTE TO STUDENT: *Fully worked-out solutions to all of the Practice Problems can be found at the back of the text starting at page SP-1*

Notice in Example 10 we changed the improper fraction to a mixed number. As answers to applications, mixed numbers are generally easier to understand.

Developing Your Study Skills

A Positive Attitude Toward Fractions

Often, students panic when they begin to study fractions in their math classes. They may think, "I have never understood fractions, and I never will!" Not true. You experience situations involving fractions every day. You may not actually perform mathematical calculations with fractions, but you find the results. Consider these two situations.

Situation: You know that if you slice an apple into quarters, you can take 1 of the 4 pieces or $\frac{1}{4}$ of the apple.

Calculation: $1 \div 4 = \frac{1}{4}$

Situation: If you take $\frac{1}{2}$ of $6, you know you have $3.

Calculation: $\frac{1}{2} \cdot 6 = 3$

As you can see, you already know how to work with fractions. Now you are ready to see how to perform the calculations so that you can find the outcome of more complex situations. How can you do this? Follow these suggestions.

1. You must have a *positive attitude* toward fractions.
2. Try to *understand the process* used to perform the calculations. You can do this by
   (a) Drawing pictures and diagrams.
   (b) Asking questions when you do not understand.
   (c) Learning all the rules.
   (d) Practicing by completing your assignments.

Verbal and Writing Skills

Fill in the blanks.

1. When we add two fractions with the same denominator, we add the _____, and the _____ stays the same.

2. When we add two fractions with different denominators, we must first find the _____.

3. Is $\dfrac{4}{5} + \dfrac{5}{9} = \dfrac{4+5}{5+9} = \dfrac{9}{14}$? Why or why not?

4. Is $\dfrac{5}{9} - \dfrac{4}{5} = \dfrac{5-4}{9-5} = \dfrac{1}{4}$? Why or why not?

Fill in each box with the correct value.

5. $\dfrac{\square}{7} + \dfrac{3}{7} = \dfrac{5}{7}$

6. $\dfrac{\square}{9} + \dfrac{4}{9} = \dfrac{7}{9}$

7. $\dfrac{\square}{4} - \dfrac{1}{4} = \dfrac{1}{4}$

8. $\dfrac{\square}{7} - \dfrac{4}{7} = \dfrac{2}{7}$

Perform the operation indicated. Be sure to simplify your answer.

9. $\dfrac{6}{17} + \dfrac{9}{17}$

10. $\dfrac{5}{35} + \dfrac{3}{35}$

11. $\dfrac{6}{23} - \dfrac{5}{23}$

12. $\dfrac{8}{43} - \dfrac{2}{43}$

13. $\dfrac{-13}{28} + \left(\dfrac{-11}{28}\right)$

14. $\dfrac{-17}{74} + \left(\dfrac{-41}{74}\right)$

15. $\dfrac{-31}{51} + \dfrac{11}{51}$

16. $\dfrac{-27}{43} + \dfrac{15}{43}$

17. $\dfrac{9}{y} - \dfrac{8}{y}$

18. $\dfrac{12}{x} - \dfrac{4}{x}$

19. $\dfrac{31}{a} + \dfrac{8}{a}$

20. $\dfrac{22}{a} + \dfrac{13}{a}$

21. $\dfrac{x}{7} - \dfrac{5}{7}$

22. $\dfrac{x}{12} - \dfrac{11}{12}$

23. $\dfrac{y}{3} + \dfrac{14}{3}$

24. $\dfrac{y}{5} + \dfrac{42}{5}$

Find the least common denominator (LCD) of the fractions.

25. $\dfrac{1}{5}, \dfrac{1}{6}$

26. $\dfrac{1}{3}, \dfrac{1}{8}$

27. $\dfrac{1}{9}, \dfrac{1}{15}$

28. $\dfrac{1}{21}, \dfrac{1}{14}$

The LCD of the following fractions is 60. Write equivalent fractions that have 60 as the denominator.

29. $\dfrac{1}{5} = \dfrac{?}{60}$

30. $\dfrac{2}{15} = \dfrac{?}{60}$

31. $\dfrac{5}{6} = \dfrac{?}{60}$

32. $\dfrac{3}{10} = \dfrac{?}{60}$

Perform the operation indicated. Be sure to simplify your answer.

33. $\dfrac{11}{15} - \dfrac{31}{45}$

34. $\dfrac{29}{12} - \dfrac{23}{24}$

35. $\dfrac{17}{24} - \dfrac{1}{6}$

36. $\dfrac{11}{28} - \dfrac{1}{7}$

37. $\dfrac{3}{8} + \dfrac{4}{7}$

38. $\dfrac{7}{4} + \dfrac{5}{9}$

39. $\dfrac{-3}{4} + \dfrac{1}{10}$

40. $\dfrac{-5}{6} + \dfrac{3}{4}$

41. $\dfrac{-2}{13} + \dfrac{7}{26}$

42. $\dfrac{-4}{15} + \dfrac{11}{30}$

43. $\dfrac{-3}{14} + \left(\dfrac{-1}{10}\right)$

44. $\dfrac{-4}{15} + \left(\dfrac{-1}{6}\right)$

45. $\dfrac{7}{10} - \dfrac{5}{14}$

46. $\dfrac{7}{20} - \dfrac{3}{16}$

47. $\dfrac{11}{15} - \dfrac{5}{12}$

48. $\dfrac{4}{15} - \dfrac{2}{25}$

Perform the operation indicated. Be sure to simplify your answer.

49. $\dfrac{5}{2x} + \dfrac{8}{x}$

50. $\dfrac{7}{5x} + \dfrac{3}{x}$

51. $\dfrac{2}{7x} + \dfrac{3}{x}$

52. $\dfrac{2}{5x} + \dfrac{5}{x}$

53. $\dfrac{3}{2x} + \dfrac{5}{6x}$

54. $\dfrac{2}{4x} + \dfrac{5}{8x}$

55. $\dfrac{3}{x} + \dfrac{4}{y}$

56. $\dfrac{5}{x} + \dfrac{3}{y}$

57. $\dfrac{4}{a} - \dfrac{9}{b}$

58. $\dfrac{6}{x} - \dfrac{4}{y}$

59. $\dfrac{2x}{15} + \dfrac{3x}{5}$

60. $\dfrac{7x}{12} + \dfrac{5x}{6}$

61. $\dfrac{-3x}{10} - \dfrac{7x}{20}$

62. $\dfrac{-11x}{14} - \dfrac{3x}{28}$

63. $\dfrac{x}{3} + \left(\dfrac{-11x}{12}\right)$

64. $\dfrac{x}{4} + \left(\dfrac{-7x}{16}\right)$

Mixed Practice

65. $\dfrac{5}{6} + \dfrac{3}{10}$

66. $\dfrac{3}{7} + \dfrac{7}{2}$

67. $\dfrac{3}{16} + \left(\dfrac{-9}{20}\right)$

68. $\dfrac{7}{18} + \left(\dfrac{-5}{27}\right)$

69. $\dfrac{9}{y} + \dfrac{1}{x}$

70. $\dfrac{6}{y} + \dfrac{1}{x}$

71. $\dfrac{2x}{15} + \dfrac{3x}{20}$

72. $\dfrac{7x}{10} - \dfrac{2x}{15}$

Applications

73. *Sweets Purchased* Pat bought $\frac{3}{4}$ pound of peanut butter fudge and $\frac{7}{8}$ pound of fudge with nuts. How many pounds of fudge did Pat buy?

74. *Miles Walked* Leon walked $\frac{3}{8}$ mile to his friend's house and then $\frac{2}{3}$ mile to the park. How far did Leon walk?

75. *Fruit Bar Recipe* A chewy fruit bar recipe calls for $\frac{3}{4}$ cup of brown sugar and $\frac{1}{2}$ cup of granulated sugar.

  (a) How many cups of sugar are in the recipe?

  (b) How many more cups of brown sugar than granulated sugar are in the recipe?

76. *Ham Recipe* A ham glaze recipe calls for $\frac{1}{2}$ teaspoon of dry mustard, $\frac{1}{4}$ teaspoon of ground ginger, and $\frac{1}{4}$ teaspoon of salt.

  (a) What is the quantity of dry ingredients in the recipe?

  (b) How many more teaspoons of dry mustard than salt are in the recipe?

77. *Painting a Home* A mother and her teenage son are painting their home. In one day, the mother completes $\frac{1}{3}$ of the job and the son completes $\frac{1}{4}$ of the job. How much more of the job did the mother complete than the son?

78. *Homework Completed* Mary Ann finished $\frac{3}{4}$ of her math homework before dinner and $\frac{1}{5}$ after dinner. How much more homework did Mary Ann complete before dinner than after dinner?

79. *Inheritance* Eric inherited $\frac{1}{8}$ of his grandfather's estate, and his cousin inherited $\frac{1}{12}$ of the estate.

   (a) What part of the estate did Eric and his cousin inherit?

   (b) How much more of the estate did Eric inherit than his cousin?

80. *Family Business* Thu Tran owns $\frac{2}{9}$ of the family business, and her brother Bao owns $\frac{4}{15}$ of the business.

   (a) What part of the family business do Thu and Bao own together?

   (b) How much more of the family business does Bao own than Thu?

One Step Further *Perform the operations indicated.*

81. $\dfrac{7}{30} + \dfrac{3}{40} + \dfrac{1}{8}$

82. $\dfrac{1}{12} + \dfrac{3}{14} + \dfrac{4}{21}$

83. $\dfrac{1}{3} + \dfrac{1}{12} - \dfrac{1}{6}$

84. $\dfrac{1}{5} + \dfrac{2}{3} - \dfrac{11}{15}$

Cumulative Review *Evaluate each of the following for the given values.*

85. **[2.4.4]** $\dfrac{-a}{b}$ for $a = -24$ and $b = 6$

86. **[2.4.4]** $\dfrac{-x}{-y}$ for $x = -10$ and $y = -2$

87. **[2.6.2]** $\dfrac{(a^2 - b)}{-4}$ for $a = 3$ and $b = 1$

88. **[2.6.2]** $9x - x^2$ for $x = -2$

Solve the applications in exercises 89 and 90.

89. **[1.9.3]** *Household Budget* A family's monthly budget for household expenses is $3033. After $1295 is spent for the house payment, $469 for food, $387 for clothing, and $287 for entertainment, how much is left in the budget?

90. **[1.9.3]** *College Living Expense* Joan has a $500 monthly expense allowance from her parents while she is living in the dorm at college. Her expenses this month were: food $190, gas $43, telephone $42, school supplies $96, and entertainment $55. How much money did she have left after expenses?

Quick Quiz 5.3 *Perform the operations indicated.*

1. $\dfrac{1}{y} - \dfrac{2}{9y}$

3. $\dfrac{2x}{15} + \dfrac{5x}{6}$

2. **(a)** $\dfrac{5}{12} + \dfrac{3}{20}$ **(b)** $\dfrac{3}{14} - \dfrac{1}{21}$

4. **Concept Check**

   (a) What is a common denominator for the fractions $\frac{3x}{20}$ and $\frac{5x}{6}$?

   (b) Explain how you would add the fractions.

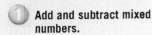
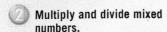
1 Adding and Subtracting Mixed Numbers

We add and subtract mixed numbers in a manner similar to the one used for proper fractions. The only difference is that we work with the whole number and the fractional parts separately.

ADDING AND SUBTRACTING MIXED NUMBERS

We add or subtract the fractions first and then the whole numbers.

EXAMPLE 1 Add. $4\frac{1}{8} + 3\frac{3}{8}$

Solution

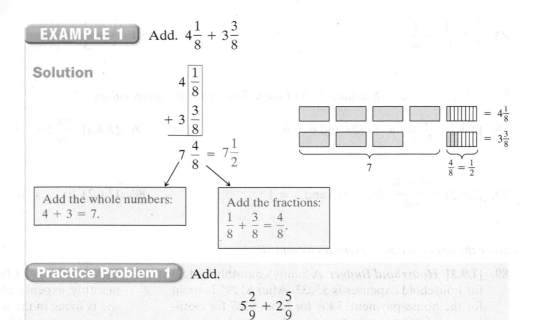

$$4\frac{1}{8}$$
$$+ 3\frac{3}{8}$$
$$\overline{7\frac{4}{8}} = 7\frac{1}{2}$$

Add the whole numbers: $4 + 3 = 7$.

Add the fractions: $\frac{1}{8} + \frac{3}{8} = \frac{4}{8}$.

Practice Problem 1 Add.

$$5\frac{2}{9} + 2\frac{5}{9}$$

If the fractional parts of the mixed numbers do not have common denominators, we find the LCD and build equivalent fractions to obtain common denominators before adding.

EXAMPLE 2 Add. $4\frac{2}{3} + 2\frac{1}{4}$

Solution The LCD of $\frac{2}{3}$ and $\frac{1}{4}$ is 12, so we build equivalent fractions with this denominator.

$$4\frac{2}{3} \cdot \frac{4}{4} = 4\frac{8}{12}$$
$$+ 2\frac{1}{4} \cdot \frac{3}{3} = + 2\frac{3}{12}$$
$$\overline{6\frac{11}{12}}$$

Add the fractions: $\frac{8}{12} + \frac{3}{12} = \frac{11}{12}$.

Add the whole numbers.

Practice Problem 2 Add.

$$5\frac{1}{3} + 6\frac{3}{5}$$

NOTE TO STUDENT: *Fully worked-out solutions to all of the Practice Problems can be found at the back of the text starting at page SP-1*

EXAMPLE 3   Add. $2\frac{5}{7} + 6\frac{2}{3}$

Solution   The LCD of $\frac{5}{7}$ and $\frac{2}{3}$ is 21.

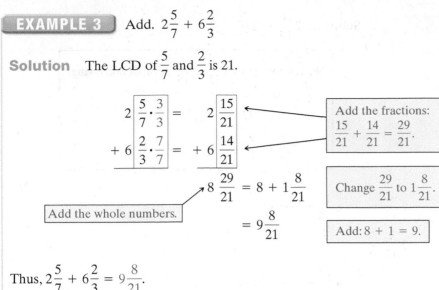

Add the fractions:
$$\frac{15}{21} + \frac{14}{21} = \frac{29}{21}.$$

$$8\frac{29}{21} = 8 + 1\frac{8}{21}$$ Change $\frac{29}{21}$ to $1\frac{8}{21}$.

Add the whole numbers.

$$= 9\frac{8}{21}$$ Add: $8 + 1 = 9$.

Thus, $2\frac{5}{7} + 6\frac{2}{3} = 9\frac{8}{21}$.

Practice Problem 3   Add.

$$7\frac{3}{4} + 2\frac{4}{5}$$

NOTE TO STUDENT: *Fully worked-out solutions to all of the Practice Problems can be found at the back of the text starting at page SP-1*

CARRYING

In Example 3 we simplified $8\frac{29}{21}$ to $9\frac{8}{21}$ because the fractional part of a mixed number must be a proper fraction. We used a process similar to *carrying* with whole numbers.

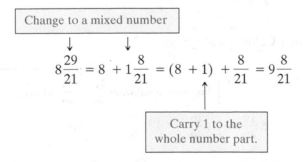

Change to a mixed number

$$8\frac{29}{21} = 8 + 1\frac{8}{21} = (8 + 1) + \frac{8}{21} = 9\frac{8}{21}$$

Carry 1 to the whole number part.

BORROWING

When subtracting mixed numbers, it is sometimes necessary to *borrow*. The process used to borrow with mixed numbers is the opposite of carrying with mixed numbers.

Write 9 as the sum $8 + 1$.   Borrow 1 from the whole number part and add to the fraction part.

$$9\frac{8}{21} = (8 + 1) + \frac{8}{21} = 8 + 1\frac{8}{21} = 8\frac{29}{21}$$

Change $1\frac{8}{21}$ to the improper fraction $\frac{29}{21}$.

Thus $9\frac{8}{21}$ is written as $8\frac{29}{21}$ when borrowing is necessary.

EXAMPLE 4 Subtract. $7\dfrac{4}{15} - 2\dfrac{7}{15}$

Solution

> We cannot subtract $\dfrac{4}{15} - \dfrac{7}{15}$, without borrowing.
>
> $7\dfrac{4}{15} = 6 + 1\dfrac{4}{15}$ We write 7 as the sum $6 + 1$ (borrowing from 7).
>
> $= 6 + \dfrac{19}{15}$ We change $1\dfrac{4}{15}$ to $\dfrac{19}{15}$.

$$
\begin{aligned}
7\dfrac{4}{15} &= \quad 6\dfrac{19}{15} \longleftarrow \\
-2\dfrac{7}{15} &= -2\dfrac{7}{15} \\
\hline
&\quad\ 4\dfrac{12}{15} \longleftrightarrow
\end{aligned}
$$

Subtract fractions: $\dfrac{19}{15} - \dfrac{7}{15} = \dfrac{12}{15}$.

Subtract whole numbers.

We simplify: $4\dfrac{12}{15} = 4\dfrac{4}{5}$. Thus, $7\dfrac{4}{15} - 2\dfrac{7}{15} = 4\dfrac{4}{5}$.

Practice Problem 4 Subtract.

$$5\dfrac{3}{12} - 3\dfrac{5}{12}$$

EXAMPLE 5 Subtract. $5\dfrac{2}{5} - 3\dfrac{7}{8}$

Solution   The LCD of $\dfrac{2}{5}$ and $\dfrac{7}{8}$ is 40.

$$
\begin{aligned}
5\dfrac{2\cdot 8}{5\cdot 8} &= \quad 5\dfrac{16}{40} \longleftarrow \\
-3\dfrac{7\cdot 5}{8\cdot 5} &= -3\dfrac{35}{40}
\end{aligned}
$$

> We cannot subtract $\dfrac{16}{40} - \dfrac{35}{40}$, without borrowing.
>
> $5\dfrac{16}{40} = 4 + 1\dfrac{16}{40}$ We write 5 as the sum $4 + 1$ (borrowing from 5).
>
> $4 + \dfrac{56}{40}$ We change $1\dfrac{16}{40}$ to $\dfrac{56}{40}$.

$$
\begin{aligned}
5\dfrac{16}{40} &= \quad 4\dfrac{56}{40} \longleftarrow \\
-3\dfrac{35}{40} &= -3\dfrac{35}{40} \\
\hline
&\quad\ 1\dfrac{21}{40} \longleftarrow
\end{aligned}
$$

Subtract fractions: $\dfrac{56}{40} - \dfrac{35}{40} = \dfrac{21}{40}$.

Subtract whole numbers.

Thus $5\dfrac{2}{3} - 3\dfrac{7}{8} = 1\dfrac{21}{40}$.

Practice Problem 5 Subtract.

$$6\dfrac{1}{7} - 2\dfrac{3}{4}$$

Understanding the Concept

Should We Change to an Improper Fraction?

When combining mixed numbers, we can change the numbers to improper fractions, and then add or subtract. To illustrate, we work Example 5 this way.

Change to   Build
improper   equivalent
fractions.   fractions.
↓   ↓

$$5\frac{2}{5} = \frac{27}{5} = \frac{216}{40}$$

$$-3\frac{7}{8} = -\frac{31}{8} = -\frac{155}{40}$$

$$\frac{61}{40} \text{ or } 1\frac{21}{40} \quad \text{Subtract improper fractions.}$$

As you can see, the result is the same as the result obtained in Example 5. Which method should you use? Well, there are advantages to both methods. We do not have to carry or borrow when we change to improper fractions. But if the numbers are large, changing to improper fractions can be more difficult.

Exercise

1. Add the following numbers using both methods. Which way is easier? Why?

$$25\frac{3}{5} + 32\frac{5}{8}$$

EXAMPLE 6   Subtract. $8 - 3\frac{1}{4}$

Solution

$$8 \ = \ 7\frac{4}{4} \quad 8 = (7 + 1) = 7 + \frac{4}{4} \text{ or } 7\frac{4}{4}$$

$$-3\frac{1}{4} = -3\frac{1}{4}$$

$$4\frac{3}{4}$$

When we borrowed 1 from 8 we changed the 1 to $\frac{4}{4}$ because we wanted a fraction that had the same denominator as $\frac{1}{4}$.

Practice Problem 6   Subtract.

$$9 - 4\frac{1}{3}$$

NOTE TO STUDENT: Fully worked-out solutions to all of the Practice Problems can be found at the back of the text starting at page SP-1

2   Multiplying and Dividing Mixed Numbers

In Chapter 4 we learned that the mixed number $2\frac{1}{4}$ means $2 + \frac{1}{4}$. To multiply $3 \cdot 2\frac{1}{4}$ we have $3\left(2 + \frac{1}{4}\right)$, which requires use of the distributive property.

$$3 \cdot 2\frac{1}{4} = 3\left(2 + \frac{1}{4}\right) = 3 \cdot \left(2 + \frac{1}{4}\right) = 3 \cdot 2 + 3 \cdot \frac{1}{4} = 6 + \frac{3}{4} = 6\frac{3}{4}$$

with $3 \cdot 2$ indicated above and $3 \cdot \frac{1}{4}$ indicated below.

Changing the mixed number to an improper fraction simplifies the calculations.

$$3 \cdot 2\frac{1}{4} = \frac{3}{1} \cdot \frac{9}{4} = \frac{27}{4} = 6\frac{3}{4}$$

> Change mixed numbers to improper fractions before multiplying or dividing.

EXAMPLE 7   Multiply. $5\frac{5}{12} \cdot 3\frac{11}{15}$

Solution   We change the mixed numbers to improper fractions and then multiply.

$$5\frac{5}{12} \cdot 3\frac{11}{15} = \frac{65}{12} \cdot \frac{56}{15} = \frac{\cancel{5} \cdot 13 \cdot \cancel{4} \cdot 14}{3 \cdot \cancel{4} \cdot \cancel{5} \cdot 3} = \frac{182}{9} \text{ or } 20\frac{2}{9}$$

Practice Problem 7   Multiply.
$$6\frac{3}{7} \cdot 1\frac{13}{15}$$

CAUTION: When *adding* and *subtracting* mixed numbers, we normally *don't* change to improper fractions before we add or subtract. **However, when *multiplying* and *dividing* mixed numbers, we must change to improper fractions *before* we multiply or divide to avoid using the distributive property.**

EXAMPLE 8   Divide. $2\frac{1}{4} \div (-5)$

Solution   Recall that to divide we invert the second fraction and multiply.

$$2\frac{1}{4} \div (-5) = \frac{9}{4} \div \frac{(-5)}{1} \qquad \text{Change to an improper fraction.}$$

$$= \frac{9}{4} \cdot \left(-\frac{1}{5}\right) \qquad \text{Find the reciprocal of (invert) } \frac{-5}{1}.$$

$$= -\frac{9}{20} \qquad \text{Multiply.}$$

Practice Problem 8   Divide.
$$1\frac{1}{4} \div (-2)$$

 Solving Applied Problems Involving Mixed Numbers

When solving applied problems, it is important to identify which operation to use. In Sections 5.1 and 5.2 we reviewed the addition, subtraction, multiplication, and division situations we learned in Chapter 1. We summarize these, as well as other key words and phrases, below.

Multiplication Situations and Key Words
- Situations that require repeated addition or taking a fraction *of* something
- Key words: *double, triple,* and *times*

Division Situations and Key Words
- Situations that require splitting an amount into a certain number of equal parts or finding how many times one number is in another number
- Key words: *quotient, divided by*

Addition Key Phrases
- "How many," "find the total"

Subtraction Key Phrases
- "How much more," "how much is left"

When solving applications involving fractions, it is helpful to draw pictures or diagrams.

▲ **EXAMPLE 9**   Ester uses a small piece of painted wood as the base for each centerpiece she makes for banquet tables. She has a long piece of wood that measures $13\frac{1}{2}$ feet. She needs to cut it into pieces that are $\frac{1}{2}$ foot long for the centerpiece bases. How many centerpiece bases will she be able to cut from the long piece of wood?

Solution   *Understand the problem.* We draw a picture.

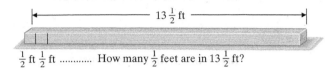

$\frac{1}{2}$ ft $\frac{1}{2}$ ft .... How many $\frac{1}{2}$ feet are in $13\frac{1}{2}$ ft?

Solve and state the answer. This is a division situation since we want to know how many $\frac{1}{2}$s are in $13\frac{1}{2}$. Therefore we must divide $13\frac{1}{2} \div \frac{1}{2}$.

$$13\frac{1}{2} \div \frac{1}{2} = \frac{27}{2} \div \frac{1}{2} \quad \text{We change } 13\frac{1}{2} \text{ to an improper fraction.}$$

$$= \frac{27}{2} \cdot \frac{2}{1} \quad \text{We invert } \frac{1}{2} \text{ and change the division to multiplication.}$$

$$= 27 \quad \text{We simplify.}$$

Ester can make 27 centerpiece bases from the piece of wood.

Practice Problem 9   A recipe uses $4\frac{1}{2}$ tablespoons of brown sugar. If Sara only has a $\frac{1}{2}$-tablespoon measuring utensil, how many times must she fill this utensil to get the desired amount of sugar?

▲ **EXAMPLE 10**   A plumber has a pipe $5\frac{3}{4}$ feet long. He needs $\frac{1}{3}$ of the length of the pipe for a repair job. What length must he cut off the pipe to get the desired size?

Solution   *Understand the problem.* We draw a picture.

$5\frac{3}{4}$ ft

? ft
$\frac{1}{3}$ of the length

Solve and state the answer. The key word of ($\frac{1}{3}$ of the length) indicates that we must multiply to find the length the plumber must cut off.

$$\frac{1}{3} \cdot 5\frac{3}{4} = \frac{1}{3} \cdot \frac{23}{4} = \frac{23}{12} \text{ or } 1\frac{11}{12}$$

The plumber must cut off $1\frac{11}{12}$ feet of pipe.

▲ **Practice Problem 10**   Jerome has $32\frac{1}{2}$ feet of fencing material. He needs $\frac{1}{10}$ of this material to repair a portion of the fence on his land. How much fencing material does Jerome need to repair his fence?

Verbal and Writing Skills

1. Marcy multiplied two mixed numbers and got the following results.

$$2\frac{2}{3} \cdot 3\frac{4}{5} \rightarrow 2 \cdot 3 = 6 \quad \text{and} \quad \frac{2}{3} \cdot \frac{4}{5} = \frac{8}{15}$$

$$2\frac{2}{3} \cdot 3\frac{4}{5} = 6\frac{8}{15} \quad \text{This answer is wrong.}$$

(a) What did Marcy do wrong?

(b) What is the correct answer?

2. Lester divided two mixed numbers and got the following results.

$$8\frac{1}{2} \div 4\frac{4}{7} \rightarrow 8 \div 4 = 2 \quad \text{and} \quad \frac{1}{2} \cdot \frac{4}{7} = \frac{2}{7}$$

$$8\frac{1}{2} \div 4\frac{4}{7} = 2\frac{2}{7} \quad \text{This answer is wrong.}$$

(a) What did Lester do wrong?

(b) What is the correct answer?

Add or subtract. Simplify all answers. Express as a mixed number.

3. $10\frac{4}{9} + 11\frac{1}{9}$

4. $8\frac{1}{5} + 3\frac{3}{5}$

5. $5\frac{5}{8} + 11\frac{1}{8}$

6. $7\frac{1}{6} + 2\frac{1}{6}$

7. $5\frac{2}{3} + 8\frac{1}{4}$

8. $22\frac{3}{5} + 16\frac{1}{10}$

9. $14\frac{1}{4} + 6\frac{1}{3}$

10. $13\frac{1}{2} + 7\frac{4}{5}$

11. $7\frac{5}{6} + 4\frac{3}{8}$

12. $5\frac{14}{15} + 10\frac{3}{10}$

13. $7\frac{4}{5} - 2\frac{1}{5}$

14. $6\frac{3}{8} - 2\frac{1}{8}$

15. $9\frac{2}{3} - 6\frac{1}{6}$

16. $15\frac{3}{4} - 13\frac{1}{6}$

17. $11\frac{1}{5} - 6\frac{3}{5}$

18. $25\frac{2}{7} - 16\frac{5}{7}$

19. $10\frac{5}{12} - 3\frac{9}{10}$

20. $12\frac{4}{9} - 7\frac{5}{6}$

21. $9 - 2\frac{1}{4}$

22. $4 - 2\frac{2}{7}$

Mixed Practice Exercises 23–30

Add or subtract. Simplify all answers. Express as a mixed number.

23. $8\frac{2}{5} - 6\frac{1}{7}$

24. $45\frac{3}{8} - 26\frac{1}{10}$

25. $1\frac{1}{6} + \frac{3}{8}$

26. $1\frac{2}{3} + \frac{5}{18}$

27. $8\frac{1}{4} + 3\frac{5}{6}$

28. $7\frac{3}{4} + 6\frac{2}{5}$

29. $32 - 1\frac{2}{9}$

30. $24 - 3\frac{4}{11}$

Multiply or divide and simplify your answer.

31. $2\frac{1}{5} \cdot 1\frac{2}{3}$

32. $1\frac{1}{4} \cdot 2\frac{2}{7}$

33. $4\frac{1}{3} \cdot 2\frac{1}{4}$

34. $6\frac{1}{3} \cdot 2\frac{1}{4}$

35. $-\frac{3}{4} \cdot 3\frac{5}{7}$

36. $-\frac{8}{11} \cdot 4\frac{3}{4}$

37. $2\frac{1}{4} \div (-4)$

38. $2\frac{1}{2} \div (-3)$

39. $4\frac{1}{2} \div 2\frac{1}{4}$

40. $8\frac{1}{4} \div 2\frac{3}{4}$

41. $3\frac{1}{4} \div \frac{3}{8}$

42. $-\frac{1}{2} \div 2\frac{5}{8}$

43. $-6 \div \frac{1}{4}$

44. $-6 \div \frac{1}{2}$

Mixed Practice Exercises 45–50

Multiply or divide and simplify your answer.

45. $1\frac{1}{4} \cdot 3\frac{2}{3}$

46. $2\frac{3}{5} \cdot 1\frac{4}{7}$

47. $6\frac{1}{2} \div \frac{3}{4}$

48. $-\frac{1}{4} \div 1\frac{7}{8}$

49. $7\frac{1}{2} \div (-8)$

50. $8\frac{2}{9} \div (-9)$

Applications

51. *Camping Supplies* To put up the tents for a camping trip, Andy needs several pieces of rope each $6\frac{1}{2}$ feet long. If Andy has a rope that is 26 feet long, how many pieces can he cut for his tents?

▲ **53.** *Oak Wood* A carpenter has a piece of oak wood $7\frac{1}{5}$ feet long. He needs $\frac{1}{3}$ of the length for a shelf. What length must he cut off the wood to get the desired size?

Recipes Use the given recipe to answer exercises 55–58.

55. To double the recipe, how much flour do you need?

56. To triple the recipe, how much brown sugar do you need?

57. To make four times the recipe, how many cups of chocolate chips do you need?

58. To make $\frac{1}{2}$ of the recipe, how much granulated sugar do you need?

52. *Tie Pattern* Quynh has $4\frac{1}{5}$ yards of silk. It takes $\frac{3}{5}$ of a yard to make a tie. How many ties can she make from this silk?

54. *Project* Ella has $7\frac{1}{2}$ weeks to finish a project for her employer. She must plan to allow $\frac{1}{5}$ of the time to develop a formal presentation. How many weeks should Ella allow to develop the presentation?

Ingredients for 1 Batch of Chocolate Chip Cookies	
$2\frac{1}{4}$ cups flour	$\frac{3}{4}$ cup granulated sugar
1 teaspoon baking soda	$\frac{2}{3}$ cup brown sugar
$\frac{3}{4}$ teaspoon salt	1 teaspoon vanilla
1 cup margarine	$2\frac{1}{2}$ cups chocolate chips

59. *20-mile Run* As part of a 3-day workout plan to prepare for a 20-mile endurance run, Jeff ran $9\frac{1}{8}$ miles Monday, $12\frac{1}{3}$ miles Tuesday, and $17\frac{1}{6}$ miles Wednesday. How many miles did Jeff run in the 3-day period?

60. *Purchase* Will bought $\frac{5}{8}$ pound of M&M's and $1\frac{7}{16}$ pound of jellybeans. How many pounds of candy did Will buy?

To Think About *Find the values for each of the variables.*

61. $\frac{1}{4}, \frac{1}{2}, \frac{3}{4}, 1, \frac{a}{4}, \frac{3}{2}, \frac{7}{b}, 2, \frac{9}{4}, \frac{5}{2}, \frac{11}{4}, c, \cdots$

62. $\frac{1}{8}, \frac{1}{4}, \frac{3}{8}, \frac{1}{2}, \frac{a}{8}, \frac{3}{4}, \frac{7}{b}, 1, \frac{9}{8}, \frac{5}{4}, \frac{11}{8}, \frac{c}{2}, \cdots$

Cumulative Review *Perform the operations indicated.*

63. [1.6.4] $2 + 9 \cdot 8$

64. [1.6.4] $12 - 4 \div 2$

65. [1.6.4] $\dfrac{(5 + 7)}{(2 \cdot 3)}$

66. [1.6.4] $\dfrac{(11 - 5)}{2}$

67. [1.9.3] *Water Dispenser* Aqua Water Company charges a $7 per month rental fee for dispensers and $2 for each gallon of water delivered. The company offers a $3 per month discount on the total rental fee for every 8 dispensers rented and a $5 per month discount for every 15-gallon bottle of water purchased within a 1-month period. From the invoice below, determine how much the large advertising firm *Sell It Now* paid Aqua Water Company for the rental of dispensers and the water delivered over a period of 3 months.

	Aqua Water Company Invoice		
Sell It Now	January	February	March
Number of units rented	19	26	26
Gallons of water delivered	28	36	31
Monthly charge	____	____	____

68. **[1.9.3]** Refer to exercise 67 to answer the following. A water dispenser that has hot and cold water rents for $8 per month. What would the cost of the rentals and water be for the 3-month period if the advertising firm rented all hot and cold water dispensers?

Quick Quiz 5.4   Perform the operation indicated.

1. (a) $1\dfrac{7}{9} + 3\dfrac{5}{12}$ **(b)** $10\dfrac{1}{3} - 5\dfrac{5}{12}$ **2.** $(-9) \cdot 2\dfrac{1}{3}$

3. $4\dfrac{2}{5} \div \left(-1\dfrac{1}{10}\right)$ **4. Concept Check** Explain how you would multiply $2\dfrac{1}{2} \times 3\dfrac{2}{3}$

Student Learning Objectives

After studying this section, you will be able to:

 Follow the order of operations with fractions.

 Simplify complex fractions.

 Solve applied problems involving complex fractions.

 Following the Order of Operations with Fractions

Recall that when we work a problem with more than one operation, we must follow the **order of operations.**

ORDER OF OPERATIONS

If a fraction has operations written in the numerator or in the denominator or both, these operations must be done first. We perform operations in the following order.

1. Perform operations inside grouping symbols.
2. Simplify exponents.
3. Do multiplication and division in order from left to right.
4. Do addition and subtraction last, working from left to right.

EXAMPLE 1 Simplify. $\left(\dfrac{2}{3}\right)^2 - \dfrac{2}{9} \cdot \dfrac{1}{3}$

Solution

$$\left(\frac{2}{3}\right)^2 - \frac{2}{9} \cdot \frac{1}{3} = \frac{4}{9} - \frac{2}{9} \cdot \frac{1}{3}$$

First we simplify exponents: $\left(\dfrac{2}{3}\right)^2 = \left(\dfrac{2}{3}\right)\left(\dfrac{2}{3}\right) = \dfrac{4}{9}$.

$$= \frac{4}{9} - \frac{2}{27}$$

Then we multiply: $\dfrac{2}{9} \cdot \dfrac{1}{3} = \dfrac{2}{27}$.

$$= \frac{4 \cdot 3}{9 \cdot 3} - \frac{2}{27}$$

Next we find the LCD, which is 27, and build equivalent fractions.

$$= \frac{12}{27} - \frac{2}{27}$$

Now we subtract.

$$= \frac{10}{27}$$

Last, we simplify.

CAUTION: Do not add or subtract before multiplying or dividing even though addition or subtraction comes first in the problem or appears to be easier. *Be careful not to make this error.*

NOTE TO STUDENT: *Fully worked-out solutions to all of the Practice Problems can be found at the back of the text starting at page SP-1*

Practice Problem 1 Simplify.

$$\left(\frac{5}{3}\right)^2 + \frac{20}{9} \cdot \frac{1}{5}$$

Simplifying Complex Fractions

When the numerator and/or the denominator is a fraction, we have a *complex fraction*.

> **COMPLEX FRACTION**
>
> A fraction that contains at least one fraction in the numerator or in the denominator is a **complex fraction.**

These three fractions are complex fractions.

$$\frac{\dfrac{2}{x}}{\dfrac{12}{x}}, \qquad \frac{\dfrac{3}{7} + 2}{\dfrac{1}{8}}, \qquad \frac{2 - \dfrac{1}{x}}{\dfrac{1}{6} + \dfrac{2}{9}} \quad \leftarrow \text{main fraction bar}$$

Although we usually do not write grouping symbols (parentheses or brackets) around the numerator and denominator of a complex fraction, it is understood that *they exist*. Thus we must perform operations above and then below the main fraction bar before we divide.

EXAMPLE 2 Simplify. $\dfrac{(-2)^2 + 8}{\dfrac{2}{3}}$

Solution We must follow the order of operations.

$\dfrac{[(-2)^2 + 8]}{\left(\dfrac{2}{3}\right)}$ We write grouping symbols in the numerator and denominator, since it is understood they exist.

$= \dfrac{12}{\left(\dfrac{2}{3}\right)}$ Within the brackets we simplify exponents first, and then add: $(-2)^2 = 4$ and $4 + 8 = 12$.

$= 12 \div \dfrac{2}{3}$ The main fraction bar means divide.

$= 12 \cdot \dfrac{3}{2}$ We invert the second fraction and multiply.

$= \dfrac{\overset{1}{\cancel{2}} \cdot 2 \cdot 3 \cdot 3}{\underset{1}{\cancel{2}}} = 18$ We factor 12: $12 = 2 \cdot 2 \cdot 3$. Then we simplify.

Practice Problem 2 Simplify.

$$\frac{\dfrac{4}{7}}{3^2 + (-5)}$$

NOTE TO STUDENT: Fully worked-out solutions to all of the Practice Problems can be found at the back of the text starting at page SP-1

EXAMPLE 3 Simplify. $\dfrac{\dfrac{x^2}{8}}{\dfrac{x}{4}}$

Solution Since the main fraction bar indicates division, we can divide the top fraction by the bottom fraction to simplify.

$$\frac{\dfrac{x^2}{8}}{\dfrac{x}{4}} = \frac{x^2}{8} \div \frac{x}{4} = \frac{x^2}{8} \cdot \frac{4}{x} = \frac{x^2 \cdot \cancel{4}}{2 \cdot \cancel{4} \cdot x} = \frac{\cancel{x} \cdot x}{2 \cdot \cancel{x}} = \frac{x}{2}$$

Practice Problem 3 Simplify.

$$\frac{\dfrac{x^2}{5}}{\dfrac{x}{10}}$$

EXAMPLE 4 Simplify. $\dfrac{\dfrac{2}{3} + \dfrac{1}{6}}{\dfrac{3}{4} - \dfrac{1}{2}}$

Solution We write parentheses in the numerator and denominator and follow the order of operations.

$$\frac{\left(\dfrac{2}{3} + \dfrac{1}{6}\right)}{\left(\dfrac{3}{4} - \dfrac{1}{2}\right)} = \frac{\left(\dfrac{2 \cdot 2}{3 \cdot 2} + \dfrac{1}{6}\right)}{\left(\dfrac{3}{4} - \dfrac{1 \cdot 2}{2 \cdot 2}\right)} = \frac{\left(\dfrac{4}{6} + \dfrac{1}{6}\right)}{\left(\dfrac{3}{4} - \dfrac{2}{4}\right)} = \frac{\dfrac{5}{6}}{\dfrac{1}{4}}$$

Add top fractions.

Subtract bottom fractions.

Now we divide the top fraction by the bottom fraction.

$$\frac{5}{6} \div \frac{1}{4} = \frac{5}{6} \cdot \frac{4}{1} = \frac{5 \cdot \cancel{2} \cdot 2}{3 \cdot \cancel{2}} = \frac{10}{3}$$

$$\frac{\dfrac{2}{3} + \dfrac{1}{6}}{\dfrac{3}{4} - \dfrac{1}{2}} = \frac{10}{3}$$

Practice Problem 4 Simplify.

$$\frac{\dfrac{3}{5} + \dfrac{1}{2}}{\dfrac{5}{6} - \dfrac{1}{3}}$$

Solving Applied Problems Involving Complex Fractions

EXAMPLE 5 A recipe requires $3\frac{2}{3}$ cups of flour to make bread to feed 50 people. How much flour do we need to make bread to feed 120 people?

Solution Since the problem concerns the rate of cups of flour per 50 people, we set up a proportion and solve for the missing number.

$$\frac{3\frac{2}{3}\text{ cups}}{50\text{ people}} = \frac{x\text{ cups}}{120\text{ people}}$$

$$120 \cdot 3\frac{2}{3} = 50x \qquad \text{We find the cross product.}$$

$$120 \cdot \frac{11}{3} = 50x \qquad \text{We change } 3\frac{2}{3} \text{ to an improper fraction.}$$

$$\frac{40 \cdot \overset{1}{\cancel{3}} \cdot 11}{\underset{1}{\cancel{3}}} = 50x \qquad \begin{array}{l}\text{Since the sum of the digits of 120 is divisible by 3,}\\ \text{we factor } 120 = 40 \cdot 3 \text{ and simplify.}\end{array}$$

$$40 \cdot 11 = 50x \qquad \text{Now we solve the equation for } x.$$

$$\frac{40 \cdot 11}{50} = \frac{50x}{50} \qquad \text{We divide by 50 on both sides.}$$

$$\frac{4 \cdot \overset{1}{\cancel{10}} \cdot 11}{5 \cdot \underset{1}{\cancel{10}}} = x \qquad \text{We factor and simplify.}$$

$$\frac{44}{5} = x \quad \text{or} \quad x = 8\frac{4}{5}$$

We need $8\frac{4}{5}$ cups of flour.

▲ **Practice Problem 5** A carpenter needs $6\frac{4}{5}$ feet of oak wood to make shelves for 2 small bookcases. How many feet of oak wood will the carpenter need to make 15 bookcases?

NOTE TO STUDENT: Fully worked-out solutions to all of the Practice Problems can be found at the back of the text starting at page SP-1

Verbal and Writing Skills

1. When we perform a series of calculations without grouping symbols, do we add first or multiply first?

2. When we perform a series of calculations without grouping symbols, do we divide first or subtract first?

Simplify.

3. $\dfrac{3}{5} - \dfrac{1}{3} \div \dfrac{5}{6}$

4. $\dfrac{1}{2} + \dfrac{3}{8} \div \dfrac{3}{4}$

5. $\dfrac{3}{4} + \dfrac{1}{4} \cdot \dfrac{3}{5}$

6. $\dfrac{4}{5} - \dfrac{1}{5} \cdot \dfrac{2}{3}$

7. $\dfrac{5}{7} \cdot \dfrac{1}{3} \div \dfrac{2}{7}$

8. $\dfrac{2}{7} \cdot \dfrac{3}{4} \div \dfrac{1}{2}$

9. $\left(\dfrac{3}{2}\right)^2 - \dfrac{1}{3} + \dfrac{1}{2}$

10. $\left(\dfrac{5}{6}\right)^2 + \dfrac{1}{12} - \dfrac{1}{4}$

11. $\dfrac{5}{6} \cdot \dfrac{1}{2} + \dfrac{2}{3} \div \dfrac{4}{3}$

12. $\dfrac{3}{5} \cdot \dfrac{1}{2} + \dfrac{1}{5} \div \dfrac{2}{3}$

13. $\dfrac{2}{9} \cdot \dfrac{1}{4} + \left(\dfrac{2}{3} \div \dfrac{6}{7}\right)$

14. $\dfrac{3}{4} \cdot \left(\dfrac{1}{6} + \dfrac{1}{2}\right) \div \dfrac{4}{5}$

15. $\dfrac{3}{4} \cdot \dfrac{1}{4} + \left(\dfrac{3}{4}\right)^2$

16. $\left(\dfrac{2}{5}\right)^2 + \dfrac{3}{5} \cdot \dfrac{1}{5}$

17. $\left(-\dfrac{2}{5}\right) \cdot \left(\dfrac{1}{4}\right)^2$

18. $\left(\dfrac{4}{3}\right)^2 \cdot \left(-\dfrac{1}{2}\right)$

Simplify.

19. $\dfrac{7 + (-3)^2}{\dfrac{8}{9}}$

20. $\dfrac{6 + (-4)^2}{\dfrac{2}{3}}$

21. $\dfrac{\dfrac{4}{7}}{2^3 + 8}$

22. $\dfrac{\dfrac{5}{8}}{5^2 - 10}$

23. $\dfrac{2 \cdot 3 - 1}{\dfrac{5}{8}}$

24. $\dfrac{4 \cdot 3 + 2}{\dfrac{2}{7}}$

25. $\dfrac{\dfrac{6}{7}}{\dfrac{9}{14}}$

26. $\dfrac{\dfrac{8}{9}}{\dfrac{4}{27}}$

27. $\dfrac{\dfrac{x^2}{2}}{\dfrac{x}{4}}$

28. $\dfrac{\dfrac{x^2}{5}}{\dfrac{x}{15}}$

29. $\dfrac{\dfrac{x}{3}}{\dfrac{x^2}{9}}$

30. $\dfrac{\dfrac{x}{5}}{\dfrac{x^2}{15}}$

31. $\dfrac{\dfrac{1}{2} + \dfrac{3}{4}}{\dfrac{4}{5} + \dfrac{1}{10}}$

32. $\dfrac{\dfrac{3}{7} + \dfrac{1}{14}}{\dfrac{2}{3} + \dfrac{1}{6}}$

33. $\dfrac{\dfrac{4}{25} - \dfrac{3}{50}}{\dfrac{3}{10} + \dfrac{5}{20}}$

34. $\dfrac{\dfrac{5}{12} - \dfrac{7}{24}}{\dfrac{1}{2} + \dfrac{1}{8}}$

Mixed Practice

35. $\dfrac{\dfrac{x}{10}}{\dfrac{x^2}{20}}$

36. $\dfrac{\dfrac{x}{7}}{\dfrac{x^2}{28}}$

37. $\left(\dfrac{1}{2}\right)^2 + \dfrac{2}{3} \cdot \dfrac{6}{7}$

38. $\left(\dfrac{2}{3}\right)^2 - \dfrac{1}{3} \cdot \dfrac{3}{4}$

39. $\dfrac{\dfrac{3}{8} + \dfrac{1}{4}}{\dfrac{4}{5} + \dfrac{3}{4}}$

40. $\dfrac{\dfrac{5}{6} + \dfrac{1}{3}}{\dfrac{3}{8} + \dfrac{1}{2}}$

41. $\dfrac{11 + (3)^2}{\dfrac{2}{3}}$

42. $\dfrac{\dfrac{9}{8}}{(-2)^3 + 11}$

Applications

43. Dessert Recipe A recipe requires $2\frac{3}{4}$ cups of sugar to make a dessert dish for 20 people. How much sugar is needed to make the recipe for 36 people?

44. Punch Recipe Monica is using a punch recipe that requires $5\frac{1}{2}$ cups of concentrated punch for every 4 cups of water. How many cups of concentrated punch should she use with 16 cups of water?

45. Lawn Fertilizer A gardener needs about $3\frac{3}{4}$ bags of fertilizer for every 2 lawns he feeds. Approximately how many bags of fertilizer will he need to feed 12 lawns?

46. Casserole Recipe A casserole recipe requires $2\frac{1}{2}$ teaspoons of salt to prepare a serving for 8 people. How much salt should be added to prepare a serving for 12 people?

47. Acres of Land A developer needs $2\frac{1}{4}$ acres of land for every 3 houses she builds. How many acres does she need to build 28 homes?

48. Inches and Centimeters There are approximately $2\frac{1}{2}$ centimeters in 1 inch. Approximately how many centimeters are in 12 inches?

One Step Further *Simplify.*

49. $\dfrac{\dfrac{25xy^2}{49}}{\dfrac{15x^2y}{14}}$

50. $\dfrac{\dfrac{36x^2y^2}{45}}{\dfrac{12xy}{30}}$

51. $\dfrac{\dfrac{1}{x} - \dfrac{1}{y}}{\dfrac{1}{x} + \dfrac{1}{y}}$

52. $\dfrac{\dfrac{1}{a} + \dfrac{1}{b}}{\dfrac{1}{a} - \dfrac{1}{b}}$

To Think About *Evaluate each expression for the value given.*

53. $x - \dfrac{2}{5} \div \dfrac{4}{15}$ for $x = \dfrac{7}{2}$

54. $x - \dfrac{5}{6} \div \dfrac{25}{12}$ for $x = \dfrac{7}{5}$

55. $-\dfrac{3}{8} \cdot \dfrac{16}{21} + x$ for $x = -\dfrac{4}{7}$

56. $-\dfrac{4}{9} \cdot \dfrac{18}{24} + x$ for $x = -\dfrac{1}{3}$

Cumulative Review *Perform the operations indicated.*

57. [2.4.2] $(-2)(3)(-1)(-5)$

58. [2.4.2] $(-1)(-3)(-1)(-5)$

59. [2.4.4] $-50 \div 5$

60. [2.4.4] $-36 \div (-6)$

Quick Quiz 5.5 Perform the operations indicated.

1. $\left(\dfrac{1}{3}\right)^2 + \dfrac{1}{3} \div \dfrac{5}{6}$

2. $\dfrac{\dfrac{a}{15}}{\dfrac{a}{10}}$

3. $\dfrac{\dfrac{8}{15} - \dfrac{1}{5}}{\dfrac{1}{2} + \dfrac{1}{3}}$

4. Concept Check Explain how you would simplify $\dfrac{1 + 2 \times 3}{\dfrac{1}{2}}$.

After studying this section, you will be able to:

 Solve applied problems involving fractions.

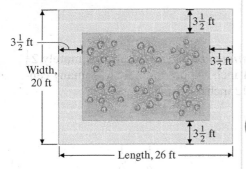

Solving Applied Problems Involving Fractions

For applied problems involving fractions, we may need to draw a picture to help us determine what operation to use.

EXAMPLE 1 Jason planted a rectangular rose garden in the center of his 26-foot by 20-foot backyard. Around the garden there is a sidewalk that is $3\frac{1}{2}$ feet wide. The garden and sidewalk take up the entire 26-foot by 20-foot yard.

(a) What are the dimensions of the rose garden?

(b) How much will it cost to put a fence around the rose garden if the fencing costs $2\frac{1}{2}$ per linear foot?

Solution *Understand the problem.* We draw a picture of the situation to help us develop a plan to solve the problem.

Mathematics Blueprint for Problem Solving

Gather the Facts	What Am I Asked to Do?	How Do I Proceed?	Key Points to Remember
Refer to the picture for dimensions. *Fencing:* costs $2\frac{1}{2}$ per foot	**(a)** Find the dimensions of the rose garden. **(b)** Calculate the cost of a fence around the rose garden.	**1.** Find the length and width of the garden. **2.** Use the length and width to find the perimeter. **3.** Multiply the perimeter times $2\frac{1}{2}$ to find the cost.	Use the perimeter formula $P = 2L + 2W$. The garden is in the center of the yard.

Solve and state the answer.

1. We find the length and width of the rose garden.
From the picture, we see the following.

length of garden		length of entire yard		width of sidewalk (left side + right side)

$$L = 26 - \left(3\frac{1}{2} + 3\frac{1}{2}\right)$$

$$L = 26 - 7 = 19$$

We find the width of the rose garden.

width of garden		width of entire yard		width of sidewalk (above + below garden)

$$W = 20 - \left(3\frac{1}{2} + 3\frac{1}{2}\right)$$

$$W = 20 - 7 = 13$$

(a) The dimensions of the garden are 19 feet by 13 feet.

2. Now we find the perimeter of the garden.

$$P = 2L + 2W = 2(19) + 2(13)$$

$$= 38 + 26 = 64 \quad \text{The perimeter is 64 ft}$$

3. We multiply $2\frac{1}{2}$ times 64 feet to find the total cost of fencing.

$$2\frac{1}{2} \cdot 64 = \frac{5}{2} \cdot \frac{64}{1} = \frac{5 \cdot \cancel{2} \cdot 32}{\cancel{2} \cdot 1} = 160$$

(b) It will cost $160 to put a fence around the rose garden.

Check. We can place the answers on the diagram to check.

Width: $3\frac{1}{2} + 13 + 3\frac{1}{2} = 20$ ft ✓

Length: $3\frac{1}{2} + 19 + 3\frac{1}{2} = 26$ ft ✓

Round the price: $2\frac{1}{2} \rightarrow \$3$.

Round the perimeter: $64 \rightarrow 60$.

Then multiply to estimate the cost of the fence: $\$3 \times 60 = \$180$, which is close to our answer. ✓

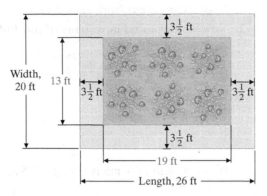

Width, 20 ft
13 ft
$3\frac{1}{2}$ ft
$3\frac{1}{2}$ ft
$3\frac{1}{2}$ ft
$3\frac{1}{2}$ ft
19 ft
Length, 26 ft

▲ **Practice Problem 1**   Larry wants to place a rug in the center of his living room floor, which measures 22 feet by 15 feet. He wants to center the rug so that there is $2\frac{1}{2}$ feet of wood flooring showing on each side of the rug.

(a) What are the dimensions of the rug Larry must buy?

(b) Larry wants to place binding around the outer edges of the carpet. If the cost to bind the carpet is $2 per linear foot, how much will Larry pay for the binding?

NOTE TO STUDENT: Fully worked-out solutions to all of the Practice Problems can be found at the back of the text starting at page SP-1

▲ **EXAMPLE 2**   Marian is planning to build a fence on her farm. She determines that she must make 115 wooden fence posts that are each $3\frac{3}{4}$ feet in length. The wood to make the fence posts is sold in 20-foot lengths. How many 20-foot pieces of wood must Marian purchase so that she can make 115 fence posts?

Solution *Understand the problem.* We draw a picture to help us develop a plan.

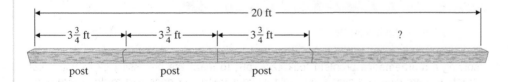

20 ft
$3\frac{3}{4}$ ft $3\frac{3}{4}$ ft $3\frac{3}{4}$ ft   ?
post   post   post

Mathematics Blueprint for Problem Solving

Gather the Facts	What Am I Asked to Do?	How Do I Proceed?	Key Points to Remember
Refer to the picture.	Find the number of 20-foot lengths of wood needed to make 115 posts.	**1.** Determine the number of posts that can be made from one 20-foot piece of wood. **2.** Use the information in step 1 to find how many 20-foot pieces are needed to make 115 posts.	We must change mixed numbers to improper fractions before we perform division.

Solve and state the answer.

1. From the picture, we see that we must divide to find how many $3\frac{3}{4}$-foot sections are in 20 feet.

$$20 \div 3\frac{3}{4} = 20 \div \frac{15}{4} = 20 \cdot \frac{4}{15} = \frac{4 \cdot \cancel{5} \cdot 4}{\cancel{5} \cdot 3} = \frac{16}{3} \quad \text{or} \quad 5\frac{1}{3}$$

5 posts can be cut from each 20-foot piece of wood, with some wood left over.

2. Now we must find how many of the 20-foot pieces are needed.

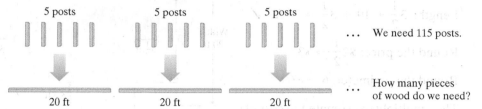

We must find how many groups of 5 are in 115. We divide $115 \div 5$.

$$115 \div 5 = \frac{115}{5} = \frac{\cancel{5} \cdot 23}{\cancel{5}} = 23$$

Marian must purchase 23 pieces of wood.

Check. We can estimate our answer by rounding the fraction $3\frac{3}{4}$ to 4 and re-working the problem.

20-foot length $\div$ 4 feet per post = 5 posts per length of wood

115 posts $\div$ 5 posts per length of wood = 23 lengths of wood ✓

NOTE TO STUDENT: *Fully worked-out solutions to all of the Practice Problems can be found at the back of the text starting at page SP-1*

▲ **Practice Problem 2**   Nancy wishes to make two bookcases, each with 4 shelves. Each shelf is $3\frac{1}{8}$ feet long. The wood for the shelves is sold as 10-foot boards. How many boards does Nancy need to buy for the shelves?

Developing Your Study Skills

Why Is Homework Necessary?

You learn mathematics by practicing, not by watching. Your instructor may make solving a mathematics problem look easy, but to learn the necessary skills you must practice them over and over again, just as your instructor once had to do. There is no other way. Learning mathematics is like learning how to play a musical instrument or to play a sport. *You must practice, not just observe, to do well.* Homework provides this practice. The amount of practice varies for each person. The more problems you do, the better you get.

Many students underestimate the amount of time each week that is required to learn math. In general, two to three hours per week per unit is a good rule of thumb. This means that for a three-unit class you should spend six to nine hours a week studying math. Spread this time throughout the week, not just in a few sittings. Your brain gets overworked just as your muscles do!

Exercise

1. Start keeping a log of the time that you spend studying math. If your performance is not up to your expectations, increase your study time.

Applications

When solving the following application problems, you may want to use a Mathematics Blueprint for Problem Solving to help organize your work.

1. Workout Program Joan planned a workout program that included increasing the amount of time she exercised by $\frac{1}{4}$ hour each week for the first 4 weeks. If Joan starts week 1 with a $\frac{1}{2}$-hour workout, how long will her workout program be at the beginning of week 4?

△ 2. Bolt Length In assembling her bookshelves, Keri finds that she needs a bolt that will reach through the $\frac{5}{8}$-inch wood, a $\frac{1}{8}$-inch-thick washer, and a $\frac{1}{4}$-inch-thick nut. How long must the bolt be?

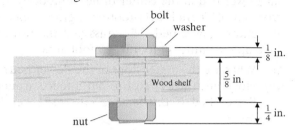

3. Average Speed Andrew must drive 305 miles to a sales conference. If it takes him $4\frac{1}{2}$ hours to drive to the sales conference, what is his average speed in miles per hour?

4. Metal Cutter A machine that cuts metal is calibrated to cut strips $1\frac{3}{8}$ inches long from a piece of metal that is 22 inches long. How many strips will the machine cut from this one piece?

Recipe vs. Servings *Use the given recipe to answer exercises 5 and 6.*

5. To make 6 servings, how much of each ingredient would you need?

6. To make 12 servings, how much of each ingredient would you need?

Cereal Preparation Directions

Ingredient	Servings	
	1	2
Water	$1\frac{1}{4}$ cups	$2\frac{1}{2}$ cups
Salt	$\frac{1}{8}$ tsp.	$\frac{1}{4}$ tsp.
Cereal	$\frac{1}{4}$ cup	$\frac{1}{2}$ cup

Use the given chart to answer exercises 7 and 8.

7. Fabric Needed To make 5 long skirts in size 8, how much 45-inch-wide material would you need?

8. To make a short skirt and a bodice in size 14, how much material would it take if the material were 60 inches wide?

Pattern Directions

Skirt Pattern							
Sizes		4	6	8	10	12	14
Sizes–European		30	32	34	36	38	40
Long skirt	45″	$2\frac{3}{4}$	$2\frac{3}{4}$	$2\frac{3}{4}$	$2\frac{3}{4}$	$2\frac{3}{4}$	$2\frac{3}{4}$ yd
	60″	$2\frac{1}{4}$	$2\frac{1}{4}$	$2\frac{3}{8}$	$2\frac{1}{2}$	$2\frac{1}{2}$	$2\frac{3}{4}$ yd
Short skirt	45″	$1\frac{3}{4}$	$1\frac{3}{4}$	$1\frac{3}{4}$	$1\frac{3}{4}$	$1\frac{3}{4}$	$1\frac{3}{4}$ yd
	60″	1	1	1	1	1	$1\frac{1}{4}$ yd
Bodice A or B	45″	$\frac{1}{2}$	$\frac{1}{2}$	$\frac{1}{2}$	$\frac{5}{8}$	$\frac{5}{8}$	$\frac{3}{4}$ yd
	60″	$\frac{1}{2}$	$\frac{1}{2}$	$\frac{1}{2}$	$\frac{1}{2}$	$\frac{1}{2}$	$\frac{1}{2}$ yd

9. Gas Mileage John had $15\frac{2}{3}$ gallons of gasoline in his car before traveling to Los Angeles. When he arrived, he only had $9\frac{1}{2}$ gallons left.

(a) How much gasoline did he use to travel to Los Angeles?

(b) If his car gets 24 miles per gallon, how many miles did John travel to Los Angeles?

△ 10. Bathroom Tiles Each tile that Amy wants covers $3\frac{1}{2}$ square inches of space. She wants to cover 245 square inches in her bathroom with the tile.

(a) How many tiles will she need to purchase?

(b) If each box of tiles contains 12 tiles, how many boxes must Amy purchase?

11. ***Money and Savings*** The Tran family is receiving a $2400 tax refund. They decide to spend $\frac{1}{4}$ of the money on a vacation, and use $\frac{1}{8}$ of the money to pay off bills. They will put the remainder of the tax refund money into a savings account. How much money will they put in the savings account?

▲**13.** ***Flower Bed Dimensions*** Monica planted a rectangular flower bed in the center of her 40-foot by 25-foot front lawn. There is a $4\frac{3}{4}$-foot-wide grass area around the entire flower bed. The grass and the flower bed take up the entire 40-foot by 25-foot area.

(a) What are the dimensions of the flower bed?
(b) How much will it cost to put a fence around the flower bed if the fencing costs $2\frac{1}{4}$ per linear foot?

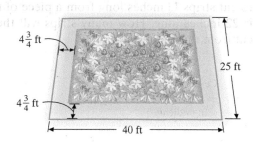

15. ***Bookcase Material*** Brenda wishes to build 3 bookcases, each with 4 shelves. Each shelf will be $3\frac{3}{4}$ feet long. The wood for the shelves is sold in 8-foot boards. How many boards does Brenda need to buy for the shelves?

12. ***Pep Club Banner*** The Pep Club has $18\frac{2}{3}$ feet of paper on a roll of paper used to make banners. The club must make 3 banners, each $3\frac{3}{4}$ feet in length. How much paper will be left on the roll after the club makes the 3 banners?

▲**14.** ***Pool Dimensions*** Howard put a rectangular pool in his yard, which is $45\frac{1}{2}$ feet by 20 feet. There is a grass area 5 feet wide around the entire perimeter of the pool. The pool and grass take up the entire $45\frac{1}{2}$-foot by 20-foot yard.

(a) What are the dimensions of the pool?
(b) How much will it cost to put a row of tile around the edge of his pool if the tile costs $3\frac{1}{2}$ per linear foot?

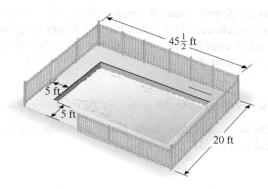

16. ***Bookcase Material*** Julie wishes to build 2 bookcases, each with 5 shelves. Each shelf will be $2\frac{3}{4}$ feet long. The wood for the shelves is sold in 6-foot boards. How many boards does Julie need to buy for the shelves?

▲**17.** ***Pool Tile Cost*** Mamadou put a rectangular pool in his yard, which is 50 feet by 30 feet. There is a slate tile area $5\frac{1}{2}$ feet wide around the entire perimeter of the pool. The pool and the tile area take up the entire 50-foot by 30-foot yard.

(a) What are the dimensions of the pool?
(b) How much will it cost to put a row of tile around the edge of the pool if the tile costs $2\frac{1}{2}$ per linear foot?

▲**18.** ***Cost for Metal Stripe*** Lester wants to cut a square hole in the center of a square piece of wood that has a 6-foot side. He wants each edge of the square hole to be $2\frac{1}{2}$ feet from the edge of the wood.

(a) What are the dimensions of the square hole?

(b) How much will it cost for Lester to put a strip of metal around the hole, if the metal costs $1\frac{1}{2}$ per linear foot?

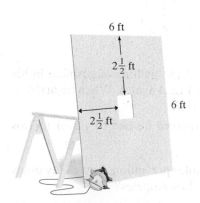

▲ **19.** *Yard Fence* Shannon is planning to build a picket fence around 3 sides of her front yard. She determines that she must make 56 wooden posts that are each $2\frac{3}{4}$ feet in length. The wood to make the posts comes in 10-foot lengths. How many 10-foot pieces of wood must Shannon purchase so that she can make 56 wooden posts?

20. *Ribbon for Bows* Aleksandra must make 90 bows. She needs $1\frac{3}{4}$ feet of ribbon for each bow. The ribbon is sold in spools that contain 21 feet of ribbon. How many spools of ribbon must Aleksandra purchase to make the 90 bows?

One Step Further

21. *Distance Traveled* A space probe took $4\frac{1}{2}$ days to travel 240,000 miles.

(a) How many miles per day did the spacecraft travel?

(b) How many miles per hour did the spacecraft travel?

22. *Titanic Cruise Ship* The night of the *Titanic* cruise ship disaster, the captain decided to run his ship at $22\frac{1}{2}$ knots (nautical miles per hour). The *Titanic* traveled at that speed for $4\frac{3}{4}$ hours before it met its tragic demise. How far did the *Titanic* travel at this excessive speed before the disaster?

Cumulative Review *Solve and check your solution.*

23. [3.2.1] $3x = 12$ **24.** [3.2.1] $5x = 45$ **25.** [3.1.2] $x - 5 = 12$ **26.** [3.1.2] $x + 3 = -1$

Quick Quiz 5.6

1. Alex wishes to build 3 bookcases, each with 5 shelves. Each shelf is $3\frac{1}{3}$ feet long. The wood to make the shelves is sold in 12-foot lengths. How many 12-foot pieces of wood must Alex purchase so he can make 3 bookcases?

2. Ella weighed 134 pounds on August 1. She weighed herself weekly and found that the first week her weight went up $2\frac{1}{4}$ pounds, and the second week her weight went down $2\frac{3}{8}$ pounds. The third week it rose $1\frac{1}{2}$ pounds.

(a) What was Ella's weight at the end of week 3?

(b) How much more did she weigh in week 3 than on August 1?

3. Martha put a rectangular pavilion in the center of her $32\frac{1}{2}$-foot by 28-foot backyard. There is a grass area $5\frac{1}{2}$ feet wide around the entire perimeter of the pavilion. The pavilion and grass take up the entire $32\frac{1}{2}$-foot by 28-foot yard.

(a) What are the dimensions of the pavilion?

(b) How much will it cost to put a row of tile around the outside of the pavilion if the tile costs $2 per linear foot?

4. **Concept Check** Choose the correct operation you must use to answer each of the following questions: Add, Subtract, Multiply, or Divide. You do not need to calculate the answer.

(a) Jason ran $2\frac{1}{3}$ miles, and Lester ran $2\frac{7}{8}$ miles. How much farther did Lester run than Jason?

(b) Beatrice earns $780 per week and has $\frac{1}{13}$ of her paycheck placed in a savings account. How much money does she put in her savings each week?

(c) Samuel has 14 pounds of candy and must place it in $\frac{2}{3}$-pound bags. How many bags can he fill?

5.7 SOLVING EQUATIONS OF THE FORM $\frac{x}{a} = c$

Student Learning Objective

After studying this section, you will be able to:

 Solve equations using the multiplication principle of equality.

 ## Solving Equations Using the Multiplication Principle of Equality

As we saw in Chapter 3, to solve the equation $5x = 30$ we can divide both sides of the equation by the same nonzero number.

$$5x = 30$$

$$\frac{5x}{5} = \frac{30}{5}$$

$$\frac{\overset{1}{\cancel{5}}x}{\underset{1}{\cancel{5}}} = \frac{30}{5}$$

$$x = 6$$

We *divided* by 5 to *undo* the *multiplication* by 5 so that we could get x alone on one side of the equation, that is, in the form $x = $ some number. Now, to solve $\frac{x}{2} = 8$, can we *multiply* by 2 on both sides of the equation to *undo* the *division* by 2 and get x alone?

Let's return to our example of a balanced seesaw to answer this question. If we doubled the number of weights on each side (we are multiplying each side by 2), the seesaw should still balance. In mathematics, a similar principle is observed. Thus we can multiply both sides of the equation by a number without changing the solution.

We can now state the multiplication principle.

> ### MULTIPLICATION PRINCIPLE OF EQUALITY
>
> If both sides of an equation are multiplied by the same nonzero number, the results on both sides are equal in value.
>
> For any numbers a, b, and c, with c not equal to 0:
>
> If $a = b$, then $ca = cb$.

To solve an equation like $\frac{x}{5} = 30$ we can simply think: "What can we do to the left side of the equation so that $\frac{x}{5}$ becomes simply x?" Since x is divided by 5, we can *undo* the *division* and obtain x alone by *multiplying* by 5. However, whatever we do to one side of the equation, we must do to the other side of the equation.

$$\frac{x}{5} = 30 \rightarrow \frac{5 \cdot x}{5} = 30 \cdot 5 \quad \text{We multiply both sides of the equation by 5.}$$

$$\frac{\overset{1}{\cancel{5}} \cdot x}{\underset{1}{\cancel{5}}} = 150$$

$$x = 150$$

336

EXAMPLE 1   Solve. $\dfrac{x}{-4} = 28$

Solution   Since we are dividing the variable x by -4, we can *undo* the division and get x alone by multiplying by -4.

$$\frac{x}{-4} = 28 \qquad \text{The variable } x \text{ is } divided \text{ by } -4.$$

$$\frac{-4 \cdot x}{-4} = 28 \cdot (-4) \quad \text{We undo the division by } multiplying \text{ both sides by } -4.$$

$$x = -112 \qquad \text{Simplify: } \frac{-4x}{-4} = x, \text{ and } 28 \cdot (-4) = -112.$$

Be sure that you *check* your solution.

Practice Problem 1   Solve.

$$\frac{a}{-2} = 17$$

NOTE TO STUDENT: Fully worked-out solutions to all of the Practice Problems can be found at the back of the text starting at page SP-1

It is important that we remember to perform any necessary simplification of an equation before we find the solution.

EXAMPLE 2   Solve. $\dfrac{x}{2^3} = 12 \cdot 5 + 1$

Solution   We simplify each side of the equation first and then we find the solution.

$$\frac{x}{2^3} = 12 \cdot 5 + 1$$

$$\frac{x}{8} = 60 + 1 \qquad \text{Simplify: } 2^3 = 8; \quad 12 \cdot 5 = 60.$$

$$\frac{x}{8} = 61 \qquad 60 + 1 = 61$$

$$\frac{8 \cdot x}{8} = 61 \cdot 8 \qquad \text{We } undo \text{ the division by multiplying both sides by 8.}$$

$$x = 488 \qquad \text{Multiply to find the solution.}$$

We leave the check for the student.

Practice Problem 2   Solve.

$$\frac{x}{3^2} = 11 \cdot 4 + 9$$

SIDELIGHT

Sometimes the coefficient of the variable is a fraction such as in $\frac{2}{3}x = 5$. Think: "what can we do to the left side of the equation so x will stand alone?" Recall that when you multiply a fraction by its reciprocal, the product is 1. For example, $\frac{3}{2} \cdot \frac{2}{3} = 1$. We will use this idea to solve the equation $\frac{2}{3}x = 5$.

$$\frac{2}{3}x = 5$$

$$\frac{3}{2} \cdot \frac{2}{3}x = \frac{5}{1} \cdot \frac{3}{2}$$

$$1 \cdot x = \frac{15}{2}$$

$$x = \frac{15}{2}$$

EXAMPLE 3 Solve for the variable and check your solution. $-\dfrac{3}{4}x = 12$

Solution

$$-\frac{3}{4}x = 12$$

$$\left(-\frac{4}{3}\right)\left(-\frac{3}{4}\right)x = 12\left(-\frac{4}{3}\right)$$ Multiply both sides of the equation by $-\dfrac{4}{3}$ because $\left(-\dfrac{4}{3}\right)\left(-\dfrac{3}{4}\right) = 1.$

$$1x = -\frac{4 \cdot \cancel{3} \cdot 4}{\cancel{3}}$$

$$x = -16$$

Check:

$$-\frac{3}{4}x = 12$$

$$\left(-\frac{3}{4}\right)(-16) \overset{?}{=} 12 \quad \text{Replace } x \text{ with } -16.$$

$$12 = 12 \quad \checkmark$$

Practice Problem 3 Solve for the variable and check your solution.

$$-\frac{3}{8}x = 9$$

Developing Your Study Skills

Keep Trying

Do you wish you could improve your math grade? Are you frustrated and starting to become discouraged? Don't give up! Take note of the following suggestions. They will help make a difference.

- *Be patient.* Would you expect to learn how to play the piano easily, without a lot of effort? Of course, those who have had experience with various instruments earlier in life might learn more easily and faster than someone who has not. Developing the skills to do math is like learning to play a musical instrument. *Learning mathematics is a process that takes time and effort.* Those who have had more experience working with mathematics may learn more easily, but for many students this is catch-up time.

- *Increase your study time.* It is not unusual to study mathematics for 8 to 12 hours a week. Perfecting math skills requires the same intensity as preparing to play a sport. Baseball players practice many hours each day to perfect their swing or curveball. *Increasing your study time will help you improve your understanding of math.*

Yes, it can be slow moving at first, but eventually, as your skills develop, you will find that math will become easier and you will understand concepts more quickly.

- *Seek help.* Make an appointment with your instructor for help or use any tutorial services that are available. Too often, students *give up* and skip topics they don't understand. Missing a few topics can make it difficult to understand new topics because math builds on previous concepts and skills.

- *Be positive.* Don't let past frustrations stand in your way. Start fresh with a positive attitude and work hard and practice the study skills in this book. Then as you become more successful, your confidence in your mathematical ability will grow.

Exercise

1. Re-examine your time management schedule and insert a few more hours each week to study math. If you have not been using a time management schedule, refer to Developing Your Study Skills in Section 2.5 for assistance.

Verbal and Writing Skills *Fill in the blanks.*

1. When you multiply a nonzero fraction by its reciprocal, the product is _____.

2. A nonzero number divided by itself is equal to _____.

3. To solve $\frac{x}{6} = 2$, we _____ by 6 on both sides of the equation.

4. To solve $\frac{6}{7}x = 42$, we multiply by the _____ of $\frac{6}{7}$ on both sides of the equation.

Fill in each box to complete each solution.

5. $\dfrac{x}{12} = -3$

$\dfrac{\boxed{} \cdot x}{12} = -3 \cdot \boxed{}$

$x = \boxed{}$

6. $\dfrac{x}{7} = -8$

$\dfrac{\boxed{} \cdot x}{7} = -8 \cdot \boxed{}$

$x = \boxed{}$

7. $\dfrac{x}{-5} = 4$

$\dfrac{\boxed{} \cdot x}{-5} = 4 \cdot \boxed{}$

$x = \boxed{}$

8. $\dfrac{x}{-3} = 6$

$\dfrac{\boxed{} \cdot x}{-3} = 6 \cdot \boxed{}$

$x = \boxed{}$

9. $\dfrac{2}{5}x = -8$

$\dfrac{\boxed{}}{\boxed{}} \cdot \dfrac{2}{5}x = -8 \cdot \dfrac{\boxed{}}{\boxed{}}$

$x = \boxed{}$

10. $\dfrac{3}{4}x = -6$

$\dfrac{\boxed{}}{\boxed{}} \cdot \dfrac{3}{4}x = -6 \cdot \dfrac{\boxed{}}{\boxed{}}$

$x = \boxed{}$

11. $\dfrac{-5}{7}x = 10$

$\dfrac{\boxed{}}{\boxed{}} \cdot \dfrac{(-5)}{7}x = 10 \cdot \dfrac{\boxed{}}{\boxed{}}$

$x = \boxed{}$

12. $\dfrac{-4}{9}x = 16$

$\dfrac{\boxed{}}{\boxed{}} \cdot \dfrac{(-4)}{9} = 16 \cdot \dfrac{\boxed{}}{\boxed{}}$

$x = \boxed{}$

Solve and check your solutions.

13. $\dfrac{y}{8} = 12$

14. $\dfrac{x}{9} = 16$

15. $\dfrac{x}{7} = 31$

16. $\dfrac{m}{6} = 10$

17. $\dfrac{m}{13} = -30$

18. $\dfrac{a}{8} = -14$

19. $\dfrac{x}{15} = -5$

20. $\dfrac{m}{19} = -7$

21. $-15 = \dfrac{a}{4}$

22. $-44 = \dfrac{m}{2}$

23. $-4 = \dfrac{a}{-20}$

24. $-6 = \dfrac{m}{-42}$

Simplify, then solve and check your solution.

25. $\frac{x}{3^2} = 2 + 6 \div 3$

26. $\frac{x}{2^2} = 6 + 8 \div 4$

27. $\frac{x}{-7} = -2 + 9$

28. $\frac{x}{-5} = -6 + (-9)$

29. $\frac{y}{2^3} = 2 \cdot 3 + 1$

30. $\frac{y}{3^3} = 4 \cdot 2 + 3$

Solve and check your solutions.

31. $\frac{3}{5}y = 12$

32. $\frac{6}{7}y = 30$

33. $\frac{4}{9}x = 12$

34. $\frac{2}{3}x = 14$

35. $\frac{1}{2}x = -15$

36. $\frac{1}{5}x = -12$

37. $\frac{-5}{8}x = 30$

38. $\frac{-3}{7}x = 21$

Mixed Practice *Solve and check your solution.*

39. $3 = \frac{a}{11}$

40. $10 = \frac{x}{7}$

41. $\frac{x}{3^2} = 4 + 6 \div 2$

42. $\frac{y}{2^2} = 12 - 3 \div 3$

43. $\frac{-3}{4}y = -12$

44. $\frac{-2}{9}y = -12$

45. $-1 = \frac{m}{30}$

46. $-9 = \frac{x}{15}$

To Think About *Solve and check your solution.*

47. (a) $4x = 52$

   (b) $\frac{x}{4} = 52$

48. (a) $3y = 39$

   (b) $\frac{y}{3} = 39$

49. (a) $4x = -52$

   (b) $\frac{x}{4} = -52$

50. (a) $3y = -39$

   (b) $\frac{y}{3} = -39$

51. (a) $x - 7 = 21$

   (b) $x + 12 = 33$

   (c) $5x = 3$

   (d) $\frac{x}{5} = 11$

52. (a) $x - 4 = 19$

   (b) $x + 6 = 23$

   (c) $5x = 4$

   (d) $\frac{x}{3} = 12$

53. (a) $x - 7 = -12$

   (b) $3x = -2$

   (c) $\frac{x}{6} = -9$

   (d) $x + 11 = -34$

54. (a) $x + 15 = -31$

   (b) $13x = -7$

   (c) $\frac{x}{2} = -8$

   (d) $x - 3 = -10$

One Step Further *Name the fraction $\frac{a}{b}$ that makes each statement true.*

55. $\dfrac{a}{b}x = 6$

$\dfrac{3}{2} \cdot \dfrac{a}{b}x = 6 \cdot \dfrac{3}{2}$

$x = 9$

$\dfrac{a}{b} = \,?$

56. $\dfrac{a}{b}x = 10$

$\dfrac{3}{5} \cdot \dfrac{a}{b}x = 10 \cdot \dfrac{3}{5}$

$x = 6$

$\dfrac{a}{b} = \,?$

57. $\dfrac{a}{b}x = 9$

$\dfrac{7}{3} \cdot \dfrac{a}{b}x = 9 \cdot \dfrac{7}{3}$

$x = 21$

$\dfrac{a}{b} = \,?$

58. $\dfrac{a}{b}x = 8$

$\dfrac{5}{2} \cdot \dfrac{a}{b}x = 8 \cdot \dfrac{5}{2}$

$x = 20$

$\dfrac{a}{b} = \,?$

Cumulative Review *Combine like terms.*

59. **[2.6.1]** $3a + 7b - 9a - 10ab + 2b$

60. **[2.6.1]** $-2x + 3xy - 4y - 6x - 5xy$

Simplify.

61. **[3.4.3]** $3x^2(x^4 + 8x)$

62. **[3.4.3]** $-2x^3(x^2 - 6)$

▲ **63.** **[5.6.1]** *Stained Glass Window* Find the area of the stained glass window with length $L = 4\frac{2}{3}$ feet and width $W = 3\frac{3}{8}$ feet.

64. **[5.6.1]** *Bread Recipe* Juan uses $2\frac{1}{2}$ cups of flour for one loaf of bread. How many cups of flour will he need for 4 loaves of bread?

Quick Quiz 5.7 Solve.

1. $\dfrac{x}{5} = 2 - 3^2$

2. $\dfrac{3}{5}a = 18$

3. $\dfrac{y}{8} = -9$

4. Concept Check To solve the equation $\frac{x}{-5} = 6$, Amy multiplied both sides of the equation by 5 to obtain $x = 30$. Is this correct? Why or why not?

CHAPTER 7

We often use patterns to create designs. Did you know that recognizing a pattern can help you when you must make a business decision?

Solving Equations

Student Learning Objectives

After studying this section, you will be able to:

 1 Solve equations using the addition principle of equality.

2 Solve equations using the multiplication principle of equality.

3 Solve equations using the division principle of equality.

1 **Solving Equations Using the Addition Principle of Equality**

In Chapter 3 we learned how to solve equations of the form $x - a = c$, $x + a = c$, and $ax = c$ using the addition and division principles of equality. In Chapter 5 we used the multiplication principle to solve equations of the form $\frac{x}{a} = c$. In this section we will study all four forms, $x - a = c$, $x + a = c$, $ax = c$, and $\frac{x}{a} = c$, within one section and focus on how to determine which principle to use. This skill will prepare you for the next section, which requires that you use more than one principle of equality to solve equations of the form $ax + b = c$.

Before we begin our discussion on solving equations, we restate in words the principle of equality presented in Chapter 3.

> **ADDITION PRINCIPLE OF EQUALITY**
>
> If the *same number* or *variable term* is added to both sides of the equation, the results on each side are equal in value.

We can restate it in symbols this way.

> For any numbers a, b, and c, if $a = b$, then $a + c = b + c$.

It is important to keep in mind that an equation is like a balanced seesaw. Whatever we do to one side of the equation, we must do to the other side to maintain the balance.

The goal when solving an equation is to get the variable alone on one side of the equation, that is, to get the equation in the form $x = some\ number$ or $some\ number = x$.

We have a balanced seesaw.

We add the same amount to both sides and the seesaw remains balanced.

EXAMPLE 1 Solve $x - 2 = -42$ and check your solution.

Solution We want an equation of the form $x = some\ number$. To obtain this we think, "What can we add to each side of the equation so that $x - 2$ becomes simply x?" We add the opposite of -2, or $+2$, to both sides.

$$
\begin{array}{ll}
x - 2 = -42 & \text{We want to get } x \text{ alone.} \\
\underline{+\ \ +2 = +2} & \text{We add the opposite of } -2, \text{ or } +2, \text{ to both sides.} \\
x + 0 = -40 & -2 + 2 = 0; -42 + 2 = -40 \\
\ x = -40 & x + 0 = x
\end{array}
$$

Check:
$$
\begin{array}{c}
x - 2 = -42 \\
-40 - 2 \overset{?}{=} -42 \\
-42 = -42 \quad \checkmark
\end{array}
$$

Practice Problem 1 Solve $x - 6 = -56$ and check your solution.

EXAMPLE 2   Solve. $-12 - 15 = 9x + 15 - 8x - 6$

Solution   First we simplify each side of the equation, and then we solve for x.

$$-12 - 15 = 9x + 15 - 8x - 6$$
$$-27 = 9x + 15 - 8x - 6 \quad \text{We calculate: } -12 - 15 = -12 + (-15) = -27.$$
$$-27 = 9x + 15 - 8x - 6$$
$$-27 = x + 9 \qquad\qquad \text{We simplify: } 9x - 8x = x, \text{ and } 15 - 6 = 9.$$

Now we solve for x.

$$
\begin{array}{rl}
-27 = x + 9 & \text{The opposite of } +9 \text{ is } -9. \\
+\quad -9 = \quad -9 & \text{We add } -9 \text{ to both sides of the equation.} \\
\hline
-36 = x &
\end{array}
$$

We leave the check to the student.

Practice Problem 2   Solve. $-11 - 17 = 5y + 12 - 4y - 1$.

NOTE TO STUDENT: *Fully worked-out solutions to all of the Practice Problems can be found at the back of the text starting at page SP-1*

Solving Equations Using the Multiplication Principle of Equality

We learned how to use the multiplication principle in Chapter 5. We restate this principle in words for your review.

MULTIPLICATION PRINCIPLE OF EQUALITY

If both sides of an equation are *multiplied* by the same nonzero number, the results on each side are equal in value.

We can restate it in symbols as follows.

For any numbers a, b, and c with c not equal to 0, if $a = b$, then $a \cdot c = b \cdot c$.

Our goal when solving equations is to get the variable alone on one side of the equation. We must remember that whatever we do to one side of the equation, we must do to the other side of the equation.

EXAMPLE 3   Solve $\dfrac{y}{-5} = -10 + 2^3$ and check your solution.

Solution   First we simplify each side of the equation, and then we solve for y.

$$\frac{y}{-5} = -10 + 2^3$$

$$\frac{y}{-5} = -2 \qquad\qquad \text{We simplify } 2^3 = 8 \text{ and } -10 + 8 = -2.$$

To solve the equation $\frac{y}{-5} = -2$, we can think, "What can we do to the left side of the equation so that $\frac{y}{-5}$ becomes simply y?" Since y is *divided by* -5, we can *undo* the division and obtain y alone by *multiplying by* -5.

$$\frac{-5 \cdot y}{-5} = -2 \cdot (-5) \qquad \text{We undo the division by multiplying by } -5.$$

$$y = 10 \qquad \text{We simplify: } \frac{-5y}{-5} = y \text{ and } -2 \cdot (-5) = 10.$$

Check:
$$\frac{y}{-5} = -10 + 2^3$$

$$\frac{10}{-5} \overset{?}{=} -10 + 2^3 \qquad \text{We replace } y \text{ with } 10.$$

$$-2 = -2 \checkmark$$

Practice Problem 3 Solve $\dfrac{y}{-3} = 2^2 - 8$ and check your solution.

Recall from Chapter 5 that to solve an equation such as $\frac{2}{3}x = 5$ we multiply both sides of the equation by the reciprocal of $\frac{2}{3}$.

$$\frac{2}{3}x = 5$$

$$\frac{3}{2} \cdot \frac{2}{3}x = 5 \cdot \frac{3}{2} \qquad \text{We multiply both sides by } \frac{3}{2}, \text{ the reciprocal of } \frac{2}{3}.$$

$$x = \frac{15}{2}$$

Be sure to simplify each side of the equation as your first step before solving for the variable.

EXAMPLE 4 Solve. $\dfrac{3}{4}a = 5^2 + 2$

Solution First we simplify $5^2 + 2$, and then we solve for a.

$$\frac{3}{4}a = 5^2 + 2$$

$$\frac{3}{4}a = 27 \qquad \text{Simplify: } 5^2 + 2 = 25 + 2 = 27.$$

$$\frac{4}{3} \cdot \frac{3}{4}a = 27 \cdot \frac{4}{3} \qquad \text{Multiply both sides by } \frac{4}{3}.$$

$$a = 36 \qquad \frac{27 \cdot 4}{3} = \frac{\overset{1}{\cancel{3}} \cdot 9 \cdot 4}{\underset{1}{\cancel{3}}} = 36$$

Check:
$$\frac{3}{4}a = 5^2 + 2$$

$$\frac{3}{4} \cdot 36 \overset{?}{=} 5^2 + 2 \qquad \text{Replace } a \text{ with } 36.$$

$$27 = 27 \checkmark \qquad \frac{3}{4} \cdot 36 = \frac{3 \cdot \overset{1}{\cancel{4}} \cdot 9}{\underset{1}{\cancel{4}}} = 27$$

NOTE TO STUDENT: Fully worked-out solutions to all of the Practice Problems can be found at the back of the text starting at page SP-1

Practice Problem 4 Solve. $\dfrac{4}{5}a = 3^2 + 7$

Solving Equations Using the Division Principle of Equality

In Chapter 3 we saw that to solve an equation in the form $3x = -27$, we can use the division principle of equality, which states that we can divide both sides of the equation by 3. We restate this principle in words for your review.

DIVISION PRINCIPLE OF EQUALITY

If both sides of the equation are divided by the same nonzero number, the results on each side are equal in value.

The division principle of equality is an alternate form of the multiplication principle. This is because dividing by c is the same as multiplying by $\frac{1}{c}$. We will explore this in the To Think About on page 394.

Since division by zero is not defined, we put a restriction on the number by which we are dividing. We restate this principle in this way.

For any numbers a, b, and c, with c not equal to 0, if $a = b$, then $\dfrac{a}{c} = \dfrac{b}{c}$.

There are two things we must remember when we solve an equation.

1. First we must be sure that each side of the equation is simplified.
2. Next, we use the principles of equality to get the variable alone on one side of the equation; that is, we find an equivalent equation of the form $x = some\ number$ or $some\ number = x$.

EXAMPLE 5   Solve $\dfrac{-20}{5} = -2(5x) + 7x$ and check your solution.

Solution   We begin by simplifying each side of the equation.

$$\frac{-20}{5} = -2(5x) + 7x$$

$-4 = -2(5x) + 7x$ Simplify: $\dfrac{-20}{5} = -4.$

$-4 = -10x + 7x$ Multiply: $-2(5x) = -10x.$

$-4 = -3x$ Add: $-10x + 7x = -3x.$

Now that both sides of the equation are simplified, we use the division principle of equality to transform the equation into the form $some\ number = x$.

$$\frac{-4}{-3} = \frac{-3x}{-3}$$ Dividing by -3 on both sides *undoes* the multiplication by -3.

$$\frac{4}{3} = x$$ Simplify: $\dfrac{-4}{-3} = \dfrac{4}{3}$ and $\dfrac{-3x}{-3} = x.$

If we leave the solution as an improper fraction, it will be easier to check it in the original equation.

Check: $\dfrac{-20}{5} = -2(5x) + 7x$

$$\dfrac{-20}{5} \overset{?}{=} -2\left(5 \cdot \dfrac{4}{3}\right) + 7 \cdot \dfrac{4}{3}$$

$$-4 \overset{?}{=} \dfrac{-40}{3} + \dfrac{28}{3} \qquad -2\left(5 \cdot \dfrac{4}{3}\right) \overset{?}{=} -2\left(\dfrac{20}{3}\right) = \dfrac{-40}{3}; \quad 7 \cdot \dfrac{4}{3} = \dfrac{28}{3}$$

$$-4 \overset{?}{=} \dfrac{-12}{3}$$

$$-4 = -4 \ \checkmark$$

Practice Problem 5 Solve $\dfrac{16}{-4} = 4x + 3(-3x)$ and check your solution.

You may have to rewrite an equation so that a coefficient of 1 or -1 is obvious: $-x = -1x$ or $x = 1x$. With practice you will be able to recognize the coefficient without actually rewriting it.

EXAMPLE 6 Solve. $-x = 36$

Solution

$-1x = 36$ Rewrite the equation: $-x$ is the same as $-1x$.

$\dfrac{-1x}{-1} = \dfrac{36}{-1}$ Dividing by -1 on both sides *undoes* the multiplication by -1.

$x = -36$

Although checking the solution is not always illustrated in the examples, you should always do so.

Practice Problem 6 Solve. $-x = 25$

NOTE TO STUDENT: *Fully worked-out solutions to all of the Practice Problems can be found at the back of the text starting at page SP-1*

TO THINK ABOUT: The Multiplication Principle of Equality Can you think of another way to solve the equation $-x = 36$ in Example 6? What other operation can we do to transform the equation to the form $x = $ *some number*? Try multiplying both sides of the equation by -1 and see what happens. Do you see why we can solve the equation this way?

Let's summarize a few facts to help you solve equations using the principles of equality.

- Subtraction *undoes* addition.
- Addition *undoes* subtraction.
- Division *undoes* multiplication.
- Multiplication *undoes* division.

Verbal and Writing Skills

Fill in the blanks.

1. To solve the equation $y + 8 = -17$, we add the opposite of $+8$, which is ____, to both sides of the equation.

2. To solve the equation $y - 1 = -11$, we add the opposite of -1, which is ___, to both sides of the equation.

3. To solve the equation $x - 15 = 82$, we add ____ to both sides of the equation.

4. To solve the equation $x + 21 = 33$, we add _____ to both sides of the equation.

5. Before we solve the equation $7x + 2 - 6x - 9 = 2 - 8$, we must first _____ each side of the equation.

6. Before we solve the equation $3x + 4 - 2x - 9 = 10 - 11$, we must first _____ each side of the equation.

Fill in each blank with the missing phrase.

7. To solve the equation $-9y = -36$, we _____ on both sides of the equation.

8. To solve the equation $-14 = 3x$, we _____ on both sides of the equation.

9. To solve the equation $\dfrac{y}{-9} = 2$, we _____ on both sides of the equation.

10. To solve the equation $-14 = \dfrac{x}{3}$, we _____ on both sides of the equation.

11. We _____ on both sides of the equation when we solve $14 = x + 3$.

12. We _____ on both sides of the equation when we solve $14 = x - 3$.

Solve and check your answer.

13. $x - 7 = -20$

14. $y - 3 = -11$

15. $a + 9 = -1$

16. $x + 12 = -4$

17. $-5 = x + 5$

18. $-2 = y + 3$

19. $7 - 9 = y - 4$

20. $8 - 11 = x - 4$

21. $7 - 12 = x - 6 + 3^2$

22. $8 - 13 = x - 2 + 3^2$

23. $-8 + 4^2 = a + 6 - 4$

24. $-5 + 3^2 = a + 5 - 7$

25. $12x - 1 - 11x - 1 = -5$

26. $8x + 7 - 7x + 2 = -3$

27. $12 - 16 = 4y + 8 - 3y$

28. $8 - 9 = 3x - 4 - 2x$

29. $6x - 6 - 5x + 1 = -2 + 4$

30. $11x + 12 - 10x - 1 = -4 + 11$

Solve and check your solution.

31. $-16 = \dfrac{x}{3}$

32. $2 = \dfrac{x}{-2}$

33. $14 = \dfrac{y}{-2}$

34. $-3 = \dfrac{a}{6}$

35. $\dfrac{a}{-4} = -6 + 9$

36. $\dfrac{y}{-3} = 9 - 11$

37. $\dfrac{x}{4} = -8 + 6$

38. $\dfrac{x}{5} = -6 + 2$

39. $\frac{y}{-2} = 4 + 2^2$ **40.** $\frac{x}{-1} = 5 + 4^2$ **41.** $\frac{3}{5}x = 9$ **42.** $\frac{5}{7}x = 15$

43. $\frac{-2}{3}a = 18$ **44.** $\frac{-5}{8}a = 15$ **45.** $\frac{7}{6}y = 4^2 + 5$ **46.** $\frac{3}{7}y = 5^2 - 4$

Solve and check your solution.

47. $3(2x) = 24$ **48.** $4(6x) = 48$ **49.** $-6 = 2(-5x)$ **50.** $-2 = 6(-4x)$

51. $8x + 4(4x) = 48$ **52.** $6x + 3(3x) = 45$ **53.** $6(-2x) - 3x = -30$ **54.** $5(-5x) - 4x = -29$

55. $\frac{-10}{2} = 3(4x) + 2x$ **56.** $\frac{6}{-3} = 2(3x) + 3x$ **57.** $\frac{21}{3} = 5x + 3(-4x)$ **58.** $\frac{32}{8} = 8x + 2(-2x)$

59. $-x = 9$ **60.** $-x = 16$ **61.** $-x = -4$ **62.** $-x = -6$

Mixed Practice *Solve.*

63. (a) $2x = -12$ **64.** (a) $5y = -20$ **65.** (a) $y - 10 = 9$ **66.** (a) $x - 6 = 11$

   (b) $\frac{x}{2} = -12$ (b) $\frac{y}{5} = -20$ (b) $y + 10 = 9$ (b) $x + 6 = 11$

   (c) $x - 2 = -12$ (c) $y - 5 = -20$ (c) $\frac{y}{-10} = 9$ (c) $\frac{x}{-6} = 11$

   (d) $x + 2 = -12$ (d) $y + 5 = -20$ (d) $-10y = 9$ (d) $-6x = 11$

67. $-15 = a + 5$ **68.** $-2 = y + 7$ **69.** $5x + 2 - 4x = 9$ **70.** $7x + 3 - 6x = 4$

71. $\frac{x}{7} = -2 + 3^2$ **72.** $\frac{y}{9} = -6 + 2^2$ **73.** $-x = 12$ **74.** $-y = 8$

75. $\frac{20}{5} = 3x + 2(-6x)$ **76.** $\frac{12}{-6} = 4(2x) + 3x$ **77.** $\frac{6}{7}x = 3^2 + 3$ **78.** $\frac{3}{4}y = 2^2 + 5$

To Think About *As stated earlier, the division principle is another form of the multiplication principle. To see why this is true, complete exercise 79.*

79. (a) Solve $-2x = 8$ using the division principle.

(b) Solve $-2x = 8$ using the multiplication principle. (*Hint:* multiply each side of the equation by the reciprocal of -2.)

(c) What can you say about the answers?

(d) Why do you think this is true?

A magic square is an array of numbers with a special property. In this type of array all the numbers in each column, each row, and in each of the two diagonals add up to the same number.

80. The sum of each row, each column, and each diagonal in the magic square is 15.

8	z	6
3	5	7
x	9	y

(a) Form an equation using the 1st column by writing the sum of 8, 3, and x equal to 15. Solve the equation for x. Then in the array below, replace x with the value of x.

(b) Complete the same process using the 2nd and 3rd columns to find the values of y and z.

(c) Check your answer by verifying that the sum of each diagonal is 15.

8		6
3	5	7
	9	

81. The sum of each row, each column, and each diagonal in the magic square is 18.

9	z	y
x	6	10
7	8	3

(a) Form an equation using the 1st column by writing the sum of 9, x, and 7 equal to 18. Solve the equation for x. Then in the array below, replace x with the value of x.

(b) Complete the same process using the 2nd and 3rd columns to find the values of y and z.

(c) Check your answer by verifying that the sum of each diagonal is 18.

9		
	6	10
7	8	3

82. Use the properties of magic squares to find the values of a, b, c, d, and e.

5	a	18
b	15	c
d	e	25

5		18
	15	
		25

▲ *The sum of the interior angles of a triangle is 180°. A right triangle is a special kind of triangle in which one angle is 90°. This angle is identified by the symbol ⌐. Find the missing angle for the following right triangles.*

Interior angle

83.

x
30°

84.

x
60°

▲ *Find the measure of each angle.*

85.

86.

Cumulative Review *Express as a product of prime numbers.*

87. [4.1.3] 210

88. [4.1.3] 112

89. [1.3.5] *Earth and Sun* The distance between the sun and Earth varies because Earth travels around the sun in an orbit that has an elliptical (oval) shape. The shortest distance from Earth to the sun is approximately 91,400,000 miles, and the greatest distance is about 94,500,000. What is the difference between the greatest and shortest distance?

Quick Quiz 7.1 Solve and check your solution.

1. $-3y + 4y + 8 = -9 + 5$

2. $\dfrac{x}{-5} = 3^2 - 7$

3. $2(-7b) + 8b = -24$

4. Concept Check Which of the following equations would you solve by dividing by 7 on both sides of the equation? Explain why this operation is used to solve for x.

(a) $x - 7 = -21$

(b) $\dfrac{x}{7} = -21$

(c) $7x = -21$

(d) $x + 7 = -21$

7.2 SOLVING EQUATIONS USING MORE THAN ONE PRINCIPLE OF EQUALITY

To solve equations such as $4x - 9 = 78$, we use more than one principle of equality. In this section we will see how to use the principles of equality to solve these more complex equations.

Student Learning Objectives

After studying this section, you will be able to:

1. Solve equations using more than one principle of equality.

2. Simplify and solve equations.

 ## Solving Equations Using More Than One Principle of Equality

When we solve an equation that requires using more than one principle of equality, we must be able to determine which principle to use first. We can use the following sequence of steps to solve an equation such as $3x + 6 = 9$.

PROCEDURE TO SOLVE AN EQUATION IN THE FORM
$ax + b =$ SOME NUMBER

1. First, use the addition principle to get the variable term ax alone on one side of the equation:

$$ax = some\ number$$

2. Then apply the multiplication or division principle to get the variable x alone on one side of the equation:

$$x = some\ number$$

EXAMPLE 1 Solve $3x + 7 = 88$ and check your solution.

Solution First, we use the addition principle to get the variable term, $3x$, alone.

$$
\begin{array}{rl}
3x + 7 = 88 & \\
\underline{+ \quad -7 \quad -7} & \text{Add } -7 \text{ to both sides of the equation.} \\
3x \quad = 81 & \text{The variable term, } 3x, \text{ is alone.}
\end{array}
$$

Then we apply the division principle to get the variable, x, alone.

$$3x = 81$$

$$\frac{3x}{3} = \frac{81}{3} \qquad \textit{Divide by } 3 \text{ on both sides of the equation.}$$

$$x = 27 \qquad \text{The variable, } x, \text{ is alone.}$$

Check:
$$3x + 7 = 88$$
$$3(27) + 7 \stackrel{?}{=} 88$$
$$81 + 7 \stackrel{?}{=} 88$$
$$88 = 88 \quad \checkmark$$

Practice Problem 1 Solve $8x + 9 = 105$ and check your solution.

Calculator

 Checking Solutions to Equations

We can use a scientific calculator to check our solutions. To check that 5 is a solution to $3x - 1 = 14$, enter:

$$3 \boxed{\times} 5 \boxed{-} 1 \boxed{=}$$

The display should read:

$$\boxed{14}$$

Remember that you should use the addition principle before you use the division or multiplication principle.

EXAMPLE 2   Solve. $-6x - 4 = 74$

Solution   First, we must get the variable term, $-6x$, alone by using the addition principle.

$$
\begin{array}{rcl}
-6x - 4 &=& 74 \\
+ \qquad + 4 &=& +4 \qquad \text{\textit{Add} 4 to both sides of the equation.} \\
\hline
-6x \qquad &=& 78 \qquad \text{The variable term, } -6x, \text{ is alone.}
\end{array}
$$

Then we apply the division principle to get the variable, x, alone.

$$-6x = 78$$
$$\frac{-6x}{-6} = \frac{78}{-6} \qquad \text{\textit{Divide by} } -6 \text{ on both sides of the equation.}$$
$$x = -13 \qquad \text{The variable, } x, \text{ is alone.}$$

We leave the check to the student.

Practice Problem 2   Solve. $-5m - 10 = 115$

EXAMPLE 3   Solve $-3 = 6 - 4y$ and check your solution.

Solution   We use the addition principle to get the variable term, $-4y$, alone.

$$
\begin{array}{rcl}
-3 &=& 6 - 4y \\
+ -6 & & -6 \qquad \text{\textit{Add} } -6 \text{ to both sides of the equation.} \\
\hline
-9 &=& \quad - 4y
\end{array}
$$

Now we use the division principle to get y alone on the right side of the equation.

$$\frac{-9}{-4} = \frac{-4y}{-4} \qquad \text{Divide by } -4 \text{ on both sides of the equation.}$$

$$\frac{9}{4} = y \qquad \frac{-9}{-4} = \frac{9}{4} \text{ and } \frac{-4y}{-4} = y.$$

Check:
$$-3 = 6 - 4y$$
$$-3 \overset{?}{=} 6 - 4\left(\frac{9}{4}\right)$$
$$-3 \overset{?}{=} 6 - 9$$
$$-3 = -3 \quad \checkmark$$

Practice Problem 3   Solve $-2 = 4 - 5x$ and check your solution.

② Simplifying and Solving Equations

As we have said, the process of solving an equation is easier if we simplify each side of the equation before we begin to solve it. Many students find that it is helpful to have a written procedure to follow when solving more-involved equations.

PROCEDURE TO SOLVE EQUATIONS

1. *Parentheses.* Remove any parentheses.

2. *Simplify each side of the equation.* Combine like terms and simplify numerical work.

3. *Isolate the ax term.* Use the addition principle to get *all* terms with the variable on *one side* of the equation and the numerical values on the other side.

4. *Isolate the x.* Use the multiplication or division principle to get the variable alone on one side of the equation.

5. *Check* your solution.

Sometimes there is a variable term on *both* sides of the equation. In this case, we must rewrite the equation so that all variable terms are on one side. Then we continue to work toward the form $x = some number$.

EXAMPLE 4   Solve $5x - 3 = 6x + 2$ and check your solution.

Solution   First, we add $-6x$ to both sides of the equation so that all variable terms are on one side of the equation.

$$
\begin{array}{rcr}
5x - 3 = & & 6x + 2 \\
+\,-6x & & -6x \\
\hline
-x - 3 = & & 2
\end{array}
$$

Then, we solve the equation.

$$
\begin{array}{rcl}
-x - 3 = & 2 & \\
+\quad +3 & +3 & \text{Add 3 to both sides of the equation.} \\
\hline
-x \quad = & 5 & \\
\dfrac{-1x}{-1} = & \dfrac{5}{-1} & \text{Write } -x \text{ as } -1x, \text{ and divide by } -1 \\
& & \text{on both sides.} \\
x = & -5 &
\end{array}
$$

Another way to solve $-1x = 5$ is to multiply both sides of the equation by -1. $-1x = 5 \rightarrow -1(-1x) = -1(5) \rightarrow x = -5$. We leave the check to the student.

Practice Problem 4   Solve $3x - 1 = 4x - 6$ and check your solution.

NOTE TO STUDENT: Fully worked-out solutions to all of the Practice Problems can be found at the back of the text starting at page SP-1

Understanding the Concept

Variables on Both Sides of an Equation

When a variable appears on both sides of an equation, does it matter which side is cleared of variable terms? No. To see why, let's look at the equation $9x + 1 = 7x - 4$.

Add $-7x$ to both sides:

$$
\begin{array}{rcr}
9x + 1 = & & 7x - 4 \\
+\,-7x & & -7x \\
\hline
2x + 1 = & & -4
\end{array}
$$

$$\boxed{2x + 1 = -4}$$

$$
\begin{array}{rcll}
2x = & -5 & & \text{Add } -1 \text{ to both sides.} \\
x = & -\dfrac{5}{2} & & \text{Divide both sides by 2.}
\end{array}
$$

Add $-9x$ to both sides:

$$
\begin{array}{rcr}
9x + 1 = & & 7x - 4 \\
+\,-9x & & -9x \\
\hline
1 = & & -2x - 4
\end{array}
$$

$$\boxed{1 = -2x - 4}$$

$$
\begin{array}{rcll}
5 = & -2x & & \text{Add 4 to both sides.} \\
-\dfrac{5}{2} = & x & & \text{Divide both sides by } -2.
\end{array}
$$

As we can see, the answers are the same—the only difference being that in one case we have an equation with the variable on the *left side* and in the other case we have an equation with the variable on the *right side*.

Some students prefer to bring the variable terms together on one side of the equation so that there is a positive coefficient on the remaining variable term. Others prefer always to have the variable on the left side. This is just a preference; either way is correct.

EXAMPLE 5 Solve $2y - 3 + 3y + 7 = 6y + 21$ and check your solution.

Solution

$$
\begin{array}{ll}
2y - 3 + 3y + 7 = 6y + 21 & \\
5y - 3 \qquad + 7 = 6y + 21 & 2y + 3y = 5y \\
5y + 4 = 6y + 21 & \text{Combine: } -3 + 7 = 4. \\
\underline{+ \quad -5y \qquad\qquad -5y} & \text{Add } -5y \text{ to both sides of the equation.} \\
4 = y + 21 & \\
\underline{+ -21 = \qquad - 21} & \text{Add } -21 \text{ to both sides of the equation.} \\
-17 = y &
\end{array}
$$

Check:

$$2y - 3 + 3y + 7 = 6y + 21$$

$$2(-17) - 3 + 3(-17) + 7 \overset{?}{=} 6(-17) + 21$$

$$-34 - 3 - 51 + 7 \overset{?}{=} -102 + 21$$

$$-81 = -81 \checkmark$$

Practice Problem 5 Solve $-2 + 6y + 4 = 8y + 15$ and check your solution.

Developing Your Study Skills

Mathematics and Careers

Students often question the value of mathematics. They see little real use for it in their everyday lives. However, mathematics is often the key that opens the door to a better-paying job. Studying mathematics sharpens your mind and helps you sort out and solve real-life situations that *do not* require the use of mathematics.

In our present-day technological world, people use mathematics daily. Many vocational and professional areas—such as the fields of business, statistics, economics, psychology, finance, computer science, chemistry, physics, medicine, engineering, electronics, nuclear energy, banking, quality control, and teaching—require a certain level of expertise in mathematics. Those who want to work in these fields must be able to function at a given mathematical level. Those who cannot will not be able to enter these job areas.

So, whatever your field, be sure to realize the importance of mastering the basics of this course. It will very likely help you advance to the career of your choice.

Keep in mind that mathematical thinking does not always require performing math calculations. Organizing and planning skills are enhanced when you study mathematics!

Exercise

1. Make a list of the types of jobs you plan to seek when you finish your education. Talk with your instructor, counselor, or job placement director about the level and type of mathematics, as well as the planning and organizational skills, that are required for these jobs.

Verbal and Writing Skills

Write in words the question asked by each equation.

1. $1 + 2n = 5$

2. $3x - 2 = 7$

Fill in the boxes in each step with the values needed to solve each equation.

3.
$$3x + 6 = 5x + 9$$
$$+ \boxed{} \qquad \boxed{}$$
$$0 + 6 = 2x + 9$$
$$+ \boxed{} \qquad \boxed{}$$
$$-3 = 2x + 0$$
$$\frac{-3}{\boxed{}} = \frac{2x}{\boxed{}}$$
$$-\frac{3}{2} = x$$

4.
$$8 - 5x = 7x + 3$$
$$+ \boxed{} \qquad \boxed{}$$
$$8 + 0 = 12x + 3$$
$$+ \boxed{} \qquad \boxed{}$$
$$5 = 12x + 0$$
$$\frac{5}{\boxed{}} = \frac{12x}{\boxed{}}$$
$$\frac{5}{12} = x$$

5.
$$6 - 2x = 5 - 9x$$
$$+ \boxed{} \qquad \boxed{}$$
$$6 + 7x = 5 + 0$$
$$\boxed{} \qquad \boxed{}$$
$$0 + 7x = -1$$
$$\frac{7x}{\boxed{}} = \frac{-1}{\boxed{}}$$
$$x = -\frac{1}{7}$$

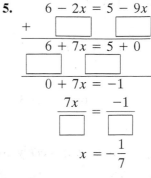

6.
$$-3 + 8x = 9x - 4$$
$$+ \boxed{}$$
$$-3 + 0 = x - 4$$
$$+ \boxed{} \qquad \boxed{}$$
$$1 = x$$

7.
$$-4x + 2 + 3x = 13$$
$$\boxed{}x + 2 = 13$$
$$+ \boxed{} \qquad \boxed{}$$
$$\frac{-1x}{\boxed{}} + 0 = \frac{11}{\boxed{}}$$
$$x = -11$$

8.
$$-6x + 4 + 5x = 10$$
$$\boxed{}x + 4 = 10$$
$$+ \boxed{} \qquad \boxed{}$$
$$\frac{-1x}{\boxed{}} + 0 = \frac{6}{\boxed{}}$$
$$x = -6$$

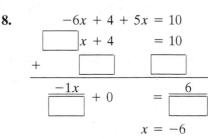

Solve and check your solution.

9. $3x - 9 = 27$

10. $8x + 3 = 19$

11. $5x - 15 = 20$

12. $6x - 15 = 9$

13. $18 = 4x - 10$

14. $24 = 2x + 6$

15. $5x - 1 = 16$

16. $3x - 2 = 12$

17. $-4y + 9 = 65$

18. $-8w + 5 = 69$

19. $-6m - 10 = 88$

20. $-5y - 9 = 74$

21. $52 = -2x - 10$

22. $16 = -3x - 5$

23. $-1 = -7 - 5y$

24. $-2 = -9 - 4x$

25. $2 = 4 + 2x$

26. $8 = 5 - 3x$

27. $-6 = 6 - 3y$

28. $-2 = 8 - 2y$

Simplify the left side of the equation by combining like terms and then solve.

29. $8y + 6 - 2y = 18$

30. $7x + 3 - 4x = 12$

31. $9x - 2 + 2x = 6$

32. $3m - 1 + 4m = 5$

33. $7x + 8 - 8x = 11$

34. $4x + 7 - 5x = 12$

Solve and check your solution. You may collect the variable terms on the right or on the left.

35. $15x = 9x + 48$

36. $16x = 7x + 36$

37. $4x = -12x + 7$

38. $14x = -2x + 11$

39. $8x + 2 = 5x - 4$

40. $7x + 6 = 2x - 9$

41. $11x + 20 = 12x + 2$

42. $6y - 5 = 13y + 9$

43. $-2 + y + 5 = 3y + 9$

44. $-9 + 2y + 6 = y + 11$

45. $13y + 9 - 2y = 6y - 8$

46. $14y - 6 + 4y = 8y - 1$

47. $-9 - 3x + 8 = -6x + 3 - 3x$

48. $-1 - 6x + 2 = -4 + 3x - 5x$

Mixed Practice *Solve and check your solution.*

49. $-2y + 6 = 12$

50. $-8x + 4 = 20$

51. $3x - 4 = 11$

52. $7x - 2 = 19$

53. $5x + 5 - 2x = 15$

54. $4x + 3 - 2x = 12$

55. $13x = 8x + 20$

56. $15x = 6x + 30$

57. $4x - 24 = 6x - 8$

58. $9x - 4 = 3x - 10$

One Step Further *Solve.*

59. $2x - 6 + 2(4x) + 13 = -2 - 5x + (3^2 - 3)$

60. $9x - 8 - 2(3x) + (4^2 + 3) = -4x - 3 + 2x$

Cumulative Review

Multiply.

61. **[2.6.3]** $-3(x - 4)$

62. **[2.6.3]** $2(-3 + y)$

Find the value of x in each proportion.

63. **[4.6.3]** $\dfrac{13}{21} = \dfrac{65}{x}$

64. **[4.6.3]** $\dfrac{15}{17} = \dfrac{x}{85}$

Quick Quiz 7.2 Solve and check your solution.

1. $-5a = 3a + 40$

2. $3y + 8 - 6y = -13$

3. $4x + 9 = 6x - 3$

4. **Concept Check** Explain the steps to solve the equation $8x + 3 - 4x = 15$.

Solving Equations with Parentheses

As we have seen, we must simplify each side of an equation before we can begin the process of solving the equation for a variable. If equations contain parentheses, we remove the parentheses first. Then when we combine like terms, the equations become just like those encountered previously. We review the procedure to solve equations presented in Section 7.2.

Student Learning Objective

After studying this section, you will be able to:

 Solve equations with parentheses.

PROCEDURE TO SOLVE EQUATIONS

1. *Parentheses.* Remove any parentheses.

2. *Simplify each side of the equation.* Combine like terms and simplify numerical work.

3. *Isolate the ax term.* Use the addition principle to get all terms with the variable on one side of the equation and the numerical values on the other side.

4. *Isolate the x.* Use the multiplication or division principle to get the variable alone on one side of the equation.

5. *Check* your solution.

EXAMPLE 1 Solve $-3(2x + 1) + 4x = 27$ and check your solution.

Solution We use the distributive property to remove parentheses and then we simplify and solve.

$$-3(2x + 1) + 4x = 27$$

$$-6x - 3 + 4x = 27 \quad \text{Multiply: } (-3)(2x) = -6x; (-3)(+1) = -3.$$

$$-2x - 3 = 27 \quad \text{Combine like terms: } -6x + 4x = -2x.$$

$$\underline{+\quad +3 \quad +3} \quad \text{Add 3 to both sides of the equation.}$$

$$-2x \quad = 30$$

$$\frac{-2x}{-2} = \frac{30}{-2} \quad \text{Divide by } -2 \text{ on both sides of the equation.}$$

$$x = -15$$

Check:
$$-3(2x + 1) + 4x = 27$$
$$-3[2(-15) + 1] + 4(-15) \overset{?}{=} 27$$
$$-3(-30 + 1) + (-60) \overset{?}{=} 27$$
$$-3(-29) + (-60) \overset{?}{=} 27$$
$$27 = 27 \quad \checkmark$$

Practice Problem 1 Solve $-5(3x + 2) - 6x = 32$ and check your solution.

NOTE TO STUDENT: Fully worked-out solutions to all of the Practice Problems can be found at the back of the text starting at page SP-1

When simplifying and solving equations, pay special attention to the *sign* of each term.

EXAMPLE 2 Solve $5(y + 8) = -6(y - 2) + 94$ and check your solution.

Solution

$$5(y + 8) = -6(y - 2) + 94$$

$$5 \cdot y + 5 \cdot 8 = -6 \cdot y - 6(-2) + 94 \quad \text{Remove parentheses.}$$

$$5y + 40 = -6y + 12 + 94$$

$$5y + 40 = -6y + 106 \qquad \text{Simplify each side of the equation separately.}$$

$$\underline{+\ 6y \qquad\qquad +6y}$$

$$11y + 40 = \qquad 106 \qquad\qquad \begin{array}{l}\text{Add } 6y \text{ to both sides so that all } y \\ \text{terms are on one side of the equation.}\end{array}$$

$$11y + 40 = \ 106 \qquad\qquad \begin{array}{l}\text{Continue to use the principles of equality}\\\text{to solve for } y.\end{array}$$

$$\underline{+ \quad -40 \quad -40}$$

$$11y \quad = \quad 66$$

$$\frac{11y}{11} = \frac{66}{11}$$

$$y = 6$$

Check: $\quad 5(y + 8) = -6(y - 2) + 94$

$$5(6 + 8) \stackrel{?}{=} -6(6 - 2) + 94$$

$$5(14) \stackrel{?}{=} -6(4) + 94$$

$$70 \stackrel{?}{=} -24 + 94$$

$$70 = 70 \ \checkmark$$

Practice Problem 2 Solve $2(x + 4) = -7(x - 3) + 2$ and check your solution.

Recall from Section 6.1 that when a negative sign is in front of parentheses, we find the opposite of the expression by changing the sign of each term inside the parentheses. We sometimes encounter this situation when solving equations.

EXAMPLE 3 Solve. $(2x^2 + 3x + 1) - (2x^2 + 6) = 4x + 1$

Solution Since there is a minus sign in front of the parentheses, $-(2x^2 + 6)$, we change the sign of each term inside the parentheses.

$$(2x^2 + 3x + 1) - (2x^2 + 6) = \quad 4x + 1$$

$$2x^2 + 3x + 1 - 2x^2 - 6 = \quad 4x + 1 \qquad \begin{array}{l}\text{Change the sign of each term}\\\text{and remove parentheses.}\end{array}$$

$$3x - 5 = \quad 4x + 1 \qquad 2x^2 - 2x^2 = 0; \ 1 - 6 = -5.$$

$$\underline{+ -3x \qquad\qquad -3x} \qquad\qquad \text{Solve for } x.$$

$$-5 = \quad x + 1$$

$$\underline{+ -1 \qquad\qquad - 1}$$

$$-6 = \quad x \qquad \text{or} \ \ x = -6$$

We leave the check for the student.

Practice Problem 3 Solve. $(4x^2 + 6x + 3) - (4x^2 + 2) = 3x + 1$

PRACTICE   WATCH   DOWNLOAD   READ   REVIEW

Verbal and Writing Skills

Fill in the blanks with the correct justification for each step of the solution to each equation.

1. $-5(3x + 2) + 2x = 16$

$-15x - 10 + 2x = 16$ _____

$-13x - 10 = 16$ _____

$-13x = 26$ _____

$x = -2$ _____

2. $-3(4x + 1) + 3x = 15$

$-12x - 3 + 3x = 15$ _____

$-9x - 3 = 15$ _____

$-9x = 18$ _____

$x = -2$ _____

Solve and check your solution.

3. $-3(2x + 1) = 15$

4. $-6(2x + 3) = 18$

5. $4(3x - 1) = 12$

6. $2(3x - 2) = 15$

7. $36 = -2(4y + 2)$

8. $35 = -5(2y - 1)$

9. $-5(2x + 1) + 3x = 37$

10. $-4(2x + 2) + 4x = 12$

11. $-2(5y - 1) + 4y = -4$

12. $-7(4y - 1) + 15y = -6$

13. $-4(2x + 1) = -5 - 3x$

14. $-2(3x + 2) = -9 - 2x$

15. $3(y - 4) + 6(y + 1) = 57$

16. $5(y - 2) + 2(y + 4) = 26$

17. $2(x - 1) + 4(x + 2) = 18$

18. $3(x - 4) + 6(x + 1) = 21$

19. $10 = -2(x - 2) + 6(x - 1)$

20. $16 = -3(x - 3) + 4(x - 1)$

21. $6(x - 4) = -9(x + 1) + 10$

22. $4(x - 2) = -2(x + 6) + 31$

23. $2(y + 3) = -6(y - 1) - 8$

24. $3(y + 1) = -2(y - 2) - 6$

25. $(6x^2 + 4x - 1) - (6x^2 + 9) = 14$

26. $(9y^2 + 8y - 2) - (9y^2 + 5) = 9$

27. $(5x^2 + x + 3) - (5x^2 + 9) = 4x + 1$

28. $(8x^2 + 8x - 2) - (8x^2 + 5) = 6x + 2$

Mixed Practice *Solve and check your solution.*

29. $6(x - 1) + 2(x + 1) = 10 - 5x$

30. $7(x - 1) + 3(x + 1) = 20 - 4x$

31. $4(-6x + 2) - 6x = 68$

32. $2(-7x + 3) - 2x = 38$

33. $(4x^2 + 3x + 1) - (4x^2 - 2) = 5x - 2$

34. $(3x^2 - 2x + 4) - (3x^2 + 1) = 6x + 2$

One Step Further *Solve and check your solution.*

35. $(2x^2 - 6x - 3) - (x^2 + 4) = x^2 + 6$

36. $3x^2 + 4x - 9 - (2x^2 - 1) = x^2 - 5$

37. $(x^2 + 3x - 1) - (2x + 1) = x^2 - 5$

38. $(y^2 + 2y - 5) - (3y + 2) = y^2 - 1$

To Think About

39. Is $x = 19$ a solution to $(2x + 9) + (3x - 2) - (5x + 1) = 2(x - 6) - (x - 1)$?

40. Is $a = 2$ a solution to $(9a + 2) + (4a - 1) - (6a + 3) = 4(a - 1) + 8$?

Cumulative Review *Find the least common denominator.*

41. [5.3.2] $\dfrac{2}{3}, \dfrac{1}{4}, \dfrac{5}{2}$

42. [5.3.2] $\dfrac{3}{4}, \dfrac{4}{2}, \dfrac{1}{5}$

43. [5.3.2] $\dfrac{1}{2x}, \dfrac{7}{x}$

44. [5.3.2] $\dfrac{2}{x}, \dfrac{3}{5x}$

45. [5.6.1] *Weighing Produce* The cashier at the produce store charged Israel for $\frac{4}{5}$ pound of grapes. When the cashier's scale was later tested for accuracy, it was determined that the scale was inaccurate. The actual weight of the grapes was $\frac{2}{3}$ pound. Was Israel overcharged or undercharged for his purchase?

46. [5.6.1] *Pressure on Diver* The formula for calculating the pressure P in pounds per square inch on an object submerged to a depth D in feet is given by $P = 15 + \frac{1}{2}D$. Find the pressure on a diver who is submerged underwater at a depth of $13\frac{1}{4}$ feet.

Quick Quiz 7.3 Solve and check your solution.

1. $-4(3x - 5) - 2x = 34$

2. $-8(x + 1) = 4(2x - 5) - 20$

3. $(4a^2 + 2a - 1) - (4a^2 - 3a + 4) = 3a + 1$

4. **Concept Check** **(a)** The first step we should perform to solve $2(y - 1) + 2 = -3(y - 2)$ is to simplify the equation using the _____ property.

(b) Complete this simplification, then explain the rest of the steps needed to solve the equation so that the variable is on the left side of the equation: $y = $ some number.

Student Learning Objective

After studying this section, you will be able to:

 Solve equations using the LCD method.

Solving Equations Using the LCD Method

Solving equations such as $\frac{x}{2} + \frac{x}{7} = 11$ can be a lengthy process. To avoid unnecessary work, we can transform the given equation containing fractions to an equivalent equation that does not contain fractions. This process is often referred to as **clearing the fractions.** How do we *clear the fractions* from the equation? We multiply *all terms* on both sides of the equation by the least common denominator (LCD) of all the fractions contained in the equation.

EXAMPLE 1 Solve $\frac{x}{3} + \frac{x}{2} = 5$ and check your solution.

Solution First, we clear the fractions from the equation by multiplying each term by the LCD = 6; then we solve the equation.

$$6\left(\frac{x}{3}\right) + 6\left(\frac{x}{2}\right) = 6(5) \qquad \text{Multiply each term by the LCD to clear the fractions.}$$

$$2x + 3x = 30 \qquad \text{Simplify: } \frac{6x}{3} = 2x \text{ and } \frac{6x}{2} = 3x. \text{ We cleared the fractions from the equation.}$$

$$5x = 30 \qquad \text{Combine like terms.}$$

$$\frac{5x}{5} = \frac{30}{5} \qquad \text{Divide both sides by 5.}$$

$$x = 6$$

Note that the equation $2x + 3x = 30$ is equivalent to $\frac{x}{3} + \frac{x}{2} = 5$ and much easier to work with.

Check:

$$\frac{x}{3} + \frac{x}{2} = 5$$

$$\frac{6}{3} + \frac{6}{2} \stackrel{?}{=} 5$$

$$2 + 3 = 5 \checkmark$$

CAUTION: It is important to multiply **every term on both sides** of the equation by the least common denominator. A common mistake made when solving $\frac{x}{3} + \frac{x}{2} = 5$ is to multiply the fractions, $\frac{x}{3}$ and $\frac{x}{2}$, by the LCD but not the 5.

NOTE TO STUDENT: Fully worked-out solutions to all of the Practice Problems can be found at the back of the text starting at page SP-1

Practice Problem 1 Solve $\frac{x}{5} + \frac{x}{2} = 7$ and check your solution.

Let's now write down the steps we have used.

PROCEDURE TO SOLVE AN EQUATION CONTAINING FRACTIONS
1. Determine the LCD of all the denominators.
2. Multiply *every term* of the equation by the LCD (clear the fractions).
3. Solve the resulting equation.
4. Check your solution.

EXAMPLE 2 Solve. $-4x + \dfrac{3}{2} = \dfrac{2}{5}$

Solution The LCD is 10. We multiply each term by 10.

$$10(-4x) + 10\left(\dfrac{3}{2}\right) = 10\left(\dfrac{2}{5}\right)$$ Multiply each term by the LCD, 10.

$$-40x + 15 = 4$$ Simplify: $10 \cdot \dfrac{3}{2} = 15$ and $10 \cdot \dfrac{2}{5} = 4$.

$$-40x + 15 = 4$$ Solve for x.

$$\dfrac{+\quad -15 \quad -15}{-40x \quad\quad = -11}$$

$$\dfrac{-40x}{-40} = \dfrac{-11}{-40}$$

$$x = \dfrac{11}{40}$$

We leave the check to the student.

Practice Problem 2 Solve. $-5x + \dfrac{2}{7} = \dfrac{3}{2}$

EXAMPLE 3 Solve. $\dfrac{x}{7} + x = 8$

Solution There is only one denominator; thus the LCD is 7.

$$7\left(\dfrac{x}{7}\right) + 7(x) = 7(8)$$ Multiply each term by the LCD, 7.

$$1x + 7x = 56$$ Simplify: $\dfrac{7x}{7} = 1x$.

$$8x = 56$$ Combine like terms.

$$\dfrac{8x}{8} = \dfrac{56}{8}$$ Divide both sides by 8.

$$x = 7$$

Practice Problem 3 Solve. $\dfrac{x}{4} + x = 5$

NOTE TO STUDENT: Fully worked-out solutions to all of the Practice Problems can be found at the back of the text starting at page SP-1

Verbal and Writing Skills

Fill in the blanks.

1. To solve $\dfrac{x}{3} + \dfrac{x}{5} = 10$, we multiply each term by ___, so that we clear the fractions.

2. To solve $\dfrac{x}{2} - \dfrac{x}{7} = -7$, we multiply each term by ___, so that we clear the fractions.

Fill in each box with the correct number to complete each solution.

3. $\dfrac{x}{4} + \dfrac{x}{3} = 7$

$\boxed{} \cdot \dfrac{x}{4} + \boxed{} \cdot \dfrac{x}{3} = \boxed{} \cdot 7$

$\boxed{}x + \boxed{}x = 84$

$\boxed{}x = 84$

$x = \boxed{}$

4. $\dfrac{x}{5} + \dfrac{x}{3} = 8$

$\boxed{} \cdot \dfrac{x}{5} + \boxed{} \cdot \dfrac{x}{3} = \boxed{} \cdot 8$

$\boxed{}x + \boxed{}x = 120$

$\boxed{}x = 120$

$x = \boxed{}$

Solve and check your solution.

5. $\dfrac{x}{6} + \dfrac{x}{2} = 8$

6. $\dfrac{x}{3} + \dfrac{x}{6} = 9$

7. $\dfrac{x}{6} + \dfrac{x}{4} = 5$

8. $\dfrac{x}{8} + \dfrac{x}{12} = 5$

9. $\dfrac{x}{2} - \dfrac{x}{5} = 6$

10. $\dfrac{x}{2} - \dfrac{x}{9} = 7$

11. $3x + \dfrac{2}{3} = \dfrac{9}{2}$

12. $2x + \dfrac{1}{4} = \dfrac{2}{3}$

13. $5x + \dfrac{1}{8} = \dfrac{3}{4}$

14. $3x + \dfrac{2}{5} = \dfrac{1}{2}$

15. $5x - \dfrac{1}{2} = \dfrac{1}{8}$

16. $3x - \dfrac{1}{3} = \dfrac{1}{9}$

17. $-2x + \dfrac{1}{2} = \dfrac{3}{7}$

18. $-3x + \dfrac{1}{4} = \dfrac{1}{3}$

19. $-4x + \dfrac{2}{3} = \dfrac{1}{6}$

20. $-2x + \dfrac{1}{5} = \dfrac{1}{10}$

21. $\dfrac{x}{3} + x = 8$

22. $\dfrac{x}{3} + x = 4$

23. $\dfrac{x}{3} + x = 6$

24. $\dfrac{x}{7} + x = 8$

25. $\dfrac{x}{2} + x = 6$

26. $\dfrac{x}{5} - 2x = 8$

27. $\dfrac{x}{4} - 2x = 3$

28. $\dfrac{x}{3} - 4x = 5$

Mixed Practice *Solve and check your solution.*

29. $2x + \dfrac{1}{3} = \dfrac{1}{6}$

30. $5x + \dfrac{1}{2} = \dfrac{1}{4}$

31. $\dfrac{x}{3} + x = 8$

32. $\dfrac{x}{5} + x = 6$

33. $\dfrac{x}{2} + \dfrac{x}{5} = 7$

34. $\dfrac{x}{3} + \dfrac{x}{2} = 5$

One Step Further *Solve and check your solution.*

35. $\dfrac{5}{2} + \dfrac{x}{3} = \dfrac{1}{6}$

36. $\dfrac{1}{9} + \dfrac{x}{6} = \dfrac{2}{3}$

37. $\dfrac{3}{2} + \dfrac{x}{10} = \dfrac{1}{5}$

38. $\dfrac{2}{7} + \dfrac{x}{14} = \dfrac{1}{2}$

39. $\dfrac{x}{2} - \dfrac{2}{6} = -\dfrac{5}{6}$

40. $\dfrac{x}{3} - \dfrac{4}{5} = -\dfrac{2}{5}$

To Think About *Solve.*

41. $x + \dfrac{2}{3} + 2 = \dfrac{3}{2} + \dfrac{1}{4}$

42. $2x + \dfrac{3}{4} + 3 = \dfrac{2}{3} + \dfrac{1}{6}$

43. $4 + \dfrac{6}{x} + \dfrac{2}{5} = \dfrac{3}{2x}$

44. $3 + \dfrac{2}{x} + \dfrac{5}{6} = \dfrac{5}{3x}$

45. $\dfrac{1}{3}\left(\dfrac{x}{2} + 3\right) + \dfrac{1}{4} = \dfrac{5}{6}$

46. $\dfrac{3}{4}(x - 3) + \dfrac{1}{2} = \dfrac{2}{3}$

Cumulative Review *Translate using symbols.*

47. **[1.7.1]** Six more than twice a number

48. **[1.3.2]** Twelve less than some number

49. **[1.2.1]** The sum of 4 and x

50. **[1.7.1]** Two times the sum of 5 and y

51. **[5.6.1]** *Partnership Investments* Three investors own a restaurant. One partner owns $\frac{1}{3}$ of the restaurant, while the second partner owns $\frac{1}{4}$. How much does the third partner own?

52. **[5.6.1]** *Weight Loss* A boxer must lose 11 pounds in 3 weeks to be eligible for his weight category in the next boxing match. If he loses $4\frac{1}{4}$ pounds the first week and $3\frac{1}{2}$ pounds the second week, how much does he need to lose the third week to achieve the 11-pound goal?

Quick Quiz 7.4 Solve.

1. $\dfrac{x}{3} + \dfrac{x}{2} = 20$

2. $3a + \dfrac{2}{3} = \dfrac{4}{5}$

3. $\dfrac{y}{4} + y = 25$

4. **Concept Check** Explain the steps to solve the equation $-2x + \dfrac{3}{4} = \dfrac{1}{2}$.

Student Learning Objectives

After studying this section, you will be able to:

 Solve applied problems involving geometric figures.

 Solve applied problems involving comparison.

One of the first steps in solving many real-life applications is writing the equation that represents the situation. In this section we learn how to write the equations needed to solve an applied problem.

 Solving Applied Problems Involving Geometric Figures

Before we begin our discussion, let's review some of the formulas we learned in earlier chapters. To find the perimeter of a shape, we find the sum of all the sides. For a rectangle, we can use the formula $P = 2L + 2W$ to find the perimeter, and $A = LW$ to find the area.

▲ **EXAMPLE 1** Art has a rectangular planter box in his front yard that has width = 2 ft and length = 6 ft. Art plans to increase the length by x ft so that the new perimeter is 32 ft.

$$L = 6 \text{ ft} + x$$
$W = 2 \text{ ft}$ ☐ $P = 32 \text{ ft}$

(a) How much should the length be enlarged?

(b) What will the length of the enlarged planter box be?

Solution *Understand the problem.* We organize the information in a Mathematics Blueprint for Problem Solving.

Mathematics Blueprint for Problem Solving

Gather the Facts	What Am I Asked to Do?	How Do I Proceed?	Key Points to Remember
$L = x + 6$ $W = 2$ $P = 32 \text{ ft}$	**(a)** *Find x:* the number of feet the length should be enlarged. **(b)** *Find L:* the length of the enlarged planter box.	**(a)** To find x, start with $P = 2L + 2W$ and replace P, L, and W with the given values. Then solve for x. **(b)** To find L, use the equation $L = x + 6$.	Place the unit "ft" in the answer.

Solve and state the answer.

(a) How much should the length be enlarged? We must find x to answer this question.

$$P = 2L + 2W \qquad \text{Write the formula for the perimeter.}$$
$$32 = 2(x + 6) + 2(2) \qquad \text{Replace } P, L, \text{ and } W \text{ with the values given.}$$

Now we simplify and solve for x.

$$32 = 2x + 12 + 4 \qquad \text{Multiply.}$$
$$32 = 2x + 16 \qquad \text{Simplify.}$$
$$\underline{+ -16 = \qquad -16} \qquad \text{Solve the equation.}$$
$$16 = 2x$$
$$\frac{16}{2} = \frac{2x}{2}$$
$$8 = x \qquad \text{The length should be enlarged 8 ft.}$$

(b) What will the length of the enlarged planter box be?

To find L, we replace x with 8 in the expression that represents the length.

$$L = x + 6$$
$$L = 8 + 6 = 14 \quad \text{The length of the planter box will be 14 ft.}$$

$L = x + 6$ or 14 ft

$W = 2$ ft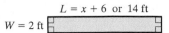

Check. We evaluate the formula for perimeter with our answer to check our calculations:

$$P = 2L + 2W$$
$$32 \stackrel{?}{=} 2(14) + 2(2)$$
$$32 = 32 \checkmark$$

▲ **Practice Problem 1** Refer to Example 1 to answer the following. Art increases the length by x ft so that the new perimeter is 36 ft.

$L = 6$ ft $+ x$

$W = 2$ ft

$P = 36$ ft

(a) How much should the length be enlarged?

(b) What will the length of the enlarged planter box be?

NOTE TO STUDENT: Fully worked-out solutions to all of the Practice Problems can be found at the back of the text starting at page SP-1

② Solving Applied Problems Involving Comparisons

In Section 6.3 we saw how to write variable expressions. In this section we will review this topic and then see how to use these expressions to form an equation and solve applied problems.

When an applied problem involves comparing two or more quantities, we must write a variable expression that describes one quantity *in terms of another* as the first step to solving the problem. We usually let a variable represent the quantity *to which things are being compared*. For example, if Laura earns $3 per hour more than Jessica, and Wendy earns $2 per hour less than Jessica, we are *comparing all the hourly wages to Jessica's* hourly wage. Therefore, we use the variable x to represent Jessica's hourly wage, and then we describe Laura's and Wendy's wages in terms of Jessica's.

$$\text{Jessica's hourly wage} = x$$
$$\text{Laura's hourly wage} = x + 3$$
$$\text{Wendy's hourly wage} = x - 2$$

We include writing variable expressions as part of a six-step process that will help you organize a Mathematics Blueprint for Problem Solving.

PROCEDURE TO SOLVE APPLIED PROBLEMS

1. Read the problem carefully to get an overview.
2. Write down formulas or draw pictures if possible.
3. Define the variable expressions.
4. Write an equation using the variable expressions selected.
5. Solve the equation and determine the values asked for in the problem.
6. Check your answer. Ask yourself if the answers obtained are reasonable.

EXAMPLE 2 For the following applied problem:

(a) Define the variable expressions.

(b) Write an equation.

(c) Solve the equation and determine the values asked for.

(d) Check your answers.

Linda is a store manager. The assistant manager, Erin, earns $8500 less annually than Linda does. The sum of Linda's annual salary and Erin's annual salary is $72,000. How much does each earn annually?

Solution *Understand the problem.* To help us understand the problem, we use a Mathematics Blueprint for Problem Solving.

Mathematics Blueprint for Problem Solving

Gather the Facts	What Am I Asked to Do?	How Do I Proceed?	Key Points to Remember
Erin earns $8500 less than Linda. The sum of the two salaries is $72,000.	Find Linda's and Erin's salaries.	**(a)** Let L represent Linda's salary and write an expression for Erin's salary. **(b)** Form an equation by setting the sum of expressions equal to $72,000. **(c)** Solve the equation.	I must find both Linda's and Erin's salaries, and check my answers.

(a) We write the variable expressions. Since we are *comparing* Erin's salary *to Linda's*, we let the variable L represent Linda's salary.

$$\text{Linda's salary} = L$$
$$\text{Erin's salary} = (L - 8500) \quad \text{\$8500 less than Linda's salary}$$

(b) We form an equation.

Linda's salary	+	Erin's salary	=	total annual salary for both people
L	+	$(L - 8500)$	=	$72,000$

The equation is $L + (L - 8500) = 72,000.$

Solve and state the answer.

(c) We solve the equation.

$$L + (L - 8500) = 72,000$$
$$2L - 8500 = 72,000$$
$$\underline{+\quad\quad 8500 \quad\quad 8,500}$$
$$2L = 80,500$$
$$\frac{2L}{2} = \frac{80,500}{2} \quad\quad L = 40,250 \quad \text{Linda earns \$40,250 annually.}$$

Now we find Erin's salary.

$$L - \$8500 = \text{Erin's salary (\$8500 less than Linda's salary)}$$
$$\$40,250 - \$8500 = \$31,750 \quad\quad \text{Erin earns \$31,750 annually.}$$

(d) *Check.* Is the sum of their salaries equal to $72,000?

$31,750 + \$40,250 \overset{?}{=} \$72,000$ $\$72,000 = \$72,000$ ✓

Practice Problem 2   For the following applied problem:

(a) Define the variable expressions.

(b) Write an equation.

(c) Solve the equation and determine the values asked for.

(d) Check your answers.

Jason is a foreman for a construction company. The apprentice for the company earns $7400 less annually than Jason does. The sum of Jason's annual salary and the apprentice's annual salary is $83,000. How much does each earn annually?

NOTE TO STUDENT: Fully worked-out solutions to all of the Practice Problems can be found at the back of the text starting at page SP-1

Understanding the Concept

Forming Equations

In this section we saw how to translate English expressions into mathematical symbols, and then form an equation. Sometimes we must write the English expression ourselves by observing a pattern in a set of numbers as illustrated below.

Suppose we must investigate the mathematical relationship between the following two sequences.

$$x \text{ is: } 1, 2, 3, 4, 5, \ldots$$
$$y \text{ is: } 1, 4, 9, 16, 25, \ldots$$

The mathematical operations that are commonly used in sequences are listed in the table below.

To Obtain Each Number in Sequence *y*:	
(a) Add the same number to each x.	**(d)** Multiply or divide each x by the same number.
(b) Subtract the same number from each x.	
(c) Add or subtract a sequence of numbers to each x: 1, 5, 1, 5, …	**(e)** Raise x to a power
	(f) Any combination of **(a)**–**(e)**.

Referring to **(e)** in the table we can state the relationship between x and y in words as follows.

We raise each value in x to the power of 2 to obtain each corresponding value in y.

Now we can translate this statement and write the equation or formula, $x^2 = y$. Then we can use this equation to find other numbers in the sequences. For example,

The next number in the sequence x is 6. x is: 1, 2, 3, 4, 5, 6, …
We evaluate $6^2 = 36$ to find the next y is: 1, 4, 9, 16, 25, 36, …
number in y.

Exercise

1. Find the next two numbers in the sequence x, and then find the corresponding values in y.

Developing Your Study Skills

Real-Life Mathematics Applications

Applied, or word, problems are the very life of mathematics! They are the reason for doing mathematics because they teach you how to put into use the mathematical skills you have developed. Learning mathematics without ever doing word problems is similar to learning all the skills of a sport without ever playing a game or learning all the notes on an instrument without ever playing a song.

The key to success is practice. Make yourself do as many problems as you can. You may not be able to work them all correctly at first, but keep trying. Do not give up whenever you reach a difficult one. If you cannot solve it, just try another one. Then come back and try the problem again later. Ask for help from your teacher or the tutoring lab. Ask other classmates how they solved the problem.

A misconception among students when they begin studying applied problems is that each problem is different. At first the problems may seem this way, but as you practice more and more, you will begin to see the similarities, the different "types." You will see patterns in solving problems, which will enable you to solve problems of a given type more easily.

Exercise

1. Spend this week thinking about situations that you have encountered that require the use of mathematics. Write out the facts for one of these situations, then form an applied problem. Share this applied problem with other students in your class.

For exercises 1–6:

(a) *Write an equation.*   **(b)** *Solve the equation.*

1. If three times a number is increased by nine, the result is fifteen. What is the number?

2. If three times a number is increased by one, the result is nineteen. What is the number?

3. If triple a number is decreased by four, the result is five. What is the number?

4. If double a number is decreased by six, the result is eight. What is the number?

5. If the sum of 4 and a number is multiplied by 2, the result is 12. What is the number?

6. If the sum of 8 and a number is multiplied by 6, the result is 54. What is the number?

Use the appropriate formula to solve exercises 7–12.

▲ **7.** Find the value of x in the following rectangle if the perimeter is 60 meters.

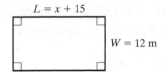

$L = x + 15$

$W = 12$ m

▲ **8.** Find the value of x in the following rectangle if the perimeter is 66 meters.

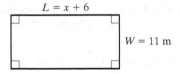

$L = x + 6$

$W = 11$ m

▲ **9.** Find the length of each side of the following triangle if the perimeter is 12 centimeters.

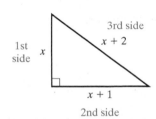

1st side x

3rd side $x + 2$

$x + 1$

2nd side

▲ **10.** Find the length of each side of the following triangle if the perimeter is 24 decimeters.

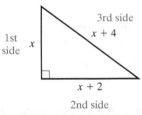

1st side x

3rd side $x + 4$

$x + 2$

2nd side

▲ **11.** Find the value of x in the following rectangle if the area is 90 square inches.

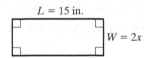

$L = 15$ in.

$W = 2x$

▲ **12.** Find the value of x in the following rectangle if the area is 216 square inches.

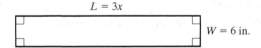

$L = 3x$

$W = 6$ in.

Applications

▲ **13.** *Geometry* Natalie's family room has width = 12 ft and length = 15 ft. She is enlarging the room by increasing the width x ft so that the new perimeter of the room is 70 ft.

(a) How much should the width be enlarged?
(b) What will the width of the enlarged family room be?

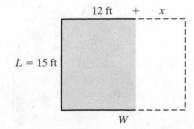

12 ft   + x

$L = 15$ ft

W

▲ **14.** *Geometry* Juan's concrete patio has width = 5 ft and length = 12 ft. He is enlarging the patio by increasing the width x ft so that the new perimeter of the patio is 44 ft.

(a) How much should the width be enlarged?
(b) What will the width of the enlarged concrete patio be?

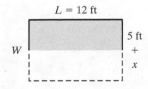

$L = 12$ ft

W

5 ft + x

▲ **15.** *Geometry* Richard is planning to enlarge a rectangular space with length = 9 ft and width = 7 ft so that the new area is 105 ft^2.

   (a) How much should the length be enlarged? (Recall that $A = LW$.)

   (b) What will the length of the enlarged space be?

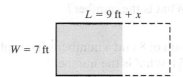

$L = 9\text{ ft} + x$

$W = 7$ ft

▲ **16.** *Geometry* Samantha is planning to enlarge a small rectangular space with length = 20 in. and width = 15 in. so that the new area is 450 in.^{2}.

   (a) How much should the length be enlarged? (Recall that $A = LW$.)

   (b) What will the length of the enlarged space be?

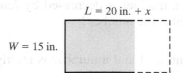

$L = 20\text{ in.} + x$

$W = 15$ in.

17. *Salary Comparison* Mark is a teaching assistant at a local community college. A tutor at the college works the same number of hours as Mark but earns $11,400 less annually. The sum of Mark's annual salary and the tutor's annual salary is $28,890. How much does each earn?

   (a) Define the variable expressions.

   (b) Write an equation.

   (c) Solve the equation and determine the values asked for.

   (d) Check your answer.

18. *Salary Comparison* Lena is a sales supervisor. The salesclerk earns $6200 less annually than Lena does. The sum of Lena's annual salary and the clerk's annual salary is $58,000. How much does each earn?

   (a) Define the variable expressions.

   (b) Write an equation.

   (c) Solve the equation and determine the values asked for.

   (d) Check your answer.

19. *Distance Traveled* Over two days Cal drove 825 miles to attend a wedding. He drove 165 more miles the second day than the first day. How far did he drive each day?

   (a) Define the variable expressions.

   (b) Write an equation.

   (c) Solve the equation and determine the values asked for.

   (d) Check your answer.

20. *Miles Walked* Andrew walked 4 miles less than Dave last week in a Boys and Girls Club "walk for the homeless" program. The two boys together walked 34 miles. How many miles did each boy walk?

   (a) Define the variable expressions.

   (b) Write an equation.

   (c) Solve the equation and determine the values asked for.

   (d) Check your answer.

WALK FOR THE HOMELESS

21. **_Flying Time_** The total flying time for two flights is 15 hours. The flight time for the first flight is half of the second. How long is each flight?

(a) Define the variable expressions.

(b) Write an equation.

(c) Solve the equation and determine the values asked for.

(d) Check your answer.

▲ **22.** **_Geometry_** The perimeter of a rectangle is 48 feet. The length is 4 feet less than triple the width. What are the dimensions of the rectangle?

(a) Define the variable expressions.

(b) Write an equation.

(c) Solve the equation and determine the values asked for.

(d) Check your answer.

▲ **23.** **_Geometry_** A triangle has a perimeter of 120 meters. The length of the second side is double the first side. The length of the third side is 12 meters longer than the first side. Find the length of each side.

(a) Define the variable expressions.

(b) Write an equation.

(c) Solve the equation and determine the values asked for.

(d) Check your answer.

▲ **24.** **_Geometry_** A triangle has a perimeter of 176 feet. The second side is 25 feet longer than the first. The third side is 5 feet shorter than the first. Find the length of each side.

(a) Define the variable expressions.

(b) Write an equation.

(c) Solve the equation and determine the values asked for.

(d) Check your answer.

▲ **25.** **_Geometry_** The perimeter of a rectangle is 68 meters. The length is 2 meters less than triple the width. What are the dimensions of the rectangle?

(a) Define the variable expressions.

(b) Write the equation.

(c) Solve the equation and determine the values asked for.

(d) Check your answer.

▲ **26.** **_Geometry_** The perimeter of a rectangle is 74 feet. The length is 2 feet less than double the width. What are the dimensions of the rectangle?

(a) Define the variable expressions.

(b) Write the equation.

(c) Solve the equation and determine the values asked for.

(d) Check your answer.

27. **_Enrollment Comparison_** Last year a total of 395 students took English. 95 more students took it in the spring than in the fall. 75 fewer students took it in the summer than in the fall. How many students took it during each semester?

(a) Define the variable expressions.

(b) Write the equation.

(c) Solve the equation and determine the values asked for.

(d) Check your answer.

28. **_Student Housing_** A small community college has a total of 1704 students. 115 more students live on campus than live in nearby off-campus housing. 55 fewer students live at home and commute than live in nearby off-campus housing. How many students are there in each of the three categories?

(a) Define the variable expressions.

(b) Write the equation.

(c) Solve the equation and determine the values asked for.

(d) Check your answer.

One Step Further

▲ 29. Find the value of x in the following pair of supplementary angles.

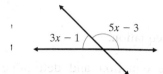

▲ 30. Since the triangle below is an isosceles triangle, the measures of $\angle a$ and $\angle b$ are equal. Find x in the following isosceles triangle.

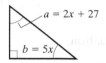

To Think About

▲ 31. **Geometry** If the perimeter and area of a square are equal in value, what is the length of the side of this square?

▲ 32. **Geometry** A triangle with all sides of equal length is called an *equilateral triangle*. If the perimeter of an equilateral triangle is equal to the length of a side squared, what is the length (in feet) of each side of the triangle?

The charts in exercises 33–36 list the numbers in two different but related sequences. The first sequence is labeled x, and the second y. Refer to the table below to determine the mathematical relationship between x and y.

To Obtain Each Number in Sequence y:
(a) Add the same number to each x.
(b) Subtract the same number from each x.
(c) Add or subtract a sequence of numbers to each x: $1, 5, 1, 5, \ldots$
(d) Multiply or divide each x by the same number.
(e) Raise x to a power.
(f) Any combination of **(a)–(e)**.

33. **(a)** Find the missing numbers for sequence x, then place these values in the appropriate place in the chart.

x	1	2	3	4	5	6		...	30
y	3	6	9	12	15			...	

(b) Determine the mathematical relationship between x and y, then write this relationship in your own words.

(c) Translate the statement in **(b)** into an equation.

(d) Use this equation to find the missing numbers for y and place these values in the chart.

34. **(a)** Find the missing numbers for sequence x, then place these values in the appropriate place in the chart.

x	25	20	15	10		0		...	−50
y	19	14	9	4		−6		...	

(b) Determine the mathematical relationship between x and y, then write this relationship in your own words.

(c) Translate the statement in **(b)** into an equation.

(d) Use this equation to find the missing numbers for y and place these values in the chart.

35. **(a)** Find the missing numbers for sequence x, then place these values in the appropriate place in the chart.

x	0	1	2	3		5		...	45
y	1	4	7	10		16		...	

(b) Determine the mathematical relationship between x and y, then write this relationship in your own words.

(c) Translate the statement in **(b)** into an equation.

(d) Use this equation to find the missing numbers for y and place these values in the chart.

36. **(a)** Find the missing numbers for sequence x, then place these values in the appropriate place in the chart.

x	2	3	4	5		7		...	20
y	3	8	15	24		48		...	

(b) Determine the mathematical relationship between x and y, then write this relationship in your own words.

(c) Translate the statement in **(b)** into an equation.

(d) Use this equation to find the missing numbers for y and place these values in the chart.

Cumulative Review

▲ **37.** **[5.6.1]** *Checker Board* The dimensions of an opened checker game board are $13\frac{1}{2}$ in. by $13\frac{1}{2}$ in. by $\frac{5}{8}$ in. What are the dimensions of the board when it is folded in half?

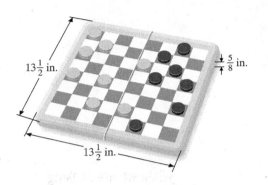

▲ **38.** **[5.6.1]** *Brick Steps*

(a) What are the length and the width of the step made of bricks if there is grout between the bricks and between the bricks and the wall?

(b) What is the perimeter of the step?

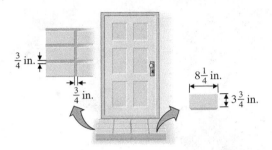

Quick Quiz 7.5 Use the following information for problems 1–3.
The perimeter of a triangle is 29 meters. The first side is 5 meters longer than the third side. The second side is twice the length of the third side. Find the length of each side of the triangle.

1. Define the variable expressions.

2. Write an equation.

3. Solve the equation and determine the values asked for.

4. Concept Check The high school marching band fundraiser for uniforms requires that students find donors to pledge money based on the number of laps they run on the school track field. This year Miguel ran 2 more laps than Sam, and Alicia ran 4 fewer laps than Sam. The total laps completed by all three was 29.

Eduardo wanted to calculate the number of laps Alicia completed. To find this information, he let S represent the number of laps that Sam ran, and then solved the equation $(S + 2) + (4 - S) = 29$ to find the number of laps completed by Alicia.

(a) Did Eduardo use the correct equation? Why or why not?

(b) How many laps did Miguel complete for the fundraiser?

When we are seeking employment we must evaluate all the benefits and costs involved with each job offer before we determine which one will fit our needs and budget. How far must I travel? What extra expenses will the job add to my budget? Which job nets more money after expenses?

Decimals and Percents

Writing Word Names for Decimal Fractions

Student Learning Objectives

After studying this section, you will be able to:

1 Write word names for decimal fractions.

2 Convert between decimals and fractions.

3 Compare and order decimals.

4 Round decimals.

A **decimal fraction** is a fraction whose denominator is a power of 10: 10, 100, 1000, and so on.

$\dfrac{9}{10}$ is a decimal fraction. $\dfrac{41}{100}$ is a decimal fraction.

We can represent the shaded part of a whole as a decimal fraction in different ways (forms): using word names, as a fraction, or in decimal form.

In Words	*In Fractional Form*	*In Decimal Form*
three-tenths	$\dfrac{3}{10}$	.3

All mean the same quantity, namely, 3 out of 10 equal parts of a whole. The "." in the decimal form .3 is called a **decimal point.** Usually a zero is placed in front of the decimal point to make sure that we don't miss seeing the decimal point.

.3 has the same value as 0.3

↑ decimal point   ↑ extra zero used only for clarity

Since situations may require that we use different forms of decimal fractions, it is important that we understand the meaning of decimal fractions as well as how to write decimal fractions in each form. A **place-value chart** is helpful.

Hundreds	Tens	Ones	Decimal Point	Tenths	Hundredths	Thousandths	Ten Thousandths
100	10	1	"and"	$\dfrac{1}{10}$	$\dfrac{1}{100}$	$\dfrac{1}{1000}$	$\dfrac{1}{10,000}$

This place-value chart is an extension of the one we used in Chapter 1 to name whole numbers. From the chart we see the following.

1. The names for the place values to the right of the decimal point end with *"ths"* compared to those to the left of the decimal point. Therefore, we must take care when stating the name of the place value.

   "3 hundreds" names the number 300. "3 hundred*ths*" names the number $\dfrac{3}{100}$.

2. The word name for a decimal point is *and*.

We can use the place-value chart to help us write a word name for a decimal fraction.

EXAMPLE 1   Write a word name for the decimal 0.561.

Solution   The place value of the *last digit* is the *last word* in the word name. The last digit is 1 and is in the *thousandths* place.

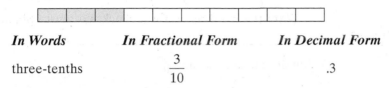

We do not include 0 as part of word name. ⟶   ⟵ thousandths place

0.561

Five hundred sixty-one *thousandths*

Practice Problem 1   Write a word name for each decimal.

(a) 0.365   **(b)** 5.32

NOTE TO STUDENT: Fully worked-out solutions to all of the Practice Problems can be found at the back of the text starting at page SP-1

Decimal notation is used when writing a check. Often, we write an amount that is less than 1 dollar, such as 35 cents, as $\frac{35}{100}$ dollar.

June Schultz 3 Barker Road Placentia, CA 92870	**2882**
	DATE *April 6* 20 *09*
PAY to the ORDER of *Jason Briggs*	$ *8.35*
Eight and $^{35}/_{100}$	DOLLARS
Norwalk Central Bank **Norwalk, California**	
MEMO_____	*June Schultz*
⑈58005200⑈ 20550522⑈' 2882	

EXAMPLE 2 Write the word name for a check written to Shandell Strong for $126.87. _____ Dollars

Solution One hundred twenty-six and $\frac{87}{100}$

Practice Problem 2 Write the word name for a check written to Wendy King for $245.09. _____ Dollars

 Converting Between Decimals and Fractions

Decimal fractions can be written with numerals in two ways: decimal notation or fractional notation.

Decimal Notation	Fractional Notation
0.7	$\frac{7}{10}$
3.49	$3\frac{49}{100}$
0.021	$\frac{21}{1000}$

From the table, note the following.

$$0.7 \quad = \quad \frac{7}{10} \qquad\qquad 0.021 \quad = \quad \frac{21}{1000}$$

| 1 decimal place | 1 zero | 3 decimal places | 3 zeros |

PROCEDURE TO CHANGE FROM DECIMAL TO FRACTIONAL NOTATION

1. Write the whole number (if any).

    $9.\underline{7653} \rightarrow 9$

    4 decimal places

2. Count the number of decimal places.

3. Write the decimal part over a denominator that has a 1 and the same number of zeros as the number of decimal places found in step 2.

    $9\dfrac{7653}{10,000}$

    4 zeros

EXAMPLE 3   Write 0.86132 using fractional notation. Do not simplify.

Solution

We do not need to write 0 as part of the fraction.

$$0.86132 = \frac{86{,}132}{100{,}000}$$

5 decimal places   5 zeros

Practice Problem 3   Write 8.723 using fractional notation. Do not simplify.

If a fraction has a denominator that is a power of 10 (10, 100, 1000, and so on), we use a similar procedure to change the fraction to a decimal.

PROCEDURE TO CHANGE FRACTIONAL NOTATION TO DECIMAL NOTATION WHEN THE DENOMINATOR IS A POWER OF 10

1. Count the number of zeros in the denominator.

$$9\frac{7653}{10{,}000} \quad \text{4 zeros}$$

2. In the numerator, move the decimal point as many places to the left as the number of zeros in step 1. If there are not enough places, add zeros until there are. Then delete the denominator.

$$9\frac{7653}{10{,}000} \rightarrow 9.7653$$

4 places

EXAMPLE 4   Write $7\frac{56}{1000}$ as a decimal.

Solution

Move decimal point 3 places to the left.

$$7\frac{56}{1000} = 7\frac{056}{1000} = 7.056$$

3 zeros

Note that we had to insert a 0 before 56 so we could move the decimal point 3 places to the left.

Practice Problem 4   Write $\frac{17}{1000}$ as a decimal.

In Section 8.3 we will see how to change fractions to decimals when the denominator is not a power of 10.

Comparing and Ordering Decimals

In Chapter 1 we studied the inequality symbols "<" and ">." Recall that

$$a < b \text{ is read "} a \text{ is less than } b.\text{"}$$

$$a > b \text{ is read "} a \text{ is greater than } b.\text{"}$$

To compare and order decimals using inequality symbols, we compare each digit.

PROCEDURE TO COMPARE TWO POSITIVE NUMBERS IN DECIMAL NOTATION

1. Start with the leftmost digit and compare corresponding digits. If the digits are the same, move one place to the right.

2. When two digits are different, the larger number is the one with the larger digit.

Note: We must write decimals such as .21 as 0.21 for the above procedure to apply.

It is easier to compare two decimals if the decimal parts of each have the same number of digits. Whenever necessary, extra zeros can be written to the right of the last digit—that is, to the *right* of the *last digit after* the decimal point—without changing the value of the decimal. To see why, let's look at $\dfrac{3}{10}, \dfrac{30}{100}, \dfrac{300}{1000}$.

$$\frac{300}{1000} = \frac{30}{100} = \frac{3}{10} \quad \frac{3}{10} \text{ is the simplified form of the fractions } \frac{300}{1000} \text{ and } \frac{30}{100}.$$

$$\downarrow \qquad \downarrow \qquad \downarrow$$

$$0.300 = 0.30 = 0.3 \quad \text{We can think of 0.3 as the simplified form of 0.300 and 0.30.}$$

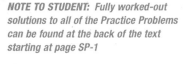 **EXAMPLE 5** Replace the ? with $<$ or $>$. 0.24 ? 0.244

Solution

0.24 ? 0.244	
0.240 ? 0.244	Add a zero to 0.24 so that both decimal parts have the same number of digits.
0.240 ? 0.244	The tenths digits are equal and the hundredths digits are equal.
0.240 ? 0.244	The thousandths digits differ.

Since $0 < 4,\ 0.240 < 0.244$.

 Practice Problem 5 Replace the ? with $<$ or $>$. 0.77 ? 0.771

NOTE TO STUDENT: *Fully worked-out solutions to all of the Practice Problems can be found at the back of the text starting at page SP-1*

④ Rounding Decimals

Just as with whole numbers, we must sometimes round decimals. The rule for rounding is similar to the one we used in Chapter 1 for whole numbers.

PROCEDURE TO ROUND DECIMALS

1. Identify the round-off place digit.

2. If the digit to the *right* of the round-off place digit is:
   (a) *Less than 5*, do not change the round-off place digit.
   (b) *5 or more*, increase the round-off place digit by 1.

3. In either case, drop all digits to the right of the round-off place digit.

Thus, when rounding decimals we either *increase* the round-off place digit by 1 or *leave it the same*. We drop all digits to the right of the round-off place digit.

EXAMPLE 6   Round 237.8435 to the nearest hundredth.

Solution   The round-off place digit is in the *hundredths place*.

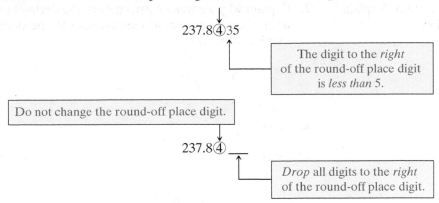

237.8④35

The digit to the *right* of the round-off place digit is *less than* 5.

Do not change the round-off place digit.

237.8④ ___

Drop all digits to the *right* of the round-off place digit.

237.8435 rounded to the nearest hundredth is 237.84.

Practice Problem 6   Round 369.2649 to the nearest hundredth.

Remember that rounding up to the next digit in a position may result in several digits being changed.

EXAMPLE 7   Round to the nearest hundredth. Alex and Lisa used 204.9954 kilowatt-hours of electricity in their house in June.

Solution   We locate and circle the digit in the hundredths place.

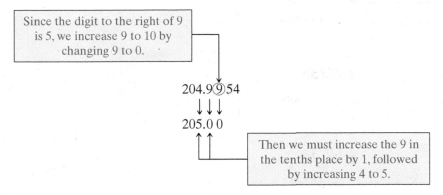

Since the digit to the right of 9 is 5, we increase 9 to 10 by changing 9 to 0.

204.9⑨54
↓ ↓ ↓
205.0 0

Then we must increase the 9 in the tenths place by 1, followed by increasing 4 to 5.

Note that we *must* include the two zeros after the decimal point because we were asked to round to the nearest hundredth.

205.0 0   When rounding to the nearest hundredth, the last digit should be in the hundredths place.

Thus 204.9954 rounds to 205.00 kilowatt-hours.

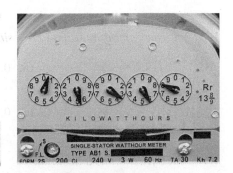

Practice Problem 7   Round to the nearest tenth. Last month the college auditorium used 16,499.952 kilowatt-hours of electricity.

Verbal and Writing Skills

1. 12.97 rounded to the nearest tenth is 13.0. Explain how rounding 9 up is similar to carrying.

2. Explain why we write a zero before the decimal point when there is no whole number part to the decimal fraction as in 0.23.

Write a word name for each decimal.

3. 5.32

4. 11.78

5. 0.428

6. 0.983

Write in decimal notation.

7. Three hundred twenty-four thousandths

8. One hundred twenty-six thousandths

9. Fifteen and three hundred forty-six ten thousandths

10. Twenty-four and one hundred seventy-six ten thousandths

Write the word name for the amount on each check.

11.

PAY to the ORDER of *Orange Coast College* $ *25.54*

_____ DOLLARS

12.

PAY to the ORDER of *Rita Smith* $ *8.75*

_____ DOLLARS

13.

PAY to the ORDER of *The Gas Company* $ *143.56*

_____ DOLLARS

14.

PAY to the ORDER of *Pep Boys Auto Parts* $ *146.32*

_____ DOLLARS

Write in fractional notation. Do not simplify.

15. 0.7

16. 0.3

17. 4.17

18. 6.23

19. 32.081

20. 0.8436

21. 0.5731

22. 20.022

Write each fraction as a decimal.

23. $6\frac{7}{10}$

24. $3\frac{7}{10}$

25. $12\frac{37}{1000}$

26. $63\frac{31}{1000}$

27. $\frac{1}{100}$

28. $\frac{3}{100}$

29. $\frac{3}{1000}$

30. $\frac{7}{1000}$

Replace the ? with < or >.

31. 0.426 ? 0.429   **32.** 0.526 ? 0.521   **33.** 0.09 ? 0.11   **34.** 0.93 ? 0.94

35. 0.36 ? 0.366   **36.** 0.12 ? 0.127   **37.** 0.7431 ? 0.743   **38.** 0.6362 ? 0.636

39. 0.3 ? 0.05   **40.** 0.6 ? 0.57   **41.** 0.502 ? 0.52   **42.** 0.703 ? 0.73

Round to the nearest hundredth.

43. 523.7235   **44.** 124.6345   **45.** 43.961   **46.** 76.996

Round to the nearest tenth.

47. 9.0546   **48.** 21.057   **49.** 462.931   **50.** 125.942

Round to the nearest thousandth.

51. 312.95144   **52.** 63.44431   **53.** 1286.3496   **54.** 2563.4895

Round to the nearest ten thousandth.

55. 0.063148   **56.** 0.043629   **57.** 0.047362   **58.** 0.095253

Applications

59. *Mars and Earth* Mars was only 42.5 million miles from Earth in June 2001. That was the closest it had been to Earth in 13 years. The two planets were only 34.6 million miles apart in August 2003. This was the nearest they'd been in 5000 years! Round these values to the nearest million. (*Source:* mars.fpl.nasa.gov)

60. *El Niño* In any given year the average rainfall in Santiago Peak, California, is 33.46 inches. From July 1, 1997, to May 29, 1998, Santiago Peak had an increase in rainfall due to an El Niño condition, receiving 105.12 inches of rain. Round the average rainfall, and the rainfall during the El Niño season, to the nearest tenth. (*Source:* Orange County Register)

The menu at Emerald's Dinner House reads as follows.

Emerald's Dinner House

Grilled chicken breast . . . . $ 12.95
New York steak . . . . $ 15.25
Stuffed pork chops . . . . . . $ 13.75
Fish of the day . . . . $ 14.50
Lobster . . . . $ 18.25
Prime rib . . . . $ 15.75

61. Round the price of the New York steak to the nearest dollar.

62. Round the price of the prime rib to the nearest dollar.

63. The Austin family ordered three meals: stuffed pork chops, lobster, and prime rib. Round the price of each meal to the nearest dollar and estimate the cost of the three meals.

64. Lester, Marian, and Sean ordered three meals: grilled chicken breast, New York steak, and lobster. Round the price of each meal to the nearest dollar and estimate the cost of the three meals.

To Think About

65. Arrange in order from largest to smallest. 0.0069, 0.73, $\frac{7}{10}$, 0.007, 0.071

66. Arrange in order from smallest to largest. 0.053, 0.005, 0.52, 0.0059, $\frac{5}{100}$

Cumulative Review   *Perform the operations indicated.*

67. **[2.3.1]** $-15 - (-6)$

68. **[2.4.1]** $(356)(-28)$

69. **[2.4.4]** $-45 \div 9$

70. **[1.5.4]** $15{,}708 \div 231$

71. **[5.6.1]** *Mixed Nuts* Tory bought $\frac{2}{3}$ lb of cashews and $\frac{1}{2}$ lb of mixed nuts. How many total pounds of nuts did Tory buy?

72. **[5.6.1]** *Term Paper* An English instructor has specific layout requirements for the final term paper. The layout must include a top margin of $\frac{3}{4}$ inch and a bottom margin of $\frac{1}{2}$ inch. How much page length is lost because of the margins?

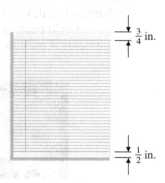

Quick Quiz 8.1

1. Write the word name. 7.21

2. (a) Write in fractional notation. 0.0217

    (b) Write as a decimal. $4\frac{32}{1000}$

3. Round 156.748 to the nearest tenth.

4. **Concept Check** Explain how you know how many zeros to put in your answer when you write 8.6711 as a fraction.

8.2 ADDING AND SUBTRACTING DECIMAL EXPRESSIONS

1 Adding and Subtracting Decimal Expressions

We often add or subtract decimals when we work with money. For example, if we buy a drink for $1.25 and a sandwich for $3.55, how much is the total bill? It is $1.25 + $3.55, or $4.80. Now, if we pay with a $5 bill, how much change do we receive? $5.00 − $4.80, or $0.20 (20 cents).

We can relate addition and subtraction of fractions to decimals. For example,

$$2\frac{3}{10} = 2.3 \qquad\qquad 8\frac{5}{10} = 8.5$$

$$+5\frac{6}{10} = 5.6 \qquad -3\frac{2}{10} = 3.2$$

$$\overline{7\frac{9}{10} = 7.9} \qquad \overline{5\frac{3}{10} = 5.3}$$

What do you notice about the sum and difference in the examples above? Do you see that addition and subtraction of decimals are very much like those of whole numbers, except that we must consider placement of the decimal point?

PROCEDURE TO ADD OR SUBTRACT DECIMALS

1. Write the numbers vertically and *line up* the decimal points. Extra zeros may be written to the right of the decimal points if needed.

2. Add or subtract all the digits with the same place value, starting with the right column and moving to the left. Use carrying or borrowing as needed.

3. Place the decimal point of the answer in line with the decimal points of all the numbers added or subtracted.

Calculator

 Adding and Subtracting Decimals

The calculator can be used to verify your work. To find 13.04 + 2.33, enter

$$13.04 \boxed{+} 2.33 \boxed{=}$$

The display should read:

$$\boxed{15.37}$$

EXAMPLE 1 Add. 40 + 8.77 + 0.9

Solution We can write any whole number as a decimal by placing a decimal point at the end of the number: 40 = 40.

$$
\begin{array}{r}
\overset{1}{40.00} \\
8.77 \\
+0.90 \\
\hline
49.67
\end{array}
$$

Line up decimal points.

Add zeros so that each number has the same number of decimal places.

Place the decimal point in the answer in line with other decimal points.

Practice Problem 1 Add. 50 + 4.39 + 0.7

EXAMPLE 2 Subtract. 19.02 − 8.6

Solution

$$
\begin{array}{r}
\overset{8}{1}\overset{10}{9}.02 \\
-8.60 \\
\hline
10.42
\end{array}
$$

Line up decimal points.

Add a zero.

The decimal point in the difference is in line with the other decimal points.

Practice Problem 2 Subtract. 26.01 − 5.7

When we add or subtract positive and negative decimals we use the same rules stated in Chapter 2.

EXAMPLE 3   Perform the operation indicated. $-9.79 - (-0.68)$

Solution   To subtract, we add the opposite of the second number.

$$-9.79 - (-0.68)$$
$$-9.79 + (0.68)$$

Add   the opposite of (-0.68).

Next, to add numbers with different signs, we *"keep the sign of the larger absolute value and subtract."*

$$\begin{array}{r} -9.79 \\ \underline{0.68} \\ -9.11 \end{array}$$ We subtract.
The answer will be negative since $|-9.79|$ is larger than $|0.68|$.

Practice Problem 3   Perform the operation indicated. $-3.02 - (-5.1)$

NOTE TO STUDENT: *Fully worked-out solutions to all of the Practice Problems can be found at the back of the text starting at page SP-1*

 Combining Like Terms

Recall that to combine like terms we add coefficients of like terms and the variable part stays the same.

EXAMPLE 4   Combine like terms. $11.2x + 3.6x - 7.1y$

Solution $11.2x$ and $3.6x$ are like terms, so we add them.

$$\begin{array}{r} 11.2x \\ \underline{+\ 3.6x} \\ 14.8x \end{array}$$ We line up decimal points and add.

We have $\underbrace{11.2x + 3.6x}\ - 7.1y$

$$= 14.8x - 7.1y$$

We cannot combine $14.8x$ and $7.1y$ since they are not like terms.

Practice Problem 4   Combine like terms. $4.5y + 7.2y - 5.6x$

 Evaluating Algebraic Expressions Involving Decimals

Recall that to evaluate an expression we replace the variable with the given number and simplify.

EXAMPLE 5   Evaluate $x + 3.12$ for $x = 0.11$.

Solution   We replace the variable with 0.11.

$$x + 3.12 = 0.11 + 3.12$$

Next we line up decimal points and add.

$$\begin{array}{r} 3.12 \\ \underline{+\ 0.11} \\ 3.23 \end{array}$$

Practice Problem 5   Evaluate $-6.2 + x$ for $x = 1.2$.

Estimating Sums and Differences

We can estimate a sum or difference of decimals by rounding each decimal to the nearest whole number.

EXAMPLE 6   Julie runs on her treadmill every day. She wants to run approximately 25 miles each week to prepare for a track race. She logged the distance she ran each day this week on the following chart. *Estimate* the total number of miles Julie ran this week.

Monday	Tuesday	Wednesday	Thursday	Friday	Saturday	Sunday
2.13 mi	2.79 mi	2.9 mi	3.11 mi	3.8 mi	4.12 mi	4.9 mi

Solution   We round each decimal to the nearest whole number and then add.

$$2 + 3 + 3 + 3 + 4 + 4 + 5 = 24 \text{ miles}$$

Julie ran approximately 24 miles.

Practice Problem 6   Allen ate at restaurants for two days while on a business trip. He logged his expenses on the chart located in the margin. *Estimate* the total cost of meals.

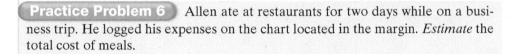

(4)	(5)	MEALS		(6)
DAY	BREAK-FAST	LUNCH	DINNER	
Tuesday	7.29	8.99	19.10	
Wednesday	6.99	9.20	21.76	

 Solving Applied Problems Involving Decimals

EXAMPLE 7   In May 2001 Allen Iverson, a 6-foot, 165-pound guard for the Philadelphia 76ers, became the shortest and lightest player to be named the NBA Most Valuable Player. The table on the right compares some of the top players' average season statistics.

(a) How many more points did Iverson average than Bryant?

(b) Find the total of the average number of rebounds made by Iverson, Duncan, and O'Neal.

Name	Team	Points	Rebounds	Assists
1. Allen Iverson	76ers	31.1	3.1	4.6
2. Tim Duncan	Spurs	22.2	12.2	3.0
3. Shaquille O'Neal	Lakers	28.7	12.7	3.7
4. Kobe Bryant	Lakers	28.5	5.9	5.0

Source: Orange County Register

Solution

(a) The key phrase "how many more" indicates the operation subtraction.

$$
\begin{array}{r}
\overset{\scriptsize 10}{} \\[-6pt]
\overset{\scriptsize 2\ \cancel{0}\ 11}{3\cancel{1}.\cancel{1}} \quad \text{We borrow and then subtract.} \\
\text{Allen Iverson's points} \\
\text{Kobe Bryant's points} \quad -28.5 \\
\hline
2.6 \text{ more points}
\end{array}
$$

(b) We add to find the total.

$$
\begin{array}{rr}
\text{Iverson} & 3.1 \\
\text{Duncan} & 12.2 \\
\text{O'Neal} & 12.7 \\
\hline
& 28.0 \text{ rebounds}
\end{array}
$$

Practice Problem 7   Refer to the table in Example 7 to answer the following. Find the total of the average number of assists for all four players listed on the chart.

NOTE TO STUDENT: *Fully worked-out solutions to all of the Practice Problems can be found at the back of the text starting at page SP-1*

Verbal and Writing Skills *Fill in the blanks.*

1. To add numbers in decimal notation, we _____ the decimal points.

2. When adding decimals, we place the decimal point in the answer _____ with the decimal points in the problem.

3. When subtracting decimals, we place the decimal point in the answer _____ with the decimal points in the problem.

4. When subtracting $73 - 23.4$, we rewrite 73 as _____ so that we can line up _____.

Add.

5. $0.34 + 7.21$

6. $0.63 + 2.73$

7. $1.01 + 3.46$

8. $0.74 + 9.32$

9. $63.2 + 0.2348$

10. $35.4 + 0.8759$

11. $73 + 7.54 + 0.483$

12. $59 + 1.27 + 0.345$

13. $73.1 + 0.3169$

14. $74.2 + 0.4524$

15. $15 + 2.73 + 0.423$

16. $0.658 + 23 + 6.24$

Subtract.

17. $53.783 - 2.46$

18. $48.575 - 5.44$

19. $16.54 - 3.9$

20. $125.43 - 2.8$

21. $20 - 0.36$

22. $30 - 0.82$

23. $-12.1 - 0.23$

24. $-13.6 - 0.51$

25. $-91.13 - 14.213$

26. $-88.14 - 16.315$

27. $-8.69 - (-4.12)$

28. $-7.22 - (-2.11)$

Combine like terms.

29. $2.3x + 3.9x$

30. $4.6x + 1.7x$

31. $24.8y - 9.2y$

32. $15.6y - 8.2y$

33. $3.5x + 9.1x - y$

34. $5.5x + 3.2x - 3y$

35. $1.4x + 6.2y + 3.5x$

36. $2.6x + 3.1y + 4.2x$

Mixed Problems 37–40 *Perform the operations indicated.*

37. (a) $-3.4 + (-2.1)$
    (b) $9.7 - (-5.4)$
    (c) $-9.2 - 4.1$

38. (a) $-1.13 + (-8.84)$
    (b) $8.31 - (-2.36)$
    (c) $-4.99 - 1.73$

39. (a) $4.6x + 2x$
    (b) $3.04y - 7.5y$
    (c) $x - 0.25x$

40. (a) $3.4x + 5x$
    (b) $2.06y - 1.2y$
    (c) $x - 0.44x$

Evaluate for the given value.

41. $y - 0.861$ for $y = 9$

42. $16.011 - n$ for $n = 9.7$

43. $211.2 - n$ for $n = 5.42$

44. $y - 0.12$ for $y = 7$

45. $x + 2.3$ for $x = -6.7$

46. $x - (-19.2)$ for $x = -0.09$

Applications

47. *Payroll Deductions* John makes $1763.24 a month. $161.96 is deducted for federal income tax, $61.23 for Social Security, and $47.82 for state taxes. *Estimate* to the nearest dollar how much money he takes home each month after the deductions are taken out.

48. *Checking Account Balance* Karen has $321.45 in her checking account. She makes deposits of $38.97 and $86.23. She writes checks for $23.10, $45.67, and $8.97. *Estimate* the new balance in her checking account.

Use the following bar graph to answer exercises 49–52.

The NASDAQ was founded in 1971 and is the largest U.S. electronic stock market with about 3200 companies. The bar graph shows the closing numbers of the NASDAQ index during a selected week.

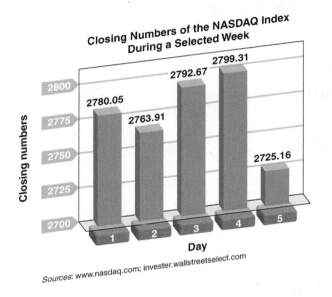

Closing Numbers of the NASDAQ Index During a Selected Week

Sources: www.nasdaq.com; invester.wallstreetselect.com

49. *Estimate* the difference between closing numbers for Day 1 and Day 2.

50. *Estimate* the difference between closing numbers for Day 3 and Day 5.

51. What two days have the largest difference in closing numbers? *Estimate* this difference.

52. What two days have the smallest difference in closing numbers? *Estimate* this difference.

53. *Change from Purchase* Ann spent $72.31 on groceries for her family. If she gives the clerk a 100-dollar bill, how much change should she get?

54. *Odometer Reading* Charles checked his odometer before the summer began. It read 2301.2 miles. He traveled 1236.9 miles that summer in his car. What was the odometer reading at the end of the summer?

55. *Olympic Record* How much faster was the 1988 Olympic 100-meter winning time by Florence Griffith Joyner than the one by Gail Devers in the 1992 Olympics?

56. *Olympic Record* How much slower was the 1960 Olympic 100-meter winning time by Wilma Rudolph than the record set by Evelyn Ashford in 1984?

Women's 100-meter Winning Time

GREECE 2004
10.93, Yuliya Nesterenko, Belarus
SYDNEY 2000
11.12, Ekaterini Thanou, Greece
ATLANTA 1996
10.94, Gail Devers, U.S.
BARCELONA 1992
10.82, Gail Devers, U.S.
SEOUL 1988
10.54, Florence Griffith Joyner, U.S.
LOS ANGELES 1984
10.97, Evelyn Ashford, U.S.
MOSCOW 1980
11.06, Lyudmila Kondratyeva, USSR
MONTREAL 1976
11.08, Annegret Richter, W. Germany
MUNICH 1972
11.07, Renate Stecher, E. Germany
MEXICO CITY 1968
11.08, Wyomia Tyus, U.S.
TOKYO 1964
11.40, Wyomia Tyus, U.S.
ROME 1960
11.00, Wilma Rudolph, U.S.

57. *Olympic Record* What is the difference between the fastest and the slowest 100-meter Olympic winning times for the years 1960 to 2004?

58. *Olympic Record* Which pair or pairs of consecutive Olympic games had the largest difference in 100-meter winning times? Which had the smallest difference?

One Step Further *Perform the operations indicated.*

59. $-2.3 - (-0.24) + 4.6 - 9$

60. $-3.8 - (-0.46) + 8.2 - 14$

61. $\dfrac{3}{10} - 1.26 + (-2.3)$

62. $\dfrac{7}{10} - 4.36 + (-3.1)$

To Think About *Guess the next seven digits in each of the following.*

63. 5.636336333633336...

64. 6.1213314441...

65. 8.181181118...

66. 3.043004300043...

67. 12.98987987698765...

68. 7.6574839201102938...

Cumulative Review *Multiply.*

69. **[1.4.4]** $(231)(14)$

70. **[2.4.1]** $(-12)(92)$

Divide.

71. **[1.5.4]** $2940 \div 12$

72. **[2.4.4]** $3105 \div (-3)$

Quick Quiz 8.2

1. Perform the operations indicated.
   (a) $42.09 + 3.1$
   (b) $5.03 - 2.68$
   (c) $28.61 - (-4.21)$

3. Evaluate. $y - 18.75$ for $y = -20.96$

2. Combine like terms. $5.6x + 2.13x + 9.01$

4. **Concept Check** Explain how you would evaluate $x - 3.1$ for $x = 0.866$.

8.3 MULTIPLYING AND DIVIDING DECIMAL EXPRESSIONS

① Multiplying Decimals

Just as with addition and subtraction, we can relate multiplication of fractions to decimals. For example:

$$\frac{5}{10} \times \frac{9}{100} = \frac{45}{1000} \quad \text{Fractional notation}$$
$$\downarrow \qquad \downarrow \qquad \downarrow$$
$$0.5 \times 0.09 = 0.045 \quad \text{Decimal notation}$$

In both cases we multiply $9 \times 5 = 45$. When we multiply using decimal notation, we must decide where to place the decimal point in the product, 45. We determine this by adding the number of decimal places in each factor.

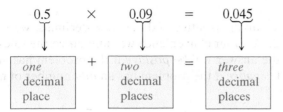

$0.5 \qquad \times \qquad 0.09 \qquad = \qquad 0.045$

| one decimal place | + | two decimal places | = | three decimal places |

PROCEDURE TO MULTIPLY DECIMALS

1. Multiply the numbers just as you would multiply whole numbers.

2. Find the total number of decimal places in the factors.

3. Place the decimal point in the product so that the product has the same number of decimal places as the total in step 2. To do this, you may need to write zeros to the left of the answer from step 1.

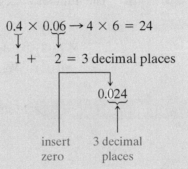

$0.4 \times 0.06 \rightarrow 4 \times 6 = 24$

$1 + \quad 2 = 3 \text{ decimal places}$

0.024

insert zero   3 decimal places

EXAMPLE 1 Multiply. 0.08×0.04

Solution

$0.08 \quad \times \quad 0.04 \rightarrow 8 \times 4 = 32$ Multiply just as you would whole numbers.

$0.08 \quad \times \quad 0.04 \qquad = 0.0032$

| 2 decimal places | + | 2 decimal places | = | 4 decimal places |

Note that we had to insert two zeros to the left of 32 in order to have 4 decimal places in the product.

Practice Problem 1 Multiply. 0.05×0.07

When multiplying larger numbers, it is usually easier to perform the calculation if we multiply vertically, placing the factor with the fewer number of nonzero digits underneath the other factor.

Student Learning Objectives

After studying this section, you will be able to:

① Multiply decimals.

② Multiply a decimal by a power of 10.

③ Divide a decimal by a whole number.

④ Divide a decimal by a decimal.

⑤ Change a fraction to a decimal.

NOTE TO STUDENT: Fully worked-out solutions to all of the Practice Problems can be found at the back of the text starting at page SP-1

EXAMPLE 2 Multiply. 5.33×7.2

Solution We write the multiplication just as we would if there were no decimal points.

$$
\begin{array}{r}
5.33 \quad \text{2 decimal places} \\
\times\ 7.2 \quad \text{1 decimal place} \\
\hline
1066 \\
3731 \\
\hline
38.376 \quad \text{We need 3 decimal places (2 + 1 = 3).}
\end{array}
$$

Note that we *do not* line up the decimal points when we multiply.

Practice Problem 2 Multiply. 20.1×4.32

To multiply or divide positive and negative decimals, we use the same rules stated in Chapter 2. For your convenience we summarize the rules.

The sign of the answer will be *positive* if the problem has an *even* number of negative signs and *negative* if the problem has an *odd* number of negative signs.

EXAMPLE 3 Multiply. $(-2)(4.51)$

Solution The number of negative signs, 1, is odd so the product is negative.

$$
\begin{array}{r}
4.51 \quad \text{2 decimal places} \\
\times\ (-2) \quad \text{0 decimal places} \\
\hline
-9.02 \quad \text{We need 2 decimal places (2 + 0 = 2).}
\end{array}
$$

Practice Problem 3 Multiply. $(-3)(6.22)$

 ## Multiplying a Decimal by a Power of 10

Observe the following pattern.

| *one* zero | Decimal point moves *one* place to the right. |

$0.042 \times 10^1 = 0.042 \times 10 = 0.42$

| *two* zeros | Decimal point moves *two* places to the right. |

$0.042 \times 10^2 = 0.042 \times 100 = 4.2$

| *three* zeros | Decimal point moves *three* places to the right. |

$0.042 \times 10^3 = 0.042 \times 1000 = 42.$

PROCEDURE TO MULTIPLY A DECIMAL BY A POWER OF 10

To multiply a decimal by a power of 10, move the decimal point to the *right* the same number of places as the number of zeros in the power of 10. It may be necessary to add zeros at the end of the number.

 Calculator

Multiplying Decimals

The calculator can be used to verify your work. To find -3×1.4, enter

3 $\boxed{+/-}$ $\times$ 1.4 $\boxed{=}$

The display should read:

$\boxed{-4.2}$

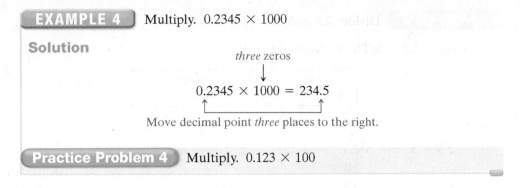

EXAMPLE 4 Multiply. 0.2345×1000

Solution

three zeros

$$0.2345 \times 1000 = 234.5$$

Move decimal point *three* places to the right.

Practice Problem 4 Multiply. 0.123×100

If the number that is a power of 10 is in exponent form, move the decimal point to the right the same number of places as the number that is the exponent.

EXAMPLE 5 Multiply. 15×10^4

Solution Since 10^4 has 4 zeros ($10^4 = 10,000$), we must move the decimal point to the right 4 places.

$$(15)(10^4) = (15.0)(10^4) = 150000. \quad \text{or} \quad 150,000$$

Rewrite in decimal notation.   Add zeros and move decimal point.

Practice Problem 5 Multiply. $(0.6944)(10^3)$

NOTE TO STUDENT: *Fully worked-out solutions to all of the Practice Problems can be found at the back of the text starting at page SP-1*

③ Dividing a Decimal by a Whole Number

Just as with addition, subtraction, and multiplication, the only new rule we must learn when dividing decimal numbers concerns the placement of the decimal point. To divide a decimal by a whole number, we place the decimal point in the quotient directly above the decimal point in the dividend.

To divide $33.6 \div 6$, we proceed as follows.

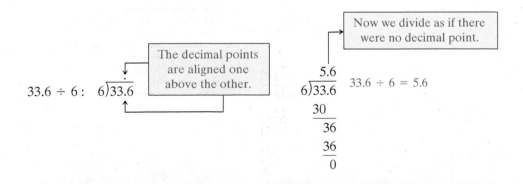

The decimal points are aligned one above the other.

Now we divide as if there were no decimal point.

$$33.6 \div 6 : \quad 6\overline{)33.6}$$

$$\begin{array}{r} 5.6 \\ 6\overline{)33.6} \\ \underline{30} \\ 36 \\ \underline{36} \\ 0 \end{array} \qquad 33.6 \div 6 = 5.6$$

PROCEDURE TO DIVIDE A DECIMAL BY A WHOLE NUMBER

1. Place the decimal point in the answer directly above the decimal point in the dividend.

2. Divide as if there were no decimal point involved.

Often, we must add extra zeros to the right end of the dividend so that we can continue dividing.

EXAMPLE 6   Divide. $2.3 \div 5$

Solution $2.3 \div 5$: Think "5 goes into 2.3."

> We place the decimal point directly above the decimal point in the dividend.

$$
2.3 \div 5 \longrightarrow
\begin{array}{r}
0.4 \\
5\overline{)2.3} \\
\underline{2\,0} \\
3
\end{array}
$$

Now we divide as if there were no decimal point.

$$
\begin{array}{r}
0.46 \\
5\overline{)2.30} \\
\underline{2\,0} \\
30 \\
\underline{30} \\
0
\end{array}
$$

We add a zero so that we can continue to divide.

We bring down a zero.

$$2.3 \div 5 = 0.46$$

Practice Problem 6   Divide. $1.3 \div 2$

Sometimes a division problem does not yield a remainder of zero, or we must carry out the division many decimal places before we get a remainder of zero. In such cases we may be asked to round the answer to a specified place.

EXAMPLE 7   Divide $-0.185 \div 13$. Round your answer to the nearest thousandth.

Solution   We must divide *one place* beyond the thousandths place—that is, to the ten thousandths place—so we can round to the nearest thousandth.

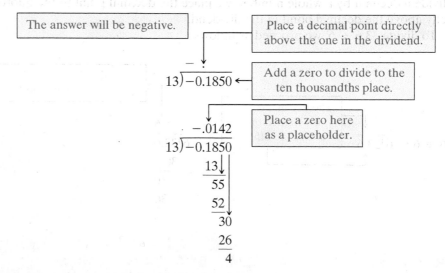

-0.0142 rounded to the nearest thousandth is -0.014; $-0.185 \div 13 \approx -0.014$. Note that we used the symbol $\approx$ to indicate that our answer is an approximate value.

Practice Problem 7   Divide $-0.3624 \div 14$. Round your answer to the nearest hundredth.

Dividing a Decimal by a Decimal

So far we have considered only division by whole numbers. When the *divisor is not a whole number,* we must adjust the placement of the decimal point so that we have an equivalent division problem with a whole number as the divisor.

EXAMPLE 8   Divide. $6.93 \div 2.2$

Solution   Since the divisor, 2.2, is *not* a whole number, let's write the division problem using fractional notation.

$$6.93 \div 2.2 = \frac{6.93}{2.2}$$

Now, if we multiply the numerator and denominator by 10, the divisor becomes a whole number.

$$\frac{(6.93)(10)}{(2.2)(10)} = \frac{69.3}{22} = 69.3 \div 22 \quad \text{The divisor is a whole number.}$$

Once the divisor is a whole number, we can divide as usual.

$$
\begin{array}{r}
3.15 \\
22\overline{)69.30} \\
\end{array}
$$
   We add a zero so that we can continue the division.

$$
\begin{array}{r}
66 \\
\hline
33 \\
22 \\
\hline
110 \\
110 \\
\hline
0 \\
\end{array}
$$

$6.93 \div 2.2 = 3.15$

Practice Problem 8   Divide. $14.56 \div 3.5$

NOTE TO STUDENT: *Fully worked-out solutions to all of the Practice Problems can be found at the back of the text starting at page SP-1*

Since multiplying by a power of 10 is the same as moving the decimal point to the *right,* we could have rewritten the division statement in Example 8 by moving the decimal point to the right one place in both the divisor and dividend.

$6.93 \div 2.2$ Move the decimal point one place to the right.

or

$69.3 \div 22.0$ The divisor is a whole number.

We can summarize the process for dividing with decimals as follows.

PROCEDURE TO DIVIDE WITH DECIMALS

1. If the divisor is a decimal, change it to a whole number by moving the decimal point to the right as many places as necessary.

2. Then move the decimal point in the dividend to the right the *same* number of places.

3. Place the decimal point in the answer directly above the decimal point in the dividend.

4. Divide until the remainder becomes zero, or the remainder repeats itself, or the desired number of decimal places is achieved.

EXAMPLE 9   Divide. $0.7 \div 1.5$

Solution

The divisor is *not* a whole number.
↓

1.5)0.7   Move the decimal point *one place* to the right.

Now that the divisor is a whole number, we rewrite the problem and divide.

$$
\begin{array}{r}
0.466 \\
15\overline{)7.000} \\
6\,0 \\
\hline
1\,00 \\
90 \\
\hline
100 \\
90 \\
\hline
10
\end{array}
$$
Add zeros.

Decimals that have a digit, or a group of digits, that repeats are called **repeating decimals.** We often indicate the repeating pattern with a bar over the repeating group of digits. Thus $0.7 \div 1.5 = 0.4\overline{6}$ because if we continued dividing, the 6 would repeat.

Practice Problem 9   Divide. $1.1 \div 1.8$

Changing a Fraction to a Decimal

Earlier we saw how to change fractions to decimals when the fraction had a power of 10 as a denominator: $\frac{2}{10} = 0.2$, $\frac{3}{100} = 0.03$, and so on. In this section we see how to change fractions whose denominators are not a power of 10 to decimals.

The fraction $\frac{21}{5}$ can be written as $21 \div 5$. Thus, to change a fraction to a decimal, we divide the numerator by the denominator.

Fraction	*Division*	*Decimal*
$\dfrac{21}{5}$ =	$21 \div 5$ =	4.2

PROCEDURE TO CONVERT A FRACTION TO A DECIMAL

Divide the denominator into the numerator until

(a) the remainder becomes zero, *or*

(b) the remainder repeats itself, *or*

(c) the desired number of decimal places is achieved.

EXAMPLE 10 Write as a decimal. $5\dfrac{7}{11}$

Solution

We divide.

$$5\dfrac{7}{11} \text{ means } 5 + \boxed{\dfrac{7}{11}}$$

$$
\begin{array}{r}
0.6363 \\
11\overline{)7.000} \\
66 \\
\hline
40 \\
33 \\
\hline
70 \\
66 \\
\hline
40 \\
33
\end{array}
$$

We can see that the pattern repeats

Thus $\dfrac{7}{11} = 0.\overline{63}$ and $5\dfrac{7}{11} = 5.\overline{63}$.

Practice Problem 10 Write as a decimal.

$$2\dfrac{5}{11}$$

NOTE TO STUDENT: Fully worked-out solutions to all of the Practice Problems can be found at the back of the text starting at page SP-1

Developing Your Study Skills

Preparing for the Final Exam

To do well on the final exam, you should begin to prepare many weeks before the exam. Cramming for any test, especially the final one, often causes anxiety and fatigue and impairs your performance. Complete the following in several 1- to 2-hour study sessions.

- Review all your tests and quizzes.
- Ask your instructor or tutor how to work the problems you missed and still do not understand.
- Complete the Cumulative Test for Chapters 1–8.
- Complete any review sheets that your instructor has given you.
- If you come across a topic that you cannot understand even after seeking assistance, move on to another topic. When you finish reviewing all the topics for the final exam, return to this topic and try again.
- Find a few students in your class to study with. When you study in groups, you can help each other. Discussing mathematics with others in the group (verbalizing) is an important part of the learning cycle.
- Repeat this process after Chapter 9.
- Finally, get a good night's sleep the night before the final.

Verbal and Writing Skills *Fill in the blanks.*

1. If one factor has 4 decimal places and the second factor has 2 decimal places, the product has _____ decimal places.

2. If one factor has 4 decimal places and the second factor has 3 decimal place, the product has _____ decimal places.

3. When we divide $4.62\overline{)12.7}$, we rewrite the equivalent division problem _____ and then divide.

4. When we divide $8.23\overline{)19.2}$, we rewrite the equivalent division problem _____ and then divide.

Multiply.

5. 0.03×0.04

6. 0.09×0.02

7. 0.05×0.07

8. 0.05×0.06

9. 7.43×8.3

10. 2.5×6.34

11. 15.2×4.3

12. 21.7×2.2

13. $(-3)(2.35)$

14. $(-7)(2.13)$

15. $(-4.23)(2.7)$

16. $(-3.16)(4.1)$

17. $(-25)(-0.613)$

18. $(-31)(-0.314)$

19. $(12.1)(-2.81)$

20. $(-11.3)(4.11)$

Multiply by powers of 10.

21. 0.1498×100

22. 0.1931×100

23. $8.554 \times 10,000$

24. $96.12 \times 10,000$

25. 41×10^4

26. 35×10^3

27. 0.6×10^4

28. 0.4×10^3

Divide.

29. $17.28 \div 8$

30. $12.6 \div 6$

31. $3.22 \div 14$

32. $5.12 \div 16$

33. $3.616 \div 64$

34. $12.6672 \div 39$

35. $82.824 \div 24$

36. $44.95 \div 31$

Divide. Round your answer to the nearest hundredth when necessary.

37. $3.25 \div 14$

38. $8.23 \div 11$

39. $-0.2988 \div 3.7$

40. $-0.2726 \div 2.9$

41. $-20.8 \div (-1.7)$

42. $-36.5 \div (-1.6)$

43. $8.343 \div 0.27$

44. $8.378 \div 0.41$

45. $13.7592 \div 5.88$

46. $15.4947 \div 4.11$

Divide. If a repeating decimal is obtained, use notation such as $0.\overline{9}$ or $0.\overline{14}$.

47. $3 \div 1.8$ **48.** $14 \div 1.5$ **49.** $0.6 \div 1.1$ **50.** $0.5 \div 3.7$

51. $11.3 \div 2.2$ **52.** $100 \div 3.3$ **53.** $200 \div 6.6$ **54.** $140 \div 1.5$

Write as a decimal. Round to the nearest hundredth.

55. $\dfrac{11}{6}$ **56.** $\dfrac{15}{7}$ **57.** $12\dfrac{7}{15}$ **58.** $14\dfrac{3}{16}$

Divide. If a repeating decimal is obtained, use notation such as $0.\overline{9}$ or $0.\overline{14}$.

59. $\dfrac{1}{3}$ **60.** $\dfrac{1}{6}$ **61.** $\dfrac{2}{15}$ **62.** $\dfrac{9}{11}$

Mixed Practice *Divide. If a repeating decimal is obtained, use notation such as $0.\overline{9}$ or $0.\overline{14}$.*

63. $20.35 \div 0.44$ **64.** $16.87 \div 0.35$

65. $\dfrac{2}{9}$ **66.** $\dfrac{5}{12}$

Multiply.

67. -3.5×4.24 **68.** -5.7×3.22

69. 0.4×0.8 **70.** 0.6×0.9

Applications

71. *Detecting Motion* A fly can detect motion in $\frac{1}{300}$ of a second, whereas the human eye detects motion in $\frac{1}{30}$ of a second.

  (a) Write $\frac{1}{300}$ of a second as a decimal.

  (b) Write $\frac{1}{30}$ of a second as a decimal.

72. *Inheritance* Erin inherited $\frac{1}{3}$ of her father's estate, and the family's favorite charity inherited $\frac{1}{60}$ of his estate.

  (a) Write $\frac{1}{3}$ as a decimal.

  (b) Write $\frac{1}{60}$ as a decimal.

Divide. Round to the nearest thousandth.

73. $-562.53 \div 13.123$

74. $-2104.03 \div 0.2346$

To Think About *Observe the pattern and then fill in the table with the missing values.*

75.

Fraction	$\frac{1}{9}$	$\frac{2}{9}$	$\frac{3}{9}$	$\frac{4}{9}$	$\frac{5}{9}$
Decimal	$0.11\ldots$	$0.22\ldots$	$0.33\ldots$		

76.

Fraction	$\frac{1}{11}$	$\frac{2}{11}$	$\frac{3}{11}$	$\frac{4}{11}$	$\frac{5}{11}$	$\frac{6}{11}$	$\frac{7}{11}$
Decimal	$0.\overline{09}$	$0.\overline{18}$	$0.\overline{27}$	$0.\overline{36}$			

Cumulative Review *Solve and check your solution.*

77. **[3.2.1]** $12x = 96$

78. **[3.1.2]** $x - 25 = -30$

79. **[3.1.2]** $x + 45 = 17$

80. **[3.2.1]** $15x = 225$

Quick Quiz 8.3

1. Multiply.
  (a) $(5.07)(3.1)$
  (b) $(4.39)(10^3)$

3. Write as a decimal. $\frac{29}{9}$

2. Divide. $36.54 \div 6.3$

4. **Concept Check** Marc multiplied 0.097×0.5 and obtained the answer 0.485. Is Marc's answer correct? Why or why not?

8.6 PERCENTS

We use percents in business, science, sports, and our everyday life: a suit you want to buy is on sale for 25% off; you receive a 5% increase in pay; and so on. What does this mean? How do we calculate percents? In this section we gain the knowledge to answer these questions.

Student Learning Objectives

After studying this section, you will be able to:

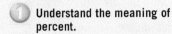 Understand the meaning of percent.

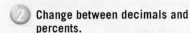 Change between decimals and percents.

③ Change between fractions, decimals, and percents.

① Understanding the Meaning of Percent

As stated in Section 8.5 we use decimals, fractions, or percents to describe parts of a whole. **Percents** can be described as ratios whose denominators are 100. The symbol % means "parts per 100." For example, 17% means 17 out of 100 parts.

It is important to know that 17% means 17 out of 100 parts. It can also be written $\frac{17}{100}$. Understanding the meaning of the notation allows you to work with percents as well as change from one notation to another.

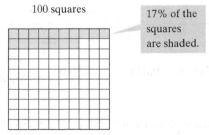

100 squares

17% of the squares are shaded.

17 of 100 squares are shaded.

EXAMPLE 1 State using percents. 13 out of 100 radios are defective.

Solution

$$\frac{13}{100} = 13\% \quad \text{13\% of the radios are defective.}$$

Practice Problem 1 State using percents. 42 out of 100 students in the class voted.

Percents can be larger than 100% or less than 1%. Consider the following situations.

EXAMPLE 2 Last year's attendance at the school's winter formal was 100 students. This year the attendance was 121. Write this year's attendance as a percent of last year's.

Solution We must write this year's attendance (121) as a percent of last year's (100).

$$\text{This year's attendance} \rightarrow \frac{121}{100} = 121\%$$
$$\text{Last year's attendance} \rightarrow 100$$

This year's attendance at the formal was 121% of last year's.

Note that we have 121 parts out of 100 parts, which means we have *more than* one whole amount and thus more than 100%.

Practice Problem 2 Ten years ago a lawn mower cost $100. Now the average price for a lawn mower is $215. Write the present cost as a percent of the cost ten years ago.

EXAMPLE 3   There are 100 milliliters (mL) of solution in a container. Sara takes 0.3 mL of the solution. What percentage of the solution does Sara take?

Solution   Sara takes 0.3 mL out of 100 mL, or

$$\frac{0.3}{100} = 0.3\% \text{ of the solution}$$

Practice Problem 3   There are 100 mL of solution in a container. Julio takes 0.7 mL of the solution. What percentage of the solution does Julio take?

NOTE TO STUDENT: Fully worked-out solutions to all of the Practice Problems can be found at the back of the text starting at page SP-1

 Changing Between Decimals and Percents

Earlier we saw how to change between fractional and decimal notation. We review below.

Fraction → Decimal	Decimal → Fraction
$\dfrac{5}{8} = 5 \div 8 = 0.625$	$0.625 = \dfrac{625}{1000} = \dfrac{5}{8}$

Now we combine this skill with our knowledge of percents to see how to change between percents and decimals. Observe the pattern in the following illustrations.

We write a decimal as a percent.

Decimal → Percent

$$0.27 = \frac{27}{100} = 27\% \text{ or } 27.0\%$$

$$0.27 \quad = \quad 27.0\%$$

Decimal point moves 2 places to the *right*.

We reverse the process to write a percent as a decimal.

Decimal ← Percent

$$0.27 \quad = \quad 27.0\%$$

Decimal point moves 2 places to the *left*.

When we say we "move" the decimal point to the *right* to change a decimal to a percent, we mean we are multiplying by 100, which gives us the same result. When we say we "move" the decimal point 2 places to the *left*, we are really dividing by 100. We summarize below.

PROCEDURE TO CHANGE BETWEEN PERCENTS AND DECIMALS

To write a decimal as a percent:

1. Move the decimal point 2 places to the *right*.
2. Write the percent symbol at the end of the number.

Decimal → Percent

$$0.712 \quad = \quad 71.2\%$$

To write a percent as a decimal:

1. Move the decimal point 2 places to the *left*.
2. Drop the percent symbol.

Decimal ← Percent

$$0.712 \quad = \quad 71.2\%$$

Using the following chart can be helpful when changing between decimal and percent form since the decimal point moves the same direction as you move on the chart.

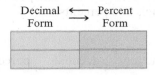

Decimal ⟷ Percent
Form   Form

EXAMPLE 4

(a) Write 3.8% as a decimal.   **(b)** Write 0.009 as a percent.

Solution

(a)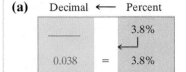

Decimal ⟵ Percent   We write the chart.

| 3.8% |

We move *left* on the chart, so the decimal point moves *2 places left*.

0.038 = 3.8%   We must place an extra zero to the left of the 3.

(b)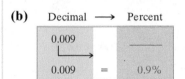

Decimal ⟶ Percent   We write the chart.

0.009

We move *right* on the chart, so the decimal point moves *2 places right*.

0.009 = 0.9%

Practice Problem 4   **(a)** Write 2.6% as a decimal.

(b) Write 0.001 as a percent.

EXAMPLE 5   Complete the table of equivalent notations.

Decimal Form	Percent Form
0.457	
	58.2%
	0.6%
2.9	

Solution

Decimal Form	Percent Form
0.457	45.7%
0.582	58.2%
0.006	0.6%
2.9	290%

We must insert two zeros. → (row 0.006)

← We must insert a zero. (row 2.9 / 290%)

Practice Problem 5   Complete the table of equivalent notations.

Decimal Form	Percent Form
0.511	
	84.1%
	0.2%
6.7	

Changing Between Fractions, Decimals, and Percents

Now that you can change between decimals and percents, you are ready to change between fractions and decimals and percents.

$$\text{fraction} \underset{\longrightarrow}{\overset{\longleftarrow}{}} \text{decimal} \underset{\longrightarrow}{\overset{\longleftarrow}{}} \text{percent}$$

EXAMPLE 6

(a) Write $\dfrac{211}{500}$ as a percent.   **(b)** Write 42.2% as a fraction.

Solution

(a) Using a chart often helps.

Fraction	$\longrightarrow$	Decimal	$\longrightarrow$	Percent	
$\dfrac{211}{500}$	$\rightarrow$	0.422		?	Compute: $211 \div 500 = 0.422$.
$\dfrac{211}{500}$	$\rightarrow$	0.422	$\rightarrow$	42.2%	Move the decimal point 2 places to the right.

(b) We reverse the process to write 42.2% as a fraction.

Fraction	$\longleftarrow$	Decimal	$\longleftarrow$	Percent	
?		0.422	$\leftarrow$	42.2%	Move the decimal point 2 places to the left.
$\dfrac{211}{500}$	$\leftarrow$	0.422	$\leftarrow$	42.2%	$0.422 = \dfrac{422}{1000} = \dfrac{211}{500}$.

NOTE TO STUDENT: Fully worked-out solutions to all of the Practice Problems can be found at the back of the text starting at page SP-1

Practice Problem 6

(a) Write $\dfrac{7}{40}$ as a percent.   **(b)** Write 17.5% as a fraction.

Changing some fractions to decimals results in a repeating decimal. For example, $\frac{1}{3} = 0.333\ldots$. In such cases, we usually round as directed. If we are not asked to round, we use a notation such as $0.\overline{3}$.

EXAMPLE 7

(a) Write $\dfrac{5}{9}$ as a percent. Round to the nearest hundredth of a percent.

(b) Write $\dfrac{1}{4}\%$ as a fraction.

Solution

(a) First we change $\frac{5}{9}$ to a decimal: $5 \div 9 = 0.55555\ldots$. We must carry out the division at least *five* places beyond the decimal point so that we can move the decimal point to the right *two* places, and we then round to the nearest hundredth of a percent.

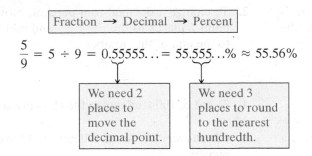

$$\frac{5}{9} = 5 \div 9 = 0.55555\ldots = 55.555\ldots\% \approx 55.56\%$$

We need 2 places to move the decimal point.

We need 3 places to round to the nearest hundredth.

Remember that if you are *not* asked to round, $\frac{5}{9} = 55.\overline{5}\%$.

(b) A percent can be written in the form of a whole number, fraction, or decimal. $\frac{1}{4}\%$ is a percent written in fraction form. We can rewrite the percent in its decimal form so that we can use the decimal shift method.

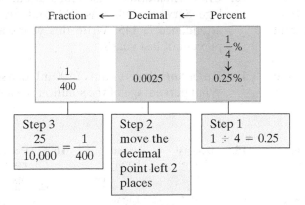

Fraction ← Decimal ← Percent

$$\frac{1}{400} \qquad 0.0025 \qquad \frac{1}{4}\% \downarrow 0.25\%$$

Step 3
$$\frac{25}{10,000} = \frac{1}{400}$$

Step 2
move the decimal point left 2 places

Step 1
$1 \div 4 = 0.25$

Practice Problem 7

(a) Write $\frac{3}{7}$ as a percent. Round to the nearest hundredth of a percent.

(b) Write $\frac{1}{5}\%$ as a fraction.

Certain percents occur very often, especially in money matters. Here are some common equivalents that you may already know. If not, be sure to memorize them.

$$\frac{1}{4} = 0.25 = 25\% \qquad \frac{1}{3} = 0.3\overline{3} = 33\frac{1}{3}\% \qquad \frac{1}{10} = 0.10 = 10\%$$

$$\frac{1}{2} = 0.5 = 50\% \qquad \frac{2}{3} = 0.6\overline{6} = 66\frac{2}{3}\% \qquad \frac{3}{4} = 0.75 = 75\%$$

Verbal and Writing Skills *Fill in the blanks.*

1. To change a percent to a decimal, move the decimal point 2 places to the _____ and drop the _____ .

2. To change a decimal to a percent, move the decimal point 2 places to the _____ and add the _____ to the end of the number.

State the percents.

3. 42 out of 100 students in the class voted.

4. 71 out of 100 students in the class are women.

5. **Radar Navigation** 63 out of 100 power boats had a radar navigation system.

6. **CD Players** 97 out of 100 new cars have compact disc players.

7. **Electric Toothbrushes** 28 out of 100 people use electric toothbrushes. What percentage of people use electric toothbrushes?

8. **Organized Sports** 58 out of 100 people play organized sports. What percentage of people play organized sports?

9. **School Attendance** Last year's attendance at the medical school was 100 students. This year the attendance is 113. Write this year's attendance as a percent of last year's.

10. **Club Attendance** Last year's attendance at the College Service Club was 100 students. This year the attendance is 145. Write this year's attendance as a percent of last year's.

11. **Grams of Fat** 0.9 out of 100 grams of fat is saturated fat. What percentage is saturated fat?

12. **Water Solution** 0.7 out of 100 mL of a solution is water. What percentage of the solution is water?

Complete each table of equivalent notations.

13.

Decimal Form	Percent Form
0.576	
	24.9%
	0.3%
1.546	

14.

Decimal Form	Percent Form
0.139	
	57.8%
	0.9%
5.612	

15.

Decimal Form	Percent Form
3.7	
	23.8%
	0.6%
12.882	

16.

Decimal Form	Percent Form
2.8	
	42.4%
	0.1%
13.145	

17. Write 36% as a decimal.

18. Write 61% as a decimal.

19. Write 53.8% as a decimal.

20. Write 24.4% as a decimal.

21. Write 0.075 as a percent.

22. Write 0.007 as a percent.

23. Write 2.33% as a decimal.

24. Write 5.2% as a decimal.

25. In Alaska, 0.03413 of the state is covered by water. Write the part of the state that is covered by water as a percent.

26. In Florida, 0.07689 of the state is covered by water. Write the part of the state that is covered by water as a percent.

Complete each table of equivalent notations.

27.

Fraction Form	Decimal Form	Percent Form
$\frac{4}{5}$		
	0.27	
		0.7%
$4\frac{1}{3}$		

28.

Fraction Form	Decimal Form	Percent Form
$\frac{9}{12}$		
	0.61	
		2.8%
$9\frac{5}{8}$		

29.

Fraction Form	Decimal Form	Percent Form
$\frac{5}{16}$		
	2.6	
		$\frac{1}{10}$%
$6\frac{1}{2}$		

30.

Fraction Form	Decimal Form	Percent Form
$\frac{8}{15}$		
	3.5	
		$\frac{1}{8}$%
$5\frac{1}{4}$		

31. Write $\frac{4}{32}$ as a percent.

32. Write $\frac{129}{250}$ as a percent.

33. Write $\frac{1}{5}$% as a fraction.

34. Write $\frac{1}{2}$% as a fraction.

35. (a) Write $\frac{14}{40}$ as a percent.

    (b) Write 22.3% as a fraction.

36. (a) Write $\frac{32}{80}$ as a percent.

    (b) Write 72.1% as a fraction.

37. *Seamstress* A seamstress wastes $1\frac{1}{4}$% of the material used to make a dress. Write this percent as a fraction.

38. *Photo Paper* Arran Copy Center wastes $2\frac{1}{2}$% of its paper supply due to poor quality of the photocopies produced. Write this percent as a fraction.

39. *Brain Size* The brain represents $\frac{1}{40}$ of an average person's weight. Express this fraction as a percent.

40. *Blinking the Eye* During waking hours a person blinks $\frac{9}{2000}$ of the time. Express the fraction as a percent.

Write each fraction as a percent. Round to the nearest hundredth of a percent.

41. $\frac{9}{14}$

42. $\frac{16}{35}$

43. $\frac{7}{9}$

44. $\frac{4}{9}$

Applications *Use the bar graph to answer exercises 45–49.*

Prescription Drugs In 1980 5.5% of all personal health care spending was for prescription drugs, compared to 10.2% in 2000. Write as a fraction the percent of health care costs that was spent on prescription drugs for the following years.

45. 1980

46. 1990

47. 2002

48. 2007

49. 2010

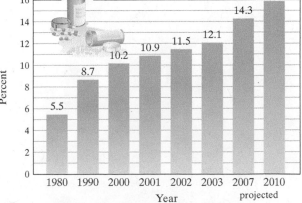

Drug Costs as a Percentage of All Personal Health Spending

Year	Percent
1980	5.5
1990	8.7
2000	10.2
2001	10.9
2002	11.5
2003	12.1
2007	14.3
2010 projected	15.9

Source: National Health Care Expenditures Projections: 2000–2010

To Think About *Observe the pattern and then fill in the table with the missing values.*

50.

Fraction	$\frac{1}{10}$	$\frac{2}{10}$	$\frac{3}{10}$	$\frac{4}{10}$	$\frac{5}{10}$
Percent	10%	20%			50%

51.

Fraction	$\frac{1}{5}$	$\frac{2}{5}$	$\frac{3}{5}$	$\frac{4}{5}$	$\frac{5}{5}$
Percent	20%	40%			100%

52.

Fraction	2	$2\frac{1}{4}$	$2\frac{1}{2}$	$2\frac{3}{4}$	3
Percent	200%		250%		300%

53.

Fraction	4	$4\frac{1}{8}$	$4\frac{2}{8}$	$4\frac{3}{8}$	$4\frac{4}{8}$	$4\frac{5}{8}$
Percent	400%	412.5%			450%	462.5%

Cumulative Review *Translate and solve.*

54. **[3.2.3]** Three times what number is equal to forty-eight?

55. **[3.2.3]** Twice what number is equal to three hundred thirty?

56. **[5.1.3]** One-fourth of what number is equal to 60?

57. **[5.1.3]** What is one-third of sixty-nine?

58. **[8.2.5]** *Apartment Expenses* The utility bills for an apartment are as follows: $64.55, phone; $34.50, gas; $55.90, electricity. If the total cost of utilities is divided equally among the three roommates, how much must each contribute?

59. **[8.2.5]** *Land Mass* The area of the United States is 3.7 million square miles, while the area of Antarctica is 5.1 million square miles. What is the difference in area between the United States and Antarctica?

Quick Quiz 8.6 Complete the table of equivalent notations.

	Fraction Form	Decimal Form	Percent Form
1.	$\frac{15}{24}$	(a)	(b)
2.	(a)	0.14	(b)
3.	(a)	(b)	0.05%

4. **Concept Check** Explain how you would change 0.43% to a decimal, then to a fraction.

1 Translating and Solving Percent Problems

Percents are used to describe parts of a whole base amount. For example, 75% describes the amount: *3 parts out of 4.*

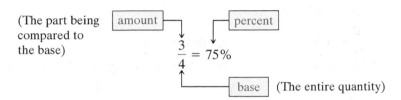

We know that the fraction $\frac{3}{4} = 75\%$. Now let's look at each of the three parts of this relationship—3, 4, and 75%.

(The part being compared to the base)
amount
percent

$$\frac{3}{4} = 75\%$$

base (The entire quantity)

We can write the relationship $\frac{3}{4} = 75\%$ as *amount = percent × base.*

$$\text{amount} = \text{percent} \times \text{base}$$
$$3 = 75\% \times 4$$

When one of the parts of the relationship (percent, amount, or base) is unknown we can solve the equation for the unknown quantity.

It should be noted that a *percent* is used primarily for comparative and descriptive purposes. *When we perform calculations with percents we must first change the percent to its equivalent decimal or fraction form and then perform the calculations.*

To solve applied percent problems, we must understand what each of these three parts means. Therefore, we draw a picture of each situation. Then we translate the statement by replacing "of" with ×; "is" with =; "find" with $n =$; "what" with n; "percent" with %.

EXAMPLE 1 Translate into an equation and solve.

(a) What is 25% of 40?   **(b)** 10 is 25% of what number?

(c) 10 is what percent of 40?

Solution We translate each into the form amount = percent × base .

(a) What is 25% of 40?
$\downarrow \quad \downarrow \quad \downarrow \quad \downarrow \quad \downarrow$

$n \;=\; 25\% \times 40$ Write in symbols.

We want to find the *amount,* that is, the *part of* (25% of) the *base* of 40.

$n =\ 25\%\ \text{of } 40$

$n =\ 0.25\ \times\ 40$ Change 25% to decimal form.

$n = 10$ Multiply.

10 is 25% of 40.

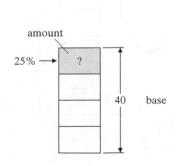

Student Learning Objectives

After studying this section, you will be able to:

 Translate and solve percent problems.

 Solve applied percent problems using equations.

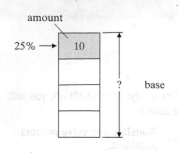

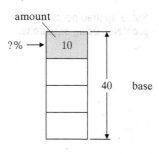

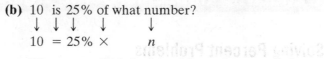

(b) 10 is 25% of what number?

$$10 = 25\% \times n$$

We want to find the *base* (the entire quantity).

$$10 = 0.25 \times n \quad \text{Change 25\% to a decimal.}$$

$$\frac{10}{0.25} = n \quad \text{Solve the equation for } n.$$

$$40 = n \quad \text{Divide.}$$

10 is 25% of 40.

(c) 10 is what percent of 40?

$$10 = n \quad \% \quad \times \quad 40$$

We want to find the *percent*.

$$10 = n\% \times 40$$

$$\frac{10}{40} = n\% \quad \text{Solve the equation for } n\%.$$

$$0.25 = n\% \quad \text{The \% symbol reminds us to write 0.25 as a percent.}$$

$$25 = n$$

10 is 25% of 40.

Note that when forming the equation we used the percent symbol, %, to represent the word *percent* and remind us that the answer must be in percent form.

NOTE TO STUDENT: *Fully worked-out solutions to all of the Practice Problems can be found at the back of the text starting at page SP-1*

Practice Problem 1 Translate into an equation and solve.

(a) What is 40% of 90? **(b)** 36 is 40% of what number?

(c) 36 is what percent of 90?

Sometimes we have more than 100%—this means that the *amount* is more than the *base*.

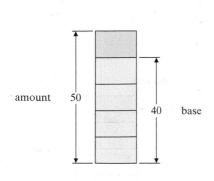

EXAMPLE 2 Translate into an equation and solve. 50 is what percent of 40?

Solution We should expect to get more than 100% since 50 is more than the base 40.

$$50 \text{ is what percent of } 40?$$

$$50 = n \quad \% \quad \times 40$$

$$50 = n\% \times 40$$

$$\frac{50}{40} = n\% \quad \text{Solve for } n\%.$$

$$1.25 = n\% \quad \text{Divide.}$$

$$125 = n$$

50 is 125% of 40.

Practice Problem 2 Translate into an equation and solve. 80 is what percent of 20?

CAUTION: We must remember to change the percent to its equivalent decimal or fraction form before we perform calculations.

EXAMPLE 3   Find 55% of 36.

Solution

$$\begin{array}{ccccc} \text{Find} & 55\% & \text{of} & 36. \\ \downarrow & \downarrow & \downarrow & \downarrow \end{array}$$

$$\begin{aligned} n &= 55\% \times 36 && \text{Translate "}find\text{" to } n = \text{ since it has the same} \\ & && \text{meaning as "}what\ is\text{."} \\ &= 0.55 \times 36 && \text{Change 55\% to a decimal.} \\ &= 19.8 && \text{Multiply.} \end{aligned}$$

19.8 is 55% of 36.

Practice Problem 3   Find 22% of 60.

Solving Applied Percent Problems Using Equations

We can solve applied problems that involve percents by using the following three-step process.

> **PROCEDURE TO SOLVE APPLIED PERCENT PROBLEMS**
>
> 1. Write a percent statement to represent the situation.
> 2. Translate the statement into an equation.
> 3. Solve the equation.

EXAMPLE 4   Marilyn has 850 out of 1000 points possible in her English class. What percent of the total points does Marilyn have?

Solution   We must find the *percent,* so we write the statement that represents the percent situation.

$$\begin{array}{cccccc} 850 & \text{is} & \text{what} & \text{percent} & \text{of} & 1000? \\ \downarrow & \downarrow & \downarrow & \downarrow & \downarrow & \downarrow \end{array}$$

$$\begin{aligned} 850 &= n \quad\% \times 1000 && \text{Form an equation.} \\ \frac{850}{1000} &= n\% && \text{Solve the equation.} \\ 0.85 &= n\% \\ 85 &= n \end{aligned}$$

Marilyn has 85% of the total points.

There are several ways to write equivalent statements for a percent situation. We could have written, "What percent of 1000 is 850?" Try translating and solving this statement to verify that it is equivalent.

Practice Problem 4   Alisha received 35 out of 50 points on a quiz. What percent of the total points did Alisha earn on the quiz?

NOTE TO STUDENT: Fully worked-out solutions to all of the Practice Problems can be found at the back of the text starting at page SP-1

EXAMPLE 5 Sean's bill for his dinner at the Spaghetti House was $19.75. How much should he leave for a 15% tip? Round this amount to the nearest cent.

Solution We must find the *amount,* that is, the *part of* (15% of) the *base* of $19.75.

What is 15% of $19.75?   Write the statement for this situation.

$$n = 15\% \times \$19.75 \qquad \text{Form an equation.}$$
$$= 0.15 \times \$19.75$$
$$= 2.9625 \qquad \text{Solve the equation.}$$
$$\approx \$2.96 \qquad \text{Round.}$$

The tip is $2.96.

Note that rounding to the nearest cent is the same as rounding to the nearest hundredth. Why?

Practice Problem 5 Frances left a $3.50 tip for her dinner, which cost $18.55. What percent of the total bill did Frances leave for a tip? Round your answer to the nearest hundredth of a percent.

What do we mean when we say "100% of the price of an item"? We are referring to the *entire price* of the item. That is, if a sofa costs $400 then 100% of the cost of the sofa is $400. If an item costs x dollars, then 100% $x = the price of the item.$ We often write x as 100%x when we are dealing with markup problems.

EXAMPLE 6 Sergio stayed in a luxury hotel on a Saturday night and paid $230 for that night. If the rate on Saturday night is 15% higher than it is on Sunday night, how much will Sergio pay for the room on Sunday night?

Solution *Understand the problem.*

Mathematics Blueprint for Problem Solving

Gather the Facts	What Am I Asked to Do?	How Do I Proceed?	Key Points to Remember
Room rate for Saturday night is $230. The Saturday night rate is 15% *higher* than the rate on Sunday.	Find the room rate for Sunday.	Let x = the room rate on Sunday. Find the sum: The Sunday night rate *plus* the markup equals the Saturday night rate.	The markup is 15% of the rate on Sunday.

Calculate and state the answer.

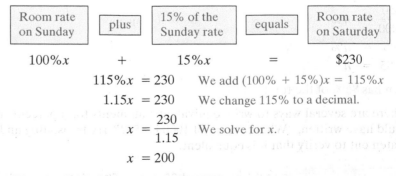

Room rate on Sunday	plus	15% of the Sunday rate	equals	Room rate on Saturday
100%x	+	15%x	=	$230

$$115\%x = 230 \qquad \text{We add } (100\% + 15\%)x = 115\%x$$
$$1.15x = 230 \qquad \text{We change 115\% to a decimal.}$$
$$x = \frac{230}{1.15} \qquad \text{We solve for } x.$$
$$x = 200$$

Sergio will pay a rate of $200 to stay Sunday night.

Practice Problem 6 Refer to Example 6 to answer the following. If the rate on Saturday night is 20% higher than it is on Sunday night, how much will Sergio pay to stay Sunday? Round to the nearest cent.

Verbal and Writing Skills

Since we use the following percents often, we should memorize them.

25% of a number is the same as $\frac{1}{4}$ of the number.   50% of a number is the same as $\frac{1}{2}$ of the number.

Knowing these facts, explain why it is obvious that there is an error in the following statements.

1. 35 is 50% of 40.

2. 50% of 30 is 40.

3. 25% of 10 is 9.

4. 200 is 25% of 60.

Each of the following requires finding the "amount" of a number in a percent equation.

Translate into an equation and solve.

5. What is 32% of 90?

6. What is 26% of 72?

7. Find 26% of 145.

8. Find 53% of 210.

9. What is 52% of 60?

10. What is 18% of 66?

11. What is 150% of 40?

12. What is 120% of 36?

Applications *Solve each applied problem by finding the "amount" of a number in the percent equation.*

13. Restaurant Tip The bill for Bui's dinner was $18.45. How much should he leave for a 15% tip? Round your answer to the nearest cent.

14. Farm Acres The Boyd farm is 250 acres. 70% of it is suitable land for farming. How many acres can be used to farm?

15. Transfer Students 60% of the graduates of Trinity, a two-year college, transfer to a four-year college. If the graduating class at Trinity has 650 students, how many are transferring to a four-year college?

16. Defective Parts H&B Manufacturing claims that no more than 0.5% of its parts are defective. If a client orders 8600 parts from H&B Manufacturing, what is the largest number of parts that could be defective?

Each of the following requires finding a "percent" in the percent equation.

Translate into an equation and solve. Round to the nearest hundredth of a percent.

17. 54 is what percent of 30?

18. 400 is what percent of 80?

19. What percent of 650 is 70?

20. What percent of 350 is 20?

21. What percent of 60 is 18?

22. What percent of 120 is 15?

Solve each applied problem by finding the "percent" in the percent equation.

23. Calories and Fat A snack bar has 80 calories. If 15 of those calories are from fat, what percent of the calories are from fat?

24. Sales Tax Wesley paid $21 tax when he bought a mountain bike for $300. What percent tax did he pay?

25. Soccer In a soccer game Tasha made 2 out of 5 shots on goal. What percent of shots did she make?

26. Basketball On the Almen High School basketball team, 9 out of the 24 players are over 6 feet tall. What percent of the players are over 6 feet tall?

Each of the following requires finding the "base" in a percent equation.

Translate into an equation and solve.

27. 56 is 70% of what number?

28. 72 is 25% of what number?

29. 24 is 40% of what number?

30. 32 is 64% of what number?

31. 70 is 20% of what number?

32. 90 is 45% of what number?

Solve each applied problem by finding the "base" in the percent equation.

33. Employees with Flu 24% of the employees at Jack's Sporting Goods Store called in sick with the flu. If 12 employees called in sick, how many employees are there at the company?

34. Scholarships 25% of the graduating class at Springdale Community College received a scholarship. If 1800 students received a scholarship, how many students graduated from the college?

35. Nature Trail The new 8-mile nature trail is 125% of the length of the original trail. How long was the original trail?

36. Auditorium Capacity The new 350-seat auditorium contains 140% of the number of seats in the original auditorium. How many seats were in the original auditorium?

37. Golfing Cost A small country club charges nonmembers $128 to play a game of golf at the club. If the fee to play a game of golf for nonmembers is 60% more than the fee for club members, what do club members pay to play a game of golf?

38. Hotel Charges A hotel charges a rate of $120 per room to individuals who are not attending a conference at the hotel. If this rate is 20% more than the rate charged to those attending the conference, how much is the room rate for a person attending a conference at the hotel?

39. Electric Bill Mary Beth's first electric bill for her new apartment was $95 for the month of June. When she complained to the landlord about the high cost of electricity, she was informed that summer electric bills are about 90% higher than winter because of the periodic summer use of air conditioners. How much can Mary Beth expect her winter electric bill to be?

40. Restaurant Bill Vu Nguyen and his wife have $46 to spend on dinner. What is the maximum amount they can spend on the meals and drinks so that they have enough money left to leave a 15% tip?

Mixed Practice *Translate each of these different types of percent statements into equations and then solve.*

41. 44 is 50% of what number?

42. 90 is 50% of what number?

43. 125% of 60 is what number?

44. 118% of 48 is what number?

45. What is 27% of 78?

46. What is 32% of 85?

47. 15.66 is what percent of 87?

48. 39.96 is what percent of 74?

49. 135 is 45% of what number?

50. 160 is 25% of what number?

51. 110 is what percent of 440?

52. 80 is what percent of 320?

One Step Further *When we work with large numbers such as millions, we can simplify the calculations if we write the abbreviation "mil" in place of the zeros and then perform the calculations. For example, to divide 22,000,000 by 2 we can write* 22 mil ÷ 2 = 11 mil.

Roses Sold *Roses are a popular Valentine's Day flower. One year there were 130 million roses sold on Valentine's Day. Use this information to answer exercises 53 and 54.*

53. If 73% of the roses sold on Valentine's Day were red, how many red roses were sold on Valentine's Day?

54. If 48% of the cut flowers sold on Valentine's Day were roses, how many cut flowers were sold? Round your answer to the nearest tenth.

Write the statement that represents each of these different types of percent situations. Then solve the equation.

55. **Test Score** Robert got 86 out of the 92 questions right on his test. What percent did he get correct? Round your answer to the nearest percent.

56. **Basketball** A basketball player has made 25 of her 30 free throws. What percent of free throws did she make? Round your answer to the nearest percent.

Trash Recycling *About 208 million tons of residential and commercial trash are generated each year. Use the information in the illustration below to answer exercises 57 and 58.*

57. How much greater is the percentage of aluminum recycled than the percentage of glass recycled?

58. How much greater is the percentage of yard waste recycled than the percentage of plastics recycled?

Percent of Residential and Commercial Trash Recycled Annually

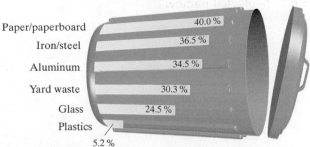

Paper/paperboard	40.0 %
Iron/steel	36.5 %
Aluminum	34.5 %
Yard waste	30.3 %
Glass	24.5 %
Plastics	5.2 %

Income Budget *Jeremy has a monthly income of $1250. He allocates it as shown on the circle graph. Use the graph to answer exercises 59–62.*

59. What percent does he spend on recreation?

60. How much money does he spend on food?

61. How much money does he save each month?

62. After rent, food, and clothing, how much does he have left each month?

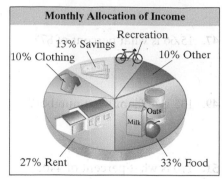

Monthly Allocation of Income

Recreation
13% Savings
10% Clothing
10% Other
Oats
Milk
27% Rent
33% Food

 63. What is 67.3% of 348.9?

 64. What percent of 875 is 625?

 65. 368 is 20% of what number?

 66. What is 18.9% of $9500?

 67. *Surfers* 34.6% of the 1,400,000 U.S. surfers are women. How many U.S. surfers are women?

 68. *Snowboarders* 1,501,200 U.S. snowboarders are women. What percent of the 5,400,000 U.S. snowboarders are women?

Cumulative Review *Solve.*

69. [7.2.1] $2x + 3 = 13$

70. [7.2.2] $3x - 1 = 2x + 4$

71. [7.2.2] $5x - 3 = 3x + 9$

72. [7.3.1] $2(3x + 1) = 2x - 6$

Quick Quiz 8.7

1. What is 35% of 60?

2. 15 is what percent of 50?

3. 8 is 20% of what number?

4. **Concept Check** The owner of M&R Windows determined that 0.8% of the products ordered from the manufacturer are defective. Explain how you would determine how many windows the owner should expect to be defective in a shipment from the manufacturer of 375 windows.

Identifying the Parts of a Percent Proportion

In Section 8.7 we showed you how to use an equation to solve a percent problem. Some students find it easier to use proportions to solve percent problems. We will show you how to use proportions in this section. The two methods work equally well. Using percent proportions allows you to see another of the many uses of the proportions that we studied in Chapter 4.

Consider the following relationship.

$$\frac{17}{68} = 25\%$$

This can be written as follows.

$$\frac{17}{68} = \frac{25}{100}$$

In general, we can write this relationship using the following percent proportion.

$$\frac{\text{amount}}{\text{base}} = \frac{\text{percent number}}{100}$$

To use this equation effectively, we need to identify the *amount, base,* and *percent number* in an applied problem. The easiest of these three parts to identify is the percent number. We use the letter p (a variable) to represent the percent number.

EXAMPLE 1 Identify the percent number p.

(a) Find 15% of 360.
(b) 28% of what is 25?
(c) What percent of 18 is 4.5?

Solution

(a) Find 15% of 360.   The value of p is 15.
(b) 28% of what is 25?   The value of p is 28.
(c) What percent of 18 is 4.5?
              p

We let p represent the unknown percent number.

Practice Problem 1 Identify the percent number p.

(a) Find 83% of 460.
(b) 15% of what number is 60?
(c) What percent of 45 is 9?

We use the letter b to represent the *base* number. The base is the entire quantity or the total involved. The number that is the base usually appears after the word *of.* The *amount,* which we represent by the letter a, is the *part* being compared to the whole.

Student Learning Objectives

After studying this section, you will be able to:

1 Identify the parts of a percent proportion.

2 Use the percent proportion to solve percent problems.

3 Solve applied percent problems using proportions.

NOTE TO STUDENT: Fully worked-out solutions to all of the Practice Problems can be found at the back of the text starting at page SP-1

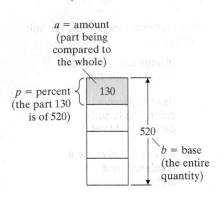

a = amount (part being compared to the whole)

p = percent (the part 130 is of 520)

b = base (the entire quantity)

EXAMPLE 2   Identify the base b and the amount a.

(a) 25% of 520 is 130.

(b) 19 is 50% of what?

Solution

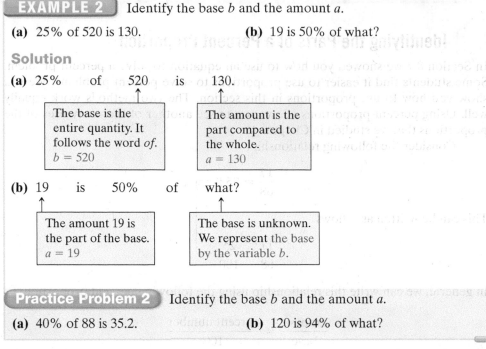

(a) 25%   of   520   is   130.

> The base is the entire quantity. It follows the word *of*.
> $b = 520$

> The amount is the part compared to the whole.
> $a = 130$

(b) 19   is   50%   of   what?

> The amount 19 is the part of the base.
> $a = 19$

> The base is unknown. We represent the base by the variable b.

Practice Problem 2   Identify the base b and the amount a.

(a) 40% of 88 is 35.2.

(b) 120 is 94% of what?

When identifying the percent p, base b, and amount a in a problem, it is easiest to identify p and b first. The remaining quantity or variable is then a.

EXAMPLE 3   Find the percent p, base b, and amount a.

(a) What is 77% of 210?

(b) What percent of 21 is 17?

Solution

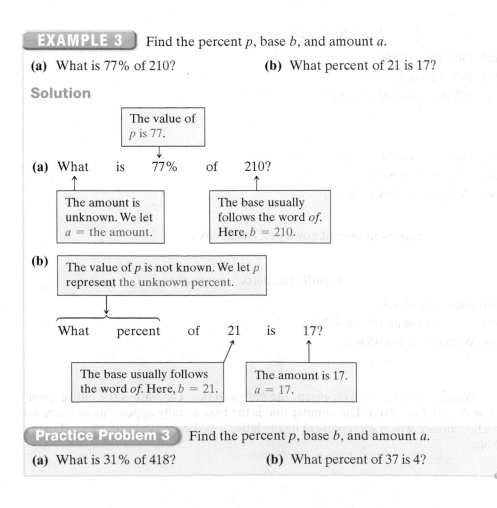

> The value of p is 77.

(a) What   is   77%   of   210?

> The amount is unknown. We let a = the amount.

> The base usually follows the word *of*. Here, $b = 210$.

(b)

> The value of p is not known. We let p represent the unknown percent.

What   percent   of   21   is   17?

> The base usually follows the word *of*. Here, $b = 21$.

> The amount is 17. $a = 17$.

Practice Problem 3   Find the percent p, base b, and amount a.

(a) What is 31% of 418?

(b) What percent of 37 is 4?

Using the Percent Proportion to Solve Percent Problems

In order to solve a percent proportion, we need to be given enough information to state the numerical value for two of the three variables a, b, p in the proportion.

$$\frac{a}{b} = \frac{p}{100}$$

We first identify those two values and then substitute those values into the proportion. Then we use the skills that we acquired for solving proportions in Chapter 4 to find the value we do not know.

EXAMPLE 4 Find 260% of 40.

Solution   The percent $p = 260$. The number that is the base usually appears after the word *of*. The base $b = 40$. The amount is unknown. We use the variable a. Thus

$$\frac{a}{b} = \frac{p}{100} \qquad \text{becomes} \qquad \frac{a}{40} = \frac{260}{100}$$

If we simplify the fraction on the right-hand side, we have the following.

$$\frac{a}{40} = \frac{13}{5} \qquad \frac{260}{100} = \frac{13}{5}$$

$$5a = (40)(13) \quad \text{Cross-multiply.}$$

$$5a = 520 \qquad \text{Simplify.}$$

$$\frac{5a}{5} = \frac{520}{5} \qquad \text{Divide both sides of the equation by 5.}$$

$$a = 104$$

Thus 260% of 40 is 104.

Practice Problem 4 Find 340% of 70.

NOTE TO STUDENT: Fully worked-out solutions to all of the Practice Problems can be found at the back of the text starting at page SP-1

EXAMPLE 5 65% of what is 195?

Solution   The percent $p = 65$. The base is unknown. We use the variable b. The amount a is 195. Thus

$$\frac{a}{b} = \frac{p}{100} \qquad \text{becomes} \qquad \frac{195}{b} = \frac{65}{100}$$

If we simplify the fraction on the right-hand side, we have the following.

$$\frac{195}{b} = \frac{13}{20} \qquad \frac{65}{100} = \frac{13}{20}$$

$$(20)(195) = 13b \quad \text{Cross-multiply.}$$

$$3900 = 13b \quad \text{Simplify.}$$

$$\frac{3900}{13} = \frac{13b}{13} \quad \text{Divide both sides by 13.}$$

$$300 = b$$

Thus 65% of 300 is 195.

Practice Problem 5 82% of what is 246?

EXAMPLE 6   19 is what percent of 95?

Solution   The percent is unknown. We use the variable p. The base $b = 95$. The amount $a = 19$. Thus

$$\frac{a}{b} = \frac{p}{100} \quad \text{becomes} \quad \frac{19}{95} = \frac{p}{100}$$

Cross-multiplying, we have the following.

$$(100)(19) = 95p$$
$$1900 = 95p$$
$$\frac{1900}{95} = \frac{95p}{95} \quad \text{Divide both sides of the equation by 95.}$$
$$20 = p$$

Thus 19 is 20% of 95.

Practice Problem 6   42 is what percent of 140?

 Solving Applied Percent Problems Using Proportions

EXAMPLE 7   Sonia has $29.75 deducted from her weekly salary of $425 for a retirement plan.

(a) What percent of Sonia's salary is withheld for the retirement plan?

(b) What percent of Sonia's salary is *not* withheld for the retirement plan?

Solution

(a) We must find the percent p. The base $b = 425$. The amount $a = 29.75$. Thus

$$\frac{a}{b} = \frac{p}{100} \quad \text{becomes} \quad \frac{29.75}{425} = \frac{p}{100}$$

When we cross-multiply, we obtain the following.

$$100(29.75) = 425p \quad \text{Cross-multiply.}$$
$$2975 = 425p \quad (29.75)100 = 2975$$
$$\frac{2975}{425} = \frac{425p}{425} \quad \text{Divide both sides by 425.}$$
$$7 = p$$

Since p represents percent, we see that 7% of Sonia's salary is deducted for the retirement plan.

(b) We can subtract the percents to determine the percent of Sonia's salary that is *not* deducted.

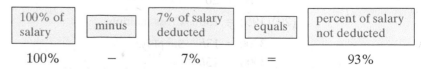

100% of salary	minus	7% of salary deducted	equals	percent of salary not deducted
100%	−	7%	=	93%

93% of Sonia's salary is not deducted for the retirement plan.

Practice Problem 7   The manager of an office building has 70% of the 120 offices in the building occupied.

(a) What percent of the offices are *not* occupied?

(b) How many offices are *not* occupied?

NOTE TO STUDENT: *Fully worked-out solutions to all of the Practice Problems can be found at the back of the text starting at page SP-1*

Verbal and Writing Skills

1. Why is it obvious that 150% of 80 is a number greater than 80?

2. Why is it obvious that 99% of 80 is equal to a number a little less than 80?

Identify the percent p, base b, and amount a. Do not solve for the unknown.

	p	b	a
3. 16% of 250 is 40.	_____	_____	_____
4. 45% of 650 is 292.5	_____	_____	_____
5. What is 95% of 420?	_____	_____	_____
6. What is 56% of 600?	_____	_____	_____
7. 69% of what is 8230?	_____	_____	_____
8. 46% of what is 189?	_____	_____	_____
9. 63 is what percent of 90?	_____	_____	_____
10. 140 is what percent of 82?	_____	_____	_____
11. What percent of 47 is 10?	_____	_____	_____
12. What percent of 29 is 6?	_____	_____	_____
13. 400 is 160% of what?	_____	_____	_____
14. 900 is 225% of what?	_____	_____	_____

In exercises 15–32, solve by using the percent proportion.

$$\frac{a}{b} = \frac{p}{100}$$

In exercises 15–20, the amount a is not known.

15. 24% of 200 is what?

16. 65% of 500 is what?

17. Find 250% of 30.

18. Find 250% of 60.

19. 0.6% of 4000 is what?

20. 0.9% of 2000 is what?

In exercises 21–26, the base b is not known.

21. 82 is 50% of what?

22. 96 is 80% of what?

23. 150% of what is 75?

24. 125% of what is 75?

25. 4000 is 0.8% of what?

26. 6300 is 0.7% of what?

In exercises 27–32, the percent p is not known.

27. 70 is what percent of 280?

28. 90 is what percent of 450?

29. What percent of 140 is 11.2?

30. What percent of 170 is 3.4?

31. What percent of $5000 is $90?

32. What percent of $4000 is $64?

Mixed Practice *Solve by using the percent proportion.*

33. 26% of 350 is what?

34. 56% of 650 is what?

35. 180% of what is 720?

36. 160% of what is 320?

37. 75 is what percent of 400?

38. 88 is what percent of 500?

39. Find 0.2% of 650.

40. Find 0.5% of 500.

41. What percent of 25 is 15.2?

42. What percent of 49 is 34.3?

43. 68 is 40% of what?

44. 52 is 40% of what?

45. 94.6 is what percent of 220?

46. 85.8 is what percent of 260?

47. What is 12.5% of 380?

48. What is 20.5% of 320?

49. Find 0.05% of 5600.

50. Find 0.04% of 8700.

Applications *Solve using the percent proportion.*

51. *Apartment Renting* An apartment owner must keep 80% of the apartments rented in order to cover the costs of ownership. If there are 250 apartments, how many must be rented in order to cover the owner's costs?

52. *Midterm Grade* In a class of 25 students, 40% of the students received an A on the midterm. How many student received an A?

53. *Preschool Registration* A new preschool predicts that 60% of the 150 spaces open for registration will be filled during the first week of registration.

(a) What percent of the openings should be available *after* the first week of registration?

(b) How many spaces should be open *after* the first week of registration?

54. *Promotional Sale* The marketing division of a company predicts that 72% of the 250 special promotional sale items will sell on the first day of the sale.

(a) What percent of the promotional items should be available *after* the first day of the sale?

(b) How many special promotional items should be available *after* the first day of the sale?

55. *Vacation Savings* Owen has $42.90 deducted from his monthly salary of $1950 for a vacation savings plan.
- **(a)** What percent of Owen's salary is withheld for the vacation savings plan?
- **(b)** What percent of Owen's salary is *not* withheld for the vacation savings plan?

56. *Child Care Expenses* Dave has $120 deducted from his weekly salary of $600 to pay for the on-site child care offered by his company.
- **(a)** What percent of Dave's salary is deducted for child care expenses?
- **(b)** What percent of Dave's salary is *not* deducted for child care expenses?

57. *Office Usage* In an office building, 90 offices are currently being rented. This represents 75% of the total units. How many offices are there in the building?

58. *Mobile Homes Destroyed* Fifteen percent of the mobile homes in Senior Park Community were destroyed by a tornado. If 21 mobile homes were destroyed, how many mobile homes were in Senior Park Community?

59. *Quiz Score* Delroy got 6 out of 9 questions right on the quiz. What percent did he get correct? Round your answer to the nearest percent.

60. *Payroll Deduction* A cashier has $29.15 deducted from his weekly gross earnings of $265 for federal income taxes. What percent of the cashier's pay is withheld for federal taxes?

Solve each percent problem. Round to the nearest hundredth.

61. What is $19\frac{1}{4}\%$ of 798?

62. $140\frac{1}{2}\%$ of what number is 10,397?

63. Find 18% of 20% of $3300. (*Hint:* First find 20% of $3300.)

64. Find 42% of 16% of $5500. (*Hint:* First find 16% of $5500.)

Cumulative Review

▲ 65. **[3.3.2]** Find the area of a rectangle with $L = 7$ in. and $W = 4$ in.

▲ 66. **[3.3.3]** Find the volume of a cube with $L = 8$ cm, $W = 4$ cm, and $H = 6$ cm.

▲ 67. **[3.3.2]** Find the area of a square with a side of 2 ft.

▲ 68. **[3.3.1]** Find the perimeter of a square with a side of 3 in.

Quick Quiz 8.8 Solve by using the percent proportion.

1. What is 18% of 90?

2. 45 is what percent of 125?

3. 56 is 80% of what number?

4. **Concept Check** In the following percent proportion, what can you say about the *percent number* if the value of the *amount* is larger than the *base*?

$$\frac{\text{amount}}{\text{base}} = \frac{\text{percent number}}{100}$$

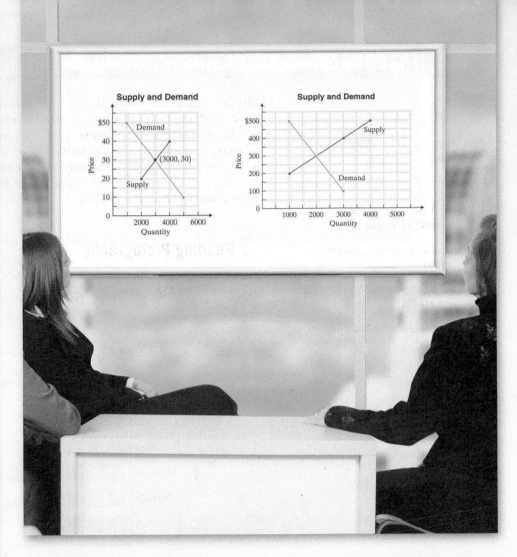

CHAPTER

9

To efficiently manage a business we must be able to analyze consumers' purchase patterns and to make decisions about the sale price and demand for an item. Displaying this information on graphs allows us to see the entire financial picture in a comparative way.

Graphing and Statistics

Student Learning Objectives

After studying this section, you will be able to:

1. Read pictographs.

2. Read circle graphs with percentage values.

3. Read and interpret double-bar graphs.

4. Read and interpret comparison line graphs.

5. Construct double-bar and line graphs.

Statistics is that branch of mathematics that collects and studies data. Once the data are collected, the data must be organized so that the information is easily readable. As we have seen in earlier chapters, graphs give a visual representation of the data that is easy to read. Their visual nature allows them to communicate information efficiently about the complicated relationships among statistical data. For this reason, newspapers often use the types of graphs we will study in this section to help their readers grasp information quickly.

1 Reading Pictographs

A **pictograph** uses a visually appropriate symbol to represent a number of items. A pictograph is used in Example 1.

EXAMPLE 1 Consider the following pictograph.

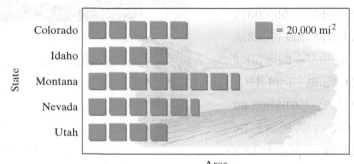

Areas of Selected States

= 20,000 mi^2

State: Colorado, Idaho, Montana, Nevada, Utah

Area
(in square miles rounded to the nearest ten thousand)

Source: World Book Encyclopedia

(a) How many square miles is the area of Idaho?

(b) Which of the states listed on the pictograph has the largest area?

(c) How many more square miles is the area of Colorado than the area of Utah?

Solution

(a) Since there are four symbols (■) beside the state of Idaho on the pictograph, and each one equals 20,000 square miles, we have $4 \times 20,000 = 80,000$ square miles.

(b) Montana has the most symbols on the pictograph and thus has the largest area.

(c) Colorado is 20,000 square miles more in area than Utah because there is one extra symbol beside Colorado. (Each ■ equals 20,000 square miles.)

Practice Problem 1 Consider the pictograph in Example 1.

(a) How many square miles is the area of Utah?

(b) Which of the states listed has the smallest area?

(c) How many fewer square miles is Idaho than Nevada?

NOTE TO STUDENT: Fully worked-out solutions to all of the Practice Problems can be found at the back of the text starting at page SP-1

Reading Circle Graphs with Percentage Values

A **circle graph** indicates how a whole quantity is divided into parts. These graphs help us to visualize the relative sizes of the parts. Each piece of the pie or circle is called a **sector.** We sometimes refer to circle graphs as **pie graphs.**

EXAMPLE 2 Together, the Great Lakes form the largest body of freshwater in the world. The total area of these five lakes is about 290,000 square miles, almost all of which is suitable for boating. The percentage of this total area taken up by each of the Great Lakes is shown in the pie graph.

(a) What percentage of the area is taken up by Lake Michigan?

(b) What lake takes up the largest percentage of the total area?

(c) What percentage of the total area is *not* taken up by Lake Erie?

(d) How many square miles are taken up by Lake Huron and Lake Michigan together?

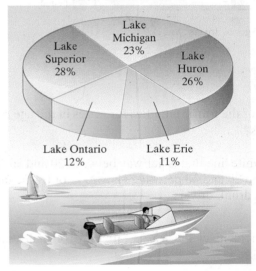

Area of Great Lakes

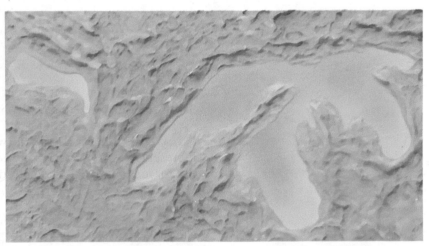

Solution

(a) Lake Michigan takes up 23% of the area.

(b) Lake Superior takes up the largest percentage.

(c) The entire circle represents 100%, and Lake Erie takes up 11% of the area. Thus, we subtract $100 - 11 = 89$, so 89% of the total area is *not* taken up by Lake Erie.

(d) If we add $26 + 23$, we get 49. Thus Lake Huron and Lake Michigan together take up 49% of the total area.

$$49\% \text{ of } 290{,}000 = (0.49)(290{,}000) = 142{,}100 \text{ square miles}$$

Practice Problem 2 Refer to Example 2 to answer the following.

(a) What percentage of the area is taken up by Lake Superior and Lake Michigan together?

(b) What percentage of the total area is *not* taken up by Lake Superior and Lake Michigan together?

(c) How many square miles are taken up by Lake Erie and Lake Ontario together?

Reading and Interpreting Double-Bar Graphs

Double-bar graphs are useful for making comparisons. The following double-bar graph compares the percent of all traffic fatalities for each age group that involved drunk drivers. The groups are separated by gender for the year 2005. Use this graph for the following Examples and Practice Problems.

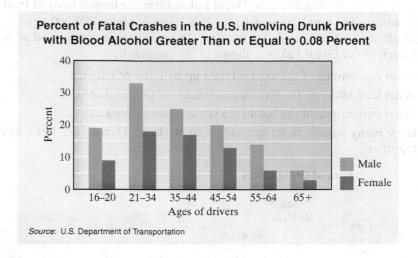

Percent of Fatal Crashes in the U.S. Involving Drunk Drivers with Blood Alcohol Greater Than or Equal to 0.08 Percent

Source: U.S. Department of Transportation

EXAMPLE 3 What percent of the traffic fatalities for males in the age range 35–44 years involved drunk drivers?

Solution The bar rises to the white line that is halfway between 20 and 30. This represents a value halfway between 20 and 30 percent. Thus 25% of traffic fatalities for males ages 35–44 involved drunk drivers.

Practice Problem 3 What percent of the traffic fatalities for males ages 45–54 years involved drunk drivers?

EXAMPLE 4 In which age group was the percent of drunk-driving fatalities the highest for males? For females?

Solution From the double-bar graph, we see that the percent of fatalities for 21–34 year olds was the highest for both males and females.

Practice Problem 4 Estimate the highest percent of drunk-driving fatalities for males.

NOTE TO STUDENT: *Fully worked-out solutions to all of the Practice Problems can be found at the back of the text starting at page SP-1*

Reading and Interpreting Comparison Line Graphs

Two or more sets of data can be compared by using a **comparison line graph.** A comparison line graph shows two or more line graphs together. A different style or color for each line distinguishes them. Note that using a blue line and a yellow line in the following graph makes it easy to read. Use this graph for the following Examples and Practice Problems.

EXAMPLE 5 Fill in the blank. Approximately 19% of people in the _____ age group do their grocery shopping on Friday.

Solution The blue solid line represents the under-35 age group. Since the dot corresponding to Friday on the blue solid line is near 20%, we know that approximately 19% of the under-35 age group shops on Friday.

Practice Problem 5

Fill in the blank. Approximately 9% of people in the _____ age group do their grocery shopping on Monday.

EXAMPLE 6 On what day(s) are there more grocery shoppers from the over-55 age group than the under-35 age group?

Solution Since the yellow solid line indicates the shopping days for the over-55 age group, we look for those days that have a yellow dot higher on the graph than a blue dot. Thus, Tuesday, Wednesday, and Thursday are the days that have more shoppers from the over-55 age group.

Grocery Shopping in the U.S.

- Shoppers under 35 years of age
- Shoppers over 55 years of age

Percent of people who grocery shop

Day of the week

Source: Chicago Tribune

Practice Problem 6 Which day is the busiest shopping day for the under-35 age group? For the over-55 age group?

 Constructing Double-Bar and Line Graphs

There are several ways to construct line and bar graphs. How you design a graph usually depends on the data you must graph and the visual appearance you want. For both types of graphs, the intervals on the horizontal and vertical lines must be equally spaced.

EXAMPLE 7   Construct a comparison line graph of the information given in the table.

Category	Activity	Hours Spent per Week
Single men	Gym	6
	Outdoor sports	4
	Dating	7
	Reading and TV	3
Single women	Gym	4
	Outdoor sports	2
	Dating	7
	Reading and TV	9

Solution   We plan our graph.

1. First, we draw a vertical and a horizontal line.
2. Since we are comparing *Hours per Week* to type of activity, we place this label on the vertical line. Mark intervals with equally spaced notches and label 0 to 9.
3. We place the label *Activity* on the horizontal line. We mark intervals with equally spaced notches and label with the name of each activity.
4. Now we place dots on the graph that correspond to the data given.
5. We choose a different color line for each of the categories we are comparing (men and women) and connect the dots with line segments.

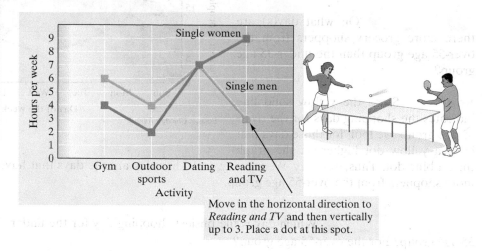

Move in the horizontal direction to *Reading and TV* and then vertically up to 3. Place a dot at this spot.

Note that instead of colored lines, we could use a solid line and a dashed line.

Practice Problem 7   Construct a comparison line graph of the information given in the table.

Apartment Rent

Size	Beach Area	Inland
Studio	$800	$650
1 bedroom	$1050	$800
2 bedroom	$1400	$1100
3 bedroom	$1800	$1350

EXAMPLE 8   Construct a double-bar graph of the information given in the table.

The Window Store Profits*

Window Covering	2009	2010
Miniblinds	$12,000	$15,000
Vertical blinds	11,000	16,000
Shutters	16,000	14,000
Drapes	9,000	7,000

*Profits rounded to the nearest thousand.

Solution   We plan our graph.

1. First, we draw a vertical and a horizontal line.
2. Since we are comparing the annual profits for the items, we place the label *Profit* on the vertical line. Mark intervals with equally spaced notches and label 7,000 to 17,000.
3. We label the horizontal line with the store's products.
4. We next label a shaded and a nonshaded bar for the years we are displaying (2009 and 2010).
5. Now, we draw a bar to the appropriate height for each category of window coverings.

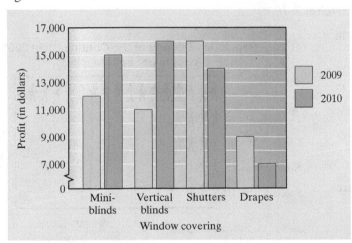

Sidelight   When we construct bar graphs, sometimes the heights of many of the bars we draw do not rise exactly to one of the intervals marked on the vertical axis. When this happens we can place each bar's data above it, so that the exact number is displayed, and we can avoid estimating when reading the graph.

Practice Problem 8   Construct a double-bar graph with the information given. Place the given data above each bar so that estimating is not necessary when reading the graph.

2006 Average Yearly Earnings and Highest Degree Earned*

Degree Earned	Men	Women
AA	$51,000	$40,000
BA	$77,000	$53,000
MA	$97,000	$63,000

*Rounded to the nearest thousand
Source: U.S. Census Bureau

NOTE TO STUDENT: Fully worked-out solutions to all of the Practice Problems can be found at the back of the text starting at page SP-1

Applications

Fastest Growing Occupations *Use the pictograph to answer exercises 1–6.*

1. Which profession will require the greatest number of new people?

2. Which profession will require the fewest new people?

3. How many additional computer support specialists and desktop publishers will be needed?

4. How many more systems software engineers will be needed by the end of 2014 than were needed at the start of 2004?

5. How many more new computer support specialists will be needed than new network systems and data communications analysts?

6. How many more new network and computer system administrators will be needed than new desktop publishers?

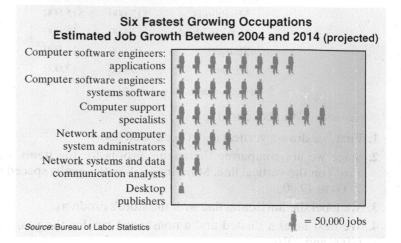

Six Fastest Growing Occupations
Estimated Job Growth Between 2004 and 2014 (projected)

Computer software engineers: applications
Computer software engineers: systems software
Computer support specialists
Network and computer system administrators
Network systems and data communication analysts
Desktop publishers

Source: Bureau of Labor Statistics

= 50,000 jobs

Population Density *Use this pictograph to answer exercises 7–10.*

7. How many people per square mile are there in Asia?

8. How many people per square mile are there in Africa?

9. How many more people per square mile are there in Europe than in South America?

10. How many more people per square mile are there in Asia than in North America?

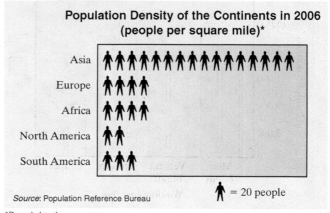

Population Density of the Continents in 2006
(people per square mile)*

Asia
Europe
Africa
North America
South America

Source: Population Reference Bureau

= 20 people

*Rounded to the nearest ten

Household Expenses *In 2005 the average household expenses for a consumer under 25 years of age were approximately $27,776. The circle graph divides this average expense into basic expense categories. Use the circle graph to answer exercises 11–16.*

11. What percent of the household expenses went for housing?

12. What percent of the household expenses went for food away from home?

13. (a) What are the two largest expenses?

    (b) What is the total percent of these two expenses?

14. What percent of expenses are for categories other than housing and transportation?

15. How much on the average was spent for housing?

16. How much on the average was spent for education?

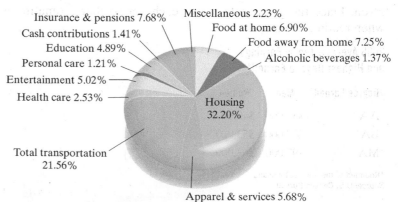

Estimated Household Expenses for People Under 25 Years of Age

Insurance & pensions 7.68%
Cash contributions 1.41%
Education 4.89%
Personal care 1.21%
Entertainment 5.02%
Health care 2.53%
Miscellaneous 2.23%
Food at home 6.90%
Food away from home 7.25%
Alcoholic beverages 1.37%
Housing 32.20%
Total transportation 21.56%
Apparel & services 5.68%

Source: U.S. Bureau of Labor Statistics

Emergency Room Visits *In the United States approximately one-quarter of all emergency room (ER) visits of people ages 5 to 24 are caused by sports. Use the circle graph to answer exercises 17–22.*

17. What percent of ER visits were caused by basketball injuries?

18. What percent of ER visits were caused by soccer injuries?

19. What percent of injuries were caused by football or cycling?

20. What percent of injuries were caused by snow sports or water sports?

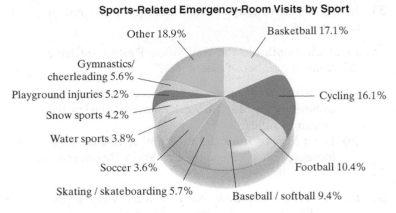

Sports-Related Emergency-Room Visits by Sport

Other 18.9%
Basketball 17.1%
Gymnastics/ cheerleading 5.6%
Playground injuries 5.2%
Cycling 16.1%
Snow sports 4.2%
Water sports 3.8%
Soccer 3.6%
Football 10.4%
Skating / skateboarding 5.7%
Baseball / softball 9.4%

Source: Centers for Disease Control and Prevention

21. What percent of injuries were *not* caused by basketball?

22. What percent of injuries were *not* caused by water sports?

Snowfall *In March of a recent year, when most of the season's snow had fallen, the snowfall totals for most cities were below the average yearly totals. The double-bar graph compares the average yearly snowfall totals to the season snowfall totals as of March for selected cities in the United States. Use this graph to answer exercises 23–32.*

23. What is the average yearly snowfall total in Boston, Massachusetts?

24. As of March, what was the season snowfall total in Denver, Colorado?

25. For what cities was the average yearly snowfall less than the season snowfall as of March?

26. For which city is the average yearly snowfall the greatest?

27. For Great Falls, Montana, what was the difference between the average yearly snowfall and the season snowfall as of March?

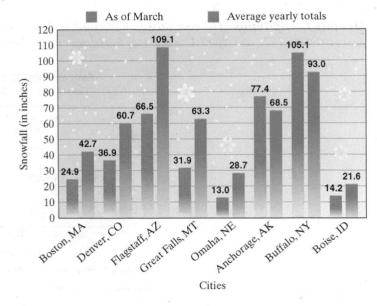

As of March   Average yearly totals

109.1
105.1
93.0
77.4
68.5
66.5
63.3
60.7
42.7
36.9
31.9
28.7
24.9
21.6
14.2
13.0

Snowfall (in inches)

Boston, MA   Denver, CO   Flagstaff, AZ   Great Falls, MT   Omaha, NE   Anchorage, AK   Buffalo, NY   Boise, ID

Cities

28. For Omaha, Nebraska, what was the difference between the average yearly snowfall and the season snowfall as of March?

29. For which city was the difference between the average yearly snowfall and the season snowfall as of March the greatest?

30. For which city was the difference between the average yearly snowfall and the season snowfall as of March the smallest?

31. In which cities were snowfalls as of March greater than the average yearly snowfall in Denver, CO?

32. In which cities were the average yearly snowfalls greater than the snowfalls as of March in Anchorage, AK?

Restaurant Customers *The comparison line graph illustrates the number of customers per month coming into the Bay Shore Restaurant and the Lilly Cafe. Use this graph to answer exercises 33–38.*

33. In which month did the Lilly Cafe have the fewest customers?

34. In which month did the Bay Shore Restaurant have the greatest number of customers?

35. (a) Approximately how many customers per month came into the Bay Shore Restaurant during the month of June?

    (b) From May to June, did the number of customers increase or decrease at the Bay Shore Restaurant?

36. (a) Approximately how many customers came into the Lilly Cafe during the month of May?

    (b) From March to April, did the number of customers increase or decrease at the Lilly Cafe?

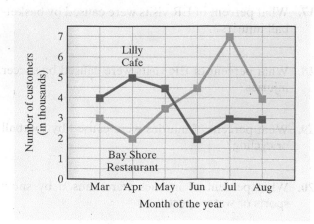

37. Between what two months is the *increase* in customers the largest at the Bay Shore Restaurant?

38. Between what two months did the biggest *decrease* in customers occur at the Lilly Cafe?

Monthly Precipitation *The comparison line graph indicates average monthly precipitation at two city airports for the thirty years between 1971 and 2000. Use this graph to answer exercises 39–44.*

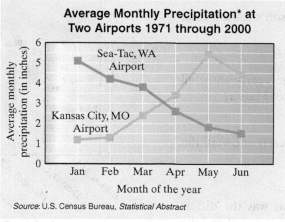

39. During which month was the average precipitation highest at the Sea-Tac (Seattle-Tacoma) airport? At the Kansas City airport?

40. During which month was the average precipitation lowest at the Sea-Tac (Seattle-Tacoma) airport? At the Kansas City airport?

41. During what months was the average precipitation at the Sea-Tac airport less than the average precipitation at the Kansas City airport?

42. During what months was the average precipitation at the Sea-Tac airport greater than the average precipitation at the Kansas City airport?

43. What was the average precipitation for June at the Sea-Tac airport?

44. At what airport was the average precipitation the highest for any month?

45. *High Low Reading* Use the table to make a double-bar graph that compares the high and low daily temperatures given in the table.

City	High °F	Low °F
Albany	50	24
Anchorage	30	16
Boise	55	30
Chicago	20	11

46. *Fat and Carbohydrates* Use the table to make a double-bar graph that compares the number of grams of fat and carbohydrates in the "fast foods" named in the following table.

Type of Sandwich	Fat (g)	Carbohydrates (g)
Wendy's Baconator™	51	35
Wendy's Ultimate Chicken Grill Sandwich	7	36
Burger King's Bacon Cheeseburger	18	31
McDonald's McChicken Sandwich	16	40

Sources: www.bk.com, www.mcdonalds.com, www.wendys.com

Life Insurance Use the information in the table to answer exercises 47 and 48.

Estimated Monthly Premiums for $200,000 5-year Term Life Insurance (Non-Nicotine User)

Age	25	30	35	40	45	50	55	60
Male	$25	$25	$30	$45	$60	$80	$130	$190
Female	$20	$20	$25	$30	$45	$60	$95	$140

47. Construct a comparison line graph that compares the male and female premiums for the ages 25–45.

48. Construct a double-bar graph that compares the male and female premiums for the ages 45–60.

Company Profit Use the information in the table for exercises 49 and 50.

Profit for Douglas Electronics

Quarter	2006	2007	2008	2009
1st	$12,000	$10,000	$15,000	$14,000
2nd	14,000	11,000	13,000	13,000
3rd	15,000	13,000	10,000	11,000
4th	10,000	15,000	12,000	14,000

49. Construct a comparison line graph that compares the profits in 2006 and 2007.

50. Construct a comparison line graph that compares the profits in 2007 and 2008.

Sport Event Tickets Use the circle graph for exercise 51a–d.

Ticket Allocation for Super Bowl 34

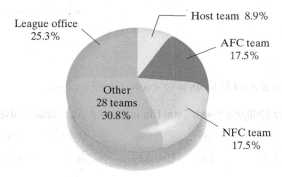

League office 25.3%
Host team 8.9%
AFC team 17.5%
Other 28 teams 30.8%
NFC team 17.5%

Source: Orange County Register

51. **(a)** What percent of the tickets were allocated to individual teams?

(b) If 100,000 tickets were available, how many went to the host team?

(c) If the average ticket price was $102, what was the ticket revenue for the AFC or the NFC team?

(d) If the league office gave away 25% of its tickets as promotion, what was the value of the promotion?

Quick Quiz 9.1

1. Use the information in the table for exercises 49–50 to construct a double-bar graph that compares profits in 2008 and 2009.

2. Refer to the circle graph in exercise 51 to answer the following. What percent of the Super Bowl tickets were *not* allocated to individual teams?

3. Use the information in the table to construct a comparison line graph that compares the number of male and female customers in a coffee shop.

Category	Time of Day	Number of Customers
Male	5:01–6 A.M.	20
	6:01–7 A.M.	35
	7:01–8 A.M.	35
	8:01–9 A.M.	20
Female	5:01–6 A.M.	10
	6:01–7 A.M.	25
	7:01–8 A.M.	40
	8:01–9 A.M.	45

4. **Concept Check** The college administration is gathering data to determine the number of students who enroll in morning, afternoon, evening, and weekend courses. So far the following information has been gathered: 45% of students enroll in morning courses, while 10% enroll in weekend courses.

   (a) If the enrollment in the afternoon is twice the weekend enrollment, explain how you would determine the percent of students enrolled in evening and in afternoon courses.

   (b) If you create a circle graph (pie graph), describe how you would construct a pie slice that describes the percent of students enrolled in evening courses.

Student Learning Objectives

After studying this section, you will be able to:

 Find the mean of a set of numbers.

2 Find the median of a set of numbers.

3 Find the mode of a set of numbers.

1 Finding the Mean of a Set of Numbers

We often want to know the *middle value* of a group of numbers. In this section we learn that in statistics there is more than one way of describing this middle value. There is the *mean* of the group of numbers, and there is the *median* of the group of numbers. In some situations it's more helpful to look at the mean, and in others it's more helpful to look at the median. We'll learn to tell which situations lend themselves to one or the other.

The **mean** of a set of values is the sum of the values divided by the number of values. The mean is often called the **average.**

EXAMPLE 1 Find the average or mean test score of a student who has test scores of 71, 83, 87, 99, 80, and 90.

Solution We take the sum of the six test scores and divide the sum by 6.

Sum of test scores →
Number of tests → $\dfrac{71 + 83 + 87 + 99 + 80 + 90}{6} = \dfrac{510}{6} = 85$

The mean is 85.

Practice Problem 1 Find the average or mean of the following test scores: 88, 77, 84, 97, and 89.

The mean value is often rounded to a certain decimal-place accuracy.

EXAMPLE 2 Carl and Wally each kept a log of the miles per gallon achieved by their cars for the last two months. Their results are recorded on the graph. What is the mean miles per gallon figure for the last 8 weeks for Carl? Round your answer to the nearest mile per gallon.

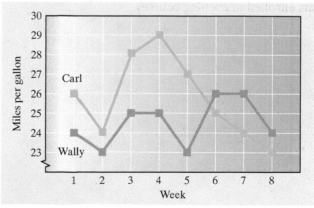

Solution Sum of values →
Number of values → $\dfrac{26 + 24 + 28 + 29 + 27 + 25 + 24 + 23}{8}$

$= \dfrac{206}{8} \approx 26$ Rounded to the nearest whole number.

The mean miles per gallon figure is 26.

Practice Problem 2 Use the double-line graph in Example 2 to find the mean miles per gallon figure for the last 8 weeks for Wally. Round your answer to the nearest mile per gallon.

Finding the Median of a Set of Numbers

> If a set of numbers is arranged in order from smallest to largest, the **median** is that value that has the same number of values above it as below it.

EXAMPLE 3 The total minutes of daily telephone calls made by Sara and Brad during one week are indicated on the double-bar graph. Find the median value for the total minutes of Sara's daily calls.

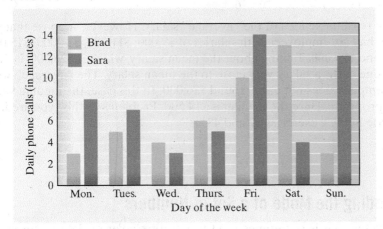

Solution We arrange the numbers for Sara's calls in order from smallest to largest.

$$\underbrace{3, \quad 4, \quad 5}_{\text{three numbers}} \qquad \underset{\underset{\text{middle}}{\uparrow}}{7} \qquad \underbrace{8, \quad 12, \quad 14}_{\text{three numbers}}$$

number

There are three numbers smaller than 7 and three numbers larger than 7. Thus 7 is the median.

Practice Problem 3 Use the double-bar graph in Example 3 to find the median value for Brad's daily calls.

If a list of numbers contains an even number of different items, then of course there is no one middle number. In this situation we obtain the median by taking the average of the two middle numbers.

EXAMPLE 4 Find the median of the following numbers: 13, 16, 18, 26, 31, 33, 38, and 39.

Solution $\underbrace{13, \quad 16, \quad 18}_{\text{three numbers}} \qquad \underset{\underset{\text{numbers}}{\text{two middle}}}{\underset{\uparrow}{26, \quad 31}} \qquad \underbrace{33, \quad 38, \quad 39}_{\text{three numbers}}$

The average (mean) of 26 and 31 is $\dfrac{26 + 31}{2} = \dfrac{57}{2} = 28.5$.

Thus the median value is 28.5.

Practice Problem 4 Find the median value of the following numbers: 88, 90, 100, 105, 118, and 126.

Understanding the Concept

Use the Mean or the Median?

When would someone want to use the mean, and when would someone want to use the median? Which is more helpful? The mean (average) is used more frequently. It is most helpful when the data are distributed fairly evenly, that is, when no one value is "much larger" or "much smaller" than the rest. For example, suppose a company had employees with annual salaries of $9,000, $11,000, $14,000, $15,000, $17,000, and $20,000. All the salaries fall within a fairly limited range. The mean salary (rounded to the nearest cent),

$$\frac{9000 + 11,000 + 14,000 + 15,000 + 17,000 + 20,000}{6} \approx \$14,333.33$$

gives us a reasonable idea of the "average" salary. However, suppose that the company had six employees with salaries of $9,000, $11,000, $14,000, $15,000, $17,000, and **$90,000.** Talking about the mean salary, which is $26,000, is deceptive. No one earns a salary very close to the mean salary. The "average" worker in that company does not earn around $26,000. In this case, the median value is more appropriate. Here the median is $14,500. Problems of this type are included in Exercise Set 9.2, exercises 47 and 48.

Finding the Mode of a Set of Numbers

Another value that is sometimes used to describe a set of data is the **mode.** The *mode* of a set of data is the *number or numbers that occur most often.* If two values occur most often, we say that the data have two modes (*or* are **bimodal**).

EXAMPLE 5 Find the mode of each of the following.

(a) A student's test scores of 89, 94, 96, 89, and 90.

(b) The ages of students in a calculus class: 33, 27, 28, 28, 21, 19, 18, 25, 26, and 33.

Solution

(a) The mode of 89, 94, 96, 89, and 90 is 89 since it occurs twice in the set of data.

(b) The data 33, 27, 28, 28, 21, 19, 18, 25, 26, and 33 are bimodal since both 28 and 33 occur twice.

Practice Problem 5 Find the mode of each of the following.

(a) The number of video rentals per day during a 1-week period: 121, 156, 131, 121, 142, 149, 131.

(b) Test scores: 99, 76, 79, 92, 76, 84, 83, 76.

NOTE TO STUDENT: Fully worked-out solutions to all of the Practice Problems can be found at the back of the text starting at page SP-1

A set of numbers may have *no mode* at all. For example, the set of numbers 10, 20, 30, 40 has *no mode* because each number occurs just once. Likewise, if all numbers occur the same number of times, there is *no mode*. The set of numbers 10, 10, 20, 20 has *no mode* because each number occurs twice.

Verbal and Writing Skills

1. Define the mean (average).

2. Explain the difference between the median and the mode.

Find the mean. Round to the nearest tenth when necessary.

3. *Quiz Grade* A student received grades of 84, 91, 86, 95, and 98 on math quizzes.

4. *Quiz Grade* A student received grades of 77, 88, 90, 92, 83, and 84 on history quizzes.

5. *Television Viewing* Sam watched television last week for the following number of hours per day.

Mon.	Tues.	Wed.	Thurs.	Fri.	Sat.	Sun.
2	3	3	4	2.5	2.5	4

6. *Mileage* Joyce's car got the following miles per gallon results during the last 6 months.

Jan.	Feb.	Mar.	Apr.	May	June
23	22	25	28	28	30

7. *Calls Received* The Windy City Passport Photo Center received the following numbers of telephone calls over the last 6 days: 23, 45, 63, 34, 21, and 42.

8. *Car Rental* The local Hertz rental car office received the following numbers of inquiries over the last 7 days: 34, 57, 61, 22, 43, 80, and 39.

9. *Homes Sold* The last five houses built in town sold for the following prices: $189,000, $185,000, $162,000, $145,000, and $162,000.

10. *Sofa Price* Luis priced a sofa at six local stores. The prices were $499, $359, $600, $450, $529, and $629.

Sales Record *The double-bar graph shows the number of sales made by Alex and Lisa from June through October. Use the graph to answer exercises 11 and 12.*

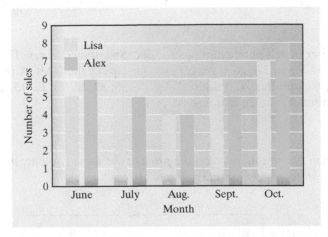

11. Find the average number of sales by Alex for the 5-month period.

12. Find the average number of sales by Lisa for the 5-month period.

13. *Baseball* The captain of the college baseball team achieved the following results.

	Game 1	Game 2	Game 3	Game 4	Game 5
Hits	0	2	3	2	2
Times at bat	5	4	6	5	4

Find his batting average by dividing his total number of hits by the total times at bat.

14. *Bowling* The captain of the college bowling team had the following results after practice.

	Practice 1	Practice 2	Practice 3	Practice 4
Score (pins)	541	561	840	422
Number of games	3	3	4	2

Find her bowling average by dividing the total number of pins scored by the total number of games.

15. *Gasoline Mileage* Frank and Wally traveled to the West Coast during the summer. The number of miles they drove and the number of gallons of gas they used each day are recorded below.

	Day 1	Day 2	Day 3	Day 4
Miles driven	276	350	391	336
Gallons of gas	12	14	17	14

Find the average miles per gallon achieved by the car on the trip by dividing the total number of miles driven by the total number of gallons used.

16. *Gasoline Mileage* Cindy and Andrea traveled to Boston this fall. The number of miles they drove and the number of gallons of gas they used each day are recorded below.

	Day 1	Day 2	Day 3	Day 4
Miles driven	260	375	408	416
Gallons of gas	10	15	17	16

Find the average miles per gallon achieved by the car on the trip by dividing the total number of miles driven by the total number of gallons used.

Find the median value.

17. 22, 42, 45, 47, 51, 50, 58

18. 37, 39, 46, 53, 57, 60, 63

19. 1052, 968, 1023, 999, 865, 1152

20. 1400, 1329, 1200, 1386, 1427, 1350

21. 0.52, 0.69, 0.71, 0.34, 0.58

22. 0.26, 0.12, 0.35, 0.43, 0.28

23. 3.7, 1.1, 3.4, 3.9, 2.8, 2.9

24. 5.3, 2.1, 4.4, 4.9, 2.9, 5.9

25. *Salaries* The annual salaries of the employees of a local cable television office are $17,000, $11,600, $23,500, $15,700, $26,700, and $31,500.

26. *Car Costs* The costs of six cars recently purchased by the Weston Company were $18,270, $11,300, $16,400, $9,100, $12,450, and $13,800.

27. *Cell Phone Usage* The number of cell phone minutes used on the phone per day by a San Diego teenager is 40 minutes, 108 minutes, 62 minutes, 12 minutes, 24 minutes, 31 minutes, 20 minutes, and 26 minutes.

28. *Swimmers' Ages* The ages of 10 people swimming laps at the YMCA pool one morning were 60, 18, 24, 36, 39, 32, 70, 12, 15, and 85.

Price Comparison The comparison line graph indicates the price of the same compact disc sold at music stores and online during a 6-year period. Use the graph to answer exercises 29 and 30.

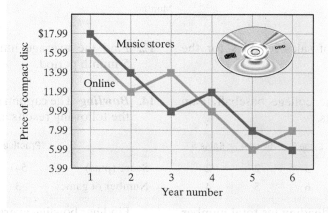

29. Find the median value of the prices at the music stores.

30. Find the median value of the prices online.

Find the median value.

31. *Actors in a Play* The numbers of potential actors who tried out for the school play at Hamilton-Wenham Regional High School over the last 10 years: 36, 48, 44, 64, 60, 71, 22, 36, 53, and 37.

32. *Football Injuries* The number of injuries during the high school football season for the Badgers over the last 8 years: 10, 17, 14, 29, 30, 19, 25, and 21.

Find the mode.

33. 60, 65, 68, 60, 72, 59, 80

34. 86, 84, 86, 87, 84, 83, 90

35. 121, 150, 117, 150, 121, 180, 127, 123

36. 144, 143, 140, 141, 149, 144, 141, 150

37. *Bikes Sold* The last six bicycles sold at the Skol Bike shop cost $249, $649, $439, $259, $269, and $249.

38. *TVs Sold* The last six color television sets sold at the local Circuit City cost $315, $430, $515, $330, $430, and $615.

Mixed Practice *Find the mean, median, and mode for each set of numbers.*

39. 21, 82, 42, 55, 42, 45, 49
  (a) Mean
  (b) Median
  (c) Mode

40. 11, 32, 21, 74, 32, 25, 29
  (a) Mean
  (b) Median
  (c) Mode

41. 2.7, 7.1, 6.9, 7.5, 6.1
  (a) Mean
  (b) Median
  (c) Mode

42. 3.6, 7.4, 3.9, 6.2, 7.6
  (a) Mean
  (b) Median
  (c) Mode

43. *Quiz Scores* Damian's quiz scores in his history class were 97, 81, 92, 73, 86, and 81. Find the mean, median, and mode for his quiz scores.

44. *Website Inquiries* Joanna's Website received the following numbers of inquiries over the last six days: 35, 55, 22, 61, 55, and 12. Find the mean, median, and mode.

One Step Further *Use the table for exercises 45–46. Round to the nearest tenth if necessary.*

Inco Systems: Office Staff Positions	Inco Systems: Monthly Salary Scale
File clerk	$1350
Receptionist	$1600
Secretary	$2400
Office manager	$2800
Administrative assistant	$3200

45. **(a)** Find the average salary.
  (b) Find the median salary.
  (c) Find the mode.

46. All the staff at Inco Systems get a holiday bonus at the end of the year of 8.25% of their monthly salary.
  (a) What is the holiday bonus for the highest paid position?
  (b) What is the holiday bonus for the lowest paid position?
  (c) Find the mean for the holiday bonus.
  (d) Find the median for the holiday bonus.

To Think About

47. *Monthly Salaries* A local travel office has 10 employees. Their monthly salaries are $1500, $1700, $1650, $1300, $1440, $1580, $1820, $1380, $2900, and $6300.
   (a) Find the mean.
   (b) Find the median.
   (c) Which of these numbers best represents what the "average person" earns? Why?

48. *Track Meet* A college track star in California ran the 100-meter event in 8 track meets. Her times were 11.7 seconds, 11.6 seconds, 12.0 seconds, 12.1 seconds, 11.9 seconds, 18 seconds, 11.5 seconds, and 12.4 seconds.
   (a) Find the mean.
   (b) Find the median.
   (c) Which of these numbers best represents her "average running time"? Why?

Find the median value.

49. 2576; 8764; 3700; 5000; 7200; 4700; 9365; 1987

50. 15.276; 21.375; 18.90; 29.2; 14.77; 19.02

Cumulative Review *Evaluate.*

51. [2.6.2] $\dfrac{x}{2} + 4$ for $x = 26$

52. [2.6.2] $\dfrac{35}{x} - 9$ for $x = 7$

53. [2.6.2] $2x + 1$ for $x = 5$

54. [2.6.2] $3x - 7$ for $x = 0$

55. [5.1.3] *Roofing Cost* Wesley is putting a new roof on his house and must pay the contractor $\frac{3}{8}$ of the cost of the roof before she will begin the work. If the roof costs $9200, how much must Wesley give the contractor before she starts the job?

56. [2.3.3] *Mountain Altitude* The highest mountain in the United States, Mt. McKinley in Alaska, is 20,320 feet at its highest point. What is the difference in altitude between the lowest point in South America, the Valdes Peninsula, which has an altitude of 131.2 feet below sea level, and Mt. McKinley?

Quick Quiz 9.2

1. Find the average or mean quiz score for Jake if he has quiz scores of 15, 13, 14, 11, 13, 12.

2. Find the median of each of the following.
   (a) 17, 9, 5, 14, 11, 19, 3
   (b) 35, 50, 40, 20, 75, 65

3. Find the mode of each of the following.
   (a) Sara scored the following number of goals in the last six soccer seasons: 6, 9, 5, 7, 6, 4.
   (b) The number of cell phones sold each day by Peter are 5, 6, 4, 3, 5, 7, and 4.

4. Concept Check An internet site had the following number of inquiries over the last seven days: 926, 887, 778, 887, 926, 297, 801. Would you select the mean, median, or mode to determine the most realistic estimate of how many inquires there were that particular week? Why?

10

With the high price we must pay for gasoline, many of us would like to reduce the amount of money we spend at the pump. One important step is to choose a vehicle that matches our budget and our driving needs. How can we perform calculations and make decisions to determine which vehicle is the best fit?

Measurement and Geometric Figures

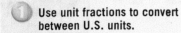

10.1 USING UNIT FRACTIONS WITH U.S. AND METRIC UNITS

Student Learning Objectives

After studying this section, you will be able to:

1. Use unit fractions to convert between U.S. units.

2. Solve applied problems involving U.S. units.

3. Convert between metric units.

4. Solve applied problems involving metric units.

We have worked with units of measurement throughout the book. Now we will see how to change (convert) from one U.S. unit to another. We present a table that shows the relationships between units.

Length	Weight
12 inches (in.) = 1 foot (ft)	16 ounces (oz) = 1 pound (lb)
3 feet (ft) = 1 yard (yd)	2000 pounds (lb) = 1 ton
5280 feet (ft) = 1 mile (mi)	

Volume	Time
2 cups (c) = 1 pint (pt)	60 seconds (sec) = 1 minute (min)
2 pints (pt) = 1 quart (qt)	60 minutes (min) = 1 hour (hr)
4 quarts (qt) = 1 gallon (gal)	24 hours (hr) = 1 day
	7 days = 1 week

 Using Unit Fractions to Convert Between U.S. Units

For many simple problems such as 24 inches = ? feet, we can easily see how to convert from inches to feet.

$$24 \text{ inches} = 12 \text{ inches} + 12 \text{ inches}$$
$$= 1 \text{ foot} + 1 \text{ foot} \qquad (12 \text{ inches} = 1 \text{ foot})$$
$$24 \text{ inches} = 2 \text{ feet}$$

For more complicated problems, for example, those with larger numbers, we need another conversion method so that the process is simple and efficient. The method we use involves multiplying by a unit fraction.

> A **unit fraction** is a fraction that shows the relationship between units and is equal to 1.

For example, since 12 in. = 1 ft, we can say that there are 12 inches per 1 foot or 1 foot per 12 inches. If we read the fraction bar as *per,* we have the following unit fractions that are equal to 1:

$$\text{per} \rightarrow \frac{12 \text{ in.}}{1 \text{ ft}} = \frac{1 \text{ ft}}{12 \text{ in.}} = 1 \qquad \frac{12 \text{ in.}}{1 \text{ ft}} \text{ and } \frac{1 \text{ ft}}{12 \text{ in.}} \quad \begin{array}{l}\text{are called} \\ \textit{unit fractions.}\end{array}$$

We can multiply a quantity by a unit fraction since its value is equal to 1 and we know that multiplying by 1 does not change the value of the quantity.

EXAMPLE 1 Convert 35 yards to feet.

Solution We write the relationship between feet and yards as a unit fraction. Since 3 ft = 1 yd, we have the unit fraction $\frac{3 \text{ ft}}{1 \text{ yd}}$.

$$35 \text{ yd} = \underline{\quad ? \quad} \text{ ft}$$

$$35 \text{ yd} \times \frac{3 \text{ ft}}{1 \text{ yd}} \qquad \text{Multiply by the unit fraction.}$$

$$= 35 \; \cancel{\text{yd}} \times \frac{3 \text{ ft}}{1 \; \cancel{\text{yd}}} \qquad \text{Divide out the units "yd."}$$

$$= 35 \times 3 \text{ ft} = 105 \text{ ft} \qquad \text{Multiply.}$$

Practice Problem 1 Convert 420 minutes to hours.

NOTE TO STUDENT: *Fully worked-out solutions to all of the Practice Problems can be found at the back of the text starting at page SP-1*

How did we know what unit fraction to use in Example 1? We use the unit fraction that relates the units we are working with; in this case it is *feet* and *yards*. Now, to determine which unit to put in the numerator and denominator of the fraction, we must consider what unit we want to end up with. In Example 1 we wanted to end up with feet, so we placed feet in the numerator.

$$35 \text{ yd} \times \frac{3 \text{ ft}}{1 \text{ yd}} = \frac{?}{} \text{ ft}$$

We want to end up with feet, so we place 3 ft in the numerator.

The yards divide out, and we end up with feet.

PROCEDURE TO CONVERT FROM ONE UNIT TO ANOTHER

1. Write the relationship between the units.
2. Identify the unit you want to end up with.
3. Write a unit fraction that has the unit you want to end up with in the numerator.
4. Multiply by the unit fraction.

EXAMPLE 2   Convert 560 quarts to gallons.

Solution   We write the relationship between quarts and gallons: 4 qt = 1 gal. We want to end up with gallons, so we write *1 gal* in the numerator of the unit fraction: $\frac{1 \text{ gal}}{4 \text{ qt}}$.

$$560 \text{ qt} = \frac{?}{} \text{ gal}$$

$$560 \text{ qt} \times \frac{1 \text{ gal}}{4 \text{ qt}} \qquad \text{We multiply by the appropriate unit fraction.}$$

$$= 560 \text{ qt} \times \frac{1 \text{ gal}}{4 \text{ qt}} \qquad \text{We divide out the units "qt."}$$

$$= 560 \times \frac{1}{4} \text{ gal} = \frac{560 \text{ gal}}{4} = 140 \text{ gal}$$

Practice Problem 2   Convert 144 ounces to pounds.

2   Solving Applied Problems Involving U.S. Units

EXAMPLE 3   A computer printout shows that a particular job took 144 seconds. How many minutes is that? (Express your answer as a decimal.)

Solution   We must change seconds to minutes.

$$144 \text{ sec} \times \frac{1 \text{ min}}{60 \text{ sec}} = \frac{144}{60} \text{ min} = 2.4 \text{ min}$$

Practice Problem 3   Joe's time card read, "Hours worked today: 7.2." How many minutes are in 7.2 hours?

EXAMPLE 4 The all-night garage charges $1.50 per hour for parking both day and night. A businessman left his car there for $2\frac{1}{4}$ days. How much was he charged?

Solution *Understand the problem.* We organize the information in a Mathematics Blueprint for Problem Solving.

Mathematics Blueprint for Problem Solving

Gather the Facts	What Am I Asked to Do?	How Do I Proceed?	Key Points to Remember
The charge for parking is $1.50 per (for each) hour. The car was in the garage $2\frac{1}{4}$ days.	Find the total parking charge for $2\frac{1}{4}$ days.	1. Change $2\frac{1}{4}$ days to hours to find the total number of hours the car was in the garage. 2. Multiply the total hours by $1.50 to find the cost for parking.	Change the number of days to a decimal so calculations are easier.

Calculate and state the answer.

1. $2\frac{1}{4} = 2.25$ days   We change $\frac{1}{4}$ to a decimal: $1 \div 4 = 0.25$.

   $2.25 \; \cancel{\text{days}} \times \dfrac{24 \text{ hr}}{1 \; \cancel{\text{day}}} = 54 \text{ hr}$ We change days to hours.

2. Now we must find the total charge for parking.

   $$54 \; \cancel{\text{hr}} \times \dfrac{\$1.50}{1 \; \cancel{\text{hr}}} = \$81$$

Check. Is our answer in the desired units? Yes. The answer is in dollars, and we would expect it to be in dollars. ✓

You may want to redo the calculation or use a calculator to check. The check is up to you.

Practice Problem 4 A businesswoman parked her car at a garage for $1\frac{3}{4}$ days. The garage charges $1.50 per hour. How much did she pay to park the car?

Understanding the Concept

Multiplying by a Unit Fraction

How did people first come up with the idea of multiplying by a unit fraction? What mathematical principles are involved here? Actually, this is the same as solving a proportion. Consider a situation where we change 34 quarts to 8.5 gallons by multiplying by a unit fraction.

$$34 \; \cancel{\text{qt}} \times \dfrac{1 \text{ gal}}{4 \; \cancel{\text{qt}}} = \dfrac{34}{4} \text{ gal} = 8.5 \text{ gal}$$

What we were actually doing is setting up the proportion, 1 gal is to 4 qt as n gal is to 34 qt, and solving for n.

$$\dfrac{1 \text{ gal}}{4 \text{ qt}} = \dfrac{n \text{ gal}}{34 \text{ qt}}$$

We cross-multiply: 34 qt × 1 gal = 4 qt × n gal. We divide both sides of the equation by 4 quarts.

$$\frac{34 \ \cancel{qt} \times 1 \ gal}{4 \ \cancel{qt}} = \frac{\cancel{4} \ \cancel{qt} \times n \ gal}{\cancel{4} \ \cancel{qt}}$$

$$1 \ gal \times \frac{34}{4} = n \ gal$$

$$8.5 \ gal = n \ gal$$

Thus the number of gallons is 8.5. Using proportions takes a little longer, so multiplying by a unit fraction is the more popular method.

Converting Between Metric Units

Now let's see how to change from one metric unit to another. We start by looking at the relationship between metric units. The basic metric units are the gram, the liter, and the meter. Units that are larger than the *basic unit* use the prefixes *kilo,* meaning 1000; *hecto,* meaning 100; and *deka,* meaning 10. For units smaller than the basic unit we use the prefixes *deci,* meaning $\frac{1}{10}$; *centi,* meaning $\frac{1}{100}$; and *milli,* meaning $\frac{1}{1000}$.

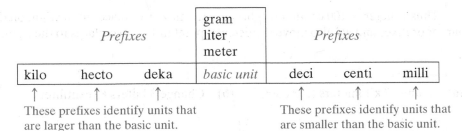

			gram liter meter			
Prefixes				*Prefixes*		
kilo	hecto	deka	*basic unit*	deci	centi	milli

These prefixes identify units that are larger than the basic unit.   These prefixes identify units that are smaller than the basic unit.

We list the relationships between units that are commonly used in the metric system.

COMMONLY USED METRIC MEASUREMENTS

Weight

1 kilogram (kg) = 1000 grams

1 gram (g)   the basic unit

1 milligram (mg) = 0.001 gram

Length

1 kilometer (km) = 1000 meters

1 meter (m)   the basic unit

1 centimeter (cm) = 0.01 meter

1 millimeter (mm) = 0.001 meter

Volume

1 kiloliter (kL) = 1000 liters

1 liter (L)   the basic unit

1 milliliter (mL) = 0.001 liter

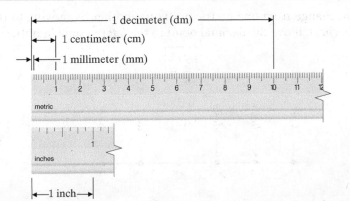

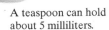

A teaspoon can hold about 5 milliliters.

A 1-liter bottle can hold 1000 milliliters.

1 nickel weighs about 5 grams.

200 nickels weigh about 1000 grams or 1 kilogram (kg).

How do we convert from one metric unit to another? For example, how do we change 5 kilometers into an equivalent number of meters?

Recall from Chapter 8 that when we multiply by 10, we move the decimal point 1 place to the right. When we divide by 10, we move the decimal point 1 place to the left. Let's see how we use that idea to change from one metric unit to another.

CHANGING FROM LARGER METRIC UNITS TO SMALLER ONES

When you change from one metric prefix to another by moving to the *right* on this prefix chart, move the decimal point to the *right* the same number of places.

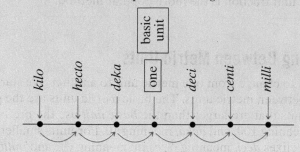

Thus 1 meter = 100 centimeters because we move two places to the right on the chart of prefixes and we also move the decimal point in 1.00 two places to the right.

EXAMPLE 5

(a) Change 7 kilometers to meters.   (b) Change 30 liters to centiliters.

Solution

(a) To go from kilometer to meter (basic unit), we move *3 places to the right on the prefix chart,* so we move the decimal point 3 places to the right.

$$7 \text{ km} = 7.000 \text{ m (move 3 places)} = 7000 \text{ m}$$

(b) To go from liter (basic unit) to centiliter, we move *2 places to the right on the prefix chart.* Thus we move the decimal point 2 places to the right.

$$30 \text{ L} = 30.00 \text{ cL (move 2 places)} = 3000 \text{ cL}$$

Practice Problem 5   (a) Change 4 meters to centimeters.

(b) Change 30 centigrams to milligrams.

Now let us see how we can change a measurement stated in a smaller unit to an equivalent measurement in larger units.

CHANGING FROM SMALLER METRIC UNITS TO LARGER ONES

When you change from one metric prefix to another by moving to the *left* on this prefix chart, move the decimal point to the *left* the same number of places.

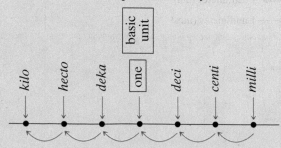

NOTE TO STUDENT: Fully worked-out solutions to all of the Practice Problems can be found at the back of the text starting at page SP-1

EXAMPLE 6

(a) Change 7 centigrams to grams.

(b) Change 56 millimeters to kilometers.

Solution

(a) To go from centigrams to grams, we move 2 places to the left on the prefix chart. Thus we move the decimal point 2 places to the left.

$$7 \text{ cg} = 0.07 \text{ g} \qquad \text{Move the decimal point 2 places to the left.}$$

$$= 0.07 \text{ g}$$

(b) To go from *milli*meters to *kilo*meters, we move 6 places to the left on the prefix chart. Thus we move the decimal point 6 places to the left.

$$56 \text{ mm} = 0.000056 \text{ km} \qquad \text{Move the decimal point 6 places to the left.}$$

$$= 0.000056 \text{ km}$$

Practice Problem 6

(a) Change 3 milliliters to liters.

(b) Change 47 centimeters to kilometers.

NOTE TO STUDENT: *Fully worked-out solutions to all of the Practice Problems can be found at the back of the text starting at page SP-1*

EXAMPLE 7 Convert.

(a) 426 decimeters to kilometers

(b) 9.47 hectometers to meters

Solution

(a) We are converting from a smaller unit, *dm,* to a larger one, *km*. Therefore, there will be fewer kilometers than decimeters (the number we get will be smaller than 426). We move the decimal point 4 places to the left.

$$426 \text{ dm} = 0.0426 \text{ km} \qquad \text{Move the decimal point 4 places to the left.}$$

$$= 0.0426 \text{ km}$$

(b) We are converting from a larger unit, *hm,* to a smaller one, *m*. Therefore, there will be more meters than hectometers (the number will be larger than 9.47). We move the decimal point 2 places to the right.

$$9.47 \text{ hm} = 947. \text{ m} \qquad \text{Move the decimal point 2 places to the right.}$$

$$= 947 \text{ m}$$

Practice Problem 7 Convert.

(a) 389 millimeters to dekameters

(b) 0.48 hectometer to centimeters

1 liter

Cleaning
Fluid

1 milliliter

(4) Solving Applied Problems Involving Metric Units

EXAMPLE 8 A special cleaning fluid used to rinse test tubes in a chemistry lab costs $40.00 per liter. What is the cost per milliliter?

Solution *Understand the problem.* We organize the information in a Mathematics Blueprint for Problem Solving.

Mathematics Blueprint for Problem Solving

Gather the Facts	What Am I Asked to Do?	How Do I Proceed?	Key Points to Remember
The fluid costs $40 per liter.	Find out how much 1 milliliter of fluid costs.	1. Change 1 liter to milliliters. 2. Find the unit cost per milliliter.	To go from liters to milliliters we move 3 places to the right on the prefix chart. Thus we move the decimal point 3 places to the right.

Calculate and state the answer.

1. 1 L = 1000 mL   Change liters to milliliters.
2. We write $40 per liter as a rate.

$$\frac{\$40}{1 \text{ L}} = \frac{\$40}{1000 \text{ mL}} \qquad \text{Replace 1 L with 1000 mL.}$$

$$= \$0.04 \text{ per mL} \quad 40 \div 1000 = 0.04$$

Check: A milliliter is a very small part of a liter. Therefore it should cost much less for 1 milliliter of fluid than it does for 1 liter. $0.04 is much smaller than $40.00, so our answer seems reasonable.

NOTE TO STUDENT: *Fully worked-out solutions to all of the Practice Problems can be found at the back of the text starting at page SP-1*

Practice Problem 8 A purified acid costs $110 per liter. What does it cost per milliliter?

Verbal and Writing Skills *From memory, write the equivalent values.*

1. 1 foot = _____ inches

2. 1 yard = _____ feet

3. _____ pints = 1 quart

4. _____ feet = 1 mile

5. 1 ton = _____ pounds

6. 1 pound = _____ ounces

7. _____ quarts = 1 gallon

8. _____ cups = 1 pint

9. 7 days = _____ week

10. 1 day = _____ hours

11. _____ seconds = 1 minute

12. _____ minutes = 1 hour

Convert.

13. 21 feet = _____ yards

14. 84 inches = _____ feet

15. 7920 feet = _____ miles

16. 41 yards = _____ feet

17. 69 inches = _____ feet

18. 192 ounces = _____ pounds

19. 13 tons = _____ pounds

20. 2.25 pounds = _____ ounces

21. 7 gallons = _____ quarts

22. 660 minutes = _____ hours

23. 11 days = _____ hours

24. 70 minutes = _____ seconds

Applications

25. *Javelin Record* Randy threw his javelin 218 feet 10 inches. How many inches did his javelin fly?

26. *Mountain Height* Mount Whitney in California is approximately 2.745 miles high. How many feet is that? Round your answer to the nearest 10 feet.

27. *Parking Costs* A stockbroker left his car in an all-night garage for $2\frac{1}{2}$ days. The garage charges $2.25 per hour. How much did he pay for parking?

28. *Wild Mushroom Sauce* Judy is making a wild mushroom sauce for a pasta dinner for a large group of friends. She bought 26 ounces of wild mushrooms at $6.00 per pound. How much did the mushrooms cost?

29. *Gourmet Cheese Purchase* Phoebe bought 24 ounces of gourmet cheese for a fondue. If the cheese sells for $4.00 per pound, how much did Phoebe pay for 24 ounces of gourmet cheese?

30. *Housesitting Expenses* Darlene's housesitter charges $1.25 per hour to stay at Darlene's home while she is out of town. How much will the housesitter charge for $2\frac{1}{4}$ days?

Memorize this chart and use it when converting between metric units. Fill in the blanks with the correct values.

31. 50 cm = _____ mm

32. 44 cm = _____ mm

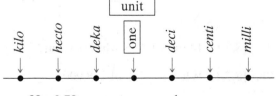

33. 3.6 km = _____ m

34. 7.6 km = _____ m

35. 2.43 kL = _____ mL

36. 1.76 kL = _____ mL

37. 1834 mL = _____ kL

38. 5261 mL = _____ kL

39. 0.78 g = _____ kg

40. 294 g = _____ kg

41. 5.9 kg = _____ mg

42. 6328 mg = _____ g

43. 7 mL = _____ L = _____ kL

44. 18 mL = _____ L = _____ kL

45. 413 mg = _____ g = _____ kg

46. 49 mg = _____ g = _____ kg

47. 35 mm = _____ cm = _____ m

48. 83 mm = _____ cm = _____ m

49. 3582 mm = _____ m = _____ km

50. 7812 mm = _____ m = _____ km

51. 0.32 cm = _____ m = _____ km

52. 0.81 cm = _____ m = _____ km

Applications

53. *Vaccines* A pharmaceutical firm developed a new vaccine that costs $6.00 per milliliter to produce. How much will it cost the firm to produce 1 liter of the vaccine?

54. *Anticancer Drug* A new anticancer drug costs $95.50 per gram. How much would it cost to buy 6 kilograms of the drug?

55. *Rare Flower* A very rare essence of an almost extinct flower found in the Amazon jungle of South America is extracted by a biogenetic company trying to copy and synthesize it. The company estimates that if the procedure is successful, the product will cost the company $850 per milliliter to produce. How much will it cost the company to produce 0.4 liter of the engineered essence?

56. *Longest Train Run* The world's longest train run is on the Trans-Siberian line in Russia, from Moscow to Nakhodka on the Sea of Japan. The length of the run, which makes 97 stops, measures 94,380,000 centimeters. The run takes 8 days, 4 hours, and 25 minutes.

(a) How many meters is the run?

(b) How many kilometers is the run?

57. *Highest Railroad* The highest railroad line in the world is a track on the Morococha branch of the Peruvian state railways at La Cima. The track is 4818 meters high.

(a) How many centimeters high is the track?

(b) How many kilometers high is the track?

58. *Dam Height* A dam is 335 meters high.

(a) How many kilometers high is the dam?

(b) How many centimeters high is the dam?

Mixed Practice

59. 5280 feet = _____ yards

60. 8 pints = _____ quarts

61. 4 miles = _____ feet

62. 12 feet = _____ inches

63. 9 tons = _____ pounds

64. 18 hours = _____ seconds

65. 14.6 kg = _____ g

66. 0.83 kg = _____ mg

67. 3.22 kL = _____ L

68. 3607 mL = _____ L = _____ kL

69. 7183 mg = _____ g = _____ kg

To Think About
*Metric prefixes are also used for computers. A **byte** is the amount of computer memory needed to store one alphanumeric character. In reference to computers you may hear the following words: kilobytes, megabytes, and gigabytes. Use the following chart to convert the measurements in exercises 70–73.*

70. 1.2 gigabytes = _____ bytes

71. 528 megabytes = _____ bytes

72. 78.9 kilobytes = _____ bytes

73. 24.9 gigabytes = _____ bytes

1 gigabyte (GB) = one billion bytes	= 1,000,000,000 bytes
1 megabyte (MB) = one million bytes[*]	= 1,000,000 bytes
1 kilobyte (KB) or K = one thousand bytes[†]	= 1000 bytes

*Sometimes in computer science 1 megabyte is considered to be 1,048,576 bytes.
†Sometimes in computer science 1 kilobyte is considered to be 1024 bytes.

Cumulative Review

74. [8.7.1] 14 out of 70 is what percent?

75. [8.7.1] What is 23% of 250?

76. [8.7.1] What is 1.7% of $18,900?

77. [8.7.1] *Furniture Sold* A salesperson earns a commission of 8%. She sold furniture worth $8960. How much commission will she earn?

Quick Quiz 10.1

1. Mount Whitney is 14,496 feet high. How many miles is that? Round your answer to the nearest hundredth.

2. Convert 500 milliliters to meters.

3. Convert 9 kilograms to milligrams.

4. Concept Check Explain how you would convert 240 ounces to pounds.

① Converting Units of Length, Volume, and Weight Between the Metric and U.S. Systems

So far we've seen how to convert units when working *within* either the U.S. or the metric system. Many people, however, work with *both* the metric and U.S. systems. If you study such fields as chemistry, electromechanical technology, business, X-ray technology, nursing, or computers, you will probably need to convert measurements between the two systems. We learn that skill in this section.

To convert between U.S. and metric units, it is necessary to know equivalent values. The most commonly used equivalents are listed below. Most of these equivalents are approximate, denoted by ≈.

Student Learning Objectives

After studying this section, you will be able to:

 Convert units of length, volume, and weight between the metric and U.S. systems.

 Convert between Fahrenheit and Celsius degrees of temperature.

Equivalent Measures

	U.S. to Metric	Metric to U.S.
Units of length	1 mile ≈ 1.61 kilometers 1 yard ≈ 0.914 meter 1 foot ≈ 0.305 meter 1 inch = 2.54 centimeters*	1 kilometer ≈ 0.62 mile 1 meter ≈ 1.09 yards 1 meter ≈ 3.28 feet 1 centimeter ≈ 0.394 inch
Units of volume	1 gallon ≈ 3.79 liters 1 quart ≈ 0.946 liter	1 liter ≈ 0.264 gallon 1 liter ≈ 1.06 quarts
Units of weight	1 pound ≈ 0.454 kilogram 1 ounce ≈ 28.35 grams	1 kilogram ≈ 2.2 pounds 1 gram ≈ 0.0353 ounce

*Exact value

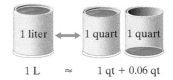

1 liter ⟷ 1 quart 1 quart

1 L ≈ 1 qt + 0.06 qt

Remember that to convert from one unit to another we multiply by a unit fraction that is equivalent to 1. We create a fraction from the equivalent measures table so that the unit in the numerator is the unit we want to end up with. To change 5 miles to kilometers, we look in the table and find that 1 mile ≈ 1.61 kilometers. We will use the fraction

$$\frac{1.61 \text{ km}}{1 \text{ mi}}$$

We want to have 1.61 kilometers in the numerator.

$$5 \text{ mi} \times \frac{1.61 \text{ km}}{1 \text{ mi}} = 5 \times 1.61 \text{ km} = 8.05 \text{ km}$$

Thus 5 miles is approximately 8.05 kilometers.

EXAMPLE 1

(a) Convert 26 m to yd.
(b) Convert 1.9 km to mi.
(c) Convert 14 gal to L.
(d) Convert 2.5 L to qt.
(e) Convert 5.6 lb to kg.
(f) Convert 152 g to oz.

Solution

(a) $26 \text{ m} \times \dfrac{1.09 \text{ yd}}{1 \text{ m}} = 28.34 \text{ yd}$

(b) $1.9 \text{ km} \times \dfrac{0.62 \text{ mi}}{1 \text{ km}} = 1.178 \text{ mi}$

(c) $14 \text{ gal} \times \dfrac{3.79 \text{ L}}{1 \text{ gal}} = 53.06 \text{ L}$

(d) $2.5 \text{ L} \times \dfrac{1.06 \text{ qt}}{1 \text{ L}} = 2.65 \text{ qt}$

(e) $5.6 \text{ lb} \times \dfrac{0.454 \text{ kg}}{1 \text{ lb}} = 2.5424 \text{ kg}$

(f) $152 \text{ g} \times \dfrac{0.0353 \text{ oz}}{1 \text{ g}} = 5.3656 \text{ oz}$

Practice Problem 1

(a) Convert 17 m to yd.
(b) Convert 29.6 km to mi.
(c) Convert 26 gal to L.
(d) Convert 6.2 L to qt.
(e) Convert 16 lb to kg.
(f) Convert 280 g to oz.

Although the calculations in Example 1 show "=", keep in mind that most conversions are approximations and have been rounded.

Some conversions require more than one step.

EXAMPLE 2 Convert 235 cm to feet. Round your answer to the nearest hundredth of a foot.

Solution Our first unit fraction converts centimeters to inches. Our second unit fraction converts inches to feet.

$$235 \text{ cm} \times \frac{0.394 \text{ in.}}{1 \text{ cm}} \quad \text{We convert to inches.}$$

$$235 \times \frac{0.394 \text{ in.}}{1} \times \frac{1 \text{ ft}}{12 \text{ in.}} = \frac{92.59}{12} \text{ ft} = 7.71583$$

Rounded to the nearest hundredth we have 7.72 ft.

Practice Problem 2 Convert 180 cm to feet.

The same rules can be followed to convert a rate such as 100 kilometers per hour to miles per hour.

EXAMPLE 3 Convert 100 km/hr to mi/hr.

Solution We multiply by the unit fraction that relates mi to km.

$$\frac{100 \text{ km}}{\text{hr}} \times \frac{0.62 \text{ mi}}{1 \text{ km}} = 62 \text{ mi/hr}$$

Thus 100 km/hr is approximately equal to 62 mi/hr.

Practice Problem 3 Convert 88 km/hr to mi/hr.

EXAMPLE 4 A camera film that is 35 mm wide is how many inches wide?

Solution We first convert from millimeters to centimeters by moving the decimal point in the number 35 one place to the left.

$$35 \text{ mm} = 3.5 \text{ cm}$$

Then we convert to inches using a unit fraction.

$$3.5 \text{ cm} \times \frac{0.394 \text{ in.}}{1 \text{ cm}} = 1.379 \text{ in.}$$

Practice Problem 4 The city police use 9-mm automatic pistols. If such a pistol fires a bullet 9 mm wide, how many inches wide is it? (Round to the nearest hundredth.)

Understanding the Concept

Changing the Area of a Rectangle from U.S. to Metric Units

Suppose we consider a rectangle that measures 2 yd wide by 4 yd long. The area would be 2 yd × 4 yd = 8 yd². How could you change 8 yd² to m²? Suppose that we look at 1 yd². Each side is 1 yd long, which is approximately 0.914 m.

Area = 1 yd × 1 yd ≈ 0.914 m × 0.914 m

Area = 1 yd² ≈ 0.8354 m² (rounded to the ten-thousandths place)

Thus 1 yd² ≈ 0.8354 m². Therefore, we change 8 yd² to m² as follows:

$$8 \text{ yd}^2 \times \frac{0.8354 \text{ m}^2}{1 \text{ yd}^2} = 6.6832 \text{ m}^2$$

8 yd² ≈ 6.6832 m². Thus, 8 square yards is approximately 6.6832 square meters.

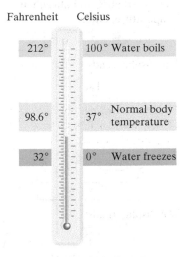

Fahrenheit   Celsius

212° — 100° Water boils

98.6° — 37° Normal body temperature

32° — 0° Water freezes

② Converting Between Fahrenheit and Celsius Degrees of Temperature

In the metric system, temperature is measured on the **Celsius scale.** Water boils at 100° (100°C) and freezes at 0° (0°C) on the Celsius scale. In the **Fahrenheit system,** water boils at 212° (212°F) and freezes at 32° (32°F).

To convert a Celsius temperature to Fahrenheit, we can use the formula

$$F = 1.8 \times C + 32$$

and to convert a Fahrenheit temperature to Celsius, we can use the formula

$$C = \frac{5 \times F - 160}{9}$$

where F is the number of Fahrenheit degrees and C is the number of Celsius degrees.

EXAMPLE 5   Convert 176°F to Celsius temperature.

Solution   We use the formula that gives us Celsius degrees.

$$C = \frac{5 \times F - 160}{9}$$

$$= \frac{5 \times 176 - 160}{9} \qquad \text{We multiply, then subtract.}$$

$$= \frac{880 - 160}{9} = \frac{720}{9} = 80$$

The temperature is 80°C.

Practice Problem 5   Convert 181°F to Celsius temperature. Round to the nearest degree.

NOTE TO STUDENT: Fully worked-out solutions to all of the Practice Problems can be found at the back of the text starting at page SP-1

EXAMPLE 6   Hester is planning a visit from his home in Rhode Island to Brazil. He checked the weather report for the part of Brazil where he will visit and finds that the temperature during the day is 37°C. If the temperature in Rhode Island is currently 87°F, what is the difference between the higher and lower temperatures in degrees Fahrenheit?

Solution   We want to convert the Celsius temperature to Fahrenheit so we use the following formula.

$$F = 1.8 \times C + 32$$
$$= 1.8 \times 37 + 32 \quad \text{We replace } C \text{ with the Celsius temperature.}$$
$$= 66.6 + 32 \qquad \text{We multiply before we add.}$$
$$= 98.6$$

It is 98.6°F in Brazil.
    Now we find the difference in Fahrenheit temperatures.

$$98.6° - 87° = 11.6°F$$

Practice Problem 6   On a cold winter day in England, Erin notices that the temperature reads 4°C. She calls home in Los Angeles, California, and finds out that the temperature is 79°F. What is the difference between the higher and lower temperatures in degrees Fahrenheit?

Calculator

Converting Temperature

You can use your calculator to convert temperature readings between Fahrenheit and Celsius. To convert 30°C to Fahrenheit temperature, enter:

1.8 ⟨×⟩ 30 ⟨+⟩ 32 ⟨=⟩

The display reads:

    86

The temperature is 86°F.
To convert 82.4°F to Celsius temperature, enter:

5 ⟨×⟩ 82.4 − 160

⟨=⟩ ⟨÷⟩ 9 ⟨=⟩

The display reads:

    28

The temperature is 28°C.

Perform each conversion. Round your answer to the nearest hundredth when necessary.

1. 4 ft to m

2. 11 ft to m

3. 14 m to yd

4. 18 m to yd

5. 15 km to mi

6. 12 km to mi

7. 24 yd to m

8. 31 yd to m

9. 82 mi to km

10. 68 mi to km

11. 25 m to ft

12. 35 m to ft

13. 17.5 cm to in.

14. 19.6 cm to in.

15. 5 gal to L

16. 7 gal to L

17. 4.5 L to qt

18. 6.5 L to qt

19. 7 oz to g

20. 9 oz to g

21. 11 kg to lb

22. 14 kg to lb

23. 126 g to oz

24. 186 g to oz

The following problems involve a double conversion.

25. 4 kg to oz

26. 6 kg to oz

27. 230 cm to ft

28. 142 cm to ft

29. 16.5 ft to cm

30. 19.5 ft to cm

Perform each conversion. Round your answer to the nearest tenth when necessary.

31. 50 km/hr to mi/hr

32. 60 km/hr to mi/hr

33. 45 mi/hr to km/hr

34. 40 mi/hr to km/hr

Perform each conversion. Round your answer to the nearest hundredth when necessary.

35. A wire that is 13 mm wide is how many inches wide?

36. A bolt that is 7 mm wide is how many inches wide?

37. 0°C to Fahrenheit

38. 60°C to Fahrenheit

39. 85°C to Fahrenheit

40. 105°C to Fahrenheit

41. 168°F to Celsius

42. 112°F to Celsius

43. 86°F to Celsius

44. 98°F to Celsius

Mixed Practice *Perform each conversion. Round your answer to the nearest hundredth when necessary.*

45. 9 in. to cm

46. 13 in. to cm

47. 32.2 m to yd

48. 29.3 m to yd

49. 19 L to gal

50. 15 L to gal

51. 32 lb to kg

52. 27 lb to kg

53. 12°C to Fahrenheit

54. 21°C to Fahrenheit

55. 68°F to Celsius

56. 131°F to Celsius

Applications *Solve. Round your answer to the nearest hundredth when necessary.*

57. *Male's Weight* One of the heaviest human males documented in medical records weighed 635 kg in 1978. What would have been his weight in pounds?

58. *Child's Weight* The average weight for a 7-year-old girl is 22.2 kilograms. What is the average weight in pounds?

59. *Boat Travel* Mr. and Mrs. Weston have traveled 67 miles on a boat cruise from Seattle, Washington, to Victoria Island, Vancouver, B.C., Canada. They have 36 kilometers until their rendezvous point with another boat. How many kilometers in total will they have traveled?

60. *Land Travel* Marcia is traveling from Ixtapa to a beach in Zihuatenejo in Mexico. The odometer on her American car shows that the first part of her trip was 4 miles. Then she sees a sign posted: "Zihuatenejo 14 KILOMETERS." How many kilometers in total will she have traveled when she arrives at her destination?

61. *Gasoline Use* Pierre had a Jeep imported into France. During a trip from Paris to Lyon, he used 38 liters of gas. The tank, which he filled before starting the trip, holds 15 gallons of gas. How many liters of gas were left in the tank when he arrived in Lyon?

62. *Surgical Procedure* A surgeon is irrigating an abdominal cavity after a cancerous growth is removed. There is a supply of 3 gallons of distilled water in the operating room. The surgeon uses a total of 7 liters of the water during the procedure. How many liters of water are left after the operation?

63. *Temperature Comparison* Hillina is vacationing in Spain, where the temperature during the day is 32°C. She is planning her trip home, where the temperature currently is 80°F. What is the difference between the higher and lower temperatures in degrees Fahrenheit?

64. *Temperature Comparison* Jessica lives in Los Angeles, California, and is planning a trip to Germany. The temperature in the part of Germany where she will visit is 25°C. If it is currently 85°F in Los Angeles, what is the difference between the higher and lower temperatures in degrees Fahrenheit?

65. *Temperature Comparison* In central Australia at 4 o'clock in the morning, the temperature is 19°C. After 7 o'clock in the morning, the temperature can reach 45°C. What would be equivalent Fahrenheit temperatures at 4 o'clock and 7 o'clock in the morning?

66. *Roasting a Turkey* A holiday turkey in Buenos Aires, Argentina, was roasted at 200°C for 4 hours, (20 minutes per pound). What would have been the cooking temperature in Fahrenheit in Joplin, Missouri?

Round your answer to the nearest thousandth.

 67. *Lead Poisoning* A pathologist found 0.768 oz of lead in the liver of a child who had died of lead poisoning. How many grams of toxic lead were in the child's liver?

 68. *Gold Nugget Weight* While panning in a river in the Yukon, in Alaska, a prospector found a gold nugget that weighed 2.552 oz. How many grams did the nugget weigh?

Cumulative Review *Perform the operations indicated in the correct order.*

69. [1.6.4] $2^3 \times 6 - 4 + 3$

70. [1.6.4] $5 + 2 - 3 + 5 \times 3^2$

71. [1.6.4] $2^2 + 3^2 + 4^3 + 2 \times 7$

72. [1.6.4] $5^2 + 4^2 + 3^2 + 3 \times 8$

Quick Quiz 10.2

1. The Australian copperhead is a highly venomous snake growing to as long as 1.8 meters. How many feet is 1.8 meters? Round your answer to the nearest whole number.

2. The anaconda snake lives in the rain forests and river systems of the Amazon. This snake's average weight is 149 kg. How many pounds is this? Round your answer to the nearest whole number.

3. The center hole of a CD is 1.5 centimeters across. How many inches is this? Round your answer to the nearest hundredth.

4. Concept Check Explain how you would convert 50 km/hr to mi/hr.

Subject Index

A

Absolute value, 107–108
  symbol for, 108
Acute angle, 587–588
Addends, 10
Addition
  associative property of, 12–13
  commutative property of, 11–13
  of decimal expressions, 441–442
  of fractional expressions, 303–310
  of integers, 113–117
  of mixed numbers, 314–317
  of polynomials, 351
  of several digit numbers, 14–16
  of whole numbers, 10
Addition principle of equality
  definition, 168, 390
  solving equations using, 168–170,
    390–391
Additive inverse property, 117, 168
Adjacent angles, 171, 589–590
Algebraic expressions
  definition, 64
  distributive property and, 65–66
  evaluating, 14, 64, 118, 154–155
  in exponent form, 56–57
  involving decimals, 442
  least common multiple of, 296–298
  multiples of, 296
  multiplying, 202–204
  simplifying, 153–155
Alternate interior angles, 590–591
Angle(s), 171
  adjacent, 171
  complement of, 588–589
  definition, 587
  naming, 587
  solving problems involving, 171–172
  supplement of, 588–589
  supplementary, 171
  types of, 587–600
Applied problems. *See* Problem solving.
  See also Applications index
Area, 188
  of a parallelogram, 187–190, 192
  of a rectangle, 187–190, 192
  of a square, 192
Array, 33
Associative property
  of addition, 12–13
  of multiplication, 35–37
Average, 528. *See also* Mean
Axis, 537

B

Base
  of exponent, 55, 188
  of triangle, 601
Bimodal data, 530
Binomial(s). *See also* Polynomial(s)
  definition, 204
  multiplying times a trinomial, 358
  multiplying using FOIL method,
    358–360
Borrowing, 25–27

C

Carrying, 14–16
Celsius scale, 583
  Celsius to Fahrenheit conversions,
    583–584
Center (of a circle), 606
Charts and diagrams, 83–84

Circle(s)
  area of, 608–609
  center of, 606
  definition, 606
  diameter, 606–608
  radius, 606–608
Circle graphs, 517
Clearing the fractions, 410
Coefficient, 69, 202
Commissions, 496
Common denominator, 303
Commutative property
  of addition, 11–13
  of multiplication, 35–37
Comparison line graphs, 519
  constructing, 519–521
Comparison problems, 415–417
Complementary angles, 588–589
Complex fractions
  applications involving, 327
  definition, 325
  simplifying, 325–326
Composite number, 220–221
Cone volume, 613–614
Constant term, 69
Coordinates, 539–540. *See also* Rectangular
    coordinate system
Corresponding angles, 590–591
  of similar triangles, 618
Corresponding sides, 618
Cross product, 264
Cylinder volume, 612–613

D

Decimal(s). *See also* Decimal expressions
  changing between fractions, percents, and,
    476–477
  comparing and ordering, 435–436
  converting to and from fractions, 434–435,
    452–453
  converting to and from percents, 474–475
  dividing by decimals, 451–452
  dividing by whole numbers, 449–450
  equations involving, 457–458
  estimating sum or difference, 443
  multiplying, 447–449
  rounding, 436–437, 443
Decimal expressions
  adding, 441–442
  subtracting, 441–442
Decimal fraction(s)
  definition, 433
  writing word names for, 433–434
Decimal notation, 433–434
Decimal point, 433
Degrees
  of angles, 587
  temperatures. *See* Celsius scale; Fahrenheit
    system
Denominator, 228
  common, 303
Diameter (of a circle), 606–608
Difference, 23–24
Digits, 2
Discount problems, 496–498
Distributive property
  definition, 65
  integers and, 155
  multiplying polynomials and, 204–205
  simplifying algebraic expressions
    and, 65–66
  solving equations, 357, 405, 414
Dividend, 45

Divisibility, 220
Division
  algebraic expressions and, 64–65
  applied problems involving, 50–51
  of decimals, 449–452
  definition, 44
  dividend, 45
  divisor, 45
  facts, 46–47
  of integers, 142–143
  involving one and zero, 47, 229
  long, 47–50
  of mixed numbers, 317–318
  quotient, 45
  remainder and, 47–50
  of whole numbers, 44–51
Division ladder, 222
Division principle of equality, 177–179,
    393–394
  definition, 393
  solving equations using, 393–394
Divisor, 45
Double-bar graphs, 518
  constructing, 519–521

E

Equality test for fractions, 264
Equations, 389–423. *See also* Linear
    equations; Solving equations
  addition principle of equality and, 168–170,
    390–391
  additive inverse property and, 117, 168
  applied problems with, 414–417
  checking solutions to, 399
  division principle of equality and, 177–179,
    393–394
  of the form $ax + b = c$, 399–400, 457–458
  of the form $x/a = c$, 336–338
  of the form $x + a = c$ and $x - a = c$,
    168–172, 390–391
  involving comparisons, 415–417
  involving decimals, 457–458
  involving fractions, 410–411
  involving geometric figures, 414–415
  involving perimeter, 186–187, 191
  involving volume, 190–192
  LCD method of solving, 410–411
  linear, 69–75
  linear with two variables, 546–553
  multiplication principle of equality and,
    336–338, 391–392
  parentheses in, 405–406
  simplifying, 400–402
  solving using basic arithmetic facts, 72–75
  translating English statements into, 71–75,
    179–180
  using more than one principle of equality,
    399–400
  using percents, 481–484
  variables on both sides of, 401
Equivalent fractions, 236–237
Even numbers, 138
Expanded notation, 3–4
Exponents, 55–59
  additional power rule, 250
  evaluating, 56–57
  exponent form, 55
  in fractions, 247–250
  multiplying expressions with, 202–204
  negative numbers and, 141–142
  parentheses and, 142
  product rule for, 201–202, 287, 357
  quotient rule for, 247–249, 289–290, 328

Applications Index

Elementary & Intermediate Algebra

Third Edition

by George Woodbury

Review of Real Numbers

This chapter reviews properties of real numbers and arithmetic that are necessary for success in algebra. The chapter also introduces several algebraic properties.

STUDY STRATEGY

Study Groups Throughout this book, study strategies will help you learn and be successful in this course. This chapter will focus on getting involved in a study group.

Working with a study group is an excellent way to learn mathematics, improve your confidence and level of interest, and improve your performance on quizzes and tests. When working with a group, you will be able to work through questions about the material you are studying. Also, by being able to explain how to solve a particular problem to another person in your group, you will increase your ability to retain this knowledge.

We will revisit this study strategy throughout this chapter so you can incorporate it into your study habits. See the end of Section 1.1 for tips on how to get a study group started.

1.1

Integers, Opposites, and Absolute Value

OBJECTIVES

1. **Graph whole numbers on a number line.**
2. **Determine which is the greater of two whole numbers.**
3. **Graph integers on a number line.**
4. **Find the opposite of an integer.**
5. **Determine which is the greater of two integers.**
6. **Find the absolute value of an integer.**

A **set** is a collection of objects, such as the set consisting of the numbers 1, 4, 9, and 16. This set can be written as {1, 4, 9, 16}. The braces, { }, are used to denote a set, and the values listed inside are said to be **elements**, or members, of the set. A set with no elements is called the **empty set** or **null set**. A **subset** of a set is a collection of some or all of the elements of the set. For example, {1, 9} is a subset of the set {1, 4, 9, 16}. A subset also can be an empty set.

Whole Numbers

Objective 1 Graph whole numbers on a number line. For the most part, this text deals with the set of real numbers. The set of real numbers is made up of the set of rational numbers and the set of irrational numbers.

> ### Rational Numbers
>
> A **rational number** is a number that can be expressed as a fraction, such as $\frac{3}{4}$ and $\frac{2}{9}$. Decimal numbers that terminate, such as 2.57, and decimal numbers that repeat, such as $0.444\ldots$, are also rational numbers.

> ### Irrational Numbers
>
> An **irrational number** is a number that cannot be expressed as a fraction, but instead is a decimal number that does not terminate or repeat. The number π is an example of an irrational number: $\pi = 3.14159\ldots$.

One subset of the set of real numbers is the set of natural numbers.

> ### Natural Numbers
>
> The set of **natural numbers** is the set $\{1, 2, 3, \ldots\}$.

If we include the number 0 with the set of natural numbers, we have the set of **whole numbers**.

> ### Whole Numbers
>
> The set of **whole numbers** is the set $\{0, 1, 2, 3, \ldots\}$. This set can be displayed on a number line as follows:
>
>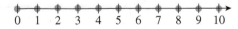

The arrow on the right-hand side of the number line indicates that the values continue to increase in this direction. There is no largest whole number, but we say that the values approach infinity (∞).

To graph any particular number on a number line, we place a point, or dot, at that location on the number line.

EXAMPLE 1   Graph the number 6 on a number line.

SOLUTION   To graph any number on a number line, place a point at that number's location.

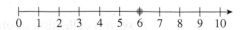

Quick Check 1

Graph the number 4 on a number line.

Inequalities

Objective 2 Determine which is the greater of two whole numbers. When comparing two whole numbers a and b, we say that a is **greater than** b, denoted $a > b$, if the number a is to the right of the number b on the number line. The number a is **less than** b, denoted $a < b$, if a is to the left of b on the number line. The statements $a > b$ and $a < b$ are called **inequalities**.

EXAMPLE 2 Write the appropriate symbol, $<$ or $>$, between the following:
6 _____ 4

SOLUTION   Let's take a look at the two values graphed on a number line.

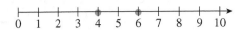

Because the number 6 is to the right of the number 4 on the number line, 6 is greater than 4. So $6 > 4$.

EXAMPLE 3 Write the appropriate symbol, $<$ or $>$, between the following:
2 _____ 5

SOLUTION   Because 2 is to the left of 5 on the number line, $2 < 5$.

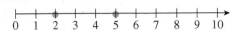

Quick Check 2

Write the appropriate symbol, $<$ or $>$, between the following:

a) 8 _____ 3

b) 19 _____ 23

Integers

Objective ③ **Graph integers on a number line.** Another important subset of the real numbers is the set of integers.

Integers —
The set of **integers** is the set $\{\ldots, -3, -2, -1, 0, 1, 2, 3, \ldots\}$. We can display the set of integers on a number line as follows:

The arrow on the left side indicates that the values continue to decrease in this direction, and they are said to approach negative infinity $(-\infty)$.

Opposites

Objective ④ **Find the opposite of an integer.** The set of integers is the set of whole numbers together with the opposites of the natural numbers. The **opposite** of a number is a number on the other side of 0 on the number line and the same distance from 0 as that number. We denote the opposite of a real number a as $-a$. For example, -5 and 5 are opposites because both are 5 units away from 0 and one is to the left of 0 while the other is to the right of 0.

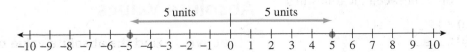

Numbers to the left of 0 on the number line are called **negative numbers**. Negative numbers represent a quantity less than 0. For example, if you have written checks that the balance in your checking account cannot cover, your balance will be a negative number. A temperature that is below 0° F, a golf score that is below par, and an elevation that is below sea level are other examples of quantities that can be represented by negative numbers.

EXAMPLE 4   What is the opposite of 7?

SOLUTION   The opposite of 7 is −7 because −7 also is 7 units away from 0 but is on the opposite side of 0.

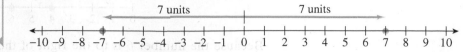

EXAMPLE 5   What is the opposite of −6?

SOLUTION   The opposite of −6 is 6.

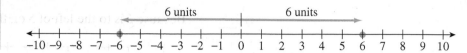

The opposite of 0 is 0 itself. Zero is the only number that is its own opposite.

Inequalities with Integers

Objective 5 Determine which is the greater of two integers. Inequalities for integers follow the same guidelines as they do for whole numbers. If we are given two integers *a* and *b*, the number that is greater is the number that is to the right on the number line.

EXAMPLE 6   Write the appropriate symbol, < or >, between the following:
−3 _____ 5

SOLUTION   Looking at the number line, we can see that −3 is to the left of 5; so −3 < 5.

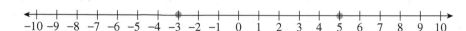

EXAMPLE 7   Write the appropriate symbol, < or >, between the following:
−2 _____ −7

SOLUTION   On the number line, −2 is to the right of −7; so −2 > −7.

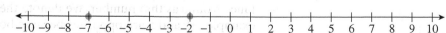

Absolute Values

Objective 6 Find the absolute value of an integer.

Absolute Value

The **absolute value** of a number *a*, denoted $|a|$, is the distance between *a* and 0 on the number line.

Distance cannot be negative, so the absolute value of a number *a* is always 0 or higher.

Quick Check 3
Find the opposite of the given integer.

a) −13   **b)** 8

Quick Check 4
Write the appropriate symbol, < or >, between the following:

a) −14 _____ −11
b) 6 _____ −20

EXAMPLE 8   Find the absolute value of 6.

SOLUTION   The number 6 is 6 units away from 0 on the number line, so $|6| = 6$.

EXAMPLE 9   Find the absolute value of -4.

SOLUTION   The number -4 is 4 units away from 0 on the number line, so $|-4| = 4$.

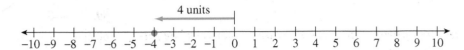

Quick Check 5
Find the absolute value of -9.

BUILDING YOUR STUDY STRATEGY

Study Groups, 1 With Whom to Work? To form a study group, you must begin with this question: With whom do I want to work? Look for students who are serious about learning, who are prepared for each class, and who ask intelligent questions during class.

Look for students with whom you believe you can get along. You are about to spend a great deal of time working with this group, sometimes under stressful conditions.

If you take advantage of tutorial services provided by your college, keep an eye out for classmates who do the same. There is a strong chance that classmates who use the tutoring center are serious about learning mathematics and earning good grades.

Exercises 1.1   MyMathLab

PRACTICE   WATCH   DOWNLOAD   READ   REVIEW

Vocabulary

1. A set with no elements is called the _____.
2. A number m is _____ than another number n if it is located to the left of n on a number line.
3. The arrow on the right side of a number line indicates that the values approach _____.
4. $c > d$ if c is located to the _____ of d on a number line.

Graph the following whole numbers on a number line.

5. 7

6. 3

7. 6

8. 9

9. 2

10. 13

Write the appropriate symbol, $<$ or $>$, between the following whole numbers.

11. 3 ____ 13   12. 7 ____ 9

13. 8 ____ 6   14. 12 ____ 5

15. 45 ____ 42   16. 33 ____ 37

Graph the following integers on a number line.

17. -4

18. -7

19. 5

20. -9

21. -12

22. 4

Find the opposite of the following integers.

23. -7

24. 5

25. 22

26. -13

27. 0

28. -39

Write the appropriate symbol, $<$ or $>$, between the following integers.

29. -7 ___ -9

30. -5 ___ -2

31. -13 ___ -11

32. -8 ___ -14

33. -16 ___ 0

34. 5 ___ -3

35. 9 ___ -14

36. -10 ___ 6

Find the following absolute values.

37. $|-15|$

38. $|9|$

39. $|0|$

40. $|-6|$

41. $|-7|$

42. $|-12|$

43. $-|7|$

44. $-|12|$

45. $-|-29|$

46. $-|-8|$

Write the appropriate symbol, $<$ or $>$, between the following integers.

47. $|-7|$ ___ 4

48. $|-17|$ ___ $|13|$

49. -16 ___ $|-16|$

50. $|8|$ ___ $|-19|$

51. $-|-24|$ ___ $|-47|$

52. $|-8|$ ___ $-|8|$

Identify whether the given number is a member of the following sets of numbers: A. natural numbers, B. whole numbers, C. integers, D. real numbers.

53. 8

54. -6

55. 0

56. 3.14

57. -9

58. 20

Find the missing number if possible. There may be more than one number that works, so find as many as possible. There may be no number that works.

59. $|?| = 5$

60. $|?| = 18$

61. $|?| = -7$

62. $|?| = 0$

63. $|?| - 8 = 6$

64. $4 \cdot |?| + 3 = 27$

Writing in Mathematics

Answer in complete sentences.

65. A fellow student tells you that to find the absolute value of any number, make the number positive. Is this always true? Explain in your own words.

66. True or false: The opposite of the opposite of a number is the number itself.

67. If the opposite of a nonzero integer is equal to the absolute value of that integer, is the integer positive or negative? Explain your reasoning.

68. If an integer is less than its opposite, is the integer positive or negative? Explain your reasoning.

1.2

Operations with Integers

OBJECTIVES

1. Add integers.
2. Subtract integers.
3. Multiply integers.
4. Divide integers.

Addition and Subtraction of Integers

Objective 1 Add integers. Using the number line can help us learn how to add and subtract integers. Suppose we are trying to add the integers 3 and -7, which could be written as $3 + (-7)$. On a number line, we will start at 0 and move 3 units in the positive, or right, direction. Adding −7 tells us to move 7 units in the negative, or left, direction.

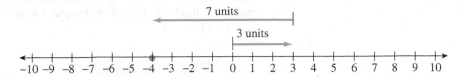

Ending up at −4 tells us that 3 + (−7) = −4.

We can use a similar approach to verify an important property of opposites: the sum of two opposites is equal to 0.

Sum of Two Opposites

For any real number a, $a + (-a) = 0$.

Suppose that we want to add the opposites 4 and −4. Using the number line, we begin at 0 and move 4 units to the right. We then move 4 units to the left, ending at 0. So 4 + (−4) = 0.

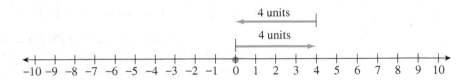

We also can see that 3 + (−7) = −4 through the use of manipulatives, which are hands-on tools used to demonstrate mathematical properties. Suppose we had a bag of green and red candies. Let each piece of green candy represent a positive 1 and each piece of red candy represent a negative 1. To add 3 + (−7), we begin by combining 3 green candies (positive 3) with 7 red candies (negative 7). Combining 1 red candy with 1 green candy has a net result of 0, as the sum of two opposites is equal to 0. So each time we make a pair of a green candy and a red candy, these two candies cancel each other's effect and can be discarded. After doing this, we are left with 4 red candies. The answer is −4.

Now we will examine another technique for finding the sum of a positive number and a negative number. In the sum 3 + (−7), the number 3 contributes to the sum in a positive fashion while the number –7 contributes to the sum in a negative fashion. The two numbers contribute to the sum in an opposite manner. We can think of the sum as the difference between these two contributions.

Adding a Positive Number and a Negative Number

1. **Take the absolute value of each number and find the difference between these two absolute values.** This is the difference between the two numbers' contributions to the sum.

2. **Note that the sign of the result is the same as the sign of the number that has the largest absolute value.**

For the sum $3 + (-7)$, we begin by taking the absolute value of each number: $|3| = 3, |-7| = 7$. The difference between the absolute values is 4. The sign of the sum is the same as the sign of the number that has the larger absolute value. In this case, -7 has the larger absolute value, so the result is negative. Therefore, $3 + (-7) = -4$.

EXAMPLE 1   Find the sum $12 + (-8)$.

SOLUTION

$\|12\| = 12;$ $\|8\| = 8$	Find the absolute value of each number.
$12 - 8 = 4$	The difference between the absolute values is 4.
$12 + (-8) = 4$	Because the number with the larger absolute value is positive, the result is positive.

Quick Check 1
Find the sum $14 + (-6)$.

Notice in the previous example that $12 + (-8)$ is equivalent to $12 - 8$, which also equals 4. What the two expressions have in common is that there is one number (12) contributes to the total in a positive fashion and a second number (8) that contributes to the total in a negative fashion.

EXAMPLE 2   Find the sum $3 + (-11)$.

SOLUTION   Again, one number (3) contributes to the total in a positive way and a second number (11) contributes in a negative way. The difference between their contributions is 8 and because the number making the larger contribution is negative, the result is -8.

$$3 + (-11) = -8$$

Quick Check 2
Find the sum $4 + (-17)$.

Note that $-11 + 3$ also equals -8. The rules for adding a positive integer and a negative integer still apply when the first number is negative and the second number is positive.

Adding Two (or More) Negative Numbers
1. Total the negative contributions of each number.
2. Note that the sign of the result is negative.

EXAMPLE 3   Find the sum $-3 + (-7)$.

SOLUTION   Both values contribute to the total in a negative fashion. Totaling the negative contributions of 3 and 7 results in 10, and the result is negative because both numbers are negative.

$$-3 + (-7) = -10$$

Quick Check 3
Find the sum $-2 + (-9)$.

Objective 2 Subtract integers. To subtract a negative integer from another integer, we use the following property:

Subtraction of Real Numbers
For any real numbers a and b, $a - b = a + (-b)$.

This property says that adding the opposite of b to a is the same as subtracting b from a. Suppose we are subtracting a negative integer, as in the example $-8 - (-19)$. The property for subtraction of real numbers says that subtracting -19 is the same as adding its opposite (19); so we convert this subtraction to $-8 + 19$. Remember that subtracting a negative number is equivalent to adding a positive number.

EXAMPLE 4 Subtract $6 - (-27)$.

SOLUTION

$$6 - (-27) = 6 + 27 \quad \text{Subtracting } -27 \text{ is the same as adding 27.}$$
$$= 33 \qquad \text{Add.}$$

Quick Check 4
Subtract $11 - (-7)$.

General Strategy for Adding/Subtracting Integers

- Rewrite "double signs." *Adding a negative number,* $4 + (-5)$, *can be rewritten as subtracting a positive number,* $4 - 5$. *Subtracting a negative number,* $-2 - (-7)$, *can be rewritten as adding a positive number,* $-2 + 7$.
- Look at each integer and determine whether it is contributing positively or negatively to the total.
- Add any integers contributing positively to the total, resulting in a single positive integer. In a similar fashion, add all integers that are contributing to the total negatively, resulting in a single negative integer. Finish by finding the sum of these two integers.

Rather than saying to add or subtract, the directions for a problem may state to "simplify" a numerical expression. To **simplify** an expression means to perform all arithmetic operations.

EXAMPLE 5 Simplify $17 - (-11) - 6 + (-13) - (-21) + 3$.

SOLUTION Begin by working on the *double signs*. This produces the following:

$$17 - (-11) - 6 + (-13) - (-21) + 3$$
$$= 17 + 11 - 6 - 13 + 21 + 3 \qquad \text{Rewrite double signs.}$$
$$= 52 - 19 \qquad\qquad\qquad\quad \text{The four integers that contribute in a positive fashion}$$
$$\qquad\qquad\qquad\qquad\qquad\qquad (17, 11, 21, \text{and } 3) \text{ total } 52. \text{ The}$$
$$\qquad\qquad\qquad\qquad\qquad\qquad \text{two integers that contribute in}$$
$$\qquad\qquad\qquad\qquad\qquad\qquad \text{a negative fashion total } -19.$$
$$= 33 \qquad\qquad\qquad\qquad\quad \text{Subtract.}$$

Quick Check 5
Simplify $14 - 9 - (-22) - 6 + (-30) + 5$.

Multiplication and Division of Integers

Objective 3 **Multiply integers.** The result obtained when multiplying two numbers is called the **product** of the two numbers. The numbers that are multiplied are called **factors.** When we multiply two positive integers, their product also is a positive integer. For example, the product of the two positive integers 4 and 7 is the positive integer 28. This can be written as $4 \cdot 7 = 28$. The product $4 \cdot 7$ also can be written as $4(7)$ or $(4)(7)$.

The product $4 \cdot 7$ is another way to represent the repeated addition of 7 four times.

$$4 \cdot 7 = 7 + 7 + 7 + 7$$
$$= 28$$

This concept can be used to show that the product of a positive integer and a negative integer is a negative integer. Suppose we want to multiply 4 by -7. We can rewrite this as -7 being added four times, or $(-7) + (-7) + (-7) + (-7)$. From our work earlier in this section, we know that this total is -28; so $4(-7) = -28$. Anytime we multiply a positive integer and by a negative integer, the result is negative. So $(-7)(4)$ also is equal to -28.

Products of Integers

$$(\text{Positive}) \cdot (\text{Negative}) = \text{Negative}$$
$$(\text{Negative}) \cdot (\text{Positive}) = \text{Negative}$$

EXAMPLE 6   Multiply $5(-8)$.

SOLUTION   We begin by multiplying 5 and 8, which equals 40. The next step is to determine the sign of the result. Whenever we multiply a positive integer by a negative integer, the result is negative.

$$5(-8) = -40$$

Quick Check 6
Multiply $10(-6)$.

A WORD OF CAUTION Note the difference between $5 - 8$ (a subtraction) and $5(-8)$ (a multiplication). A set of parentheses *without* a sign in front of them is used to imply multiplication.

Product	Result
(3)(−5)	−15
(2)(−5)	−10
(1)(−5)	−5
(0)(−5)	0
(−1)(−5)	?
(−2)(−5)	?

The product of two negative integers is a positive integer. Let's try to understand why this is true by considering the example $(-2)(-5)$. Examine the table to the left, which shows the products of some integers and −5.

Notice the pattern in the table. Each time the integer multiplied by −5 decreases by 1, the product increases by 5. As we go from $0(-5)$ to $(-1)(-5)$, the product should increase by 5. So $(-1)(-5) = 5$ and, by the same reasoning, $(-2)(-5) = 10$.

Product of Two Negative Integers

$$(\text{Negative}) \cdot (\text{Negative}) = \text{Positive}$$

EXAMPLE 7 Multiply $(-9)(-8)$.

SOLUTION We begin by multiplying 9 and 8, which equals 72. The next step is to determine the sign of the result. Whenever we multiply a negative integer by a negative integer, the result is positive.

$$(-9)(-8) = 72$$

Quick Check 7
Multiply $(-7)(-9)$.

Products of Integers

- If a product contains an *odd number* of negative factors, the result is negative.
- If a product contains an *even number* of negative factors, the result is positive.

The main idea behind this principle is that every two negative factors multiply to be positive. If there are three negative factors, the product of the first two is a positive number. Multiplying this positive product by the third negative factor produces a negative product.

EXAMPLE 8 Multiply $7(-2)(-5)(-3)$.

SOLUTION Because there are three negative factors, the product will be negative.

$$7(-2)(-5)(-3) = -210$$

Quick Check 8
Multiply $-4(-10)(5)(-2)$.

Using Your Calculator Here is how the screen looks when you are using the TI-84 to multiply the expression in the previous example:

```
7(-2)(-5)(-3)
                -210
```

Notice that parentheses can be used to indicate multiplication without using the ⊠ key.

Before continuing on to division, let's consider multiplication by 0. Any real number multiplied by 0 is 0; this is the multiplication property of 0.

Multiplication Property of 0

For any real number x,

$$0 \cdot x = 0$$
$$x \cdot 0 = 0.$$

Objective 4 Divide integers. When dividing one number called the **dividend** by another number called the **divisor**, the result obtained is called the **quotient** of the two numbers:

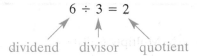

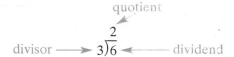

The statement "6 divided by 3 is equal to 2" is true because the product of the quotient and the divisor, $2 \cdot 3$, is equal to the dividend 6.

$$6 \div 3 = 2 \longleftrightarrow 2 \cdot 3 = 6$$

When we divide two integers that have the same sign (both positive or both negative), the quotient is positive. When we divide two integers that have different signs (one negative, one positive), the quotient is negative. Note that this is consistent with the rules for multiplication.

Quotients of Integers

(Positive) ÷ (Positive) = Positive   (Positive) ÷ (Negative) = Negative

(Negative) ÷ (Negative) = Positive   (Negative) ÷ (Positive) = Negative

---

EXAMPLE 9 Divide $(-54) \div (-6)$.

SOLUTION   When we divide a negative number by another negative number, the result is positive.

$$(-54) \div (-6) = 9 \quad \text{Note that } -6 \cdot 9 = -54.$$

EXAMPLE 10 Divide $(-33) \div 11$.

SOLUTION   When we divide a negative number by a positive number, the result is negative.

$$(-33) \div 11 = -3$$

Whenever 0 is divided by any integer (except 0), the quotient is 0. For example, $0 \div 16 = 0$. We can check that this quotient is correct by multiplying the quotient by the divisor. Because $0 \cdot 16 = 0$, the quotient is correct.

Quick Check 9

Divide $72 \div (-8)$.

Division by Zero

Whenever an integer is divided by 0, the quotient is said to be **undefined**.

Use the word **undefined** to state that an operation cannot be performed or is meaningless. For example, $41 \div 0$ is undefined. Suppose there was a real number a for which $41 \div 0 = a$. In that case, the product $a \cdot 0$ would be equal to 41. Because the product of 0 and any real number is equal to 0, such a number a does not exist.

Exercises 1.2

PRACTICE   WATCH   DOWNLOAD   READ   REVIEW

Vocabulary

1. When finding the sum of a positive integer and a negative integer, the sign of the result is determined by the sign of the integer with the _____ absolute value.

2. The sum of two negative integers is a(n) _____ integer.

3. Subtracting a negative integer can be rewritten as adding a(n) _____ integer.

4. The product of a positive integer and a negative integer is a(n)_____ integer.

5. The product of a negative integer and a negative integer is a(n) _____ integer.

6. If a product contains a(n) _____ number of negative integers, the product is negative.

7. In a division problem, the number you divide by is called the _____.

8. Division by 0 results in a quotient that is _____.

Add.

9. $8 + (-13)$

10. $16 + (-11)$

11. $6 + (-33)$

12. $52 + (-87)$

13. $(-4) + 5$

14. $-9 + 2$

15. $-14 + 22$

16. $(-35) + 50$

17. $-5 + (-6)$

18. $-9 + (-9)$

Subtract.

19. $8 - 6$

20. $13 - 9$

21. $5 - 11$

22. $4 - 12$

23. $(-5) - 3$

24. $(-9) - 6$

25. $-9 - 13$

26. $-47 - 16$

27. $36 - (-25)$

28. $64 - (-19)$

29. $-42 - (-33)$

30. $-27 - (-60)$

Simplify.

31. $8 - 13 - 6$

32. $-6 + 12 - 20$

33. $-9 + 7 - 4$

34. $-5 - 8 + 23$

35. $6 - (-16) + 5$

36. $18 - 21 - (-62)$

37. $4 + (-15) - 13 - (-25)$

38. $-13 + (-12) - (-1) - 29$

39. A mother with $30 in her purse paid $22 for her family to go to a movie. How much money did she have remaining?

40. A student had $60 in his checking account prior to writing an $85 check to the bookstore for books and supplies. What is his account's new balance?

41. The temperature at 6 A.M. in Fargo, North Dakota, was $-8°$C. By 3 P.M., the temperature had risen by $12°$ C. What was the temperature at 3 P.M.?

42. If a golfer completes a round at 3 strokes under par, her score is denoted -3. A professional golfer had rounds of $-4, -2, 3,$ and -6 in a recent tournament. What was her total score for this tournament?

43. Dylan drove from a town located 400 feet below sea level to another town located 1750 feet above sea level. What was the change in elevation traveling from one town to another?

44. After withdrawing $80 from her bank using an ATM card, Alycia had $374 remaining in her savings account.

How much money did Alycia have in her account prior to withdrawing the money?

83. A group of 4 friends went out to dinner. If each person paid $23, what was the total bill?

84. Three friends decided to start investing in stocks together. In the first year, they lost a total of $13,500. How much did each person lose?

Multiply.

45. 7(−6)

46. −4(9)

47. −8 · 5

48. −6(−8)

49. −15(−12)

50. −11 · 17

51. 82(−1)

52. −1 · 19

53. −6 · 0

54. 0(−240)

55. −6(−3)(5)

56. −2(−4)(−8)

57. 5 · 3(−2)(−6)

58. −7 · 2(−7)(−2)

Divide if possible.

59. 45 ÷ (−5)

60. 56 ÷ (−7)

61. −36 ÷ 6

62. −91 ÷ 13

63. −32 ÷ (−8)

64. −75 ÷ (−5)

65. 126 ÷ (−9)

66. −420 ÷ 14

67. 0 ÷ (−13)

68. 0 ÷ 11

69. 29 ÷ 0

70. −15 ÷ 0

Mixed Practice, 71–82

Simplify.

71. −11(−12)

72. 126 ÷ (−6)

73. 5 − 13

74. 5(−13)

75. 17 − (−11) − 49

76. 8(−7)(−6)

77. −432 ÷ 3

78. −5 · 17

79. 9(−24)

80. 9 + (−24)

81. 5 · 3(−17)(−29)(0)

82. −16 + (−11) − 42 − (−58)

85. Tina owns 400 shares of a stock that dropped in value by $3 per share last month. She also owns 500 shares of a stock that went up by $2 per share last month. What is Tina's net income on these two stocks for last month?

86. Mario took over as the CEO for a company that lost $20 million dollars in 2007. The company lost three times as much in 2008. The company went on to lose $13 million more in 2009 than it had lost in 2008. How much money did Mario's company lose in 2009?

87. When a certain integer is added to −34, the result is −15. What is that integer?

88. Thirty-five less than a certain integer is −13. What is that integer?

89. When a certain integer is divided by −8, the result is 16. What is that integer?

90. When a certain integer is multiplied by −4 and that product is added to 22, the result is −110. What is that integer?

True or False (If false, give an example that shows why the statement is false.)

91. The sum of two integers is always an integer.

92. The difference of two integers is always an integer.

93. The sum of two whole numbers is always a whole number.

94. The difference of two whole numbers is always a whole number.

Writing in Mathematics

Explain each of the following in your own words.

95. Explain why subtracting a negative integer from another integer is the same as adding the opposite of that integer to it. Use the example $11 - (-5)$ in your explanation.

96. Explain why a positive integer times a negative integer produces a negative integer.

97. Explain why a negative integer times another negative integer produces a positive integer.

98. Explain why $7 \div 0$ is undefined.

1.3

Fractions

OBJECTIVES

1. Find the factor set of a natural number.
2. Determine whether a natural number is prime.
3. Find the prime factorization of a natural number.
4. Simplify a fraction to lowest terms.
5. Change an improper fraction to a mixed number.
6. Change a mixed number to an improper fraction.

Factors

Objective 1 **Find the factor set of a natural number.** To factor a natural number, express it as the product of two natural numbers. For example, one way to factor 12 is to rewrite it as $3 \cdot 4$. In this example, 3 and 4 are said to be factors of 12. The collection of all factors of a natural number is called its **factor set**. The factor set of 12 can be written as $\{1, 2, 3, 4, 6, 12\}$ because $1 \cdot 12 = 12, 2 \cdot 6 = 12,$ and $3 \cdot 4 = 12$.

> **EXAMPLE 1** Write the factor set for 18.
>
> SOLUTION Because 18 can be factored as $1 \cdot 18, 2 \cdot 9,$ and $3 \cdot 6$, its factor set is $\{1, 2, 3, 6, 9, 18\}$.

Quick Check 1

Write the factor set for 36.

Prime Numbers

Objective 2 **Determine whether a natural number is prime.**

Prime Numbers

A natural number is **prime** if it is greater than 1 and its only two factors are 1 and itself.

For instance, the number 13 is prime because its only two factors are 1 and 13. The first 10 prime numbers are 2, 3, 5, 7, 11, 13, 17, 19, 23, and 29. The number 8 is not prime because it has factors other than 1 and 8, namely, 2 and 4. A natural number greater than 1 that is not prime is called a **composite** number. The number 1 is considered to be neither prime nor composite.

EXAMPLE 2 Determine whether the following numbers are prime or composite:

a) 26   **b)** 37

SOLUTION

a) The factor set for 26 is {1, 2, 13, 26}. Because 26 has factors other than 1 and itself, it is a composite number.

b) Because the number 37 has no factors other than 1 and itself, it is a prime number.

Quick Check 2

Determine whether the following numbers are prime or composite.

a) 57
b) 47
c) 48

Prime Factorization

Objective 3 Find the prime factorization of a natural number. When we rewrite a natural number as a product of prime factors, we obtain the **prime factorization** of the number. The prime factorization of 12 is $2 \cdot 2 \cdot 3$ because 2 and 3 are prime numbers and $2 \cdot 2 \cdot 3 = 12$. A **factor tree** is a useful tool for finding the prime factorization of a number. Here is an example of a factor tree for 72.

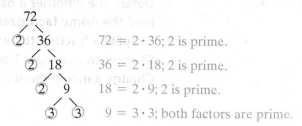

$72 = 2 \cdot 36$; 2 is prime.
$36 = 2 \cdot 18$; 2 is prime.
$18 = 2 \cdot 9$; 2 is prime.
$9 = 3 \cdot 3$; both factors are prime.

The prime factorization of 72 is $2 \cdot 2 \cdot 2 \cdot 3 \cdot 3$. We could have begun by rewriting 72 as $8 \cdot 9$ and then factored those two numbers. The process for creating a factor tree for a natural number is not unique, although the prime factorization for the number is unique.

EXAMPLE 3 Find the prime factorization of 60.

SOLUTION

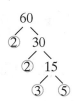

The prime factorization is $2 \cdot 2 \cdot 3 \cdot 5$.

Quick Check 3

Find the prime factorization of 63.

Fractions

Objective 4 Simplify a fraction to lowest terms. Recall from Section 1.1 that a rational number is a real number that can be written as the quotient (or ratio) of two integers, the second of which is not zero. An irrational number is a real number that cannot be written this way, such as the number π.

Rational numbers are often expressed using fraction notation such as $\frac{3}{7}$. Whole numbers such as 7 can be written as a fraction whose denominator is $1: \frac{7}{1}$. The number on the top of the fraction is called the **numerator**, and the number on the bottom of the fraction is called the **denominator**.

$$\frac{\text{numerator}}{\text{denominator}}$$

If the numerator and denominator do not have any common factors other than 1, the fraction is said to be in **lowest terms**.

To simplify a fraction to lowest terms, begin by finding the prime factorization of both the numerator and denominator. Then divide the numerator and the denominator by their common factors.

EXAMPLE 4 Simplify $\frac{18}{30}$ to lowest terms.

SOLUTION

$$\frac{18}{30} = \frac{2 \cdot 3 \cdot 3}{2 \cdot 3 \cdot 5}$$ Find the prime factorization of the numerator and denominator. $18 = 2 \cdot 3 \cdot 3$, $30 = 2 \cdot 3 \cdot 5$.

$$= \frac{\overset{1}{\cancel{2}} \cdot \overset{1}{\cancel{3}} \cdot 3}{\underset{1}{\cancel{2}} \cdot \underset{1}{\cancel{3}} \cdot 5}$$ Divide out common factors.

$$= \frac{3}{5}$$ Simplify.

EXAMPLE 5 Simplify $\frac{4}{24}$ to lowest terms.

SOLUTION

$$\frac{4}{24} = \frac{2 \cdot 2}{2 \cdot 2 \cdot 2 \cdot 3}$$ Find the prime factorization of the numerator and denominator.

$$\frac{\overset{1}{\cancel{2}} \cdot \overset{1}{\cancel{2}}}{\underset{1}{\cancel{2}} \cdot \underset{1}{\cancel{2}} \cdot 2 \cdot 3}$$ Divide out common factors.

$$= \frac{1}{6}$$ Simplify.

Quick Check 4
Simplify to lowest terms:

a) $\frac{45}{210}$ **b)** $\frac{24}{384}$

A WORD OF CAUTION It is customary to leave off the denominator of a fraction if it is equal to 1. For example, rather than writing $\frac{19}{1}$, we usually write 19. However, we cannot omit a numerator that is equal to 1. In the previous example, it would have been a mistake if we had written 6 instead of $\frac{1}{6}$.

Mixed Numbers and Improper Fractions

Objective 5 **Change an improper fraction to a mixed number.** An **improper fraction** is a fraction whose numerator is greater than or equal to its denominator, such as $\frac{7}{4}$, $\frac{400}{150}$, $\frac{8}{8}$, and $\frac{35}{7}$. (In contrast, a proper fraction's numerator is smaller than its denominator.) An improper fraction is often converted to a **mixed number**, which is the sum of a whole number and a proper fraction. For example, the improper fraction $\frac{14}{3}$ can be represented by the mixed number $4\frac{2}{3}$, which is equivalent to $4 + \frac{2}{3}$.

To convert an improper fraction to a mixed number, begin by dividing the denominator into the numerator. The quotient is the whole number portion of the mixed number. The remainder becomes the numerator of the fractional part, while the denominator of the fractional part is the same as the denominator of the improper function.

Denominator of fractional portion of mixed number $\longrightarrow 3\overline{)14}$ ← Whole-number portion of mixed number

-12

2 ← Numerator of fractional portion of mixed number

EXAMPLE 6 Convert the improper fraction $\frac{71}{9}$ to a mixed number.

SOLUTION Begin by dividing 9 into 71, which divides in 7 times with a remainder of 8.

$$9\overline{)71} \\ \underline{-63} \\ 8$$

with a 7 above.

The mixed number for $\frac{71}{9}$ is $7\frac{8}{9}$.

Quick Check 5

Convert the improper fraction $\frac{121}{13}$ to a mixed number.

Objective 6 Change a mixed number to an improper fraction. Often we have to convert a mixed number such as $2\frac{7}{15}$ into an improper fraction before proceeding with arithmetic operations.

Rewriting a Mixed Number as an Improper Fraction

- Multiply the whole number part of the mixed number by the denominator of the fractional part of the mixed number.
- Add this product to the numerator of the fractional part of the mixed number.
- The sum is the numerator of the improper fraction. The denominator stays the same.

Add product to numerator

$$2\frac{7}{15}$$

Multiply

$$2\frac{7}{15} = \frac{37}{15}$$

EXAMPLE 7 Convert the mixed number $5\frac{4}{7}$ to an improper fraction.

SOLUTION Begin by multiplying $5 \cdot 7 = 35$. Add this product to 4 to produce a numerator of 39.

$$5\frac{4}{7} = \frac{39}{7}$$

Quick Check 6

Convert the mixed number $8\frac{1}{6}$ to an improper fraction.

BUILDING YOUR STUDY STRATEGY

Study Groups, 3 Where to Meet

- Some study groups prefer to meet off campus in the evening. One good place to meet is at a coffee shop with tables large enough to accommodate everyone, provided that the surrounding noise is not too distracting.
- Some groups take advantage of study rooms at public libraries.
- Other groups like to meet at members' homes. This typically provides a comfortable, relaxing atmosphere in which to work.

Exercises 1.3

Vocabulary

1. The collection of all factors of a natural number is called its _____.

2. A natural number greater than 1 is _____ if its only factors are 1 and itself.

3. A natural number greater than 1 that is not prime is called a(n) _____ number.

4. Define the prime factorization of a natural number.

5. The numerator of a fraction is the number written on the _____ of the fraction.

6. The denominator of a fraction is the number written on the _____ of the fraction.

7. A fraction is in lowest terms if its numerator and denominator contain no _____ other than 1.

8. A fraction whose numerator is less than its denominator is called a(n) _____ fraction.

9. A fraction whose numerator is greater than or equal to its denominator is called a(n) _____ fraction.

10. An improper fraction can be rewritten as a whole number or as a(n) _____.

11. Is 7 a factor of 247?

12. Is 13 a factor of 273?

13. Is 6 a factor of 4836?

14. Is 9 a factor of 32,057?

15. Is 15 a factor of 2835?

16. Is 103 a factor of 1754?

Write the factor set for the following numbers.

17. 48

18. 60

19. 27

20. 15

21. 20

22. 16

23. 81

24. 64

25. 31

26. 103

27. 91

28. 143

Write the prime factorization of the following numbers. (If the number is prime, state this.)

29. 18

30. 20

31. 42

32. 36

33. 39

34. 50

35. 27

36. 32

37. 125

38. 49

39. 29

40. 76

41. 99

42. 90

43. 31

44. 209

45. 120

46. 109

Simplify the following fractions to lowest terms.

47. $\dfrac{10}{16}$

48. $\dfrac{35}{42}$

49. $\dfrac{9}{45}$

50. $\dfrac{38}{2}$

51. $\dfrac{168}{378}$

52. $\dfrac{60}{84}$

53. $\dfrac{27}{64}$

54. $\dfrac{66}{154}$

55. $\dfrac{160}{176}$

56. $\dfrac{56}{45}$

57. $\dfrac{49}{91}$

58. $\dfrac{72}{140}$

Convert the following mixed numbers to improper fractions.

59. $3\dfrac{4}{5}$

60. $7\dfrac{2}{9}$

61. $2\dfrac{16}{17}$

62. $6\dfrac{5}{14}$

63. $13\dfrac{8}{11}$

64. $17\dfrac{16}{33}$

Convert the following improper fractions to whole numbers or mixed numbers.

65. $\dfrac{39}{5}$

66. $\dfrac{56}{8}$

67. $\dfrac{101}{7}$

68. $\dfrac{12}{4}$

69. $\dfrac{141}{19}$

70. $\dfrac{109}{8}$

71. List four fractions that are equivalent to $\frac{3}{4}$.

72. List four fractions that are equivalent to $1\frac{2}{3}$.

73. List four whole numbers that have at least three different prime factors.

74. List four whole numbers greater than 100 that are prime.

Writing in Mathematics

Answer in complete sentences.

75. Describe a real-world situation involving fractions. Describe a real-world situation involving mixed numbers.

76. Describe a situation in which you should convert an improper fraction to a mixed number.

1.4

Operations with Fractions

OBJECTIVES

1. Multiply fractions and mixed numbers.
2. Divide fractions and mixed numbers.
3. Add and subtract fractions and mixed numbers with the same denominator.
4. Find the least common multiple (LCM) of two natural numbers.
5. Add and subtract fractions and mixed numbers with different denominators.

Multiplying Fractions

Objective 1 Multiply fractions and mixed numbers. To multiply fractions, we multiply the numerators together and multiply the denominators together. When multiplying fractions, we may simplify any individual fraction, as well as divide out a common factor from a numerator and a different denominator. Dividing out a common factor in this fashion is often referred to as **cross-canceling**.

EXAMPLE 1 Multiply $\frac{4}{11} \cdot \frac{5}{6}$.

SOLUTION The first numerator (4) and the second denominator (6) have a common factor of 2 that we can eliminate through division.

$$\frac{4}{11} \cdot \frac{5}{6} = \frac{\overset{2}{\cancel{4}}}{11} \cdot \frac{5}{\underset{3}{\cancel{6}}}$$ Divide out the common factor 2.

$$= \frac{2}{11} \cdot \frac{5}{3}$$ Simplify.

$$= \frac{10}{33}$$ Multiply the two numerators and the two denominators.

Quick Check 1

Multiply $\frac{10}{63} \cdot \frac{9}{16}$.

EXAMPLE 2 Multiply $3\frac{1}{7} \cdot \frac{14}{55}$.

SOLUTION When multiplying a mixed number by another number, convert the mixed number to an improper fraction before proceeding.

$$3\frac{1}{7} \cdot \frac{14}{55} = \frac{22}{7} \cdot \frac{14}{55} \quad \text{Convert } 3\frac{1}{7} \text{ to the improper fraction } \frac{22}{7}.$$

$$= \frac{\overset{2}{\cancel{22}}}{\underset{1}{\cancel{7}}} \cdot \frac{\overset{2}{\cancel{14}}}{\underset{5}{\cancel{55}}} \quad \text{Divide out the common factors 11 and 7.}$$

$$= \frac{4}{5} \quad \text{Multiply.}$$

Quick Check 2

Multiply $2\frac{2}{3} \cdot 8\frac{5}{8}$.

Dividing Fractions

Objective ② **Divide fractions and mixed numbers.**

> **Reciprocal**
>
> When we invert a fraction such as $\frac{3}{5}$ to $\frac{5}{3}$, the resulting fraction is called the **reciprocal** of the original fraction.

Consider the fraction $\frac{a}{b}$, where a and b are nonzero real numbers. The reciprocal of this fraction is $\frac{b}{a}$. Notice that if we multiply a fraction by its reciprocal, such as $\frac{a}{b} \cdot \frac{b}{a}$, the result is 1. This property will be important in Chapter 2.

> **Reciprocal Property**
>
> For any nonzero real numbers a and b, $\frac{a}{b} \cdot \frac{b}{a} = 1$.

To divide a number by a fraction, invert the divisor and then multiply.

EXAMPLE 3 Divide $\frac{16}{25} \div \frac{22}{15}$.

SOLUTION

$$\frac{16}{25} \div \frac{22}{15} = \frac{16}{25} \cdot \frac{15}{22} \quad \text{Invert the divisor and multiply.}$$

$$= \frac{\overset{8}{\cancel{16}}}{\underset{5}{\cancel{25}}} \cdot \frac{\overset{3}{\cancel{15}}}{\underset{11}{\cancel{22}}} \quad \text{Divide out the common factors 2 and 5.}$$

$$= \frac{24}{55} \quad \text{Multiply.}$$

Quick Check 3

Divide $\frac{12}{25} \div \frac{63}{10}$.

A WORD OF CAUTION When dividing a number by a fraction, we must invert the divisor (not the dividend) before dividing out a common factor from a numerator and a denominator.

When performing a division involving a mixed number, begin by rewriting the mixed number as an improper fraction.

EXAMPLE 4   Divide $2\frac{5}{8} \div 3\frac{3}{10}$.

SOLUTION   Begin by rewriting each mixed number as an improper fraction.

$$2\frac{5}{8} \div 3\frac{3}{10} = \frac{21}{8} \div \frac{33}{10}$$ Rewrite each mixed number as an improper fraction.

$$= \frac{21}{8} \cdot \frac{10}{33}$$ Invert the divisor and multiply.

$$= \frac{\overset{7}{\cancel{21}}}{\underset{4}{\cancel{8}}} \cdot \frac{\overset{5}{\cancel{10}}}{\underset{11}{\cancel{33}}}$$ Divide out common factors.

$$= \frac{35}{44}$$ Multiply.

Quick Check 4

Divide $\frac{20}{21} \div 2\frac{2}{3}$.

Adding and Subtracting Fractions

Objective 3 Add and subtract fractions and mixed numbers with the same denominator. To add or subtract fractions that have the same denominator, we add or subtract the numerators, placing the result over the common denominator. Make sure you simplify the result to lowest terms.

EXAMPLE 5   Subtract $\frac{3}{8} - \frac{9}{8}$.

SOLUTION   The two denominators are the same (8), so we subtract the numerators. When we subtract $3 - 9$, the result is -6. Although we may leave the negative sign in the numerator, it often appears in front of the fraction itself.

$$\frac{3}{8} - \frac{9}{8} = -\frac{6}{8}$$ Subtract the numerators.

$$= -\frac{3}{4}$$ Simplify to lowest terms.

Quick Check 5

Subtract $\frac{17}{20} - \frac{5}{20}$.

When performing an addition involving a mixed number, begin by rewriting the mixed number as an improper fraction.

EXAMPLE 6   Add $3\frac{5}{12} + 2\frac{11}{12}$.

SOLUTION   Begin by rewriting each mixed number as an improper fraction.

$$3\frac{5}{12} + 2\frac{11}{12} = \frac{41}{12} + \frac{35}{12}$$ Rewrite $3\frac{5}{12}$ and $2\frac{11}{12}$ as improper fractions.

$$= \frac{76}{12}$$ Add the numerators.

$$= \frac{19}{3}$$ Simplify to lowest terms.

$$= 6\frac{1}{3}$$ Rewrite as a mixed number.

It is not necessary to rewrite the result as a mixed number, but this is often done when you perform arithmetic operations on mixed numbers.

Quick Check 6

Add $6\frac{1}{8} + 5\frac{5}{8}$.

Objective 4 Find the least common multiple (LCM) of two natural numbers. Two fractions are said to be **equivalent fractions** if they have the same numerical value and both can be simplified to the same fraction when simplified to lowest terms. To add or subtract two fractions with different denominators, we must first convert them to equivalent fractions with the same denominator. To do this, we find the **least common multiple (LCM)** of the two denominators. This is the smallest number that is a multiple of both denominators. For example, the LCM of 4 and 6 is 12 because 12 is the smallest multiple of both 4 and 6.

To find the LCM for two numbers, begin by factoring them into their prime factorizations.

Finding the LCM of Two or More Numbers

- Find the prime factorization of each number.
- Find the common factors of the numbers.
- Multiply the common factors by the remaining factors of the numbers.

EXAMPLE 7 Find the LCM of 24 and 30.

SOLUTION Begin with the prime factorizations of 24 and 30.

$$24 = 2 \cdot 2 \cdot 2 \cdot 3$$
$$30 = 2 \cdot 3 \cdot 5$$
$$24 = ②\cdot 2 \cdot 2 \cdot ③$$
$$30 = ②\cdot ③ \cdot 5$$

The common factors are 2 and 3. Additional factors are a pair of 2's as well as a 5. So to find the LCM, multiply the common factors (2 and 3) by the additional factors (2, 2, and 5).

$$2 \cdot 3 \cdot 2 \cdot 2 \cdot 5 = 120$$

The least common multiple of 24 and 30 is 120.

Quick Check 7

Find the least common multiple of 18 and 42.

Another technique for finding the LCM for two numbers is to start listing the multiples of the larger number until we find a multiple that also is a multiple of the smaller number. For example, the first few multiples of 6 are

$$6: 6, 12, 18, 24, 30, \ldots$$

The first multiple listed that also is a multiple of 4 is 12, so the LCM of 4 and 6 is 12.

Objective 5 **Add and subtract fractions and mixed numbers with different denominators.** When adding or subtracting two fractions that do not have the same denominator, we first find a common denominator by finding the LCM of the two denominators. Then convert each fraction to an equivalent fraction whose denominator is that common denominator. Once we rewrite the two fractions so they have the same denominator, we can add (or subtract) as done previously in this section.

Adding or Subtracting Fractions with Different Denominators

- Find the LCM of the denominators.
- Rewrite each fraction as an equivalent fraction whose denominator is the LCM of the original denominators.
- Add or subtract the numerators, placing the result over the common denominator.
- Simplify to lowest terms if possible.

EXAMPLE 8 Add $\frac{5}{12} + \frac{9}{14}$.

SOLUTION The prime factorization of 12 is $2 \cdot 2 \cdot 3$, and the prime factorization of 14 is $2 \cdot 7$. The two denominators have a common factor of 2. If we multiply this common factor by the other factors of these two numbers, 2, 3, and 7, we see that the LCM of these two denominators is 84. Begin by rewriting each fraction as an equivalent fraction whose denominator is 84. Multiply the first fraction by $\frac{7}{7}$ and the second fraction by $\frac{6}{6}$. Because $\frac{7}{7}$ and $\frac{6}{6}$ are both equal to 1, we do not change the value of either fraction.

$$\frac{5}{12} + \frac{9}{14} = \frac{5}{12} \cdot \frac{7}{7} + \frac{9}{14} \cdot \frac{6}{6} \qquad \text{Multiply the first fraction's numerator and denominator by 7. Multiply the second fraction's numerator and denominator by 6.}$$

$$= \frac{35}{84} + \frac{54}{84} \qquad \text{Multiply.}$$

$$= \frac{89}{84} \qquad \text{Add.}$$

This fraction is already in lowest terms.

Quick Check 8
Add $\frac{4}{9} + \frac{2}{15}$.

When performing an addition or a subtraction involving a mixed number, we can begin by rewriting the mixed number as an improper fraction.

EXAMPLE 9 Subtract $4\frac{1}{3} - \frac{3}{4}$.

SOLUTION Begin by rewriting $4\frac{1}{3}$ as an improper fraction.

$$4\frac{1}{3} - \frac{3}{4} = \frac{13}{3} - \frac{3}{4} \qquad \text{Rewrite } 4\frac{1}{3} \text{ as an improper fraction.}$$

$$= \frac{13}{3} \cdot \frac{4}{4} - \frac{3}{4} \cdot \frac{3}{3} \qquad \text{The LCM of the denominators is 12. Multiply the first fraction by } \frac{4}{4}. \text{ Multiply the second fraction by } \frac{3}{3}.$$

$$= \frac{52}{12} - \frac{9}{12} \qquad \text{Multiply.}$$

$$= \frac{43}{12} \qquad \text{Subtract.}$$

$$= 3\frac{7}{12} \qquad \text{Rewrite as a mixed number.}$$

Quick Check 9
Subtract $5\frac{1}{5} - 3\frac{5}{6}$.

BUILDING YOUR STUDY STRATEGY

Study Groups, 4 Going Over Homework A study group can go over homework assignments together. It is important that each group member work on the assignment before arriving at the study session. If you struggled with a problem or could not do it at all, ask for help or suggestions from your group members.

If there was a problem that you seem to understand better than the members of your group do, share your knowledge; explaining how to do a certain problem increases your chances of retaining that knowledge until the exam and beyond.

At the end of each session, quickly review what the group accomplished.

Exercises 1.4

  PRACTICE   WATCH   DOWNLOAD READ   REVIEW

Vocabulary

1. Before multiplying by a mixed number, convert it to a(n) _____.

2. When a fraction is inverted, the result is called its _____.

3. Explain how to divide by a fraction.

4. When fractions are added or subtracted, they must have the same _____.

5. The smallest number that is a multiple of two numbers is called their _____.

6. A board is cut into two pieces that measure $4\frac{1}{6}$ feet and $3\frac{3}{8}$ feet, respectively. Which operation will give the length of the original board?

   a) $4\frac{1}{6} + 3\frac{3}{8}$ b) $4\frac{1}{6} - 3\frac{3}{8}$

   c) $4\frac{1}{6} \cdot 3\frac{3}{8}$ d) $4\frac{1}{6} \div 3\frac{3}{8}$

Multiply. Your answer should be in lowest terms.

7. $\frac{3}{8} \cdot \frac{4}{27}$

8. $\frac{6}{35} \cdot \frac{25}{29}$

9. $\frac{20}{21} \cdot \left(-\frac{77}{90}\right)$

10. $-\frac{9}{30} \cdot \frac{28}{42}$

11. $4\frac{2}{7} \cdot \frac{14}{25}$

12. $-3\frac{5}{9} \cdot 2\frac{1}{6}$

13. $5 \cdot 6\frac{3}{10}$

14. $8 \cdot \frac{7}{12}$

15. $\frac{2}{3} \cdot \frac{8}{9}$

16. $-\frac{12}{35}\left(-\frac{14}{99}\right)$

Divide. Your answer should be in lowest terms.

17. $\frac{6}{25} \div \frac{8}{45}$

18. $\frac{15}{32} \div \frac{9}{20}$

19. $-\frac{22}{56} \div \frac{33}{147}$

20. $-\frac{24}{91} \div \left(-\frac{9}{39}\right)$

21. $\frac{17}{40} \div \frac{1}{2}$

22. $\frac{7}{30} \div \left(-\frac{1}{5}\right)$

23. $\frac{4}{11} \div 3\frac{1}{5}$

24. $3\frac{3}{8} \div 6$

25. $-2\frac{4}{5} \div 6\frac{2}{3}$

26. $7\frac{1}{9} \div 13\frac{3}{8}$

Add or subtract.

27. $\frac{7}{15} + \frac{4}{15}$

28. $\frac{1}{8} + \frac{5}{8}$

29. $\frac{5}{9} + \frac{4}{9}$

30. $\frac{3}{10} + \frac{9}{10}$

31. $\frac{2}{5} - \frac{4}{5}$

32. $\frac{17}{18} - \frac{5}{18}$

33. $\frac{9}{16} - \frac{3}{16}$

34. $\frac{13}{42} - \frac{29}{42}$

Find the LCM of the given numbers.

35. $10, 15$

36. $8, 12$

37. $12, 42$

38. $9, 30$

39. $16, 80$

40. $16, 27$

41. $8, 10, 14$

42. $20, 35, 50$

Simplify. Your answer should be in lowest terms.

43. $\frac{4}{5} + \frac{3}{4}$

44. $\frac{4}{7} + \frac{1}{4}$

45. $\frac{7}{10} + \frac{5}{8}$

46. $\frac{3}{4} + \frac{5}{6}$

47. $6\frac{1}{5} + 5$

48. $3 + 8\frac{3}{7}$

49. $6\frac{2}{3} + 5\frac{1}{6}$

50. $11\frac{4}{9} + 5\frac{1}{3}$

51. $\frac{2}{3} - \frac{7}{15}$

52. $\frac{1}{2} - \frac{7}{9}$

53. $\frac{3}{4} - \frac{2}{7}$

54. $\frac{5}{8} - \frac{5}{6}$

55. $7\frac{1}{2} - 3\frac{1}{4}$

56. $12\frac{2}{3} - 6\frac{2}{5}$

57. $12\frac{3}{10} - 9$

58. $6 - 4\frac{3}{4}$

59. $-\frac{5}{9} - \frac{7}{12}$

60. $-\frac{9}{10} - \frac{11}{14}$

61. $-\frac{9}{16} + \frac{5}{24}$

62. $-\frac{3}{8} + \frac{13}{24}$

63. $\frac{6}{7} - \left(-\frac{8}{15}\right)$

64. $\frac{1}{12} - \left(-\frac{19}{30}\right)$

65. $-\frac{4}{15} + \left(-\frac{13}{18}\right)$

66. $-\frac{17}{24} + \left(-\frac{25}{42}\right)$

67. $\dfrac{3}{16} + \dfrac{9}{20} - \dfrac{11}{12}$

68. $\dfrac{10}{21} - \dfrac{13}{18} + \dfrac{8}{15}$

Mixed Practice, 69–88

Simplify.

69. $\dfrac{8}{9} \cdot \dfrac{3}{5}$

70. $\dfrac{3}{4} + \dfrac{7}{10}$

71. $\dfrac{7}{30} \div \dfrac{35}{48}$

72. $\dfrac{12}{35} \cdot \dfrac{14}{27}$

73. $\dfrac{1}{6} - \dfrac{7}{8}$

74. $\dfrac{7}{24} - \dfrac{29}{40}$

75. $\dfrac{19}{30} + \dfrac{11}{18}$

76. $3\dfrac{1}{5} \cdot 4\dfrac{3}{8}$

77. $13 \div \dfrac{1}{8}$

78. $\dfrac{3}{5} - \dfrac{2}{3} - \dfrac{7}{10}$

79. $3\dfrac{4}{7} + 6\dfrac{3}{5} - 8$

80. $12\dfrac{1}{3} + 7\dfrac{1}{6} - 5\dfrac{1}{2}$

81. $\dfrac{15}{56} + \left(-\dfrac{16}{21}\right)$

82. $\dfrac{7}{12} - \left(-\dfrac{23}{30}\right)$

83. $-\dfrac{9}{13} + \dfrac{19}{36}$

84. $-\dfrac{3}{8} - \dfrac{81}{100}$

Find the missing number.

85. $\dfrac{11}{24} + \dfrac{5}{?} = \dfrac{13}{12}$

86. $\dfrac{?}{10} - \dfrac{1}{3} = \dfrac{1}{6}$

87. $\dfrac{10}{21} \cdot \dfrac{?}{75} = \dfrac{4}{45}$

88. $\dfrac{11}{40} + \dfrac{?}{40} = \dfrac{9}{10}$

89. Bruce is fixing a special dinner for his girlfriend. The three recipes he is preparing call for $\frac{1}{2}$ cup, $\frac{3}{4}$ cup, and $\frac{1}{3}$ cup of flour, respectively. In total, how much flour does Bruce need to make these three recipes?

90. Sue gave birth to twins. One of the babies weighed $4\frac{7}{8}$ pounds at birth, and the other baby weighed $5\frac{1}{4}$ pounds. Find the total weight of the twins at birth.

91. A chemist has $\frac{23}{40}$ fluid ounce of a solution. If she needs $\frac{1}{8}$ fluid ounce of the solution for an experiment, how much of the solution will remain?

92. A popular weed spray concentrate recommends using $1\frac{1}{4}$ tablespoons of concentrate for each quart of water. How much concentrate needs to be mixed with 6 quarts of water?

93. A board that is $4\frac{1}{5}$ feet long needs to be cut into 6 pieces of equal length. How long will each piece be?

94. Ross makes a batch of hot sauce that will be poured into bottles that hold $5\frac{3}{4}$ fluid ounces. If Ross has 115 fluid ounces of hot sauce, how many bottles can he fill?

95. A craftsperson is making a rectangular picture frame. Each of two sides will be $\frac{5}{6}$ of a foot long, while each of the other two sides will be $\frac{2}{3}$ of a foot long. If the craftsperson has one board that is $2\frac{3}{4}$ feet long, is this enough to make the picture frame? Explain.

96. A pancake recipe calls for $1\frac{1}{3}$ cups of whole wheat flour to make 12 pancakes. How much flour is needed to make 48 pancakes?

97. A pancake recipe calls for $1\frac{1}{3}$ cups of whole wheat flour to make 12 pancakes. How much flour is needed to make 6 pancakes?

Writing in Mathematics

Answer in complete sentences.

98. Explain, using your own words, the difference between dividing a number in half and dividing a number by one-half.

99. Explain why you cannot divide a common factor of 2 from the numbers 4 and 6 in the expression $\frac{4}{7} \cdot \frac{6}{11}$.

100. Explain why it would be a bad idea to rewrite fractions with a common denominator before multiplying them.

1.5

Decimals and Percents

OBJECTIVES

1. **Perform arithmetic operations with decimals.**
2. **Rewrite a fraction as a decimal number.**
3. **Rewrite a decimal number as a fraction.**
4. **Rewrite a fraction as a percent.**
5. **Rewrite a decimal as a percent.**
6. **Rewrite a percent as a fraction.**
7. **Rewrite a percent as a decimal.**

Decimals

Rational numbers also can be represented using **decimal notation**. The decimal 0.23 is equivalent to the fraction $\frac{23}{100}$, or twenty-three hundredths. The digit 2 is in the tenths place, and the digit 3 is in the hundredths place. The following chart shows several place values for decimals:

$$0.123456\ldots$$

Tenths ─────────── Millionths
Hundredths ─────────── Hundred Thousandths
Thousandths ─────────── Ten Thousandths

Objective 1 Perform arithmetic operations with decimals. Here is a brief summary of arithmetic operations using decimals.

- To add or subtract two decimal numbers, align the decimal points and add or subtract as you would with integers.

$$3.96 + 12.072$$

$$\begin{array}{r} 3.96 \\ +\ 12.072 \\ \hline 16.032 \end{array}$$

- To multiply two decimal numbers, multiply them as you would integers. The total number of decimal places in the two factors shows how many decimal places are in the product.

$$-2.09 \cdot 3.1$$

In this example, the two factors have a total of three decimal places, so the product must have three decimal places. Multiply these two numbers as if they were 209 and 31 and then insert the decimal point in the appropriate place, leaving three digits to the right of the decimal point.

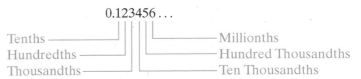

$$\begin{array}{r} -209 \\ \times\ 31 \\ \hline -6479 \end{array} \qquad \begin{array}{r} -2.09 \\ \times\ 3.1 \\ \hline -6.479 \end{array}$$

3 places

• To divide two decimal numbers, move the decimal point in the divisor to the right so that it becomes an integer. Then move the decimal point in the other number (dividend) to the right by the same number of spaces. The decimal point in the answer will be aligned with this new location of the decimal point in the dividend.

$$8.24 \div 0.4$$

$$0.4\overline{)8.24}$$ Begin by moving *each* decimal point one place to the right

$$0.4\overline{)8.24}$$

$$\begin{array}{r} 20.6 \\ 4\overline{)82.4} \end{array}$$ Then perform the division.

Rewriting Fractions as Decimals and Decimals as Fractions

Objective 2 Rewrite a fraction as a decimal number. To rewrite any fraction as a decimal, we divide its numerator by its denominator. The fraction line is simply another way to write "÷".

EXAMPLE 1   Rewrite the fraction $\frac{5}{8}$ as a decimal.

SOLUTION   To rewrite this fraction as a decimal, divide 5 by 8.

Now begin the division, adding a decimal point after the 5 and 0's to the end of the dividend until there is no remainder.

$$\begin{array}{r} 0.625 \\ 8\overline{)5.000} \\ -4.8 \\ \hline 20 \\ -16 \\ \hline 40 \\ -40 \\ \hline 0 \end{array}$$

$$\frac{5}{8} = 0.625$$

Quick Check 1

Rewrite the fraction $\frac{3}{4}$ as a decimal.

EXAMPLE 2   Rewrite the fraction $\frac{23}{30}$ as a decimal.

SOLUTION   When we divide 23 by 30, the result is a decimal that does not terminate (0.76666 . . .). The pattern continues repeating the digit 6 forever. This is an example of a **repeating decimal**. We may place a bar over the repeating digit(s) to denote a repeating decimal.

$$\frac{23}{30} = 0.7\overline{6}$$

Quick Check 2

Rewrite the fraction $\frac{5}{18}$ as a decimal.

Objective 3 Rewrite a decimal number as a fraction. Suppose we want to rewrite a decimal number such as 0.48 as a fraction. This decimal is read as "forty-eight hundredths" and is equivalent to the fraction $\frac{48}{100}$. Simplifying this fraction shows that $0.48 = \frac{12}{25}$.

EXAMPLE 3 Rewrite the decimal 0.164 as a fraction in lowest terms.

SOLUTION   This decimal ends in the thousandths place, so start with a fraction of $\frac{164}{1000}$.

$$0.164 = \frac{164}{1000} \quad \text{Rewrite as a fraction whose denominator is 1000.}$$

$$= \frac{41}{250} \quad \text{Simplify to lowest terms.}$$

Quick Check 3
Rewrite the decimal 0.425 as a fraction in lowest terms.

Using Your Calculator   To rewrite a decimal as a fraction using the TI-84, key the decimal, press the [MATH] key, and select option 1. The following screens show how to rewrite the decimal 0.164 as a fraction using the TI-84, as in Example 3.

Key the decimal.	Press the [MATH] key.	Result

Percents

Objective ④ **Rewrite a fraction as a percent.** **Percents** (%) are used to represent numbers as parts of 100. One percent, which can be written as 1%, is equivalent to 1 part of 100, or $\frac{1}{100}$, or 0.01. The fraction $\frac{27}{100}$ is equivalent to 27%. Percents, decimals, and fractions are all ways to write a rational number. We will learn to convert back and forth between percents and fractions as well as between percents and decimals.

Rewriting Fractions and Decimals as Percents

To rewrite a fraction or a decimal as a percent, we multiply it by 100%. Because 100% is equal to 1 this will not change the value of the fraction or decimal number.

EXAMPLE 4 Rewrite as a percent: a) $\frac{2}{5}$,   b) $\frac{3}{8}$.

SOLUTION

a) Begin by multiplying by 100% and simplifying.

$$\frac{2}{\underset{1}{\cancel{5}}} \cdot \overset{20}{\cancel{100}}\% = 40\%$$

b) Again, multiply by 100%. Occasionally, as in this example, we will end up with an improper fraction, which can be changed to a mixed number.

$$\frac{3}{\underset{2}{\cancel{8}}} \cdot \overset{25}{\cancel{100}}\% = \frac{75}{2}\%, \text{ which can be rewritten as } 37\frac{1}{2}\%.$$

Quick Check 4

a) Rewrite $\frac{7}{10}$ as a percent.

b) Rewrite $\frac{21}{40}$ as a percent.

Objective 5 Rewrite a decimal as a percent.

EXAMPLE 5 Rewrite 0.3 as a percent.

SOLUTION   When we multiply a decimal by 100, the result is the same as moving the decimal point two places to the right.

$$0.30_{\curvearrowright}$$

$$0.3 \cdot 100\% = 30\%$$

Quick Check 5
Rewrite 0.42 as a percent.

Rewriting Percents as Fractions and Decimals

Objective 6 Rewrite a percent as a fraction. To rewrite a percent as a fraction or a decimal, we can divide it by 100 and omit the percent sign. When rewriting a percent as a fraction, we may choose to multiply by $\frac{1}{100}$ rather than dividing by 100.

EXAMPLE 6 Rewrite as a fraction: a) 44%,   b) $16\frac{2}{3}\%$.

SOLUTION

a) Begin by multiplying by $\frac{1}{100}$ and omitting the percent sign.

$$\overset{11}{\cancel{44}} \cdot \frac{1}{\underset{25}{\cancel{100}}} = \frac{11}{25}$$

b) Rewrite the mixed number $16\frac{2}{3}$ as an improper fraction $\left(\frac{50}{3}\right)$, multiply by $\frac{1}{100}$, and simplify.

$$\frac{\overset{1}{\cancel{50}}}{3} \cdot \frac{1}{\underset{2}{\cancel{100}}} = \frac{1}{6}$$

▶ Quick Check 6

a) Rewrite 35% as a fraction.
b) Rewrite $11\frac{2}{3}\%$ as a fraction.

Objective 7 Rewrite a percent as a decimal. In the next example, we will rewrite percents as decimals rather than as fractions.

EXAMPLE 7 Rewrite as a decimal: a) 56%,   b) 143%.

SOLUTION

a) Begin by dropping the percent sign and dividing by 100. Keep in mind that dividing a decimal number by 100 is the same as moving the decimal point two places to the left.

$$.56_{\curvearrowleft}$$

$$56 \div 100 = 0.56$$

b) When a percent is greater than 100%, its equivalent decimal must be greater than 1.

$$143 \div 100 = 1.43$$

▶ Quick Check 7

a) Rewrite 8% as a decimal.   **b)** Rewrite 240% as a decimal.

BUILDING YOUR STUDY STRATEGY

Study Groups, 5 Three Questions Another way to structure a group study session is to have each member bring a list of three questions to the meeting. The questions can be about specific homework problems or about topics or procedures that have been covered in class. Once the members have asked their questions, the group should attempt to come up with answers that each member understands. If the group cannot answer a question, see your instructor at the beginning of the next class or during office hours, asking him or her for an explanation.

Exercises 1.5

MyMathLab® Powered by CourseCompass™ and MathXL®

PRACTICE   WATCH   DOWNLOAD   READ   REVIEW

Vocabulary

1. The first place to the right of a decimal point is the _____ place.
2. The third place to the right of a decimal point is the _____ place.
3. To rewrite a fraction as a decimal divide the _____ by the _____.
4. To rewrite a fraction as a percent _____ it by 100%.
5. To rewrite a percent as a fraction _____ it by 100 and omit the percent sign.
6. Percents are used to represent numbers as parts of _____.

Simplify the following decimal expressions.

7. $4.23 + 3.62$
8. $13.89 - 2.54$
9. $-7(5.2)$
10. $69.54 \div 6$
11. $8.4 - 3.7$
12. $-7.9 + (-4.5)$
13. $13.568 \div 0.4$
14. $3.6(4.7)$
15. $-2.2 \cdot 3.65$
16. $6.2 - 15.9$
17. $13.47 - (-21.562)$
18. $5.283 \div 0.25$
19. $-6.3(3.9)(-2.25)$
20. $-4.84 \div (-0.016)$
21. $37.278 + 56.722$
22. $109.309 - 27.46 - 52.3716$

Rewrite the following fractions as decimal numbers.

23. $\dfrac{9}{10}$
24. $\dfrac{2}{5}$

25. $-\dfrac{23}{8}$
26. $\dfrac{59}{4}$
27. $\dfrac{13}{25}$
28. $-\dfrac{11}{16}$
29. $24\dfrac{29}{50}$
30. $7\dfrac{3}{20}$

Rewrite the following decimal numbers as fractions in lowest terms.

31. 0.2
32. 0.5
33. 0.85
34. 0.36
35. -0.74
36. -0.56
37. 0.375
38. 0.204

39. The normal body temperature for humans is 98.6° F. If Melody has a temperature that is 2.8° F above normal, what is her temperature?

40. Paul spent the following amounts on gifts for his wife's birthday: $32.95, $16.99, $47.50, $12.37, and $285. How much did Paul spend on gifts for his wife?

41. The balance of Carie's checking account is $427.36. If she writes checks for $19.95, $34.40, and $148.68, what will her new balance be?

42. At the close of the stock market on Tuesday, the price for one share of Google was $426.17. Over the next three days, the stock went down by $9.63, up by $14.08, and down by $7.84. What was the price of the stock at the end of Friday's session?

43. An office manager bought 12 cases of paper. If each case cost $21.47, what was the total cost for the 12 cases?

44. Jean gives Chris a $20 bill and tells him to go to the grocery store and buy as many hot dogs as he can. If each package of hot dogs costs $2.65, how many packages can Chris buy? How much change will Chris have?

Rewrite as percents.

45. $\frac{3}{4}$ **46.** $\frac{3}{5}$

47. $\frac{4}{5}$ **48.** $\frac{5}{8}$

49. $\frac{7}{8}$ **50.** $\frac{11}{12}$

51. $\frac{27}{4}$ **52.** $\frac{12}{5}$

53. 0.4   **54.** 0.6

55. 0.15   **56.** 0.87

57. 0.09   **58.** 0.03

59. 3.2   **60.** 2.75

Rewrite as fractions.

61. 84%   **62.** 80%

63. 7%   **64.** 2%

65. $11\frac{1}{9}\%$ **66.** $18\frac{2}{11}\%$

67. 520%   **68.** 275%

Rewrite as decimals.

69. 54%   **70.** 71%

71. 16%   **72.** 29%

73. 7%   **74.** 9%

75. 0.3%   **76.** 61.3%

77. 400%   **78.** 320%

79. Find three fractions that are equivalent to 0.375.

80. Find three fractions that are equivalent to 0.4.

Complete the following table.

	Fraction	Decimal	Percent
81.		0.2	
82.	$\frac{7}{40}$		
83.			32%
84.			45%
85.	$\frac{13}{8}$		
86.		0.64	

Writing in Mathematics

Answer in complete sentences.

87. Stock prices at the New York Stock Exchange used to be reported as fractions. Now prices are reported as decimals. Do you think this was a good idea? Explain.

88. Describe a real-world application involving decimals.

1.6
Basic Statistics

OBJECTIVES

1 Calculate basic statistics for a set of data.
2 Construct a histogram for a set of data.

In today's data-driven society, we often see graphs presenting data or information on television news as well as in newspapers, magazines, and online. This section focuses on the calculation of statistics used to describe a set of data as well as the creation of a histogram to represent a set of data.

Objective 1 Calculate basic statistics for a set of data. There are two basic types of statistics—those that describe the typical value for a set of data and those that describe how varied the values are. Statistics that describe the typical value for a set of data are often called **measures of center**, while statistics that describe how varied a set of data is are often called **measures of spread**.

> ### Mean
> The **mean** of a set of data is one measure of center for a set of data. To calculate the mean for a set of data, we simply add all of the values and divide by how many values there are. The mean is the arithmetic average of the set of data.
>
> $$\text{Mean} = \frac{\text{Sum of All Values}}{\text{Number of Values}}$$

EXAMPLE 1 Eight students were asked how far they drive to school each day. Here are the results, in miles: 17, 8, 30, 1, 2, 5, 15, 10. Calculate the mean for this set of data.

SOLUTION   The total of these eight values is 88.

$$\text{Mean} = \frac{88}{8} = 11$$

The mean mileage for these students is 11 miles.

Quick Check 1

Five families were asked how much they spend on groceries each month. Here are the results: $850, $1020, $970, $635, $795. Calculate the mean for this set of data.

> ### Median
> The **median** of a set of data is another measure of center for a set of data, often used for types of data that have unusually high or low values, such as home prices and family income. To find the median for a set of data, we begin by writing the values in ascending order. If a set of data has an odd number of values, the single value in the middle of the set of data is the median. If a set of data has an even number of values, the median is the average of the two center values.

EXAMPLE 2 Find the median of the given set of values.

a) 37, 16, 59, 18, 30, 4, 75, 46, 62

b) 65, 72, 74, 81, 71, 83, 89, 82, 53, 48, 77, 65

SOLUTION

a) Begin by rewriting the values in ascending order: 4, 16, 18, 30, 37, 46, 59, 62, 75. Because there is an odd number of values (9), the median is the single value in the center of the list.

4   16   18   30   37   46   59   62   75

↑
Median

The median is 37.

b) Here are the values in ascending order: 48, 53, 65, 65, 71, 72, 74, 77, 81, 82, 83, 89. Because there is an even number of values (12), the median is the average of the two values in the center of the list.

48 53 65 65 71 (72 74) 77 81 82 83 89

$$\text{Median} = \frac{72 + 74}{2} = \frac{146}{2} = 73$$

The median is 73.

Quick Check 2

Find the median of the given set of values.

a) 54, 21, 39, 16, 7, 75
b) 51, 3, 29, 60, 62, 25, 43, 102, 14

Mode and Midrange

The **mode** and **midrange** are two other measures of center for a set of data. The mode is the value that is repeated most often.

- If there are no repeated values, the set of data has no mode. The set 1, 2, 3, 4, 5 has no mode because no value is repeated.
- A set of data can have more than one mode if two or more values are repeated the same number of times. The set 5, 5, 7, 8, 8 has two modes—5 and 8.

The midrange is the average of the set's minimum value and maximum value.

$$\text{Midrange} = \frac{\text{Minimum Value} + \text{Maximum Value}}{2}$$

EXAMPLE 3 During a medical trial, the LDL cholesterol levels of 16 adult males were measured. Here are the results.

104 122 115 90 116 88 167 105 154 129 81 157 143 122 106 87

Find the mode and the midrange for this data.

SOLUTION Only one value, 122, has been repeated; so the mode is 122. To find the midrange, identify the maximum and minimum values for this set of data. The smallest value in this set is 81, and the largest value is 167.

$$\text{Midrange} = \frac{81 + 167}{2} = \frac{248}{2} = 124$$

The midrange is 124.

▶ **Quick Check 3**

Here are the heights, in inches, of 10 adult females.

| 56 | 65 | 66 | 66 | 65 | 66 | 65 | 60 | 61 | 65 |

Find the mode and the midrange for this data.

Range

The **range** is a measure of spread for a set of data, showing how varied the values are. To find the range of a set of values, we subtract the minimum value in the set from the maximum value in the set.

$$\text{Range} = \text{Maximum Value} - \text{Minimum Value}$$

EXAMPLE 4   Here are the test scores of 9 math students.

| 65 | 75 | 96 | 91 | 78 | 81 | 73 | 92 | 61 |

Find the range of these test scores.

SOLUTION   To find the range, identify the maximum and minimum values for this set of data. The maximum value in this set is 96, and the minimum value is 61.

$$\text{Range} = 96 - 61 = 35$$

The range is 35 points.

▶ Quick Check 4

Here are the heights, in centimeters, of 8 adult males.

| 165 | 168 | 174 | 179 | 182 | 159 | 171 | 180 |

Find the range for this data.

Histogram

Objective 2 **Construct a histogram for a set of data.**

A **histogram** is a graph that can be used to show how a set of data is distributed, giving an idea of where the data values are centered as well as how they are dispersed. To construct a histogram, we begin with a **frequency distribution**, which divides the data into groups, called **classes**, and lists how many times each class is represented in the set of data. Here is a frequency distribution showing the ages of U.S. Presidents at inauguration.

Age	Frequency
40 to 44	2
45 to 49	7
50 to 54	13
55 to 59	12
60 to 64	7
65 to 69	3

This frequency distribution shows that two presidents were between 40 and 44 years old when they were inaugurated, seven presidents were between the ages of 45 and 49, and so on.

To construct a histogram, we begin by drawing two axes as shown. Mark the beginning of each class at the bottom of the graph on the horizontal axis, including the value that would be the lower limit of the next class. In the example, that will be the numbers 40, 45, 50, 55, 60, 65, and 70. On the vertical axis, mark the frequencies. Make sure your axis goes at least to the highest frequency in the frequency distribution.

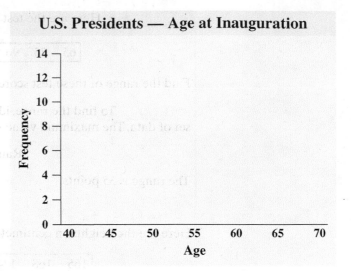

A bar is drawn above each class, and the height of the bar is determined by the frequency of that class. The first bar, from 40 to 45, should have a height of 2; the second bar should have a height of 7; and so on. Here is the histogram.

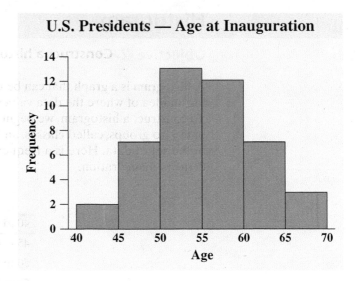

From this histogram, we can see that the bulk of the values are between 50 and 60, which is the center of the values.

EXAMPLE 5   Here is a frequency distribution showing the ages of 30 students enrolled in an online algebra class.

Age	Frequency
17 to 20	17
21 to 24	6
25 to 28	2
29 to 32	1
33 to 36	3
37 to 40	1

Draw a histogram for the frequency distribution.

SOLUTION   On the horizontal axis, we begin the labels at 17 and increase by 4 until we reach 41. On the vertical axis, we must have labels that reach at least 17, which is the largest frequency.

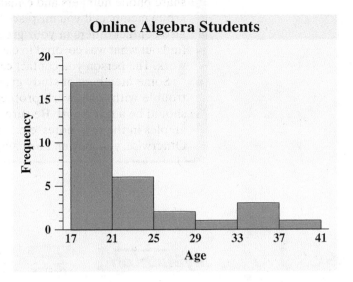

▶ Quick Check 5

Here is a frequency distribution showing the ages of 86 passengers on a cruise.

Ages	Frequency
25 to 34	3
35 to 44	7
45 to 54	6
55 to 64	15
65 to 74	35
75 to 84	20

Draw a histogram for the frequency distribution.

BUILDING YOUR STUDY STRATEGY

Study Groups, 6 Keeping in Touch It is important for group members to share phone numbers and e-mail addresses. This will allow you to contact other group members if you misplace the homework assignment for that day. You can also contact others in your group if you have to miss class. This allows you to find out what was covered in class and which problems were assigned for homework. The person you contact can also give you advice on certain problems.

Some members of study groups agree to call each other if they are having trouble with homework problems. Calling a group member for this purpose should be a last resort. Be sure that you have used all available resources (examples in the text, notes, etc.) and have given the problem your fullest effort. Otherwise, you may end up calling for help on all of the problems.

Exercises 1.6

   PRACTICE WATCH DOWNLOAD READ REVIEW

Vocabulary

1. Statistics that describe the typical value for a set of data are often called measures of _____.

2. Statistics that describe how varied a set of data is are often called measures of _____.

3. The _____ of a set of data is the sum of all of the values divided by the number of values.

4. The _____ of a set of data is the value in the center of the data once the values are arranged in ascending order.

5. The _____ of a set of data is the value that is repeated most often.

6. The _____ of a set of data is the average of its minimum and maximum values.

7. The _____ of a set of data is the difference between its maximum and minimum values.

8. A(n) _____ is a graph that can be used to show how a set of data is distributed.

Find the mean for the given values.

9. 63, 98, 21, 42, 71

10. 84, 37, 29, 46, 15, 65

11. 5, 17, 21, 35, 42, 59, 89, 106

12. 30, 70, 74, 82, 95, 113, 128, 140

Find the median for the given values.

13. 97, 76, 22, 103, 80, 45, 66

14. 87, 3, 20, 62, 55, 73, 101, 49, 75

15. 68, 47, 32, 90, 85, 40, 83, 39, 50, 77

16. 123, 304, 290, 175, 260, 209, 321, 275

Find the mode, if it exists, for the given values.

17. 70, 56, 63, 35, 56, 63, 36, 56, 19

18. 80, 50, 70, 80, 50, 70, 80, 40, 60

19. 7, 41, 32, 56, 41, 19, 8, 32, 25

20. 61, 47, 47, 17, 29, 16, 25, 92, 16

21. 5, 35, 89, 106, 42, 17, 59, 21

22. 88, 45, 6, 99, 32, 75, 16, 100, 42

For the given values, find the midrange and the range.

23. 70, 140, 87, 62, 196, 125, 155

24. 93, 47, 28, 80, 94, 60, 93

25. 406, 354, 509, 427, 516, 379

26. 165, 82, 97, 155, 79, 203, 121, 99

For Exercises 27–34, find the a) mean, b) median, c) mode, d) midrange, and e) range.

27. 22, 13, 16, 30, 32, 19, 24, 30, 21

28. 59, 41, 46, 62, 41, 50, 65

29. 48, 45, 63, 36, 50, 38, 73, 63

30. 98, 84, 44, 40, 50, 82, 43, 84, 46, 70

31. 63, 86, 76, 85, 59, 71, 34, 44, 30, 67, 44, 77, 50, 83, 76

32. 48, 91, 38, 101, 93, 66, 31, 57, 84, 47, 73, 41, 86, 90, 96, 86, 62

33. 196, 295, 213, 69, 371, 77, 253, 210, 298, 210, 426, 327, 270, 323, 262, 70, 459, 481, 278, 192

34. 257, 50, 23, 223, 125, 249, 197, 191, 99, 194, 239, 227, 192, 96, 50, 147, 259, 296

Find the mean for the given set of data.

35. IQ of 12 college students

95 82 104 119 118 126 82 96 116 85 90 90

36. Red Sox home runs (2001–2008)

2001	2002	2003	2004	2005	2006	2007	2008
198	177	238	222	199	192	166	173

37. Systolic blood pressure of seven 60-year-old men

133   112   142   154   102   139   149

38. Systolic blood pressure of nine 60-year-old women

119   160   121   92   109   95   114   112   122

39. Weight (in ounces) of 10 newborn baby girls

101   110   125   120   106   113   102   108   132   135

40. Starting salary for 5 bachelor's degrees

Chemical Engineering	Computer Science	Mathematics	Political Science	English
$61,800	$54,200	$43,500	$39,400	$36,700

(*Source: PayScale.com*)

Find the median for the given set of data.

41. Number of Facebook friends for 6 college math instructors

243   18   21   152   93   125

42. Serum glucose level (mg/dL) of 8 people

90   91   94   122   113   142   59   92

43. Math test scores of 9 members of a study group

80   96   100   89   74   96   95   98   87

44. Pregnancy duration (days) for 11 women

267 255 263 261 265 273 264 267 268 275 273

45. Number of hours spent studying last week by 10 college students

25   12   17   3   20   20   16   34   1   9

46. Number of hours spent working last week by 10 college students

8   4   20   0   12   32   8   40   20   16

For exercises 47–52, find the a) mean, b) median, c) mode, d) midrange, and e) range.

47. Room rate at 10 Las Vegas hotels (Valentine's Day, 2010)

$219	$259	$127	$199	$259	$169
$219	$229	$299	$199		

48. Touchdown passes thrown by Joe Montana by year (16 seasons)

1 15 19 17 26 28 27 8 31 18 26 26 0 2 13 16

49. Time (in seconds) of the 8 songs on Bruce Springsteen's "Born to Run"

289   191   180   390   271   270   198   574

50. Number of calories in 16 different brands of beer

188 166 163 165 149 209 135 150 96 145 170
124 158 110 314 94

51. Cell phone minutes used by 14 families last month

636   754   662   884   1346   659   1006   1357
1129   904   1747   1336   1234   388

52. Systolic blood pressure of thirteen 65-year-old smokers (mmHg)

110   118   137   127   134   163   129   102
102   136   150   130   113

Find the missing value x that satisfies the given condition for the set of values.

53. Mean: 75

80   86   100   81   30   57   90 x

54. Mean: 82.5

43   96   90 x 81   104   111   72   66   89

55. Median: 101.5

112   98   121   72 x 65

56. Median: 93

97   x 81   100   104   88   121   79

57. Range: 84; midrange: 52

| 66 | 25 | 94 | 37 | x | 85 | 42 |

58. Range: 47; midrange: 35.5

| 30 | 29 | 58 | 12 | 16 | 45 | x | 50 |

Construct a histogram for the given frequency distribution.

59. Average 2007 SAT math score for the 50 states and Washington, D.C.

(*Source: The College Board*)

Average Score	Frequency
460 to 479	2
480 to 499	6
500 to 519	14
520 to 539	6
540 to 559	6
560 to 579	8
580 to 599	5
600 to 619	4

60. Scores of 40 students on an algebra exam

Score	Frequency
40 to 49	1
50 to 59	3
60 to 69	4
70 to 79	7
80 to 89	14
90 to 99	11

61. High school graduation rates for the 50 states (2005)

Graduation Rate	Frequency
45.0% to 49.9%	1
50.0% to 54.9%	2
55.0% to 59.9%	2
60.0% to 64.9%	4
65.0% to 69.9%	7
70.0% to 74.9%	16
75.0% to 79.9%	13
80.0% to 84.9%	5

62. Daily caloric intake of 60 participants in a health study

Calories	Frequency
1400 to 1599	1
1600 to 1799	6
1800 to 1999	15
2000 to 2199	21
2200 to 2399	9
2400 to 2599	8

Complete the frequency distribution for the given data and use it to construct a histogram.

63. Number of heads in 1000 coin flips, repeated by 60 students

471	505	515	503	506	507	471	522	548	478	514	490
511	463	515	514	490	485	467	531	487	482	500	506
504	492	522	497	508	499	515	499	516	495	499	496
510	520	509	500	488	512	501	506	488	497	498	503
496	488	522	505	517	497	500	502	472	525	477	506

Number of Heads	Frequency
450 to 469	
470 to 489	
490 to 509	
510 to 529	
530 to 549	

64. Starting salaries of 50 Certified Public Accountants (CPAs)

$52,500	$57,700	$55,100	$60,400	$61,900
$57,700	$52,600	$57,200	$52,700	$59,200
$58,300	$58,800	$61,400	$56,600	$56,900
$60,300	$57,700	$55,400	$56,200	$59,300
$59,000	$58,300	$52,300	$56,000	$59,400
$60,100	$53,400	$54,700	$55,600	$62,800
$62,300	$55,000	$56,300	$57,200	$59,600
$56,200	$62,300	$55,900	$50,100	$64,500
$55,900	$56,600	$57,200	$59,600	$60,300
$55,900	$63,400	$62,100	$55,800	$63,100

Salary	Frequency
$50,000 to $52,499	
$52,500 to $54,999	
$55,000 to $57,499	
$57,500 to $59,999	
$60,000 to $62,499	
$62,500 to $64,999	

65. IQs of 36 college students

104	114	88	96	105	120	92	107	134	110	95	133
132	119	115	116	129	114	100	95	105	140	110	131
97	113	104	120	95	128	128	106	96	114	127	133

IQ	Frequency
85 to 94	
95 to 104	
105 to 114	
115 to 124	
125 to 134	
135 to 144	

66. Blood glucose level (mg/dL) of 40 women participating in a clinical study

63	141	84	108	93	64	94	80	95	100
90	115	96	89	68	114	130	111	86	75
85	93	116	102	72	87	95	105	109	74
115	120	119	101	92	100	84	148	97	100

Blood Glucose Level	Frequency
60 to 74	
75 to 89	
90 to 104	
105 to 119	
120 to 134	
135 to 149	

Use the given histogram to create a frequency distribution.

67.

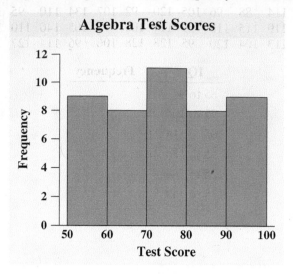

69.

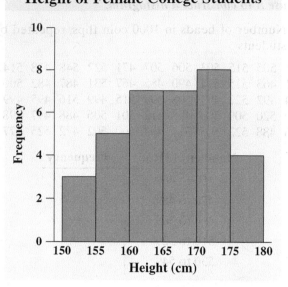

68.

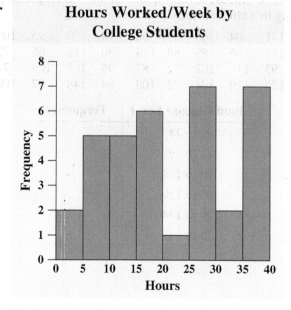

70.

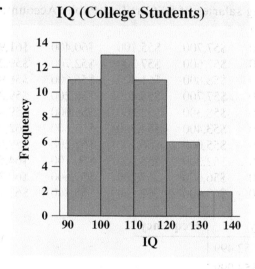

1.7

Exponents and Order of Operations

OBJECTIVES

1. **Simplify exponents.**
2. **Use the order of operations to simplify arithmetic expressions.**

Exponents

Objective 1 Simplify exponents. The same number used repeatedly as a factor can be represented using **exponential notation**. For example, $3 \cdot 3 \cdot 3 \cdot 3 \cdot 3$ can be written as 3^5.

Base, Exponent

For the expression 3^5, the number being multiplied (3) is called the **base**. The **exponent** (5) tells how many times the base is used as a factor.

We read 3^5 as *three raised to the fifth power* or simply *three to the fifth power*. When raising a base to the second power, we usually say that the base is being **squared**. When raising a base to the third power, we usually say that the base is being **cubed**. Exponents of 4 or higher do not have a special name.

EXAMPLE 1 Simplify 2^7.

SOLUTION In this example, 2 is a factor seven times.

$$2^7 = 2 \cdot 2 \cdot 2 \cdot 2 \cdot 2 \cdot 2 \cdot 2 \quad \text{Write 2 as a factor seven times.}$$
$$= 128 \quad \text{Multiply.}$$

Quick Check 1
Simplify 4^3.

Using Your Calculator Many calculators have a key that can be used to simplify expressions with exponents. When using the TI-84, use the ⌃ key. Other calculators may have a key that is labeled $\boxed{y^x}$ or $\boxed{x^y}$. Here is the screen you should see when using the TI-84 to simplify the expression in Example 1.

```
2^7
          128
```

EXAMPLE 2 Simplify $\left(\frac{2}{3}\right)^3$.

SOLUTION When the base is a fraction, the same rules apply. Use $\frac{2}{3}$ as a factor three times.

$$\left(\frac{2}{3}\right)^3 = \frac{2}{3} \cdot \frac{2}{3} \cdot \frac{2}{3} \quad \text{Write as a product.}$$
$$= \frac{8}{27} \quad \text{Multiply.}$$

Quick Check 2
Simplify $\left(\frac{1}{8}\right)^4$.

Consider the expression $(-3)^2$. The base is -3; so we multiply $(-3) \cdot (-3)$, and the result is positive 9. However, in the expression -2^4, the negative sign is not included in a set of parentheses with the 2. So the base of this expression is 2, not -2. We will use 2 as a factor 4 times and then take the opposite of the result: $-2^4 = -(2 \cdot 2 \cdot 2 \cdot 2) = -16$.

Order of Operations

Objective ② **Use the order of operations to simplify arithmetic expressions.** Suppose we were asked to simplify the expression $2 + 4 \cdot 3$. We could obtain two different results depending on whether we performed the addition or the multiplication first. Performing the addition first would give us $6 \cdot 3 = 18$, while performing the multiplication first would give us $2 + 12 = 14$. Only one result is correct. The **order of operations agreement** is a standard order in which arithmetic operations are performed, ensuring a single correct answer.

Order of Operations

1. **Remove grouping symbols.** Begin by simplifying all expressions within parentheses, brackets, and absolute value bars. Also perform any operations in the numerator or denominator of a fraction. This is done by following Steps 2–4, presented next.
2. **Perform any operations involving exponents.** After all grouping symbols have been removed from the expression, simplify any exponential expressions.
3. **Multiply and divide.** These two operations have equal priority. Perform multiplications or divisions in the order they appear from left to right.
4. **Add and subtract.** At this point, the only remaining operations should be additions and subtractions. Again, these operations are of equal priority, and we perform them in the order they appear from left to right. We also can use the strategy for totaling integers from Section 1.2.

Considering this information, when we simplify $2 + 4 \cdot 3$, the correct result is 14 because multiplication takes precedence over the addition.

$$2 + 4 \cdot 3 = 2 + 12 \quad \text{Multiply } 4 \cdot 3.$$
$$= 14 \quad \text{Add.}$$

EXAMPLE 3 Simplify $4 + 3 \cdot 5 - 2^6$.

SOLUTION In this example, the operation with the highest priority is 2^6, because simplifying exponents takes precedence over addition or multiplication. Note that the base is 2, not -2, because the negative sign is not grouped with 2 inside a set of parentheses.

$$4 + 3 \cdot 5 - 2^6 = 4 + 3 \cdot 5 - 64 \quad \text{Raise 2 to the 6th power.}$$
$$= 4 + 15 - 64 \quad \text{Multiply } 3 \cdot 5.$$
$$= -45 \quad \text{Simplify.}$$

Quick Check 3
Simplify $-2 \cdot 7 + 11 - 3^4$.

EXAMPLE 4 Simplify $(-5)^2 - 4(-2)(6)$.

SOLUTION Begin by squaring negative 5, which equals 25.

$$(-5)^2 - 4(-2)(6) = 25 - 4(-2)(6) \quad \text{Square } -5.$$
$$= 25 - (-48) \quad \text{Multiply } 4(-2)(6).$$
$$= 25 + 48 \quad \text{Write as a sum, eliminating the double signs.}$$
$$= 73$$

Quick Check 4
Simplify $9^2 - 4(-2)(-10)$.

A WORD OF CAUTION When we square a negative number such as $(-5)^2$ in the previous example, the result is a positive number.

$$(-5)^2 = (-5)(-5) = 25$$

EXAMPLE 5 Simplify $8 \div 2 + 3(7 - 4 \cdot 5)$.

SOLUTION The first step is to simplify the expression inside the set of parentheses. Here the multiplication takes precedence over the subtraction. Once we have simplified the expression inside the parentheses, we proceed to multiply and divide. We finish by subtracting.

$$
\begin{aligned}
8 \div 2 + 3(7 - 4 \cdot 5) &= 8 \div 2 + 3(7 - 20) && \text{Multiply } 4 \cdot 5.\\
&= 8 \div 2 + 3(-13) && \text{Subtract } 7 - 20.\\
&= 4 + 3(-13) && \text{Divide } 8 \div 2.\\
&= 4 - 39 && \text{Multiply } 3(-13).\\
&= -35 && \text{Subtract.}
\end{aligned}
$$

Quick Check 5
Simplify $20 \div 5 \cdot 10(3 \cdot 6 - 9)$.

Using Your Calculator When using your calculator to simplify an expression using the order of operations, you may want to perform one operation at a time. However, if you are careful to enter all of the parentheses, you can enter the entire expression at one time. Here is how to simplify the expression in Example 5 using the TI-84.

```
8/2+3(7-4*5)
             -35
```

Occasionally, an expression will have one set of grouping symbols inside another set, such as the expression $3[7 - 4(9 - 3)] + 5 \cdot 4$. This is called **nesting** grouping symbols. We begin by simplifying the innermost set of grouping symbols and work our way out from there.

EXAMPLE 6 Simplify $3[7 - 4(9 - 3)] + 5 \cdot 4$.

SOLUTION We begin by simplifying the expression inside the set of parentheses. Once we do that, we simplify the expression inside the square brackets.

$$
\begin{aligned}
&3[7 - 4(9 - 3)] + 5 \cdot 4 && \text{Subtract } 9 - 3 \text{ to simplify the expression inside}\\
&= 3[7 - 4 \cdot 6] + 5 \cdot 4 && \text{the parentheses. Then turn our attention to simplifying the expression inside the square brackets.}\\
&= 3[7 - 24] + 5 \cdot 4 && \text{Multiply } 4 \cdot 6.\\
&= 3[-17] + 5 \cdot 4 && \text{Subtract } 7 - 24.\\
&= -51 + 20 && \text{Multiply } 3[-17] \text{ and } 5 \cdot 4.\\
&= -31 && \text{Simplify.}
\end{aligned}
$$

Quick Check 6
Simplify $4[3^2 + 5(2 - 8)]$.

BUILDING YOUR STUDY STRATEGY

Study Groups, 7 Productive Group Members For any group or team to be effective, it must be made up of members who are committed to giving their full effort to success. Here are some pointers for being a productive study group member:

- **Arrive at each session fully prepared.** Make sure you have completed all required homework assignments. Bring a list of any questions you have.
- **Stay focused during study sessions.** Do not spend your time socializing.
- **Be open-minded.** During study sessions, you may be told that you are wrong. Keep in mind that the goal is to learn mathematics, not always to be correct initially.
- **Consider the feelings of others.** When a person has made a mistake, be supportive and encouraging.
- **Know when to speak and when to listen.** A study group works best when it is a collaborative body.

Exercises 1.7

MyMathLab

 PRACTICE

 WATCH

 DOWNLOAD

READ

 REVIEW

Vocabulary

1. In exponential notation, the factor being multiplied repeatedly is called the _____.

2. In exponential notation, the exponent tells us how many times the _____ is repeated as a(n) _____.

3. When a base is _____, it is raised to the second power.

4. When a base is _____, it is raised to the third power.

5. Symbols such as ( ) and [ ] are called _____ symbols.

6. When simplifying arithmetic expressions, once all grouping symbols have been removed, we perform any operations involving _____.

Rewrite the given expression using exponential notation.

7. $2 \cdot 2 \cdot 2$

8. $9 \cdot 9 \cdot 9 \cdot 9 \cdot 9$

9. $(-2)(-2)(-2)(-2)$

10. $(-6)(-6)(-6)(-6)(-6)$

11. $-3 \cdot 3 \cdot 3 \cdot 3 \cdot 3$

12. $-8 \cdot 8 \cdot 8 \cdot 8$

13. *five to the third power*

14. *seven squared*

Simplify the given expression.

15. 3^4

16. 4^3

17. 7^5

18. 2^9

19. 10^6

20. 10^5

21. 1^{723}

22. 0^{2364}

23. $\left(\dfrac{3}{4}\right)^3$

24. $\left(\dfrac{1}{5}\right)^5$

25. 0.2^5

26. 0.5^4

27. $(-3)^4$

28. -3^4

29. -2^7

30. $(-2)^7$

31. $2^3 \cdot 5^2$

32. $9^2 \cdot 4^4$

33. $-6^2 \cdot (-2)^2$

34. $-3^2 \cdot (-8)^2$

Simplify the given expression.

35. $9 + 3 \cdot 4$

36. $8 - 2 \cdot 7$

37. $20 \div 5 \cdot 2^2$

38. $80 - 16 \div 2^3$

39. $8 \cdot 5 - 9 \cdot 7$

40. $8(5 - 9 \cdot 7)$

41. $3.2 + 2.8(-6.3)$

42. $(3.2 + 2.8) - 6.3$

43. $17.1 - 8.58 \div 3.9$

44. $4.7 \cdot 13.9 - 3.6^2$

45. $(-3)^2 - 4(-5)(-4)$

46. $(-6)^2 - 4(2)(7)$

47. $3^2 + 4^2$

48. $(3 + 4)^2$

49. $-4 - 5(7 - 3 \cdot 6)$

50. $3 - 6(5^2 - 4 + 2 \cdot 7)$

51. $\dfrac{1}{2} + \dfrac{1}{2} \cdot \dfrac{4}{7}$

52. $\dfrac{3}{5} \cdot \dfrac{2}{3} + \dfrac{15}{7} \cdot \dfrac{21}{20}$

53. $\dfrac{2}{9} \div \dfrac{5}{3} \cdot \dfrac{33}{50}$

54. $4 \cdot \dfrac{3}{8} - \left(\dfrac{7}{6}\right)^2$

55. $\dfrac{1}{9}\left(\dfrac{19}{28} - \dfrac{1}{4}\right)$

56. $\dfrac{8}{25} \div \left(\dfrac{4}{15} - \dfrac{1}{3} + \dfrac{3}{5}\right) \cdot \dfrac{7}{18}$

57. $\dfrac{2^2 - 9}{3^3 - 7}$

58. $\dfrac{3 + 5 \cdot 7 - 4 \cdot 2}{1 + 2 \cdot 17}$

59. $\dfrac{(3 + 5) \cdot 6 - 8}{1 + 3^2 + 2}$

60. $\dfrac{10^3 + 9^3}{1^3 + 12^3}$

61. $3 - [4(5 - 6 \cdot 7)]$

62. $18 + [9 - (4 - 5 \cdot 8)] \div 3^2$

63. $-4 \cdot 9 - |-7(3 + 5)| - 2^3$

64. $-6^2 + 2|(7 - 49) \div (2 \cdot 3)|$

65. $9 - |3^2 + 2^3 - 10 \cdot 9|$

66. $|-4^2 + 19| - |(-7)^2 + 5(10)|$

67. $-21(|4 - 3 \cdot 9| + |8(13 - 4)|)$

68. $(6 \cdot 5 + 40 \div 20)(|8^2 - 2 \cdot 17| - |10^2 - 2 \cdot 51|)$

Construct an "order-of-operations problem" of your own that involves at least four numbers and produces the given result. Answers will vary. Examples are shown.

69. 41

70. 0

71. -13

72. -19

The size of a computer's memory is measured by the number of bytes that it can store. The following table lists the number of bytes in commonly used storage units.

1 kilobyte (KB)	2^{10} bytes
1 megabyte (MB)	2^{20} bytes
1 gigabyte (GB)	2^{30} bytes
1 terabyte (TB)	2^{40} bytes

Calculate the number of bytes in each of the following.

73. 1 kilobyte

74. 1 megabyte

75. 1 gigabyte

76. 1 terabyte

Find the missing number.

77. $5^? = 125$

78. $6^? = 7776$

79. $?^3 = 729$

80. $?^4 = 2401$

81. $\left(\dfrac{3}{?}\right)^4 = \dfrac{81}{4096}$

82. $\left(\dfrac{2}{5}\right)^? = \dfrac{64}{15,625}$

Insert the arithmetic operation signs $+$, $-$, $\cdot$, and $\div$ between the values to produce the desired results. (You may use parentheses as well.)

83. 3   5   9   8 = 14

84. 4   7   2   6 = 14

85. 3   7   9   2 = 33

86. 8   2   3   14   4   7 = 2

 Writing in Mathematics

Answer in complete sentences.

87. Explain the difference between $(-2)^6$ and -2^6.

88. *Newsletter* Write a newsletter explaining how to use the order of operations to simplify an expression.

1.8

Introduction to Algebra

OBJECTIVES

1. Build variable expressions.
2. Evaluate algebraic expressions.
3. Use the commutative, associative, and distributive properties of real numbers.
4. Identify terms and their coefficients.
5. Simplify variable expressions.

Variables

The number of students absent from a particular English class changes from day to day, as does the closing price for a share of Microsoft stock and the daily high temperature in Providence, Rhode Island. Quantities that change, or vary, are often represented by variables. A **variable** is a letter or symbol that is used to represent a quantity that changes or that has an unknown value.

Variable Expressions

Objective 1 **Build variable expressions.** Suppose a buffet restaurant charges $7 per person to eat. To determine the bill for a family to eat in the restaurant, we multiply the number of people by $7. The number of people can change from family to family, so we can represent this quantity by a variable such as x. The bill for a family with x people can be written as $7 \cdot x$, or simply $7x$. This expression for the bill, $7x$, is known as a variable expression. A **variable expression** is a combination of one or more variables with numbers or arithmetic operations. When the operation is multiplication such as $7 \cdot x$, we often omit the multiplication dot. Here are other examples of variable expressions.

$$3a + 5 \qquad x^2 + 3x - 10 \qquad \frac{y + 5}{y - 3}$$

EXAMPLE 1 Write an algebraic expression for *the sum of a number and 17*.

SOLUTION   Choose a variable to represent the unknown number. Let x represent the number. The expression is $x + 17$.

Other terms to look for that suggest addition are *plus, increased by, more than,* and *total.*

Quick Check 1

Write an algebraic expression for *9 more than a number.*

EXAMPLE 2 Write an algebraic expression for *five less than a number.*

SOLUTION   Let x represent the number. The expression is $x - 5$.

Be careful with the order of subtraction when the expression *less than* is used. *Five less than a number* says that we need to subtract 5 from that number. A common error is to write the subtraction in the opposite order.

Other terms that suggest subtraction are *difference, minus,* and *decreased by.*

Quick Check 2

Write an algebraic expression for *a number decreased by 25.*

A WORD OF CAUTION *Five less than a number* is written as $x - 5$, not $5 - x$.

EXAMPLE 3 Write an algebraic expression for *the product of 3 and two different numbers.*

SOLUTION   Because we are building an expression involving two different unknown numbers, we need to introduce two variables. Let x and y represent the two numbers. The expression is $3xy$.

Other terms that suggest multiplication are *times, multiplied by, of,* and *twice.*

Quick Check 3

Write an algebraic expression for *twice a number.*

EXAMPLE 4 Four friends decide to rent a fishing boat for the day. Assuming that all 4 friends decide to split the cost of renting the boat evenly, write a variable expression for the amount each friend will pay.

SOLUTION   Let c represent the cost of the boat. The expression is $c \div 4$ or $\frac{c}{4}$.

Other terms that suggest division are *quotient, divided by,* and *ratio.*

Quick Check 4

Write an algebraic expression for *the quotient of a number and 20.*

Here are some phrases that translate to $x + 5$, $x - 10$, $8x$, and $\frac{x}{6}$:

$x + 5$	$x - 10$
The sum of a number and 5	10 less than a number
A number plus 5	The difference of a number and 10
A number increased by 5	A number minus 10
5 more than a number	A number decreased by 10
The total of a number and 5	

$8x$	$\frac{x}{6}$
The product of 8 and a number	The quotient of a number and 6
8 times a number	A number divided by 6
8 multiplied by a number	The ratio of a number and 6

Evaluating Variable Expressions

Objective 2 Evaluate algebraic expressions. We often will have to evaluate variable expressions for particular values of variables. To do this, we substitute the appropriate numerical value for each variable and then simplify the resulting expression using the order of operations.

EXAMPLE 5 Evaluate $2x - 7$ for $x = 6$.

SOLUTION   The first step in evaluating a variable expression is to rewrite the expression, replacing each variable with a set of parentheses. For example, rewrite $2x - 7$ as $2(\ ) - 7$. Then we can substitute the appropriate value for each variable and simplify.

$$2x - 7$$
$$2(6) - 7 \quad \text{Substitute 6 for } x.$$
$$= 12 - 7 \quad \text{Multiply.}$$
$$= 5 \quad \text{Subtract.}$$

The expression $2x - 7$ is equal to 5 for $x = 6$.

Quick Check 5
Evaluate $5x + 2$ for $x = 11$.

EXAMPLE 6 Evaluate $x^2 - 5x + 6$ for $x = -5$.

SOLUTION

$$x^2 - 5x + 6$$
$$(-5)^2 - 5(-5) + 6 \quad \text{Substitute } -5 \text{ for } x.$$
$$= 25 - 5(-5) + 6 \quad \text{Square } -5.$$
$$= 25 + 25 + 6 \quad \text{Multiply.}$$
$$= 56 \quad \text{Add.}$$

Quick Check 6
Evaluate $x^2 - 13x - 40$ for $x = -8$.

EXAMPLE 7 Evaluate $b^2 - 4ac$ for $a = 3, b = -2$, and $c = -10$.

SOLUTION

$$b^2 - 4ac$$
$$(-2)^2 - 4(3)(-10) \quad \text{Substitute 3 for } a, -2 \text{ for } b, \text{ and } -10 \text{ for } c.$$
$$= 4 - 4(3)(-10) \quad \text{Square negative 2.}$$
$$= 4 - (-120) \quad \text{Multiply.}$$
$$= 4 + 120 \quad \text{Rewrite without double signs.}$$
$$= 124 \quad \text{Add.}$$

Quick Check 7
Evaluate $b^2 - 4ac$ for $a = -1$, $b = 5$, and $c = 18$.

Properties of Real Numbers

Objective 3 Use the commutative, associative, and distributive properties of real numbers. Now we examine three properties of real numbers. The first is the **commutative property**, which is used for addition and multiplication.

┌─ **Commutative Property** ───────────
For all real numbers a and b,

$$a + b = b + a \qquad \text{and} \qquad a \cdot b = b \cdot a.$$
└────────────────────────────────────

This property states that changing the order of the numbers a sum or a product does not change the result. For example, $3 + 9 = 9 + 3$ and $7 \cdot 8 = 8 \cdot 7$. Note that this property does not work for subtraction or division. Changing the order of the numbers in subtraction or division generally changes the result.

The second property is the **associative property**, which also holds for addition and multiplication.

Associative Property

For all real numbers a, b, and c,

$$(a + b) + c = a + (b + c) \quad \text{and} \quad (ab)c = a(bc).$$

This property states that changing the grouping of the numbers in a sum or a product does not change the result. Notice that $(2 + 7) + 3$ is equal to $2 + (7 + 3)$.

$$
\begin{array}{ll}
(2 + 7) + 3 & 2 + (7 + 3) \\
= 9 + 3 & = 2 + 10 \\
= 12 & = 12
\end{array}
$$

Also notice that $5(12x)$ can be rewritten using the associative property as $(5 \cdot 12)x$, which is equal to $60x$.

The third property of real numbers is the **distributive property**.

Distributive Property

For all real numbers a, b, and c,

$$a(b + c) = ab + ac.$$

This property says that we can distribute the factor outside the parentheses to each number being added in the parentheses, perform the multiplications, and then add. (This property also holds true when the operation inside the parentheses is subtraction.) Consider the expression $3(5 + 4)$. The order of operations says that this is equal to $3 \cdot 9$, or 27. Here is how to simplify the expression using the distributive property.

$$
\begin{array}{ll}
3(5 + 4) = 3 \cdot 5 + 3 \cdot 4 & \text{Apply the distributive property.} \\
= 15 + 12 & \text{Multiply } 3 \cdot 5 \text{ and } 3 \cdot 4. \\
= 27 & \text{Add.}
\end{array}
$$

Either way we get the same result.

EXAMPLE 8 Simplify $2(4 + 3x)$ using the distributive property.

SOLUTION

$$
\begin{array}{ll}
2(4 + 3x) = 2 \cdot 4 + 2 \cdot 3x & \text{Distribute the 2.} \\
= 8 + 6x & \text{Multiply. Recall from the associative property} \\
& \text{that } 2 \cdot 3x \text{ equals } 6x.
\end{array}
$$

Quick Check 8

Simplify $7(5x - 4)$ using the distributive property.

A WORD OF CAUTION The expression $8 + 6x$ is not equal to $14x$.

EXAMPLE 9 Simplify $7(2 + 3a - 4b)$ using the distributive property.

SOLUTION   When more than two terms are inside the parentheses, distribute the factor to each term. Also, it is a good idea to distribute the factor and multiply mentally.

Quick Check 9

Simplify $12(x - 2y + 3z)$ using the distributive property.

$$7(2 + 3a - 4b) = 14 + 21a - 28b$$

EXAMPLE 10 Simplify $-4(2x - 5)$ using the distributive property.

SOLUTION   When the factor outside the parentheses is negative, the negative number must be distributed to each term inside the parentheses. This will change the sign of each term inside the parentheses.

$$\begin{aligned}
-4(2x - 5) &= (-4) \cdot 2x - (-4) \cdot 5 &&\text{Distribute the } -4. \\
&= -8x - (-20) &&\text{Multiply.} \\
&= -8x + 20 &&\text{Rewrite without double signs.}
\end{aligned}$$

Quick Check 10
Simplify $-6(4x + 11)$ using the distributive property.

Simplifying Variable Expressions

Objective 4 Identify terms and their coefficients. In an algebraic expression, a **term** is a number, a variable, or a product of a number and variables. Terms in an algebraic expression are separated by addition. The expression $7x - 5y + 3$, has three terms: $7x$, $-5y$, and 3. The numerical factor of a term is its **coefficient**. The coefficients of these terms are 7, -5, and 3.

EXAMPLE 11 For the expression $-5x + y + 3xy - 19$, determine the number of terms, list them, and state the coefficient for each term.

SOLUTION   This expression has four terms: $-5x$, y, $3xy$, and -19.
What is the coefficient for the second term? Although y does not appear to have a coefficient, its coefficient is 1. This is because y is the same as $1 \cdot y$. So the four coefficients are -5, 1, 3, and -19.

▸ **Quick Check 11**
For the expression $x^3 - x^2 + 23x - 59$, determine the number of terms, list them, and state the coefficient for each term.

Objective 5 Simplify variable expressions. Two terms that have the same variable factors with the same exponents, or that are both constants, are called **like terms**. Consider the expression $9x + 8y + 6x - 3y + 8z - 5$. There are two sets of like terms in this expression: $9x$ and $6x$ as well as $8y$ and $-3y$. There are no like terms for $8z$ because no other term has z as its sole variable factor. Similarly, there are no like terms for the constant term -5.

> ┌ **Combining Like Terms** ────────────────
> When simplifying variable expressions, we can combine like terms into a single term with the same variable part by adding or subtracting the coefficients of the like terms.

EXAMPLE 12 Simplify $4x + 11x$ by combining like terms.

SOLUTION   These two terms are like terms because they both have the same variable factors. We can simply add the two coefficients to produce the expression $15x$.

$$4x + 11x = 15x$$

Quick Check 12
Simplify $3x + 7y + y - 5x$ by combining like terms.

A general strategy for simplifying algebraic expressions is to begin by applying the distributive property. We can then combine any like terms.

EXAMPLE 13 Simplify $8(3x - 5) - 4x + 7$.

SOLUTION The first step is to use the distributive property by distributing the 8 to each term inside the parentheses. Then we will be able to combine like terms.

$$8(3x - 5) - 4x + 7 = 24x - 40 - 4x + 7 \quad \text{Distribute the 8}$$
$$= 20x - 33 \quad \text{Combine like terms.}$$

▶ **Quick Check 13**

Simplify $5(2x + 3) + 9x - 8$.

EXAMPLE 14 Simplify $5(9 - 7x) - 10(3x + 4)$.

SOLUTION We must make sure that we distribute the *negative* 10 into the second set of parentheses.

$$5(9 - 7x) - 10(3x + 4) = 45 - 35x - 30x - 40 \quad \text{Distribute the 5 to each term in the first set of parentheses and distribute the } -10 \text{ to each term in the second set of parentheses.}$$
$$= -65x + 5 \quad \text{Combine like terms.}$$

Usually we write the simplified result with variable terms preceding constant terms, but it also is correct to write $5 - 65x$ because of the commutative property.

▶ **Quick Check 14**
Simplify $3(2x - 7) - 8(x - 9)$.

A WORD OF CAUTION If a factor in front of a set of parentheses is negative or has a subtraction sign in front of it, we must distribute the negative sign along with the factor.

BUILDING YOUR STUDY STRATEGY

Study Groups, 8 Dealing with Unproductive Group Members Occasionally, a group will have a member who is not productive or is even disruptive. You should not allow one person to prevent your group from being successful. If you have a group member who is not contributing to the group in a positive way, talk to that person one-on-one discreetly.

Try to find solutions that will be acceptable to the group and the group member in question. Seek advice from your instructor. Undoubtedly, your instructor has seen a similar situation and may have valuable advice for you.

Try to be professional about the situation rather than adversarial. Remember, you will continue to see this person in class each day and you want to stay on good terms.

Exercises 1.8

MyMathLab PRACTICE WATCH DOWNLOAD READ REVIEW

Vocabulary

1. A(n) _____ is a letter or symbol used to represent a quantity that changes or has an unknown value.

2. A combination of one or more variables with numbers and/or arithmetic operations is a(n) _____ expression.

3. To _____ a variable expression, substitute the appropriate numerical value for each variable and then simplify the resulting expression using the order of operations.

4. For any real numbers a and b, the _____ property states that $a + b = b + a$ and $a \cdot b = b \cdot a$.

5. For any real numbers a, b, and c, the _____ property states that $(a + b) + c = a + (b + c)$ and $(a \cdot b) \cdot c = a \cdot (b \cdot c)$.

6. For any real numbers a, b, and c, the _____ property states that $a(b + c) = ab + ac$.

7. A(n) _____ is a number, a variable, or a product of numbers and variables.

8. A(n) _____ is the numerical factor of a term.

9. Two terms that have the same variable factors, or that are constant terms, are called _____.

10. To combine two like terms, add their _____.

Build a variable expression for the following phrases.

11. A number increased by 15

12. A number decreased by 33

13. Twenty-four less than a number

14. Forty-one more than a number

15. Three times a number

16. A number divided by 8

17. Nineteen more than twice a number

18. Seven less than 4 times a number

19. The sum of two different numbers

20. One number divided by another

21. Seven times the difference of two numbers

22. Half the sum of a number and 25

23. A college charges $325 per credit for tuition. Letting c represent the number of credits that a student is taking, build a variable expression for the student's tuition.

24. The admission charge for a particular amusement park is $54.95 per person. Letting p represent the number of people that attended the amusement park yesterday, build a variable expression for the total admission charges the park collected yesterday.

25. A professional baseball player is appearing at a baseball card convention. The promoter agreed to pay the player a flat fee of $25,000 plus $22 per autograph signed. Letting a represent the number of autographs signed, build a variable expression for the amount of money the player will be paid.

26. Jim Rockford, a private investigator from the 1970's TV show *The Rockford Files,* charged $200 per day plus expenses to take a case. Letting d represent the number of days Rockford worked on a case and assuming that he had $425 in expenses, build a variable expression for the amount of money he would charge for the case.

Write the given expression using words.

27. $x - 9$

28. $x + 16$

29. $7x$

30. $6x + 5$

31. $8x - 10$

32. $2x - 7$

Evaluate the following algebraic expressions under the given conditions.

33. $8x + 31$ for $x = 6$

34. $27 - 4x$ for $x = 9$

35. $7a - 13b$ for $a = 8$ and $b = 11$

36. $9m + 10n$ for $m = 15$ and $n = -5$

37. $2(3x + 8)$ for $x = 5$

38. $6x + 16$ for $x = 5$

39. $x^2 + 9x + 18$ for $x = 5$

40. $a^2 - 7a - 30$ for $a = 3$

41. $y^2 + 4y - 17$ for $y = -3$

42. $x^2 - 5x - 9$ for $x = -4$

43. $m^2 - 9$ for $m = 3$

44. $5 - x^2$ for $x = -2$

45. $b^2 - 4ac$ for $a = 2$, $b = 5$, and $c = -3$

46. $b^2 - 4ac$ for $a = -5$, $b = 7$, and $c = -4$

47. $b^2 - 4ac$ for $a = -1$, $b = -2$, and $c = 10$

48. $b^2 - 4ac$ for $a = 15$, $b = -6$, and $c = 9$

49. $5(x + h) - 17$ for $x = -3$ and $h = 0.01$

50. $-3(x + h) + 4$ for $x = -6$ and $h = 0.001$

51. $(x + h)^2 - 5(x + h) - 14$ for $x = -3$ and $h = 0.1$

52. $(x + h)^2 + 4(x + h) - 28$ for $x = 6$ and $h = 1$

53. The commutative property works for addition but does not work in general for subtraction.

a) Give an example of two numbers a and b such that $a - b \neq b - a$.

b) Can you find two numbers a and b such that $a - b = b - a$?

54. The commutative property works for multiplication but does not work in general for division.

a) Give an example of two numbers a and b such that $\frac{a}{b} \neq \frac{b}{a}$.

b) Can you find two numbers a and b such that $\frac{a}{b} = \frac{b}{a}$?

Simplify where possible.

55. $3(x - 9)$

56. $4(2x + 5)$

57. $5(3 - 7x)$

58. $12(5x - 7)$

59. $-2(5x + 7)$

60. $-3(8x + 3)$

61. $-6(9x - 5)$

62. $-4(-10x + 1)$

63. $7x + 9x$

64. $14x + 3x$

65. $3x - 8x$

66. $22a - 15a$

67. $3x - 7 + 4x + 11$

68. $15x + 32 - 19x - 57$

69. $5x - 3y - 7x - 19y$

70. $15m - 11n - 6m + 22n$

71. $3(2x - 5) + 4x + 7$

72. $8 - 19k + 6(3k - 5)$

73. $2(4x - 9) - 11$

74. $3(2a + 11b) - 13a$

75. $6y - 5(3y - 17)$

76. $5 - 9(3 - 4x)$

77. $3(4z - 7) + 9(2z + 3)$

78. $-6(5x - 9) - 7(13 - 12x)$

79. $-2(5a + 4b - 13c) + 3b$

80. $-7(-2x + 3y - 17z) - 5(3x - 11)$

For the following expressions:

a) *Determine the number of terms.*

b) *Write down each term.*

c) *Write down the coefficient for each term.*

Make sure you simplify each expression before answering.

81. $5x^3 + 3x^2 - 7x - 15$

82. $-3a^2 - 7a - 10$

83. $3x - 17$

84. $9x^4 - 10x^3 + 13x^2 - 17x + 329$

85. $5(3x^2 - 7x + 11) - 6x$

86. $4(3a - 5b - 7c - 11) - 2(6b - 5c)$

87. $5(-7a - 3b + 5c) - 3(6b - 9c - 23)$

88. $2(-4x + 7y) - (3x + 9y)$

Writing in Mathematics

Answer in complete sentences.

89. Give an example of a real-world situation that can be described by the variable expression $60x$. Explain why the expression fits your situation.

90. Give an example of a real-world situation that can be described by the variable expression $20x + 35$. Explain why the expression fits your situation.

91. *Solutions Manual* Write a solutions manual page for the following problem.

Simplify $4(2x - 5) - 3(3x - 8) - 7x$.

CHAPTER 2

Linear Equations

In this chapter, we will learn to solve linear equations and investigate applications of this type of equation. The chapter also discusses applications involving percents and proportions. The chapter concludes with a section on linear inequalities.

STUDY STRATEGY

Using Your Textbook In this chapter, we will focus on how to get the most out of your textbook. Students who treat their books solely as a source of homework exercises are turning their backs on one of their best resources.

Throughout this chapter, we will revisit this study strategy and help you incorporate it into your study habits.

2.1

Introduction to Linear Equations

OBJECTIVES

1. Identify linear equations.
2. Determine whether a value is a solution of an equation.
3. Solve linear equations using the multiplication property of equality.
4. Solve linear equations using the addition property of equality.
5. Solve applied problems using the multiplication property of equality or the addition property of equality.

Linear Equations

Objective 1 Identify linear equations. An **equation** is a mathematical statement of equality between two expressions. It is a statement that asserts that the value of the expression on the left side of the equation is equal to the value of the expression on the right side. Here are a few examples of equations.

$$2x = 8 \qquad x + 17 = 20 \qquad 3x - 8 = 2x + 6 \qquad 5(2x - 9) + 3 = 7(3x + 16)$$

63

All of these are examples of linear equations. A **linear equation** in one variable has a single variable, and the exponent for that variable is 1. For example, if the variable in a linear equation is x, the equation cannot have terms containing x^2 or x^3. The variable in a linear equation cannot appear in a denominator either. Here are some examples of equations that are not linear equations.

$$x^2 - 5x - 6 = 0 \qquad \text{Variable is squared.}$$
$$m^3 - m^2 + 7m = 7 \qquad \text{Variable has exponents greater than 1.}$$
$$\frac{5x + 3}{x - 2} = -9 \qquad \text{Variable is in denominator.}$$

Solutions of Equations

Objective 2 Determine whether a value is a solution of an equation. A **solution** of an equation is a value that when substituted for the variable in the equation, produces a true statement, such as $5 = 5$.

EXAMPLE 1 Is $x = 3$ a solution of $9x - 7 = 20$?

SOLUTION To check whether a particular value is a solution of an equation, we substitute that value for the variable in the equation. If after simplifying both sides of the equation we have a true mathematical statement, the value is a solution.

$$9x - 7 = 20$$
$$9(3) - 7 = 20 \qquad \text{Substitute 3 for } x.$$
$$27 - 7 = 20 \qquad \text{Multiply.}$$
$$20 = 20 \qquad \text{Subtract.}$$

Because 20 is equal to 20, we know that $x = 3$ is a solution.

EXAMPLE 2 Is $x = -2$ a solution of $3 - 4x = -5$?

SOLUTION Again, substitute for x and simplify both sides of the equation.

$$3 - 4x = -5$$
$$3 - 4(-2) = -5 \qquad \text{Substitute } -2 \text{ for } x.$$
$$3 + 8 = -5 \qquad \text{Multiply.}$$
$$11 = -5 \qquad \text{Add.}$$

This statement, $11 = -5$, is not true because 11 is not equal to -5. Therefore, $x = -2$ is not a solution of the equation.

Quick Check 1

Is $x = -7$ a solution of $4x + 23 = -5$?

The set of all solutions of an equation is called its **solution set**. The process of finding an equation's solution set is called **solving the equation**. When we find all of the solutions to an equation, we write those values using set notation inside braces { }.

When solving a linear equation, our goal is to convert it to an equivalent equation that has the variable isolated on one side with a number on the other side (for example, $x = 3$). The value on the opposite side of the equation from the variable after it has been isolated is the solution of the equation.

Multiplication Property of Equality

Objective 3 Solve linear equations using the multiplication property of equality. The first tool for solving linear equations is the **multiplication property of equality**. It says that for any equation, if we multiply both sides of the equation by the same nonzero number, both sides remain equal to each other.

Multiplication Property of Equality

For any algebraic expressions A and B and any nonzero number n,

$$\text{if } A = B, \text{ then } n \cdot A = n \cdot B.$$

Think of a scale that holds two weights in balance. If we double the amount of weight on each side of the scale, will the scale still be balanced? Of course it will.

Think of an equation as a scale and the expressions on each side as the weights that are balanced. Multiplying both sides by the same nonzero number leaves both sides still balanced and equal to each other.

Why is it important to multiply both sides of an equation by a *nonzero* number? Multiplying both sides of an equation by 0 can take an equation that is false and make it true. For example, we know that $5 = 3$ is false. If we multiply both sides of that equation by 0, the resulting equation is $0 = 0$, which is true.

EXAMPLE 3   Solve $\frac{x}{3} = 4$ using the multiplication property of equality.

SOLUTION   The goal when solving this linear equation is to isolate the variable x on one side of the equation. We begin by multiplying both sides of the equation by 3. The expression $\frac{x}{3}$ is equivalent to $\frac{1}{3}x$; so when we multiply by 3, we are multiplying by the reciprocal of $\frac{1}{3}$. The product of reciprocals is equal to 1, so the resulting expression on the left side of the equation is $1x$, or x.

Another way to think of $\frac{x}{3}$ is as $x \div 3$. Division and multiplication are inverse operations, and we solve the equation by multiplying both sides of the equation by 3. This will "undo" dividing by 3.

$$\frac{x}{3} = 4$$

$$3 \cdot \frac{x}{3} = 3 \cdot 4 \qquad \text{Multiply both sides by 3.}$$

$$\overset{1}{3} \cdot \frac{x}{\underset{1}{3}} = 3 \cdot 4 \qquad \text{Divide out common factors.}$$

$$x = 12 \qquad \text{Multiply.}$$

The solution that we found is $x = 12$. Before moving on, we must check this value to ensure that we made no mistakes and that it is a solution.

Check

$$\frac{x}{3} = 4$$

$$\frac{12}{3} = 4 \qquad \text{Substitute 12 for } x.$$

$$4 = 4 \qquad \text{Divide.}$$

This is a true statement; so $x = 12$ is a solution, and the solution set is $\{12\}$.

Quick Check 2
Solve $\frac{x}{8} = -2$ using the multiplication property of equality.

The multiplication property of equality also allows us to divide both sides of an equation by the same nonzero number without affecting the equality of the two sides. This is because dividing both sides of an equation by a nonzero number, n, is equivalent to multiplying both sides of the equation by the reciprocal of the number, $\frac{1}{n}$.

EXAMPLE 4 Solve $5y = 40$ using the multiplication property of equality.

SOLUTION Begin by dividing both sides of the equation by 5, which will isolate the variable y.

$$5y = 40$$

$$\frac{5y}{5} = \frac{40}{5} \quad \text{Divide both sides by 5.}$$

$$\frac{\overset{1}{\cancel{5}}y}{\cancel{5}} = \frac{40}{5} \quad \text{Divide out common factors on the left side.}$$

$$y = 8 \quad \text{Simplify.}$$

Again, check the solution before writing it in solution set notation.

Check

$$5y = 40$$

$$5(8) = 40 \quad \text{Substitute 8 for } y.$$

$$40 = 40 \quad \text{Multiply.}$$

$y = 8$ is indeed a solution, and the solution set is $\{8\}$.

Quick Check 3

Solve $4a = 56$ using the multiplication property of equality.

If the coefficient of the variable term is negative, we must divide both sides of the equation by that negative number.

EXAMPLE 5 Solve $-7n = -56$ using the multiplication property of equality.

SOLUTION In this example, the coefficient of the variable term is -7. To solve this equation, we need to divide both sides by -7.

$$-7n = -56$$

$$\frac{-7n}{-7} = \frac{-56}{-7} \quad \text{Divide both sides by } -7.$$

$$n = 8 \quad \text{Simplify.}$$

The check of this solution is left to the reader. The solution set is $\{8\}$.

Quick Check 4

Solve $-9a = 144$ using the multiplication property of equality.

A WORD OF CAUTION When dividing both sides of an equation by a negative number, keep in mind that this will change the sign of the number on the other side of the equation.

Consider the equation $-x = 16$. The coefficient of the variable term is -1. To solve this equation, we can multiply both sides of the equation by -1 or divide both sides by -1. Either way, the solution is $x = -16$. We also could have solved the equation by inspection by reading the equation $-x = 16$ as *the opposite of x is 16*. If the opposite of x is 16, we know that x must be equal to -16.

We will now learn how to solve an equation in which the coefficient of the variable term is a fraction.

EXAMPLE 6 Solve $\frac{3}{8}a = -\frac{5}{2}$ using the multiplication property of equality.

SOLUTION In this example, we have a variable multiplied by a fraction. In such a case, we can multiply both sides of the equation by the reciprocal of the fraction. When we multiply a fraction by its reciprocal, the result is 1. This will leave the variable isolated.

$$\frac{3}{8}a = -\frac{5}{2}$$

$$\frac{\overset{1}{\cancel{8}}}{\underset{1}{\cancel{3}}} \cdot \frac{\overset{1}{\cancel{3}}}{\underset{1}{\cancel{8}}}a = \frac{\overset{4}{\cancel{8}}}{3}\left(-\frac{5}{\underset{1}{\cancel{2}}}\right) \quad \text{Multiply by the reciprocal of the fraction } \frac{3}{8} \text{ and divide out common factors.}$$

$$a = -\frac{20}{3} \quad \text{Simplify.}$$

The check of this solution is left to the reader. The solution set is $\left\{-\frac{20}{3}\right\}$.

Quick Check 5
Solve $\frac{9}{16}x = \frac{21}{8}$ using the multiplication property of equality.

Addition Property of Equality

Objective 4 Solve linear equations using the addition property of equality.
The **addition property of equality** says that we can add the same number to both sides of an equation or subtract the same number from both sides of an equation without affecting the equality of the two sides.

┌─ **Addition Property of Equality** ──────────────────────
│ For any algebraic expressions A and B and any number n,
│
│ $\qquad$ if $\quad A = B$, $\quad$ then $\quad A + n = B + n$
│ $\qquad\qquad\qquad$ and $\quad A - n = B - n$.
└──

This property helps us solve equations in which a number is added to or subtracted from a variable on one side of an equation.

EXAMPLE 7 Solve $x + 4 = 11$ using the addition property of equality.

SOLUTION In this example, the number 4 is being added to the variable x. To isolate the variable, use the addition property of equality to subtract 4 from both sides of the equation.

$$x + 4 = 11$$
$$x + 4 - 4 = 11 - 4 \quad \text{Subtract 4 from both sides.}$$
$$x = 7 \quad \text{Simplify.}$$

To check this solution, substitute 7 for x in the original equation.

Check

Quick Check 6
Solve $a + 22 = -8$ using the addition property of equality.

$$x + 4 = 11$$
$$7 + 4 = 11 \quad \text{Substitute 7 for } x.$$
$$11 = 11 \quad \text{Add.}$$

The statement is true, so the solution set is $\{7\}$.

EXAMPLE 8 Solve $13 = y - 9$ using the addition property of equality.

SOLUTION When a value is subtracted from a variable, isolate the variable by adding the value to both sides of the equation. In this example, add 9 to both sides.

$$13 = y - 9$$
$$13 + 9 = y - 9 + 9 \quad \text{Add 9 to both sides.}$$
$$22 = y \quad \text{Add.}$$

Check

$$13 = y - 9$$
$$13 = 22 - 9 \quad \text{Substitute 22 for } y.$$
$$13 = 13 \quad \text{Subtract.}$$

This is a true statement, so the solution set is $\{22\}$.

In the next section, we will learn how to solve equations requiring us to use both the multiplication and addition properties of equality.

Quick Check 7

Solve $-13 = x - 28$ using the addition property of equality.

Applications

Objective 5 Solve applied problems using the multiplication property of equality or the addition property of equality. This section concludes with an example of an applied problem that can be solved with a linear equation.

EXAMPLE 9 Admission to the county fair is $8 per person; so the admission price for a group of x people can be represented by $8x$. If a Cub Scout group paid a total of $208 for admission to the county fair, how many people were in the group?

SOLUTION We can express this relationship in an equation using the idea that the total cost of admission is equal to $208. Because the total cost for x people can be represented by $8x$, the equation is $8x = 208$.

$$8x = 208$$
$$\frac{8x}{8} = \frac{208}{8} \quad \text{Divide both sides by 8.}$$
$$x = 26 \quad \text{Divide.}$$

We can verify that this value checks as a solution. Whenever we work on an applied problem, we should write the solution as a complete sentence. There were 26 people in the Cub Scout group at the county fair.

▶ Quick Check 8

Josh spent a total of $26.50 to take his date to a movie. This left him with only $38.50 in his pocket. How much money did he have with him before going to the movie?

BUILDING YOUR STUDY STRATEGY

Using Your Textbook, 1 Reading Ahead One effective way to use your textbook is to read a section in the text before it is covered in class. This will give you an idea about the main concepts covered in the section, and your instructor can clarify these concepts in class.

When reading ahead, you should scan the section. Look for definitions that are introduced; as well as procedures that are developed. Pay close attention to the examples. If you find a step in the examples that you do not understand, ask your instructor about it in class.

Exercises 2.1

Vocabulary

1. A(n) _____ is a mathematical statement of equality between two expressions.

2. A(n) _____ of an equation is a value that when substituted for the variable in the equation, produces a true statement.

3. The _____ of an equation is the set of all solutions to that equation.

4. State the multiplication property of equality.

5. State the addition property of equality.

6. Freebird's Pizza charges \$12 for a pizza. If the bill for an office pizza party is \$168, which equation can be used to determine the number of pizzas that were ordered?

a) $x + 12 = 168$

b) $x - 12 = 168$

c) $12x = 168$

d) $\dfrac{x}{12} = 168$

Is the given equation a linear equation? If not, explain.

7. $5x^2 - 7x = 3x + 8$

8. $4x - 9 = 17$

9. $3x - 5(2x + 3) = 8 - x$

10. $\dfrac{7}{x^2} - \dfrac{5}{x} - 13 = 0$

11. $y = 5$

12. $x^4 - 1 = 0$

13. $\dfrac{3x}{11} - \dfrac{5}{4} = \dfrac{2x}{7}$

14. $x \cdot 4 - 1 = 0$

15. $x + \dfrac{3}{x} + 18 = 0$

16. $3(4x - 9) + 7(2x + 5) = 15$

Check to determine whether the given value is a solution of the equation.

17. $x = 7,$ $5x - 9 = 26$

18. $x = 3,$ $2x - 11 = x + 2$

19. $a = 8,$ $3 - 2a = a + 2a - 11$

20. $m = 4,$ $15 - 8m = 3m - 29$

21. $z = \dfrac{1}{4},$ $\dfrac{2}{3}z + \dfrac{11}{6} = 2$

22. $t = \dfrac{5}{3},$ $\dfrac{1}{10}t + \dfrac{1}{3} = \dfrac{1}{2}$

23. $m = 3.4,$ $3m - 2 = 2m + 0.4$

24. $a = -2.5,$ $4a - 6 = 9 + 10a$

Solve using the multiplication property of equality.

25. $7x = -91$

26. $9a = 72$

27. $6y = 84$

28. $11x = -1331$

29. $8b = 22$

30. $20z = -35$

31. $5a = 0$

32. $0 = 12x$

33. $-5t = 35$

34. $-11x = -44$

35. $-2x = -28$

36. $-9h = 54$

37. $-t = 45$

38. $-y = -31$

39. $\dfrac{x}{3} = 7$

40. $\dfrac{x}{4} = 3$

41. $-\dfrac{t}{8} = 12$

42. $-\dfrac{g}{13} = -7$

43. $\dfrac{7}{12}x = \dfrac{14}{3}$

44. $\dfrac{3}{4}x = -\dfrac{9}{2}$

45. $-\dfrac{2}{5}x = 4$

46. $-\dfrac{5}{6}x = 15$

47. $3.2x = 6.944$

48. $-4.7x = 15.04$

Solve using the addition property of equality.

49. $a + 9 = 16$

50. $b + 4 = 28$

51. $x + 11 = 3$

52. $x + 5 = -18$

53. $n - 13 = 30$

54. $n - 9 = -23$

55. $a + 3.2 = 5.7$

56. $x - 4.9 = -11.2$

57. $12 = x + 3$

58. $4 = m + 10$

59. $b - 7 = 13$

60. $a - 9 = 99$

61. $t - 7 = -4$

62. $n - 3 = -18$

63. $-4 + x = 19$

64. $-15 + x = -7$

65. $x + 9 = 0$

66. $b - 17 = 0$

67. $9 + a = 5$

68. $7 + b = -22$

69. $a + 5 + 6 = 7$

70. $x + 4 - 9 = -3$

Mixed Practice, 71–88

Solve the equation.

71. $60 = 5a$

72. $-m = -15$

73. $x - 27 = -11$

74. $\frac{3}{14}x = \frac{5}{2}$

75. $-\frac{b}{10} = -3$

76. $b + 39 = 30$

77. $x + 24 = -17$

78. $\frac{x}{5} = 13$

79. $11 = -\frac{n}{7}$

80. $47 = y + 35$

81. $0 = x + 56$

82. $x - 38 = -57$

83. $-t = 18$

84. $\frac{t}{15} = -7$

85. $\frac{4}{9}x = -\frac{14}{15}$

86. $x - 3 = -9$

87. $0 = 45m$

88. $40 = -6m$

Provide an equation that has the given solution.

89. $x = 7$

90. $x = -13$

91. $n = \frac{5}{2}$

92. $m = -\frac{3}{10}$

Set up a linear equation and solve it for the following problems.

93. Zoe has only nickels in her pocket. If she has $1.35 in her pocket, how many nickels does she have?

94. Fruit smoothies were sold at a campus fund-raiser for $3.25. If total sales were $217.75, how many smoothies were sold?

95. A local garage band, the Grease Monkeys, held a rent party. They charged $3 per person for admission, with

the proceeds used to pay the rent. If the rent is $425 and they ended up with an extra $52 after paying the rent, how many people came to see them play?

96. Ross organized a tour of a local winery. Attendees paid Ross $12 to go on the tour, plus another $5 for lunch. If Ross collected $493, how many people came on the tour?

97. An insurance company hired 8 new employees. This brought the total to 174 employees. How many employees did the company have before these 8 people were hired?

98. Geena scored 17 points lower than Jared on the last math exam. If Geena's score was 65, find Jared's score.

99. As a cold front was moving in, the temperature in Visalia dropped by 19°F in a two-hour period. If the temperature dropped to 37°F, what was the temperature before the cold front moved in?

100. A company was forced to lay off 37 workers due to an economic downturn. If the company now has 144 employees, how many workers were employed before the layoffs?

✎ Writing in Mathematics

Answer in complete sentences.

101. Explain why the equation $0x = 15$ cannot be solved.

102. Find a value for x such that the expression $x + 21$ is less than -39.

2.2 Solving Linear Equations: A General Strategy

OBJECTIVES

1. Solve linear equations using both the multiplication property of equality and the addition property of equality.
2. Solve linear equations containing fractions.
3. Solve linear equations using the five-step general strategy.
4. Identify linear equations with no solution.
5. Identify linear equations with infinitely many solutions.
6. Solve literal equations for a specified variable.

In the previous section, we solved equations that required only one operation to isolate the variable. In this section, we will learn how to solve equations requiring the use of both the multiplication and addition properties of equality.

Solving Linear Equations

Objective 1 **Solve linear equations using both the multiplication property of equality and the addition property of equality.** Suppose we needed to solve the equation $4x - 7 = 17$. Should we divide both sides by 4 first? Should we add 7 to both sides first? We refer to the order of operations. This says that in the expression $4x - 7$, we multiply 4 by x and then subtract 7 from the result. To isolate the variable x, we undo these operations in the opposite order. We first add 7 to both sides to undo the subtraction and then divide both sides by 4 to undo the multiplication.

Solution	Check

$$4x - 7 = 17 \qquad\qquad 4(6) - 7 = 17$$
$$4x - 7 + 7 = 17 + 7 \qquad 24 - 7 = 17$$
$$4x = 24 \qquad\qquad 17 = 17$$
$$\frac{4x}{4} = \frac{24}{4}$$
$$x = 6$$

Because the solution $x = 6$ checks, the solution set is $\{6\}$.

EXAMPLE 1 Solve the equation $3x + 41 = 8$.

SOLUTION To solve this equation, begin by subtracting 41 from both sides. This will isolate the term $3x$. Then divide both sides of the equation by 3 to isolate the variable x.

$$3x + 41 = 8$$
$$3x + 41 - 41 = 8 - 41 \qquad \text{Subtract 41 from both sides to isolate } 3x.$$
$$3x = -33 \qquad \text{Subtract.}$$
$$\frac{3x}{3} = -\frac{33}{3} \qquad \text{Divide both sides by 3 to isolate } x.$$
$$x = -11 \qquad \text{Simplify.}$$

Now check the solution.

$$3x + 41 = 8$$
$$3(-11) + 41 = 8 \quad \text{Substitute } -11 \text{ for } x.$$
$$-33 + 41 = 8 \quad \text{Multiply.}$$
$$8 = 8 \quad \text{Simplify.}$$

Because $x = -11$ produced a true statement, the solution set is $\{-11\}$.

Quick Check 1

Solve the equation $5x - 2 = 33$.

EXAMPLE 2 Solve the equation $-8x - 19 = 13$.

SOLUTION

$$-8x - 19 = 13$$
$$-8x - 19 + 19 = 13 + 19 \quad \text{Add 19 to both sides to isolate } -8x.$$
$$-8x = 32 \quad \text{Add.}$$
$$\frac{-8x}{-8} = \frac{32}{-8} \quad \text{Divide by } -8 \text{ to isolate } x.$$
$$x = -4 \quad \text{Simplify.}$$

Now check the solution.

$$-8x - 19 = 13$$
$$-8(-4) - 19 = 13 \quad \text{Substitute } -4 \text{ for } x.$$
$$32 - 19 = 13 \quad \text{Multiply.}$$
$$13 = 13 \quad \text{Simplify.}$$

The solution set is $\{-4\}$.

Quick Check 2

Solve the equation
$6 - 4x = 38$.

Solving Linear Equations Containing Fractions

Objective ② **Solve linear equations containing fractions.** If an equation contains fractions, we may find it helpful to convert it to an equivalent equation that does not contain fractions before we solve it. This can be done by multiplying both sides of the equation by the LCM of the denominators.

EXAMPLE 3 Solve the equation $\frac{2}{3}x - \frac{5}{6} = \frac{1}{2}$.

SOLUTION This equation contains three fractions, and the denominators are 3, 6, and 2. The LCM of these denominators is 6, so begin by multiplying both sides of the equation by 6.

$$\frac{2}{3}x - \frac{5}{6} = \frac{1}{2}$$

$$6\left(\frac{2}{3}x - \frac{5}{6}\right) = 6\left(\frac{1}{2}\right) \quad \text{Multiply both sides by the LCM 6.}$$

$$\overset{2}{\cancel{6}} \cdot \frac{2}{\cancel{3}_1}x - \overset{1}{\cancel{6}} \cdot \frac{5}{\cancel{6}_1} = \overset{3}{\cancel{6}} \cdot \frac{1}{\cancel{2}_1} \quad \text{Distribute and divide out common factors.}$$

$$4x - 5 = 3 \quad \text{Multiply.}$$

$$4x - 5 + 5 = 3 + 5 \quad \text{Add 5 to both sides to isolate } 4x.$$

$$4x = 8 \quad \text{Add.}$$

$$\frac{4x}{4} = \frac{8}{4} \quad \text{Divide by 4 to isolate } x.$$

$$x = 2 \quad \text{Simplify.}$$

Now check the solution.

$$\frac{2}{3}x - \frac{5}{6} = \frac{1}{2}$$

$$\frac{2}{3}(2) - \frac{5}{6} = \frac{1}{2} \quad \text{Substitute 2 for } x.$$

$$\frac{4}{3} - \frac{5}{6} = \frac{1}{2} \quad \text{Simplify.}$$

$$\frac{8}{6} - \frac{5}{6} = \frac{1}{2} \quad \text{Rewrite } \frac{4}{3} \text{ as } \frac{8}{6}.$$

$$\frac{3}{6} = \frac{1}{2} \quad \text{Subtract.}$$

$$\frac{1}{2} = \frac{1}{2} \quad \text{Simplify.}$$

Quick Check 3

Solve the equation $\frac{2}{7}x + \frac{1}{2} = \frac{4}{3}$.

The solution set is $\{2\}$.

A WORD OF CAUTION When multiplying both sides of an equation by the LCM of the denominators, make sure you multiply each term by the LCM, including any terms that do not contain fractions.

A General Strategy for Solving Linear Equations

Objective 3 **Solve linear equations using the five-step general strategy.** Now we will examine a process that can be used to solve any linear equation. This process works not only for types of equations we have already learned to solve, but also for more complicated equations such as $7x + 4 = 3x - 20$ and $5(2x - 9) + 3x = 7(3 - 8x)$.

Solving Linear Equations

1. **Simplify each side of the equation completely.**
   - Use the distributive property to clear any parentheses.
   - If there are fractions in the equation, multiply both sides of the equation by the LCM of the denominators to clear the fractions from the equation.
   - Combine any like terms that are on the same side of the equation. After you have completed this step, the equation should contain, at most, one variable term and one constant term on each side.

2. **Collect all variable terms on one side of the equation.** If there is a variable term on each side of the equation, use the addition property of equality to place both variable terms on the same side of the equation.

3. **Collect all constant terms on the other side of the equation.** If there is a constant term on each side of the equation, use the addition property of equality to isolate the variable term.

4. **Divide both sides of the equation by the coefficient of the variable term.** At this point the equation should be of the form $ax = b$. Use the multiplication property of equality to find the solution.

5. **Check your solution.** Check that the value creates a true equation when substituted for the variable in the original equation.

In the next example, we will solve equations that have variable terms and constant terms on both sides of the equation.

EXAMPLE 4 Solve the equation $3x + 8 = 7x - 6$.

SOLUTION   In this equation, there are no parentheses or fractions to clear and there are no like terms to be combined. Begin by gathering the variable terms on one side of the equation.

$$3x + 8 = 7x - 6$$
$$3x + 8 - 3x = 7x - 6 - 3x \qquad \text{Subtract } 3x \text{ from both sides to gather the variable terms on the right side of the equation.}$$
$$8 = 4x - 6 \qquad \text{Subtract.}$$
$$8 + 6 = 4x - 6 + 6 \qquad \text{Add 6 to both sides to isolate } 4x.$$
$$14 = 4x \qquad \text{Add.}$$
$$\frac{14}{4} = \frac{4x}{4} \qquad \text{Divide both sides by 4 to isolate } x.$$
$$\frac{7}{2} = x \qquad \text{Simplify.}$$

Quick Check 4

Solve the equation
$6x + 19 = 3x - 8$.

The check of this solution is left to the reader. The solution set is $\left\{\frac{7}{2}\right\}$.

Using Your Calculator You can use a calculator to check the solutions to an equation. Substitute the value for the variable and simplify the expressions on each side of the equation. Here is how the check of the solution $x = \frac{7}{2}$ would look on the TI-84.

Because each expression is equal to 18.5 when $x = \frac{7}{2}$, this solution checks.

```
3(7/2)+8
                    18.5
7(7/2)-6
                    18.5
```

In the next example, we will solve an equation containing like terms on the same side of the equation.

EXAMPLE 5 Solve the equation $13x - 43 - 9x = 6x + 37 + 5x - 66$.

SOLUTION This equation has like terms on each side of the equation, so begin by combining these like terms.

$$13x - 43 - 9x = 6x + 37 + 5x - 66$$

$$4x - 43 = 11x - 29 \qquad \text{Combine like terms on each side.}$$

$$4x - 43 - 4x = 11x - 29 - 4x \qquad \text{Subtract } 4x \text{ from both sides to gather variable terms on the right side of the equation.}$$

$$-43 = 7x - 29 \qquad \text{Simplify.}$$

$$-43 + 29 = 7x - 29 + 29 \qquad \text{Add 29 to both sides to isolate } 7x.$$

$$-14 = 7x \qquad \text{Simplify.}$$

$$-\frac{14}{7} = \frac{7x}{7} \qquad \text{Divide both sides by 7 to isolate } x.$$

$$-2 = x \qquad \text{Divide.}$$

The check of this solution is left to the reader. The solution set is $\{-2\}$.

Quick Check 5
Solve the equation
$6x - 9 + 4x = 3x + 13 - 8$.

EXAMPLE 6 Solve the equation $6(3x - 8) + 14 = x - 3(x - 5) + 1$.

SOLUTION Begin by distributing the 6 on the left side of the equation and the -3 on the right side of the equation. Then combine like terms before solving.

$$6(3x - 8) + 14 = x - 3(x - 5) + 1$$

$$18x - 48 + 14 = x - 3x + 15 + 1 \qquad \text{Distribute 6 and } -3.$$

$$18x - 34 = -2x + 16 \qquad \text{Combine like terms.}$$

$$18x - 34 + 2x = -2x + 16 + 2x \qquad \text{Add } 2x \text{ to both sides to gather variable terms on the left side of the equation.}$$

$$20x - 34 = 16 \qquad \text{Simplify.}$$

$$20x - 34 + 34 = 16 + 34 \qquad \text{Add 34 to both sides to isolate } 20x.$$

$$20x = 50 \qquad \text{Simplify.}$$

$$\frac{20x}{20} = \frac{50}{20} \qquad \text{Divide by 20 to isolate } x.$$

$$x = \frac{5}{2} \qquad \text{Simplify.}$$

The check of this solution is left to the reader. The solution set is $\left\{\frac{5}{2}\right\}$.

Quick Check 6
Solve the equation
$3(2x - 7) + x = 2(x - 9) - 18$.

In the next example, we will clear the equation of fractions before solving.

EXAMPLE 7 Solve the equation $\frac{3}{5}x - \frac{2}{3} = 2x + \frac{5}{6}$.

SOLUTION   Begin by finding the LCM of the three denominators (5, 3, and 6), which is 30. Then multiply both sides of the equation by 30 to clear the equation of fractions.

$$\frac{3}{5}x - \frac{2}{3} = 2x + \frac{5}{6}$$

$$30\left(\frac{3}{5}x - \frac{2}{3}\right) = 30\left(2x + \frac{5}{6}\right) \qquad \text{Multiply both sides by LCM (30).}$$

$$\overset{6}{\cancel{30}} \cdot \frac{3}{\cancel{5}}x - \overset{10}{\cancel{30}} \cdot \frac{2}{\cancel{3}} = 30 \cdot 2x + \overset{5}{\cancel{30}} \cdot \frac{5}{\cancel{6}} \qquad \text{Distribute and divide out common factors.}$$

$$18x - 20 = 60x + 25 \qquad \text{Multiply.}$$

$$18x - 20 - 18x = 60x + 25 - 18x \qquad \text{Subtract } 18x \text{ from both sides to gather variable terms on the right side of the equation.}$$

$$-20 = 42x + 25 \qquad \text{Simplify.}$$

$$-20 - 25 = 42x + 25 - 25 \qquad \text{Subtract 25 from both sides to isolate } 42x.$$

$$-45 = 42x \qquad \text{Simplify.}$$

$$-\frac{45}{42} = \frac{42x}{42} \qquad \text{Divide both sides by 42 to isolate } x.$$

$$-\frac{15}{14} = x \qquad \text{Simplify.}$$

The check of this solution is left to the reader. The solution set is $\left\{-\frac{15}{14}\right\}$.

Quick Check 7

Solve the equation
$\frac{1}{10}x - \frac{2}{5} = \frac{1}{20}x - \frac{7}{10}$.

Contradictions and Identities

Objective 4 Identify linear equations with no solution. Each equation we have solved to this point has had exactly one solution. This will not always be the case. Now we consider two special types of equations: contradictions and identities.

A **contradiction** is an equation that is always false regardless of the value substituted for the variable. A contradiction has no solution, so its solution set is the empty set { }. The empty set also is known as the **null set** and is denoted by the symbol $\varnothing$.

EXAMPLE 8 Solve the equation $3(x + 1) + 2(x + 4) = 5x + 6$.

SOLUTION   Begin solving this equation by distributing on the left side of the equation.

$$3(x + 1) + 2(x + 4) = 5x + 6$$

$$3x + 3 + 2x + 8 = 5x + 6 \qquad \text{Distribute.}$$

$$5x + 11 = 5x + 6 \qquad \text{Combine like terms.}$$

$$5x + 11 - 5x = 5x + 6 - 5x \qquad \text{Subtract } 5x \text{ from both sides.}$$

$$11 = 6 \qquad \text{Simplify.}$$

We are left with an equation that is a false statement because 11 is never equal to 6. This equation is a contradiction and has no solutions. Its solution set is $\varnothing$.

Quick Check 8

Solve the equation
$3x - 4 = 3x + 4$.

Objective 5 Identify linear equations with infinitely many solutions. An **identity** is an equation that is always true. If we substitute any real number for the variable in an identity, it will produce a true statement. The solution set for an identity is the set of all real numbers. We denote the set of all real numbers as $\mathbb{R}$. An identity has infinitely many solutions rather than a single solution.

EXAMPLE 9   Solve the equation $9x - 5 = 2(4x - 1) + x - 3$.

SOLUTION   Begin to solve this equation by distributing on the right side of the equation.

$$
\begin{aligned}
9x - 5 &= 2(4x - 1) + x - 3 \\
9x - 5 &= 8x - 2 + x - 3 &&\text{Distribute.} \\
9x - 5 &= 9x - 5 &&\text{Combine like terms.} \\
9x - 5 - 9x &= 9x - 5 - 9x &&\text{Subtract } 9x \text{ from both sides.} \\
-5 &= -5 &&\text{Simplify.}
\end{aligned}
$$

Because -5 is always equal to -5 regardless of the value of x, this equation is an identity. Its solution set is the set of all real numbers $\mathbb{R}$.

Quick Check 9

Solve the equation
$5a + 4 = 4 + 5a$.

Literal Equations

Objective 6 Solve literal equations for a specified variable. A **literal equation** is an equation that contains two or more variables. Literal equations are often used in real-world applications involving many unknowns, such as geometry problems.

> ### Perimeter of a Rectangle
>
> The **perimeter of a rectangle** is a measure of the distance around the rectangle. The formula for the perimeter (P) of a rectangle with length L and width W is $P = 2L + 2W$.
>
>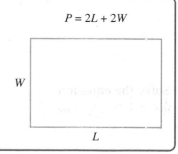

The equation $P = 2L + 2W$ is a literal equation with three variables. We may be asked to solve literal equations for one variable in terms of the other variables in the equation. The equation $P = 2L + 2W$ is solved for the variable P. If we solved for the width W in terms of the length L and the perimeter P, we would have a formula for the width of a rectangle if we knew its length and perimeter.

We solve literal equations by isolating the specified variable. We use the same general strategy that we used to solve linear equations. We treat the other variables in the equation as if they were constants.

EXAMPLE 10   Solve the literal equation $P = 2L + 2W$ (perimeter of a rectangle) for W.

SOLUTION   Gather all terms containing the variable W on one side of the equation and gather all other terms on the other side. This can be done by subtracting $2L$ from both sides.

$$
\begin{aligned}
P &= 2L + 2W \\
P - 2L &= 2L + 2W - 2L &&\text{Subtract } 2L \text{ to isolate } 2W. \\
P - 2L &= 2W &&\text{Simplify.} \\
\frac{P - 2L}{2} &= \frac{2W}{2} &&\text{Divide by 2 to isolate } W. \\
\frac{P - 2L}{2} &= W
\end{aligned}
$$

Quick Check 10

Solve the literal equation
$x + 2y = 5$ for y.

We usually rewrite the equation so that the variable we solved for appears on the left side: $W = \frac{P - 2L}{2}$.

EXAMPLE 11 Solve the literal equation $A = \frac{1}{2}bh$ (area of a triangle) for h.

SOLUTION   Because this equation has a fraction, begin by multiplying both sides by 2.

$$A = \frac{1}{2}bh$$

$$2 \cdot A = 2 \cdot \frac{1}{2}bh \qquad \text{Multiply both sides by 2 to clear fractions.}$$

$$2 \cdot A = \overset{1}{2} \cdot \frac{1}{\underset{1}{2}}bh \qquad \text{Divide out common factors.}$$

$$2A = bh \qquad \text{Multiply.}$$

$$\frac{2A}{b} = \frac{bh}{b} \qquad \text{Divide both sides by } b \text{ to isolate } h.$$

$$\frac{2A}{b} = h \quad \text{or} \quad h = \frac{2A}{b}$$

Quick Check 11

Solve the literal equation
$\frac{1}{5}xy = z$ for x.

Some geometry formulas contain the symbol π, such as $C = 2\pi r$ and $A = \pi r^2$. The symbol π is the Greek letter pi. It is used to represent an irrational number that is approximately equal to 3.14. When solving literal equations containing π, do not replace it with its approximate value.

BUILDING YOUR STUDY STRATEGY

Using Your Textbook, 2 Quick Check Exercises The Quick Check exercises following most examples in this text are similar to the examples in the book. After reading through and possibly reworking an example, try the corresponding Quick Check exercise. You can then decide whether you need more practice.

Exercises 2.2

Vocabulary

1. To clear fractions from an equation, multiply both sides of the equation by the _____ of the denominators.

2. An equation that is never true is a(n) _____.

3. The solution set to a contradiction can be denoted $\varnothing$, which represents _____.

4. An equation that is always true is a(n) _____.

5. To solve the equation $2x - 9 = 7$, the best first step is to _____.

   a) divide both sides of the equation by 2
   b) add 9 to both sides of the equation
   c) subtract 7 from both sides of the equation

6. To solve the equation $3(4x + 5) = 11$, the best first step is to _____.

   a) distribute 3 on the left side of the equation
   b) divide both sides of the equation by 4
   c) subtract 5 from both sides of the equation

Solve.

7. $5x + 31 = 16$

8. $2x + 9 = 31$

9. $23 - 4x = 9$

10. $33 - 6x = -24$

11. $6 = 2a + 20$

12. $-29 = 6b - 17$

13. $9x + 24 = 24$

14. $-4x + 30 = -34$

15. $16.2x - 43.8 = 48.54$

16. $-9.5x - 72.35 = 130$

17. $7a + 11 = 5a - 9$

18. $3m - 11 = 9m + 5$

19. $16 - 4x = 2x + 61$

20. $6n + 14 = 27 + 6n$

21. $5x - 9 = -9 + 5x$

22. $x - 7 = 11 - 3x$

23. $16 - 5x = 2x - 5$

24. $-31 + 11n = 4n + 60$

25. $3.2x + 8.3 = 1.3x + 19.7$

26. $4x - 29.2 = 7.5x - 6.8$

27. $3x + 8 + x = 2x - 9 + 13$

28. $3x + 14 + 8x - 90 = 4x + 11 + x + 27$

29. $x + (x + 1) + (x + 2) = 378$

30. $x + (x + 2) + (x + 4) = 447$

31. $2L + 2(L - 5) = 94$

32. $2(w + 7) + 2w = 74$

33. $2(2w - 3) + 2w = 102$

34. $2L + 2(3L - 50) = 68$

35. $4(2x - 3) - 5x = 3(x + 4)$

36. $2(5x - 3) + 4(x - 8) = 11$

37. $13(3x + 4) - 7(2x - 5) = 5x - 13$

38. $3(2x - 8) - 5(15 - 6x) = 9(4x - 11)$

39. $0.06x + 0.03(4000 - x) = 156$

40. $0.11x + 0.05(7500 - x) = 675$

41. $0.17x - 0.4(x + 1700) = -2566$

42. $0.09x - 0.02(x - 2100) = 322$

43. $0.48x + 0.72(120 - x) = 0.66(120)$

44. $0.3x + 0.55(95 - x) = 0.45(95)$

45. $\dfrac{1}{4}x - \dfrac{1}{3} = \dfrac{5}{12}$

46. $\dfrac{3}{11}x + \dfrac{5}{2} = 8$

47. $\dfrac{x}{12} - \dfrac{11}{6} = \dfrac{5}{4}$

48. $\dfrac{2}{5} - \dfrac{3}{8}x = -\dfrac{11}{10}$

49. $\dfrac{1}{2}x - 3 = \dfrac{11}{5} - \dfrac{3}{4}x$

50. $\dfrac{3}{5} - \dfrac{5}{6}x = 2x + \dfrac{4}{3}$

51. $\dfrac{2}{9}x + \dfrac{3}{4} = \dfrac{1}{6}x - \dfrac{5}{3}$

52. $\dfrac{4}{7}x - \dfrac{3}{2} = x - \dfrac{5}{4}$

53. Write a linear equation that is a contradiction.

54. Write a linear equation that is an identity.

55. Write an equation that has infinitely many solutions.

56. Write an equation that has no solutions.

57. Write an equation whose single solution is negative.

58. Write an equation whose single solution is a fraction.

Solve the following literal equations for the specified variable.

59. $5x + y = -2$ for y

60. $-6x + y = 9$ for y

61. $7x + 2y = 4$ for y

62. $9x + 4y = 20$ for y

63. $-4x + 3y = 10$ for y

64. $-8x + 5y = -6$ for y

65. $P = a + b + c$ for b

66. $P = a + b + 2c$ for c

67. $d = r \cdot t$ for t

68. $d = r \cdot t$ for r

69. $C = 2\pi r$ for r

70. $S = 2\pi rh$ for r

To convert a Celsius temperature (C) to a Fahrenheit temperature (F), use the formula $F = \dfrac{9}{5}C + 32$.

71. If the temperature outside is 68°F, find the Celsius temperature.

72. If the normal body temperature for a person is 98.6°F, find the Celsius equivalent.

73. A number is tripled and then added to 64. If the result is 325, find the number.

74. If two-thirds of a number is added to 48, the result is 74. Find the number.

2.4

Applications Involving Percents; Ratio and Proportion

OBJECTIVES

1. Use the basic percent equation to find an unknown amount, base, or percent.
2. Solve applied problems using the basic percent equation.
3. Solve applied problems involving percent increase or percent decrease.
4. Solve problems involving interest.
5. Solve mixture problems.
6. Solve for variables in proportions.
7. Solve applied problems involving proportions.

The Basic Percent Equation

Objective 1 Use the basic percent equation to find an unknown amount, base, or percent. We know that 40 is one-half of 80. Because the fraction $\frac{1}{2}$ is the same as 50%, we also can say that 40 is 50% of 80. In this example, the number 40 is referred to as the **amount** and the number 80 is referred to as the **base**. The basic equation relating these two quantities reflects that the amount is a percentage of the base, or

$$\text{Amount} = \text{Percent} \cdot \text{Base}.$$

In this equation, it is important to express the percent as a decimal or a fraction rather than a percent. Obviously, it is crucial to identify the amount, the percent, and the base correctly. It is a good idea to write the information in the following form:

$$\underset{\text{(Amount)}}{\underline{\hspace{2cm}}} \text{ is } \underset{\text{(Percent)}}{\underline{\hspace{2cm}}} \text{ \% of } \underset{\text{(Base)}}{\underline{\hspace{2cm}}}$$

EXAMPLE 1 What number is 40% of 45?

SOLUTION Letting n represent the unknown number, write the information as follows:

$$\underset{\text{(Amount)}}{\underline{\quad n \quad}} \text{ is } \underset{\text{(Percent)}}{\underline{\quad 40 \quad}} \% \text{ of } \underset{\text{(Base)}}{\underline{\quad 45 \quad}}$$

We see that the amount is n; the percent is 40%, or 0.4; and the base is 45.

Now translate this information to an equation, making sure the percent is written as a decimal rather than a percent.

$$n = 0.4(45)$$
$$n = 18 \qquad \text{Multiply.}$$

We find that 18 is 40% of 45.

Quick Check 1
25% of 44 is what number?

A WORD OF CAUTION When using the basic percent equation, make sure you rewrite the percent as a decimal or a fraction before solving for an unknown amount or base.

EXAMPLE 2 Eight percent of what number is 12?

SOLUTION Letting n represent the unknown number, rewrite the information as follows:

$$\underset{\text{(Amount)}}{\underline{\quad 12 \quad}} \text{ is } \underset{\text{(Percent)}}{\underline{\quad 8 \quad}} \% \text{ of } \underset{\text{(Base)}}{\underline{\quad n \quad}}$$

The amount is 12, the percent is 8%, and the base is unknown. Make sure you write the percent as a decimal before working with the equation.

$$12 = 0.08n$$
$$\frac{12}{0.08} = \frac{0.08n}{0.08} \qquad \text{Divide both sides by 0.08.}$$
$$150 = n \qquad \text{Simplify.}$$

Eight percent of 150 is 12.

Quick Check 2
39 is 60% of what number?

EXAMPLE 3 What percent of 75 is 39?

SOLUTION In this problem, the percent is unknown. Letting p represent the percent, write the information as follows:

$$\underset{\text{(Amount)}}{\underline{\quad 39 \quad}} \text{ is } \underset{\text{(Percent)}}{\underline{\quad p \quad}} \% \text{ of } \underset{\text{(Base)}}{\underline{\quad 75 \quad}}$$

Now translate directly to the basic percent equation and solve it.

$$39 = p \cdot 75$$
$$\frac{39}{75} = \frac{p \cdot 75}{75} \qquad \text{Divide both sides by 75.}$$
$$0.52 = p \qquad \text{Simplify.}$$

0.52 is equivalent to 52%, so 39 is 52% of 75.

Quick Check 3
56 is what percent of 80?

A WORD OF CAUTION After using the basic percent equation to solve for an unknown percent, make sure you rewrite the solution as a percent by multiplying by 100%.

When using the basic percent equation to solve for an unknown percent, keep in mind that the base is not necessarily the larger of the two given numbers. For example, if we are trying to determine what percent of 80 is 200, the base is the smaller number (80).

Applications

Objective 2 Solve applied problems using the basic percent equation.
Now we will use the basic percent equation to solve applied problems. We will continue to use the strategy for solving applied problems developed in Section 2.3.

> **EXAMPLE 4** There are 7107 female students at a certain community college. If 60% of all students at the college are female, what is the total enrollment of the college?

> **SOLUTION** We know that 60% of the students are female, so the number of female students (7107) is 60% of the total enrollment. Letting n represent the unknown total enrollment, write the information as follows:

$$\underset{\text{(Amount)}}{\underline{\quad 7107 \quad}} \text{ is } \underset{\text{(Percent)}}{\underline{\quad 60 \quad}} \text{ % of } \underset{\text{(Base)}}{\underline{\quad n \quad}}$$

Translate this sentence to an equation and solve.

$$7107 = 0.6n$$
$$11{,}845 = n \qquad \text{Divide both sides by 0.6.}$$

There are 11,845 students at the college.

Quick Check 4

Of the 500 children who attend an elementary school, 28% buy their lunch at school. How many children buy their lunch at this school?

Percent Increase and Percent Decrease

Objective 3 Solve applied problems involving percent increase or percent decrease. **Percent increase** is a measure of how much a quantity has increased from its original value. The amount of increase is the amount in the basic percent equation, while the original value is the base.

$$\text{Amount of Increase} = \text{Percent} \cdot \text{Original}$$

Percent decrease is a similar measure of how much a quantity has decreased from its original value.

> **EXAMPLE 5** An art collector bought a lithograph for $2500. After three years, the lithograph was valued at $3800. Find the percent increase in the value of the lithograph over the three years.

> **SOLUTION** The amount of increase in value is $1300 because $3800 - 2500 = 1300$. We need to determine what percent of the original value is the increase in value. Letting p represent the unknown percent, write the information as follows:

$$\underset{\text{(Amount)}}{\underline{\quad 1300 \quad}} \text{ is } \underset{\text{(Percent)}}{\underline{\quad p \quad}} \text{ % of } \underset{\text{(Base)}}{\underline{\quad 2500 \quad}}$$

This translates to the equation $1300 = p \cdot 2500$, which we can solve.

$$1300 = p \cdot 2500$$
$$0.52 = p \qquad \text{Divide both sides by 2500.}$$

Quick Check 5

Lee bought a new car for $30,000 three years ago, and now it is worth $13,800. Find the percent decrease in the value of the car.

Converting this decimal result to a percent, we see that the lithograph increased in value by 52%.

A WORD OF CAUTION When solving problems involving percent increase or percent decrease, remember that the base is always the *original amount*.

Percents are involved in many business applications. One such problem is determining the sale price of an item after a percent discount has been applied.

EXAMPLE 6 A department store is having a "20% off" sale, so all prices have been reduced by 20% of the original price. If a robe was originally priced at $37.50, what is the sale price after the 20% discount?

SOLUTION Begin by finding the amount by which the original price has been discounted. Let d represent the amount of the discount. Because the amount of the discount is 20% of the original price ($37.50), we can write the information as follows:

$$\underset{\text{(Amount)}}{\underline{\quad d \quad}} \text{ is } \underset{\text{(Percent)}}{\underline{\quad 20 \quad}} \% \text{ of } \underset{\text{(Base)}}{\underline{\quad \$37.50 \quad}}$$

This translates to the equation $d = 0.2(37.50)$, which we solve for d.

$$d = 0.2(37.50)$$
$$d = 7.50 \qquad \text{Multiply.}$$

The discount is $7.50, so the sale price is $37.50 − $7.50, or $30.00.

Quick Check 6

A department store bought a shipment of MP3 players for $42 each wholesale. If the store marks the MP3 players up by 45%, what is the selling price of an MP3 player?

Interest

Objective 4 Solve problems involving interest. Interest is a fee a borrower pays for the privilege of borrowing a sum of money. Banks also pay interest to customers who deposit money in their institutions. Simple interest is calculated as a percentage of the **principal**, which is the amount borrowed or deposited. If r is the annual interest rate, the simple interest (I) owed on a principal (P) is given by the formula $I = P \cdot r \cdot t$, where t is time in years.

If an investor deposited $3000 in an account that paid 4% annual interest for one year, we could determine how much money would be in the account at the end of one year by substituting 3000 for P, 0.04 for r, and 1 for t in the formula $I = P \cdot r \cdot t$.

$$I = P \cdot r \cdot t$$
$$I = 3000(0.04)(1) \qquad \text{Substitute 3000 for } P, 0.04 \text{ for } r, \text{ and 1 for } t.$$
$$I = 120 \qquad \text{Multiply.}$$

The interest earned in one year is $120. There is $3000 plus the $120 in interest, or $3120, in the account after one year.

EXAMPLE 7 Martha invested some money in an account that paid 6% annual interest. Her friend Stuart found an account that paid 7% interest, and he invested $5000 more in this account than Martha did in her account. If the pair earned a total of $1650 in interest from the two accounts in one year, how much did Martha invest? How much did Stuart invest?

SOLUTION Letting x represent the amount Martha invested at 6%, use $x + 5000$ to represent the amount Stuart invested at 7%. The equation for this problem comes from the fact that the interest earned in each account must add up to $1650. Use a table to display the important information for this problem.

Investor	Principal (P)	Rate (r)	Time (t)	Interest $I = P \cdot r \cdot t$
Martha	x	0.06	1	$0.06x$
Stuart	$x + 5000$	0.07	1	$0.07(x + 5000)$
Total				1650

The interest from the first account is $0.06x$, and the interest from the second account is $0.07(x + 5000)$; so their sum must be $1650. Essentially, we can find this equation in the final column in the table.

$$0.06x + 0.07(x + 5000) = 1650$$
$$0.06x + 0.07x + 350 = 1650 \qquad \text{Distribute.}$$
$$0.13x + 350 = 1650 \qquad \text{Combine like terms.}$$
$$0.13x = 1300 \qquad \text{Subtract 350 from both sides.}$$
$$x = 10,000 \qquad \text{Divide both sides by 0.13.}$$

Because $x = 10,000$, the amount Martha invested at 6% interest (x) is $10,000 and the amount Stuart invested at 7% interest ($x + 5000$) is $15,000. You may verify that Martha earned $600 in interest and Stuart earned $1050 in interest, which totals $1650.

Quick Check 7

Mark invested money in two accounts. One account paid 3% annual interest, and the other account paid 5% annual interest. He invested $2000 more in the account that paid 5% interest than in the account that paid 3% interest. If Mark earned a total of $500 in interest from the two accounts in one year, how much did he invest in each account?

EXAMPLE 8 Donald loaned a total of $13,500 to two borrowers, Carolyn and George. Carolyn paid 8% annual interest, while George paid 12%. If Donald earned a total of $1320 in interest from the two borrowers in one year, how much did Carolyn borrow? How much did George borrow?

SOLUTION Letting x represent the amount that Carolyn borrowed, use $13,500 - x$ to represent the amount George borrowed. (By subtracting the amount Carolyn borrowed from $13,500, we are left with the amount George borrowed.) The equation for this problem comes from the fact that the interest earned by Donald must add up to $1320. Again, use a table to display the important information for this problem.

Borrower	Principal (P)	Rate (r)	Time (t)	Interest $I = P \cdot r$
Carolyn	x	0.08	1	$0.08x$
George	$13,500 - x$	0.12	1	$0.12(13,500 - x)$
Total	13,500			1320

The interest paid by Carolyn is $0.08x$, and the interest paid by George is $0.12(13,500 - x)$; so their sum must be $1320. Again, we can find this equation in the final column in the table.

$$0.08x + 0.12(13,500 - x) = 1320$$
$$0.08x + 1620 - 0.12x = 1320 \qquad \text{Distribute.}$$
$$-0.04x + 1620 = 1320 \qquad \text{Combine like terms.}$$
$$-0.04x = -300 \qquad \text{Subtract 1620 from both sides.}$$
$$x = 7500 \qquad \text{Divide both sides by } -0.04.$$

Because $x = 7500$, the amount Carolyn borrowed is $7500 and the amount George borrowed ($13,500 - x$) is $6000. You may verify that Carolyn paid $600 in interest and George paid $720 in interest, which totals $1320.

Quick Check 8

Patsy invested a total of $1900 in two accounts. One account paid 4% annual interest, and the other account paid 5% annual interest. If Patsy earned a total of $86.50 in interest from the two accounts, how much did she invest in each account?

Mixture Problems

Objective 5 Solve mixture problems. The next example is a **mixture problem**. In this problem, we will be mixing two solutions that have different concentrations of alcohol to produce a mixture whose concentration of alcohol is somewhere between the two individual solutions. We will determine how much of each solution should be used to produce a mixture of the desired specifications.

EXAMPLE 9 A chemist has two solutions. The first is 20% alcohol, and the second is 30% alcohol. How many milliliters (mL) of each solution should she use if she wants to make 40 mL of a solution that is 24% alcohol?

SOLUTION   Let x represent the volume of the 20% alcohol solution in milliliters. We need to express the volume of the 30% solution in terms of x as well. Because the two quantities must add up to 40 mL, the volume of the 30% solution can be represented by $40 - x$.

The equation that solves this problem is based on the volume of alcohol in each solution as well as the volume of alcohol in the mixture. When we add the volume of alcohol that comes from the 20% solution to the volume of alcohol that comes from the 30% solution, it should equal the volume of alcohol in the mixture.

Because we want to end up with 40 mL of a solution that is 24% alcohol, this solution should contain $0.24(40) = 9.6$ mL of alcohol. The following table, which is similar to the one used in the previous example involving interest, presents all of the information:

Solution	Volume of Solution (mL)	% Alcohol	Volume of Alcohol (mL)
Solution 1 (20%)	x	0.2	$0.2x$
Solution 2 (30%)	$40 - x$	0.3	$0.3(40 - x)$
Mixture	40	0.24	$0.24(40) = 9.6$

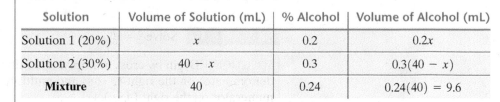

Alcohol from Solution 1 + Alcohol from Solution 2 = Alcohol in Mixture
$$0.2x \quad + \quad 0.3(40 - x) \quad = \quad 9.6$$

Now solve the equation for x.

$$0.2x + 0.3(40 - x) = 9.6$$
$$0.2x + 12 - 0.3x = 9.6 \qquad \text{Distribute.}$$
$$-0.1x + 12 = 9.6 \qquad \text{Combine like terms.}$$
$$-0.1x = -2.4 \qquad \text{Subtract 12 from both sides.}$$
$$x = 24 \qquad \text{Divide both sides by } -0.1.$$

Because x represented the volume of the 20% alcohol solution that the chemist should use, she should use 24 mL of the 20% solution. Subtracting this amount from 40 mL tells us that she should use 16 mL of the 30% alcohol solution.

Quick Check 9

Marie had one solution that was 30% alcohol and a second solution that was 42% alcohol. How many milliliters of each solution should be mixed to make 80 milliliters of a solution that is 39% alcohol?

Ratio and Proportion

A **ratio** is a comparison of two quantities using division and is usually written as a fraction. Suppose a first-grade student has 20 minutes to eat her lunch, and this is followed by a 30-minute recess. The ratio of the time for lunch to the time for recess is $\frac{20}{30}$, which can be simplified to $\frac{2}{3}$. This means that for every 2 minutes of eating time, there are 3 minutes of recess time.

Objective 6 Solve for variables in proportions. Ratios are important tools for solving some applied problems involving proportions. A **proportion** is a statement of equality between two ratios. In other words, a proportion is an equation in which two ratios are equal to each other. Here are a few examples of proportions.

$$\frac{5}{8} = \frac{n}{56} \qquad \frac{8}{11} = \frac{5}{n} \qquad \frac{9}{2} = \frac{4x + 5}{x}$$

The **cross products** of a proportion are the two products obtained when we multiply the numerator of one fraction by the denominator of the other fraction. The two cross products for the proportion $\frac{a}{b} = \frac{c}{d}$ are $a \cdot d$ and $b \cdot c$.

When we solve a proportion, we are looking for the value of the variable that produces a true statement. We use the fact that the cross products of a proportion are equal if the proportion is indeed true.

$$\text{If } \frac{a}{b} = \frac{c}{d}, \text{then } a \cdot d = b \cdot c.$$

Consider the two equal fractions $\frac{3}{6}$ and $\frac{5}{10}$. If we write these two fractions in the form of an equation $\frac{3}{6} = \frac{5}{10}$, both cross products ($3 \cdot 10$ and $6 \cdot 5$) are equal to 30. This holds true for any proportion.

To solve a proportion, we multiply each numerator by the denominator on the other side of the equation and set the products equal to each other. We then solve the resulting equation for the variable in the problem. This process is called **cross multiplying** and will be demonstrated in the next example.

EXAMPLE 10 Solve $\frac{3}{4} = \frac{n}{68}$.

SOLUTION Begin by cross multiplying. Multiply the numerator on the left by the denominator on the right ($3 \cdot 68$) and multiply the denominator on the left by the numerator on the right ($4 \cdot n$).

Then write an equation that states that the two products are equal to each other and solve the equation.

$$\frac{3}{4} = \frac{n}{68}$$

$$3 \cdot 68 = 4 \cdot n \quad \text{Cross multiply.}$$
$$204 = 4n \quad \text{Multiply.}$$
$$51 = n \quad \text{Divide both sides by 4.}$$

The solution set is $\{51\}$.

Quick Check 10
Solve $\frac{3}{17} = \frac{n}{187}$.

A WORD OF CAUTION When solving a proportion, cross multiply. *Do not "cross-cancel."*

Applications of Proportions

Objective **7** **Solve applied problems involving proportions.** Now we turn our attention to applied problems involving proportions.

EXAMPLE 11 Studies show that 1 out of every 9 people is left-handed. In a sample of 216 people, how many would be left-handed according to these studies?

SOLUTION Begin by setting up a ratio based on the known information. Because 1 person out of every 9 is left-handed, the ratio is $\frac{1}{9}$. Notice that the numerator represents the number of left-handed people while the denominator represents the number of all people. When setting up a proportion, keep this ordering consistent. This given ratio will be the left side of the proportion. To set up the right side of the proportion, write a second ratio relating the unknown quantity to the given quantity. The unknown quantity is the number of left-handed people in the group of 216 people. Let n represent the number of left-handed people. The proportion then is $\frac{1}{9} = \frac{n}{216}$. Again, make sure the ratio on the left side $\left(\frac{\text{left-handed}}{\text{total}}\right)$ is consistent with the ratio on the right side. Thus,

$$\frac{1}{9} = \frac{n}{216}$$

$216 = 9n$ Cross multiply.

$24 = n$ Divide both sides by 9.

According to these studies, there should be 24 left-handed people in the group of 216 people.

▶ Quick Check 11

Studies show that 4 out of 5 dentists recommend sugarless gum for their patients who chew gum. In a group of 85 dentists, according to these studies, how many would recommend sugarless gum to their patients?

Another use of proportions is for **dimensional analysis**: the process of converting from one unit to another. Here is a set of unit conversions that will allow us to convert from the English system of measurement to the metric system of measurement.

┌─ Conversions ───┐

Length

1 kilometer (km) ≈ 0.62 mile (mi)   1 mi ≈ 1.61 km

1 meter (m) ≈ 3.28 feet (ft)   1 ft ≈ 0.305 m

1 centimeter (cm) ≈ 0.39 inch (in.)   1 in. ≈ 2.54 cm

Volume

1 liter (L) ≈ 0.264 gallons (gal)   1 gal ≈ 3.785 L

Mass

1 kilogram (kg) ≈ 2.2 pounds (lb)   1 lb ≈ 0.454 kg

1 gram (g) ≈ 0.035 ounce (oz)   1 oz ≈ 28.35 g

└───┘

EXAMPLE 12   Convert 80 meters to feet.

SOLUTION   To convert from meters to feet, we have a choice of two conversion factors: 1 m ≈ 3.28 ft or 1 ft ≈ 0.305 m. (Note that depending on which conversion factor is used, answers may vary slightly.) Use 1 m ≈ 3.28 ft to set up a proportion, letting n represent the number of feet in 80 m.

$$\frac{1}{3.28} = \frac{80}{n}$$ Set up the proportion with meters in the numerator and feet in the denominator.

$n = 262.4$ Cross multiply.

There are 262.4 ft in 80 m. (If we had used 1 ft ≈ 0.305 m as the conversion factor, the answer would have been 262.3 feet.)

▶ Quick Check 12

Use the fact that 1 lb ≈ 0.454 kg to convert 175 pounds to kilograms.

BUILDING YOUR STUDY STRATEGY

Using Your Textbook, 4 Creating Note Cards Your textbook can be used to create a series of note cards for studying new terms and procedures or difficult problems. Each time you find a new term in the textbook, write the term on one side of a note card and the definition on the other side. Collect all of these cards and cycle through them, reading the term and trying to recite the definition by memory. You can do the same thing for each new procedure introduced in the textbook.

If you are struggling with a particular type of problem, find an example that has been worked out in the text. Write the problem on the front of the card and write the complete solution provided on the back of the card. As you cycle through the cards, try to solve the problem and then check the solution provided on the back of the card.

Some students have trouble recalling only the first step for solving particular problems. If you are in this group, you can write a series of problems on the front of some note cards and the first step on the back of the cards. You can then cycle through these cards in the same way.

Exercises 2.4

PRACTICE   WATCH   DOWNLOAD   READ   REVIEW

Vocabulary

1. State the basic percent equation.

2. In a percent problem, the _____ is a percentage of the base.

3. Percent increase is a measure of how much a quantity has increased from its _____.

4. Simple interest is calculated as a percentage of the _____.

5. State the formula for calculating simple interest.

6. A(n) _____ is a comparison of two quantities using division and is usually written as a fraction.

7. A(n) _____ is a statement of equality between two ratios.

8. If $\frac{a}{b} = \frac{c}{d}$, then $a \cdot d =$ ____.

9. Forty-five percent of 80 is what number?

10. What percent of 130 is 91?

11. Forty percent of what number is 92?

12. Fifty-seven is 6% of what number?

13. What percent of 256 is 224?

14. What number is 37% of 94?

15. What is $37\frac{1}{2}$% of 104?

16. Fifteen is what percent of 36?

17. What is 240% of 68?

18. What percent of 24 is 108?

19. Fifty-five is 125% of what number?

20. What is 600% of 53?

21. Thirty percent of the M&Ms in a bowl are brown. If there are 280 M&Ms in the bowl, how many are brown?

22. A doctor helped 320 women deliver their babies last year. Sixteen of these women had twins. What percent of the doctor's patients had twins?

23. Forty percent of the registered voters in a certain precinct are registered as Democrats. If 410 of the registered voters in the precinct are registered as Democrats, how many registered voters are in the precinct?

24. An online retailer adds a 15% charge to all items for shipping and handling. If a shipping-and-handling fee of $96 is added to the cost of a computer, what was the original price of the computer?

25. A certain brand of rum is 40% alcohol. How many milliliters of alcohol are there in a 750-milliliter bottle of rum?

26. A certificate of deposit (CD) pays 3.08% interest. Find the amount of interest earned in one year on a $5000 CD.

27. Marlana invested $3500 in the stock market. After one year, her portfolio had increased in value by 17%. What is the new value of her portfolio?

28. Kristy bought shares of a stock valued at $48.24. If the stock price dropped to $30.15, find the percent decrease in the value of the stock.

29. The price of a gallon of milk increased by 26 cents. This represented a price increase of 8%. What was the original price of the milk?

30. A bookstore charges its customers 32% over the wholesale cost of the book. How much does the bookstore charge for a book that has a wholesale price of $64?

31. A community college has 1600 parking spots on campus. When it builds its new library, the college will lose 120 of its parking spots. What will be the percent decrease in the number of available parking spots?

32. A community college had its budget slashed by $3,101,000. This represents a cut of 7% of its total budget from last year. What was last year's budget?

33. Last year the average SAT math score for students at a high school was 500.
    a) This year the average math score decreased by 20%. Find the new average score.
    b) By how many points must the average math score increase to get back to last year's average?
    c) By what percent do scores need to increase next year to bring the average score back to 500?

34. During 2008, an auto plant produced 25% fewer cars than it had in 2007. Production fell by another 20% during 2009. By what percent will production have to increase in 2010 to make the same number of cars as the plant produced in 2007?

35. Tina invested $30,000 in a stock. In the first year, the stock increased in value by 10%. In the second year, the stock decreased in value by 20%. What percentage gain is required in the third year for Tina's stock to return to its original value? (Round to the nearest tenth of a percent.)

36. Khalid invested $100,000 in a mutual fund. In the first year, the mutual fund decreased in value by 25%. In the second year, the mutual fund increased in value by 20%. What percentage gain is required in the third year for Khalid's mutual fund to return to its original value? (Round to the nearest tenth of a percent.)

37. In 2007, Donald's stock portfolio decreased in value by 25%. In 2008, his stock portfolio decreased in value by another 40%. What percentage gain is required in 2009 for Donald's stock portfolio to return to the value it had at the beginning of 2007? (Round to the nearest tenth of a percent.)

38. In 2007, Giada's retirement fund decreased in value by 8%. In 2008, her retirement fund decreased in value by another 10%. What percentage gain is required in 2009 for Giada's retirement fund to return to the value it had at the beginning of 2007? (Round to the nearest tenth of a percent.)

39. Janet invested her savings in two accounts. One of the accounts paid 2% interest, and the other paid 5% interest. Janet put twice as much money in the account that paid 5% as she put in the account that paid 2%. If she earned a total of $84 in interest from the two accounts in one year, find the amount invested in each account.

40. One of Jaleel's mutual funds made a 10% profit last year, while the other mutual fund made an 8% profit. Jaleel had invested $1400 more in the fund that made an 8% profit than he did in the fund that made a 10% profit. If he made a $715 profit last year, how much was invested in each fund?

41. Kamiran deposits a total of $6500 in savings accounts at two different banks. The first bank pays 4% interest, while the second bank pays 5% interest. If he earns a total of $300 in interest in one year, how much was deposited at each bank?

42. Dianne was given $35,000 when she retired. She invested some at 7% interest and the rest at 9% interest. If she earned $2910 in interest in one year, how much was invested in each account?

43. Aurora invested $8000 in two stocks. One stock decreased in value by 8%; the other, by 20%. If she lost a total of $1000 on these two stocks, how much was invested in the stock that decreased in value by 8%?

44. Lebron invested $20,000 in two stocks. The first stock decreased in value by 3%, and the other decreased in value by 32%. If he lost a total of $5675 on these two stocks, how much was invested in the stock that decreased in value by 32%?

45. Marquis invested $4800 in two mutual funds. Last year one of the funds went up by 6% and the other fund went down by 5%. If his portfolio increased in value by $90 last year, how much did Marquis invest in the fund that earned a 6% profit?

46. Veronica received a $50,000 insurance settlement. She invested some of the money in a bank CD that paid 3.5% annual interest and invested the rest in a stock. In one year, the stock decreased in value by 30%. If Veronica lost $1600 from her $50,000 investment, how much did she put in the bank CD?

47. A mechanic has two antifreeze solutions. One is 70% antifreeze, and the other is 40% antifreeze. How much of each solution should be mixed to make 60 gallons of a solution that is 52% antifreeze?

48. A chemist has two saline solutions. One is 2% salt, and the other is 6% salt. How much of each solution should be mixed to make 2 liters of a saline solution that is 3% salt?

49. A dairyfarmer has some milk that is 5% butterfat as well as some lowfat milk that is 2% butterfat. How much of each needs to be mixed together to make 1000 gallons of milk that is 3.2% butterfat?

50. Patti has two solutions. One is 27% acid, and the other is 39% acid. How much of each solution should

be mixed together to make 9 liters of a solution that is 29% acid?

51. A chemist has two solutions. One is 27% salt, and the other is 43% salt. How much of each solution should be mixed together to make 44 milliliters of a solution that is 39% salt?

52. A chemist has two solutions. One is 6% acid and the other is 9% acid. How much of each solution should be mixed together to make 72 milliliters of a solution that is 8.5% acid?

53. A chemist has two solutions. One is 40% alcohol, and the other is pure alcohol. How much of each solution should be mixed together to make 1.6 liters of a solution that is 52% alcohol?

54. A chemist has 60 milliliters of a solution that is 65% alcohol. She plans to add pure alcohol until the solution is 79% alcohol. How much pure alcohol should she add to this solution?

55. Paula has 400 milliliters of a solution that is 80% alcohol. She plans to dilute it so that it is only 50% alcohol. How much water must she add to do this?

56. A bartender has rum that is 40% alcohol. How much rum and how much cola need to be mixed together to make 5 liters of rum and cola that is 16% alcohol?

Solve the proportion.

57. $\dfrac{2}{3} = \dfrac{n}{48}$

58. $\dfrac{5}{8} = \dfrac{n}{32}$

59. $\dfrac{20}{n} = \dfrac{45}{81}$

60. $\dfrac{22}{30} = \dfrac{55}{n}$

61. $\dfrac{3}{4} = \dfrac{n}{109}$

62. $\dfrac{7}{10} = \dfrac{n}{86}$

63. $\dfrac{13.8}{n} = \dfrac{2}{9}$

64. $\dfrac{7.2}{n} = \dfrac{5}{8}$

65. $\dfrac{3}{4} = \dfrac{n + 12}{28}$

66. $\dfrac{5}{9} = \dfrac{3n - 2}{18}$

67. $\dfrac{2n + 15}{18} = \dfrac{5n + 13}{24}$

68. $\dfrac{n + 10}{40} = \dfrac{1 - n}{48}$

Set up a proportion and solve it for the following problems.

69. At a certain community college, 3 out of every 5 students are female. If the college has 9200 students, how many are female?

70. A day care center has a policy that there will be at least 4 staff members present for every 18 children. How many staff members are necessary to accommodate 63 children?

71. The directions for a powdered plant food state that 3 tablespoons of the food need to be mixed with 2 gallons of water. How many tablespoons need to be mixed with 15 gallons of water?

72. Eight out of every 9 people are right-handed. If a factory has 352 right-handed workers, how many left-handed workers are there at the factory?

73. If 5 out of every 6 teachers in a city meet the minimum qualifications to be teaching and the city has 864 teachers, how many do not meet the minimum qualifications?

74. A survey showed that 7 out of every 10 registered voters in a county are in favor of a bond measure to raise money for a new college campus. If there are 140,000 registered voters in the county, how many are not in favor of the bond measure?

Convert the given quantity to the desired unit. Round to the nearest tenth if necessary.

75. 60 cm to in.

76. 150 mi to km

77. 15.2 L to gal

78. 6 gal to L

79. 80 kg to lb

80. 35 oz to g

Writing in Mathematics

Answer in complete sentences.

81. Write a word problem for the following table and equation. Explain how you created the problem.

	Principal (P)	Rate (r)	Time (t)	Interest $I = P \cdot r \cdot t$
	x	0.03	1	$0.03x$
	$x + 10{,}000$	0.05	1	$0.05(x + 10{,}000)$
Total				2100

Equation: $0.03x + 0.05(x + 10{,}000) = 2100$

82. Write a word problem for the following table and equation. Explain how you created the problem.

Solution	Amount of Solution (ml)	% Alcohol	Amount of Alcohol (ml)
Solution 1	x	0.38	$0.38x$
Solution 2	$60 - x$	0.5	$0.5(60 - x)$
Mixture	60	0.4	24

Equation: $0.38x + 0.5(60 - x) = 24$

Quick Review Exercises

Solve.

1. $4x + 17 = 41$

2. $5x - 19 = 3x - 51$

3. $2x + 2(x + 8) = 68$

4. $x + 3(x + 2) = 2(x + 4) + 30$

2.5

Linear Inequalities

OBJECTIVES

1. Present the solutions of an inequality on a number line.
2. Present the solutions of an inequality using interval notation.
3. Solve linear inequalities.
4. Solve compound inequalities involving the union of two linear inequalities.
5. Solve compound inequalities involving the intersection of two linear inequalities.
6. Solve applied problems using linear inequalities.

Suppose you went to a doctor and she told you that your temperature was normal. This would mean that your temperature was 98.6° F. However, if the doctor told you that you had a fever, could you tell what your temperature was? No, all you would know is that it was above 98.6° F. If you let the variable t represent your temperature, this relationship could be written as $t > 98.6$. The expression $t > 98.6$ is an example of an inequality. An inequality is a mathematical statement comparing two quantities using the symbols $<$ (*less than*) or $>$ (*greater than*). It states that one quantity is smaller than (or larger than) the other quantity.

Two other symbols that may be used in an inequality are $\leq$ and $\geq$. The symbol $\leq$ is read as *less than or equal to,* and the symbol $\geq$ is read as *greater than or equal to.* The inequality $x \leq 7$ is used to represent all real numbers that are less than 7 or are equal to 7. Inequalities involving the symbols $\leq$ or $\geq$ are often called **weak inequalities**, while inequalities involving the symbols $<$ or $>$ are called **strict inequalities** because they involve numbers that are strictly less than (or greater than) a given value.

Presenting Solutions of Inequalities Using a Number Line

Objective 1 **Present the solutions of an inequality on a number line.**

> **Linear Inequality**
>
> A **linear inequality** is an inequality containing linear expressions.

A linear inequality often has infinitely many solutions, and it is not possible to list every solution. Consider the inequality $x < 3$. There are infinitely many solutions of this inequality, but the one thing the solutions share is that they are all to the left of 3 on the number line. Values located to the right of 3 on the number line are greater than 3. All shaded numbers to the left are solutions of the inequality and can be represented on a number line as follows:

An **endpoint** of an inequality is a point on a number line that separates values that are solutions from values that are not. The open circle at $x = 3$ tells us that the endpoint is not included in the solution because 3 is not less than 3. If the inequality were $x \le 3$, we would fill in the circle at $x = 3$.

Here are three more inequalities with their solutions graphed on a number line:

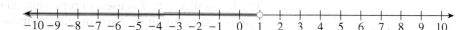

Inequality	Solution
$x \le -2$	
$x > 5$	
$x \ge -4$	

Saying that a is less than b is equivalent to saying that b is greater than a. In other words, the inequality $a < b$ is equivalent to the inequality $b > a$. This is an important piece of information, as we will want to rewrite an inequality so that the variable is on the left side of the inequality before we graph it on a number line.

EXAMPLE 1   Graph the solutions of the inequality $1 > x$ on a number line.

SOLUTION   To avoid confusion about which direction should be shaded on the number line, before graphing the solutions, rewrite the inequality so that the variable is on the left side. Saying that 1 is greater than x is the same as saying that x is less than 1, or $x < 1$. The values that are less than 1 are to the left of 1 on the number line.

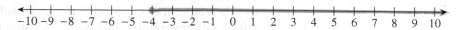

Quick Check 1
Graph the solutions of the inequality $8 < x$ on a number line.

Interval Notation

Objective 2 Present the solutions of an inequality using interval notation.   Another way to present the solutions of an inequality is by using **interval notation**. A range of values on a number line, such as the solutions of the inequality $x \ge 4$, is called an **interval**. Inequalities typically have one or more intervals as their solutions. Interval notation presents an interval that is a solution by listing its left and right endpoints. We use parentheses around the endpoints if the endpoints are not included as solutions, and we use brackets if the endpoints are included as solutions.

When an interval continues on indefinitely to the right on a number line, we will use the symbol ∞ (infinity) in place of the right endpoint and follow it with a parenthesis. Let's look again at the number line associated with the solutions of the inequality $x \ge -4$.

The solutions begin at -4 and include any number that is greater than -4. The interval is bounded by -4 on the left side and extends without bound on the right side, which can be written in interval notation as $[-4, \infty)$. The endpoint -4

is included in the interval, so we write a square bracket in front of it because it is a solution. We always write a parenthesis after ∞, because it is not an actual number that ends the interval at that point.

If the inequality had been $x > -4$ instead of $x \geq -4$, we would have written a parenthesis rather than a square bracket before -4. In other words, the solutions of the inequality $x > -4$ can be expressed in interval notation as $(-4, \infty)$.

For intervals that continue indefinitely to the left on a number line, we use $-\infty$ in place of the left endpoint.

Here is a summary of different inequalities with the solutions presented on a number line and in interval notation.

Inequality	Number Line	Interval Notation
$x > 4$		$(4, \infty)$
$x \geq 4$		$[4, \infty)$
$x < 4$		$(-\infty, 4)$
$x \leq 4$		$(-\infty, 4]$

Solving Linear Inequalities

Objective 3 Solve linear inequalities. Solving a linear inequality such as $7x - 11 \leq -32$ is similar to solving a linear equation. In fact, there is only one difference between the two procedures:

> Whenever you multiply both sides of an inequality by a negative number or divide both sides by a negative number, the direction of the inequality changes.

Why is this? Consider the inequality $3 < 5$, which is a true statement. If we multiply each side by -2, is the left side $(-2 \cdot 3 = -6)$ still less than the right side $(-2 \cdot 5 = -10)$? No, $-6 > -10$ because -6 is located to the right of -10 on the number line. Changing the direction of the inequality after multiplying (or dividing) by a negative number produces an inequality that is still a true statement.

EXAMPLE 2 Solve the inequality $7x - 11 \leq -32$. Present your solutions on a number line and in interval notation.

SOLUTION   Think about the steps you would take to solve the equation $7x - 11 = -32$. You follow the same steps when solving this inequality.

$$7x - 11 \leq -32$$
$$7x \leq -21 \qquad \text{Add 11 to both sides.}$$
$$x \leq -3 \qquad \text{Divide both sides by 7.}$$

Now present the solution on a number line.

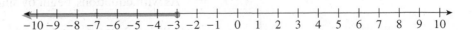

This can be expressed in interval notation as $(-\infty, -3]$.

Quick Check 2

Solve the inequality $4x + 3 < 31$. Present your solutions on a number line and in interval notation.

EXAMPLE 3 Solve the inequality $-2x - 5 > 9$. Present your solutions on a number line and in interval notation.

SOLUTION   Begin by solving the inequality.

$$-2x - 5 > 9$$
$$-2x > 14 \quad \text{Add 5 to both sides.}$$
$$\frac{-2x}{-2} < \frac{14}{-2} \quad \text{Divide both sides by } -2 \text{ to isolate } x. \text{ Notice that the}$$
$$\text{direction of the inequality must change because you}$$
$$\text{are dividing by a negative number.}$$
$$x < -7 \quad \text{Simplify.}$$

Now present the solutions.

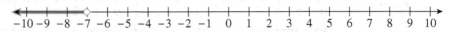

In interval notation, this is $(-\infty, -7)$.

▶ Quick Check 3

Solve the inequality $7 - 4x \leq -13$. Present your solutions on a number line and in interval notation.

EXAMPLE 4 Solve the inequality $5x - 12 > 8 - 3x$. Present your solutions on a number line and in interval notation.

SOLUTION   Collect all variable terms on one side of the inequality and all constant terms on the other side.

$$5x - 12 > 8 - 3x$$
$$8x - 12 > 8 \qquad \text{Add } 3x \text{ to both sides.}$$
$$8x > 20 \qquad \text{Add 12 to both sides.}$$
$$x > \frac{5}{2} \qquad \text{Divide both sides by 8 and simplify.}$$

Here is the solution on a number line.

In interval notation, this is written as $\left(\frac{5}{2}, \infty\right)$.

▶ Quick Check 4

Solve the inequality $3x + 8 < x + 2$. Present your solutions on a number line and in interval notation.

EXAMPLE 5 Solve the inequality $3(7 - 2x) + 6x \leq 5x - 4$. Present your solutions on a number line and in interval notation.

SOLUTION   As with equations, begin by simplifying each side completely.

$$3(7 - 2x) + 6x \leq 5x - 4$$
$$21 - 6x + 6x \leq 5x - 4 \qquad \text{Distribute.}$$
$$21 \leq 5x - 4 \qquad \text{Combine like terms.}$$
$$25 \leq 5x \qquad \text{Add 4 to both sides.}$$
$$5 \leq x \qquad \text{Divide both sides by 5.}$$

We can rewrite this solution as $x \geq 5$, which will help when you display the solutions on a number line.

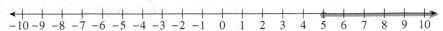

This can be expressed in interval notation as $[5, \infty)$.

▸ Quick Check 5

Solve the inequality $(11x - 3) - (2x - 13) \geq 4(2x + 1)$. Present your solutions on a number line and in interval notation.

Compound Inequalities

Objective ④ **Solve compound inequalities involving the union of two linear inequalities.** A **compound inequality** is made up of two or more individual inequalities. One type of compound inequality involves the word *or*. In this type of inequality, we are looking for real numbers that are solutions of one inequality or the other. For example, the solutions of the compound inequality $x < 2$ or $x > 4$ are real numbers that are less than 2 or greater than 4. The solutions of this compound inequality can be displayed on a number line as follows:

To express the solutions using interval notation, we write both intervals with the symbol for **union** ($\cup$) between them. The interval notation for $x < 2$ or $x > 4$ is $(-\infty, 2) \cup (4, \infty)$.

To solve a compound inequality involving *or*, we simply solve each inequality separately.

EXAMPLE 6 Solve $9x + 20 < -34$ or $5 + 4x \geq 19$.

SOLUTION Solve each inequality separately. Begin with $9x + 20 < -34$.

$$9x + 20 < -34$$
$$9x < -54 \quad \text{Subtract 20 from both sides.}$$
$$x < -6 \quad \text{Divide both sides by 9.}$$

Now solve the second inequality, $5 + 4x \geq 19$.

$$5 + 4x \geq 19$$
$$4x \geq 14 \quad \text{Subtract 5 from both sides.}$$
$$x \geq \frac{7}{2} \quad \text{Divide both sides by 4 and simplify.}$$

Combine the solutions on a single number line.

The solutions can be expressed in interval notation as $(-\infty, -6) \cup \left[\frac{7}{2}, \infty\right)$.

▸ Quick Check 6

Solve $3x - 2 \leq 10$ or $4x - 13 \geq 15$.

Objective 5 Solve compound inequalities involving the intersection of two linear inequalities. Another type of compound inequality involves the word *and*, and the solutions of this compound inequality must be solutions of each inequality. For example, the solutions of the inequality $x > -5$ and $x < 1$ are real numbers that are, at the same time, greater than -5 and less than 1. This type of inequality is generally written in the condensed form $-5 < x < 1$. You can think of the solutions as being between -5 and 1.

To solve a compound inequality of this type, we need to isolate the variable in the middle part of the inequality between two real numbers. A key aspect of the approach is to work on all three parts of the inequality at once.

EXAMPLE 7   Solve $-5 \le 2x - 1 < 9$.

SOLUTION   We are trying to isolate x in the middle of this inequality. The first step is to add 1 to all three parts of this inequality, after which we will divide by 2.

$$-5 \le 2x - 1 < 9$$
$$-4 \le 2x < 10 \quad \text{Add 1 to each part of the inequality.}$$
$$-2 \le x < 5 \quad \text{Divide each part of the inequality by 2.}$$

The solutions are presented on the following number line:

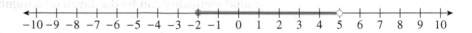

These solutions can be expressed in interval notation as $[-2, 5)$.

▶ Quick Check 7
Solve $-11 < 4x + 1 < 7$.

Applications

Objective 6 Solve applied problems using linear inequalities. Many applied problems involve inequalities rather than equations. Here are some key phrases and their translations into inequalities.

Key Phrases for Inequalities

x is greater than a x is more than a x is higher than a x is above a	$x > a$
x is at least a x is a or higher	$x \ge a$
x is less than a x is lower than a x is below a	$x < a$
x is at most a x is a or lower	$x \le a$
x is between a and b, exclusive x is more than a but less than b	$a < x < b$
x is between a and b, inclusive x is at least a but no more than b	$a \le x \le b$

EXAMPLE 8 A sign next to an amusement park ride says that you must be at least 48″ tall to get on the ride. Set up an inequality that shows the heights of people who can get on the ride.

SOLUTION   Let h represent the height of a person. If a person must be at least 48″ tall, his or her height must be 48″ or above. In other words, the person's height must be greater than or equal to 48″. The inequality is $h \geq 48$.

A WORD OF CAUTION The phrase *at least* means "greater than or equal to" ($\geq$) and does not mean "less than."

EXAMPLE 9 An instructor tells her students that on the final exam, they need a score of 70 or higher out of a possible 100 to pass. Set up an inequality that shows the scores that are not passing.

SOLUTION   Let s represent a student's score. Because a score of 70 or higher will pass, any score lower than 70 will not pass. This inequality can be written as $s < 70$. If we happen to know that the lowest possible score is 0, we also could write the inequality as $0 \leq s < 70$.

▶ Quick Check 8
The Brainiac Club has a bylaw stating that a person must have an IQ of at least 130 to be admitted to the club. Set up an inequality that shows the IQs of people who are unable to join the club.

Now we will set up and solve applied problems involving inequalities.

EXAMPLE 10 If a student averages 90 or higher on the five tests given in a math class, the student will earn a grade of A. Sean's scores on the first four tests are 82, 87, 93, and 92. What score on the fifth test will give Sean an A?

SOLUTION   To find the average of five test scores, add the five scores and divide by 5. Let x represent the score of the fifth test. The average can then be expressed as $\frac{82 + 87 + 93 + 92 + x}{5}$. We are interested in which scores on the fifth test give an average that is 90 or higher.

$$\frac{82 + 87 + 93 + 92 + x}{5} \geq 90$$

$$\frac{354 + x}{5} \geq 90 \qquad \text{Simplify the numerator.}$$

$$5 \cdot \frac{354 + x}{5} \geq 5 \cdot 90 \qquad \text{Multiply both sides by 5 to clear the fraction.}$$

$$354 + x \geq 450 \qquad \text{Simplify.}$$

$$x \geq 96 \qquad \text{Subtract 354 from both sides.}$$

Sean must score at least 96 on the fifth test to earn an A.

▶ Quick Check 9
If a student averages lower than 70 on the four tests given in a math class, the student will fail the class. Bobby's scores on the first three tests are 74, 78, and 80. What scores on the fourth test will result in Bobby failing the class?

BUILDING YOUR STUDY STRATEGY

Using Your Textbook, 5 A Word of Caution/Using Your Calculator Two features of this textbook you may find helpful are labeled "A Word of Caution" and "Using Your Calculator." Each Word of Caution box warns you about common errors for certain problems and tells you how to avoid repeating the same mistake. Look through the section for this feature before attempting the homework exercises.

Using Your Calculator shows how you can use the Texas Instruments TI-84 calculator to help with selected examples in the text. If you own one of these calculators, look for this feature before beginning your homework.

Exercises 2.5

MyMathLab *Powered by CourseCompass™ and MathXL®*

 PRACTICE   WATCH   DOWNLOAD   READ   REVIEW

Vocabulary

1. A(n) _____ is an inequality containing linear expressions.

2. When graphing an inequality, use a(n) _____ circle to indicate an endpoint that is not included as a solution.

3. You can express the solutions of an inequality using a number line or _____ notation.

4. When solving a linear inequality, you change the direction of the inequality whenever you multiply or divide both sides of the inequality by a(n) _____ number.

5. An inequality that is composed of two or more individual inequalities is called a(n) _____ inequality.

6. Which inequality can be associated with the statement *The person's height is at least 80 inches*?

   a) $x \leq 80$ **b)** $x < 80$ **c)** $x \geq 80$ **d)** $x > 80$

Graph each inequality on a number line and present it in interval notation.

7. $x < 3$

8. $x > -6$

9. $x \geq -1$

10. $x \leq 13$

11. $-2 < x < 8$

12. $3 < x \leq 12$

13. $x > \dfrac{9}{2}$

14. $x > 5.5$

15. $x > 8$ or $x \leq 2$

16. $x < -5$ or $x > 0$

Write an inequality associated with the given graph or interval notation.

17.
```
←+++++++++++++++++·+++++→
 -10 -8  -6  -4  -2   0   2   4   6   8  10
```

18.
```
←+++++++++++++++++++++++→
 -10 -8  -6  -4  -2   0   2   4   6   8  10
```

19.
```
←+++++++++++++++++++++++→
 -10 -8  -6  -4  -2   0   2   4   6   8  10
```

20.
```
←+++++·++++++++++++++·++→
 -10 -8  -6  -4  -2   0   2   4   6   8  10
```

21. $(-\infty, 2) \cup (9, \infty)$ **22.** $(-3, -2)$

23. $(-\infty, -4)$ **24.** $[-8, \infty)$

Solve. Present your solution on a number line and in interval notation.

25. $x + 9 < 5$

26. $x - 7 > 3$

27. $2x > 12$

28. $4x \geq -20$

29. $-5x > 15$

30. $-8x < -24$

31. $3x \geq -10.5$

32. $2x \leq 9.4$

33. $3x + 2 < 14$

34. $2x - 7 > 11$

35. $-2x + 9 \leq 29$

36. $7 - 4x > 19$

37. $8 < 3x - 13$

38. $1 \geq 5x + 16$

39. $\frac{2}{3}x > \frac{10}{9}$

40. $\frac{5}{9}x - \frac{4}{3} < 7$

41. $5x + 13 > 2x - 11$

42. $-2x + 51 < 9 - 8x$

43. $5(x + 3) + 2 > 3(x + 4) - 6$

44. $5(2x - 3) - 3 < 2(2x + 9) - 4$

45. $2x < -8$ or $x + 7 > 5$

46. $x - 3 \leq -5$ or $6x > -6$

47. $2x - 7 \leq -3$ or $2x - 7 \geq 3$

48. $3x - 6 < -9$ or $3x - 6 > 9$

49. $-2x + 17 < 5$ or $10 - x > 7$

50. $-4x + 13 \leq 9$ or $6 - 5x \geq 21$

51. $3x + 5 < 17$ or $2x - 9 < 5$

52. $7x - 1 \geq 13$ or $4x + 5 \geq -7$

53. $\frac{1}{4}x + \frac{7}{24} \leq \frac{2}{3}$ or $\frac{1}{4}x + \frac{9}{20} \geq \frac{6}{5}$

54. $\frac{1}{8}x - \frac{1}{5} < \frac{1}{12}x - \frac{3}{40}$ or $\frac{1}{2}x - \frac{3}{20} > \frac{1}{4}x + \frac{11}{10}$

55. $-4 < x - 3 < 1$

56. $2 \leq x + 7 \leq 5$

57. $-2 < 5x - 7 < 28$

58. $18 \leq 4x - 10 \leq 50$

59. $6 < 3x + 15 \leq 33$

60. $-12 \leq 4x - 18 < 7$

61. $\frac{1}{5} \leq \frac{1}{2}x - \frac{1}{3} \leq \frac{7}{4}$

62. $-\frac{3}{10} < \frac{1}{5}x - \frac{1}{2} < \frac{3}{5}$

63. In your own words, explain why the inequality $8 < 9x + 7 < 3$ has no solutions.

64. In your own words, explain why solving the compound inequality $x + 7 < 9$ or $x + 7 < 13$ is the same as solving the inequality $x + 7 < 13$ only.

65. Adrian needs to score at least 2 goals in the final game of the season to set a new scoring record. Write an inequality that shows the number of goals that will set a new record.

66. If Eddie sells fewer than 7 cars this week, he will be fired. Write an inequality that shows the number of cars that will result in Eddie being unemployed.

67. A certain type of shrub is tolerant to 30° F, which means that it can survive at temperatures down to 30° F. Write an inequality that shows the temperatures at which the shrub cannot survive.

68. To be eligible for growth funding from the state, a community college must have 11,200 or more students this semester. Write an inequality that shows the number of students that makes the college eligible for growth funding.

For 69–76, write an inequality for the given situation and solve it.

69. John is paid to get signatures on petitions. He gets paid 10 cents for each signature. How many signatures does he need to gather today to earn at least $30?

70. Carlo attends a charity wine-tasting festival. There is a $10 admission fee. In addition, there is a $4 charge for each variety tasted. If Carlo brings $40 with him, how many varieties can he taste?

71. Angelica is going out of town on business. Her company will reimburse her up to $85 for a rental car. She rents a car for $19.95 plus $0.07 per mile. How many miles can Angelica drive without going over the amount her company will reimburse?

72. An elementary school's booster club is holding a fundraiser by selling cookie dough. Each tub of cookie dough sells for $11, and the booster club gets to keep half of the proceeds. If the booster club wants to raise at least $12,000, how many tubs of cookie dough does it need to sell?

73. Charles told his son Harry that he should give at least 15% of his earnings to charity. If Harry earned $37,500 last year, how much should he have given to charity?

74. Karina is looking for a formal dress to wear to a charity event, and she has $400 to spend. If the store charges 7% sales tax on each dress, what price range should Karina be considering?

75. Students in a real estate class must have an average score of at least 80 on their exams in order to pass. If Jacqui has scored 92, 93, 85, and 96 on the first four exams, what scores on the fifth exam would allow her to pass the course?

76. Students with an average test score below 70 after the third test will be sent an Early Alert warning. Robert scored 62 and 59 on the first two tests. What scores on the third exam will save Robert from receiving an Early Alert warning?

✏ Writing in Mathematics

Answer in complete sentences.

77. In your own words, explain why you must change the direction of an inequality when dividing both sides of that inequality by a negative number.

78. *Solutions Manual* Write a solutions manual page for the following problem:
    Solve. $-10 < 3x + 2 \le 29$

CHAPTER 3

Graphing Linear Equations

In this chapter, we will examine linear equations in two variables. Equations involving two variables relate two unknown quantities to each other, such as a person's height and weight or the number of items sold by a company and the profit the company made. The primary focus is on graphing linear equations, which is the technique used to display the solutions to an equation in two variables.

STUDY STRATEGY

Making the Best Use of Your Resources In this chapter, we will focus on how to get the most out of your available resources. What works best for one student may not work for another student. Consider all of the different resources presented in this chapter, and use the ones you believe will help you.

Throughout this chapter, we will revisit this study strategy and help you incorporate it into your study habits.

3.1

The Rectangular Coordinate System; Equations in Two Variables

OBJECTIVES

1. Determine whether an ordered pair is a solution of an equation in two variables.
2. Plot ordered pairs on a rectangular coordinate plane.
3. Complete ordered pairs for a linear equation in two variables.
4. Graph linear equations in two variables by plotting points.

Equations in Two Variables and Their Solutions; Ordered Pairs

Objective 1 Determine whether an ordered pair is a solution of an equation in two variables. In this section, we will begin to examine equations in two variables, which relate two different quantities to each other. Here are some examples of equations in two variables.

$$y = 4x + 7 \qquad\qquad 2a + 3b = -6$$
$$y = 3x^2 - 2x - 9 \qquad t = \frac{4n + 9}{3n - 7}$$

As in the previous chapter, we will be looking for solutions of these equations. A **solution of an equation in two variables** is a pair of values that when substituted for the two variables produce a true statement. Consider the equation $3x + 4y = 10$. One solution of this equation is $x = 2$ and $y = 1$. We can see that this is a solution by substituting 2 for x and 1 for y into the equation.

$$3x + 4y = 10$$
$$3(2) + 4(1) = 10 \quad \text{Substitute 2 for } x \text{ and 1 for } y.$$
$$6 + 4 = 10 \quad \text{Multiply.}$$
$$10 = 10 \quad \text{Add.}$$

Because this produces a true statement, together the pair of values form a solution. Solutions to this type of equation are written as **ordered pairs** (x, y). In the example, the ordered pair $(2, 1)$ is a solution. We call it an ordered pair because the two values are listed in the specific order of x first and y second. The values are often referred to as **coordinates**.

EXAMPLE 1 Is the ordered pair $(-3, 2)$ a solution of the equation $y = 3x + 11$?

SOLUTION   To determine whether this ordered pair is a solution, substitute -3 for x and 2 for y.

$$y = 3x + 11$$
$$(2) = 3(-3) + 11 \quad \text{Substitute } -3 \text{ for } x \text{ and 2 for } y.$$
$$2 = -9 + 11 \quad \text{Multiply.}$$
$$2 = 2 \quad \text{Simplify.}$$

Because this is a true statement, the ordered pair $(-3, 2)$ is a solution of the equation $y = 3x + 11$.

EXAMPLE 2 Is $(4, 0)$ a solution of the equation $y - 2x = 8$?

SOLUTION   Again, check to see whether this ordered pair is a solution by substituting the given values for x and y. Be careful to substitute 4 for x and 0 for y, not vice versa.

$$y - 2x = 8$$
$$(0) - 2(4) = 8 \quad \text{Substitute 4 for } x \text{ and 0 for } y.$$
$$0 - 8 = 8 \quad \text{Multiply.}$$
$$-8 = 8 \quad \text{Simplify.}$$

Because this is a false statement, $(4, 0)$ is not a solution of the equation $y - 2x = 8$.

Quick Check 1

Is $(0, -6)$ a solution of the equation $3x + 2y = 12$?

The Rectangular Coordinate Plane

Objective 2 Plot ordered pairs on a rectangular coordinate plane.
Ordered pairs can be displayed graphically using the **rectangular coordinate plane**. The rectangular coordinate plane also is known as the **Cartesian plane**, named after the famous French philosopher and mathematician René Descartes.

The rectangular coordinate plane is made up of two number lines, known as **axes**. The axes are drawn at right angles to each other, intersecting at 0 on each axis. The accompanying graph shows how it looks.

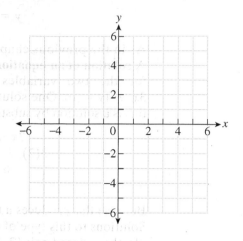

---

x-axis, y-axis, origin

The **horizontal axis,** or **x-axis,** is used to show the first value of an ordered pair. The **vertical axis,** or **y-axis,** is used to show the second value of an ordered pair. The point where the two axes cross is called the **origin** and represents the ordered pair (0, 0).

Positive values of x are found to the right of the origin, and negative values of x are found to the left of the origin. Positive values of y are found above the origin, and negative values of y are found below the origin.

We can use the rectangular coordinate plane to represent ordered pairs that are solutions of an equation. To plot an ordered pair (x, y) on a rectangular coordinate plane, we begin at the origin. The x-coordinate tells us how far to the left or right of the origin to move. The y-coordinate then tells us how far up or down to move from there.

Suppose we wanted to plot the ordered pair $(-3, 2)$ on a rectangular coordinate plane. The x-coordinate is -3, which tells us to move 3 units to the left of the origin. The y-coordinate is 2, so we move up 2 units to find the location of the ordered pair and place a point at this location. An ordered pair is often referred to as a **point** when it is plotted on a graph.

One final note about the rectangular coordinate plane is that the two axes divide the plane into four sections called **quadrants**. The four quadrants are labeled I, II, III, and IV. A point that lies on one of the axes is not considered to be in one of the quadrants.

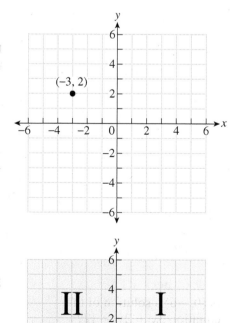

EXAMPLE 3   Plot the ordered pairs $(5, 1)$, $(4, -2)$, $(-2, -4)$, and $(-4, 0)$ on a rectangular coordinate plane.

SOLUTION   The four ordered pairs are plotted on the following graph:

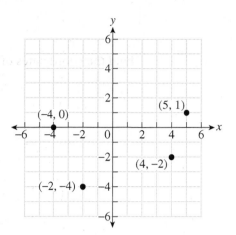

Quick Check 2

Plot the ordered pairs $(3, 8)$, $(5, -4)$, $(-3, 6)$, and $(0, 7)$ on a rectangular coordinate plane.

Choosing the appropriate scale for a graph is an important skill. To plot the ordered pair $(\frac{7}{2}, -4)$ on a rectangular coordinate plane, we could use a scale of $\frac{1}{2}$ on the axes. A rectangular plane with axes showing values ranging from -10 to 10 is not large enough to plot the ordered pair $(-45, 25)$. A good choice is to label the axes showing values that range from -50 to 50. Because this is a wide range of values, it makes sense to increase the scale. Because each coordinate is a multiple of 5, we use a scale of 5 units.

It is important to be able to read the coordinates of an ordered pair from a graph.

EXAMPLE 4   Find the coordinates of points A through G on the following graph:

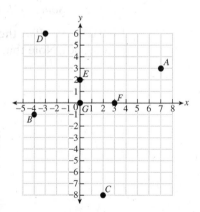

SOLUTION   To find the x-coordinate of a point, determine how far the point is to the left or right of the origin. Points to the right of the origin have positive x-coordinates, and points to the left of the origin have negative x-coordinates. Points on the y-axis have an x-coordinate of 0.

Next, determine the y-coordinate of the point by measuring how far the point is above or below the origin. If the point is above the origin, the y-coordinate is positive. If the point is below the origin, the y-coordinate is negative. Points on the x-axis have a y-coordinate of 0.

Here is a table containing the coordinates of each point.

Point	A	B	C	D	E	F	G
Coordinates	$(7, 3)$	$(-4, -1)$	$(2, -8)$	$(-3, 6)$	$(0, 2)$	$(3, 0)$	$(0, 0)$

▶ Quick Check 3

Find the coordinates of points A through E on the following graph:

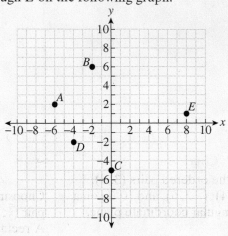

EXAMPLE 5 Plot the ordered pairs associated with the given data. (Let the year be x and the median household income be y.)

Year	1967	1977	1987	1997	2007
Median Household Income ($1000's)	7	14	26	37	50

(Source: U.S. Census Bureau)

SOLUTION   Plot the ordered pairs $(1967, 7)$, $(1977, 14)$, $(1987, 26)$, $(1997, 37)$, and $(2007, 50)$. Note that we focus on x values from 1967 to 2007.

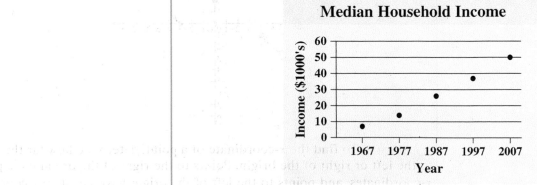

▶ Quick Check 4

Plot the ordered pairs associated with the given data. (Let the year be x and the number of subscribers be y.)

Year	2004	2005	2006	2007	2008
Subscribers (millions)	2.6	4.2	6.3	7.5	9.4

(Source: Netflix)

Linear Equations in Two Variables

Objective 3 **Complete ordered pairs for a linear equation in two variables.**

> ### Standard Form of a Linear Equation
> A linear equation in two variables is an equation that can be written in the form $Ax + By = C$, where A, B, and C are real numbers and A and B are not both 0. This is called the **standard form** of a linear equation in two variables.

A linear equation has multiple solutions. To find an ordered pair that is a solution of a linear equation, we can select an arbitrary value for one of the variables, substitute this value into the equation, and solve for the remaining variable. The next example provides practice finding solutions of linear equations in two variables.

EXAMPLE 6 Find the missing coordinate such that the ordered pair $(2, \_\!\_)$ is a solution of the equation $y = 5x - 4$.

SOLUTION We are given an x-coordinate of 2, so we substitute this for x in the equation.

$$y = 5(2) - 4 \quad \text{Substitute 2 for } x \text{ and solve for } y.$$
$$y = 10 - 4 \quad \text{Multiply.}$$
$$y = 6 \quad \text{Subtract.}$$

The ordered pair $(2, 6)$ is a solution of this equation.

Quick Check 5

Find the missing coordinate such that the ordered pair $(3, \_\!\_)$ is a solution of the equation $y = -3x + 5$.

The solutions of any linear equation in two variables follow a pattern. Now we will begin to explore this pattern.

EXAMPLE 7 Complete the following table of ordered pairs with solutions of the linear equation $x + y = 5$.

x	y
3	
	−2
0	

Plot the solutions on a rectangular coordinate plane.

SOLUTION The first ordered pair has an x-coordinate of 3. Substituting this for x results in the equation $(3) + y = 5$, which has a solution of $y = 2$. $(3, 2)$ is a solution.

The second ordered pair has a y-coordinate of -2. Substituting for y, this produces the equation $x + (-2) = 5$. The solution of this equation is $x = 7$, so $(7, -2)$ is a solution.

The third ordered pair has an x-coordinate of 0. When substituting this for x, we get the equation $(0) + y = 5$. This equation has a solution of $y = 5$, so $(0, 5)$ is a solution. The completed table follows.

x	y
3	2
7	−2
0	5

When we plot these three points on a rectangular coordinate plane, it looks like the following graph. Notice that the three points appear to fall on a straight line.

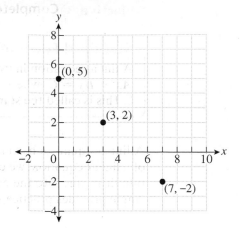

Graphing Linear Equations by Plotting Points

Objective **4** **Graph linear equations in two variables by plotting points.** In the previous example, notice that the three points appear to be in line with each other. We can draw a straight line that passes through each of the three points. In addition to the three points on the graph, every point that lies on the line is a solution of the equation. Every ordered pair that is a solution must lie on this line.

We can sketch a graph of the solutions of a linear equation by plotting ordered pairs that are solutions and then drawing the straight line through these points. The line we sketch continues indefinitely in both directions. Although only two points are needed to determine a line, we will find three points. The third point is used as a check to make sure the first two points are accurate. We will pick three arbitrary values for one of the variables and find the other coordinates.

EXAMPLE 8 Graph the linear equation $y = 3x - 4$.

SOLUTION When the equation has y isolated on one side of the equal sign, it is a good idea to select values for x and find the corresponding y-values. We find three points on the line by letting $x = 0$, $x = 1$, and $x = 2$. These values were chosen arbitrarily. If we start with other values, the ordered pairs will still be on the same line.

$x = 0$	$x = 1$	$x = 2$
$y = 3(0) - 4$	$y = 3(1) - 4$	$y = 3(2) - 4$
$y = 0 - 4$	$y = 3 - 4$	$y = 6 - 4$
$y = -4$	$y = -1$	$y = 2$
$(0, -4)$	$(1, -1)$	$(2, 2)$

Plot these three points on a rectangular coordinate plane and draw a line through them.

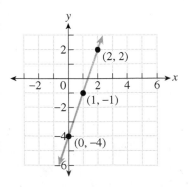

Exercises 3.1

PRACTICE   WATCH   DOWNLOAD   READ   REVIEW

Vocabulary

1. The standard form of a linear equation in two variables is _____ .

2. Solutions to an equation in two variables are written as a(n) _____.

3. The _____ is used to show the first coordinate of an ordered pair on a rectangular coordinate plane.

4. The _____ is used to show the second coordinate of an ordered pair on a rectangular coordinate plane.

5. The point at $(0, 0)$ is called the _____.

6. A(n) _____ on a rectangular coordinate plane is used to show the solutions of a linear equation in two variables.

Is the ordered pair a solution of the given equation?

7. $(7, 6), 5x + 3y = 53$

8. $(2, 9), 2x + 9y = 85$

9. $(4, -3), 6x - 2y = 18$

10. $(9, 5), 2x + 7y = 53$

11. $(10, 9), y = \frac{3}{2}x - 6$

12. $(8, 7), y = -\frac{1}{4}x + 5$

13. $(3, 2), -2x + 5y = 4$

14. $(5, -2), -x + 7y = -9$

15. $(-3, 0), -4x + y = 12$

16. $(0, 4), 2x - 5y = -20$

Plot the points on a rectangular coordinate plane.

17. $(5, 2), (3, 4), (2, -6),$
    $(-4, 1)$

18. $(-3, -5), (-5, 3),$
    $(4, -3), (-2, -1)$

19. $(0, 4), (-2, 0), (-4, 2),$
    $(2, 4)$

20. $(-4, 0), (-5, 0),$
    $(0, -3), (0, 2)$

21. $\left(\frac{7}{2}, 5\right), \left(-2, \frac{13}{4}\right),$
    $\left(-\frac{23}{8}, -1\right), \left(\frac{3}{2}, -\frac{5}{2}\right)$

22. $(-70, 30), (20, -90), (45, 25), (-50, -68)$

Find the coordinates of the labeled points A, B, C, and D.

23.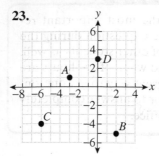

24.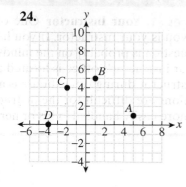

36. Median home prices in California from 2003–2008.
(*Source: California Association of Realtors*)

Year	2003	2004	2005	2006	2007	2008
Median Price ($1000's)	$373	$451	$524	$557	$558	$381

25.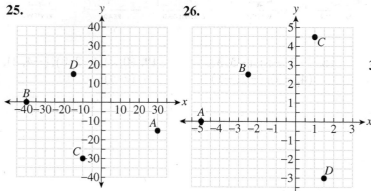

26.

37. Number of Starbucks stores worldwide from 2003–2008. (*Source: Starbucks*)

Year	2003	2004	2005	2006	2007	2008
Stores	7225	8569	10,241	12,440	15,011	16,680

In which quadrant (I, II, III, or IV) is the given point?

27. $(5, -1)$

28. $(-2, 8)$

29. $(3, 4)$

30. $(-6, -4)$

31. $(2, 5)$

32. $(-3, -3)$

33. $\left(\dfrac{1}{2}, -\dfrac{3}{5}\right)$

34. $(-700, 1000)$

Plot the ordered pairs associated with the given data. (Let the first row be x and the second row be y.)

35. Number of identity theft complaints filed. (*Source: Federal Trade Commission*)

Year	2000	2002	2004	2006	2008
Complaints (1000's)	31	162	247	246	314

38. U.S. cell phone subscribers, in millions, for selected years. (*Source: Cellular Telecommunications & Internet Associates*)

Year	1987	1992	1997	2002	2007
Subscribers (millions)	1	11	55	141	250

39. Estimated number of bariatric (weight-loss) surgeries performed from 2002–2008. (*Source: American Society for Metabolic and Bariatric Surgery*)

Year	2002	2003	2004	2005	2006	2007	2008
Surgeries (thousands)	63	103	141	171	178	205	220

40. Total value of online retail sales in the United States, in billions, from 2000–2007. (*Source: U.S. Census Bureau*)

Year	2000	2001	2002	2003	2004	2005	2006	2007
Sales	$24	$31	$41	$54	$67	$84	$108	$128

Using the given coordinate, find the other coordinate that makes the ordered pair a solution of the equation.

41. $3x - 2y = 8$, $(2, \underline{\quad})$

42. $x + 4y = 7$, $(\underline{\quad}, 3)$

43. $7x - 4y = -11$, $(\underline{\quad}, -6)$

44. $5x + 4y = 12$, $(-4, \underline{\quad})$

45. $y = 2x - 7$, $(9, \underline{\quad})$

46. $y = -5x + 4$, $(3, \underline{\quad})$

47. $7x - 11y = -22$, $(0, \underline{\quad})$

48. $4x + 3y = -20$, $(\underline{\quad}, 0)$

49. $3x + \dfrac{1}{2}y = -2$, $(\underline{\quad}, 8)$

50. $\dfrac{1}{5}x + 3y = 20$, $(10, \underline{\quad})$

51. $6x + 2y = 9$, $(\frac{2}{3}, \underline{\quad})$

52. $3x + 4y = 15$, $(\underline{\quad}, \frac{7}{2})$

Complete each table with ordered pairs that are solutions.

53. $5x - 3y = -12$

x	y
-3	
0	
3	

54. $-2x + 4y = -16$

x	y
-2	
0	
2	

55. $y = 4x - 9$

x	y
0	
1	
$\frac{3}{2}$	

56. $y = -3x + 5$

x	y
0	
$\frac{1}{3}$	
2	

57. $y = \dfrac{2}{3}x - 2$

x	y
-3	
0	
6	

58. $y = \dfrac{7}{5}x + 1$

x	y
-5	
0	
5	

59. Find three equations that have the ordered pair $(5, 2)$ as a solution.

60. Find three equations that have the ordered pair $(3, -4)$ as a solution.

61. Find three equations that have the ordered pair $(0, 6)$ as a solution.

62. Find three equations that have the ordered pair $(-8, 0)$ as a solution.

Find three ordered pairs that are solutions of the given linear equation and use them to graph the equation.

63. $y = 4x + 1$

64. $y = 2x - 3$

65. $y = -2x + 7$ **66.** $y = -3x + 6$ **71.** $y = -\dfrac{3}{5}x + 6$ **72.** $y = -\dfrac{5}{2}x + 4$

67. $y = -2x$ **68.** $y = 4x$

73. $3x + y = 9$ **74.** $2x + 3y = 6$

69. $y = \dfrac{1}{4}x + 3$ **70.** $y = \dfrac{1}{2}x - 3$

◼︎ Writing in Mathematics

Answer in complete sentences.

75. In your own words, explain why the order of the coordinates in an ordered pair is important. Is there a difference between plotting the ordered pair (a, b) and the ordered pair (b, a)?

76. If the ordered pair (a, b) is in quadrant II, in which quadrant is (b, a)? In which quadrant is $(-a, b)$? Explain how you determined your answers.

3.2

Graphing Linear Equations and Their Intercepts

OBJECTIVES

1. Find the *x*- and *y*-intercepts of a line from its graph.
2. Find the *x*- and *y*-intercepts of a line from its equation.
3. Graph linear equations using their intercepts.
4. Graph linear equations that pass through the origin.
5. Graph horizontal lines.
6. Graph vertical lines.
7. Interpret the graph of an applied linear equation.

In the previous section, we learned to use a rectangular coordinate plane to display the solutions of an equation in two variables. We also learned that all of the solutions of a linear equation in two variables are on a straight line. In this section, we will learn to graph the line associated with a linear equation in two variables in a more systematic fashion.

Intercepts

Objective ① Find the *x*- and *y*-intercepts of a line from its graph.

> A point at which a graph crosses the *x*-axis is called an ***x*-intercept,** and a point at which a graph crosses the *y*-axis is called a ***y*-intercept.**

EXAMPLE 1   Find the coordinates of any *x*-intercepts and *y*-intercepts.

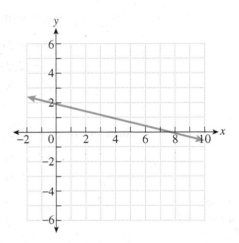

SOLUTION   An *x*-intercept is a point at which the graph crosses the *x*-axis. This graph crosses the *x*-axis at the point $(8, 0)$, so the *x*-intercept is the point $(8, 0)$. This graph crosses the *y*-axis at the point $(0, 2)$, so the *y*-intercept is $(0, 2)$.

Quick Check 1

Find the coordinates of any *x*-intercepts and *y*-intercepts.

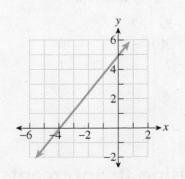

Some lines do not have both an *x*- and *y*-intercept.

This horizontal line does not cross the *x*-axis, so it does not have an *x*-intercept. Its *y*-intercept is the point $(0, -6)$.

The *x*-intercept of this vertical line is the point $(4, 0)$. This graph does not cross the *y*-axis, so it does not have a *y*-intercept.

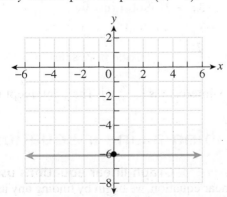

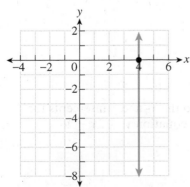

Objective 2 Find the x- and y-intercepts of a line from its equation. Any point that lies on the x-axis has a y-coordinate of 0. Similarly, any point that lies on the y-axis has an x-coordinate of 0. We can use these facts to find the intercepts of an equation's graph algebraically. To find an x-intercept, we substitute 0 for y and solve for x. To find a y-intercept, we substitute 0 for x and solve for y.

Finding Intercepts

To Find an x-Intercept

Substitute 0 for y and solve the resulting equation for x. The ordered pair will be of the form $(x, 0)$.

To Find a y-Intercept

Substitute 0 for x and solve the resulting equation for y. The ordered pair will be of the form $(0, y)$.

EXAMPLE 2 Find the x- and y-intercepts for the equation $5x - 2y = 10$.

SOLUTION   Begin with the x-intercept by substituting 0 for y and solving for x.

$$5x - 2y = 10$$
$$5x - 2(0) = 10 \quad \text{Substitute 0 for } y.$$
$$5x = 10 \quad \text{Simplify the left side of the equation.}$$
$$x = 2 \quad \text{Divide both sides by 5.}$$

The x-intercept is $(2, 0)$. To find the y-intercept, substitute 0 for x and solve for y.

$$5x - 2y = 10$$
$$5(0) - 2y = 10 \quad \text{Substitute 0 for } x.$$
$$-2y = 10 \quad \text{Simplify the left side of the equation.}$$
$$y = -5 \quad \text{Divide both sides by } -2.$$

The y-intercept is $(0, -5)$.

Quick Check 2

Find the x- and y-intercepts for the equation $-3x + 4y = -12$.

EXAMPLE 3 Find the x- and y-intercepts for the equation $y = -3x - 7$.

SOLUTION

x-intercept	**y-intercept**
$y = -3x - 7$	$y = -3x - 7$
$0 = -3x - 7$ Substitute 0 for y.	$y = -3(0) - 7$ Substitute 0 for x.
$3x = -7$ Add $3x$ to both sides.	$y = -7$ Simplify.
$x = -\dfrac{7}{3}$ Divide both sides by 3.	

The x-intercept is $\left(-\frac{7}{3}, 0\right)$. The y-intercept is $(0, -7)$.

Quick Check 3

Find the x- and y-intercepts for the equation $y = 2x - 9$.

Graphing a Linear Equation Using Its Intercepts

Objective 3 Graph linear equations using their intercepts. When graphing a linear equation, we begin by finding any intercepts. This often gives us two points for the graph. Although only two points are necessary to graph a straight line, we plot at least three points to make sure the first two points are accurate. In other words, we use a third point as a "check" for the first two points we find. We find this third point by selecting a value for x, substituting it into the equation, and solving for y.

Graphing a Line by Using Its Intercepts

- Find the x-intercept by substituting 0 for y and solving for x.
- Find the y-intercept by substituting 0 for x and solving for y.
- Select a value of x, substitute it into the equation, and solve for y to find the coordinates of a third point on the line.
- Graph the line that passes through these three points.

EXAMPLE 4   Graph $3x + y = 6$. Label any intercepts.

SOLUTION   Begin by finding the x- and y-intercepts.

x-intercept		y-intercept	
$3x + (0) = 6$	Substitute 0 for y.	$3(0) + y = 6$	Substitute 0 for x.
$3x = 6$	Simplify.	$y = 6$	Simplify.
$x = 2$	Divide both sides by 3.		

The x-intercept is $(2, 0)$. The y-intercept is $(0, 6)$.

Before looking for a third point, let's plot the two intercepts on a graph. This can help us select a value to substitute for x when finding a third point. It is a good idea to select a value for x that is somewhat near the x-coordinates of the other two points. For example, $x = 1$ is a good choice for this example. If we choose a value of x that is too far from the x-coordinates of the other two points, we may have to change the scale of the axes or extend them to show the third point.

$$3(1) + y = 6 \quad \text{Substitute 1 for } x.$$
$$3 + y = 6 \quad \text{Simplify the left side of the equation.}$$
$$y = 3 \quad \text{Subtract 3.}$$

The point $(1, 3)$ is the third point. Keep in mind that the third point can vary with our choice for x, but the three points still should be on the same line. After plotting the third point, we finish by drawing a straight line that passes through all three points.

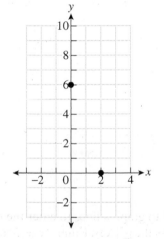

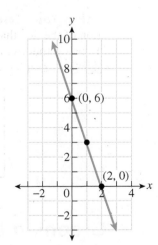

Quick Check 4

Graph $2x - 3y = 12$. Label any intercepts.

EXAMPLE 5 Graph $y = 2x + 5$. Label any intercepts.

SOLUTION Begin by finding the x- and y-intercepts.

x-intercept $(y = 0)$	y-intercept $(x = 0)$
$0 = 2x + 5$	$y = 2(0) + 5$
$-5 = 2x$	$y = 5$
$-\dfrac{5}{2} = x$	$(0, 5)$
$\left(-\dfrac{5}{2}, 0\right)$	

Choosing $x = 1$ to find the third point is a good choice: It is close to the two intercepts, and it will be easy to substitute 1 for x in the equation.

$$y = 2(1) + 5 \quad \text{Substitute 1 for } x \text{ in the equation.}$$
$$y = 7 \quad \text{Simplify.}$$

The third point is $(1, 7)$. Here is the graph.

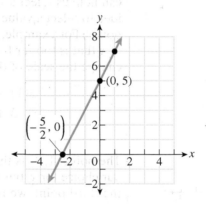

Quick Check 5

Graph $y = -3x - 9$. Label any intercepts.

Using Your Calculator You can use the TI-84 to graph a line. To enter the equation of the line that you graphed in Example 5, press the ⒴ key. Enter $2x + 5$ next to Y_1 using the key labeled ⓍＴΘⁿ to key the variable x. Then press the key labeled ⒼⓇⒶⓅⒽ to graph the line.

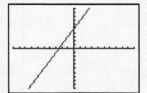

Graphing Linear Equations That Pass through the Origin

Objective ④ Graph linear equations that pass through the origin. Some lines do not have two intercepts. For example, a line that passes through the origin has its x- and y-intercepts at the same point. In this case, we need to find two additional points.

> ### Graphing a Line Passing through the Origin
> - Determine that both the x- and y-intercepts are at the origin.
> - Find a second point on the line by selecting a value of x and substituting it into the equation. Solve the equation for y.
> - Find a third point on the line by selecting another value of x and substituting it into the equation. Solve the equation for y.
> - Graph the line that passes through these three points.

EXAMPLE 6   Graph $2x - 8y = 0$. Label any intercepts.

SOLUTION   Let's start by finding the x-intercept.

$$2x - 8(0) = 0 \quad \text{Substitute 0 for } y.$$
$$2x = 0 \quad \text{Simplify.}$$
$$x = 0 \quad \text{Divide both sides by 2.}$$

The x-intercept is at the origin $(0, 0)$. This point also is the y-intercept, which we can verify by substituting 0 for x and solving for y. We need to find two more points before we graph the line. Suppose we choose $x = 1$.

$$2(1) - 8y = 0 \quad \text{Substitute 1 for } x.$$
$$2 - 8y = 0 \quad \text{Simplify.}$$
$$2 = 8y \quad \text{Add } 8y.$$
$$\frac{1}{4} = y \quad \text{Divide both sides by 8 and simplify.}$$

The point $\left(1, \frac{1}{4}\right)$ is on the line. However, it may not be easy to put this point on the graph because of its fractional y-coordinate. We can try to avoid this problem by solving the equation for y before choosing a value for x.

$$2x - 8y = 0$$
$$2x = 8y \qquad\qquad \text{Add } 8y \text{ to both sides.}$$
$$\frac{1}{4}x = y \quad \text{or} \quad y = \frac{1}{4}x \quad \text{Divide both sides by 8 and simplify.}$$

If we choose a value for x that is a multiple of 4, we will have a y-coordinate that is an integer. We will use $x = 4$ and $x = -4$, although many other choices would work.

$x = 4$	$x = -4$
$y = \dfrac{1}{4}(4)$	$y = \dfrac{1}{4}(-4)$
$y = 1$	$y = -1$
$(4, 1)$	$(-4, -1)$

Quick Check 6

Graph $y = 3x$. Label any intercepts.

Here is the graph.

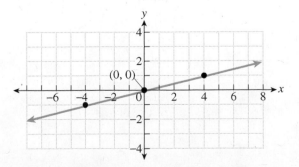

Horizontal Lines

Objective 5 Graph horizontal lines. Can we draw a line that does not cross the x-axis? Yes; here is an example.

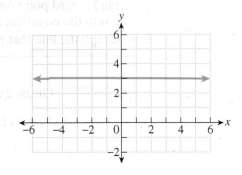

What is the equation of the line in this graph? Notice that each point has the same y-coordinate (3). The equation for the line is $y = 3$. The equation for a horizontal line is always of the form $y = b$, where b is a real number. To graph the line $y = b$, plot the y-intercept $(0, b)$ on the y-axis and draw a horizontal line through this point.

EXAMPLE 7   Graph $y = -2$. Label any intercepts.

SOLUTION   This graph will be a horizontal line, as its equation is of the form $y = b$. If an equation does not have a term containing the variable x, its graph will be a horizontal line.

   Begin by plotting the point $(0, -2)$, which is the y-intercept. Then draw a horizontal line through this point.

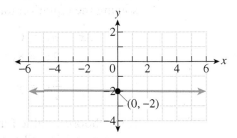

Quick Check 7

Graph $y = 7$. Label any intercepts.

Vertical Lines

Objective 6 Graph vertical lines. Vertical lines have equations of the form $x = a$, where a is a real number. Just as the equation of a horizontal line does not have any terms containing the variable x, the equation of a vertical line does not have any terms containing the variable y. We begin to graph an equation of this form by plotting its x-intercept at $(a, 0)$. Then we draw a vertical line through this point.

EXAMPLE 8   Graph $x = 6$. Label any intercepts.

SOLUTION   The x-intercept for this line is at $(6, 0)$. Plot this point and draw a vertical line through it.

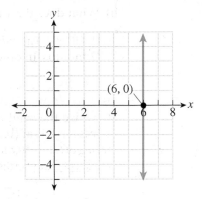

Quick Check 8

Graph $x = -15$. Label any intercepts.

Horizontal Lines	**Vertical Lines**
Equation: $y = b$	Equation: $x = a$
• Plot the y-intercept at $(0, b)$.	• Plot the x-intercept at $(a, 0)$.
• Graph the horizontal line passing through this point.	• Graph the vertical line passing through this point.

Applications of the Graphs of Linear Equations

Objective 7 Interpret the graph of an applied linear equation. The intercepts of a graph have important interpretations in the context of an applied problem. The y-intercept often provides an initial condition, such as the amount of money owed on a loan or the fixed costs to attend college before the number of units that a student is taking are added in. The x-intercept often provides a break-even point, such as when a business goes from a loss to a profit.

EXAMPLE 9   Chelsea borrowed $3600 from her friend Mack, promising to pay him $50 per month until she had paid off the loan. The amount of money (y) that Chelsea owes Mack after x months have passed is given by the equation $y = 3600 - 50x$.

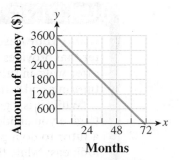

Use the graph of this equation to answer the following questions. (Because the number of months cannot be negative, the graph begins at $x = 0$.)

a) What does the *y*-intercept represent in this situation?

SOLUTION The *y*-intercept is at $(0, 3600)$. It tells us that zero months after borrowing the money from Mack, Chelsea owes him $3600.

b) What does the *x*-intercept represent in this situation?

SOLUTION The *x*-intercept is at $(72, 0)$. It tells us that Chelsea will owe Mack $0 in 72 months. In other words, her debt will be paid.

Using Your Calculator When graphing a line using the TI-84, you may need to resize the window. In Example 9, the *x*-intercept is at the point $(72, 0)$ and the *y*-intercept is at $(0, 3600)$. The graph should show these important points. After entering $3600 - 50x$ for Y_1, press the WINDOW key. Fill in the screen as follows and press the GRAPH key to display the graph.

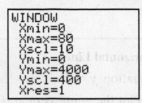 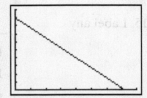

▶ Quick Check 9

Nancy invests $10,000 in a new business and expects to make a $2000 profit each month. Nancy's net profit (y) after x months have passed is given by the equation $y = 2000x - 10,000$.

Use the graph of this equation to answer the following questions. (Because the number of months cannot be negative, the graph begins at $x = 0$.)

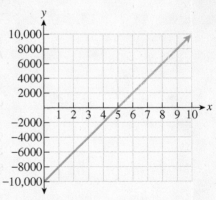

a) What does the *y*-intercept represent in this situation?

b) What does the *x*-intercept represent in this situation?

BUILDING YOUR STUDY STRATEGY

Using Your Resources, 2 Tutors Most college campuses have a tutorial center that provides free tutoring in math and other subjects. Some tutorial centers offer walk-in tutoring, others schedule appointments for one-on-one or group tutoring, and some combine these approaches.

While it is a good idea to ask a tutor if you are doing a problem correctly or to give you an idea of a starting point for a problem, it is not a good idea to ask a tutor to do a problem for you. You learn by doing, not by watching. It may look easy while the tutor is working a problem, but this will not help you do the next problem. If you do not understand a tutor's answer or directions, do not be afraid to ask for further explanation.

Exercises 3.2

PRACTICE   WATCH   DOWNLOAD   READ   REVIEW

Vocabulary

1. A point at which a graph crosses the *x*-axis is called a(n) _____.

2. A point at which a graph crosses the *y*-axis is called a(n) _____.

3. A(n) _____ line has no *y*-intercept.

4. A(n) _____ line has no *x*-intercept.

5. State the procedure for finding an *x*-intercept.

6. State the procedure for finding an *y*-intercept.

Find the x- and y-intercepts from the graph.

7.
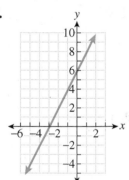

8.
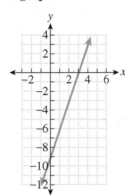

9.
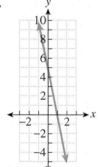

10.
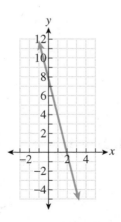

11.
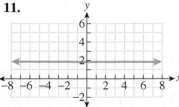

12.
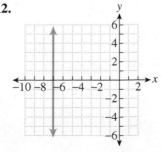

Find the x- and y-intercepts.

13. $x + y = 6$

14. $x + y = -3$

15. $x - y = -8$

16. $x - y = 4$

17. $3x + 2y = 6$

18. $2x + 5y = -10$

19. $-3x + 5y = -30$

20. $2x - 6y = 24$

21. $\frac{3}{5}x + \frac{1}{2}y = 3$

22. $\frac{2}{9}x - \frac{1}{12}y = \frac{2}{3}$

23. $y = -x + 8$

24. $y = x - 5$

25. $y = 3x - 10$

26. $y = -2x + 5$

27. $y = -2x$

28. $y = 3x$

29. $y = 2$

30. $x = 10$

31. Find three equations that have an *x*-intercept at $(4, 0)$.

32. Find three equations that have an *x*-intercept at $(-7, 0)$.

33. Find three equations that have a *y*-intercept at $(0, -10)$.

34. Find three equations that have a *y*-intercept at $(0, 2)$.

Find the intercepts and then graph the line.

35. $x + y = 4$

36. $x + y = -2$

37. $x - y = -3$

38. $x - y = 6$

45. $y = x - 4$

46. $y = x + 6$

39. $2x - 5y = 10$

40. $-4x + 2y = 8$

47. $y = -2x + 7$

48. $y = 4x - 2$

41. $3x + 4y = -24$

42. $6x + 5y = -30$

49. $y = 5x$

50. $y = -4x$

43. $-4x + 7y = 14$

44. $3x - 4y = 18$

51. $2x - 3y = 0$

52. $3x + 5y = 0$

53. $y = 4$ **54.** $y = -6$

55. $x = 3$ **56.** $x = -8$

57. A lawyer bought a new copy machine for her office in 2010, paying $12,000. For tax purposes, the copy machine depreciates at $1500 per year. If you let x represent the number of years after 2010, the value of the copier (y) after x years is given by the equation $y = 12,000 - 1500x$.

  a) Find the y-intercept of this equation. In your own words, explain what this intercept signifies.

  b) Find the x-intercept of this equation. In your own words, explain what this intercept signifies.

  c) In 2013, what will be the value of the copy machine?

58. Jerry was ordered to perform 400 hours of community service as a reading tutor. Jerry spends eight hours each Saturday teaching people to read. The equation that tells the number of hours (y) that remain on the sentence after x Saturdays is $y = 400 - 8x$.

  a) Find the y-intercept of this equation. In your own words, explain what this intercept signifies.

  b) Find the x-intercept of this equation. In your own words, explain what this intercept signifies.

  c) After 12 Saturdays, how many hours of community service does Jerry have remaining?

59. A public golf course charges a $300 annual fee to belong to its club. Members of the club pay $24 to play a round of golf. The equation that gives the cost (y) to belong to the club and to play x rounds of golf per year is $y = 300 + 24x$.

  a) Find the y-intercept of this equation. In your own words, explain what this intercept signifies.

  b) In your own words, explain why this equation has no x-intercept in the context of this problem.

  c) Find the total cost for a club member who plays 50 rounds of golf.

60. In addition to paying $185 per unit, a community college student pays a registration fee of $200 per semester. The equation that gives the cost (y) to take x units is $y = 185x + 200$.

  a) Find the y-intercept of this equation. In the context of this problem, is this cost possible? Explain.

  b) In your own words, explain why this equation has no x-intercept in the context of this problem.

  c) A full load for a student is 12 units. How much will a full-time student pay per semester?

Writing in Mathematics

Answer in complete sentences.

61. ***Solutions Manual*** Write a solutions manual page for the following problem:

  Find the x- and y-intercepts and then graph the line $3x - 4y = 18$.

Quick Review Exercises

Section 3.2

Solve for y.

1. $2x + y = 8$

2. $4x - y = 6$

3. $-8x + 2y = 10$

4. $4x + 6y = 12$

3.3

Slope of a Line

OBJECTIVES

1. Understand the slope of a line.
2. Find the slope of a line from its graph.
3. Find the slope of a line passing through two points using the slope formula.
4. Find the slopes of horizontal and vertical lines.
5. Find the slope and *y*-intercept of a line from its equation.
6. Find the equation of a line given its slope and *y*-intercept.
7. Graph a line using its slope and *y*-intercept.
8. Interpret the slope and *y*-intercept in real-world applications.

Slope of a Line

Objective 1 Understand the slope of a line. Here are four different lines that pass through the point $(0, 2)$.

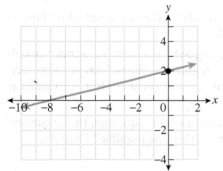 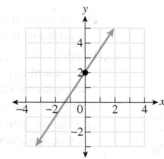 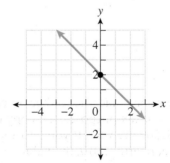 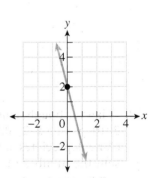

Notice that some of the lines are rising to the right, while others are falling to the right. Also, some are rising or falling more steeply than others. The characteristic that distinguishes these lines is their slope.

> **Slope**
>
> The **slope** of a line is a measure of how steeply a line rises or falls as it moves to the right. We use the letter *m* to represent the slope of a line.

If a line rises as it moves to the right, its slope is positive. If a line falls as it moves to the right, its slope is negative.

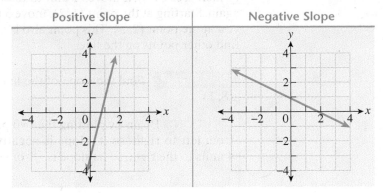

To find the slope of a line, we begin by selecting two points that are on the line. As we move from the point on the left to the point on the right, we measure how much the line rises or falls. The slope is equal to this vertical distance divided by the distance traveled from left to right. This is often referred to as "rise over run," or as the change in y divided by the change in x. Sometimes the change in y is written as Δy and the change in x is written as Δx. The Greek letter Δ (delta) is often used to represent change in a quantity. The slope of a line is represented as

$$m = \frac{\text{rise}}{\text{run}}, \quad \text{or} \quad m = \frac{\Delta y}{\Delta x}.$$

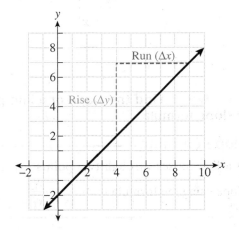
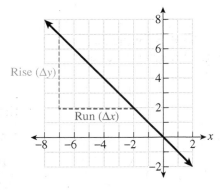

Finding the Slope of a Line from Its Graph

Objective ② **Find the slope of a line from its graph.** Consider the following line that passes through the points $(1, 2)$ and $(3, 8)$. To move from the point on the left to the point on the right, the line rises by 6 units as it moves 2 units to the right.

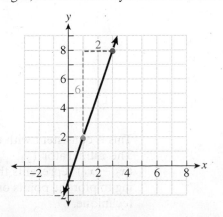

The slope m is $\frac{6}{2}$, or 3. When $m = 3$, every time the line moves up by 3 units (y increases by 3), it moves 1 unit to the right (x increases by 1). Look at the graph again. Starting at the point $(1, 2)$, move 3 units up and 1 unit to the right. This places you at the point $(2, 5)$. This point also is on the line. We can continue this pattern to find other points on the line.

EXAMPLE 1   Find the slope of the line that passes through the points $(4, 9)$ and $(8, 1)$.

SOLUTION   Begin by plotting the two points on a graph. Notice that this line falls from left to right, so its slope is negative. The line drops by 8 units as it moves 4 units to the right, so its slope is $\frac{-8}{4}$, or -2.

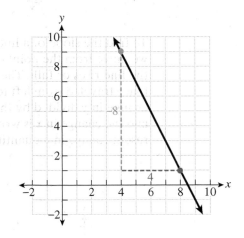

Quick Check 1

Find the slope of the line that passes through $(-2, 5)$ and $(4, -7)$.

Slope Formula

Objective 3 Find the slope of a line passing through two points using the slope formula.

> ### Slope Formula
>
> If a line passes through two points (x_1, y_1) and (x_2, y_2), we can calculate its slope using the formula $m = \dfrac{y_2 - y_1}{x_2 - x_1}$.

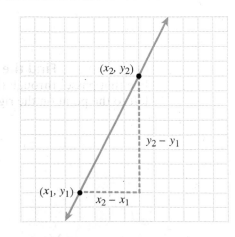

This is consistent with the technique we used to find slope in the previous example. The numerator $(y_2 - y_1)$ represents the vertical change, while the denominator $(x_2 - x_1)$ represents the horizontal change. Using this formula saves us from having to plot the points on a graph, but keep in mind that you can continue to use that technique.

We have seen that the slope of a line that passes through the points $(1, 2)$ and $(3, 8)$ is 3. Now we will use the formula $m = \dfrac{y_2 - y_1}{x_2 - x_1}$ to find the slope of the line through these two points. We will use the point $(1, 2)$ as (x_1, y_1) and the point $(3, 8)$ as (x_2, y_2).

$$m = \frac{8 - 2}{3 - 1}$$
$$= \frac{6}{2}$$
$$= 3$$

Notice that we get the same result as before. We could change the ordering of the points and still calculate the same slope. In other words, we could use the point $(3, 8)$ as (x_1, y_1) and the point $(1, 2)$ as (x_2, y_2) and still find that $m = 3$. We can subtract in either order as long as we are consistent. Whichever order we use to subtract the y-coordinates, we must subtract the x-coordinates in the same order.

EXAMPLE 2 Use the formula $m = \dfrac{y_2 - y_1}{x_2 - x_1}$ to find the slope of the line that passes through the points $(1, 7)$ and $(4, 3)$.

SOLUTION   One way to think of the numerator in this formula is *the second y-coordinate minus the first y-coordinate,* which, in the example, is $3 - 7$. Using a similar approach for the x-coordinates in the denominator, we begin with a denominator of $4 - 1$.

$$m = \frac{3 - 7}{4 - 1} \qquad \text{Substitute into the formula.}$$

$$= \frac{-4}{3} \qquad \text{Simplify numerator and denominator.}$$

The slope of the line that passes through these two points is $-\frac{4}{3}$. This line falls 4 units for every 3 units it moves to the right.

Quick Check 2

Use the formula $m = \dfrac{y_2 - y_1}{x_2 - x_1}$ to find the slope of the line that passes through the points $(1, 2)$ and $(5, 14)$.

A WORD OF CAUTION It does not matter which point is labeled as (x_1, y_1) and which point is labeled as (x_2, y_2). It *is* important that the order in which the y-coordinates are subtracted in the numerator is the order in which the x-coordinates are subtracted in the denominator.

EXAMPLE 3 Use the formula $m = \dfrac{y_2 - y_1}{x_2 - x_1}$ to find the slope of the line that passes through the points $(-5, -2)$ and $(-1, 4)$.

SOLUTION   In this example, we learn to apply the formula to points that have negative x- or y-coordinates.

$$m = \frac{4 - (-2)}{-1 - (-5)} \qquad \text{Substitute into the formula.}$$

$$= \frac{4 + 2}{-1 + 5} \qquad \text{Eliminate double signs.}$$

$$= \frac{6}{4} \qquad \text{Simplify numerator and denominator.}$$

$$= \frac{3}{2} \qquad \text{Simplify.}$$

Quick Check 3

Use the formula $m = \dfrac{y_2 - y_1}{x_2 - x_1}$ to find the slope of the line that passes through the points $(-3, 5)$ and $(1, -5)$.

The slope of this line is $\frac{3}{2}$. The line rises by 3 units for every 2 units it moves to the right.

Horizontal and Vertical Lines

Objective 4 **Find the slopes of horizontal and vertical lines.** Let's look at the horizontal line $y = 3$ that passes through the points $(1, 3)$ and $(4, 3)$.

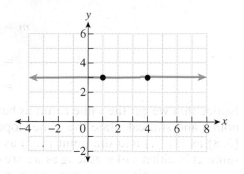

What is its slope?

$$m = \frac{3 - 3}{4 - 1}$$
$$= \frac{0}{3}$$
$$= 0$$

The slope of this line is 0. The same is true for any horizontal line. The vertical change between any two points on a horizontal line is always equal to 0, and when we divide 0 by any nonzero number, the result is equal to 0. Thus, the slope of any horizontal line is equal to 0.

Here is a brief summary of the properties of horizontal lines.

> **Horizontal Lines**
>
> Equation: $y = b$, where b is a real number
> y-intercept: $(0, b)$
> Slope: $m = 0$

Look at the following vertical line:

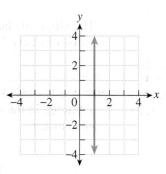

Notice that each point on this line has an x-coordinate of $x = 1$. We can attempt to find the slope of this line by selecting any two points on the line, such as $(1, 2)$ and $(1, 5)$, and using the slope formula.

$$m = \frac{5 - 2}{1 - 1}$$
$$= \frac{3}{0}$$

The fraction $\frac{3}{0}$ is undefined. Thus, the slope of a vertical line is said to be undefined.

Here is a brief summary of the properties of vertical lines.

> **Vertical Lines**
>
> Equation: $x = a$, where a is a real number
> x-intercept: $(a, 0)$
> Slope: Undefined

EXAMPLE 4   Find the slope, if it exists, of the line $x = -2$.

SOLUTION   This line is a vertical line. The slope of a vertical line is undefined, so this line has undefined slope.

Quick Check 4

Find the slope, if it exists, of the line $x = 5$.

EXAMPLE 5   Find the slope, if it exists, of the line $y = 4$.

SOLUTION   This line is a horizontal line. The slope of any horizontal line is 0, so the slope of this line is 0.

Quick Check 5

Find the slope, if it exists, of the line $y = -2$.

A WORD OF CAUTION Avoid stating that a line has "no slope." This is a vague phrase; some may take it to mean that the slope is equal to 0, while others may interpret it as meaning that the slope is undefined.

Slope–Intercept Form of a Line

Objective 5 **Find the slope and y-intercept of a line from its equation.**
If we solve a given equation for y so that it is in the form $y = mx + b$, this is the **slope–intercept form** of a line. The number being multiplied by x is the slope m, while b represents the y-coordinate of the y-intercept.

> **Slope–Intercept Form of a Line**
>
> $y = mx + b$
> m: Slope of the line
> b: y-coordinate of the y-intercept

To verify that the y-intercept is $(0, b)$, substitute 0 for x in the equation $y = mx + b$.

$$y = mx + b$$
$$y = m(0) + b$$
$$y = b$$

To verify that the slope is the coefficient of the x-term, let's look at the equation $y = 2x + 5$ by creating a table of values, as shown to the left.

Notice that the y-values increase by 2 as the x-values increase by 1; so the slope is 2.

x	$y = 2x + 5$	(x, y)
0	$y = 2(0) + 5 = 5$	$(0, 5)$
1	$y = 2(1) + 5 = 7$	$(1, 7)$
2	$y = 2(2) + 5 = 9$	$(2, 9)$
3	$y = 2(3) + 5 = 11$	$(3, 11)$

EXAMPLE 6   Find the slope and y-intercept of the line $y = -3x + 7$.

SOLUTION   Because this equation is already solved for y, we can read the slope and the y-intercept directly from the equation. The slope is -3, which is the coefficient of the term containing x in the equation. The y-intercept is $(0, 7)$ because 7 is the constant in the equation.

Quick Check 6

Find the slope and the y-intercept of the line $y = \frac{5}{2}x - 6$.

EXAMPLE 7   Find the slope and y-intercept of the line $2x + 2y = 11$.

SOLUTION   Begin by solving for y.

$$2x + 2y = 11$$
$$2y = -2x + 11 \quad \text{Subtract } 2x \text{ from both sides.}$$
$$\frac{2y}{2} = \frac{-2x}{2} + \frac{11}{2} \quad \text{Divide each term by 2.}$$
$$y = -x + \frac{11}{2} \quad \text{Simplify.}$$

Quick Check 7

Find the slope and the y-intercept of the line $6x + 2y = 10$.

The slope of this line is -1. When we see $-x$ in the equation, we need to remember that this is the same as $-1x$. The y-intercept is $\left(0, \frac{11}{2}\right)$.

A WORD OF CAUTION We cannot determine the slope and y-intercept of a line from its equation unless the equation has already been solved for y first.

Objective ⑥ Find the equation of a line given its slope and y-intercept.

EXAMPLE 8 Find the equation of a line that has a slope of 2 and a y-intercept of $(0, -15)$.

<u>SOLUTION</u> We will use the slope–intercept form $(y = mx + b)$ to help us find the equation of this line. Because the slope is 2, we can replace m with 2. Also, because the y-intercept is $(0, -15)$, we can replace b with -15. The equation of this line is $y = 2x - 15$.

Quick Check 8

Find the equation of a line that has a slope of $\frac{1}{2}$ and a y-intercept of $\left(0, -\frac{4}{7}\right)$.

Graphing a Line Using Its Slope and y-Intercept

Objective ⑦ Graph a line using its slope and y-intercept. Once we have an equation in slope–intercept form, we can use this information to graph the line. We can begin by plotting the y-intercept as the first point. We can then use the slope of the line to find a second point.

> **Graphing a Line Using Its Slope and y-Intercept**
> - Plot the y-intercept $(0, b)$
> - Use the slope m to find another point on the line.
> - Graph the line that passes through these two points.

EXAMPLE 9 Graph the line $y = -4x + 8$ using its slope and y-intercept.

<u>SOLUTION</u> We will start at the y-intercept, which is $(0, 8)$. Because the slope is -4, the line moves down 4 units as it moves 1 unit to the right. This gives us a second point at $(1, 4)$. Here is the graph.

Quick Check 9

Graph the line $y = 2x + 6$ using its slope and y-intercept.

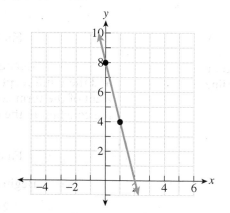

EXAMPLE 10 Graph the line $y = \frac{1}{2}x - 3$ using its slope and y-intercept.

SOLUTION   We will start by plotting the y-intercept at $(0, -3)$. The slope is $\frac{1}{2}$, which tells us that the line rises by 1 unit as it moves 2 units to the right. This will give us a second point at $(2, -2)$.

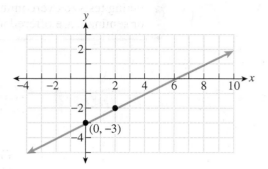

Quick Check 10

Graph the line $y = -\frac{2}{3}x + 4$ using its slope and y-intercept.

We have two techniques for graphing lines that are not horizontal or vertical lines. We can graph a line by finding its x- and y-intercepts or by using the y-intercept and the slope of the line. There are certain times when one technique is more efficient to apply than the other, and knowing which technique to use for a particular linear equation can save time and prevent errors. In general, if the equation is already solved for y, such as $y = 3x + 7$ or $y = -4x + 5$, graphing the line using the y-intercept and the slope is a good choice. If the equation is not already solved for y, such as $2x + 3y = 12$ or $5x - 2y = -10$, consider finding both the x- and y-intercepts and then drawing the line that passes through these two points.

Applications

Objective **8** **Interpret the slope and y-intercept in real-world applications.** The concept of slope becomes more important when we apply it to real-world situations.

EXAMPLE 11   The number of Americans (y), in millions, who have cell phones can be approximated by the equation $y = 13x + 77$, where x is the number of years after 1999. Interpret the slope and y-intercept of this line. (*Source: Cellular Telecommunications Industry Association*)

SOLUTION   The slope of this line is 13, which tells us that each year we can expect an additional 13 million Americans to have cell phones. (The number of Americans who have cell phones is increasing because the slope is positive.) The y-intercept at $(0, 77)$ tells us that approximately 77 million Americans had cell phones in 1999.

▸ Quick Check 11

The number of women (y) accepted to medical school in a given year can be approximated by the equation $y = 218x + 7485$, where x is the number of years after 1997. Interpret the slope and y-intercept of this line. (*Source: Association of American Medical Colleges*)

BUILDING YOUR STUDY STRATEGY

Using Your Resources, 3 Study Skills Courses Some colleges run short-term study skills courses or seminars, and these courses can be helpful to students who are learning mathematics. These courses cover everything from taking notes and taking tests to overcoming math anxiety. To find out whether study skill courses or seminars are offered at your school, talk to an academic counselor.

Exercises 3.3

MyMathLab

 PRACTICE

 WATCH

 DOWNLOAD

 READ

REVIEW

Vocabulary

1. The _____ of a line is a measure of how steeply a line rises or falls as it moves to the right.

2. A line that rises from left to right has _____ slope.

3. A line that falls from left to right has _____ slope.

4. State the formula for the slope of a line that passes through two points.

5. A(n) _____ line has a slope of 0.

6. The slope of a(n) _____ line is undefined.

7. The _____ form of the equation of a line is $y = mx + b$.

8. So that the slope of a line can be determined from its equation, the equation must be solved for _____.

Determine whether the given line has a positive or negative slope.

9.
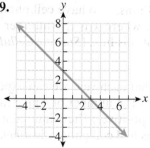

10.
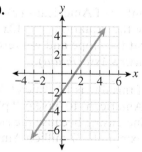

11.

12.
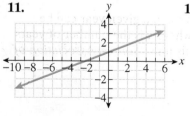

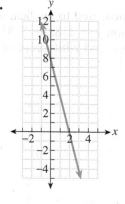

Find the slope of the given line. If the slope is undefined, state this.

13.
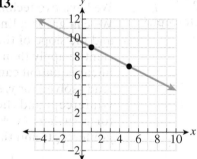

14.
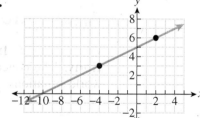

15.

16.
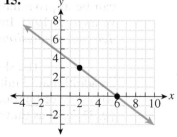
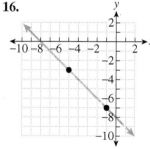

17.

18.
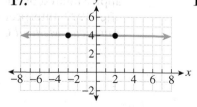
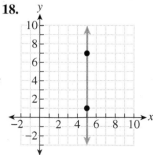

Find the slope of a line that passes through the given two points. If the slope is undefined, state this.

19. $(3, 5)$ and $(4, 7)$

20. $(2, 6)$ and $(3, 1)$

21. $(-2, 3)$ and $(-5, -6)$

22. $(5, -4)$ and $(-1, 5)$

23. $(13, -6)$ and $(7, 2)$

24. $(-11, -4)$ and $(-7, 6)$

25. $(-32, 15)$ and $(-24, -3)$

26. $(46, 33)$ and $(19, 24)$

27. $(3, 6)$ and $(-4, 6)$

28. $(-2, -6)$ and $(2, 6)$

29. $(0, 4)$ and $(0, 7)$

30. $(0, 0)$ and $(4, 7)$

Graph. Label any intercepts and determine the slope of the line. If the slope is undefined, state this.

31. $y = 4$ **32.** $x = -2$

33. $x = 3$ **34.** $y = -\dfrac{17}{5}$

35. $x = 8$ **36.** $y = -3$

Determine the equation of the given line as well as the slope of the line. If the slope is undefined, state this.

37.

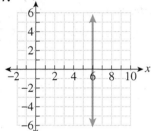

38.

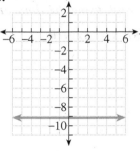

39.

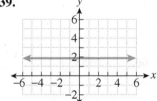

40.

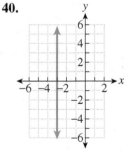

Find the slope and the y-intercept of the given line.

41. $y = 6x - 7$

42. $y = 4x + 11$

43. $y = -2x + 3$

44. $y = -5x - 8$

45. $6x + 4y = -10$

46. $2x + 3y = -12$

47. $5x - 8y = 10$

48. $8x - 6y = 12$

49. $x - 5y = 8$

50. $x + 4y = 14$

Find the equation of a line with the given slope and y-intercept.

51. Slope -2, y-intercept $(0, 5)$
52. Slope 4, y-intercept $(0, 3)$
53. Slope 3, y-intercept $(0, -6)$
54. Slope -5, y-intercept $(0, -2)$
55. Slope 0, y-intercept $(0, -4)$
56. Slope 0, y-intercept $(0, 1)$

Graph using the slope and y-intercept.

57. $y = 3x + 6$ **58.** $y = 2x - 8$

59. $y = -2x - 6$ **60.** $y = -5x + 10$

61. $y = x - 3$ **62.** $y = -x - 1$

63. $y = 4x$ **64.** $y = -2x$

65. $y = \dfrac{7}{2}x - 7$ **66.** $y = -\dfrac{5}{4}x + 10$

67. $3y = -9x - 6$ **68.** $2y = 4x + 10$

69. $-5x + 4y = 8$

70. $2x + 5y = -25$

Mixed Practice, 71–88

Graph using the most efficient technique, finding the x- and y-intercepts or using the slope and y-intercept.

71. $y = -x + 2$

72. $y = -\dfrac{1}{4}x + 2$

73. $y = -2x + 8$

74. $y = -3x + 7$

75. $y = 6x - 9$

76. $y = -2$

77. $y = -x - 5$

78. $y = -5x$

79. $3x - 2y = -12$

80. $2x + 5y = 15$

81. $y = \dfrac{4}{5}x$

82. $x = \dfrac{9}{2}$

83. $y = 4$

84. $x = -3$

85. $3x + y = 1$

86. $y = \dfrac{2}{5}x + 1$

87. $5x - y = -5$ **88.** $-8x + 2y = -10$

Graph the two lines and find the coordinates of the point of intersection.

89. $y = 3x - 6$ and $y = -x - 2$

90. $5x - 4y = 20$ and $y = \dfrac{1}{2}x + 1$

91. The value y of Dave's car x years after 2008 is given by the equation $y = -3000x + 25{,}000$.

  a) Find the slope of the equation. In your own words, explain what this slope signifies.

  b) Find the y-intercept of the equation. In your own words, explain what this y-intercept signifies.

  c) Use this equation to predict the value of the car in 2014.

92. The number of nursing students enrolled in accelerated beaccelereate programs x years after 2004 can be

approximated by the equation $y = 1200x + 6090$. (Based on 2004–2008 data. *Source: American Association of Colleges of Nursing*)

  a) Find the slope of the equation. In your own words, explain what this slope signifies.

  b) Find the y-intercept of the equation. In your own words, explain what this y-intercept signifies.

  c) Use this equation to predict the number of nursing students enrolled in accelerated baccalaureate programs in 2016.

93. The **pitch** of a roof is measure of its slope, dividing the vertical rise by the horizontal span.

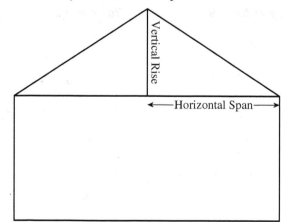

Find the pitch of the roof.

a)

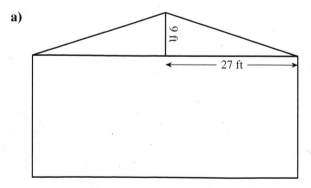

b)

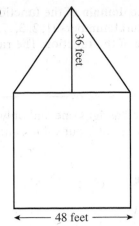

36 feet

←—— 48 feet ——→

94. A contractor is building a square house that is 72 feet wide. If he wants the pitch of the roof to be $\frac{1}{3}$, what will be the vertical rise of the roof?

95. On a 1000-foot stretch of highway through the mountains, the road rises by a total of 50 feet. Find the slope of the road.

96. George walked 1 mile (5280 feet) on a treadmill. The grade was set to 4%, which means that the slope of the treadmill is 4%, or 0.04. Over the course of his workout, how many feet did George climb (vertically)?

 Writing in Mathematics

Answer in complete sentences.

97. The governor of a state predicts that unemployment rates will increase for the next five years. Would an equation relating unemployment rate (y) to the number of years after the statement was made (x) have a positive or negative slope? Explain.

98. Consider the equations $y = -\frac{3}{8}x + 7$ and $20x - 8y = 320$. For each equation, do you believe that finding the x- and y-intercepts or using the slope and y-intercept is the most efficient way to graph the equation? Explain your choices.

99. *Solutions Manual* Write a solutions manual page for the following problem:

Find the slope of the line that passes through the points $(-2, 6)$ *and* $(4, -8)$.

3.4

Linear Functions

OBJECTIVES

1 Define *function, domain,* and *range.*
2 Evaluate functions.
3 Graph linear functions.
4 Interpret the graph of a linear function.
5 Determine the domain and range of a function from its graph.

A coffeehouse sells coffee for $2 per cup. We know that it would cost $4 to buy 2 cups, $6 for 3 cups, $8 for 4 cups, and so on. We also know that the general formula for the cost of x cups in dollars is $2 \cdot x$. The cost depends on the number of cups bought. We say that the cost is a function of the number of cups bought.

Functions; Domain and Range

Objective 1 Define *function, domain,* and *range.* A **relation** is a rule that takes an input value from one set and assigns a particular output value from another set to it. A relation for which each input value is assigned one and only one output value is called a **function**. In the example about coffee, the input value is the number of cups of coffee bought and the output value is the cost. For each number of cups bought, there is only one possible cost. The rule for determining the cost is to multiply the number of cups by $2.

Cups	1	2	3	4	...	x	...
	↓	↓	↓	↓	...	↓	
Cost	$2	$4	$6	$8		$2 \cdot x$	

The set of input values for a function is called the **domain** of the function. The domain for the example about coffee is the set of natural numbers {1, 2, 3, ...}. The set of output values for a function is called the **range** of the function. The range of the function in the coffee example is {2, 4, 6, ...}.

Function, Domain, and Range

A **function** is a relation that takes an input value and assigns one and only one output value to it. The **domain** of the function is the set of input values, and the **range** is the set of output values.

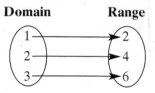

If an input value can be associated with more than one output value, the relation is not a function. For example, a relation that took a month of the year as its input and listed the people at your school who were born that month as its output would not be a function because each month has more than one person born in that month.

EXAMPLE 1 A mail-order company is selling holiday ornaments for $4 each. There is an additional $4.95 charge per order for shipping and handling. Find the function for the total cost of an order as well as the domain and range of the function.

SOLUTION To determine the cost of an order, we begin by multiplying the number of ornaments by $4. To this we still need to add $4.95 for shipping and handling.

Function: If n is the number of ornaments ordered, the cost is $4n + 4.95$.
Domain: Set of possible number of ornaments ordered {1, 2, 3, ...}
Range: Set of possible costs of the orders {$8.95, $12.95, $16.95, ...}

▶ Quick Check 1
A rental agency rents small moving trucks for $19.95 plus $0.15 per mile. Find the function for the total cost to rent a truck as well as the domain and range of the function.

Function Notation

The perimeter of a square with side x can be found using the formula $P = 4x$. This is a function that also can be expressed as $P(x) = 4x$ using function notation. **Function notation** is a way to present the output value of a function for the input x. The notation on the left side, $P(x)$, tells us the name of the function, P, as well as the input variable, x. $P(x)$ tells us that P is a function of x and is read as P *of* x. The parentheses on the left side are used to identify the input variable, not to indicate multiplication. Although we used P as the name of the function (P for perimeter), we could have used any letter. The letters f and g are frequently used for function names. The expression on the right side, $4x$, is the formula for the function.

$$P(x) = 4x \qquad\qquad P(x) = 4x \qquad\qquad P(x) = 4x$$
$$\uparrow \qquad\qquad\qquad\qquad \uparrow \qquad\qquad\qquad\qquad \uparrow$$

The variable inside the parentheses is the input variable for the function.	$P(x)$ is the output value of the function P when the input value is x.	The expression on the right side of the equation is the formula for this function.

Evaluating Functions

Objective 2 Evaluate functions. Suppose we wanted to find the perimeter of a square with a side of 3 inches. We are looking to evaluate the perimeter function, $P(x) = 4x$, for an input of 3, or, in other words, $P(3)$. Finding the output value of a function for a particular value of x is called **evaluating** the function. To evaluate a function for a particular value of the variable, we substitute that value for the variable in the function's formula and then simplify the resulting expression. To evaluate $P(3)$, we substitute 3 for x in the formula and simplify the resulting expression.

$$P(x) = 4x$$
$$P(3) = 4(3)$$
$$= 12$$

Because $P(3) = 12$, the perimeter is 12 inches.

EXAMPLE 2   Let $f(x) = 3x + 7$. Find $f(4)$.

SOLUTION   We need to replace x in the function's formula by 4 and simplify the resulting expression.

$$f(4) = 3(4) + 7 \quad \text{Substitute 4 for } x.$$
$$= 19 \qquad\qquad \text{Simplify.}$$

$f(4) = 19$. This means that when the input is $x = 4$, the output of the function is 19.

EXAMPLE 3   Let $g(x) = \dfrac{2}{3}x - 8$. Find $g(-9)$.

SOLUTION   In this example, we need to replace x with -9. As the functions become more complicated, we should use parentheses when substituting the input value.

$$g(-9) = \frac{2}{3}(-9) - 8 \quad \text{Substitute } -9 \text{ for } x.$$
$$= -6 - 8 \qquad\quad \text{Multiply.}$$
$$= -14 \qquad\qquad \text{Simplify.}$$

Quick Check 2

Let $g(x) = 2x + 9$. Find $g(-6)$.

EXAMPLE 4   Let $g(x) = 8 - 3x$. Find $g(a + 3)$.

SOLUTION   In this example, we are substituting a variable expression for x in the function. After we replace x with $a + 3$, we need to simplify the resulting variable expression.

$$g(a + 3) = 8 - 3(a + 3) \quad \text{Replace } x \text{ with } a + 3.$$
$$= 8 - 3a - 9 \qquad \text{Distribute } -3.$$
$$= -3a - 1 \qquad\quad \text{Combine like terms.}$$

Quick Check 3

Let $g(x) = 7x - 12$. Find $g(a + 8)$.

Linear Functions and Their Graphs

Objective 3 Graph linear functions.

> A **linear function** is a function of the form $f(x) = mx + b$, where m and b are real numbers.

Some examples of linear functions are $f(x) = x - 9$, $f(x) = 5x$, $f(x) = 3x + 11$, and $f(x) = 6$. We now turn our attention to graphing linear functions. We graph any function $f(x)$ by plotting points of the form $(x, f(x))$. The output value of the function $f(x)$ is treated as the variable y was when we were graphing linear equations in two variables. When we graph a function $f(x)$, the vertical axis is used to represent the output values of the function.

We can begin to graph a linear function by finding the y-intercept. As with a linear equation that is in slope–intercept form, the y-intercept for the graph of a linear function $f(x) = mx + b$ is the point $(0, b)$. For example, the y-intercept for the graph of the function $f(x) = 5x - 8$ is the point $(0, -8)$. In general, to find the y-intercept of any function $f(x)$, we can find $f(0)$. After plotting the y-intercept, we can use the slope m to find other points.

EXAMPLE 5 Graph the linear function $f(x) = \frac{1}{2}x + 2$.

Quick Check 4

Graph the linear function $f(x) = \frac{3}{4}x - 6$.

SOLUTION   We can start with the y-intercept, which is $(0, 2)$. The slope of the line is $\frac{1}{2}$; so beginning at the point $(0, 2)$, we move 1 unit up and 2 units to the right. This leads to a second point at $(2, 3)$.

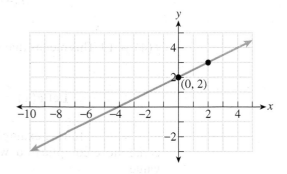

EXAMPLE 6 Graph the linear function $f(x) = -3$.

Quick Check 5

Graph the linear function $f(x) = 4$.

SOLUTION   This function is known as a **constant function**. The function is constantly equal to -3, regardless of the input value x. Its graph is a horizontal line with a y-intercept at $(0, -3)$.

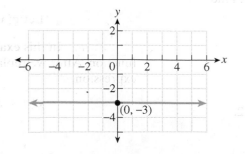

Interpreting the Graph of a Linear Function

Objective ④ **Interpret the graph of a linear function.** Here is the graph of a function $f(x)$.

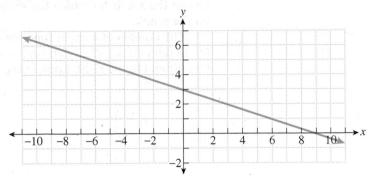

The ability to read and interpret a graph is an important skill. This line has an x-intercept at the point $(9, 0)$, so $f(9) = 0$. The y-intercept is at the point $(0, 3)$, so $f(0) = 3$.

Suppose we wanted to find $f(3)$ for this particular function. We can do so by finding a point on the line that has an x-coordinate of 3. The y-coordinate of this point is $f(3)$. In this case, $f(3) = 2$.

We also can use this graph to solve the equation $f(x) = 6$. Look for the point on the graph that has a y-coordinate of 6. The x-coordinate of this point is -9, so $x = -9$ is the solution of the equation $f(x) = 6$.

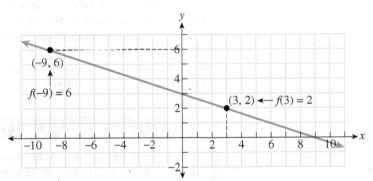

EXAMPLE 7 Consider the graph of the function $f(x)$ to the left.

a) Find $f\left(1\frac{1}{2}\right)$.

SOLUTION   We are looking for a point on the line that has an x-coordinate of $1\frac{1}{2}$. The point is $\left(1\frac{1}{2}, 4\right)$, so $f\left(1\frac{1}{2}\right) = 4$.

b) Find a value x such that $f(x) = 2$.

SOLUTION   We are looking for a point on the line that has a y-coordinate of 2, and this point is $(1, 2)$. The value that satisfies the equation $f(x) = 2$ is $x = 1$.

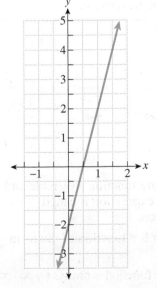

▶ Quick Check 6

Consider the following graph of a function:

a) Find $f(1)$.
b) Find a value x such that $f(x) = -2$.

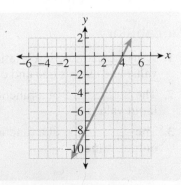

Objective 5 Determine the domain and range of a function from its graph. The domain and range of a function also can be read from a graph. Recall that the domain of a function is the set of all input values. This corresponds to all of the *x*-coordinates of the points on the graph. The domain is the interval of values on the *x*-axis for which the graph exists. We read the domain from left to right on the graph.

The domain of a linear function is the set of all real numbers, which can be written in interval notation as $(-\infty, \infty)$. The graphs of linear functions continue on to the left and to the right. Look at the following three graphs of linear functions.

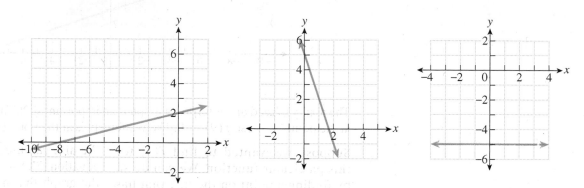

Each line continues to the left as well as to the right. This tells us that the graph exists for all values of *x* in the interval $(-\infty, \infty)$.

The range of a function can be read vertically from a graph. The range goes from the lowest point to the highest point on the graph. All linear functions have $(-\infty, \infty)$ as their range, except constant functions.

Because a constant function of the form $f(x) = c$, where *c* is a real number, has only one possible output value, its range is $\{c\}$. For example, the range of the constant function $f(x) = -5$ is $\{-5\}$.

BUILDING YOUR STUDY STRATEGY

Using Your Resources, 4 Student's Solutions Manual The student's solutions manual for a mathematics textbook can be a valuable resource when used properly, but it can be detrimental to learning when used improperly. You should refer to the solutions manual to check your work or to see where you went wrong when finding the solutions.

However, if you do nothing except essentially copy the solutions manual onto your paper, you will likely have difficulty on the next exam.

Exercises 3.4   MyMathLab

PRACTICE   WATCH   DOWNLOAD   READ   REVIEW

Vocabulary

1. A(n) _____ is a relation that takes one input value and assigns one and only one output value to it.

2. The _____ of a function is the set of all possible input values.

3. The _____ of a function is the set of all possible output values.

4. Substituting a value for the function's variable and simplifying the resulting expression is called _____ the function.

5. A(n) _____ function is a function of the form $f(x) = mx + b$.

6. The _____ of a linear function is always $(-\infty, \infty)$.

The following table contains the names of the nine American League All-Stars from 2008, along with the player's AL team.

Name	Team
Cliff Lee (P)	Cleveland Indians
Joe Mauer (C)	Minnesota Twins
Kevin Youkilis (1B)	Boston Red Sox
Dustin Pedroia (2B)	Boston Red Sox
Derek Jeter (SS)	New York Yankees
Alex Rodriguez (3B)	New York Yankees
Manny Ramirez (LF)	Boston Red Sox
Josh Hamilton (CF)	Texas Rangers
Ichiro Suzuki (RF)	Seattle Mariners

7. Would a relation that took a player's name as an input and listed his AL team as an output be a function? Why or why not?

8. Could a function be defined in the opposite direction, with the name of the AL team as the input and the All-Star player's name as the output? Why or why not?

9. Would a relation that took a person as an input and listed that person's birth mother as an output be a function? Why or why not?

10. Could a function be defined with a woman as an input and her child as an output? Why or why not?

For Exercises 11–14, determine whether a function exists with:
a) *Set A as the input and set B as the output.*
b) *Set B as the input and set A as the output.*

11. High Temperatures on December 16

Set A City	Set B High Temp.
Boston, MA	39° F
Orlando, FL	75° F
Providence, RI	39° F
Rochester, NY	26° F
Visalia, CA	57° F

12.

Set A Person	Set B Last 4 Digits of SSN
Jenny Crum	1234
Maureen O'Connor	5283
Dona Kenly	6405
Michelle Renda	5555
Lauren Morse	9200

13.

Set A Person	Set B Birthday
Greg Erb	December 15
Karen Guardino	December 17
Jolene Lehr	October 15
Siméon Poisson	June 21
Lindsay Skay	May 28
Sharon Smith	June 21

14.

Set A Competitive Eater	Set B Hot Dogs Eaten in 12 Minutes
Joey Chestnut	66
Takeru Kobayashi	63
Pat Bertoletti	49
Tim Janus	43
Sonya Thomas	39

For the given set of ordered pairs, determine whether a function could be defined for which the input would be an x-coordinate and the output would be the corresponding y-coordinate. If a function cannot be defined in this manner, explain why.

15. $\{(-2, 4), (-1, 1), (0, 0), (1, 1), (2, 4), (3, 9)\}$

16. $\{(2, -2), (1, -1), (0, 0), (1, 1), (2, 2)\}$

17. $\{(5, 3), (2, 7), (-4, -6), (5, -2), (0, 4)\}$

18. $\{(-6, 3), (-2, 3), (1, 3), (5, 3), (11, 3)\}$

19. $\{(2, -5), (2, -1), (2, 0), (2, 3), (2, 5)\}$

20. $\{(1, 1), (2, 2), (3, 3), (4, 4), (5, 5)\}$

21. A Celsius temperature can be converted to a Fahrenheit temperature by multiplying it by $\frac{9}{5}$ and then adding 32.

   a) Create a function $F(x)$ that converts a Celsius temperature x to a Fahrenheit temperature.

   b) Use the function $F(x)$ from part a to convert the following Celsius temperatures to Fahrenheit temperatures.

   0° C   100° C   30° C   −10° C   −40° C

22. To convert a Fahrenheit temperature to a Celsius temperature, subtract 32 and then multiply that difference by $\frac{5}{9}$. Create a function $C(x)$ that converts a Fahrenheit temperature x to a Celsius temperature.

23. A college student takes a summer job selling newspaper subscriptions door-to-door. She is paid $36 for a four-hour shift. She also earns $7 for each subscription sold.

  a) Create a function $f(x)$ for the amount she earns on a shift during which she sells x subscriptions.

  b) Use the function $f(x)$ to determine how much she earns on a shift during which she sells 12 subscriptions.

24. A cell phone carrier offers a plan with a $29.99 monthly fee and charges $0.40 per minute for each minute above 300 minutes for the month.

  a) Create a function $f(x)$ for the amount a person pays in a month if he or she uses x minutes above 300 minutes that month.

  b) Use the function $f(x)$ to determine the monthly bill for a subscriber who used 850 minutes last month.

25. Create a linear function whose graph has a slope of 4 and a y-intercept at $(0, 3)$.

26. Create a linear function whose graph has a slope of 5 and a y-intercept at $(0, -9)$.

27. Create a linear function whose graph has a slope of -3 and a y-intercept at $(0, -4)$.

28. Create a linear function whose graph has a slope of $-\frac{1}{2}$ and a y-intercept at $(0, \frac{2}{3})$.

29. Create a linear function whose graph has a slope of 0 and a y-intercept at $(0, 6)$.

30. Create a linear function whose graph has a slope of 0 and a y-intercept at $(0, 0)$.

Evaluate the given function.

31. $g(x) = x - 9, g(-13)$

32. $h(x) = 4x, h(-9)$

33. $f(x) = -8x + 3, f(10)$

34. $f(x) = 6x + 7, f(18)$

35. $f(x) = -\frac{2}{5}x + 9, f(-10)$

36. $f(x) = \frac{3}{4}x + 6, f(-20)$

37. $f(x) = 9x - 25, f(0)$

38. $f(x) = 6x + 13, f(0)$

39. $g(x) = 3x - 1, g\left(\frac{2}{3}\right)$

40. $g(x) = 5x + 7, g\left(\frac{9}{5}\right)$

41. $f(x) = 3x + 4, f(a)$

42. $f(x) = 2x - 3, f(b)$

43. $f(x) = 7x - 2, f(a + 3)$

44. $f(x) = 5x + 9, f(a - 7)$

45. $f(x) = 16 - 3x, f(2a - 5)$

46. $f(x) = 5 - 6x, f(3a - 4)$

47. $f(x) = 6x + 4, f(x + h)$

48. $f(x) = 3x + 11, f(x + h)$

Graph the linear function.

49. $f(x) = 6x - 6$

50. $f(x) = 2x + 6$

51. $f(x) = -3x + 3$

52. $f(x) = -x - 8$

53. $f(x) = \frac{4}{3}x + 4$

54. $f(x) = \frac{2}{5}x - 2$

55. $f(x) = \frac{8}{3}x$

56. $f(x) = -\frac{3}{7}x$

57. $f(x) = 4$ **58.** $f(x) = -6$

62. Refer to the graph of the funciton $f(x)$.
 a) Find $f(-1)$.
 b) Find a value a such that $f(a) = -8$.
 c) Find the domain and range.

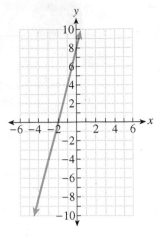

59. Refer to the graph of the function $f(x)$.
 a) Find $f(5)$.
 b) Find a value a such that $f(a) = -8$.
 c) Find the domain and range.

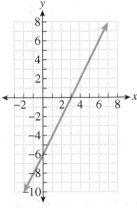

63. a) Find $f(4)$.
 b) Find the domain and range.

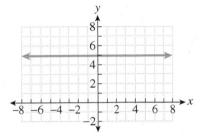

60. Refer to the graph of the function $g(x)$.
 a) Find $g(-4)$.
 b) Find a value a such that $g(a) = -2$.
 c) Find the domain and range.

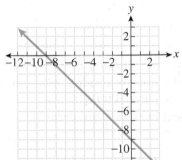

64. a) Find $f(-3)$.
 b) Find the domain and range.

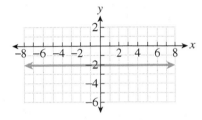

Writing in Mathematics

Answer in complete sentences.

65. Give an example of two sets A and B and a rule that is a function from set A to set B. Explain why your rule meets the definition of a function. Give another rule that would not be a function from set B to set A. Explain why your rule does not meet the definition of a function.

61. Refer to the graph of the function $f(x)$.
 a) Find $f(2)$.
 b) Find a value a such that $f(a) = 9$.
 c) Find the domain and range.

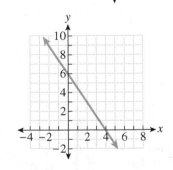

Quick Review Exercises

Section 3.4

Find the slope of the given line.

1. $6x + 2y = 17$

2. $5x - 4y = -16$

3. $x - 5y = 10$

4. $14x + 10y = 30$

3.5

Parallel and Perpendicular Lines

OBJECTIVES

1. Determine whether two lines are parallel.
2. Determine whether two lines are perpendicular.

Parallel Lines

Objective 1 Determine whether two lines are parallel. In this section, we will examine the relationship between two lines. Consider the following pair of lines:

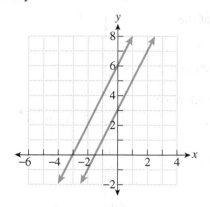

Notice that these two lines do not intersect. The lines have the same slope and are called **parallel lines**.

> **Parallel Lines**
> - Two nonvertical lines are **parallel** if they have the same slope. In other words, if we denote the slope of one line as m_1 and the slope of the other line as m_2, the two lines are parallel if $m_1 = m_2$.
> - If two lines are vertical lines, they are parallel.

Following are some examples of lines that are parallel:

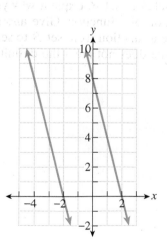 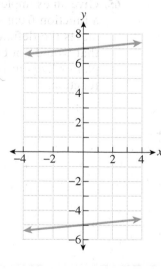 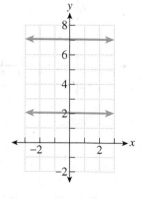 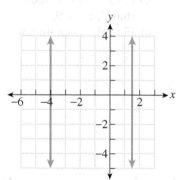

EXAMPLE 1 Are the two lines $y = 2x - 5$ and $y = 3x + 1$ parallel?

SOLUTION These two equations are in slope–intercept form, so we can see that the slope of the first line is 2 and the slope of the second line is 3. Because the slopes are not equal, these two lines are not parallel.

▸ Quick Check 1

Are the two lines $y = 4x + 3$ and $y = -4x$ parallel?

EXAMPLE 2 Are the two lines $6x + 3y = -9$ and $y = -2x + 2$ parallel?

SOLUTION To find the slope of the first line, solve the equation for y.

$$6x + 3y = -9$$
$$3y = -6x - 9 \quad \text{Subtract } 6x \text{ from both sides.}$$
$$y = -2x - 3 \quad \text{Divide by 3.}$$

The slope of the first line is -2. Because the second line is already in slope–intercept form, we see that the slope of that line also is -2. Because the two slopes are equal, the two lines are parallel.

Any two horizontal lines, such as $y = 4$ and $y = 1$, are parallel to each other because their slopes are 0. Any two vertical lines, such as $x = 2$ and $x = -1$, are, by definition, parallel to each other as well.

Quick Check 2

Are the two lines $8x + 6y = 36$ and $y = -\frac{4}{3}x + 5$ parallel?

EXAMPLE 3 Find the slope of a line that is parallel to the line $4x + 3y = 8$.

SOLUTION For a line to be parallel to $4x + 3y = 8$, it must have the same slope as this line. To find the slope of this line, we solve the equation for y.

$$4x + 3y = 8$$
$$3y = -4x + 8 \quad \text{Subtract } 4x \text{ from both sides.}$$
$$y = -\frac{4}{3}x + \frac{8}{3} \quad \text{Divide by 3.}$$

The slope of the line $4x + 3y = 8$ is $-\frac{4}{3}$. A line that is parallel to $4x + 3y = 8$ has a slope of $-\frac{4}{3}$.

Quick Check 3

Find the slope of a line that is parallel to the line $2x - 9y = 36$.

Perpendicular Lines

Objective **2** Determine whether two lines are perpendicular.

Two distinct lines that are not parallel intersect at one point. **Perpendicular lines** are one special type of intersecting lines. Here is an example of two lines that are perpendicular. Perpendicular lines intersect at right angles. Notice that one of these lines has a positive slope and the other line has a negative slope.

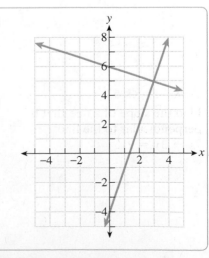

> ## Perpendicular Lines
>
> - Two nonvertical lines are **perpendicular** if their slopes are **negative reciprocals.** In other words, if we denote the slope of one line as m_1 and the slope of the other line as m_2, the two lines are perpendicular if $m_1 = -\dfrac{1}{m_2}$. (This is equivalent to saying that two lines are perpendicular if the product of their slopes is -1.)
> - A vertical line is perpendicular to a horizontal line.

Two numbers are **negative reciprocals** if they are reciprocals that have opposite signs, such as 5 and $-\frac{1}{5}$, -2 and $\frac{1}{2}$, and $-\frac{3}{10}$ and $\frac{10}{3}$.

EXAMPLE 4   Are the two lines $y = 4x + 5$ and $y = -4x + 5$ perpendicular?

SOLUTION   The slopes of these two lines are 4 and -4, respectively. While the signs of these two slopes are opposite, the slopes are not reciprocals. Therefore, the two lines are not perpendicular.

Quick Check 4

Are the two lines
$y = x + 7$ and
$y = -x + 3$ perpendicular?

EXAMPLE 5   Are the two lines $y = 3x + 7$ and $2x + 6y = 5$ perpendicular?

SOLUTION   The slope of the first line is 3. To find the slope of the second line, we solve the equation for y.

$$2x + 6y = 5$$
$$6y = -2x + 5 \quad \text{Subtract } 2x.$$
$$y = -\frac{2}{6}x + \frac{5}{6} \quad \text{Divide by 6.}$$
$$y = -\frac{1}{3}x + \frac{5}{6} \quad \text{Simplify.}$$

The slope of the second line is $-\frac{1}{3}$. The two slopes are negative reciprocals, so the lines are perpendicular.

Any vertical line, such as $x = 2$, is perpendicular to any horizontal line, such as $y = -2$.

Quick Check 5

Are the two lines
$y = \dfrac{2}{3}x + 5$ and

$6x + 4y = 12$
perpendicular?

EXAMPLE 6   Find the slope of a line that is perpendicular to the line $5x + 2y = 8$.

SOLUTION   We begin by finding the slope of this line. We do this by solving the equation $5x + 2y = 8$ for y.

$$5x + 2y = 8$$
$$2y = -5x + 8 \quad \text{Subtract } 5x \text{ from both sides.}$$
$$y = -\frac{5}{2}x + \frac{8}{2} \quad \text{Divide by 2.}$$
$$y = -\frac{5}{2}x + 4 \quad \text{Simplify.}$$

Quick Check 6

Find the slope of a line that is
perpendicular to the line
$7x - 3y = 21$.

The slope of this line is $-\frac{5}{2}$. To find the slope of a line perpendicular to this line, we take the reciprocal of this slope and change its sign from negative to positive. A line is perpendicular to $5x + 2y = 8$ if it has a slope of $\frac{2}{5}$.

Determining Whether Two Lines Are Parallel, Perpendicular, or Neither

To summarize, nonvertical lines are parallel if and only if they have the same slope and are perpendicular if and only if their slopes are negative reciprocals. Horizontal lines are parallel to other horizontal lines, and vertical lines are parallel to other vertical lines. Finally, a horizontal line and a vertical line are perpendicular to each other. These concepts are summarized in the following table:

If . . .	the lines are parallel if . . .	the lines are perpendicular if . . .
two nonvertical lines have slopes m_1 and m_2	$m_1 = m_2$	$m_1 = -\dfrac{1}{m_2}$
one of the two lines is horizontal	the other line is horizontal	the other line is vertical
one of the two lines is vertical	the other line is vertical	the other line is horizontal

EXAMPLE 7   Are the two lines $y = 6x + 2$ and $y = \frac{1}{6}x - 3$ parallel, perpendicular, or neither?

SOLUTION   The slope of the first line is 6, and the slope of the second line is $\frac{1}{6}$. The slopes are not equal, so the lines are not parallel.

The slopes are not negative reciprocals, so the lines are not perpendicular either.

The two lines are neither parallel nor perpendicular.

Quick Check 7

Are the two lines $y = 2x - 5$ and $y = -2x$ parallel, perpendicular, or neither?

EXAMPLE 8   Are the two lines $-3x + y = 7$ and $-6x + 2y = -4$ parallel, perpendicular, or neither?

SOLUTION   Find the slope of each line by solving each equation for y.

$$-3x + y = 7$$
$$y = 3x + 7 \quad \text{Add } 3x \text{ to both sides.}$$

The slope of the first line is 3. Now find the slope of the second line.

$$-6x + 2y = -4$$
$$2y = 6x - 4 \quad \text{Add } 6x \text{ to both sides.}$$
$$y = 3x - 2 \quad \text{Divide by 2.}$$

The slope of the second line also is 3.

Because the two slopes are equal, the lines are parallel.

Quick Check 8

Are the two lines $y = 4x + 3$ and $8x - 2y = 12$ parallel, perpendicular, or neither?

EXAMPLE 9   Are the two lines $10x + 2y = 0$ and $x - 5y = 3$ parallel, perpendicular, or neither?

SOLUTION   Begin by finding the slope of each line.

$$10x + 2y = 0$$
$$2y = -10x \quad \text{Subtract } 10x \text{ from both sides.}$$
$$y = -5x \quad \text{Divide by 2.}$$

The slope of the first line is -5. Now find the slope of the second line.

$$x - 5y = 3$$
$$-5y = -x + 3 \quad \text{Subtract } x \text{ from both sides.}$$
$$y = \frac{1}{5}x - \frac{3}{5} \quad \text{Divide by } -5.$$

The slope of the second line is $\frac{1}{5}$. Because the two slopes are negative reciprocals, the lines are perpendicular.

Quick Check 9

Are the two lines $y = -\frac{2}{5}x + 9$ and $5x - 2y = -8$ parallel, perpendicular, or neither?

BUILDING YOUR STUDY STRATEGY

Using Your Resources, 5 Classmates Some frequently overlooked resources are the other students in your class.

- If you have a quick question about a particular problem, a classmate can help you.
- If your notes are incomplete for a certain day, a classmate may allow you to use his or her notes to fill in the holes in your own notes.
- If you are forced to miss class, a quick call to a classmate can help you find out what was covered in class and what is the homework assignment.

Exercises 3.5

PRACTICE   WATCH   DOWNLOAD   READ   REVIEW

Vocabulary

1. Two nonvertical lines are _____ if they have the same slope.

2. Two nonvertical lines are _____ if their slopes are negative reciprocals.

3. A vertical line is parallel to a(n) _____ line.

4. A vertical line is perpendicular to a(n) _____ line.

5. Two _____ lines do not intersect.

6. Two _____ lines intersect at right angles.

Are the two given lines parallel?

7. $y = 3x + 5$, $y = 3x - 2$

8. $y = 5x - 7$, $y = -5x + 3$

9. $4x + 2y = 9$, $3y = 6x + 7$

10. $x + 3y = -4$, $3x + 9y = 8$

11. $y = 6$, $y = -6$

12. $x = 2$, $x = 7$

Are the two given lines perpendicular?

13. $y = 4x$, $y = \frac{1}{4}x - 3$

14. $y = -\frac{3}{2}x + 2$, $y = \frac{2}{3}x + 1$

15. $15x + 3y = 11$, $x - 5y = -4$

16. $x + y = 6$, $x - y = -3$

17. $x = 3$, $y = 4$

18. $y = -7$, $y = \frac{1}{7}$

Are the two given lines parallel, perpendicular, or neither?

19. $y = 6x - 2$, $y = -6x + 5$

20. $y = 7x - 9$, $y = \frac{1}{7}x + 3$

21. $y = 4x + 3$, $y = -\frac{1}{4}x - 6$

22. $y = 8x - 16$, $y = 8x - 1$

23. $8x + 6y = 12, 12x + 9y = -27$
24. $15x - 10y = 20, 6x + 9y = -45$
25. $5x - 4y = 44, 10x + 8y = -32$
26. $3y = 7x - 6, 21x - 9y = 63$
27. $y = -\dfrac{8}{7}, 8y - 7 = 0$
28. $x = \dfrac{3}{4}, x = -\dfrac{4}{3}$
29. $x = 5, y = -2$
30. $x + y = 16, y = x - 7$

Are the lines associated with the given functions parallel, perpendicular, or neither?

31. $f(x) = 7x - 5, g(x) = 7x + 3$
32. $f(x) = -2x - 5, g(x) = -\dfrac{1}{2}x + 4$
33. $f(x) = 6, g(x) = 6x + 4$
34. $f(x) = 4x + 9, g(x) = -\dfrac{1}{4}x + 3$
35. $f(x) = x + 7, g(x) = x + 2$
36. $f(x) = 5, g(x) = -5$

Find the slope of a line that is parallel to the given line. If the slope is undefined, state this.

37. $y = -6x + 7$
38. $y = 3x + 2$
39. $y = 5x$
40. $y = -3$
41. $12x + 4y = 8$
42. $2x + 6y = -7$

Find the slope of a line that is perpendicular to the given line. If the slope is undefined, state this.

43. $y = 8x - 7$
44. $y = -\dfrac{1}{5}x + 2$

45. $10x + 6y = 30$
46. $8x - 14y = -28$
47. $12x + 21y = 33$
48. $4x - 7 = 0$

49. Find the slope of a line that is parallel to the line $Ax + By = C$. (A, B, and C are real numbers, $A \neq 0$, and $B \neq 0$.)
50. Find the slope of a line that is perpendicular to the line $Ax + By = C$. (A, B, and C are real numbers, $A \neq 0$, and $B \neq 0$.)
51. Is the line that passes through $(3, 7)$ and $(5, -1)$ parallel to the line $y = -4x + 11$?
52. Is the line that passes through $(-6, 2)$ and $(4, 8)$ parallel to the line $-3x + 5y = 15$?
53. Is the line that passes through $(4, 7)$ and $(-1, 9)$ perpendicular to the line $-10x + 4y = 8$?
54. Is the line that passes through $(-3, -8)$ and $(2, 7)$ perpendicular to the line that passes through $(-5, 3)$ and $(7, 7)$?

Writing in Mathematics

Answer in complete sentences.

55. Describe three real-world examples of parallel lines.
56. Describe three real-world examples of perpendicular lines.
57. Explain the process for determining whether two lines of the form $Ax + By = C$ are parallel.
58. Explain the process for determining whether two lines of the form $Ax + By = C$ are perpendicular.

Quick Review Exercises

Section 3.5

Find the slope of a line that passes through the given two points. If the slope is undefined, state this.

1. $(5, 7)$ and $(8, 1)$
2. $(-4, 2)$ and $(2, 10)$
3. $(-9, -5)$ and $(-7, 5)$
4. $(6, 0)$ and $(-2, -6)$

3.6

Equations of Lines

OBJECTIVES

1. Find the equation of a line using the point–slope form.
2. Find the equation of a line given two points on the line.
3. Find a linear equation to describe real data.
4. Find the equation of a parallel or perpendicular line.

We are already familiar with the slope–intercept form of the equation of a line: $y = mx + b$. When an equation is written in this form, we know both the slope of the line (m) and the y-coordinate of the y-intercept (b). This form is convenient for graphing lines. In this section, we will look at another form of the equation of a line. We also will learn how to find the equation of a line if we know the slope of a line and any point through which the line passes.

Point–Slope Form of the Equation of a Line

Objective 1 Find the equation of a line using the point–slope form. In Section 3.3, we learned that if we know the slope of a line and its y-intercept, we can write the equation of the line using the slope–intercept form of a line $y = mx + b$, where m is the slope of the line and b is the y-coordinate of the y-intercept. If we know the slope of a line and the coordinates of any point on that line, not just the y-intercept, we can write the equation of the line using the point–slope form of an equation.

> **Point–Slope Form of the Equation of a Line**
>
> The **point–slope form** of the equation of a line with slope m that passes through the point (x_1, y_1) is
>
> $$y - y_1 = m(x - x_1).$$

This form can be derived directly from the slope formula $m = \dfrac{y_2 - y_1}{x_2 - x_1}$. If we let (x, y) represent an arbitrary point on the line, this formula becomes $m = \dfrac{y - y_1}{x - x_1}$. Multiplying both sides of that equation by $(x - x_1)$ produces the point–slope form of the equation of a line.

If a line has slope 2 and passes through $(3, 1)$, we find its equation by substituting 2 for m, 3 for x_1, and 1 for y_1.

$$y_1 = 1 \qquad m = 2 \qquad x_1 = 3$$

$$y - y_1 = m(x - x_1)$$
$$y - 1 = 2(x - 3)$$

The equation of the line is $y - 1 = 2(x - 3)$. This equation can be converted to slope–intercept form or to standard form.

EXAMPLE 1 Find the equation of a line with slope 4 that passes through the point $(-2, 5)$. Write the equation in slope–intercept form.

SOLUTION Substitute 4 for m, -2 for x_1, and 5 for y_1 in the point–slope form. Then solve the equation for y to write the equation in slope–intercept form.

$y - 5 = 4(x - (-2))$	Substitute into point–slope form.
$y - 5 = 4(x + 2)$	Eliminate double signs.
$y - 5 = 4x + 8$	Distribute.
$y = 4x + 13$	Add 5 to isolate y.

The equation for a line with slope 4 that passes through $(-2, 5)$ is $y = 4x + 13$. Below is the graph of the line, showing that it passes through the point $(-2, 5)$.

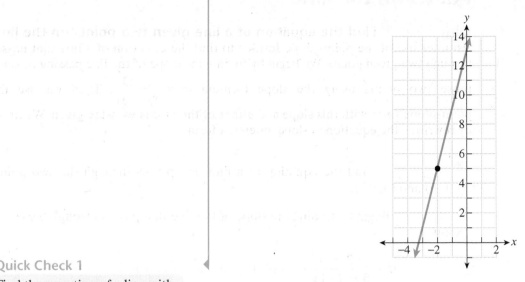

Quick Check 1

Find the equation of a line with slope 2 that passes through the point $(1, 5)$. Write the equation in slope–intercept form.

EXAMPLE 2 Find the equation of a line with slope -5 that passes through the point $(4, -3)$. Write the equation in slope–intercept form.

SOLUTION Begin by substituting -5 for m, 4 for x_1, and -3 for y_1 in the point–slope form. After substituting, solve the equation for y.

$$y - (-3) = -5(x - 4) \quad \text{Substitute into point–slope form.}$$
$$y + 3 = -5(x - 4) \quad \text{Simplify left side.}$$
$$y + 3 = -5x + 20 \quad \text{Distribute } -5.$$
$$y = -5x + 17 \quad \text{Subtract 3 to isolate } y.$$

Quick Check 2

Find the equation of a line with slope -3 that passes through the point $(4, -6)$. Write the equation in slope–intercept form.

The equation for a line with slope -5 that passes through $(4, -3)$ is $y = -5x + 17$.

In the previous example, we converted the equation from point–slope form to slope–intercept form. This is a good idea in general. We use the point–slope form because it is a convenient form for finding the equation of a line if we know its slope and the coordinates of a point on the line. We convert the equation to slope–intercept form because it is easier to graph a line when the equation is in this form.

EXAMPLE 3 The line associated with the linear function $f(x)$ has a slope of 2. If $f(-3) = -7$, find the function $f(x)$.

SOLUTION A linear function is of the form $f(x) = mx + b$. In this example, we know that $m = 2$, so $f(x) = 2x + b$. We will now use the fact that $f(-3) = -7$ to find b.

$$f(-3) = -7$$
$$2(-3) + b = -7 \quad \text{Substitute } -3 \text{ for } x \text{ in the function } f(x).$$
$$-6 + b = -7 \quad \text{Multiply.}$$
$$b = -1 \quad \text{Add 6.}$$

Quick Check 3

The line associated with the linear function $f(x)$ has a slope of -4. If $f(-2) = 13$, find the function $f(x)$.

Replace m with 2 and b with -1. The function is $f(x) = 2x - 1$.

The previous example also could have been solved by using the point–slope form with the point $(-3, -7)$.

Finding the Equation of a Line Given Two Points on the Line

Objective ② Find the equation of a line given two points on the line.
Another use of the point–slope form is to find the equation of a line that passes through two given points. We begin by finding the slope of the line passing through those two points using the slope formula $m = \dfrac{y_2 - y_1}{x_2 - x_1}$. Then we use the point–slope form with this slope and either of the points we were given. We finish by rewriting the equation in slope–intercept form.

EXAMPLE 4 Find the equation of a line that passes through the two points $(-1, 6)$ and $(3, -2)$.

SOLUTION Begin by finding the slope of the line that passes through these two points.

$$m = \frac{-2 - 6}{3 - (-1)} \quad \text{Substitute into the formula } m = \frac{y_2 - y_1}{x_2 - x_1}.$$

$$= \frac{-8}{4} \quad \text{Simplify numerator and denominator.}$$

$$= -2 \quad \text{Simplify.}$$

Now substitute into the point–slope form using either of the points with $m = -2$. Use $(3, -2)$:

$$y - (-2) = -2(x - 3) \quad \text{Substitute in point–slope form.}$$

$$y + 2 = -2x + 6 \quad \text{Simplify.}$$

$$y = -2x + 4 \quad \text{Solve for } y.$$

The equation of the line that passes through these two points is $y = -2x + 4$. If we had used the point $(-1, 6)$ instead of $(3, -2)$, the result would have been the same.

At the right is the graph of the line passing through the points $(-1, 6)$ and $(3, -2)$.

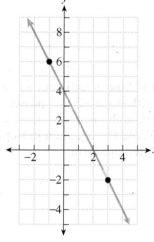

Quick Check 4

Find the equation of a line that passes through the two points $(-2, 7)$ and $(6, -5)$.

EXAMPLE 5 Find the equation of a line that passes through the two points $(8, 2)$ and $(8, 9)$.

SOLUTION Begin by attempting to find the slope of the line that passes through these two points.

$$m = \frac{9 - 2}{8 - 8} \quad \text{Substitute into the slope formula.}$$

$$= \frac{7}{0} \quad \text{Simplify numerator and denominator.}$$

Quick Check 5

Find the equation of a line that passes through the two points $(-6, 4)$ and $(3, 4)$.

The slope is undefined, so this line is a vertical line. (We could have discovered this by plotting the two points on a graph.) The equation for this line is $x = 8$.

Finding a Linear Equation to Describe Linear Data

Objective 3 **Find a linear equation to describe real data.**

EXAMPLE 6   In 2005, approximately 8.9 million U.S. households had a net worth of at least $1 million. By 2007, that number had increased to 9.9 million U.S. households. Find a linear equation that describes the number (y) of U.S. millionaire households (in millions) x years after 2005. (*Source: TNS Financial Services, Affluent Market Research Program*)

SOLUTION   Because x represents the number of years after 2005, $x = 0$ for 2005 and $x = 2$ for 2007. This tells us that two points on the line are $(0, 8.9)$ and $(2, 9.9)$. We begin by calculating the slope of the line.

$$m = \frac{9.9 - 8.9}{2 - 0} \qquad \text{Substitute into the slope formula.}$$

$$= \frac{1}{2} \qquad \text{Simplify numerator and denominator.}$$

$$= 0.5 \qquad \text{Divide.}$$

The slope is 0.5, which tells us that the number of U.S. millionaires increases by 0.5 million per year. In this example, we know that the y-intercept is $(0, 8.9)$, so we can write the equation directly in slope–intercept form. The equation is $y = 0.5x + 8.9$. (If we did not know the y-intercept of the line, we would find the equation by substituting into the point–slope form.)

▶ Quick Check 6

In 2003, 3620 master's degrees were awarded in Mathematics and Statistics. In 2007, this total increased to 4884. Find a linear equation that tells the number (y) of master's degrees awarded in Mathematics and Statistics x years after 2003. (*Source: Digest of Education Statistics, U.S. Department of Education*)

Finding the Equation of a Parallel or Perpendicular Line

Objective 4 **Find the equation of a parallel or perpendicular line.** To find the equation of a line, we must know the slope of the line and the coordinates of a point on the line. In the previous examples, we were given the slope or we calculated the slope using two points on the line. Sometimes the slope of the line is given in terms of another line. We could be given the equation of a line either parallel or perpendicular to the line for which we are trying to find the equation.

EXAMPLE 7   Find the equation of a line that is parallel to the line $y = -\frac{3}{4}x + 15$ and that passes through $(-8, 5)$.

SOLUTION   Because the line is parallel to $y = -\frac{3}{4}x + 15$, its slope must be $-\frac{3}{4}$. Substitute this slope, along with the point $(-8, 5)$, into the point–slope form to find the equation of this line.

$$y - 5 = -\frac{3}{4}[x - (-8)] \quad \text{Substitute into point–slope form.}$$

$$y - 5 = -\frac{3}{4}(x + 8) \quad \text{Eliminate double signs.}$$

$$y - 5 = -\frac{3}{4}x - \frac{3}{\underset{1}{4}} \cdot \overset{2}{8} \quad \text{Distribute and divide out common factors.}$$

$$y - 5 = -\frac{3}{4}x - 6 \quad \text{Simplify.}$$

$$y = -\frac{3}{4}x - 1 \quad \text{Add 5.}$$

Quick Check 7

Find the equation of a line that is parallel to the line $y = \frac{2}{5}x - 9$ and that passes through $(5, 4)$.

The equation of the line parallel to $y = -\frac{3}{4}x + 15$ and passing through $(-8, 5)$ is $y = -\frac{3}{4}x - 1$.

EXAMPLE 8 Find the equation of a line that is perpendicular to the line $y = -\frac{1}{2}x + 7$ and that passes through $(5, 3)$.

SOLUTION The slope of the line $y = -\frac{1}{2}x + 7$ is $-\frac{1}{2}$, so the slope of a perpendicular line must be the negative reciprocal of $-\frac{1}{2}$, or 2. Now substitute into the point–slope form.

$$y - 3 = 2(x - 5) \quad \text{Substitute into point–slope form.}$$

$$y - 3 = 2x - 10 \quad \text{Distribute.}$$

$$y = 2x - 7 \quad \text{Add 3.}$$

Quick Check 8

Find the equation of a line that is perpendicular to the line $9x - 12y = 4$ and that passes through $(6, -2)$.

The equation of the line is $y = 2x - 7$.

If we are given . . .	We find the equation by . . .
The slope and the y-intercept	Substituting m and b into the slope–intercept form $y = mx + b$
The slope and a point on the line	Substituting m and the coordinates of the point into the point–slope form $y - y_1 = m(x - x_1)$
Two points on the line	Calculating m using the slope formula $m = \dfrac{y_2 - y_1}{x_2 - x_1}$ and then substituting the slope and the coordinates of one of the points into the point–slope form $y - y_1 = m(x - x_1)$
A point on the line and the equation of a parallel line	Substituting the slope of that line and the coordinates of the point into the point–slope form $y - y_1 = m(x - x_1)$
A point on the line and the equation of a perpendicular line	Substituting the negative reciprocal of the slope of that line and the coordinates of the point into the point–slope form $y - y_1 = m(x - x_1)$

Keep in mind that if the slope of the line is undefined, the line is vertical and its equation is of the form $x = a$, where a is the x-coordinate of the given point. We do not use the point–slope form or the slope–intercept form to find the equation of a vertical line.

BUILDING YOUR STUDY STRATEGY

Using Your Resources, 6 Internet Resources Consider using the Internet as a resource to conduct further research on topics you are learning. Many websites have alternative explanations, examples, and practice problems. If you find a site that helps you with a particular topic, check that site when you are researching another topic. If you have any questions about what you find, ask your instructor.

Exercises 3.6   **MyMathLab**

PRACTICE   WATCH   DOWNLOAD   READ   REVIEW

Vocabulary

1. The point–slope form of the equation of a line with slope m that passes through the point (x_1, y_1) is

_____ .

2. State the procedure for finding the equation of a line that passes through the points (x_1, y_1) and (x_2, y_2).

Write the following equations in slope–intercept form.

3. $-6x + 2y = 10$

4. $3x + 6y = 15$

5. $x - 5y = 10$

6. $-12x - 16y = 10$

7. $7x - y = 3$

8. $6x + 4y = 0$

Find the equation of a line with the given slope and y-intercept.

9. Slope -3, y-intercept $(0, 5)$

10. Slope 2, y-intercept $(0, -4)$

11. Slope $\dfrac{2}{3}$, y-intercept $(0, -3)$

12. Slope 0, y-intercept $(0, 9)$

13. Slope 5, y-intercept $(0, 8)$

14. Slope $-\dfrac{3}{5}$, y-intercept $(0, 2)$

Find the slope–intercept form of the equation of a line with the given slope that passes through the given point.

15. Slope 3, through $(7, 4)$

16. Slope -2, through $(1, 6)$

17. Slope -4, through $(6, -2)$

18. Slope -1, through $(-6, -3)$

19. Slope $\dfrac{3}{2}$, through $(-6, -9)$

20. Slope $\dfrac{2}{5}$, through $(-5, -4)$

21. Slope 0, through $(8, 5)$

22. Undefined slope, through $(8, 5)$

23. Find a linear function $f(x)$ with slope -2 such that $f(-4) = 23$.

24. Find a linear function $f(x)$ with slope 5 such that $f(3) = 12$.

25. Find a linear function $f(x)$ with slope $\dfrac{3}{5}$ such that $f(-15) = -17$.

26. Find a linear function $f(x)$ with slope 0 such that $f(316) = 228$.

Find the slope–intercept form of the equation of a line that passes through the given points.

27. $(2, -3), (7, 2)$

28. $(4, 6), (8, 10)$

29. $(-3, -3), (1, 9)$

30. $(-6, 9), (-2, -3)$

31. $(-10, -12), (15, 18)$

32. $(6, -9), (-2, 3)$

33. $(-2, -9), (-2, -3)$

34. $(-4, 8), (2, 8)$

For Exercises 35–40, find the slope–intercept form of the equation of a line whose x-intercept and y-intercept are given.

	x-intercept	*y*-intercept
35.	$(6, 0)$	$(0, 2)$
36.	$(-9, 0)$	$(0, 3)$
37.	$(4, 0)$	$(0, -4)$
38.	$(-10, 0)$	$(0, -2)$
39.	$(6, 0)$	$(0, -6)$
40.	$(10, 0)$	$(0, 4)$

41. Jamie sells newspaper subscriptions door-to-door to help pay her tuition. She is paid a certain salary each night plus a commission on each sale she makes. On Monday, she sold 3 subscriptions and was paid $66. On Tuesday, she sold 8 subscriptions and was paid $116.

    a) Find a linear equation that calculates Jamie's pay on a night she sells x subscriptions.

    b) How much will Jamie be paid on a night she makes no sales?

42. Luis contracted with a landscaper to install a brick patio in his backyard. The landscaper charged $10,000. Luis paid the landscaper a deposit the first month and agreed to make a fixed monthly payment until the balance was paid in full. After three months, Luis owed $6800. After seven months, Luis still owed $5200.

    a) Find a linear equation for Luis's balance (y) after x months.

    b) How much was the deposit that Luis paid?

    c) How many months will it take to pay off the entire balance?

43. Members of a racquetball club pay an annual membership fee. In addition, they pay a fee each time they play racquetball. Last year Jay played racquetball 76 times and paid the club a total of $1126. Last year Sammy played racquetball 35 times and paid the club a total of $613.50.

    a) Find a linear equation for the amount paid to the club by a member who plays racquetball x times a year.

    b) What is the annual membership fee at this club?

    c) What is the fee that is charged each time a member plays racquetball?

44. A computer repairperson charges a service fee in addition to an hourly rate to fix a computer. To fix Frank's computer, the repair person took two hours and charged a total of $225 (service fee plus hourly rate for two hours of work). Bundy's computer had more problems and took six hours to fix. The charge to Bundy was $505.

    a) Find a linear equation for the charge (y) for a repair that takes x hours to perform.

    b) How much is the repairperson's service fee?

    c) How much is the repairperson's hourly rate?

45. A banquet hall hosts wedding receptions. There is a charge to rent the hall, in addition to a per person charge for the meal. Chrissy had 120 guests at her wedding and paid a total of $4100. Adaeze had 175 guests at her wedding and paid a total of $5750.

    a) Find a linear equation for the total charge (y) to host a wedding with x guests.

    b) What is the charge to rent the hall?

    c) What is the charge for each person's dinner?

    d) What would the charge be to host a wedding with 200 guests?

46. Masaru has a small business in which he caters sushi parties. He charges a flat party fee in addition to a charge for each person to cover the food costs. He charges a total of $319.50 for a party with 10 guests and $618.75 for a party with 25 guests.

    a) Find a linear equation for the total charge (y) for a party with x guests.

    b) What is the flat party fee?

    c) What is the charge for each person's food?

    d) What would the charge be for a party with 16 guests?

Find the slope–intercept form of the equation of a line that is parallel to the given line and that passes through the given point.

47. Parallel to $y = -2x + 13$, through $(-6, -3)$

48. Parallel to $y = 4x - 11$, through $(3, 8)$

49. Parallel to $-3x + y = 9$, through $(4, -6)$

50. Parallel to $10x + 2y = 40$, through $(-2, 9)$

51. Parallel to $y = 5$, through $(2, 7)$

52. Parallel to $x = -5$, through $(-6, -4)$

Find the slope–intercept form of the equation of a line that is perpendicular to the given line and that passes through the given point.

53. Perpendicular to $y = 3x - 7$, through $(9, 4)$

54. Perpendicular to $y = -\dfrac{1}{2}x + 5$, through $(1, -3)$

55. Perpendicular to $4x + 5y = 9$, through $(-4, 2)$

56. Perpendicular to $3x - 2y = 8$, through $(-6, -7)$

57. Perpendicular to $y = 3$, through $(-5, -3)$
58. Perpendicular to $x = -8$, through $(6, 1)$

Find the slope–intercept form of the equation of a line that is parallel to the graphed line and that passes through the point plotted on the graph. (Begin by finding the slope of the graphed line.)

59.

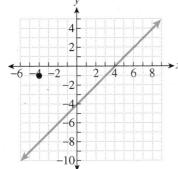

60.

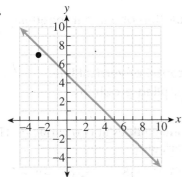

Find the slope–intercept form of the equation of a line that is perpendicular to the graphed line and that passes through the point plotted on the graph. (Begin by finding the slope of the graphed line.)

61.

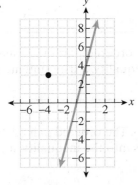

62.

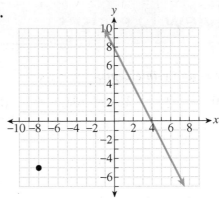

Mixed Practice, 63–72

Find the equation of a line that meets the given conditions.

63. Slope -3, passes through $(4, -8)$
64. Perpendicular to $6x - 2y = 10$, passes through $(6, -3)$

65. Parallel to $5x - 3y = -3$, passes through $(-9, 8)$

66. Passes through $(-2, 7)$ and $(4, -8)$

67. Slope 0, passes through $(13, 11)$
68. Parallel to $3x + 4y = 19$, passes through $(-12, -7)$

69. Perpendicular to $x + 4y = 8$, passes through $(-2, 13)$
70. Passes through $(-6, 14)$ and $(-6, -39)$
71. Passes through $(1, -23)$ and $(5, 33)$

72. Slope $\dfrac{4}{5}$, passes through $(-15, -11)$

Writing in Mathematics

Answer in complete sentences.

73. Explain why the equation of a vertical line has the form $x = a$ and the equation of a horizontal line has the form $y = b$.

74. Explain why a horizontal line has a slope of 0 and a vertical line has undefined slope.

Quick Review Exercises

Section 3.6

Graph. Label any x- and y-intercepts.

1. $5x - 2y = 10$

2. $y = -3x - 8$

3. $y = \dfrac{2}{3}x - 4$

4. $y = -8$

3.7

Linear Inequalities

OBJECTIVES

1 Determine whether an ordered pair is a solution of a linear inequality in two variables.

2 Graph a linear inequality in two variables.

3 Graph a linear inequality involving a horizontal or vertical line.

4 Graph linear inequalities associated with applied problems.

In this section, we will learn how to solve **linear inequalities** in two variables. Here are some examples of linear inequalities in two variables.

$$2x + 3y \leq 6 \qquad 5x - 4y \geq -8 \qquad -x + 9y < -18 \qquad -3x - 4y > 7$$

Solutions of Linear Inequalities in Two Variables

Objective 1 Determine whether an ordered pair is a solution of a linear inequality in two variables.

Solutions of Linear Inequalities

A solution of a linear inequality in two variables is an ordered pair (x, y) such that when the coordinates are substituted into the inequality, a true statement results.

For example, consider the linear inequality $2x + 3y \leq 6$. The ordered pair $(2, 0)$ is a solution because when we substitute these coordinates into the inequality, it produces the following result:

$$2x + 3y \leq 6$$
$$2(2) + 3(0) \leq 6$$
$$4 + 0 \leq 6$$
$$4 \leq 6$$

The last inequality is a true statement, so $(2, 0)$ is a solution. The ordered pair $(3, 4)$ is not a solution because $2(3) + 3(4)$ is not less than or equal to 6. Any ordered pair (x, y) for which $2x + 3y$ evaluates to be less than or equal to 6 is a solution of this inequality, and there are infinitely many solutions to this inequality. We will display our solutions on a graph.

Graphing Linear Inequalities in Two Variables

Objective 2 Graph a linear inequality in two variables. Ordered pairs that are solutions of the inequality $2x + 3y \le 6$ are one of two types: ordered pairs (x, y) for which $2x + 3y = 6$ are solutions and ordered pairs (x, y) for which $2x + 3y < 6$ are also solutions. Points satisfying $2x + 3y = 6$ lie on a line, so we begin by graphing this line. Because the equation is in standard form, a quick way to graph this line is by finding its x- and y-intercepts.

x-intercept $(y = 0)$	y-intercept $(x = 0)$
$2x + 3(0) = 6$	$2(0) + 3y = 6$
$2x + 0 = 6$	$0 + 3y = 6$
$2x = 6$	$3y = 6$
$x = 3$	$y = 2$
$(3, 0)$	$(0, 2)$

Here is the graph of the line:

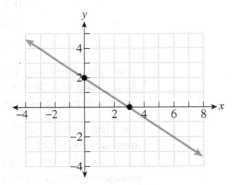

This line divides the plane into two half-planes and is the dividing line between ordered pairs for which $2x + 3y < 6$ and ordered pairs for which $2x + 3y > 6$. To finish graphing the solutions, we must determine which half-plane contains the ordered pairs for which $2x + 3y < 6$. To do this, we use a **test point,** which is a point that is not on the graph of the line whose coordinates are used for determining which half-plane contains the solutions of the inequality. We substitute the test point's coordinates into the original inequality. If the resulting inequality is true, this point and all other points on the same side of the line are solutions, and we shade that half-plane. If the resulting inequality is false, the solutions are on the other side of the line, and we shade that half-plane instead. A wise choice for the test point is the origin $(0, 0)$ if it is not on the line that has been graphed because its coordinates are easy to work with when substituting into the inequality. Because $(0, 0)$ is not on the line, we will use it as a test point.

$$\text{Test Point: } (0, 0)$$
$$2(0) + 3(0) \le 6$$
$$0 + 0 \le 6$$
$$0 \le 6$$

Because the last line is a true inequality, $(0, 0)$ is a solution, and we shade the half-plane containing this point.

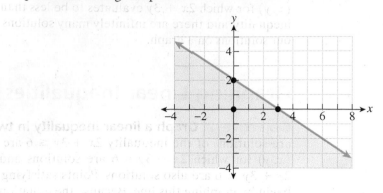

EXAMPLE 1 Graph $y \geq 4x + 3$.

SOLUTION Begin by graphing the line $y = 4x + 3$. This equation is in slope–intercept form, so we can graph it by plotting its y-intercept $(0, 3)$ and using the slope (up 4 units, 1 unit to the right) to find other points on the line.

Because the line does not pass through the origin, we can use $(0, 0)$ as a test point.

$$\text{Test Point: } (0, 0)$$
$$0 \geq 4(0) + 3$$
$$0 \geq 0 + 3$$
$$0 \geq 3$$

The last inequality is false, so the solutions are in the half-plane that does not contain the origin. The graph of the inequality is shown at the right.

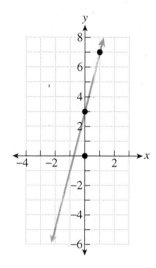

Quick Check 1

Graph $y \geq 2x - 6$.

The first two inequalities we graphed were **weak linear inequalities,** which are inequalities involving the symbols $\leq$ or $\geq$. We now turn our attention to **strict linear inequalities,** which involve the symbol $<$ or $>$. An example of a strict linear inequality is $x - 5y < 5$. Ordered pairs for which $x - 5y = 5$ are not solutions to this inequality, so the points on the line are not included as solutions. We denote this on the graph by graphing the line as a dashed or broken line. We still pick a test point and shade the appropriate half-plane as we did in the previous examples.

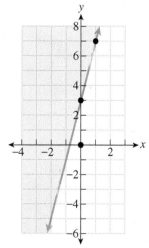

EXAMPLE 2 Graph $x - 5y < 5$.

SOLUTION Begin by graphing the line $x - 5y = 5$ as a dashed line. This equation is in standard form, so we can graph the line by finding its intercepts.

x-intercept ($y = 0$)	y-intercept ($x = 0$)
$x - 5(0) = 5$	$0 - 5y = 5$
$x - 0 = 5$	$0 - 5y = 5$
$x = 5$	$-5y = 5$
	$y = -1$
$(5, 0)$	$(0, -1)$

At the right is the graph of the line, with an x-intercept at $(5, 0)$ and a y-intercept at $(0, -1)$. Notice that the line is a dashed line.

Because the line does not pass through the origin, we will use $(0, 0)$ as a test point.

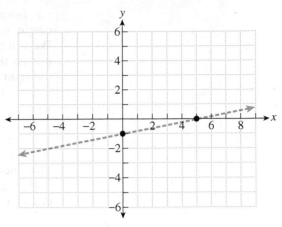

$$\text{Test Point: } (0, 0)$$
$$0 - 5(0) < 5$$
$$0 - 0 < 5$$
$$0 < 5$$

This inequality is true, so the origin is a solution. We shade the half-plane containing the origin.

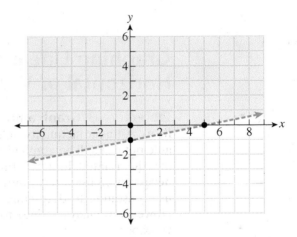

Quick Check 2
Graph $x + 2y < 6$.

EXAMPLE 3 Graph $y > 3x$.

SOLUTION This is a strict inequality, so we begin by graphing the line $y = 3x$ as a dashed line.

The equation is in slope–intercept form, with a slope of 3 and a y-intercept at $(0, 0)$. After plotting the y-intercept, we can use the slope to find a second point at $(1, 3)$. The graph of the line is shown below.

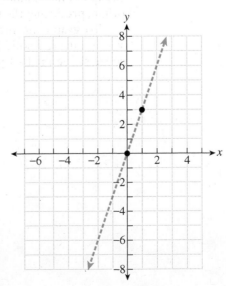

Because the line passes through the origin, we cannot use $(0, 0)$ as a test point. We will try to choose a point that is clearly not on the line, such as $(4, 0)$, which is to the right of the line.

Test Point: $(4, 0)$

$$0 > 3(4)$$

$$0 > 12$$

This inequality is false, so we shade the half-plane that does not contain the test point $(4, 0)$. At the right is the graph.

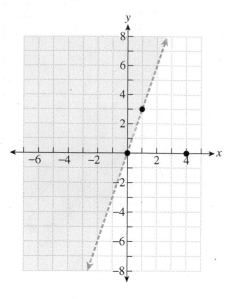

Quick Check 3

Graph $y \leq -\dfrac{4}{3}x.$

Graphing Linear Inequalities Involving Horizontal or Vertical Lines

Objective 3 Graph a linear inequality involving a horizontal or vertical line. A linear inequality involving a horizontal or vertical line has only one variable but can still be graphed on a plane rather than on a number line. After graphing the related line, we find that it is not necessary to use a test point. Instead, we can use reasoning to determine where to shade. However, we may continue to use test points if we choose.

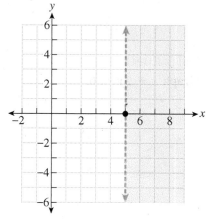

To graph the inequality $x > 5$, we begin by graphing the vertical line $x = 5$ using a dashed line. The values of x that are greater than 5 are to the right of this line, so we shade the half-plane to the right of $x = 5$. If we had used the origin as a test point, the resulting inequality $(0 > 5)$ would be false; so we would shade the half-plane that does not contain the origin, producing the same graph.

To graph the inequality $y \leq -2$, we begin by graphing the horizontal line $y = -2$ using a solid line. The values of y that are less than -2 are below this line, so we shade the half-plane below the line.

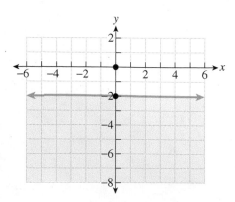

Here is a brief summary of how to graph linear inequalities in two variables.

> ## Graphing Linear Inequalities in Two Variables
>
> - Graph the line related to the inequality, which is found by replacing the inequality symbol with an equal sign.
> - If the inequality symbol includes equality ($\leq$ or $\geq$), graph the line as a solid line.
> - If the inequality symbol does not include equality ($<$ or $>$), graph the line as a dashed, or broken, line.
> - Select a test point that is not on the line. Use the origin if possible. Substitute the coordinates of the point into the original inequality. If the resulting inequality is true, shade the region on the side of the line that contains the test point. If the resulting inequality is false, shade the region on the side of the line that does not contain the test point.

Applications

Objective 4 Graph linear inequalities associated with applied problems.
We turn our attention to an application problem to end the section.

EXAMPLE 4   A movie theater has 120 seats. The number of adults and children admitted cannot exceed the number of seats. Set up and graph the appropriate inequality.

SOLUTION   There are two unknowns in this problem: the number of adults and the number of children. Let x represent the number of adults and y represent the number of children. Because the total number of adults and children cannot exceed 120, we know that $x + y \leq 120$. (We also know that $x \geq 0$ and $y \geq 0$ because we cannot have a negative number of children or adults. Therefore, we are restricted to the first quadrant, the positive x-axis and the positive y-axis.)

To graph this inequality, begin by graphing $x + y = 120$ as a solid line. Because this equation is in standard form, graph the line using its x-intercept $(120, 0)$ and its y-intercept $(0, 120)$.

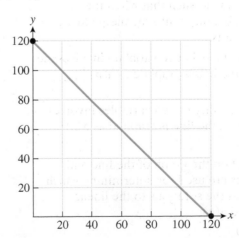

The origin is not on this line, so we can use $(0, 0)$ as a test point.

$$x + y \leq 120$$
$$0 + 0 \leq 120 \quad \text{Substitute 0 for } x \text{ and 0 for } y.$$
$$0 \leq 120 \quad \text{True.}$$

Quick Check 4

To make a fruit salad, Irv needs a total of at least 60 pieces of fruit. If Irv decides to buy only apples and pears, set up and graph the appropriate inequality.

This is a true statement, so we shade on the side of the line that contains the origin.

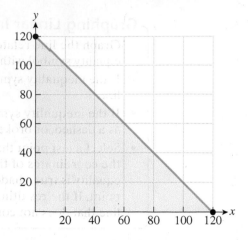

BUILDING YOUR STUDY STRATEGY

Using Your Resources, 7 MyMathLab This textbook has an online resource called MyMathLab.com. At this site, you can access video clips of lectures for each section in the book. These are useful for topics you are struggling with or for catching up if you missed a class. You also can find practice tutorial exercises that provide feedback. At this website, you also have access to sample tests, the Student's Solutions Manual, and other supplementary information.

Exercises 3.7

PRACTICE   WATCH   DOWNLOAD   READ   REVIEW

Vocabulary

1. A(n) _____ to a linear inequality in two variables is an ordered pair (x, y) such that when the coordinates are substituted into the inequality, a true statement results.

2. When a linear inequality in two variables involves the symbols $\le$ or $\ge$, the line is graphed as a(n) _____ line.

3. When a linear inequality in two variables involves the symbols $<$ or $>$, the line is graphed as a(n) _____ line.

4. A point that is not on the graph of the line and whose coordinates are used for determining which half-plane contains the solutions to the linear inequality is called a(n) _____.

Determine whether the ordered pair is a solution to the given linear inequality.

5. $5x + 3y \le 22$
   a) $(0, 0)$
   b) $(8, -4)$
   c) $(2, 4)$
   d) $(-3, 9)$

6. $2x - 4y > 6$
   a) $(0, 0)$
   b) $(2, -3)$
   c) $(7, 2)$
   d) $(5, 1)$

7. $y < 6x - 11$
   a) $(5, 8)$
   b) $(0, 0)$
   c) $(2, 1)$
   d) $(-4, -13)$

8. $x - 7y \ge -3$
   a) $(4, 1)$
   b) $(9, 2)$
   c) $(0, 0)$
   d) $(-16, -2)$

9. $y < 7$
   a) $(0, 0)$
   b) $(8, 6)$
   c) $(-3, 10)$
   d) $(6, 7)$

10. $x \le -2$
    a) $(0, 0)$
    b) $(-1, 3)$
    c) $(-2, 19)$
    d) $(-5, -4)$

Complete the solution of the linear inequality by shading the appropriate region.

11. $4x + y \geq 7$

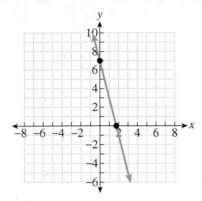

12. $-3x + 2y \leq -6$

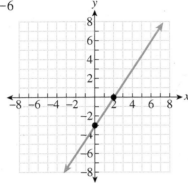

13. $2x + 8y < -4$

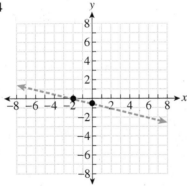

14. $10x - 2y > 0$

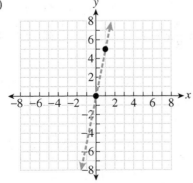

Which graph, A or B, represents the solution to the linear inequality?

15. $3x + 4y \geq 24$

A) 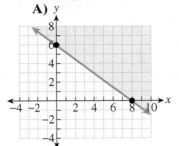   **B)**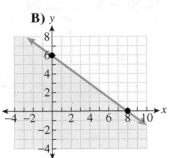

16. $y \leq \dfrac{1}{8}x$

A) 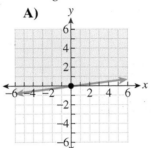   **B)**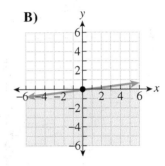

17. $3x - 2y < -18$

A) 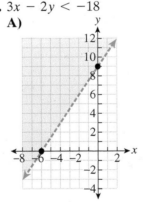   **B)**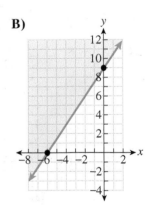

18. $5x - 4y > 20$

A) 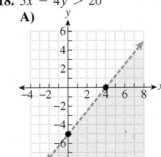   **B)**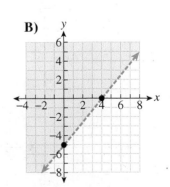

Determine the missing inequality sign (<, >, ≤, or ≥) for the linear inequality based on the given graph.

19. $8x - 3y$ _____ 24

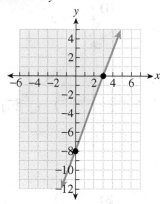

20. $3x + 6y$ _____ -27

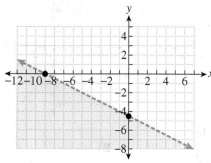

21. $-5x + 8y$ _____ 0

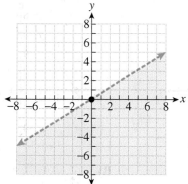

22. y _____ $4x - 6$

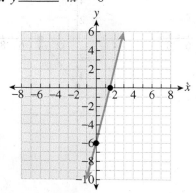

Graph the linear inequality.

23. $6x - 5y < -30$

24. $2x + 4y \le 16$

25. $-9x + 4y \le 0$

26. $y < -\dfrac{1}{4}x$

27. $y > 3$

28. $x \ge 5$

29. $y \ge \dfrac{2}{3}x - 6$

30. $y > 4x - 8$

31. $y \leq -2x - 4$ **32.** $y < -5$

33. $y > -\dfrac{3}{2}x - \dfrac{3}{2}$ **34.** $y \geq \dfrac{3}{5}x$

35. $x \leq -2$ **36.** $y < x$

38.

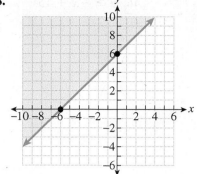

39.

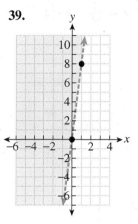

40.

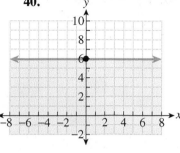

Mixed Practice, 41–50

Graph.

41. $-x + 3y \geq 9$ **42.** $y = \dfrac{3}{4}x + 5$

43. $4x - 3y = 24$ **44.** $x = -8$

Determine the linear inequality associated with the given solution. (Find the equation of the line. Then rewrite the equation as an inequality with the appropriate inequality sign: <, >, ≤, or ≥.)

37.

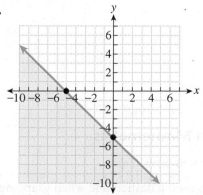

45. $5x + 4y = 0$ **46.** $y \geq -x + 15$

47. $y = -3x + 8$ **48.** $7x - 2y > -14$

b) Looking at the graph from part a, can two adults and 16 children ride the elevator at the same time?

Find the region that contains ordered pairs that are solutions to both inequalities. Graph each inequality separately; then shade the region that the two graphs have in common.

53. $x + y < 3$ and
$\quad y > x - 7$

49. $y > 2x - 30$ **50.** $x + 3y = -9$

51. More than 50 people attended a charity basketball game. Some of the people were faculty members, and the rest were students. Set up and graph an inequality involving the number of faculty members and the number of students in attendance.

54. $2x + 3y \leq 18$ and
$\quad 2x + y \geq 8$

52. An elevator has a warning posted inside the car that the maximum capacity is 1200 pounds. Suppose the average weight of an adult is 160 pounds and the average weight of a child is 60 pounds.

   a) Set up and graph an inequality involving the number of adults and the number of children that can safely ride the elevator.

✏️ Writing in Mathematics

Answer in complete sentences.

55. Explain why we used a dashed line when graphing inequalities involving the symbols $<$ and $>$ and a solid line when graphing inequalities involving the symbols $\leq$ and $\geq$.

CHAPTER 4

Systems of Equations

In this chapter, we will learn to set up and solve systems of equations. A system of equations is a set of two or more associated equations containing two or more variables. We will learn to solve systems of linear equations in two variables using three methods: graphing, the substitution method, and the addition method. We also will learn to set up systems of equations to solve applied problems. We will finish the chapter by learning to solve systems of linear inequalities in two variables.

STUDY STRATEGY

Doing Your Homework Doing a homework assignment should not be viewed as just another requirement. Homework exercises are assigned to help you learn mathematics. In this chapter, we will discuss how you should do your homework to get the most out of your effort.

4.1

Systems of Linear Equations; Solving Systems by Graphing

OBJECTIVES

1 Determine whether an ordered pair is a solution of a system of equations.
2 Identify the solution of a system of linear equations from a graph.
3 Solve a system of linear equations graphically.
4 Identify systems of linear equations with no solution or infinitely many solutions.

Systems of Linear Equations and Their Solutions

A **system of linear equations** consists of two or more linear equations. Here are some examples.

$$5x + 4y = 20 \qquad y = \frac{3}{5}x \qquad x + y = 11$$
$$2x - y = 6 \qquad y = -4x + 3 \qquad y = 5$$

Objective ① **Determine whether an ordered pair is a solution of a system of equations.** The equations in a system are examined together, and we are looking for the solution(s) that the equations have in common.

> ⌐ **Solution of a System of Linear Equations** ───────────────────
> A **solution of a system of linear equations** is an ordered pair (x, y) that is a solution of each equation in the system.

EXAMPLE 1 Is the ordered pair $(2, -3)$ a solution of the given system of equations?

$$5x + y = 7$$
$$2x - 3y = 13$$

SOLUTION   To determine whether the ordered pair $(2, -3)$ is a solution, substitute 2 for x and -3 for y in each equation. If the resulting equations are true, the ordered pair is a solution of the system. Otherwise, it is not.

$5x + y = 7$	$2x - 3y = 13$
$5(2) + (-3) = 7$	$2(2) - 3(-3) = 13$
$10 - 3 = 7$	$4 + 9 = 13$
$7 = 7$	$13 = 13$

Because $(2, -3)$ is a solution of each equation, it is a solution of the system of equations.

EXAMPLE 2 Is the ordered pair $(-5, -1)$ a solution of the given system of equations?

$$y = 2x + 9$$
$$y = 14 - 3x$$

SOLUTION   Again, begin by substituting -5 for x and -1 for y in each equation.

$y = 2x + 9$	$y = 14 - 3x$
$(-1) = 2(-5) + 9$	$(-1) = 14 - 3(-5)$
$-1 = -10 + 9$	$-1 = 14 + 15$
$-1 = -1$	$-1 = 29$

Although $(-5, -1)$ is a solution of the equation $y = 2x + 9$, it is not a solution of the equation $y = 14 - 3x$. Therefore, $(-5, -1)$ is not a solution of the system of equations.

Quick Check 1

Is the ordered pair $(-6, 3)$ a solution of the given system of equations?

$$5x - 2y = -36$$
$$-x + 7y = 27$$

Objective ② **Identify the solution of a system of linear equations from a graph.** Systems of two linear equations can be solved graphically. Because an ordered pair that is a solution of a system of two equations must be a solution of each equation, we know that this ordered pair is on the graph of each equation. To solve a system of two linear equations, we graph each line and look for points of intersection. Often this will lead to a single solution. Here are some graphical examples of systems of equations that have the ordered pair $(3, 1)$ as a solution.

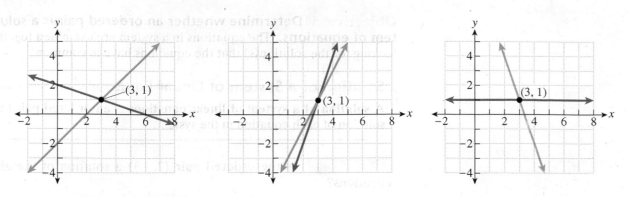

EXAMPLE 3   Find the solution of the system of equations plotted on the graph.

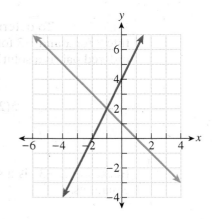

SOLUTION   The two lines intersect at the point $(-1, 2)$, so the solution of the system of equations is $(-1, 2)$.

▶ Quick Check 2
Find the solution of the system of equations plotted on the graph.

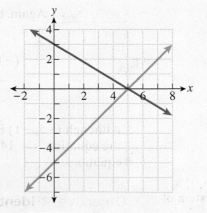

Solving Linear Systems of Equations by Graphing

Objective ③ Solve a system of linear equations graphically. Now we will solve a system of linear equations by graphing the lines and finding their point of intersection.

EXAMPLE 4   Solve the system by graphing.

$$y = 5x - 9$$

$$y = -\frac{7}{2}x + 8$$

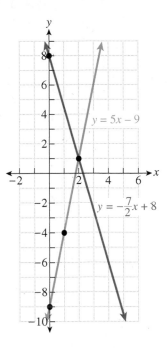

SOLUTION   Both equations are in slope–intercept form, so we will graph the lines by plotting the y-intercept and then using the slope of the line to find another point on the line.

The first line has a y-intercept at $(0, -9)$. From that point, we can find a second point by moving up 5 units and 1 unit to the right, because the slope is 5.

The y-intercept of the second line is $(0, 8)$. Because the slope of this line is $-\frac{7}{2}$, we can move down 7 units and 2 units to the right from this point to find a second point on the line. Both graphs are shown on the same set of axes at the right.

Examining the graph, we can see that the two lines intersect at the point $(2, 1)$. The solution of the system of equations is the ordered pair $(2, 1)$. We could check that this ordered pair is a solution by substituting its coordinates into both equations. The check is left to the reader.

Quick Check 3

Solve the system by graphing.

$$y = 3x - 2$$
$$y = 5x - 6$$

Using Your Calculator   To solve a system of linear equations using the TI–84, you must graph each equation and then look for points of intersection. To graph the equations from Example 4, begin by tapping the Y= key. Next to Y_1 key $5x - 9$, and next to Y_2 key $-\frac{7}{2}x + 8$. Tap the GRAPH key to display the graph.

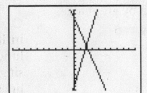

To find the points of intersection, press 2nd TRACE to access the CALC menu and select option **5: intersect.** You should see the following screen:

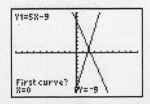

When prompted for the first curve, select Y_1 by tapping ENTER. When prompted for the second curve, select Y_2 by tapping ENTER.

Now you must make an initial guess for one of the solutions. In the next screen shot, the TI–84 asks if you would like $(0, 8)$ to be your guess. Accept this guess by tapping ENTER. The solution is the point $(2, 1)$.

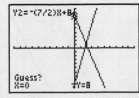
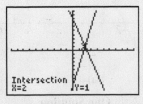

EXAMPLE 5 Solve the system by graphing.

$$2x - 3y = 12$$
$$x + y = 1$$

SOLUTION   Both equations are in general form, so we will graph them using their x- and y-intercepts.

$2x - 3y = 12$		$x + y = 1$	
x-intercept $(y = 0)$	y-intercept $(x = 0)$	x-intercept $(y = 0)$	y-intercept $(x = 0)$
$2x - 3(0) = 12$ $2x = 12$ $x = 6$ $(6, 0)$	$2(0) - 3y = 12$ $-3y = 12$ $y = -4$ $(0, -4)$	$x + (0) = 1$ $x = 1$ $(1, 0)$	$(0) + y = 1$ $y = 1$ $(0, 1)$

Here are the graphs of each line on the same set of axes.

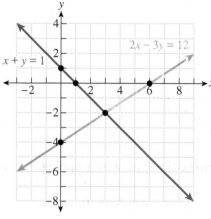

The two lines intersect at the point $(3, -2)$, so the solution of this set of equations is the ordered pair $(3, -2)$. The check is left to the reader.

Quick Check 4

Solve the system by graphing.

$$x + 5y = 5$$
$$x - y = -7$$

Objective 4 Identify systems of linear equations with no solution or infinitely many solutions. A system of two linear equations that has a single solution is called an **independent system.** Not every system of linear equations has a single solution. Suppose the graphs of the two equations are parallel lines. Parallel lines do not intersect, so such a system has no solution. A system that has no solution is called an **inconsistent system.**

Occasionally, the two equations in a system will have identical graphs. In this case, each point on the line is a solution of the system. Such a system is called a **dependent system** and has infinitely many solutions.

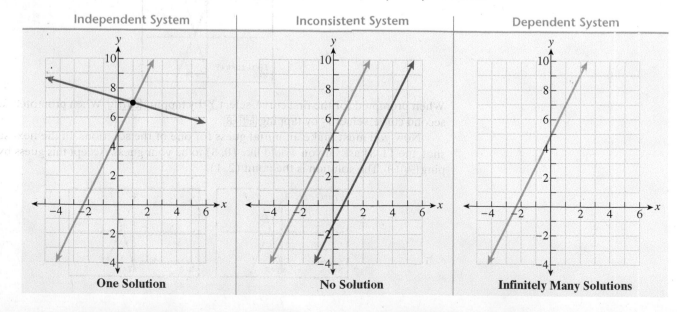

Independent System	Inconsistent System	Dependent System
One Solution	**No Solution**	**Infinitely Many Solutions**

EXAMPLE 6 Solve the system by graphing.

$$y = -3x + 5$$
$$y = -3x - 3$$

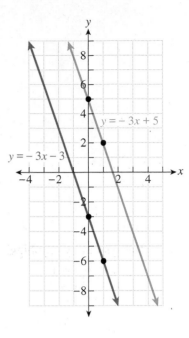

SOLUTION   Both equations are in slope–intercept form, so we can graph each line by plotting its y-intercept and then using the slope to find a second point on the line. The first line has a y-intercept at $(0, 5)$, and the slope is -3. The second line has a y-intercept at $(0, -3)$, and the slope also is -3. The graphs are at the right.

The two lines are distinct parallel lines because they have the same slope but different y-intercepts. The system is an inconsistent system and has no solution. In general, if we know that the two lines have the same slope but different y-intercepts, we know that the system is an inconsistent system and has no solution. However, if the two lines have the same slope *and* the *same* y-intercept, the system is a dependent system.

Quick Check 5

Solve the system by graphing.

$$y = -4x + 6$$
$$12x + 3y = 15$$

EXAMPLE 7 Solve the system by graphing.

$$y = 2x - 4$$
$$4x - 2y = 8$$

SOLUTION   The first line is in slope–intercept form, so we can graph it by first plotting its y-intercept at $(0, -4)$. Using its slope of 2, we see that the line also passes through the point $(1, -2)$ as shown in the graph below.

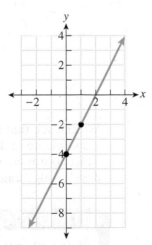

To graph the second line, we find the x- and y-intercepts, as the equation is in general form.

x-intercept $(y = 0)$	y-intercept $(x = 0)$
$4x - 2(0) = 8$	$4(0) - 2y = 8$
$4x = 8$	$-2y = 8$
$x = 2$	$y = -4$
$(2, 0)$	$(0, -4)$

After plotting these intercepts on the graph, we see that the two lines are exactly the same. This system is a dependent system. We can display the solutions of a dependent system by showing the graph of either equation. Every point on the line is a solution to the system of equations. To state the solution set, we write the general form for a point (x, y) that is on the line. To do this, we solve one of the equations for y in terms of x and replace y in the ordered pair (x, y) with this expression. In this example, we already know that $y = 2x - 4$; so our solutions are of the form $(x, 2x - 4)$.

$$y = \boxed{2x - 4}$$
$$\downarrow$$
$$(x, y)$$
$$\downarrow$$
$$(x, 2x - 4)$$

Notice that if we rewrite the equation $4x - 2y = 8$ in slope–intercept form, it is exactly the same as the first equation. Equations in a dependent linear system of equations are multiples of each other.

Quick Check 6

Solve the system by graphing.
$$4x + 6y = 12$$
$$y = -\frac{2}{3}x + 2$$

Solving systems of equations by graphing does have a major drawback. Often we will not be able to accurately determine the coordinates of the solution of an independent system. Consider the graph of the following system:

$$y = 2x - 6$$
$$y = \frac{2}{5}x + 1$$

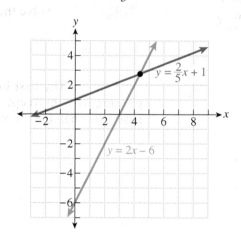

We can see that the x-coordinate of this solution is between 4 and 5 and that the y-coordinate of this solution is between 2 and 3. However, we cannot determine the exact coordinates of this solution from the graph. In the next two sections, we will develop algebraic techniques for finding solutions of linear systems of equations.

BUILDING YOUR STUDY STRATEGY

Doing Your Homework, 1 Review First Before beginning any homework assignment, it is a good idea to review. Start by going over your notes from class as a reminder of what types of problems your instructor covered and of how your instructor solved them. After reviewing your notes, keep them handy for further reference as you work through the homework assignment.

Next, you should review the appropriate section in the text. Pay particular attention to the examples. Look for the feature labeled "A Word of Caution" for advice on avoiding common errors. As you proceed through the homework assignment, refer to the section in the text as needed.

Exercises 4.1

Vocabulary

1. A(n) _____ consists of two or more linear equations.

2. Give an example of a system of two linear equations in two unknowns.

3. An ordered pair (x, y) is a(n) _____ of a system of two linear equations if it is a solution of each equation in the system.

4. A system of two linear equations is a(n) _____ system if it has exactly one solution.

5. A system of two linear equations is a(n) _____ system if it has no solution.

6. A system of two linear equations is a(n) _____ system if it has infinitely many solutions.

Is the ordered pair a solution of the given system of equations?

7. $(5, 2)$, $y = 2x - 8$
$3x + 4y = 23$

8. $(3, 9)$, $x = 5y - 42$
$7x + 2y = 39$

9. $(-6, 1)$, $3x + 2y = -16$
$2x - 5y = -7$

10. $(-7, -8)$, $x + y = -15$
$6x - 5y = -2$

11. $(-4, -10)$, $3x - 7y = 58$
$-x + 4y = -36$

12. $(5, -5)$, $4x + 9y = -25$
$3x - y = 10$

13. $(8, -6)$, $\frac{3}{4}x - \frac{2}{3}y = 2$
$\frac{1}{8}x + 2y = -11$

14. $(9, 10)$, $\frac{2}{3}x + 5y = 56$
$7x - \frac{8}{5}y = 47$

15. $\left(\frac{3}{2}, \frac{5}{6}\right)$, $8x - 12y = 2$
$5x + 9y = 15$

16. $\left(\frac{2}{3}, \frac{15}{4}\right)$, $3x + 8y = 32$
$9x - 4y = 21$

Find the solution of the system of equations on each graph. If there is no solution, state this.

17.

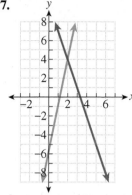

18.

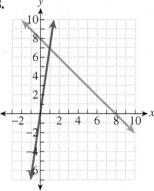

19.

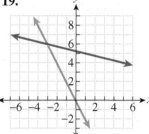

20.

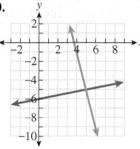

Solve the system by graphing. If the system is inconsistent and has no solution, state this. If the system is dependent, write the form of the solution for any real number x.

21. $y = x - 1$
$3x - y = 9$

22. $y = 3x - 2$
$x - y = -4$

23. $y = -2x + 8$
$y = \frac{3}{5}x - 5$

24. $4x + 2y = -8$
$y = \frac{3}{4}x + 7$

25. $y = 2x + 4$
$6x - 3y = -12$

26. $y = -5x + 6$
$3x - 4y = -24$

27. $y = \frac{3}{2}x + 3$
$7x - 2y = -14$

28. $y = -3x + 3$
$12x + 4y = 12$

29. $5x - 3y = 15$
$2x - y = 4$

30. $7x + 3y = 0$
$x + y = 4$

31. $4x - 5y = -20$
$-4x + 7y = 28$

32. $-2x + y = 10$
$2x + 3y = 6$

33. $y = 5x - 4$
$10x - 2y = 6$

34. $4x + 5y = 10$
$y = -\frac{3}{5}x + 3$

35. $9x - 2y = -18$

$y = \dfrac{1}{2}x - 7$

36. $y = -\dfrac{2}{7}x + 3$

$4x + 14y = 6$

37. Draw the graph of a linear equation that, along with the given line, forms an inconsistent system.

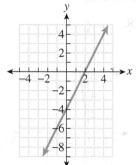

38. Draw the graph of a linear equation that, along with the given line, forms a dependent system.

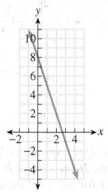

39. Draw the graph of a linear equation that, along with the given line, forms a system of equations whose single solution is the ordered pair $(5, 1)$.

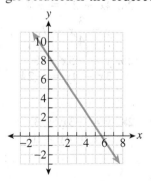

40. Draw the graphs of two linear equations that form an inconsistent system.

41. Draw the graphs of two linear equations that form a dependent system.

42. Draw the graphs of two linear equations that form a system of equations whose single solution is the ordered pair $(-3, 2)$.

Writing in Mathematics

Answer in complete sentences.

43. Explain why the solution of an independent system of equations is the ordered pair that is the point of intersection for the two lines.

44. When solving a system of equations by graphing, you may not be able to accurately determine the coordinates of the solution of an independent system. Explain.

Quick Review Exercises

Section 4.1

Solve.

1. $8x + 3(2x - 5) = 27$

2. $7x - 5(3x + 9) = -13$

3. $2(y + 6) - 3y = 17$

4. $-3(6y + 1) + 7y = 74$

4.2

Solving Systems of Equations by Using the Substitution Method

OBJECTIVES

1. Solve systems of linear equations by using the substitution method.
2. Use the substitution method to identify inconsistent systems of equations.
3. Use the substitution method to identify dependent systems of equations.
4. Solve systems of equations without variable terms with a coefficient of 1 or −1 by the substitution method.
5. Solve applied problems by using the substitution method.

Solving systems of equations by graphing each equation works well when the solution has integer coordinates. However, when the coordinates are not integers, exact solutions are difficult to find when graphing by hand. In the next two sections, we will examine algebraic methods for solving systems of linear equations. The goal of each method is to combine the two equations with two variables into a single equation with only one variable. After solving for this variable, we will substitute the value of that variable into one of the original equations and solve for the other variable.

The Substitution Method

Objective 1 Solve systems of linear equations by using the substitution method. Consider the following system of equations:

$$y = x - 5$$
$$2x + 3y = 20$$

Looking at the first equation, $y = x - 5$, we see that y is equal to the expression $x - 5$. We can use this fact to replace y with $x - 5$ in the second equation $2x + 3y = 20$. We are substituting the expression $x - 5$ for y, because the two expressions are equivalent. The first example will solve this system through use of the substitution method.

> **The Substitution Method**
>
> To solve a system of equations by using the substitution method, we solve one of the equations for one of the variables and then substitute that expression for the variable in the other equation.

EXAMPLE 1 Solve the system by substitution.

$$y = x - 5$$
$$2x + 3y = 20$$

SOLUTION Because the first equation is solved for y in terms of x, we can substitute $x - 5$ for y in the second equation.

$$y = \boxed{x - 5}$$
$$2x + 3y = 20$$

This will produce a single equation with only one variable, x.

$$2x + 3y = 20$$
$$2x + 3(x - 5) = 20 \qquad \text{Substitute } x - 5 \text{ for } y.$$
$$2x + 3x - 15 = 20 \qquad \text{Distribute.}$$
$$5x - 15 = 20 \qquad \text{Combine like terms.}$$
$$5x = 35 \qquad \text{Add 15.}$$
$$x = 7 \qquad \text{Divide both sides by 5.}$$

We are now halfway to the solution. We know that the x-coordinate of the solution is 7, and we now need to find the y-coordinate.

A WORD OF CAUTION The solution of a system of equations in two variables is an *ordered pair* (x, y), not a single value.

We can find the y-coordinate by substituting 7 for x in either of the original equations. It is easier to substitute the value into the equation $y = x - 5$, because y is already isolated in this equation. In general, it is a good idea to substitute back into the equation that was used to make the original substitution.

$$y = x - 5$$
$$y = (7) - 5 \quad \text{Substitute 7 for } x.$$
$$y = 2 \quad \text{Subtract.}$$

The solution to this system is $(7, 2)$. This solution can be checked by substituting 7 for x and 2 for y in the equation $2x + 3y = 20$. The check is left to the reader.

In the first example, one of the equations was already solved for y. To use the substitution method, we often have to solve one of the equations for x or y. When choosing which equation to work with or which variable to solve for, look for an equation that has an x or y term with a coefficient of 1 or -1 (x, $-x$, y, or $-y$). When we find one of those terms, solving for that variable can be done easily through addition or subtraction.

Quick Check 1

Solve the system by substitution.

$$y = x - 3$$
$$7x - 4y = 27$$

EXAMPLE 2   Solve the system by substitution.

$$x + 2y = 7$$
$$4x - 3y = -16$$

SOLUTION   The first equation can easily be solved for x by subtracting $2y$ from both sides of the equation. This produces the equation $x = 7 - 2y$. We can now substitute the expression $7 - 2y$ for x in the second equation $4x - 3y = -16$.

A WORD OF CAUTION Do not substitute $7 - 2y$ into the equation it came from, $x + 2y = 7$, as the resulting equation will be $7 = 7$. Substitute it into the other equation in the system. Never substitute back into the same equation.

$$4x - 3y = -16$$
$$4(7 - 2y) - 3y = -16 \quad \text{Substitute } 7 - 2y \text{ for } x.$$
$$28 - 8y - 3y = -16 \quad \text{Distribute 4.}$$
$$28 - 11y = -16 \quad \text{Combine like terms.}$$
$$-11y = -44 \quad \text{Subtract 28 from both sides.}$$
$$y = 4 \quad \text{Divide both sides by } -11.$$

Because the y-coordinate of the solution is 4, we can substitute this value for y into the equation $x = 7 - 2y$ to find the x-coordinate.

Quick Check 2

Solve the system by substitution.

$$x - y = -4$$
$$3x + 5y = 36$$

$$x = 7 - 2(4) \quad \text{Substitute 4 for } y.$$
$$x = -1 \quad \text{Simplify.}$$

The solution of this system of equations is $(-1, 4)$. We could check this solution by substituting -1 for x and 4 for y in the equation $4x - 3y = -16$. This is left to the reader. Although the first coordinate we solved for was y, keep in mind that the ordered pair must be written in the order (x, y).

Inconsistent Systems

Objective ② Use the substitution method to identify inconsistent systems of equations. Recall from the previous section that a linear system of equations with no solution is called an inconsistent system. The two lines associated with the equations of an inconsistent system are parallel lines. The next example shows how to determine that a system is an inconsistent system while using the substitution method.

EXAMPLE 3 Solve the system by substitution.

$$x = 3y - 7$$
$$3x - 9y = 18$$

SOLUTION   Because the first equation is solved for x, substitute $3y - 7$ for x in the second equation.

$$3x - 9y = 18$$
$$3(3y - 7) - 9y = 18 \quad \text{Substitute } 3y - 7 \text{ for } x.$$
$$9y - 21 - 9y = 18 \quad \text{Distribute.}$$
$$-21 = 18 \quad \text{Combine like terms.}$$

The resulting equation is false because -21 is not equal to 18. Because this equation can never be true, the system of equations has no solution ($\varnothing$) and is an inconsistent system.

Quick Check 3

Solve the system by substitution.

$$-2x + y = 3$$
$$8x - 4y = 10$$

Dependent Systems

Objective ③ Use the substitution method to identify dependent systems of equations. A dependent system of linear equations has two equations with identical graphs and is a system with infinitely many solutions. When using the substitution method to solve a dependent system, we obtain an identity, such as $3 = 3$, after making the substitution.

EXAMPLE 4 Solve the system by substitution.

$$4x - y = 3$$
$$-8x + 2y = -6$$

SOLUTION   Solve the first equation for y.

$$4x - y = 3$$
$$-y = -4x + 3 \quad \text{Subtract } 4x.$$
$$y = 4x - 3 \quad \text{Divide both sides by } -1.$$

Now substitute $4x - 3$ for y in the second equation.

$$-8x + 2y = -6$$
$$-8x + 2(4x - 3) = -6 \quad \text{Substitute } 4x - 3 \text{ for } y.$$
$$-8x + 8x - 6 = -6 \quad \text{Distribute 2.}$$
$$-6 = -6 \quad \text{Combine like terms.}$$

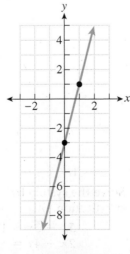

Quick Check 4

Solve the system by substitution.

$$x - 6y = 4$$
$$3x - 18y = 12$$

This equation is an identity that is true for all values of x. This system of equations is a dependent system with infinitely many solutions.

Because we have already shown that $y = 4x - 3$, the ordered pairs that are solutions have the form $(x, 4x - 3)$. The solutions are shown in the graph at the right, which is the graph of the line $y = 4x - 3$.

Objective 4 Solve systems of equations without variable terms with a coefficient of 1 or −1 by the substitution method. All of the examples in this section thus far had at least one equation containing a variable term with a coefficient of 1 or −1. Such equations are easy to solve for one variable in terms of the other. In the next example, we will learn how to use the substitution method when this is not the case.

EXAMPLE 5 Solve the system by substitution.

$$3x + 2y = -2$$
$$-2x + 7y = 43$$

SOLUTION There are no variable terms with a coefficient of 1 or −1 (x, −x, y, or −y). We will solve the first equation for y, although this selection is completely arbitrary. We could solve either equation for either variable and still find the same solution of the system.

$$3x + 2y = -2$$
$$2y = -3x - 2 \quad \text{Subtract } 3x.$$
$$y = -\frac{3}{2}x - 1 \quad \text{Divide both sides by 2.}$$

Now substitute $-\frac{3}{2}x - 1$ for y in the second equation.

$$-2x + 7y = 43$$
$$-2x + 7\left(-\frac{3}{2}x - 1\right) = 43 \quad \text{Substitute } -\frac{3}{2}x - 1 \text{ for } y.$$
$$-2x - \frac{21}{2}x - 7 = 43 \quad \text{Distribute 7.}$$
$$2\left(-2x - \frac{21}{2}x - 7\right) = 2 \cdot 43 \quad \text{Multiply both sides by 2 to clear fractions.}$$
$$2(-2x) - \overset{1}{\cancel{2}}\left(\frac{21}{\underset{1}{\cancel{2}}}x\right) - 2 \cdot 7 = 2 \cdot 43 \quad \text{Distribute and divide out common factors.}$$
$$-4x - 21x - 14 = 86 \quad \text{Multiply.}$$
$$-25x - 14 = 86 \quad \text{Combine like terms.}$$
$$-25x = 100 \quad \text{Add 14.}$$
$$x = -4 \quad \text{Divide both sides by } -25.$$

We know that the x-coordinate of the solution is −4. We will substitute this value for x in the equation $y = -\frac{3}{2}x - 1$.

$$y = -\frac{3}{2}(-4) - 1 \quad \text{Substitute } -4 \text{ for } x.$$
$$y = 5 \quad \text{Simplify.}$$

The solution to this system is $(-4, 5)$.

Quick Check 5

Solve the system by substitution.
$$5x - 3y = 17$$
$$2x + 4y = -14$$

Before turning our attention to an application of linear systems of equations, we present the following general strategy for solving these systems:

> ### Solving a System of Equations by Using the Substitution Method
>
> 1. **Solve one of the equations for either variable.** If an equation has a variable term whose coefficient is 1 or -1, try to solve that equation for that variable.
> 2. **Substitute this expression for the variable in the other equation.** At this point, we have an equation with only one variable.
> 3. **Solve this equation.** This gives us one coordinate of the ordered-pair solution. (If the equation is an identity, the system is dependent. If the equation is a contradiction, the system is inconsistent.)
> 4. **Substitute this value for the variable into the equation from Step 1.** After simplifying, this will give us the other coordinate of the solution.
> 5. **Check the solution.**

Applications

Objective 5 Solve applied problems by using the substitution method.
A college performed a play. There were 75 people in the audience. If admission was $6 for adults and $2 for children and the total box office receipts were $310, how many adults and how many children attended the play?

SOLUTION There are two unknowns in this problem: the number of adults and the number of children. We will let A represent the number of adults and C represent the number of children.

Because there are two variables, we need a system of two equations. The first equation comes from the total attendance of 75 people. Because all of these people are either adults or children, the number of adults (A) plus the number of children (C) must equal 75. The first equation is $A + C = 75$.

The second equation comes from the amount of money paid. The amount of money paid by adults ($\$6A$) plus the amount of money paid by children ($\$2C$) must equal the total amount of money paid. The second equation is $6A + 2C = 310$. Here is the system of equations we need to solve.

$$A + C = 75$$
$$6A + 2C = 310$$

Before we solve this system of equations, let's look at a table that contains all of the pertinent information for this problem.

	Number of Attendees	Cost per Ticket ($)	Money Paid ($)
Adults	A	6	$6A$
Children	C	2	$2C$
Total	75		310

Notice that the first equation in the system $A + C = 75$ can be found in the first column of the table labeled "Number of Attendees". The second equation in the system $6A + 2C = 310$ can be found in the last column in the table labeled "Money Paid ($)".

The first equation in this system can be solved for A or C; we will solve it for C. This produces the equation $C = 75 - A$, so the expression $75 - A$ can be substituted for C in the second equation.

$$6A + 2C = 310$$
$$6A + 2(75 - A) = 310 \quad \text{Substitute } 75 - A \text{ for } C.$$
$$6A + 150 - 2A = 310 \quad \text{Distribute.}$$
$$4A + 150 = 310 \quad \text{Combine like terms.}$$
$$4A = 160 \quad \text{Subtract 150.}$$
$$A = 40 \quad \text{Divide both sides by 4.}$$

There were 40 adults. We now substitute this value for A in the equation $C = 75 - A$.

$$C = 75 - (40) \quad \text{Substitute 40 for } A.$$
$$C = 35 \quad \text{Subtract.}$$

There were 40 adults and 35 children at the play.

We should check the solution for accuracy. If there were 40 adults and 35 children, that is a total of 75 people. Also, each of the 40 adults paid $6, which is $240. Each of the 35 children paid $2, which is another $70. The total paid is $310, so the solution checks.

▶ Quick Check 6

> A small business owner bought 15 new computers for his company. He paid $700 for each desktop computer and $1000 for each laptop computer. If he paid $11,700 for the computers, how many desktop computers and how many laptop computers did he buy?

BUILDING YOUR STUDY STRATEGY

Doing Your Homework, 2 Neat and Complete Two important words to keep in mind when working on your homework exercises are *neat* and *complete*. When your homework is neat, you can check your work more easily and your homework will be easier to understand when you review prior to an exam.

Be as complete as you can when working on the homework exercises. By listing each step, you are increasing your chances of being able to remember all of the steps necessary to solve a similar problem on an exam or a quiz. When you review, you may have difficulty remembering how to solve a problem if you did not write down all of the necessary steps.

Exercises 4.2

PRACTICE   WATCH   DOWNLOAD   READ   REVIEW

Vocabulary

1. To solve a system of equations by substitution, begin by solving _____
   _____.

2. Once one of the equations has been solved for one of the variables, that expression is _____ for that variable in the other equation.

3. If substitution results in an equation that is an identity, the system is a(n) _____ system.

4. If substitution results in an equation that is a contradiction, the system is a(n) _____ system.

Solve the system by substitution. If the system is inconsistent and has no solution, state this. If the system is dependent, write the form of the solution for any real number x.

5. $y = 3x - 5$
   $x + 3y = 15$

6. $x = 4y + 3$
   $2x + 5y = -7$

7. $x = 2 - 5y$
   $7x + 10y = 89$

8. $x = 1 - 4y$
   $4x + 2y = -17$

9. $y = 5x - 10$
$-10x + 2y = 20$

10. $y = 2x + 7$
$6x - 3y = -21$

11. $18x + 6y = -12$
$y = -3x - 2$

12. $x = -\frac{2}{3}y + \frac{3}{4}$
$12x + 8y = 6$

13. $y = 11 - 5x$
$-7x - 2y = 14$

14. $x = 2y - 15$
$3x + 14y = 5$

15. $y = 2.2x - 6.8$
$3x + 2y = 16$

16. $x = 4.7y - 40.6$
$5x - 2y = -31$

17. $x = \frac{2}{3}y - 4$
$6x + 7y = 75$

18. $y = \frac{3}{4}x - \frac{7}{2}$
$5x - 4y = 2$

19. $y = 4x - 3$
$y = -2x - 21$

20. $y = 5x + 2$
$y = 9x - 6$

21. $y = \frac{5}{6}x + 3$

$y = 3x - \frac{7}{2}$

22. $y = \frac{3}{2}x - 9$

$y = -\frac{7}{4}x + 4$

23. $x + 3y = 19$
$3x - 4y = -21$

24. $2x - y = -15$
$5x + 6y = 5$

25. $x + y = -6$
$4x - 3y = 46$

26. $x - y = 1$
$-2x + 7y = -42$

27. $5x + 2y = -44$
$3x + y = -26$

28. $3x + 12y = 10$
$x + 4y = 7$

29. $2x - y = -1$

$8x + 2y = 17$

30. $9x - 6y = 19$

$-x + 8y = 4$

31. $x = 4y - 5$
$2x + 2y = 90$

32. $y = 2x - 17$
$2x + 2y = 38$

33. $x + y = 40$
$0.10x + 0.25y = 8.50$

34. $x + y = 200$
$6.75x + 4.25y = 1150$

35. $x + y = 5000$
$0.04x + 0.07y = 260$

36. $x + y = 9000$
$0.06x + 0.15y = 1215$

37. $y = x + 100$
$0.02x + 0.025y = 22.75$

38. $y = x - 120$
$0.015x + 0.04y = 15$

39. $x + y = 80$
$0.18x + 0.33y = 0.24(80)$

40. $x + y = 50$
$0.25x + 0.75y = 0.60(50)$

41. $6x + y = 21$
$-18x - 3y = -63$

42. $10x - y = -23$
$-20x + 2y = -46$

43. $x + 2.8y = 3.4$
$2x - 9y = -37$

44. $-3.4x + y = -30.8$
$2.1x + 3.2y = 57.2$

45. $\frac{3}{2}x + y = -7$
$-3x + 2y = 34$

46. $x + \frac{3}{8}y = 24$
$16x - 11y = -24$

47. $4x + 2y = 10$
$5x - 4y = 6$

48. $9x + 3y = 36$
$7x - 6y = 78$

49. $3x + 5y = 14$
$6x - 5y = -32$

50. $9x + 4y = 23$
$5x - 2y = -2$

51. A college basketball team charges $5 admission to the general public for its games, while students at the college pay only $2. If the attendance for last night's

game was 1200 people and the total receipts were $5250, how many of the people in attendance were students and how many were not students?

52. Kenny walks away from a blackjack table with a total of $62 in $1 and $5 chips. If Kenny has 26 chips, how many are $1 chips and how many are $5 chips?

53. A sorority set up a charity dinner to help raise money for a local children's support group. The sorority sold chicken dinners for $8 and steak dinners for $10. If 142 people ate dinner at the fund-raiser and the sorority raised $1326, how many people ordered chicken and how many people ordered steak?

54. Jeannie has some $10 bills and some $20 bills. If she has 273 bills worth a total of $4370, how many of the bills are $10 bills and how many are $20 bills?

55. The following equations give the median age (y) for men and women at their first marriage in a particular year, where x represents the number of years after 1995.

Men: $y = 0.05x + 26.7$
Women: $y = 0.10x + 24.6$

If the current trend continues, in what year will the median age at first marriage be equal for men and women? (*Source: U.S. Census Bureau*)

56. The following equations give the number of college faculty (y) by gender in a particular year, where x represents the number of years after 1987.

Men: $y = 10,045x + 502,183$
Women: $y = 16,475x + 247,693$

If the current trend continues, in what year will the number of male and female faculty members be equal? (*Source: U.S. Department of Education*)

Writing in Mathematics

Answer in complete sentences.

57. In your own words, explain how to solve a system of linear equations using the substitution method.

58. When using the substitution method, how can you tell that a system of equations is inconsistent and has no solutions? How can you tell that a system of equations is dependent and has infinitely many solutions? Explain your answer.

59. *Solutions Manual* Write a solutions manual page for the following problem.

Solve the system of equations $y = 3x - 7$
by the substitution method. $5x - 7y = -15$

4.3

Solving Systems of Equations by Using the Addition Method

OBJECTIVES

1. Solve systems of equations by using the addition method.
2. Use the addition method to identify inconsistent and dependent systems of equations.
3. Solve systems of equations with coefficients that are fractions or decimals by using the addition method.
4. Solve applied problems by using the addition method.

The Addition Method

Objective 1 Solve systems of equations by using the addition method.
In this section, we will examine the **addition method** for solving systems of linear equations. (This method also is known as the **elimination method**.)

┌─ The Addition Method ─────────────────────────────────

The addition method is an algebraic alternative to the substitution method. The two equations in a system of linear equations will be combined into a single equation with a single variable by adding them together.

└──

In the last section, we saw that solving a system of equations by substitution is fairly easy when one of the equations contains a variable term with a coefficient of 1 or −1. The substitution method can become quite tedious for solving a system when this is not the case.

As with the substitution method, the goal of the addition method is to combine the two given equations into a single equation with only one variable. This method is based on the addition property of equality from Chapter 2, which says that when we add the same number to both sides of an equation, the equation remains true. (For any real numbers a, b, and c, if $a = b$, then $a + c = b + c$.) This property can be extended to cover adding equal expressions to both sides of an equation: if $a = b$ and $c = d$, then $a + c = b + d$.

Consider the following system:

$$3x + 2y = 20$$
$$5x - 2y = -4$$

If we add the left side of the first equation ($3x + 2y$) to the left side of the second equation ($5x - 2y$), this expression will be equal to the total of the two numbers on the right side of the equations. Here is the result of this addition.

$$\begin{array}{rcl} 3x + 2y &=& 20 \\ 5x - 2y &=& -4 \\ \hline 8x &=& 16 \end{array}$$

Notice that when we added these two equations, the two terms containing y were opposites and summed to zero, leaving an equation containing only the variable x. Next, we solve this equation for x and substitute this value for x in either of the two original equations to find y. The first example will walk through this entire process.

EXAMPLE 1 Solve the system by addition.

$$3x + 2y = 20$$
$$5x - 2y = -4$$

SOLUTION Because the two terms containing y are opposites, we can use addition to eliminate y.

$$\begin{array}{rcl} 3x + 2y &=& 20 \\ 5x - 2y &=& -4 \qquad \text{Add the two equations.} \\ \hline 8x &=& 16 \\ x &=& 2 \qquad \text{Divide both sides by 8.} \end{array}$$

The x-coordinate of the solution is 2. We now substitute this value for x in the first original equation. (We could have chosen the other equation, because it will produce exactly the same solution.)

$$\begin{array}{rcl} 3x + 2y &=& 20 \\ 3(2) + 2y &=& 20 \qquad \text{Substitute 2 for } x. \\ 6 + 2y &=& 20 \qquad \text{Multiply.} \\ 2y &=& 14 \qquad \text{Subtract 6.} \\ y &=& 7 \qquad \text{Divide both sides by 2.} \end{array}$$

Quick Check 1

Solve the system by addition.
$$4x + 3y = 31$$
$$-4x + 5y = -23$$

The solution of this system is the ordered pair $(2, 7)$. We could check this solution by substituting 2 for x and 7 for y in the equation $5x - 2y = -4$. This is left to the reader.

If the two equations in a system do not contain a pair of opposite variable terms, we can still use the addition method. We must first multiply both sides of one or both equations by a constant(s) in such a way that two of the variable terms become opposites. Then we proceed as in the first example.

EXAMPLE 2 Solve the system by addition.

$$2x - 3y = -16$$
$$-6x + 5y = 32$$

SOLUTION   Adding these two equations at this point would not be helpful, as the sum would still contain both variables. If we multiply the first equation by 3, the terms containing x will be opposites. This allows us to proceed with the addition method.

$$
\begin{array}{c}
2x - 3y = -16 \\
-6x + 5y = 32
\end{array}
\xrightarrow{\text{Multiply by 3}}
\begin{array}{c}
6x - 9y = -48 \\
-6x + 5y = 32
\end{array}
$$

$$
\begin{array}{rl}
6x - 9y = & -48 \\
-6x + 5y = & 32 \quad \text{Add.} \\
\hline
-4y = & -16 \\
y = & 4 \quad \text{Divide both sides by } -4.
\end{array}
$$

A WORD OF CAUTION Be sure to multiply *both* sides of the equation by the same number. Do not multiply just the side containing the variable terms.

Now substitute 4 for y in the equation $2x - 3y = -16$ and solve for x.

$$
\begin{array}{rl}
2x - 3(4) = -16 & \text{Substitute 4 for } y. \\
2x - 12 = -16 & \text{Multiply.} \\
2x = -4 & \text{Add 12.} \\
x = -2 & \text{Divide both sides by 2.}
\end{array}
$$

The solution of this system is $(-2, 4)$. (Be sure to write the x-coordinate first in the ordered pair even though we solved for y first.)

Quick Check 2

Solve the system by addition.
$$2x - 9y = 33$$
$$4x + 3y = 3$$

Before continuing, let's outline the basic strategy for using the addition method to solve systems of linear equations.

Using the Addition Method

1. **Write each equation in standard form $(Ax + By = C)$.** For each equation, gather all variable terms on the left side and all constants on the right side.
2. **Multiply one or both equations by the appropriate constant(s).** The goal of this step is to make the terms containing x or the terms containing y opposites.
3. **Add the two equations together.** At this point, we should have one equation containing a single variable.
4. **Solve the resulting equation.** This will give us one of the coordinates of the solution.
5. **Substitute this value for the appropriate variable in either of the original equations and solve for the other variable.** Choose the equation that you believe will be easier to solve. When we solve this equation, we find the other coordinate of the solution.
6. **Write the solution as an ordered pair.**
7. **Check your solution.**

EXAMPLE 3 Solve the system by addition.

$$5x + 8y - 22 = 0$$
$$7x = 6y + 5$$

SOLUTION   To use the addition method, we must write each equation in standard form.

$$5x + 8y = 22$$
$$7x - 6y = 5$$

Then we must decide which variable to eliminate. A wise choice for this system is to eliminate y, as the two coefficients already have opposite signs. If we multiply the first equation by 3 and the second equation by 4, the terms containing y will be $24y$ and $-24y$. Note that 24 is the LCM of 8 and 6.

$$5x + 8y = 22 \quad \xrightarrow{\text{Multiply by 3}} \quad 15x + 24y = 66$$
$$7x - 6y = 5 \quad \xrightarrow{\text{Multiply by 4}} \quad 28x - 24y = 20$$

$$\begin{array}{r} 15x + 24y = 66 \\ 28x - 24y = 20 \\ \hline 43x \phantom{{} - 24y} = 86 \end{array} \quad \text{Add to eliminate } y.$$

$$x = 2 \quad \text{Divide both sides by 43.}$$

The x-coordinate of the solution is 2. Substituting 2 for x in the equation $5x + 8y = 22$ will allow us to find the y-coordinate.

$$5(2) + 8y = 22 \quad \text{Substitute 2 for } x.$$
$$10 + 8y = 22 \quad \text{Multiply.}$$
$$8y = 12 \quad \text{Subtract 10.}$$
$$y = \frac{12}{8} \quad \text{Divide both sides by 8.}$$
$$y = \frac{3}{2} \quad \text{Simplify.}$$

Quick Check 3

Solve the system by addition.

$$3x + 2y = -26$$
$$5y = 2x + 11$$

The solution to this system is $\left(2, \dfrac{3}{2}\right)$. The check is left to the reader.

Objective 2 Use the addition method to identify inconsistent and dependent systems of equations. Recall from the previous section that when solving an inconsistent system (no solution), we obtain an equation that is a contradiction, such as $0 = -6$. When solving a dependent system (infinitely many solutions), we end up with an equation that is an identity, such as $7 = 7$. The same is true when applying the addition method.

EXAMPLE 4 Solve the system by addition.

$$3x + 5y = 15$$
$$6x + 10y = 30$$

SOLUTION   Suppose we chose to eliminate the variable x. We can do so by multiplying the first equation by -2. This produces the following system:

$$3x + 5y = 15 \quad \xrightarrow{\text{Multiply by } -2} \quad -6x - 10y = -30$$
$$6x + 10y = 30 \quad\quad\quad\quad\quad\quad 6x + 10y = 30$$

$$\begin{array}{r} -6x - 10y = -30 \\ 6x + 10y = 30 \\ \hline 0 = 0 \end{array} \quad \text{Add to eliminate } x.$$

Because the resulting equation is an identity, this is a dependent system with infinitely many solutions. To determine the form of the solutions, we can solve the equation $3x + 5y = 15$ for y.

$$3x + 5y = 15$$

$$5y = -3x + 15 \quad \text{Subtract } 3x \text{ to isolate } 5y.$$

$$y = -\frac{3}{5}x + 3 \quad \text{Divide both sides by 5 and simplify.}$$

The ordered pairs that are solutions have the form $(x, -\frac{3}{5}x + 3)$. We also could display the solutions by graphing the line $3x + 5y = 15$, or $y = -\frac{3}{5}x + 3$.

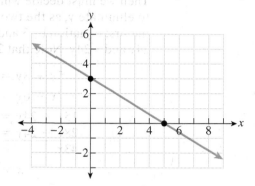

Quick Check 4

Solve the system by addition.

$$2x - 3y = 12$$
$$-4x + 6y = -24$$

EXAMPLE 5 Solve the system by addition.

$$6x - 3y = 7$$
$$-2x + y = -3$$

SOLUTION To eliminate the variable y, multiply the second equation by 3. The variable term containing y in the second equation would then be $3y$, which is the opposite of $-3y$ in the first equation.

$$6x - 3y = 7 \qquad\qquad\qquad 6x - 3y = 7$$
$$-2x + y = -3 \quad\xrightarrow{\text{Multiply by 3}}\quad -6x + 3y = -9$$

$$\begin{array}{r} 6x - 3y = 7 \\ -6x + 3y = -9 \quad \text{Add to eliminate } y. \\ \hline 0 = -2 \end{array}$$

Because the resulting equation is false, this is an inconsistent system with no solution.

Quick Check 5

Solve the system by addition.

$$3x = 4y + 11$$
$$9x - 12y = 30$$

Systems of Equations with Coefficients That Are Fractions or Decimals

Objective 3 Solve systems of equations with coefficients that are fractions or decimals by using the addition method. If one or both equations in a system of linear equations contain fractions or decimals, we can clear the fractions or decimals first and then solve the resulting system.

EXAMPLE 6   Solve the system by addition.

$$\frac{5}{4}x + \frac{1}{3}y = 3$$

$$\frac{3}{8}x - \frac{5}{6}y = \frac{13}{2}$$

SOLUTION   The LCM of the denominators in the first equation is 12; so if we multiply both sides of the first equation by 12, we can clear the equation of fractions.

$$12\left(\frac{5}{4}x + \frac{1}{3}y\right) = 12 \cdot 3 \quad \text{Multiply both sides by 12.}$$

$$\overset{3}{\cancel{12}} \cdot \frac{5}{\underset{1}{4}}x + \overset{4}{\cancel{12}} \cdot \frac{1}{\underset{1}{3}}y = 12 \cdot 3 \quad \text{Distribute and divide out common factors.}$$

$$15x + 4y = 36 \quad \text{Simplify.}$$

Multiplying both sides of the second equation by 24 will clear the fractions from that equation.

$$24\left(\frac{3}{8}x - \frac{5}{6}y\right) = 24 \cdot \frac{13}{2} \quad \text{Multiply both sides by 24.}$$

$$\overset{3}{\cancel{24}} \cdot \frac{3}{\underset{1}{8}}x - \overset{4}{\cancel{24}} \cdot \frac{5}{\underset{1}{6}}y = \overset{12}{\cancel{24}} \cdot \frac{13}{\underset{1}{2}} \quad \text{Distribute and divide out common factors.}$$

$$9x - 20y = 156 \quad \text{Simplify.}$$

Here is the resulting system of equations.

$$15x + 4y = 36$$
$$9x - 20y = 156$$

Because the coefficient of the term containing y in the second equation is a multiple of the coefficient containing y in the first equation, we will eliminate y. This can be done by multiplying the first equation by 5.

$$15x + 4y = 36 \quad \xrightarrow{\text{Multiply by 5}} \quad 75x + 20y = 180$$
$$9x - 20y = 156 \qquad\qquad\qquad\qquad 9x - 20y = 156$$

$$\begin{array}{r} 75x + 20y = 180 \\ 9x - 20y = 156 \\ \hline 84x \qquad\quad = 336 \end{array} \quad \text{Add to eliminate } y.$$

$$x = 4 \quad \text{Divide both sides by 84.}$$

The x-coordinate of the solution is 4. To solve for y, we can substitute 4 for x in either of the original equations, or we can substitute into either of the equations that was created by clearing the fractions. We will use the equation $15x + 4y = 36$.

$$15(4) + 4y = 36 \quad \text{Substitute 4 for } x.$$
$$60 + 4y = 36 \quad \text{Multiply.}$$
$$4y = -24 \quad \text{Subtract 60.}$$
$$y = -6 \quad \text{Divide both sides by 4.}$$

The solution of this system is the ordered pair $(4, -6)$.

Quick Check 6

Solve the system by addition.

$$-\frac{2}{3}x + \frac{5}{2}y = 14$$

$$\frac{5}{12}x + \frac{3}{4}y = \frac{1}{2}$$

If one or both equations in a system of linear equations contain decimals, we can clear the decimals by multiplying by the appropriate power of 10 and then solve the resulting system.

EXAMPLE 7 Solve the system by addition.

$$0.3x + 2y = 7.5$$
$$0.04x + 0.07y = 0.41$$

SOLUTION If we multiply both sides of the first equation by 10, we can clear the equation of decimals.

$$10(0.3x + 2y) = 10(7.5) \quad \text{Multiply both sides by 10.}$$
$$3x + 20y = 75 \quad \text{Distribute and multiply.}$$

For the second equation, multiply both sides by 100 to clear the decimals.

$$100(0.04x + 0.07y) = 100(0.41) \quad \text{Multiply both sides by 100.}$$
$$4x + 7y = 41 \quad \text{Distribute and multiply.}$$

Here is the resulting system of equations.

$$3x + 20y = 75$$
$$4x + 7y = 41$$

Eliminate x by multiplying the first equation by 4 and the second equation by -3.

$$3x + 20y = 75 \xrightarrow{\text{Multiply by 4}} 12x + 80y = 300$$
$$4x + 7y = 41 \xrightarrow{\text{Multiply by } -3} -12x - 21y = -123$$

$$\begin{array}{r} 12x + 80y = 300 \\ -12x - 21y = -123 \\ \hline 59y = 177 \end{array} \quad \text{Add to eliminate } x.$$

$$y = 3 \quad \text{Divide both sides by 59.}$$

The y-coordinate of the solution is 3. To solve for x, substitute 3 for y in either of the original equations or in either of the equations that was created by clearing the decimals. The equation $3x + 20y = 75$ is a good choice, as it will be easier to solve for x in an equation that does not contain decimals.

$$3x + 20(3) = 75 \quad \text{Substitute 3 for } y.$$
$$3x + 60 = 75 \quad \text{Multiply.}$$
$$3x = 15 \quad \text{Subtract 60.}$$
$$x = 5 \quad \text{Divide both sides by 3.}$$

◀ The solution to this system is the ordered pair $(5, 3)$.

Quick Check 7

Solve the system by addition.

$$0.03x + 0.05y = 29.5$$
$$x + y = 700$$

Which method is more efficient to use: substitution or addition?

The substitution and addition methods for solving a system of equations will solve any system of linear equations. There are certain times when one method is more efficient to apply than the other, and knowing which method to choose for a particular system of equations can save time and prevent errors. In general, if one of the equations in the system is already solved for one of the variables, such as $y = 3x$ or $x = -4y + 5$, using the substitution method is a good choice. The substitution method also works well when one of the equations contains a variable term with a coefficient of 1 or -1 (such as $x + 6y = 17$ or $7x - y = 14$). Otherwise, consider using the addition method.

Applications

Objective 4 Solve applied problems by using the addition method. We conclude this section with an application of solving systems of equations using the addition method.

EXAMPLE 8 Dylan has $3.20 in change in his pocket. Each coin is either a dime or a quarter. If Dylan has 17 coins in his pocket, how many are dimes and how many are quarters?

SOLUTION There are two unknowns in this problem: the number of dimes and the number of quarters. We will let d represent the number of dimes and q represent the number of quarters.

The first equation in the system comes from the fact that Dylan has 17 coins. Because all of these coins are either dimes or quarters, the number of dimes (d) plus the number of quarters (q) must equal 17. The first equation is $d + q = 17$.

The second equation comes from the amount of money Dylan has in his pocket. The amount of money in dimes ($\$0.10d$) plus the amount of money in quarters ($\$0.25q$) must equal the total amount of money he has. The second equation is $0.10d + 0.25q = 3.20$.

	Number of Coins	Value per Coin ($)	Money in Pocket ($)
Dimes	d	0.10	0.10d
Quarters	q	0.25	0.25q
Total	17		3.20

Here is the system of equations that we need to solve.

$$d + q = 17$$
$$0.10d + 0.25q = 3.20$$

Multiplying both sides of the second equation by 100 will clear the equation of decimals, producing the following system:

$$d + q = 17$$
$$10d + 25q = 320$$

Now we can eliminate d by multiplying the first equation by -10.

$$
\begin{aligned}
d + q &= 17 \\
10d + 25q &= 320
\end{aligned}
\quad \xrightarrow{\text{Multiply by } -10} \quad
\begin{aligned}
-10d - 10q &= -170 \\
10d + 25q &= 320
\end{aligned}
$$

$$
\begin{aligned}
-10d - 10q &= -170 \\
\underline{10d + 25q =\quad 320} \quad &\text{Add to eliminate } d. \\
15q &= 150 \\
q &= 10 \quad \text{Divide both sides by 15.}
\end{aligned}
$$

There are 10 quarters in Dylan's pocket. To find the number of dimes he has, we can substitute 10 for q in the equation $d + q = 17$ and solve for d.

$$d + (10) = 17 \quad \text{Substitute 10 for } q.$$
$$d = 7 \quad \text{Subtract 10.}$$

Dylan has 7 dimes and 10 quarters in his pocket. You can verify that the total amount of money in his pocket is $3.20.

Quick Check 8

Erica has $5.35 in change in her pocket. Each coin is either a nickel or a dime. If Erica has 75 coins in her pocket, how many are nickels and how many are dimes?

BUILDING YOUR STUDY STRATEGY

Doing Your Homework, 3 Difficult Problems Eventually, there will be a homework exercise that you cannot answer correctly. Rather than giving up, here are some options to consider.

- Review your class notes. A similar problem may have been discussed in class.
- Review the related section in the text. You may be able to find a similar example, or there may be a Word of Caution warning you about typical errors on that type of problem.
- Call someone in your study group. A member of your study group may be able to help you figure out what to do.

If you still cannot solve the problem, move on and try the next problem. Ask your instructor about the problem at your next class.

Exercises 4.3

MyMathLab

PRACTICE   WATCH   DOWNLOAD   READ   REVIEW

Vocabulary

1. If an equation in a system of equations contains fractions, you can clear the fractions by multiplying both sides of the equation by the _____ of the denominators.

2. If an equation in a system of equations contains decimals, you can clear the decimals by multiplying both sides of the equation by the appropriate power of _____.

3. If the addition method results in an equation that is an identity, the system is a(n) _____ system.

4. If the addition method results in an equation that is a contradiction, the system is a(n) _____ system.

Solve the system by addition. If the system is inconsistent and has no solution, state this. If the system is dependent, write the form of the solution for any real number x.

5. $5x + 4y = -56$
   $3x - 4y = -8$

6. $7x + 5y = 39$
   $-7x + 2y = -53$

7. $-3x + 6y = 36$
   $3x - 11y = -51$

8. $9x - 8y = 25$
   $-3x + 8y = 29$

9. $4x + 3y = 1$
   $13x - 6y = 82$

10. $8x + 7y = -26$
    $-4x + 9y = 138$

11. $2x - 4y = 11$
    $-4x + 8y = -22$

12. $8x - 3y = 34$
    $-2x + 9y = 8$

13. $x + 4y = 11$
    $3x + 16y = 37$

14. $10x + 2y = 44$
    $3x + 8y = 65$

15. $12x + 9y = -69$
    $3x + 5y = -31$

16. $2x + 3y = 13$
    $10x + 15y = 26$

17. $5x + 6y = -9$
    $-x + 9y = -39$

18. $8x + 3y = -33$
    $9x - y = -59$

19. $7x + 4y = 85$
    $11x - 6y = -63$

20. $8x + 5y = -87$
    $-10x + 9y = -59$

21. $-8x + 5y = -28$
    $3x + 8y = -29$

22. $5x - 5y = 45$
    $-4x + 4y = -36$

23. $4x - 3y = -6$
    $6x + 5y = 29$

24. $-7x + 4y = -25$
    $5x + 14y = 60$

25. $-6x + 9y = 17$
    $-4x + 6y = 12$

26. $3x - 11y = 43$
    $2x - 7y = 27$

27. $5x + 7y = 16$
    $4x + 8y = 14$

28. $4x + 6y = -20$
$6x + 13y = -48$

29. $4y = 3x - 13$
$6x + 5y = 52$

30. $7x = -18 - 4y$
$3x - 2y = -30$

31. $5x = 3y + 21$
$-5x + 4y = -23$

32. $5y = 2x + 13$
$4x + 3y = 65$

33. $\dfrac{1}{2}x + \dfrac{2}{5}y = \dfrac{7}{5}$
$\dfrac{1}{4}x - \dfrac{1}{6}y = \dfrac{1}{3}$

34. $\dfrac{1}{4}x + \dfrac{1}{2}y = \dfrac{11}{4}$
$-\dfrac{1}{9}x + \dfrac{1}{3}y = \dfrac{4}{9}$

35. $\dfrac{2}{3}x + \dfrac{1}{6}y = 4$
$\dfrac{5}{3}x - y = -7$

36. $\dfrac{1}{7}x + \dfrac{1}{28}y = \dfrac{1}{2}$
$\dfrac{1}{3}x - \dfrac{2}{9}y = -\dfrac{23}{18}$

37. $x + y = 3600$
$0.03x + 0.07y = 144$

38. $x + y = 6000$
$0.04x + 0.06y = 330$

39. $x + y = 120$
$8.50x + 5.75y = 827.50$

40. $x + y = 100$
$0.25x + 0.17y = 23.40$

41. $x + y = 100$
$0.36x + 0.48y = 0.45(100)$

42. $x + y = 60$
$0.42x + 0.22y = 0.36(60)$

43. A man bought roses and carnations for his wife on Valentine's Day. Each rose cost $6, and each carnation cost $4. If the man spent $68 for a total of 15 roses and carnations, how many of each type of flower did he buy?

44. For matinees, a movie theater charges $7 per adult and $4 per child. If 84 people attended a matinee and paid a total of $432, how many adults and how many children were there?

45. A family purchased 7 trees and 4 shrubs from a local nursery and paid a total of $312. Another family purchased 4 trees and 15 shrubs for a total of $280. How much does the nursery charge for each tree and each shrub?

46. A large group at Maxine's Pizzeria purchased 6 pizzas and 4 pitchers of soda for $114. Another group bought 9 pizzas and 7 pitchers of soda for $175.50. How much does the pizzeria charge for each pizza and each pitcher of soda?

47. Alycia opens her piggy bank to find only dimes and nickels inside. She counts the coins and finds that she has 81 coins totaling $6.50. How many dimes and how many nickels were in the piggy bank?

48. Charlotte has 24 postage stamps. Some of the stamps are 28¢ stamps, and the rest are 44¢ stamps. If the total value of the stamps is $9.12, how many of each type of stamp does Charlotte have?

49. Jessica has a handful of nickels and quarters worth a total of $6.95. If she has seven more nickels than quarters, how many of each type of coin does she have?

50. The cash box at a bake sale contains nickels, dimes, and quarters. The number of quarters is four more than three times the number of dimes. The number of nickels is the same as the number of dimes. If the cash box contains $16.30 in coins, how many of each type of coin are in the box?

Mixed Practice, 51–62

Solve by substitution or addition.

51. $5x - 2y = 47$
$3x + 4y = 23$

52. $x = 4y + 12$
$3x + 2y = -34$

53. $y = 2x + 20$
$8x - 5y = -86$

54. $7x - 4y = -81$
$4x + 5y = -141$

55. $y = \dfrac{3}{4}x + 1$
$3x + 8y = 116$

56. $\dfrac{2}{3}x - \dfrac{1}{2}y = 6$
$\dfrac{5}{12}x + \dfrac{3}{8}y = 1$

57. $y = 4x - 8$
$-12x + 3y = -24$

58. $14x + 21y = 28$
$12x + 18y = -24$

59. $13x - 8y = 20$
$9x + 10y = -126$

60. $x = -2y + 1$
$-3x + 17y = -72$

61. $y = 6x - 14$
$4x + 5y = -19$

62. $2x - 6y = 13$
$8x + 9y = \dfrac{115}{2}$

Writing in Mathematics

63. *Newsletter* Write a newsletter explaining how to solve a system of two linear equations by using the addition method.

4.5

Systems of Linear Inequalities

OBJECTIVES

1 Solve a system of linear inequalities by graphing.
2 Solve a system of linear inequalities with more than two inequalities.

In addition to systems of linear equations, we can have a **system of linear inequalities.** A system of linear inequalities is made up of two or more linear inequalities. As with systems of equations, an ordered pair is a solution to a system of linear inequalities if it is a solution to each linear inequality in the system.

Solving a System of Linear Inequalities by Graphing

Objective 1 Solve a system of linear inequalities by graphing. To find the solution set to a system of linear inequalities, we begin by graphing each inequality separately. If the solutions to the individual inequalities intersect, the region of intersection is the solution set to the system of inequalities.

EXAMPLE 1 Graph the system of inequalities.

$$y \geq 2x - 5$$
$$y < 3x - 7$$

SOLUTION

Begin by graphing the inequality $y \geq 2x - 5$. To do this, graph the line $y = 2x - 5$ as a solid line. Recall that we use a solid line when the points on the line are solutions to the inequality. Because this equation is in slope–intercept form, an efficient way to graph it is by plotting the y-intercept at $(0, -5)$ and then using the slope of 2 to find additional points on the line.

Because the origin is not on this line, we can use $(0, 0)$ as a test point. Substitute 0 for x and 0 for y in the inequality $y \geq 2x - 5$.

$$0 \geq 2(0) - 5$$
$$0 \geq 0 - 5$$
$$0 \geq -5$$

Substituting these coordinates into the inequality $y \geq 2x - 5$ produces a true statement; so we shade the half-plane containing $(0, 0)$.

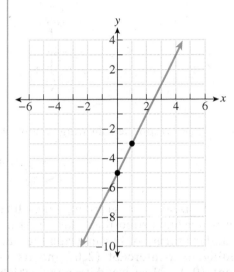

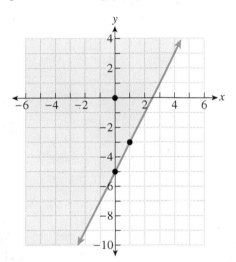

Now we turn our attention to the second inequality in the system. To graph the inequality $y < 3x - 7$, we use a dashed line to graph the equation $y = 3x - 7$. Recall that the dashed line is used to signify that no point on the line is a solution to the inequality. Again, this equation is in slope–intercept form, so we graph the line by plotting the y-intercept at $(0, -7)$ and using the slope of 3 to find additional points on the line.

We can use the origin as a test point for this inequality as well. Substituting 0 for x and 0 for y produces a false statement.

$$0 < 3(0) - 7$$
$$0 < 0 - 7$$
$$0 < -7$$

We shade the half-plane on the opposite side of the line from the origin.

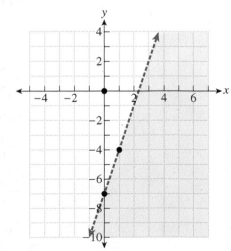

The solution of the system of linear inequalities is the region where the two solutions intersect.

Graph the system of inequalities.

$$y > x + 3$$
$$2x + 3y < 6$$

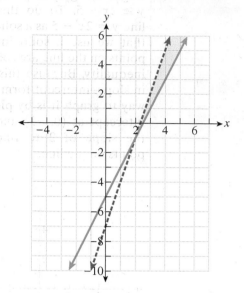

EXAMPLE 2 Graph the following system of inequalities:

$$2x + y \leq 4$$
$$y > 3x$$

SOLUTION Begin by graphing the line $2x + y = 4$ using a solid line. This equation is in standard form, so we can graph the line by finding its x-intercept $(2, 0)$ and its y-intercept $(0, 4)$. Now we determine which half-plane to shade. Because the line does not pass through the origin, we can choose $(0, 0)$ as a test point.

$$2(0) + (0) \leq 4$$
$$0 \leq 4$$

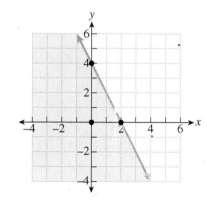

Because the test point produced a true statement, we shade the half-plane containing the origin.

Now we turn our attention to the inequality $y > 3x$. We begin by graphing the line $y = 3x$ as a dashed line. The y-intercept is at the origin, and the slope of the line is 3. We must choose a point that is clearly not on the line to use as a test point, such as $(5, 0)$.

$$0 > 3(5)$$
$$0 > 15$$

The test point produced a false statement, so we shade the half-plane that does not contain the test point.

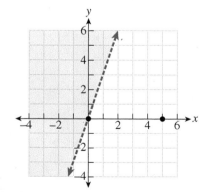

Quick Check 2
Graph the system of inequalities.

$$-3x + 4y \le 8$$
$$y \ge 0$$

The solution of the system of inequalities is the region where the two shaded regions intersect.

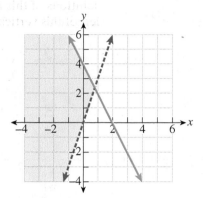

Solving a System of Linear Inequalities with More than Two Inequalities

Objective 2 Solve a system of linear inequalities with more than two inequalities. The next example involves a system of three linear inequalities. Regardless of the number of inequalities in a system, we still find the solution in the same manner. Graph each inequality individually and then find the region where the shaded regions intersect.

EXAMPLE 3 Graph the system of inequalities.

$$3x + 4y > 12$$
$$x < 6$$
$$y > 4$$

SOLUTION   Begin by graphing the line $3x + 4y = 12$ with a dashed line. This is the line associated with the first inequality. Because the equation is in standard form, we can graph it by finding its x- and y-intercepts.

$3x + 4y = 12$	
x-intercept ($y = 0$)	y-intercept ($x = 0$)
$3x + 4(0) = 12$	$3(0) + 4y = 12$
$3x = 12$	$4y = 12$
$x = 4$	$y = 3$
$(4, 0)$	$(0, 3)$

The x-intercept is at $(4, 0)$. The y-intercept of the line is at $(0, 3)$. Because the line does not pass through the origin, we can use $(0, 0)$ as a test point. When we substitute 0 for x and 0 for y in the inequality $3x + 4y > 12$, we obtain a false statement.

$$3(0) + 4(0) > 12$$
$$0 > 12$$

Because this statement is not true, we shade the half-plane on the side of the line that does not contain the point $(0, 0)$.

To graph the second inequality, begin with the graph of the vertical line $x = 6$. This line also is dashed. The solutions of this inequality are to the left of this vertical line.

For the third inequality, graph the dashed horizontal line $y = 4$. The solutions of this inequality are above the horizontal line $y = 4$.

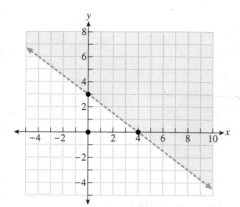

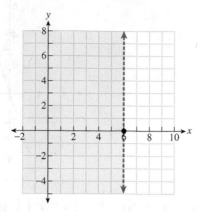

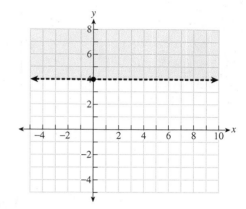

Now display the solutions to the system of inequalities by finding the region of intersection for these three inequalities, shown in the graph below.

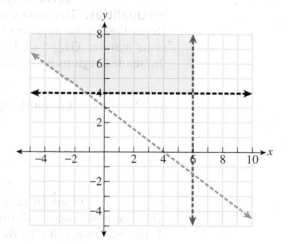

Quick Check 3

Graph the system of inequalities.

$$x + y \le 8$$
$$x \ge 1$$
$$y \ge -1$$

BUILDING YOUR STUDY STRATEGY

Doing Your Homework, 5 Homework Schedule Try to establish a regular schedule for doing your homework. Some students find it advantageous to work on their homework as soon as possible after class, while the material is still fresh in their minds. You may be able to find other students in your class who can work with you in the library.

It is crucial that you complete an assignment before the next class. Because math skills build on previous concepts, if you do not understand the material one day, you will have difficulty understanding the next day's material.

Exercises 4.5

Vocabulary

1. A(n) _____ is made up of two or more linear inequalities.

2. A linear inequality is graphed with a(n) _____ line if it involves either of the symbols $<$ or $>$.

3. A linear inequality is graphed with a(n) _____ line if it involves either of the symbols $\leq$ or $\geq$.

4. When solving a system of linear inequalities, shade the region where the solutions of the individual inequalities _____.

Graph the system of inequalities.

5. $y \geq 5x - 2$
   $y \leq -x + 1$

6. $y > 4x - 3$
   $y \leq 2x - 1$

7. $y \leq 3x - 1$
   $y > -\dfrac{3}{4}x + 6$

8. $y < 2x + 2$
   $y > 6x - 2$

9. $x + y \geq 5$
   $x - y \geq 3$

10. $x - y \geq 7$
    $x + y \leq 1$

11. $y < 5x + 5$
    $y > 5x - 5$

12. $y \leq 3x + 3$
    $y \geq 3x - 1$

13. $x + 4y < 8$
    $3x - 2y < 6$

14. $5x + 2y \leq 10$
    $-3x + y > 5$

15. $-7x + 3y > 21$
    $4x + 9y \leq 36$

16. $8x + y \geq -8$
    $3x + 4y < -12$

17. $y \geq 5$
    $5x + 2y < 0$

18. $-4x + y < 6$
    $4x - y < 2$

19. $y \geq 3x$
$\quad y > 3$

20. $x < -4$
$\quad 2x + 6y > 12$

27. $3x - 2y \leq -10$
$\quad y < -4x - 6$
$\quad -x + 3y < 12$

21. $y > -\dfrac{3}{2}x + 6$
$\quad 4x - 3y \geq -6$

22. $x < 4$
$\quad y \geq -7$

28. $x \geq -5$
$\quad x \leq 4$
$\quad y < \dfrac{1}{5}x + 2$

23. $x > 1$
$\quad 8x - 4y > 12$

24. $3x + 10y > 15$
$\quad y \leq -\dfrac{5}{2}x + 7$

29. Write a system of linear inequalities whose solution is the entire first quadrant, as shown in the graph to the right.

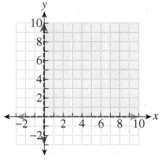

30. Write a system of linear inequalities whose solution is the entire third quadrant.

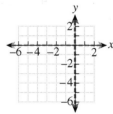

25. $y < 2x$
$\quad y < 6$
$\quad x > 2$

26. $y > x - 4$
$\quad y < -2x + 5$
$\quad y > -2$

31. Find the area of the region defined by the following system of linear inequalities:

$x \geq 2$
$y \geq 1$
$y \leq -x + 9$

32. Write a system of linear inequalities whose solution set is shown on the following graph:

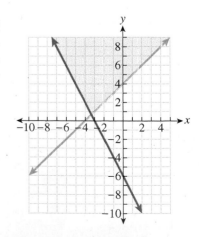

# CHAPTER 5

Exponents and Polynomials

The expressions and equations we have examined to this point in the text have been linear. In this chapter, we begin to examine expressions and functions that are nonlinear, including polynomials such as $-16t^2 + 32t + 128$ and $x^5 - 3x^4 + 8x^2 - 9x + 7$. After learning some basic definitions, we will learn to add, subtract, multiply, and divide polynomials. We will introduce properties for working with expressions containing exponents that make using these operations easier. We also will cover scientific notation, which is used to represent very large and very small numbers and to perform arithmetic calculations with them.

STUDY STRATEGY

Test Taking To be successful in a math class, understanding the material is important, but you also must be a good test taker. In this chapter, we will discuss the test-taking skills necessary for success in a math class.

5.1

Exponents

OBJECTIVES

1. Use the product rule for exponents.
2. Use the power rule for exponents.
3. Use the power of a product rule for exponents.
4. Use the quotient rule for exponents.
5. Use the zero exponent rule.
6. Use the power of a quotient rule for exponents.
7. Evaluate functions by using the rules for exponents.

We have used exponents to represent repeated multiplication of a particular factor. For example, the expression 3^7 is used to represent a product in which 3 is a factor 7 times.

$$3^7 = 3 \cdot 3 \cdot 3 \cdot 3 \cdot 3 \cdot 3 \cdot 3$$

Recall that in the expression 3^7, the number 3 is called the base and the number 7 is called the exponent.

In this section, we will introduce several properties of exponents and learn how to apply these properties to simplify expressions involving exponents.

Product Rule

Objective 1 **Use the product rule for exponents.**

> ### Product Rule
>
> For any base x, $x^m \cdot x^n = x^{m+n}$.

When multiplying two expressions with the same base, keep the base and add the exponents. Consider the example $x^3 \cdot x^7$.

$$x^3 = x \cdot x \cdot x \quad \text{and} \quad x^7 = x \cdot x \cdot x \cdot x \cdot x \cdot x \cdot x$$

So $x^3 \cdot x^7$ can be rewritten as $(x \cdot x \cdot x) \cdot (x \cdot x \cdot x \cdot x \cdot x \cdot x \cdot x)$.

Because x is being repeated as a factor 10 times, this expression can be rewritten as x^{10}.

$$x^3 \cdot x^7 = x^{3+7} = x^{10}$$

A WORD OF CAUTION When multiplying two expressions with the same base, keep the base and add the exponents. *Do not multiply the exponents.*

$$x^3 \cdot x^7 = x^{10}, \text{ not } x^{21}$$

EXAMPLE 1 Simplify $x^2 \cdot x^9$.

SOLUTION Because we are multiplying and the two bases are the same, we keep the base and add the exponents.

$$\begin{aligned} x^2 \cdot x^9 &= x^{2+9} \quad \text{Keep the base and add the exponents.} \\ &= x^{11} \quad \text{Add.} \end{aligned}$$

EXAMPLE 2 Simplify $2 \cdot 2^5 \cdot 2^4$.

SOLUTION In this example, we are multiplying three expressions that have the same base. To do this, we keep the base and add the three exponents. Keep in mind that if an exponent is not written for a factor, the exponent is a 1.

$$\begin{aligned} 2 \cdot 2^5 \cdot 2^4 &= 2^{1+5+4} \quad \text{Keep the base and add the exponents.} \\ &= 2^{10} \quad \text{Add.} \\ &= 1024 \quad \text{Raise 2 to the 10th power.} \end{aligned}$$

▸ **Quick Check 1**
Simplify.
a) $x^5 \cdot x^4$ **b)** $3^3 \cdot 3^2 \cdot 3$

EXAMPLE 3 Simplify $(x + y)^4 \cdot (x + y)^9$.

SOLUTION The base for these expressions is the sum $x + y$.

$$\begin{aligned} (x + y)^4 \cdot (x + y)^9 &= (x + y)^{4+9} \quad \text{Keep the base and add the exponents.} \\ &= (x + y)^{13} \quad \text{Add.} \end{aligned}$$

Quick Check 2
Simplify $(a - 6)^{10} \cdot (a - 6)^{17}$.

EXAMPLE 4 Simplify $(x^2y^7)(x^3y)$.

SOLUTION When we have a product involving more than one base, we can use the associative and commutative properties of multiplication to simplify the product.

$$
\begin{aligned}
(x^2y^7)(x^3y) &= x^2y^7x^3y && \text{Write without parentheses.} \\
&= x^2x^3y^7y && \text{Group like bases together.} \\
&= x^5y^8 && \text{For each base, add the exponents and} \\
& && \text{keep the base.}
\end{aligned}
$$

In future examples, we will not show the application of the associative and commutative properties of multiplication. Look for bases that are the same, add their exponents, and write each base to the calculated power.

Quick Check 3
Simplify $(a^6b^5)(a^9b^5)$.

Power Rule

Objective ② **Use the power rule for exponents.** The second property of exponents involves raising an expression with an exponent to a power.

Power Rule

For any base x, $(x^m)^n = x^{m \cdot n}$.

In essence, this property says that when we raise a power to a power, we keep the base and multiply the exponents. To show why this is true, consider the expression $(x^3)^7$.

Whenever we raise an expression to the 7th power, the expression is repeated as a factor seven times. So $(x^3)^7 = x^3 \cdot x^3 \cdot x^3 \cdot x^3 \cdot x^3 \cdot x^3 \cdot x^3$. Applying the first property from this section, $x^3 \cdot x^3 \cdot x^3 \cdot x^3 \cdot x^3 \cdot x^3 \cdot x^3 = x^{3+3+3+3+3+3+3}$, or x^{21}. This exponent could be found by multiplying 3 by 7.

$$(x^3)^7 = x^{3 \cdot 7} = x^{21}$$

A WORD OF CAUTION When raising an expression with an exponent to another power, keep the base and multiply the exponents. *Do not add the exponents.*

$$(x^3)^7 = x^{21}, \text{ not } x^{10}$$

EXAMPLE 5 Simplify $(x^5)^4$.

SOLUTION In this example, we are raising a power to another power, so we keep the base and multiply the exponents.

$$
\begin{aligned}
(x^5)^4 &= x^{5 \cdot 4} && \text{Keep the base and multiply the exponents.} \\
&= x^{20} && \text{Multiply.}
\end{aligned}
$$

Quick Check 4
Simplify $(x^9)^7$.

EXAMPLE 6 Simplify $(x^3)^9(x^7)^8$.

SOLUTION To simplify this expression, we must use both properties introduced in this section.

$$
\begin{aligned}
(x^3)^9(x^7)^8 &= x^{3 \cdot 9}x^{7 \cdot 8} && \text{Apply the power rule.} \\
&= x^{27}x^{56} && \text{Multiply.} \\
&= x^{83} && \text{Keep the base and add the exponents.}
\end{aligned}
$$

Quick Check 5
Simplify $(x^4)^6(x^5)^2$.

Power of a Product Rule

Objective 3 Use the power of a product rule for exponents. The third property introduced in this section involves raising a product to a power.

> ## Power of a Product Rule
>
> For any bases x and y, $(xy)^n = x^n y^n$.

This property says that when we raise a product to a power, we may raise each factor to that power. Consider the expression $(xy)^5$. We know that this can be rewritten as $xy \cdot xy \cdot xy \cdot xy \cdot xy$. Using the associative and commutative properties of multiplication, we can rewrite this expression as $x \cdot x \cdot x \cdot x \cdot x \cdot y \cdot y \cdot y \cdot y \cdot y$, which simplifies to $x^5 y^5$.

EXAMPLE 7 Simplify $(x^2 y^3)^6$.

SOLUTION   This example combines two properties. When we raise each factor to the 6th power, we are raising a power to a power; therefore, we multiply the exponents.

$$(x^2 y^3)^6 = (x^2)^6 (y^3)^6 \quad \text{Raise each factor to the 6th power}$$
$$= x^{12} y^{18} \quad \text{Keep the base and multiply the exponents.}$$

Quick Check 6
Simplify $(a^5 b^3)^8$.

EXAMPLE 8 Simplify $(x^2 y^3)^7 (3x^5)^2$.

SOLUTION   In this example, begin by raising each factor to the appropriate power. Then multiply expressions with the same base.

$$(x^2 y^3)^7 (3x^5)^2 = x^{14} y^{21} \cdot 3^2 x^{10} \quad \text{Raise each base to the appropriate power.}$$
$$= 9x^{24} y^{21} \quad \text{Simplify.}$$

It is a good idea to write the variables in an expression in alphabetical order, as shown in this example, although it is not necessary.

Quick Check 7
Simplify $(4a^2 b^3)^3 (a^4 b^2 c^7)^5$.

A WORD OF CAUTION This property applies only when we raise a *product* to a power, not a sum or a difference. Although $(xy)^2 = x^2 y^2$, a similar approach does not work for $(x + y)^2$ or $(x - y)^2$.

$$(x + y)^2 \neq x^2 + y^2$$
$$(x - y)^2 \neq x^2 - y^2$$

For example, let $x = 12$ and $y = 5$. In this case, $(x + y)^2$ is equal to 17^2, or 289, but $x^2 + y^2$ is equal to $12^2 + 5^2$, or 169. This shows that $(x + y)^2$ is not equal to $x^2 + y^2$ in general.

Quotient Rule

Objective 4 Use the quotient rule for exponents. The next property involves fractions containing the same base in their numerators and denominators. It also applies to dividing exponential expressions with the same base.

> ## Quotient Rule
>
> For any base x, $\dfrac{x^m}{x^n} = x^{m-n}$ $(x \neq 0)$.

Note that this property has a restriction; it does not apply when the base is 0. This is because division by 0 is undefined. This property tells us that when we are dividing two expressions with the same base, we subtract the exponent of the denominator from the exponent of the numerator. Consider the expression $\dfrac{x^7}{x^3}$. This can be rewritten as $\dfrac{x \cdot x \cdot x \cdot x \cdot x \cdot x \cdot x}{x \cdot x \cdot x}$. From our previous work, we know that this fraction can be simplified by dividing out common factors in the numerator and denominator.

$$\frac{\cancel{x} \cdot \cancel{x} \cdot \cancel{x} \cdot x \cdot x \cdot x \cdot x}{\cancel{x} \cdot \cancel{x} \cdot \cancel{x}} = x^4$$

One way to think of this is that the number of factors in the numerator has been reduced by three because there were three factors in the denominator. The property says that we can simplify this expression by subtracting the exponents, which produces the same result.

$$\frac{x^7}{x^3} = x^{7-3} = x^4$$

EXAMPLE 9   Simplify $\dfrac{y^9}{y^2}$. (Assume that $y \neq 0$.)

SOLUTION   Because the bases are the same, keep the base and subtract the exponents.

$$\frac{y^9}{y^2} = y^{9-2} \quad \text{Keep the base and subtract the exponents.}$$
$$= y^7 \quad \text{Subtract.}$$

EXAMPLE 10   Simplify $a^{21} \div a^3$. (Assume that $a \neq 0$.)

SOLUTION   Although in a different form than the previous example, $a^{21} \div a^3$ is equivalent to $\dfrac{a^{21}}{a^3}$. Keep the base and subtract the exponents.

$$a^{21} \div a^3 = a^{21-3} \quad \text{Keep the base and subtract the exponents.}$$
$$= a^{18} \quad \text{Subtract.}$$

Quick Check 8

Simplify. (Assume that $x \neq 0$.)

a) $\dfrac{x^{20}}{x^4}$ **b)** $x^{24} \div x^8$

A WORD OF CAUTION When dividing two expressions with the same base, keep the base and subtract the exponents. *Do not divide the exponents.*

$$a^{21} \div a^3 = a^{18}, \text{ not } a^7$$

EXAMPLE 11   Simplify $\dfrac{16x^{10}y^9}{2x^7y^4}$. (Assume that $x, y \neq 0$.)

SOLUTION   Although we will subtract the exponents for the bases x and y, we will not subtract the numerical factors 16 and 2. We simplify numerical factors the same way we did in Chapter 1; so $\frac{16}{2} = 8$.

$$\frac{16x^{10}y^9}{2x^7y^4} = 8x^3y^5 \quad \begin{array}{l}\text{Simplify } \frac{16}{2}. \text{ Keep the variable bases and} \\ \text{subtract the exponents.}\end{array}$$

▶ Quick Check 9

Simplify $\dfrac{20a^{10}b^{12}c^{15}}{5a^2b^6c^9}$. (Assume that $a, b, c \neq 0$.)

Zero Exponent Rule

Objective **5** **Use the zero exponent rule.** Consider the expression $\dfrac{2^7}{2^7}$. We know that any number (except 0) divided by itself is equal to 1. The previous property also tells us that we can subtract the exponents in this expression; so $\dfrac{2^7}{2^7} = 2^{7-7} = 2^0$.

Because we have shown that $\dfrac{2^7}{2^7}$ is equal to both 2^0 and 1, the expression 2^0 must be equal to 1. The following property involves raising a base to the power of zero.

> **Zero Exponent Rule**
>
> For any base x, $x^0 = 1$ ($x \neq 0$).

EXAMPLE 12 Simplify 7^0.

SOLUTION By applying the zero exponent rule, we see that $7^0 = 1$.

A WORD OF CAUTION When we raise a nonzero base to the power of zero, the result is 1, not 0.

$$7^0 = 1, \text{ not } 0$$

Quick Check 10

Simplify. (Assume that $x \neq 0$.)

a) 124^0 **b)** $(3x^2)^0$ **c)** $9x^0$

The expressions $(4x)^0$ and $4x^0$ are different ($x \neq 0$). In the first expression, the base being raised to the power of zero is $4x$. So $(4x)^0 = 1$ because any nonzero base raised to the power of zero is equal to 1. In the second expression, the base being raised to the power of zero is x, not $4x$. The expression $4x^0$ simplifies to be $4 \cdot 1$, or 4.

Power of a Quotient Rule

Objective **6** **Use the power of a quotient rule for exponents.** The power of a quotient rule is similar to the property that involves raising a product to a power.

> **Power of a Quotient Rule**
>
> For any bases x and y, $\left(\dfrac{x}{y}\right)^n = \dfrac{x^n}{y^n}$ ($y \neq 0$).

To raise a quotient to a power, we raise both the numerator and denominator to that power. The restriction $y \neq 0$ is again due to the fact that division by 0 is undefined. Consider the expression $\left(\dfrac{r}{s}\right)^3$, where $s \neq 0$. The property tells us that this is equivalent to $\dfrac{r^3}{s^3}$, and here is why.

$$\left(\frac{r}{s}\right)^3 = \frac{r}{s} \cdot \frac{r}{s} \cdot \frac{r}{s} \qquad \text{Repeat } \frac{r}{s} \text{ as a factor three times.}$$

$$= \frac{r \cdot r \cdot r}{s \cdot s \cdot s} \qquad \text{Use the definition of multiplication for fractions.}$$

$$= \frac{r^3}{s^3} \qquad \text{Rewrite the numerator and denominator using exponents.}$$

A WORD OF CAUTION When raising a quotient to a power, raise both the numerator and denominator to that power. Do not raise just the numerator to that power.

$$\left(\frac{r}{s}\right)^3 = \frac{r^3}{s^3}, \text{ not } \frac{r^3}{s} \qquad \text{(Assume that } s \neq 0.\text{)}$$

EXAMPLE 13 Simplify $\left(\dfrac{x^2 y^3}{z^4}\right)^8$. (Assume that $z \neq 0$.)

SOLUTION   Begin by raising each factor in the numerator and denominator to the 8th power; then simplify the resulting expression.

$$\left(\frac{x^2 y^3}{z^4}\right)^8 = \frac{(x^2)^8 (y^3)^8}{(z^4)^8} \qquad \text{Raise each factor in the numerator and denominator to the 8th power.}$$

$$= \frac{x^{16} y^{24}}{z^{32}} \qquad \text{Keep the bases and multiply the exponents.}$$

▶ Quick Check 11

Simplify $\left(\dfrac{ab^7}{c^3 d^4}\right)^5$. (Assume that $c, d \neq 0$.)

Here is a brief summary of the properties introduced in this section.

┌─ **Properties of Exponents** ──────────────────────────────

1. Product Rule For any base x, $x^m \cdot x^n = x^{m+n}$.

2. Power Rule For any base x, $(x^m)^n = x^{m \cdot n}$.

3. Power of a Product Rule For any bases x and y, $(xy)^n = x^n y^n$.

4. Quotient Rule For any base x, $\dfrac{x^m}{x^n} = x^{m-n}$ $(x \neq 0)$.

5. Zero Exponent Rule For any base x, $x^0 = 1$ $(x \neq 0)$.

6. Power of a Quotient Rule For any bases x and y, $\left(\dfrac{x}{y}\right)^n = \dfrac{x^n}{y^n}$ $(y \neq 0)$.

Objective 7 Evaluate functions by using the rules for exponents. We conclude this section by investigating functions containing exponents.

EXAMPLE 14 For the function $f(x) = x^4$, evaluate $f(3)$.

SOLUTION   Substitute 3 for x and simplify the resulting expression.

$$f(3) = (3)^4 \qquad \text{Substitute 3 for } x.$$

$$= 81 \qquad \text{Simplify.}$$

▶ Quick Check 12

For the function $f(x) = x^6$, evaluate $f(-4)$.

EXAMPLE 15 For the function $f(x) = x^3$, evaluate $f(a^5)$.

SOLUTION Substitute a^5 for x and simplify.

$$f(a^5) = (a^5)^3 \quad \text{Substitute } a^5 \text{ for } x.$$
$$= a^{5 \cdot 3} \quad \text{Simplify using the power rule.}$$
$$= a^{15} \quad \text{Multiply.}$$

▶ **Quick Check 13**

For the function $f(x) = x^7$, evaluate $f(a^8)$.

BUILDING YOUR STUDY STRATEGY

Test Taking, 1 Prepare Completely The first test-taking skill is preparing yourself completely. As legendary basketball coach John Wooden once said, "Failing to prepare is preparing to fail." Begin preparing for the exam well in advance; do not plan to study (or cram) the night before the exam.

Review your old homework assignments, notes, and note cards, spending more time on problems or concepts that were difficult for you. Work through the chapter review and chapter test in the text to identify any areas of weakness for you.

Create a practice test and take it under test conditions without using your text or notes. Allow yourself the same amount of time you will be given for the actual test so you know whether you are working fast enough.

Finally, get a good night's sleep the night before the exam. Tired students do not think as well as students who are rested.

Exercises 5.1

MyMathLab PRACTICE   WATCH   DOWNLOAD   READ   REVIEW

Vocabulary

1. The product rule states that for any base x, _____.

2. The power rule states that for any base x, _____.

3. The power of a product rule states that for any bases x and y, _____.

4. The quotient rule states that for any nonzero base x, _____.

5. The zero exponent rule states that for any nonzero base x, _____.

6. The power of a quotient rule states that for any bases x and y, where $y \neq 0$, _____.

Simplify.

7. $2^4 \cdot 2^2$

8. $5^2 \cdot 5^3$

9. $x^8 \cdot x^5$

10. $a^7 \cdot a^4$

11. $m^{21} \cdot m^{19}$

12. $n^{17} \cdot n^{45}$

13. $b^5 \cdot b^6 \cdot b^3$

14. $x^8 \cdot x^6 \cdot x$

15. $(2x - 3)^4 \cdot (2x - 3)^{10}$

16. $(4x + 1)^{12} \cdot (4x + 1)^9$

17. $(x^6 y^5)(x^2 y^8)$

18. $(5x^8 y^8)(2x^5 y^{11})$

Find the missing factor.

19. $x^4 \cdot ? = x^9$

20. $x^7 \cdot ? = x^{10}$

21. $? \cdot b^5 = b^6$

22. $? \cdot a^{11} = a^{20}$

Simplify.

23. $(x^4)^6$

24. $(x^5)^5$

25. $(a^7)^9$

26. $(b^{14})^4$

27. $(2^5)^2$

28. $(3^3)^3$

29. $(x^3)^7(x^4)^2$

30. $(x^2)^8(x^5)^3$

Find the missing exponent.

31. $(x^6)^? = x^{42}$

32. $(p^?)^8 = p^{112}$

33. $(x^3)^8(x^?)^4 = x^{44}$

34. $(x^9)^?(x^{11})^{12} = x^{195}$

Simplify.

35. $(3x)^4$

36. $(7m)^3$

37. $(-8x^3)^2$

38. $(-5n^6)^4$

39. $(m^8n^5)^7$

40. $(a^3b^{11})^5$

41. $(3x^4y)^4$

42. $(2x^5y^6)^8$

43. $(x^2y^5z^3)^7(y^4z^5)^8$

44. $(a^{10}b^{15}c^{20})^7(a^{11}b^7c^3)^8$

Find the missing exponent(s).

45. $(x^5y^4)^? = x^{35}y^{28}$

46. $(c^7d^{11})^? = c^{21}d^{33}$

47. $(2s^?t^?)^4 = 16s^{24}t^{52}$

48. $(m^?n^?)^9 = m^{54}n^{216}$

Simplify. (Assume that all variables are nonzero.)

49. $\dfrac{x^{12}}{x^3}$

50. $\dfrac{x^{32}}{x^4}$

51. $r^{25} \div r^{10}$

52. $z^{36} \div z^{15}$

53. $\dfrac{16x^{16}}{2x^2}$

54. $\dfrac{119x^{24}}{7x^8}$

55. $\dfrac{(a + 5b)^{13}}{(a + 5b)^{11}}$

56. $\dfrac{(2x - 17)^{11}}{(2x - 17)^5}$

57. $\dfrac{a^8b^6}{a^3b}$

58. $\dfrac{28r^6s^7t^9}{7r^3s^7t^6}$

Find the missing exponent(s). (Assume that all variables are nonzero.)

59. $\dfrac{x^{14}}{x^?} = x^2$

60. $\dfrac{y^?}{y^8} = y^9$

61. $m^? \div m^{11} = m^{19}$

62. $\dfrac{x^{15}y^?}{x^?y^{25}} = x^7y^6$

Simplify. (Assume that all variables are nonzero.)

63. 9^0

64. -8^0

65. $(-16)^0$

66. 5^0

67. $\dfrac{3}{7^0}$

68. $\left(\dfrac{4}{13}\right)^0$

69. $(13x)^0$

70. $(22x^5y^{12}z^9)^0$

Simplify. (Assume that all variables are nonzero.)

71. $\left(\dfrac{3}{4}\right)^3$

72. $\left(\dfrac{x}{2}\right)^7$

73. $\left(\dfrac{a}{b}\right)^8$

74. $\left(\dfrac{x}{y}\right)^{12}$

75. $\left(\dfrac{x^4}{y^3}\right)^5$

76. $\left(\dfrac{m^9}{n^6}\right)^8$

77. $\left(\dfrac{2a^6}{b^7}\right)^3$

78. $\left(\dfrac{x^{13}}{5y^9}\right)^5$

79. $\left(\dfrac{a^5b^4}{b^2c^7}\right)^9$

80. $\left(\dfrac{17x^5y^{19}z^{24}}{32a^{11}b^{70}c^{33}}\right)^0$

Find the missing exponent(s). (Assume that all variables are nonzero.)

81. $\left(\dfrac{3}{4}\right)^? = \dfrac{81}{256}$

82. $\left(\dfrac{x^4}{y^7}\right)^? = \dfrac{x^{12}}{y^{21}}$

83. $\left(\dfrac{a^3b^6}{c^8}\right)^? = \dfrac{a^{36}b^{72}}{c^{96}}$

84. $\left(\dfrac{ab^8}{c^5d^9}\right)^? = \dfrac{a^{15}b^{120}}{c^{75}d^{135}}$

Evaluate the given function.

85. $f(x) = x^2$, $f(4)$

86. $g(x) = x^3$, $g(9)$

87. $g(x) = x^4$, $g(-2)$

88. $f(x) = x^{10}$, $f(-1)$

89. $f(x) = x^6$, $f(a^4)$

90. $f(x) = x^5$, $f(b^7)$

Mixed Practice, 91–104

Simplify.

91. $(a^7)^6$

92. $(13a)^0$

93. $\left(\dfrac{5x^4}{2y^7}\right)^3$

94. $(x^6y^9z^2)^7$

95. $\dfrac{x^{13}}{x}$

96. $\dfrac{x^{100}}{x^{100}}$

97. $\left(\dfrac{a^8b^9}{2c^2}\right)^5$

98. $c^8 \cdot c^{12}$

99. $(b^{10})^2$

100. $\dfrac{x^8y^{13}}{xy^6}$

101. $(x^{15})^6$

102. $(2x^9yz^3)^4$

103. $\left(\dfrac{3a^2b^9}{7cd^4}\right)^4$

104. $(6x^7y^9z)^3$

The number of feet traveled by a free-falling object in t seconds is given by the function $f(t) = 16t^2$.

105. If a ball is dropped from the top of a building, how far will it fall in 3 seconds?

106. How far will a skydiver fall in 7 seconds?

The area of a square with side x is given by the function $A(x) = x^2$.

107. Use the function to find the area of a square if each side is 90 feet long.

108. Use the function to find the area of a square if each side is 17 meters long.

The area of a circle with radius r is given by the function
$A(r) = \pi r^2.$

109. Use the function to find the area of the base of a circular storage tank if the radius is 14 feet long. Use $\pi \approx 3.14$.

110. Columbus Circle in New York City is a traffic circle. The radius of the inner circle is 107 feet. Use the function to find the area of the inner circle. Use $\pi \approx 3.14$.

Writing in Mathematics

Answer in complete sentences.

111. Which expression is equal to x^9: $(x^5)^4$ or $x^5 \cdot x^4$? Explain your answer.

112. Explain the difference between the expressions $\dfrac{a^3}{b}$ and $\left(\dfrac{a}{b}\right)^3$.

5.2

Negative Exponents; Scientific Notation

OBJECTIVES

1 **Understand negative exponents.**
2 **Use the rules of exponents to simplify expressions containing negative exponents.**
3 **Convert numbers from standard notation to scientific notation.**
4 **Convert numbers from scientific notation to standard notation.**
5 **Perform arithmetic operations using numbers in scientific notation.**
6 **Use scientific notation to solve applied problems.**

Negative Exponents

Objective 1 Understand negative exponents. In this section, we introduce the concept of a **negative exponent**.

> **Negative Exponents**
>
> For any nonzero base x, $x^{-n} = \dfrac{1}{x^n}$.

For example, $2^{-3} = \dfrac{1}{2^3}$, or $\dfrac{1}{8}$.

Let's examine this definition. Consider the expression $\dfrac{2^4}{2^7}$. If we apply the property $\dfrac{x^m}{x^n} = x^{m-n}$ from the previous section, we see that $\dfrac{2^4}{2^7}$ simplifies to 2^{-3}.

$$\frac{2^4}{2^7} = 2^{4-7}$$
$$= 2^{-3}$$

If we simplify $\dfrac{2^4}{2^7}$ by dividing out common factors, the result is $\dfrac{1}{2^3}$.

$$\frac{2^4}{2^7} = \frac{\overset{1}{\cancel{2}} \cdot \overset{1}{\cancel{2}} \cdot \overset{1}{\cancel{2}} \cdot \overset{1}{\cancel{2}}}{\underset{1}{\cancel{2}} \cdot \underset{1}{\cancel{2}} \cdot \underset{1}{\cancel{2}} \cdot \underset{1}{\cancel{2}} \cdot 2 \cdot 2 \cdot 2}$$
$$= \frac{1}{2^3}$$

Because $\dfrac{2^4}{2^7}$ is equal to 2^{-3} and $\dfrac{1}{2^3}$, $2^{-3} = \dfrac{1}{2^3}$.

A WORD OF CAUTION Raising a positive base to a negative exponent is not the same as raising the opposite of that base to a positive power.

$$2^{-3} = \frac{1}{2^3}, \text{ not } -2^3$$

EXAMPLE 1 Rewrite the expression 7^{-2} without using negative exponents and simplify.

SOLUTION   When raising a number to a negative exponent, we begin by rewriting the expression without negative exponents. We finish by raising the base to the appropriate positive power.

$$7^{-2} = \frac{1}{7^2} \quad \text{Rewrite without negative exponents.}$$

$$= \frac{1}{49} \quad \text{Simplify.}$$

Quick Check 1

Rewrite 4^{-3} without using negative exponents and simplify.

EXAMPLE 2   Rewrite the expression $9x^{-6}$ without using negative exponents. (Assume that $x \neq 0$.)

SOLUTION   The base in this example is x. The exponent does not apply to the 9 because there are no parentheses. When we rewrite the expression without a negative exponent, the number 9 is unaffected. Rather than writing x^{-6} as $\frac{1}{x^6}$ first, we can move the factor directly to the denominator of a fraction whose numerator is 9 by changing the sign of its exponent.

$$9x^{-6} = \frac{9}{x^6}$$

Note the difference between the expressions $9x^{-6}$ and $(9x)^{-6}$. In the first expression, the base x is being raised to the power of -6, leaving 9 in the numerator when the expression is rewritten without negative exponents. The base in the second expression is $9x$, so we rewrite $(9x)^{-6}$ as $\frac{1}{(9x)^6}$.

Quick Check 2

Rewrite the expression a^5b^{-4} without using negative exponents. (Assume that $b \neq 0$.)

EXAMPLE 3   Rewrite the expression $\frac{x^8}{z^{-5}}$ without using negative exponents. (Assume that $z \neq 0$.)

SOLUTION   Begin by rewriting the denominator as $\frac{1}{z^5}$.

$$\frac{x^8}{z^{-5}} = \frac{x^8}{1/z^5} \quad \text{Rewrite the denominator without negative exponents.}$$

$$= x^8 \div \frac{1}{z^5} \quad \text{Rewrite as division.}$$

$$= x^8 \cdot \frac{z^5}{1} \quad \text{Invert the divisor and multiply.}$$

$$= x^8z^5 \quad \text{Simplify.}$$

When an expression has a factor in the denominator with a negative exponent, we can change its exponent to a positive number by moving the factor to the numerator.

EXAMPLE 4 Rewrite the expression $\dfrac{a^7 b^{-3}}{c^{-5} d^{12}}$ without using negative exponents. (Assume that all variables are nonzero.)

SOLUTION   Of the four factors in this example, two of them (b^{-3} and c^{-5}) need to be rewritten without using negative exponents. This can be done by changing the sign of their exponents and rewriting the factors on the other side of the fraction bar.

$$\frac{a^7 b^{-3}}{c^{-5} d^{12}} = \frac{a^7 c^5}{b^3 d^{12}}$$

▸ Quick Check 3

Rewrite without using negative exponents. (Assume that all variables are nonzero.)

a) $\dfrac{x^{12}}{y^{-7}}$ b) $\dfrac{x^{-2} y^4}{z^{-1} w^{-9}}$

Using the Rules of Exponents with Negative Exponents

Objective 2 Use the rules of exponents to simplify expressions containing negative exponents. All of the properties of exponents described in the previous section hold true for negative exponents. When we are simplifying expressions involving negative exponents, we can take two general routes. We can choose to apply the appropriate property first, then rewrite the expression without negative exponents. On the other hand, in some circumstances it will be more convenient to rewrite the expression without negative exponents before attempting to apply the appropriate property.

EXAMPLE 5 Simplify the expression $x^{11} \cdot x^{-6}$. Write the result without using negative exponents. (Assume that $x \neq 0$.)

SOLUTION   This example uses the product rule $x^m \cdot x^n = x^{m+n}$.

$$x^{11} \cdot x^{-6} = x^{11+(-6)} \quad \text{Keep the base and add the exponents.}$$
$$= x^5 \quad \text{Simplify.}$$

An alternative approach is to rewrite the expression without using negative exponents.

$$x^{11} \cdot x^{-6} = \frac{x^{11}}{x^6} \quad \text{Rewrite without negative exponents.}$$
$$= x^5 \quad \text{Keep the base and subtract the exponents.}$$

Use the approach that seems clearer to you.

Quick Check 4

Simplify the expression $x^{-13} \cdot x^6$. Write the result without using negative exponents. (Assume that $x \neq 0$.)

Quick Check 5

Simplify the expression $(x^{-6})^{-7}$. Write the result without using negative exponents. (Assume that $x \neq 0$.)

EXAMPLE 6 Simplify the expression $(y^3)^{-2}$. Write the result without using negative exponents. (Assume that $y \neq 0$.)

SOLUTION   This example uses the power rule $(x^m)^n = x^{m \cdot n}$.

$$(y^3)^{-2} = y^{-6} \quad \text{Keep the base and multiply the exponents.}$$
$$= \frac{1}{y^6} \quad \text{Rewrite without using negative exponents.}$$

EXAMPLE 7   Simplify the expression $(2a^{-7}b^9)^{-4}$. Write the result without using negative exponents. (Assume that $a, b \neq 0$.)

SOLUTION   This example uses the power of a product rule $(xy)^n = x^n y^n$.

$$
\begin{aligned}
(2a^{-7}b^9)^{-4} &= 2^{-4}a^{-7(-4)}b^{9(-4)} && \text{Raise each factor to the power of } -4. \\
&= 2^{-4}a^{28}b^{-36} && \text{Simplify each exponent.} \\
&= \frac{a^{28}}{2^4 b^{36}} && \text{Rewrite without using negative exponents.} \\
&= \frac{a^{28}}{16b^{36}} && \text{Simplify } 2^4.
\end{aligned}
$$

Quick Check 6

Simplify the expression $(9ab^{-3}c^2)^{-2}$. Write the result without using negative exponents. (Assume that $a, b, c \neq 0$.)

EXAMPLE 8   Simplify the expression $\dfrac{x^3}{x^{15}}$. Write the result without using negative exponents. (Assume that $x \neq 0$.)

SOLUTION   This example uses the quotient rule $\dfrac{x^m}{x^n} = x^{m-n}$.

$$
\begin{aligned}
\frac{x^3}{x^{15}} &= x^{-12} && \text{Keep the base and subtract the exponents.} \\
&= \frac{1}{x^{12}} && \text{Rewrite without using negative exponents.}
\end{aligned}
$$

▸ **Quick Check 7**

Simplify the expression $\dfrac{x^8}{x^{14}}$. Write the result without using negative exponents.

(Assume that $x \neq 0$.)

EXAMPLE 9   Simplify the expression $\left(\dfrac{r^4}{s^2}\right)^{-3}$. Write the result without using negative exponents. (Assume that $r, s \neq 0$.)

SOLUTION   This example uses the power of a quotient rule $\left(\dfrac{x}{y}\right)^n = \dfrac{x^n}{y^n}$.

$$
\begin{aligned}
\left(\frac{r^4}{s^2}\right)^{-3} &= \frac{r^{4(-3)}}{s^{2(-3)}} && \text{Raise the numerator and the denominator to the power of } -3. \\
&= \frac{r^{-12}}{s^{-6}} && \text{Multiply.} \\
&= \frac{s^6}{r^{12}} && \text{Rewrite without using negative exponents.}
\end{aligned}
$$

Quick Check 8

Simplify the expression $\left(\dfrac{x^5}{y^{-4}}\right)^{-4}$. Write the result without using negative exponents. (Assume that $x, y \neq 0$.)

Scientific Notation

Objective 3 **Convert numbers from standard notation to scientific notation.** **Scientific notation** is used to represent numbers that are very large, such as 93,000,000, or very small, such as 0.0000324.

Rewriting a Number in Scientific Notation

> To convert a number to scientific notation, rewrite it in the form $a \times 10^b$, where $1 \le a < 10$ and b is an integer.

First, consider the following table listing several powers of 10:

10^5	10^4	10^3	10^2	10^1	10^0	10^{-1}	10^{-2}	10^{-3}	10^{-4}	10^{-5}
100,000	10,000	1000	100	10	1	0.1	0.01	0.001	0.0001	0.00001

Notice that all of the positive powers of 10 are numbers that are 10 or higher. All of the negative powers of 10 are numbers between 0 and 1.

To convert a number to scientific notation, we first move the decimal point so that it immediately follows the first nonzero digit in the number. Count the number of decimal places the decimal point moves. This gives us the power of 10 when the number is written in scientific notation. If the original number is 10 or larger, the exponent is positive, but if the original number is between 0 and 1, the exponent is negative.

EXAMPLE 10   Convert 0.000321 to scientific notation.

SOLUTION   Move the decimal point so that it follows the first nonzero digit, which is 3.

$$0.000321$$

To do this, move the decimal point four places to the right. Because 0.000321 is less than 1, this exponent must be negative.

$$0.000321 = 3.21 \times 10^{-4}$$

EXAMPLE 11   Convert 24,000,000,000 to scientific notation.

SOLUTION   Move the decimal point so that it follows the digit 2. To do this, move the decimal point 10 places to the left. Because 24,000,000,000 is 10 or larger, the exponent will be positive.

$$24,000,000,000 = 2.4 \times 10^{10}$$

▶ Quick Check 9

Convert to scientific notation.

a) 0.0046
b) 3,570,000

Objective ④ Convert numbers from scientific notation to standard notation.

EXAMPLE 12   Convert 5.28×10^4 from scientific notation to standard notation.

SOLUTION

$$5.28 \times 10^4 = 5.28 \times 10,000 \quad \text{Rewrite } 10^4 \text{ as } 10,000.$$
$$= 52,800 \quad \text{Multiply.}$$

To multiply a decimal number by 10^4 or 10,000, move the decimal point four places to the right. Note that the power of 10 is positive in this example.

EXAMPLE 13 Convert 2.0039×10^{-5} from scientific notation to standard notation.

SOLUTION

$$2.0039 \times 10^{-5} = 2.0039 \times 0.00001 \quad \text{Rewrite } 10^{-5} \text{ as } 0.00001.$$
$$= 0.000020039 \quad \text{Multiply.}$$

To multiply a decimal number by 10^{-5}, or 0.00001, move the decimal point five places to the left. Note that the power of 10 is negative in this example.

▶ Quick Check 10

Convert from scientific notation to standard notation.

a) 3.2×10^6 **b)** 7.21×10^{-4}

If you are unsure about which direction to move the decimal point, think about whether you are making the number larger or smaller. Multiplying by positive powers of 10 makes the number larger; so move the decimal point to the right. Multiplying by negative powers of 10 makes the number smaller; so move the decimal point to the left.

Objective 5 Perform arithmetic operations using numbers in scientific notation. When we are performing calculations involving very large or very small numbers, using scientific notation can be convenient.

EXAMPLE 14 Multiply $(2.2 \times 10^7)(2.8 \times 10^{13})$. Express your answer using scientific notation.

SOLUTION   When multiplying two numbers that are in scientific notation, we may multiply the two decimal numbers first. We then multiply the powers of 10 using the product rule, $x^m \cdot x^n = x^{m+n}$.

$$(2.2 \times 10^7)(2.8 \times 10^{13}) = (2.2)(2.8)(10^7)(10^{13}) \quad \text{Reorder the factors.}$$
$$= 6.16 \times 10^{20} \quad \text{Multiply decimal numbers. Add the exponents for the base 10.}$$

▶ Quick Check 11

Multiply $(5.8 \times 10^4)(1.2 \times 10^9)$. Express your answer using scientific notation.

Using Your Calculator   The TI-84 can help you perform calculations with numbers in scientific notation. To enter a number in scientific notation, use the second function **EE** above the key labeled $\boxed{,}$. For example, to enter the number 2.2×10^7, key 2.2 $\boxed{\text{2nd}}$ $\boxed{,}$ 7. Here is the screen shot showing how to multiply $(2.2 \times 10^7)(2.8 \times 10^{13})$.

```
2.2E7*2.8E13
           6.16E20
```

EXAMPLE 15 Divide (1.2×10^{-6}) by (2.4×10^9). Express your answer using scientific notation.

SOLUTION To divide numbers that are in scientific notation, begin by dividing the decimal numbers. Then divide the powers of 10 separately, using the property $\frac{x^m}{x^n} = x^{m-n}$.

$$(1.2 \times 10^{-6}) \div (2.4 \times 10^9) = \frac{1.2 \times 10^{-6}}{2.4 \times 10^9} \qquad \text{Rewrite as a fraction.}$$

$$= \frac{1.2}{2.4} \times 10^{-6-9} \qquad \begin{array}{l}\text{Divide the decimal numbers.}\\ \text{Subtract the exponents for the}\\ \text{powers of 10.}\end{array}$$

$$= 0.5 \times 10^{-15} \qquad \begin{array}{l}\text{Divide 1.2 by 2.4. Simplify the}\\ \text{exponent.}\end{array}$$

Although this is the correct quotient, the answer is not in scientific notation, as the number 0.5 does not have a nonzero digit to the left of the decimal point. To rewrite 0.5 as 5.0, move the decimal point one place to the right. This will decrease the exponent by one, from -15 to -16. $(1.2 \times 10^{-6}) \div (2.4 \times 10^9) = 5.0 \times 10^{-16}$

Quick Check 12

Divide (9.9×10^5) by (3.3×10^{-7}). Express your answer using scientific notation.

Applications

Objective 6 Use scientific notation to solve applied problems. We finish with an applied problem using scientific notation.

EXAMPLE 16 At its farthest point, the planet Mars is 155 million miles from the sun. How many seconds does it take light from the sun to reach Mars if the speed of light is 1.86×10^5 miles per second?

SOLUTION To determine the length of time a trip takes, we divide the distance traveled by the rate of speed. To solve this problem, we need to divide the distance of 155 million (155,000,000) miles by the speed of light. We will convert the distance to scientific notation, which is 1.55×10^8.

$$\frac{1.55 \times 10^8}{1.86 \times 10^5} \approx 0.833 \times 10^3 \qquad \begin{array}{l}\text{Divide the decimal numbers; approximate with}\\ \text{a calculator. Subtract the exponents for the}\\ \text{powers of 10.}\end{array}$$

To write this result in scientific notation, we move the decimal point one place to the right. This decreases the exponent by one. The light will reach Mars in approximately 8.33×10^2, or 833, seconds, or 13 minutes and 53 seconds.

▶ **Quick Check 13**

How many seconds does it take light to travel 1,488,000,000 miles? (The speed of light is 1.86×10^5 miles per second.)

Exercises 5.2

MyMathLab

PRACTICE | WATCH | DOWNLOAD | READ | REVIEW

Vocabulary

1. For any *nonzero* base x, $x^{-n} =$ _____.

2. A number is in _____ if it is in the form $a \times 10^b$, where $1 \le a < 10$ and b is an integer.

Rewrite the expression without using negative exponents. (Assume that all variables represent nonzero real numbers.)

3. 5^{-2}

4. 8^{-2}

5. 4^{-3}

6. 7^{-3}

7. -13^{-2}

8. -3^{-4}

9. b^{-12}

10. a^{-9}

11. $12x^{-6}$

12. $6x^{-8}$

13. $-5m^{-19}$

14. $-12m^{-6}$

15. $\dfrac{1}{x^{-5}}$

16. $\dfrac{1}{x^{-7}}$

17. $\dfrac{3}{y^{-4}}$

18. $\dfrac{x^7}{y^{-5}}$

19. $\dfrac{x^{-11}}{y^{-2}}$

20. $\dfrac{x^{-10}}{y^4}$

21. $\dfrac{-8a^{-6}b^5}{c^7}$

22. $\dfrac{-10x^3y^{-5}}{z^{-4}}$

23. $\dfrac{5a^{-6}b^{-9}}{c^{-4}d^5}$

24. $\dfrac{a^3b^{-3}}{c^{-4}d^{-9}}$

Simplify the expression. Write the result without using negative exponents. (Assume that all variables represent nonzero real numbers.)

25. $x^{-12} \cdot x^7$

26. $x^8 \cdot x^{-17}$

27. $a^{16} \cdot a^{-10}$

28. $b^{-13} \cdot b^{31}$

29. $m^{-9} \cdot m^{-12}$

30. $n^{-15} \cdot n^{-21}$

31. $(x^6)^{-3}$

32. $(x^{11})^{-4}$

33. $(x^{-6})^{-7}$

34. $(x^{-9})^{-2}$

35. $(x^5y^4z^{-6})^{-2}$

36. $(x^{-3}y^3z^{-2})^{-7}$

37. $(4a^{-5}b^{-8}z^2)^{-3}$

38. $(-2x^4b^{-6}c^{-7})^5$

39. $\dfrac{x^{-5}}{x^{10}}$

40. $\dfrac{x^{-3}}{x^{15}}$

41. $\dfrac{x^{11}}{x^{-6}}$

42. $\dfrac{x^8}{x^{-8}}$

43. $\dfrac{a^{-8}}{a^{-5}}$

44. $\dfrac{a^{-2}}{a^{-9}}$

45. $\dfrac{x^7}{x^{18}}$

46. $\dfrac{x^3}{x^{12}}$

47. $\dfrac{x^5 \cdot x^{-11}}{x^{-6}}$

48. $\dfrac{x^{-13}}{x^{-17} \cdot x^4}$

49. $\left(\dfrac{x^3}{y^4}\right)^{-5}$

50. $\left(\dfrac{2x^8}{y^5}\right)^{-3}$

51. $\left(\dfrac{a^4b^7}{3c^5d^{-8}}\right)^{-2}$

52. $\left(\dfrac{x^{-8}y^5}{wz^{-6}}\right)^{-8}$

Convert the given number to standard notation.

53. 3.07×10^{-7}

54. 2.3×10^5

55. 8.935×10^9

56. 6.001×10^{-8}

57. 9.021×10^4

58. 7.0×10^{10}

Convert the given number to scientific notation.

59. 0.00027

60. 0.00000621

61. 8,600,000

62. 92,000

63. 420,000,000,000

64. 0.0000000023

Perform the following calculations. Express your answer using scientific notation.

65. $(4.1 \times 10^8)(2.3 \times 10^{11})$

66. $(3.6 \times 10^{-13})(1.6 \times 10^6)$

67. $(1.598 \times 10^{-12}) \div (4.7 \times 10^9)$

68. $(3.286 \times 10^{14}) \div (6.2 \times 10^{-7})$

69. $(5.32 \times 10^{-15})(7.8 \times 10^3)$

70. $(6.0 \times 10^{13}) \div (7.5 \times 10^{-12})$

71. $(87{,}000{,}000{,}000)(0.000002)$

72. $0.0000000064 \div 160{,}000{,}000{,}000$

73. If a computer can perform a calculation in 0.0000000008 second, how long will it take to perform 42,000,000,000,000 calculations?

74. If a computer can perform a calculation in 0.0000000008 second, how many calculations can it perform in 2 minutes (120 seconds)?

75. The speed of light is 1.86×10^5 miles per second. How far can light from the sun travel in 10 minutes?

76. The speed of light is 1.86×10^5 miles per second. At its farthest point, Pluto is 4,555,000,000 miles from the sun. How many seconds does it take light from the sun to reach Pluto?

77. If the mass of a typical star is 2.2×10^{33} grams and there are approximately 500,000,000,000 stars in the Milky Way galaxy, what is the total mass of these stars?

78. The speed of light is 1.86×10^5 miles per second. How far can light from the sun travel in one year? (This distance is often referred to as a light-year.)

79. For the 12-month period ending March 31, 2009, Microsoft showed total revenues of $\$6.118 \times 10^{10}$ and Apple showed total revenues of $\$3.369 \times 10^{10}$. What was the combined revenue for the two companies? (*Source: Capital IQ/Yahoo! Finance*)

80. Each day Burger King restaurants serve 1.57×10^7 customers worldwide. How many customers do Burger King restaurants serve in one year? (*Source: Burger King Corporation*)

81. Approximately 3.3×10^6 high school students graduated in 2008. If 70% of these graduates attended college in the fall, how many attended college in the fall? (*Source: U.S. Department of Education*)

82. In the 2003–2004 school year, there were approximately 1.73×10^7 U.S. college students. If 63% of these students received some type of financial aid, how many received some type of financial aid? (*Source: U.S. Department of Education*)

Writing in Mathematics

Answer in complete sentences.

83. Explain the difference between the expressions 4^{-2} and $(-4)^2$.

84. Describe three real-world examples of numbers using scientific notation.

Quick Review Exercises

Section 5.2

Simplify.

1. $8x + 3x$

2. $9a - 16a$

3. $-9x^2 + 4x + 3x^2 + 7x$

4. $10y^3 - y^2 + 5y + 13 + 2y^3 + 6y^2 - 18y - 50$

5.3 Polynomials; Addition and Subtraction of Polynomials

OBJECTIVES

1 Identify polynomials and understand the vocabulary used to describe them.

2 Evaluate polynomials.

3 Add and subtract polynomials.

4 Understand polynomials in several variables.

Polynomials in a Single Variable

Objective 1 Identify polynomials and understand the vocabulary used to describe them. Many real-world phenomena cannot be described by linear expressions and linear functions. For example, if a car is traveling at x miles per hour on dry pavement, the distance in feet required for the car to come to a complete stop can be approximated by the expression $0.06x^2 + 1.1x + 0.02$. This non-linear expression is an example of a **polynomial**.

Polynomials —————————————————————————————

A **polynomial in a single variable** x is a sum of **terms** of the form ax^n, where a is a real number and n is a whole number.

Here are some examples of a polynomial in a single variable x.

$$x^2 - 9x + 14 \qquad\qquad 4x^5 - 13 \qquad\qquad x^7 - 4x^5 + 8x^2 + 13x$$

An expression is *not* a polynomial if it contains a term with a variable that is raised to a power other than a whole number (such as $x^{3/4}$ or x^{-2}) or if it has a term with a variable in a denominator $\left(\text{such as } \dfrac{5}{x^3}\right)$.

Degree of a Term ——————————————————————————

The **degree of each term** in a polynomial in a single variable is equal to the variable's exponent.

For example, the degree of the term $8x^9$ is 9. A **constant term** does not contain a variable. The degree of a constant term is 0 because a constant term such as -15 can be rewritten as $-15x^0$. The polynomial $4x^5 - 9x^4 + 2x^3 - 7x - 11$ has five terms, and their degrees are 5, 4, 3, 1, and 0, respectively.

Term	$4x^5$	$-9x^4$	$2x^3$	$-7x$	-11
Degree	5	4	3	1	0

A polynomial with only one term is called a **monomial**. A **binomial** is a polynomial that has two terms, while a **trinomial** is a polynomial that has three terms. (We do not have special names to describe polynomials with four or more terms.) Here are some examples.

Monomial	Binomial	Trinomial
$2x$	$x^2 - 25$	$x^2 - 15x - 76$
$9x^2$	$7x + 3$	$4x^2 + 12x + 9$
$-4x^3$	$5x^3 - 135$	$x^6 + 11x^5 - 26x^4$

Quick Check 1

Classify as a monomial, binomial, or trinomial. List the degree of each term.
a) $x^2 - 9x + 20$ **b)** $x^2 - 81$
c) $-92x^7$

EXAMPLE 1 Classify the polynomial as a monomial, binomial, or trinomial. List the degree of each term.
a) $16x^4 - 81$ **b)** $-13x^7$ **c)** $x^6 - 7x^3 - 18x$

SOLUTION

a) $16x^4 - 81$ has two terms, so it is a binomial. The degrees of its two terms are 4 and 0.
b) $-13x^7$ has only one term, so it is a monomial. The degree of this term is 7.
c) $x^6 - 7x^3 - 18x$ is a trinomial as it has three terms. The degrees of those terms are 6, 3, and 1, respectively.

The **coefficient** of a term is the numerical part of a term. When determining the coefficient of a term, be sure to include its sign. For the polynomial $8x^3 - 6x^2 - 5x + 13$, the four terms have coefficients 8, −6, −5, and 13, respectively.

Term	$8x^3$	$-6x^2$	$-5x$	13
Coefficient	8	−6	−5	13

EXAMPLE 2 For the trinomial $x^2 - 9x + 18$, determine the coefficient of each term.

SOLUTION   The first term of this trinomial, x^2, has a coefficient of 1. Even though we do not see a coefficient in front of the term, the coefficient is 1 because $x^2 = 1 \cdot x^2$. The second term, $-9x$, has a coefficient of −9. Finally, the coefficient of the constant term is 18.

▶ Quick Check 2

For the polynomial $x^3 - 6x^2 - 11x + 32$, determine the coefficient of each term.

We write polynomials in **descending order**, writing the term of highest degree first, followed by the term of next highest degree, and so on. For example, the polynomial $3x^2 - 9 - 5x^5 + 7x$ is written in descending order as $-5x^5 + 3x^2 + 7x - 9$. The term of highest degree is called the **leading term**, and its coefficient is called the **leading coefficient**.

> **Degree of a Polynomial**
>
> The degree of the leading term also is called the **degree of the polynomial**.

EXAMPLE 3 Rewrite the polynomial $7x^2 - 9 + 3x^5 - x$ in descending order and identify the leading term, the leading coefficient, and the degree of the polynomial.

SOLUTION   To write a polynomial in descending order, write the terms according to their degree from highest to lowest. In descending order, this polynomial is $3x^5 + 7x^2 - x - 9$. The leading term is $3x^5$, and the leading coefficient is 3. The leading term has degree 5, so this polynomial has degree 5.

Quick Check 3

Rewrite the polynomial $x + 9 + 4x^2 - x^3$ in descending order and identify the leading term, the leading coefficient, and the degree of the polynomial.

Evaluating Polynomials

Objective ② **Evaluate polynomials.** To **evaluate a polynomial** for a particular value of a variable, we substitute the value for the variable in the polynomial and simplify the resulting expression.

EXAMPLE 4 Evaluate $4x^5 - 7x^3 + 12x^2 - 13x$ for $x = -2$.

SOLUTION

$4(-2)^5 - 7(-2)^3 + 12(-2)^2 - 13(-2)$	Substitute −2 for x.
$= 4(-32) - 7(-8) + 12(4) - 13(-2)$	Perform operations involving exponents.
$= -128 + 56 + 48 + 26$	Multiply.
$= 2$	Simplify.

Quick Check 4

Evaluate $x^4 - 5x^3 - 6x^2 + 10x - 21$ for $x = -3$.

A **polynomial function** is a function that is described by a polynomial, such as $f(x) = x^3 - 5x^2 - 5x + 7$. Linear functions of the form $f(x) = mx + b$ are first-degree polynomial functions.

> **EXAMPLE 5** For the polynomial function $f(x) = x^2 - 9x + 16$, find $f(3)$.
>
> SOLUTION Recall that the notation $f(3)$ says to substitute 3 for x in the function. After substituting, simplify the resulting expression.
>
> $$\begin{aligned} f(3) &= (3)^2 - 9(3) + 16 && \text{Substitute 3 for } x. \\ &= 9 - 9(3) + 16 && \text{Perform operations involving exponents.} \\ &= 9 - 27 + 16 && \text{Multiply.} \\ &= -2 && \text{Simplify.} \end{aligned}$$

Quick Check 5

For the polynomial function $f(x) = x^3 + 12x^2 - 21x$, find $f(-5)$.

Adding and Subtracting Polynomials

Objective 3 Add and subtract polynomials. Just as we can perform arithmetic operations combining two numbers, we can perform operations combining two polynomials, such as adding and subtracting.

> **Adding Polynomials** ―――――――
>
> To add two polynomials, combine their like terms.

Recall that two terms are like terms if they have the same variables with the same exponents.

> **EXAMPLE 6** Add $(7x^2 - 5x - 8) + (4x^2 - 9x - 17)$.
>
> SOLUTION To add these polynomials, drop the parentheses and combine like terms.
>
> $$\begin{aligned} &(7x^2 - 5x - 8) + (4x^2 - 9x - 17) \\ &= 7x^2 - 5x - 8 + 4x^2 - 9x - 17 && \text{Rewrite without using parentheses.} \\ &= 11x^2 - 14x - 25 && \text{Combine like terms. } 7x^2 + 4x^2 = 11x^2, \\ & && -5x - 9x = -14x, -8 - 17 = -25 \end{aligned}$$

▶ **Quick Check 6**

Add $(x^3 - x^2 - 9x + 25) + (x^2 + 12x + 144)$.

A WORD OF CAUTION The terms $11x^2$ and $-14x$ are not like terms, as the variables do not have the same exponents.

To subtract one polynomial from another, such as $(x^2 + 5x - 9) - (3x^2 - 2x + 15)$, change the sign of each term that is being subtracted and combine like terms. Changing the sign of each term in the parentheses being subtracted is equivalent to applying the distributive property with -1.

> **EXAMPLE 7** Subtract $(x^2 + 5x - 9) - (3x^2 - 2x + 15)$.
>
> SOLUTION Remove the parentheses by changing the sign of each term in the polynomial that is being subtracted. Then combine like terms as follows:
>
> $$\begin{aligned} &(x^2 + 5x - 9) - (3x^2 - 2x + 15) \\ &= x^2 + 5x - 9 - 3x^2 + 2x - 15 && \text{Distribute to remove parentheses.} \\ &= -2x^2 + 7x - 24 && \text{Combine like terms.} \end{aligned}$$

Quick Check 7

Subtract $(5x^2 + 6x + 27) - (3x^3 + 6x^2 - 9x + 22)$.

A WORD OF CAUTION When subtracting one polynomial from another polynomial, be sure to change the sign of each term in the polynomial that is being subtracted.

EXAMPLE 8 Given the polynomial functions $f(x) = x^2 + 5x + 7$ and $g(x) = 2x^2 - 7x + 11$, find $f(x) - g(x)$.

SOLUTION Substitute the appropriate expressions for $f(x)$ and $g(x)$ and simplify the resulting expression.

$$\begin{aligned}
f(x) - g(x) &= (x^2 + 5x + 7) - (2x^2 - 7x + 11) &&\text{Substitute.} \\
&= x^2 + 5x + 7 - 2x^2 + 7x - 11 &&\text{Distribute to remove parentheses.} \\
&= -x^2 + 12x - 4 &&\text{Combine like terms.}
\end{aligned}$$

▶ **Quick Check 8**

Given the polynomial functions $f(x) = 4x^2 + 30x - 45$ and $g(x) = -2x^2 + 17x + 52$, find $f(x) - g(x)$.

Polynomials in Several Variables

Objective 4 Understand polynomials in several variables. While the polynomials we have examined to this point contained a single variable, some polynomials contain two or more variables. Here are some examples.

$$x^2y^2 + 3xy - 10 \qquad 7a^3 - 8a^2b + 3ab^2 - 15b^3 \qquad x^2 + 2xh + h^2 + 5x + 5h$$

We evaluate polynomials in several variables by substituting values for each variable and simplifying the resulting expression.

EXAMPLE 9 Evaluate the polynomial $x^2 - 8xy + 2y^2$ for $x = 5$ and $y = -4$.

SOLUTION Substitute 5 for x and -4 for y. Be careful to substitute the correct value for each variable.

$$\begin{aligned}
& x^2 - 8xy + 2y^2 \\
& (5)^2 - 8(5)(-4) + 2(-4)^2 &&\text{Substitute 5 for } x \text{ and } -4 \text{ for } y \\
& = 25 - 8(5)(-4) + 2(16) &&\text{Perform operations involving exponents.} \\
& = 25 + 160 + 32 &&\text{Multiply.} \\
& = 217 &&\text{Add.}
\end{aligned}$$

Quick Check 9

Evaluate the polynomial $b^2 - 4ac$ for $a = 1, b = -9$, and $c = -52$.

For a polynomial in several variables, the degree of a term is equal to the sum of the exponents of its variable factors. For example, the degree of the term $3x^2y^5$ is $2 + 5$, or 7.

Quick Check 10

Find the degree of each term in the polynomial $x^5 - 3x^2y^6 + 8x^9y$. In addition, find the degree of the polynomial.

EXAMPLE 10 Find the degree of each term in the polynomial $a^4b^3 - 3a^7b^5 + 9ab^6$. In addition, find the degree of the polynomial.

SOLUTION The first term, a^4b^3, has degree 7. The second term, $-3a^7b^5$, has degree 12. The third term, $9ab^6$, has degree 7. The degree of a polynomial is equal to the highest degree of any of its terms, so the degree of this polynomial is 12.

To add or subtract polynomials in several variables, we need to combine like terms. Two terms are like terms if they have the same variables with the same exponents.

EXAMPLE 11   Add $4xy^2 + 7x^3y^5$ and $9x^2y - 3x^3y^5$.

SOLUTION

$(4xy^2 + 7x^3y^5) + (9x^2y - 3x^3y^5)$ Write as a sum.
$= 4xy^2 + 7x^3y^5 + 9x^2y - 3x^3y^5$ Rewrite without parentheses.
$= 4xy^2 + 4x^3y^5 + 9x^2y$ Combine like terms ($7x^3y^5$ and $-3x^3y^5$).

Quick Check 11
Add $5x^4y^2 - 6x^3y^3$ and $8x^4y^2 + 2x^3y^3$.

BUILDING YOUR STUDY STRATEGY

Test Taking, 3 Read the Test In the same way you begin to solve a word problem, you should begin to take a test by briefly reading through it. This will give you an idea of how many problems you must solve, how many word problems there are, and roughly how much time you can devote to each problem. Keep an eye on the clock to be sure you are working fast enough.

Not all problems are assigned the same point value. Identify those problems that are worth more points. You do not want to have to rush through problems that have higher point values because you did not notice them until you got to the end of the test.

Exercises 5.3

Vocabulary

1. A(n) _____ in a single variable x is a sum of terms of the form ax^n, where a is a real number and n is a whole number.

2. For a polynomial in a single variable x, the _____ of a term is equal to its exponent.

3. A polynomial with one term is called a(n) _____.

4. A polynomial with two terms is called a(n) _____.

5. A polynomial with three terms is called a(n) _____.

6. The _____ of a term is the numerical part of a term.

7. When the terms of a polynomial are written from highest degree to lowest degree, the polynomial is said to be in _____.

8. The _____ of a polynomial is the term that has the greatest degree.

List the degree of each term in the given polynomial.

9. $9x^4 - 7x^2 + 3x - 8$
10. $-4x^3 + 10x^2 + 5x + 4$
11. $13x - 8x^7 - 11x^4$
12. $5x^5 - 3x^4 + 2x^3 + x^2 - 15$

List the coefficient of each term in the given polynomial.

13. $7x^2 + x - 15$
14. $3x^3 + x^2 - 8x - 13$
15. $10x^5 - 17x^4 + 6x^3 - x^2 + 2$
16. $-5x^3 - 12x^2 - 9x - 4$

Identify the given polynomial as a monomial, binomial, or trinomial.

17. $x^2 - 9x + 20$
18. $15x^9$
19. $4x - 7$
20. $2x^5 + 13x^4$
21. $-8x^3$
22. $5x^5 - 8x^3 + 17x$

Rewrite the polynomial in descending order. Identify the leading term, the leading coefficient, and the degree of the polynomial.

23. $8x - 7 + 3x^2$
24. $13 - 9x - x^2$
25. $6x^2 - 11x + 2x^4 + 10$
26. $2x^5 - x^6 + 24 - 3x^3 + x - 5x^2$

Evaluate the polynomial for the given value of the variable.

27. $x^2 + 3x - 10$ for $x = 5$

28. $2x^2 - 7x - 32$ for $x = 8$

29. $x^4 - 8x^3 - 48$ for $x = -2$

30. $x^3 + 16x^2 + 23$ for $x = -3$

31. $-x^2 + 7x + 22$ for $x = 10$

32. $-3x^2 - 8x + 16$ for $x = 6$

Evaluate the given polynomial function.

33. $f(x) = x^2 - 7x - 10, f(8)$

34. $f(x) = x^2 + 12x - 13, f(-9)$

35. $g(x) = 3x^3 - 8x^2 + 5x + 9, g(-5)$

36. $g(x) = -2x^3 - 5x^2 + 10x + 35, g(6)$

Add or subtract.

37. $(5x^2 + 8x - 11) + (3x^2 - 14x + 14)$

38. $(2x^2 - 9x - 35) + (8x^2 - 6x + 17)$

39. $(4x^2 - 7x + 30) - (2x^2 + 10x - 50)$

40. $(x^2 + 12x - 42) - (6x^2 - 19x - 23)$

41. $(2x^3 + 7x^2 - 19x) + (x^2 + 5x - 11)$

42. $(9x^4 + 7x^2 - 6x - 15) + (3x^3 - 7x^2 + 6x - 15)$

43. $(x^3 + 5x^2 - 16) - (6x^2 - 5x - 19)$

44. $(4x^3 + 9x^2 - 6x) - (x^4 - 9x^2 - 17)$

45. $(2x^9 - 5x^4 + 7x^2) - (-7x^6 + 4x^5 - 12)$

46. $(9x^3 + x^2 - x - 13) - (9x^3 + x^2 - x - 13)$

Find the missing polynomial.

47. $(3x^2 + 8x + 11) + ? = 7x^2 + 5x - 2$

48. $(2x^3 - 4x^2 - 7x + 19) + ? = x^2 + 3x + 24$

49. $(3x^4 - 5x^3 + 6x + 12) - ? = x^4 - 2x^3 - x^2 - 5x + 1$

50. $? - (6x^3 - 11x^2 - 16x + 22) = -x^3 + 19x^2 - 12x + 9$

For the given functions $f(x)$ and $g(x)$, find $f(x) + g(x)$ and $f(x) - g(x)$.

51. $f(x) = 7x^2 + 10x + 3, g(x) = 5x^2 - 9x + 6$

52. $f(x) = 2x^2 + 11x - 5, g(x) = -x^2 - 5x + 20$

53. $f(x) = x^3 - 8x - 31, g(x) = 4x^3 + x^2 + 3x + 25$

54. $f(x) = 2x^3 - 4x^2 + 8x - 16, g(x) = x^3 + 12x^2 - 15$

Evaluate the polynomial.

55. $x^2 - 7xy + 10y^2$ for $x = 2$ and $y = 5$

56. $3x^2 + 11xy + y^2$ for $x = 4$ and $y = 3$

57. $b^2 - 4ac$ for $a = -9, b = -2$, and $c = 4$

58. $b^2 - 4ac$ for $a = 5, b = -1$, and $c = 6$

59. $3x^2yz^3 - 4xy^2z - 6x^4y^2z$ for $x = 4, y = 5$, and $z = -2$

60. $7x^2yz + 9xy^2z - 10xyz^2$ for $x = 9, y = 3$, and $z = -2$

For each polynomial, list the degree of each term and the degree of the polynomial.

61. $6x^5y^5 - 7x^3y^3 + 9x^2y$

62. $-4x^8y^6 + 3x^3y^7 + x^5y^{11}$

63. $x^5y^2z - 5x^3y^3z^3 + 6x^2y^5z^4$

64. $a^{12}b^9c^{10} + 2a^{11}b^6c^{16} + 4a^{10}b^{10}c^3$

Add or subtract.

65. $(15x^2y + 8xy^2 - 7x^2y^3) + (-8x^2y + 3xy^2 + 4x^2y^3)$

66. $(x^4y - 5x^2y^3 - 14y^5) - (6x^4y + 11x^2y^3 - 7y^5)$

67. $(a^3b^2 + 11a^5b + 24a^2b^3) - (19a^2b^3 - 2a^5b + 15a^3b^2)$

68. $(9m^4n^2 - 13m^3n^3 + 11m^2n^4) + (-4m^2n^4 - 3m^4n^2 - m^3n^3)$

69. $(2x^3yz^2 - xy^4z^3 - 10x^2y^2z^5) - (4x^2yz^3 + 14xy^4z^3 - 3x^2y^2z^5)$

70. $(22x^3y^9 - 21x^6y^4 - 7x^8y^2) - (22x^3y^9 - 21x^6y^4 - 7x^8y^2)$

71. The manager of an amusement park is considering raising the price of admission to increase revenues.

She determines that if she raises the admission price by x dollars, the total daily revenues for the park can be approximated by the function $R(x) = -400x^2 + 13,600x + 1,230,000$. Find the daily revenues if she increases the cost of admission by \$6.

72. The average cost per shirt, in dollars, to produce x T-shirts is given by the function $f(x) = 0.00015x^2 - 0.06x + 10.125$. What is the average cost per shirt to produce 250 T-shirts?

73. The number of students earning master's degrees in mathematics or statistics in the United States in a particular year can be approximated by the function $g(x) = 6x^2 - 224x + 4941$, where x represents the number of years after 1971. Use the function to estimate the number of students who earned a master's degree in mathematics or statistics in the United States in 2010. (*Source: U.S. Department of Education*)

74. The number of births, in thousands, in the United States in a particular year can be approximated by the function $f(x) = 6x^2 - 72x + 4137$, where x represents the number of years after 1990. Use the function to estimate the number of births in the United States in 2010. (*Source: National Center for Health Statistics, U.S. Department of Health and Human Services*)

Writing in Mathematics

Answer in complete sentences.

75. Explain why it is a good idea to use parentheses when evaluating a polynomial for negative values of a variable. Do you believe that using parentheses is a good idea for evaluating any polynomial?

76. A classmate made the following error when subtracting two polynomials.

$$(3x^2 + 2x - 7) - (x^2 - x + 9)$$
$$= 3x^2 + 2x - 7 - x^2 - x + 9$$

Explain the error to your classmate and give advice on how to avoid making this error.

5.4

Multiplying Polynomials

OBJECTIVES

1. Multiply monomials.
2. Multiply a monomial by a polynomial.
3. Multiply polynomials.
4. Find special products.

Multiplying Monomials

Objective 1 Multiply monomials. Now that we have learned how to add and subtract polynomials, we will explore multiplication of polynomials. We begin by learning how to multiply monomials.

┌─ **Multiplying Monomials** ──────────
When multiplying monomials, begin by multiplying their coefficients. Then multiply the variable factors using the property of exponents that states that for any real number $x, x^m \cdot x^n = x^{m+n}$.
└──────────────────────────────────

EXAMPLE 1 Multiply $3x \cdot 5x$.

SOLUTION Multiply the coefficients first; then multiply the variables.

$$3x \cdot 5x = 3 \cdot 5 \cdot x \cdot x \quad \text{Multiply coefficients, then variables.}$$
$$= 15x^{1+1} \quad \text{Multiply variables using the property } x^m \cdot x^n = x^{m+n}.$$
$$= 15x^2 \quad \text{Simplify the exponent.}$$

▶ Quick Check 1
Multiply $7x \cdot 8x$.

EXAMPLE 2   Multiply $2x^4y^3 \cdot 3x^2y^7z^4$.

SOLUTION   The procedure for multiplying monomials containing more than one variable is the same as multiplying monomials containing a single variable. After multiplying the coefficients, multiply the variables one at a time.

$$2x^4y^3 \cdot 3x^2y^7z^4 = 6x^6y^{10}z^4 \quad \text{Multiply coefficients, then variables.}$$

Notice that the variable z was a factor of only one of the monomials. The exponent of z was not changed.

Quick Check 2
Multiply $5x^6yz^7 \cdot 12x^8z^6$.

Multiplying a Monomial by a Polynomial

Objective 2 Multiply a monomial by a polynomial. We now advance to multiplying a monomial by a polynomial containing two or more terms, such as $3x(2x^2 - 5x + 2)$. To do this, we use the distributive property $a(b + c) = ab + ac$. To find the product $3x(2x^2 - 5x + 2)$, we multiply the monomial $3x$ by each term of the polynomial $2x^2 - 5x + 2$.

> **Multiplying a Monomial by a Polynomial**
>
> To multiply a monomial by a polynomial containing two or more terms, multiply the monomial by each term of the polynomial.

EXAMPLE 3   Multiply $3x(2x^2 - 5x + 2)$.

SOLUTION   Begin by distributing the monomial $3x$ to each term of the polynomial.

$$3x(2x^2 - 5x + 2) = 3x \cdot 2x^2 - 3x \cdot 5x + 3x \cdot 2 \quad \text{Distribute } 3x.$$
$$= 6x^3 - 15x^2 + 6x \quad \text{Multiply.}$$

Although we will continue to show the distribution of the monomial, your goal should be to perform this task mentally.

Quick Check 3

Multiply
$4x(7x^3 - 6x^2 + 5x - 8)$.

EXAMPLE 4   Multiply $-8x^3(x^5 - 4x^4 - 9x^2)$.

SOLUTION   Notice that the coefficient of the monomial being distributed is negative. We must distribute $-8x^3$, and multiplying by this negative term changes the sign of each term in the polynomial.

$$-8x^3(x^5 - 4x^4 - 9x^2) = (-8x^3)(x^5) - (-8x^3)(4x^4) - (-8x^3)(9x^2)$$
$$\text{Distribute } -8x^3.$$
$$= -8x^8 - (-32x^7) - (-72x^5) \quad \text{Multiply.}$$
$$= -8x^8 + 32x^7 + 72x^5 \quad \text{Simplify.}$$

▶ **Quick Check 4**
Multiply $-3x^5(-2x^4 + x^3 - x^2 - 15x + 21)$.

A WORD OF CAUTION   When multiplying a polynomial by a term with a negative coefficient, be sure to change the sign of each term in the polynomial.

Multiplying Polynomials

Objective ③ **Multiply polynomials.**

> **Multiplying Two Polynomials**
>
> To multiply two polynomials when each contains two or more terms, multiply each term in the first polynomial by each term in the second polynomial.

Suppose we wanted to multiply $(x + 9)(x + 7)$. We could distribute the factor $(x + 9)$ to each term in the second polynomial as follows:

$$(x + 9)(x + 7) = (x + 9) \cdot x + (x + 9) \cdot 7$$

We could then perform the two multiplications by distributing x in the first product and distributing 7 in the second product.

$$
\begin{aligned}
(x + 9)(x + 7) &= (x + 9) \cdot x + (x + 9) \cdot 7 \\
&= x \cdot x + 9 \cdot x + x \cdot 7 + 9 \cdot 7 \\
&= x^2 + 9x + 7x + 63 \\
&= x^2 + 16x + 63
\end{aligned}
$$

We end up with each term in the first polynomial being multiplied by each term in the second polynomial.

EXAMPLE 5   Multiply $(x + 6)(x + 4)$.

SOLUTION   Begin by taking the first term in the first polynomial, x, and multiplying it by each term in the second polynomial. Then repeat this for the second term in the first polynomial, 6.

$(x + 6)(x + 4) = x \cdot x + x \cdot 4 + 6 \cdot x + 6 \cdot 4$ Distribute the term x from the first polynomial; then distribute the 6 from the first polynomial.

$\qquad\qquad\qquad\quad = x^2 + 4x + 6x + 24$ Multiply.

$\qquad\qquad\qquad\quad = x^2 + 10x + 24$ Combine like terms.

▶ Quick Check 5

Multiply $(x + 11)(x + 9)$.

We often refer to the process of multiplying a binomial by another binomial as "FOIL." FOIL is an acronym for **F**irst, **O**uter, **I**nner, **L**ast, which describes the four multiplications that occur when we multiply two binomials. Here are the four multiplications performed in the previous example.

First	**O**uter	**I**nner	**L**ast
$x \cdot x$	$x \cdot 4$		
$(x + 6)(x + 4)$	$(x + 6)(x + 4)$	$(x + 6)(x + 4)$	$(x + 6)(x + 4)$
		$6 \cdot x$	$6 \cdot 4$

FOIL applies only when we multiply a binomial by another binomial. If we are multiplying a binomial by a trinomial, six multiplications must be performed and FOIL cannot be used. Keep in mind that each term in the first polynomial must be multiplied by each term in the second polynomial.

EXAMPLE 6 Multiply $(x - 6)(4x - 5)$.

SOLUTION When multiplying polynomials, we must be careful with the signs. When we distribute the second term of $x - 6$ to the second polynomial, we must distribute a negative 6.

$$(x - 6)(4x - 5) = x \cdot 4x - x \cdot 5 - 6 \cdot 4x + 6 \cdot 5 \qquad \text{Distribute (FOIL). The product}$$
of two negative numbers is
positive: $(-6)(-5) = 6 \cdot 5$.

$$= 4x^2 - 5x - 24x + 30 \qquad \text{Multiply.}$$
$$= 4x^2 - 29x + 30 \qquad \text{Combine like terms.}$$

Quick Check 6
Multiply $(5x - 2)(2x - 9)$.

EXAMPLE 7 Given the functions $f(x) = 3x - 2$ and $g(x) = x^2 + 4x - 7$, find $f(x) \cdot g(x)$.

SOLUTION We will substitute the appropriate expressions for $f(x)$ and $g(x)$ in parentheses and simplify the resulting expression. We need to multiply each term in the first polynomial by each term in the second polynomial.

$$f(x) \cdot g(x) = (3x - 2)(x^2 + 4x - 7) \qquad \text{Substitute for } f(x)$$
and $g(x)$.

$$= 3x \cdot x^2 + 3x \cdot 4x - 3x \cdot 7 - 2 \cdot x^2 - 2 \cdot 4x + 2 \cdot 7 \quad \text{Distribute.}$$
$$= 3x^3 + 12x^2 - 21x - 2x^2 - 8x + 14 \qquad \text{Multiply.}$$
$$= 3x^3 + 10x^2 - 29x + 14 \qquad \text{Combine like terms.}$$

Quick Check 7
Given the functions $f(x) = x + 8$ and $g(x) = 3x^2 + 6x - 2$, find $f(x) \cdot g(x)$.

Special Products

Objective 4 Find special products. We finish this section by examining some special products. The first special product is of the form $(a + b)(a - b)$. In words, this is the product of the sum and the difference of two terms. Here is the multiplication.

$$(a + b)(a - b) = a^2 - ab + ab - b^2 \qquad \text{Distribute.}$$
$$= a^2 - b^2 \qquad \text{Combine like terms.}$$

Notice that when we were combining like terms, two of the terms were opposites. This left only two terms. We can use this result whenever we multiply two binomials of the form $(a + b)(a - b)$.

$$(a + b)(a - b) = a^2 - b^2$$

EXAMPLE 8 Multiply $(x + 7)(x - 7)$.

SOLUTION

$$(x + 7)(x - 7) = x^2 - 7^2 \qquad \text{Multiply using the pattern}$$
$(a + b)(a - b) = a^2 - b^2$.

$$= x^2 - 49 \qquad \text{Simplify.}$$

Quick Check 8
Multiply $(x + 10)(x - 10)$.

EXAMPLE 9 Multiply $(3x - 5)(3x + 5)$.

SOLUTION   Although the difference is listed first, we can still multiply using the same pattern.

$$(3x - 5)(3x + 5) = (3x)^2 - 5^2$$ Multiply using the pattern $(a + b)(a - b) = a^2 - b^2$.
$$= 9x^2 - 25$$ Simplify.

Quick Check 9
Multiply $(2x + 7)(2x - 7)$.

The other special product we will examine is the square of a binomial, such as $(x + 3)^2$ and $(9x + 4)^2$. Here are the patterns for squaring binomials of the form $a + b$ and $a - b$.

$$(a + b)^2 = a^2 + 2ab + b^2$$
$$(a - b)^2 = a^2 - 2ab + b^2$$

Let's derive the first of these patterns.

$$(a + b)^2 = (a + b)(a + b)$$ To square a binomial, multiply it by itself.
$$= a^2 + ab + ab + b^2$$ Distribute (FOIL).
$$= a^2 + 2ab + b^2$$ Combine like terms.

The second pattern can be derived in the same fashion.

EXAMPLE 10 Multiply $(x - 3)^2$.

SOLUTION   We can use the pattern $(a - b)^2 = a^2 - 2ab + b^2$, substituting x for a and 3 for b.

$$a^2 - 2ab + b^2$$
$$x^2 - 2 \cdot x \cdot 3 + 3^2$$ Substitute x for a and 3 for b.
$$= x^2 - 6x + 9$$ Multiply.

Quick Check 10
Multiply $(5x - 8)^2$.

EXAMPLE 11 Multiply $(2x + 5)^2$.

SOLUTION   We can use the pattern $(a + b)^2 = a^2 + 2ab + b^2$, substituting $2x$ for a and 5 for b.

$$a^2 + 2ab + b^2$$
$$(2x)^2 + 2 \cdot (2x) \cdot 5 + 5^2$$ Substitute $2x$ for a and 5 for b.
$$= 4x^2 + 20x + 25$$ Multiply.

Quick Check 11
Multiply $(x + 6)^2$.

Although the patterns developed for these three special products may save us time when multiplying, keep in mind that we can find these types of products by multiplying as we did earlier in this section. When we square a binomial, we can start by rewriting the expression as the product of the binomial and itself. For example, we can rewrite $(8x - 7)^2$ as $(8x - 7)(8x - 7)$ and then multiply.

BUILDING YOUR STUDY STRATEGY

Test Taking, 4 Solve Easier Problems First When you take a test, work on easier problems first, saving more difficult problems for later. One benefit to this approach is that you will gain confidence as you progress through the test, making you confident when you attempt to solve a difficult problem. You also will save time to spend on the few difficult problems.

Exercises 5.4

Vocabulary

1. To multiply a monomial by another monomial, multiply the coefficients and _____ the exponents of the variable factors.

2. To multiply a monomial by a polynomial, _____ the monomial to each term in the polynomial.

3. To multiply a polynomial by another polynomial, _____ each term in the first polynomial by each term in the second polynomial.

4. The acronym _____ can be used when you are multiplying a binomial by another binomial.

Multiply.

5. $4x \cdot 9x^4$

6. $8x^3 \cdot 7x^2$

7. $9m^7(-6m^{11})$

8. $-6n^5 \cdot 10n^3$

9. $13a^7b^{10} \cdot 7a^5b$

10. $20ab^9 \cdot 16a^{13}b^{15}$

11. $-5x^3y^2z^4 \cdot 14xz^5w^4$

12. $3a^5b^8c \cdot 9bc^7d^4$

13. $2x^5 \cdot 6x^3 \cdot 7x^2$

14. $-12x^8 \cdot 5x^{10} \cdot 6x^9$

Find the missing monomial.

15. $5x^5 \cdot ? = 30x^{30}$

16. $-7x^9 \cdot ? = -28x^{16}$

17. $2x^9 \cdot ? = -24x^{18}$

18. $-6x^{10} \cdot ? = 84x^{23}$

Multiply.

19. $5(3x - 4)$

20. $3(7x + 6)$

21. $-2(6x - 9)$

22. $-4(3x + 11)$

23. $6x(3x + 5)$

24. $9x(4x - 13)$

25. $x^3(3x^2 - 4x + 7)$

26. $-x^3(2x^5 + 9x^4 - 6x)$

27. $2xy^2(3x^2 - 6xy + 7y^2)$

28. $11x^4y^3(2xy - 5x^4y^2 - 7x)$

Multiply.

29. $(x + 7)(x - 9)$

30. $(x + 6)(x + 8)$

31. $(x - 3)(x - 9)$

32. $(x - 5)(x + 10)$

33. $(4x + 3)(x - 6)$

34. $(5x - 7)(2x + 3)$

35. $(x - 8)(x + 9)$

36. $(x + 6)(x - 3)$

37. $(2x + 3)(2x - 13)$

38. $(2x - 9)(3x - 4)$

39. $(x + 6)(3x - 5)$

40. $(5x + 8)(4x + 1)$

41. $(3x + 2)(x^2 - 5x - 9)$

42. $(7x - 4)(49x^2 + 28x + 16)$

43. $(x^2 - 7x + 10)(x^2 + 3x - 40)$

44. $(2x^2 - 5x - 8)(x^2 + 3x + 9)$

45. $(x + 2y)(x - 4y)$

46. $(x - 6y)(x - 7y)$

47. $(4xy + 3)(5xy + 6)$

48. $(2xy + 7)(3xy - 2)$

Find the missing factor or term.

49. $?(2x^2 - 7x - 10) = 6x^5 - 21x^4 - 30x^3$

50. $?(3x^4 + 9x^2 + 16) = 18x^9 + 54x^7 + 96x^5$

51. $4x^4(?) = 12x^7 - 20x^6 - 48x^4$

52. $8x^9(?) = 56x^{17} + 104x^{14} - 96x^{11}$

53. $(x + ?)(x + 5) = x^2 + 8x + 15$

54. $(x - 7)(x + ?) = x^2 + 3x - 70$

55. $(x + ?)(x + ?) = x^2 + 9x + 18$

56. $(? - 5)(? + 3) = 2x^2 + x - 15$

For the given functions $f(x)$ and $g(x)$, find $f(x) \cdot g(x)$.

57. $f(x) = x - 9, g(x) = x + 2$

58. $f(x) = 4x^3, g(x) = x^2 - 8x - 14$

59. $f(x) = 6x^5, g(x) = -3x^4$

60. $f(x) = 2x^7, g(x) = 11x^6$

61. $f(x) = x^3 - 5x^2 + 8x + 3, g(x) = -4x^5$

62. $f(x) = 7x + 4, g(x) = 6x - 13$

Find the special product using the appropriate formula.

63. $(x + 9)(x - 9)$

64. $(x - 6)(x + 6)$

65. $(3x - 7)(3x + 7)$

66. $(2x + 11)(2x - 11)$

67. $(x + 7)^2$

68. $(x - 10)^2$

69. $(4x - 3)^2$

70. $(9x + 5)^2$

Find the missing factor or term.

71. $(x + 9) \cdot (?) = x^2 - 81$

72. $(5x + 7) \cdot (?) = 25x^2 - 49$

73. $(?)^2 = x^2 - 12x + 36$

74. $(?)^2 = 4x^2 + 20x + 25$

Mixed Practice, 75–92

Multiply.

75. $(x + 7)(x - 1)$

76. $2x^5 \cdot 3x^2$

77. $5x(x^2 - 8x - 9)$

78. $(x + 2)(x - 2)$

79. $-7x^2y^3 \cdot 4x^4y^6$

80. $(x - 7)^2$

81. $-5x^6(-4x^8)$

82. $(2x + 15)(3x - 7)$

83. $(5x + 3)(5x - 3)$

84. $-3x^2(x^2 - 10x - 13)$

85. $(x + 13)^2$

86. $(x + 8)(3x^2 + 7x - 6)$

87. $2x^2y(3x^2 - x^4y^3 - 7y)$

88. $9x^3(-6x^3)$

89. $(4x - 9)^2$

90. $(6 + 5x)^2$

91. $(x^2 + 3x + 4)(x^2 - 5x + 4)$

92. $-6x^5(-x^5 + 3x^3 - 11)$

✏ Writing in Mathematics

Answer in complete sentences.

93. Explain the difference between simplifying the expression $8x^2 + 3x^2$ and simplifying the expression $(8x^2)(3x^2)$. Discuss how the coefficients and exponents are handled differently.

94. To simplify the expression $(x + 8)^2$, you can multiply $(x + 8)(x + 8)$ or use the special product formula $(a + b)^2 = a^2 + 2ab + b^2$. Which method do you prefer? Explain your answer.

95. *Newsletter* Write a newsletter explaining how to multiply two binomials.

5.5

Dividing Polynomials

OBJECTIVES

1. Divide a monomial by a monomial.
2. Divide a polynomial by a monomial.
3. Divide a polynomial by a polynomial using long division.
4. Use placeholders when dividing a polynomial by a polynomial.

Dividing Monomials by Monomials

Objective 1 Divide a monomial by a monomial. In this section, we will learn to divide a polynomial by another polynomial. We will begin by reviewing how to divide a monomial by another monomial, such as $\dfrac{4x^5}{2x^2}$ or $\dfrac{30a^5b^4}{6ab^2}$.

Dividing a Monomial by a Monomial

To divide a monomial by another monomial, divide the coefficients first. Then divide the variables using the quotient rule $\frac{x^m}{x^n} = x^{m-n}$. Assume that no variable in the denominator is equal to 0.

EXAMPLE 1 Divide $\frac{18x^5}{3x^3}$. (Assume that $x \neq 0$.)

SOLUTION

$$\frac{18x^5}{3x^3} = 6x^{5-3} \quad \text{Divide coefficients. Subtract exponents of } x.$$

$$= 6x^2 \quad \text{Simplify the exponent.}$$

We can check the quotient by using multiplication. If $\frac{18x^5}{3x^3} = 6x^2$, we know that $3x^3 \cdot 6x^2$ should equal $18x^5$.

Check

$$3x^3 \cdot 6x^2 = 18x^{3+2} \quad \text{Multiply coefficients. Keep the base and add the exponents.}$$

$$= 18x^5 \quad \text{Simplify the exponent.}$$

The quotient of $6x^2$ checks.

Quick Check 1

Divide $\frac{32x^9}{4x^4}$.

(Assume that $x \neq 0$.)

EXAMPLE 2 Divide $\frac{24x^3y^2}{3xy^2}$. (Assume that $x, y \neq 0$.)

SOLUTION   When there is more than one variable, as in this example, divide the coefficients and then divide the variables one at a time.

$$\frac{24x^3y^2}{3xy^2} = 8x^2y^0 \quad \text{Divide coefficients and subtract exponents.}$$

$$= 8x^2 \quad \text{Rewrite without } y \text{ as a factor. } (y^0 = 1)$$

Quick Check 2

Divide $\frac{40x^3y^{11}}{8xy^2}$. (Assume that $x, y \neq 0$.)

Dividing Polynomials by Monomials

Objective ② Divide a polynomial by a monomial. Now we move on to dividing a polynomial by a monomial, such as $\frac{3x^5 - 9x^3 - 18x^2}{3x}$.

Dividing a Polynomial by a Monomial

To divide a polynomial by a monomial, divide each term of the polynomial by the monomial.

EXAMPLE 3 Divide $\frac{15x^2 + 10x - 5}{5}$.

SOLUTION   Divide each term in the numerator by 5.

$$\frac{15x^2 + 10x - 5}{5} = \frac{15x^2}{5} + \frac{10x}{5} - \frac{5}{5} \quad \text{Divide each term in the numerator by 5.}$$

$$= 3x^2 + 2x - 1 \quad \text{Divide.}$$

If $\dfrac{15x^2 + 10x - 5}{5} = 3x^2 + 2x - 1$, $5(3x^2 + 2x - 1)$ should equal $15x^2 + 10x - 5$. We can use this to check our work.

Check

$$5(3x^2 + 2x - 1) = 5 \cdot 3x^2 + 5 \cdot 2x - 5 \cdot 1 \quad \text{Distribute.}$$
$$= 15x^2 + 10x - 5 \qquad \text{Multiply.}$$

◄ The quotient of $3x^2 + 2x - 1$ checks.

Quick Check 3

Divide $\dfrac{7x^2 - 21x - 49}{7}$.

> **EXAMPLE 4** Divide $\dfrac{3x^5 - 9x^3 - 18x^2}{3x}$. (Assume that $x \ne 0$.)

> SOLUTION In this example, divide each term in the numerator by $3x$.

$$\frac{3x^5 - 9x^3 - 18x^2}{3x}$$

$$= \frac{3x^5}{3x} - \frac{9x^3}{3x} - \frac{18x^2}{3x} \quad \text{Divide each term in the numerator by } 3x.$$

$$= x^4 - 3x^2 - 6x \qquad \text{Divide.}$$

Quick Check 4

Divide $\dfrac{48x^{10} + 12x^7 + 30x^5}{6x^2}$.

(Assume that $x \ne 0$.)

Dividing a Polynomial by a Polynomial (Long Division)

Objective 3 Divide a polynomial by a polynomial using long division.
To divide a polynomial by another polynomial containing at least two terms, we use a procedure similar to long division. Before outlining this procedure, let's review some of the terms associated with long division.

$$\text{Divisor} \longrightarrow 2\overline{)6} \xleftarrow{\text{Dividend}} \quad \overset{\text{Quotient}}{\underset{3}{\nearrow}}$$

Suppose we were asked to divide $\dfrac{x^2 - 10x + 16}{x - 2}$. The polynomial in the numerator is the dividend, and the polynomial in the denominator is the divisor. We may rewrite this division as $x - 2\overline{)x^2 - 10x + 16}$. We must be sure to write both the divisor and the dividend in descending order. We perform the division using the following steps:

┌─ **Division by a Polynomial** ──────────────────────────

1. Divide the term in the dividend with the highest degree by the term in the divisor with the highest degree. Add this result to the quotient.
2. Multiply the monomial obtained in Step 1 by the divisor, writing the result underneath the dividend. (Align like terms vertically.)
3. Subtract the product obtained in Step 2 from the dividend. (Recall that to subtract a polynomial from another polynomial, we change the signs of its terms and then combine like terms.)
4. Repeat Steps 1–3 with the result of Step 3 as the new dividend. Keep repeating this procedure until the degree of the new dividend is less than the degree of the divisor.

EXAMPLE 5 Divide $\dfrac{x^2 - 10x + 16}{x - 2}$.

SOLUTION   Begin by writing $x - 2\overline{)x^2 - 10x + 16}$. Divide the term in the dividend with the highest degree (x^2) by the term in the divisor with the highest degree (x). Because $\dfrac{x^2}{x} = x$, write x in the quotient and multiply x by the divisor $x - 2$, writing this product underneath the dividend.

$$
\begin{array}{r}
x \phantom{{}- 10x + 16} \\
x - 2\overline{)x^2 - 10x + 16} \\
x^2 - 2x \phantom{{}+ 16}
\end{array}
\quad \text{Multiply } x \text{ by } (x - 2).
$$

To subtract, change the signs of the second polynomial and combine like terms.

$$
\begin{array}{r}
x \phantom{{}- 10x + 16} \\
x - 2\overline{)x^2 - 10x + 16} \\
\underline{\overset{-}{x^2} \overset{+}{\not{-}} 2x} \phantom{{}+ 16} \downarrow \\
-8x + 16
\end{array}
\quad \text{Change the signs and combine like terms.}
$$

Begin the process again by dividing $-8x$ by x, which equals -8. Multiply -8 by $x - 2$ and subtract.

$$
\begin{array}{r}
x - 8 \phantom{{}+ 16} \\
x - 2\overline{)x^2 - 10x + 16} \\
\underline{\overset{-}{x^2} \overset{+}{\not{-}} 2x} \phantom{{}+ 16} \downarrow \\
-8x + 16 \\
\underline{\overset{+}{\not{-}} 8x \overset{-}{\not{+}} 16} \\
0
\end{array}
\quad \begin{array}{l} \text{Multiply } -8 \text{ by } (x - 2). \\ \text{Subtract the product.} \end{array}
$$

The remainder of 0 says that we are finished because its degree is less than the degree of the divisor $x - 2$. The expression written above the division box ($x - 8$) is the quotient.

$$\frac{x^2 - 10x + 16}{x - 2} = x - 8$$

We can check our work by multiplying the quotient ($x - 8$) by the divisor ($x - 2$), which should equal the dividend ($x^2 - 10x + 16$).

Check

$$
\begin{aligned}
(x - 8)(x - 2) &= x^2 - 2x - 8x + 16 \\
&= x^2 - 10x + 16
\end{aligned}
$$

The division checks; the quotient is $x - 8$.

▶ **Quick Check 5**

Divide $\dfrac{x^2 + 13x + 36}{x + 4}$.

In the previous example, the remainder of 0 also says that $x - 2$ divides into $x^2 - 10x + 16$ evenly; so $x - 2$ is a **factor** of $x^2 - 10x + 16$. The quotient, $x - 8$, also is a factor of $x^2 - 10x + 16$.

In the next example, we will learn how to write a quotient when there is a nonzero remainder.

EXAMPLE 6   Divide $x^2 - 10x + 9$ by $x - 3$.

SOLUTION   Because the divisor and dividend are already written in descending order, we may begin to divide.

$$
\begin{array}{r}
x - 7 \\
x - 3{\overline{\smash{\big)}\,x^2 - 10x + 9}} \\
\underline{x^2 - 3x} \quad\downarrow \\
-7x + 9 \\
\underline{-7x + 21} \\
-12
\end{array}
$$

Multiply x by $x - 3$ and subtract.

Multiply -7 by $x - 3$ and subtract.

The remainder is -12. After the quotient, we write a fraction with the remainder in the numerator and the divisor in the denominator. Because the remainder is negative, we subtract this fraction from the quotient. If the remainder had been positive, we would have added this fraction to the quotient.

$$
\frac{x^2 - 10x + 9}{x - 3} = x - 7 - \frac{12}{x - 3}
$$

▶ Quick Check 6

Divide $\dfrac{x^2 - 3x - 8}{x + 7}$.

EXAMPLE 7   Divide $6x^2 + 17x + 17$ by $2x + 3$.

SOLUTION   Because the divisor and dividend are already written in descending order, we may begin to divide.

$$
\begin{array}{r}
3x + 4 \\
2x + 3{\overline{\smash{\big)}\,6x^2 + 17x + 17}} \\
\underline{6x^2 + 9x} \quad\downarrow \\
8x + 17 \\
\underline{8x + 12} \\
5
\end{array}
$$

Multiply $3x$ by $2x + 3$ and subtract.

Multiply 4 by $2x + 3$ and subtract.

The remainder is 5. We write the quotient and add a fraction with the remainder in the numerator and the divisor in the denominator.

$$
\frac{6x^2 + 17x + 17}{2x + 3} = 3x + 4 + \frac{5}{2x + 3}
$$

▶ Quick Check 7

Divide $\dfrac{12x^2 - 7x + 4}{3x - 4}$.

Using Placeholders When Dividing a Polynomial by a Polynomial

Objective 4 Use placeholders when dividing a polynomial by a polynomial. Suppose we wanted to divide $x^3 - 12x - 11$ by $x - 3$. Notice that the dividend is missing an x^2 term. When this is the case, we add the term $0x^2$ as a **placeholder**. We add placeholders to dividends that are missing terms of a particular degree.

EXAMPLE 8 Divide $(x^3 - 12x - 11) \div (x - 3)$.

SOLUTION   The degree of the dividend is 3, and each degree lower than 3 must be represented in the dividend. We will add the term $0x^2$ as a placeholder. The divisor does not have any missing terms.

$$
\begin{array}{r}
x^2 + 3x - 3 \\
x - 3 \overline{)x^3 + 0x^2 - 12x - 11} \\
\underline{x^3 \pm 3x^2 \quad\downarrow\quad\downarrow} \\
3x^2 - 12x - 11 \\
\underline{3x^2 \pm 9x \quad\downarrow} \\
-3x - 11 \\
\underline{\pm 3x \mp 9} \\
-20
\end{array}
$$

Multiply x^2 by $x - 3$ and subtract.

Multiply $3x$ by $x - 3$ and subtract.

Multiply -3 by $x - 3$ and subtract.

$$(x^3 - 12x - 11) \div (x - 3) = x^2 + 3x - 3 - \frac{20}{x - 3}.$$

Quick Check 8

Divide $\dfrac{x^3 - 3x^2 - 9}{x - 2}$.

BUILDING YOUR STUDY STRATEGY

Test Taking, 5 Review Your Test Try to leave yourself enough time to review the test at the end of the period. Check for careless errors, which can cost you a fair number of points. Also check that your answers make sense in the context of the problem. For example, if the question asks how tall a person is and your answer is 68 feet, chances are that something has gone astray.

Check for problems or parts of problems you may have skipped and left blank.

Take all of the allotted time to review the test. There is no reward for turning in a test early, and the more you work on a test, the more likely you are to find a mistake or a problem where you can gain points.

Exercises 5.5

PRACTICE   WATCH   DOWNLOAD   READ   REVIEW

Vocabulary

1. To divide a polynomial by a monomial, divide each _____ by the monomial.

2. To divide a polynomial by another polynomial containing at least two terms, use _____.

3. If one polynomial divides evenly into a second polynomial, the first polynomial is a(n) _____ of the second polynomial.

4. If a polynomial in the dividend is missing a term of a particular degree, use a(n) _____ in the dividend.

Divide. Assume that all variables are nonzero.

5. $\dfrac{24x^{24}}{3x^3}$

6. $\dfrac{16x^{16}}{4x^4}$

7. $\dfrac{-30n^{11}}{6n^4}$

8. $\dfrac{-48n^9}{3n}$

9. $\dfrac{26a^7b^5}{2ab^3}$

10. $\dfrac{35x^9y^{10}}{5x^8y^3}$

11. $(15x^6) \div (3x^2)$

12. $(70x^{13}) \div (10x^5)$

13. $\dfrac{12x^6}{8x^4}$

14. $\dfrac{-35x^9}{25x^5}$

15. $\dfrac{7x^{12}}{21x^4}$

16. $\dfrac{3x^{15}}{18x^7}$

Find the missing monomial. Assume that $x \neq 0$.

17. $\dfrac{?}{5x^4} = 2x^7$

18. $\dfrac{?}{3x^6} = -15x^8$

19. $\dfrac{24x^9}{?} = -6x^4$

20. $\dfrac{20x^9}{?} = \dfrac{5x^4}{3}$

Divide. Assume that all variables are nonzero.

21. $\dfrac{15x^2 - 25x - 40}{5}$

22. $\dfrac{8x^5 - 2x^3 + 6x^2}{2}$

23. $\dfrac{24x^4 + 30x^2 - 27x}{3x}$

24. $\dfrac{32x^4 + 44x^3 + 60x^2}{4x}$

25. $(6x^7 + 9x^6 + 15x^5) \div (3x)$

26. $(-14x^8 + 21x^6 + 7x^4) \div (7x)$

27. $\dfrac{20x^6 - 30x^4}{-10x^2}$

28. $\dfrac{-8x^5 + 2x^4 - 6x^3 - 2x^2}{-2x^2}$

29. $\dfrac{x^6y^6 - x^4y^5 + x^2y^4}{xy^2}$

30. $\dfrac{2a^{10}b^7 - 8a^3b^6 - 10a^5b}{2a^3b}$

Find the missing dividend or divisor. Assume that $x \neq 0$.

31. $\dfrac{24x^3 - 48x^2 + 36x}{?} = 4x^2 - 8x + 6$

32. $\dfrac{10x^7 - 50x^5 + 35x^3}{?} = 2x^5 - 10x^3 + 7x$

33. $\dfrac{?}{2x^3} = 3x^4 - 4x^2 - 9$

34. $\dfrac{?}{7x^5} = -x^2 - 9x + 1$

Divide using long division.

35. $\dfrac{x^2 + 13x + 40}{x + 8}$

36. $\dfrac{x^2 + 10x + 21}{x + 3}$

37. $\dfrac{x^2 - 8x - 84}{x - 14}$

38. $\dfrac{x^2 - x - 72}{x - 9}$

39. $(x^2 - 13x + 36) \div (x - 4)$

40. $(x^2 - 20x + 91) \div (x - 7)$

41. $\dfrac{x^2 - 4x - 29}{x - 8}$

42. $\dfrac{x^2 + 7x - 7}{x + 5}$

43. $\dfrac{x^3 - 11x^2 - 37x + 14}{x + 1}$

44. $\dfrac{x^3 - x^2 - 24x - 19}{x + 3}$

45. $\dfrac{2x^2 + 3x - 32}{x + 5}$

46. $\dfrac{3x^2 + 26x + 24}{x + 9}$

47. $\dfrac{6x^2 + 25x + 10}{2x + 7}$

48. $\dfrac{10x^2 - 53x + 28}{5x - 4}$

49. $\dfrac{x^2 - 169}{x + 13}$

50. $\dfrac{9x^2 - 25}{3x - 5}$

51. $\dfrac{x^4 + 2x^2 - 15x + 32}{x - 3}$

52. $\dfrac{x^5 - 9x^3 - 17x^2 + x - 15}{x + 8}$

53. $\dfrac{x^3 - 125}{x - 5}$

54. $\dfrac{x^3 + 343}{x + 7}$

Find the missing dividend or divisor.

55. $\dfrac{?}{x + 8} = x - 3$

56. $\dfrac{?}{x - 5} = x - 11$

57. $\dfrac{x^2 + 10x - 39}{?} = x - 3$

58. $\dfrac{6x^2 - 35x + 49}{?} = 3x - 7$

59. Is $x + 9$ a factor of $x^2 + 28x + 171$?

60. Is $x - 6$ a factor of $x^2 + 4x - 54$?

61. Is $2x - 5$ a factor of $4x^2 - 8x - 15$?

62. Is $3x + 4$ a factor of $9x^2 + 24x + 16$?

Mixed Practice, 63–80

Divide. Assume that all denominators are nonzero.

63. $\dfrac{x^3 + 12x^2 - 9}{x + 3}$

64. $\dfrac{x^2 + 3x - 15}{x + 7}$

65. $\dfrac{x^3 + 8x - 19}{x + 4}$

66. $\dfrac{8x^9}{2x^3}$

67. $\dfrac{12x^6 - 8x^4 + 20x^3 - 4x^2}{4x^2}$

68. $\dfrac{x^2 + 4x - 165}{x + 15}$

69. $\dfrac{8x^2 + 42x - 25}{x + 6}$

70. $\dfrac{4x^2 - 25x - 100}{x - 8}$

71. $\dfrac{20x^2 - 51x - 6}{4x - 3}$

72. $\dfrac{6x^2 - 19x + 30}{2x - 5}$

73. $\dfrac{27x^9 - 18x^7 - 6x^6 - 3x^3}{-3x^2}$

74. $\dfrac{8x^2 - 10x - 63}{2x - 7}$

75. $\dfrac{8x^3 - 38x - 39}{2x + 3}$

76. $\dfrac{16a^4b^8c^7}{4ab^7c^7}$

77. $\dfrac{6x^3 - 37x^2 + 11x + 153}{2x - 9}$

78. $\dfrac{6x^5 - 12x^4 + 18x^3}{4x^3}$

79. $\dfrac{21x^9y^6z^{17}}{-7x^7y^5z^{12}}$

80. $\dfrac{x^4 - 85}{x - 3}$

Writing in Mathematics

Answer in complete sentences.

81. *Solutions Manual* Write a solutions manual page for the following problem:

$$Divide \ \dfrac{6x^2 - 17x - 19}{2x - 7}.$$

CHAPTER 6

Factoring and Quadratic Equations

In this chapter, we will begin to learn how to solve quadratic equations. A *quadratic equation* is an equation of the form $ax^2 + bx + c = 0$, where a, b, and c are real numbers and $a \neq 0$. To solve a quadratic equation, we will attempt to rewrite the quadratic expression $ax^2 + bx + c$ as a product of two expressions. In other words, we will factor the quadratic expression. The first five sections of this chapter focus on factoring techniques.

Once we have learned how to factor polynomials, we will learn how to solve quadratic equations and to apply quadratic equations to real-world problems. We also will examine quadratic functions, which are functions of the form $f(x) = ax^2 + bx + c$, where $a \neq 0$.

STUDY STRATEGY

Overcoming Math Anxiety In this chapter, we will focus on how to overcome math anxiety, a condition that many students share. Math anxiety can prevent a student from learning mathematics, and it can seriously impact a student's performance on quizzes and exams.

6.1

An Introduction to Factoring; the Greatest Common Factor; Factoring by Grouping

OBJECTIVES

1. **Find the greatest common factor (GCF) of two or more integers.**
2. **Find the GCF of two or more variable terms.**
3. **Factor the GCF out of each term of a polynomial.**
4. **Factor a common binomial factor out of a polynomial.**
5. **Factor a polynomial by grouping.**

In the previous chapter, we learned about polynomials; in this section, we will begin to learn how to **factor** a polynomial. A polynomial has been **factored** when it is represented as the product of two or more polynomials. Being able to factor polynomials will help us solve quadratic equations such as $x^2 - 11x + 30 = 0$, as well as simplify rational expressions such as $\dfrac{x^2 + 3x - 10}{x^2 - 9x + 14}$.

Greatest Common Factor

Objective 1 Find the greatest common factor (GCF) of two or more integers. Before we begin to learn how to factor polynomials, we will go over the procedure for finding the **greatest common factor (GCF)** of two or more integers. The GCF of two or more integers is the largest whole number that is a factor of each integer.

Finding the GCF of Two or More Integers

Find the prime factorization of each integer.
Write the prime factors that are common to each integer; the GCF is the product of these prime factors.

EXAMPLE 1 Find the GCF of 30 and 42.

SOLUTION The prime factorization of 30 is $2 \cdot 3 \cdot 5$, and the prime factorization of 42 is $2 \cdot 3 \cdot 7$. (For a refresher on finding the prime factorization of a number, refer back to Section 1.3.) The prime factors they have in common are 2 and 3; so the GCF is $2 \cdot 3$, or 6. (This means that 6 is the greatest number that divides evenly into both 30 and 42.)

Quick Check 1

Find the GCF of 16 and 20.

EXAMPLE 2 Find the GCF of 108, 504, and 720.

SOLUTION Begin with the prime factorizations.

$$108 = 2^2 \cdot 3^3 \qquad 504 = 2^3 \cdot 3^2 \cdot 7 \qquad 720 = 2^4 \cdot 3^2 \cdot 5$$

The only primes that are factors of all three numbers are 2 and 3. The smallest power of 2 that is a factor of any of the three numbers is 2^2, and the smallest power of 3 that is a factor is 3^2. The GCF is $2^2 \cdot 3^2$, or 36.

Quick Check 2

Find the GCF of 48, 120, and 156.

Note that if two or more integers do not have any common prime factors, their GCF is 1. For example, the GCF of 8, 12, and 15 is 1 because no prime numbers are factors of all three numbers.

Objective 2 Find the GCF of two or more variable terms. We also can find the GCF of two or more variable terms. For a variable factor to be included in the GCF, it must be a factor of each term. As with prime factors, the exponent for a variable factor used in the GCF is the smallest exponent that can be found for that variable in any one term.

EXAMPLE 3 Find the GCF of $6x^2$ and $15x^4$.

SOLUTION The GCF of the two coefficients is 3. The variable x is a factor of each term, and its smallest exponent is 2. The GCF of these two terms is $3x^2$.

Quick Check 3

Find the GCF.

a) $12x^5$ and $28x^3$
b) $x^3y^4z^9$, $x^6y^2z^{10}$, and x^7z^4

EXAMPLE 4 Find the GCF of $a^5b^4c^2$, a^7b^3, $a^6b^9c^5$, and $a^3b^8c^3$.

SOLUTION Only the variables a and b are factors of all of the terms. (The variable c is not a factor of the second term.) The smallest power of a in any one term is 3, which is the case for the variable b as well. The GCF is a^3b^3.

Factoring Out the Greatest Common Factor

Objective ③ Factor the GCF out of each term of a polynomial. The first step for factoring a polynomial is to factor out the GCF of all of the terms. This process uses the distributive property, and you may think of it as "undistributing" the GCF from each term. Consider the polynomial $4x^2 + 8x + 20$. The GCF of these three terms is 4, and the polynomial can be rewritten as the product $4(x^2 + 2x + 5)$. Notice that the GCF has been factored out of each term and that the polynomial inside the parentheses is the polynomial we would multiply by 4 to equal $4x^2 + 8x + 20$.

$$4(x^2 + 2x + 5) = 4 \cdot x^2 + 4 \cdot 2x + 4 \cdot 5 \quad \text{Distribute.}$$
$$= 4x^2 + 8x + 20 \quad \text{Multiply.}$$

EXAMPLE 5 Factor $5x^3 - 30x^2 + 10x$ by factoring out the GCF.

SOLUTION Begin by finding the GCF, which is $5x$. The next task is to fill in the missing terms of the polynomial inside the parentheses so that the product of $5x$ and that polynomial is $5x^3 - 30x^2 + 10x$.

$$5x(? - ? + ?)$$

To find the missing terms, we can divide each term of the original polynomial by $5x$.

$$5x^3 - 30x^2 + 10x = 5x(x^2 - 6x + 2)$$

We can check the answer by multiplying $5x(x^2 - 6x + 2)$, which should equal $5x^3 - 30x^2 + 10x$. The check is left to the reader.

▶ Quick Check 4
Factor $6x^4 - 42x^3 - 90x^2$ by factoring out the GCF.

EXAMPLE 6 Factor $6x^6 + 8x^4 + 2x^3$ by factoring out the GCF.

SOLUTION The GCF for these three terms is $2x^3$. Notice that this is also the third term.

$$6x^6 + 8x^4 + 2x^3 = 2x^3(3x^3 + 4x + 1) \quad \text{Factor out the GCF.}$$

When a term in a polynomial is the GCF of the polynomial, factoring out the GCF leaves a 1 in that term's place. Why? Because we need to determine what we multiply $2x^3$ by to equal $2x^3$, and $2x^3 \cdot 1 = 2x^3$.

▶ Quick Check 5
Factor $15x^7 - 30x^5 + 3x^4$ by factoring out the GCF.

A WORD OF CAUTION When factoring out the GCF from a polynomial, be sure to write a 1 in the place of a term that was the GCF.

Objective ④ Factor a common binomial factor out of a polynomial. Occasionally, the GCF of two terms will be a binomial or some other polynomial with more than one term. Consider the expression $8x(x - 5) + 3(x - 5)$, which contains the two terms $8x(x - 5)$ and $3(x - 5)$. Each term has the binomial $x - 5$ as a factor. This common factor can be factored out of this expression.

EXAMPLE 7 Factor $x(x + 3) + 7(x + 3)$ by factoring out the GCF.

SOLUTION The binomial $x + 3$ is a common factor for these two terms. Begin by factoring out this common factor.

$$x(x + 3) + 7(x + 3)$$

$$= (x + 3)(? + ?)$$

After factoring out $x + 3$, what factors remain in the first term? The only factor that remains is x. Using the same method, we see that the only factor remaining in the second term is 7.

$$x(x + 3) + 7(x + 3) = (x + 3)(x + 7)$$

EXAMPLE 8 Factor $9x(2x + 3) - 8(2x + 3)$ by factoring out the GCF.

SOLUTION The GCF of these two terms is $2x + 3$, which can be factored out as follows:

$$9x(2x + 3) - 8(2x + 3) = (2x + 3)(9x - 8) \quad \text{Factor out the common factor } 2x + 3.$$

Notice that the second term was negative, which led to $9x - 8$, rather than $9x + 8$, as the other factor.

Again, factoring out the GCF will be the first step in factoring a polynomial. Often this will make the factoring easier, and sometimes the expression cannot be factored without factoring out the GCF.

Quick Check 6

Factor by factoring out the GCF.

a) $5x(x - 9) + 14(x - 9)$
b) $7x(x - 8) - 6(x - 8)$

Factoring by Grouping

Objective 5 Factor a polynomial by grouping. We now turn our attention to a factoring technique known as **factoring by grouping**. Consider the polynomial $3x^3 + 33x^2 + 7x + 77$. The GCF for the four terms is 1, so we cannot factor the polynomial by factoring out the GCF. However, the first pair of terms has a common factor of $3x^2$ and the second pair of terms has a common factor of 7. If we factor $3x^2$ out of the first two terms and 7 out of the last two terms, we produce the following:

$$3x^2(x + 11) + 7(x + 11)$$

Notice that the two resulting terms have a common factor of $x + 11$. This common binomial factor can then be factored out.

$$3x^3 + 33x^2 + 7x + 77$$
$$= 3x^2(x + 11) + 7(x + 11) \quad \text{Factor } 3x^2 \text{ from the first two terms and } 7 \text{ from the last two terms.}$$
$$= (x + 11)(3x^2 + 7) \quad \text{Factor out the common binomial factor } x + 11.$$

Factoring a Polynomial with Four Terms by Grouping

Factor a common factor out of the first two terms and another common factor out of the last two terms. If the two "groups" share a common binomial factor, this binomial can be factored out to complete the factoring of the polynomial.

If the two "groups" do not share a common binomial factor, we can try rearranging the terms of the polynomial in a different order. If we cannot find two "groups" that share a common factor, the polynomial cannot be factored by this method.

EXAMPLE 9 Factor $5x^3 - 30x^2 + 4x - 24$ by grouping.

SOLUTION First, check for a factor that is common to each of the four terms. Because there is no common factor other than 1, proceed to factoring by grouping.

$$5x^3 - 30x^2 + 4x - 24 = 5x^2(x - 6) + 4x - 24 \qquad \text{Factor } 5x^2 \text{ out of the first two terms.}$$
$$= 5x^2(x - 6) + 4(x - 6) \qquad \text{Factor 4 out of the last two terms.}$$
$$= (x - 6)(5x^2 + 4) \qquad \text{Factor out the common factor } x - 6.$$

As was the case earlier, we can check our factoring by multiplying the two factors. The check is left to the reader.

Quick Check 7

Factor $x^3 + 4x^2 + 7x + 28$ by grouping.

EXAMPLE 10 Factor $8x^2 + 32x - 7x - 28$ by grouping.

SOLUTION Because the four terms have no common factors other than 1, we factor by grouping. After factoring $8x$ out of the first two terms, we must factor a *negative* 7 out of the last two terms. If we factored a positive 7 rather than a negative 7 out of the last two terms, the two binomial factors would be different.

$$8x^2 + 32x - 7x - 28 = 8x(x + 4) - 7(x + 4) \qquad \text{Factor the common factor } 8x \text{ out of the first two terms and the common factor } -7 \text{ out of the last two terms.}$$
$$= (x + 4)(8x - 7) \qquad \text{Factor out the common factor } x + 4.$$

When the third of the four terms is negative, a negative common factor often needs to be factored from the last two terms.

Quick Check 8

Factor $2x^2 - 10x - 9x + 45$ by grouping.

A WORD OF CAUTION Factoring a negative common factor from two terms when factoring by grouping is often necessary.

EXAMPLE 11 Factor $10x^3 + 50x^2 + x + 5$ by grouping.

SOLUTION Again, the four terms have no common factor other than 1, so we may proceed to factor this polynomial by grouping. Notice that the last two terms have no common factor other than 1. When this is the case, we factor out the common factor of 1 from the two terms.

$$10x^3 + 50x^2 + x + 5 = 10x^2(x + 5) + 1(x + 5) \qquad \text{Factor the common factors of } 10x^2 \text{ and 1 from the first two terms and the last two terms, respectively.}$$
$$= (x + 5)(10x^2 + 1) \qquad \text{Factor out the common factor } x + 5.$$

Quick Check 9

Factor $4x^3 - 36x^2 + x - 9$ by grouping.

In the next example, the four terms have a common factor other than 1. We will factor out the GCF from the polynomial before attempting to use factoring by grouping.

EXAMPLE 12 Factor $2x^3 - 6x^2 - 20x + 60$ completely.

SOLUTION The four terms share a common factor of 2, and we will factor this out before proceeding with factoring by grouping.

$$2x^3 - 6x^2 - 20x + 60 = 2(x^3 - 3x^2 - 10x + 30)$$ Factor out the common factor 2.

$$= 2[x^2(x - 3) - 10(x - 3)]$$ Factor out the common factor x^2 from the first two terms. Factor out the common factor -10 from the last two terms.

$$= 2(x - 3)(x^2 - 10)$$ Factor out the common factor $x - 3$.

If we had not factored out the common factor 2 before factoring this polynomial by grouping, we would have factored $2x^3 - 6x^2 - 20x + 60$ to be $(x - 3)(2x^2 - 20)$. If we stop here, we have not factored this polynomial completely because $2x^2 - 20$ has a common factor of 2.

Quick Check 10

Factor $3x^2 + 24x - 12x - 96$ by grouping.

Occasionally, despite our best efforts, a polynomial cannot be factored. Here is an example of just such a polynomial. Consider the polynomial $x^2 - 5x + 3x + 15$. The first two terms have a common factor of x, and the last two terms have a common factor of 3.

$$x^2 - 5x + 3x + 15 = x(x - 5) + 3(x + 5)$$

Because the two binomials are not the same, we cannot factor a common factor out of the two terms. Reordering the terms $-5x$ and $3x$ leads to the same problem. The polynomial cannot be factored.

There are instances when factoring by grouping fails, yet the polynomial can be factored by other techniques. For example, the polynomial $x^3 + 2x^2 - 7x - 24$ cannot be factored by grouping. However, it can be shown that $x^3 + 2x^2 - 7x - 24$ is equal to $(x - 3)(x^2 + 5x + 8)$.

BUILDING YOUR STUDY STRATEGY

Overcoming Math Anxiety, 1 Understanding Math Anxiety If you have been avoiding taking a math class, if you panic when asked a mathematical question, or if you think you cannot learn mathematics, you may have a condition known as math anxiety. Like many other anxiety-related conditions, math anxiety may be traced back to an event that first triggered the negative feelings. If you are going to overcome your anxiety, the first step is to understand the cause of your anxiety.

Were you ridiculed as a child when you couldn't solve a math problem? Were you expected to be a mathematical genius like a parent or an older sibling but were not able to measure up? One negative event can trigger math anxiety, and the journey to overcome math anxiety can begin with a single success. If you are able to complete a homework assignment or show improvement on a quiz or an exam, celebrate your success. Let this be your vindication and consider your slate to have been wiped clean.

Exercises 6.1

Vocabulary

1. A polynomial has been _____ when it is represented as the product of two or more polynomials.

2. The _____ of two or more integers is the largest whole number that is a factor of each integer.

3. The exponent for a variable factor used in the GCF is the _____ exponent that can be found for that variable in any one term.

4. The process of factoring a polynomial by first breaking the polynomial into two sets of terms is called factoring by _____.

Find the GCF.

5. $6, 8$
6. $15, 21$
7. $30, 42$
8. $5, 50$
9. $16, 40, 60$
10. $8, 24, 27$
11. x^3, x^7
12. y^8, y^4
13. a^2b^3, a^5b^2
14. $a^8b^3c^4, a^5bc^2, a^3b^4c^5$
15. $4x^4, 6x^3$
16. $27x^5, 24x^{11}$
17. $15a^5b^2c, 25a^2c^3, 5a^3bc^2$
18. $30x^3y^4z^5, 12x^6y^{11}z^3, 24y^9z$

Factor the GCF out of the given expression.

19. $7x - 14$
20. $3a + 12$
21. $5x^2 + 4x$
22. $9x^2 - 20x$
23. $8x^3 + 20x$
24. $11x^5 - 33x^3$
25. $60x^2 + 36x + 6$
26. $15x^2 - 9x - 3$
27. $20x^6 - 35x^4 - 50x^3$
28. $36x^5 - 9x^4 - 45x^2$
29. $m^7n^3 - m^5n^4 + m^6n^6$
30. $a^7b^8 + a^5b^6 - a^3b^2$
31. $10x^5y^5 - 30x^7y^4 + 80x^2y^{10}$

32. $20x^6y^2 - 16xy^5 + 24x^3y^3$
33. $-8x^3 + 12x^2 - 16x$
34. $-18a^5 - 30a^3 + 24a^2$
35. $5x(2x - 7) + 8(2x - 7)$

36. $x(4x + 3) + 4(4x + 3)$
37. $x(3x - 4) - 9(3x - 4)$
38. $6x(x - 8) - 5(x - 8)$
39. $5x(4x + 7) - (4x + 7)$
40. $3x(7x - 2) + (7x - 2)$

Factor by grouping.

41. $x^2 + 10x + 3x + 30$
42. $x^2 - 7x + 5x - 35$
43. $x^3 - 9x^2 + 6x - 54$
44. $x^3 + 4x^2 + 11x + 44$
45. $x^2 - 5x - 12x + 60$
46. $x^2 + 3x - 9x - 27$
47. $3x^2 + 15x + 4x + 20$
48. $4x^2 - 24x + 7x - 42$
49. $7x^2 + 28x - 6x - 24$
50. $5x^2 - 25x - 12x + 60$
51. $3x^2 + 21x + x + 7$
52. $4x^2 - 48x + x - 12$
53. $2x^2 - 10x - x + 5$
54. $9x^2 - 81x - x + 9$
55. $x^3 + 8x^2 + 6x + 48$
56. $2x^3 - 12x^2 + 5x - 30$
57. $4x^3 + 12x + 3x^2 + 9$
58. $7x^3 + 49x + 4x^2 + 28$
59. $2x^2 + 10x + 6x + 30$
60. $3x^2 + 27x + 21x + 189$

Find a polynomial that has the given factor.

61. $x - 5$
62. $x + 3$
63. $2x + 9$
64. $3x - 4$

Writing in Mathematics

Answer in complete sentences.

65. When you are factoring a polynomial, how do you check your work?

66. Explain why it is necessary to factor a negative common factor from the last two terms of the polynomial $x^3 - 5x^2 - 7x + 35$ to factor it by grouping.

Quick Review Exercises

Section 6.1

Multiply.

1. $(x + 7)(x + 4)$

2. $(x - 9)(x - 11)$

3. $(x + 5)(x - 8)$

4. $(x - 10)(x + 6)$

6.2

Factoring Trinomials of the Form $x^2 + bx + c$

OBJECTIVES

1 Factor a trinomial of the form $x^2 + bx + c$ when c is positive.

2 Factor a trinomial of the form $x^2 + bx + c$ when c is negative.

3 Factor a perfect square trinomial.

4 Determine that a trinomial is prime.

5 Factor a trinomial by first factoring out a common factor.

6 Factor a trinomial in several variables.

In this section, we will learn how to factor trinomials of degree 2 with a leading coefficient of 1. Some examples of this type of polynomial are $x^2 + 12x + 32$, $x^2 - 9x + 14$, $x^2 + 8x - 20$, and $x^2 - x - 12$.

> **Factoring Trinomials of the Form $x^2 + bx + c$**
>
> If $x^2 + bx + c$, where b and c are integers, is factorable, it can be factored as the product of two binomials of the form $(x + m)(x + n)$, where m and n are integers.

We will begin by multiplying two binomials of the form $(x + m)(x + n)$ and using the result to help us learn to factor trinomials of the form $x^2 + bx + c$.

Multiply the two binomials $x + 4$ and $x + 8$.

$$(x + 4)(x + 8) = x^2 + 8x + 4x + 32 \quad \text{Distribute.}$$
$$= x^2 + 12x + 32 \quad \text{Combine like terms.}$$

The two binomials have a product that is a trinomial of the form $x^2 + bx + c$ with $b = 12$ and $c = 32$. Notice that the two numbers 4 and 8 have a product of 32 and a sum of 12; in other words, their product is equal to c and their sum is equal to b.

$$4 \cdot 8 = 32$$
$$4 + 8 = 12$$

We will use this pattern to help us factor trinomials of the form $x^2 + bx + c$. We will look for two integers m and n with a product equal to c and a sum equal to b. If we can find two such integers, the trinomial will factor as $(x + m)(x + n)$.

Factoring $x^2 + bx + c$ When c Is Positive

Objective 1 Factor a trinomial of the form $x^2 + bx + c$ when c is positive.

EXAMPLE 1 Factor $x^2 + 9x + 18$.

SOLUTION   We begin, as always, by looking for common factors. The terms in this trinomial have no common factors other than 1. We are looking for two integers m and n whose product is 18 and whose sum is 9. Here are the factors of 18.

Factors	$1 \cdot 18$	$2 \cdot 9$	$3 \cdot 6$
Sum	19	11	9

The pair of factors that have a sum of 9 are 3 and 6. The trinomial $x^2 + 9x + 18$ factors to be $(x + 3)(x + 6)$. Be aware that this also can be written as $(x + 6)(x + 3)$.

We can check our work by multiplying $x + 3$ by $x + 6$. If the product equals $x^2 + 9x + 18$, we have factored correctly. The check is left to the reader.

EXAMPLE 2 Factor $x^2 - 11x + 24$.

SOLUTION   The major difference between this trinomial and the previous one is that the x term has a negative coefficient. We are looking for two integers m and n whose product is 24 and whose sum is -11. Because the product of these two integers is positive, they must have the same sign. The sum of these two integers is negative, so each integer must be negative. Here are the negative factors of 24.

Factors	$(-1)(-24)$	$(-2)(-12)$	$(-3)(-8)$	$(-4)(-6)$
Sum	-25	-14	-11	-10

The pair that has a sum of -11 is -3 and -8. $x^2 - 11x + 24 = (x - 3)(x - 8)$.

From the previous examples, we see that when the constant term c is positive, such as in $x^2 + 9x + 18$ and $x^2 - 11x + 24$, the two numbers we are looking for (m and n) will have the same sign. Both numbers will be positive if b is positive, and both numbers will be negative if b is negative.

Quick Check 1

Factor.

a) $x^2 + 7x + 10$
b) $x^2 - 11x + 30$

Factoring $x^2 + bx + c$ When c Is Negative

Objective 2 **Factor a trinomial of the form $x^2 + bx + c$ when c is negative.** If the product of two numbers is negative, one of the numbers must be negative and the other number must be positive. So if the constant term c is negative, m and n must have opposite signs.

EXAMPLE 3 Factor $x^2 + 8x - 33$.

SOLUTION   These three terms do not have any common factors, so we look for two integers m and n with a product of -33 and a sum of 8. Because the product is negative, we are looking for one negative number and one positive number. Here are the factors of -33, along with their sums.

Factors	$-1 \cdot 33$	$-3 \cdot 11$	$-11 \cdot 3$	$-33 \cdot 1$
Sum	32	8	-8	-32

The pair of integers we are looking for are -3 and 11. $x^2 + 8x - 33 = (x - 3)(x + 11)$.

EXAMPLE 4   Factor $x^2 - 3x - 40$.

SOLUTION   Because there are no common factors to factor out, we are looking for two integers m and n that have a product of -40 and a sum of -3. Here are the factors of -40.

Factors	$-1 \cdot 40$	$-2 \cdot 20$	$-4 \cdot 10$	$-5 \cdot 8$	$-8 \cdot 5$	$-10 \cdot 4$	$-20 \cdot 2$	$-40 \cdot 1$
Sum	39	18	6	3	-3	-6	-18	-39

◀ The integers m and n are -8 and 5. $x^2 - 3x - 40 = (x - 8)(x + 5)$.

Quick Check 2

Factor.

a) $x^2 + 9x - 36$
b) $x^2 - x - 42$

It is not necessary to list each set of factors as in the previous examples. We can often find the two integers m and n quickly through trial and error.

EXAMPLE 5   Factor.

a) $x^2 - 10x - 24$

SOLUTION   The two integers whose product is -24 and sum is -10 are -12 and 2.

$$x^2 - 10x - 24 = (x - 12)(x + 2)$$

b) $x^2 + 10x + 24$

SOLUTION   This example is similar to the last example, but we are looking for two integers that have a product of *positive* 24 instead of -24. Also, the sum of these two integers is 10 instead of -10. The two integers whose product is 24 and whose sum is 10 are 4 and 6.

$$x^2 + 10x + 24 = (x + 4)(x + 6)$$

Quick Check 3

Factor.

a) $x^2 + 5x - 6$
b) $x^2 + 5x + 6$
c) $x^2 - 5x + 6$
d) $x^2 - 5x - 6$

c) $x^2 + 10x - 24$

SOLUTION   The two integers that have a product of -24 and a sum of 10 are -2 and 12.

$$x^2 + 10x - 24 = (x - 2)(x + 12)$$

d) $x^2 - 10x + 24$

SOLUTION   The integers -4 and -6 have a product of 24 and a sum of -10.

$$x^2 - 10x + 24 = (x - 4)(x - 6)$$

Factoring a Perfect Square Trinomial

Objective 3 Factor a perfect square trinomial.

EXAMPLE 6   Factor $x^2 - 6x + 9$.

SOLUTION   We begin by looking for two integers that have a product of 9 and a sum of -6. Because the product of -3 and -3 is 9 and their sum is -6, $x^2 - 6x + 9 = (x - 3)(x - 3)$. Notice that the same factor is listed twice. We can ◀ rewrite this as $(x - 3)^2$.

Quick Check 4

Factor $x^2 + 10x + 25$.

> When a trinomial factors to equal the square of a binomial, we call it a **perfect square trinomial**.

Trinomials That Are Prime

Objective 4 Determine that a trinomial is prime. Not every trinomial of the form $x^2 + bx + c$ can be factored. For example, there may not be a pair of integers that have a product of c and a sum of b. In this case, we say that the trinomial cannot be factored; it is **prime**. For example, $x^2 + 9x + 12$ is prime because we cannot find two numbers with a product of 12 and a sum of 9.

EXAMPLE 7   Factor $x^2 + 11x - 18$.

SOLUTION   As there are no common factors to factor out, we are looking for two integers m and n that have a product of -18 and a sum of 11. Here are the factors of -18.

Factors	$-1 \cdot 18$	$-2 \cdot 9$	$-3 \cdot 6$	$-6 \cdot 3$	$-9 \cdot 2$	$-18 \cdot 1$
Sum	17	7	3	-3	-7	-17

No two integers have a product of -18 and a sum of 11, so the trinomial $x^2 + 11x - 18$ is prime.

Quick Check 5

Factor $x^2 + 9x - 20$.

Factoring a Trinomial Whose Terms Have a Common Factor

Objective 5 Factor a trinomial by first factoring out a common factor. We now turn our attention to factoring trinomials whose terms contain common factors other than 1. After we factor out a common factor, we will attempt to factor the remaining polynomial factor.

EXAMPLE 8   Factor $4x^2 + 48x + 80$.

SOLUTION   The GCF of these three terms is 4.

A WORD OF CAUTION When factoring a polynomial, begin by factoring out the GCF of *all* of the terms.

After factoring out the GCF, we have $4(x^2 + 12x + 20)$. We now try to factor the trinomial $x^2 + 12x + 20$ by finding two integers that have a product of 20 and a sum of 12. The integers that satisfy these conditions are 2 and 10.

$$4x^2 + 48x + 80 = 4(x^2 + 12x + 20) \quad \text{Factor out the GCF 4.}$$
$$= 4(x + 2)(x + 10) \quad \text{Factor } x^2 + 12x + 20.$$

Quick Check 6

Factor $5x^2 + 40x + 60$.

A WORD OF CAUTION When a common factor is factored out of a polynomial, that common factor *must* be written in all following stages of factoring. *Do not "lose" the common factor!*

EXAMPLE 9   Factor $-x^2 - 7x + 60$.

SOLUTION   The leading coefficient for this trinomial is -1, but to factor the trinomial using our technique, the leading coefficient must be a *positive* 1. We begin by factoring out a -1 from each term, which will change the sign of each term.

$$-x^2 - 7x + 60 = -(x^2 + 7x - 60) \quad \text{Factor out } -1 \text{ so that the leading coefficient is 1.}$$
$$= -(x - 5)(x + 12) \quad \text{Factor } x^2 + 7x - 60 \text{ by finding two integers whose product is } -60 \text{ and whose sum is 7.}$$

Quick Check 7

Factor $-x^2 + 14x - 48$.

If a trinomial's leading coefficient is not 1 or if the degree of the trinomial is not 2, we should factor out a common factor so that the trinomial factor is of the form $x^2 + bx + c$. At this point in the text, this is the only type of trinomial we know how to factor. We will learn techniques to factor other trinomials in the next section.

Factoring Trinomials in Several Variables

Objective 6 Factor a trinomial in several variables. Trinomials in several variables also can be factored. In the next example, we will explore the similarities and differences between factoring trinomials in two variables and trinomials in one variable.

EXAMPLE 10 Factor $x^2 + 13xy + 36y^2$.

SOLUTION These three terms have no common factors, and the leading coefficient is 1. Suppose the variable y were not included; in other words, suppose we were asked to factor $x^2 + 13x + 36$. After looking for two integers whose product is 36 and whose sum is 13, we would see that $x^2 + 13x + 36 = (x + 4)(x + 9)$. Now we can examine the changes that are necessary because of the second variable y. Note that $4 \cdot 9 = 36$, not $36y^2$. However, $4y \cdot 9y$ does equal $36y^2$ and $x \cdot 9y + x \cdot 4y$ does equal $13xy$. This trinomial factors to be $(x + 4y)(x + 9y)$.

Quick Check 8
Factor $x^2 - 4xy - 32y^2$.

We can factor a trinomial in two or more variables by ignoring all of the variables except the first variable. After determining how the trinomial factors for the first variable, we can determine where the rest of the variables appear in the factored form of the trinomial. We can check that our factoring is correct by multiplying, making sure the product is equal to the trinomial.

EXAMPLE 11 Factor $p^2r^2 - 9pr - 10$.

SOLUTION If the variable r did not appear in the trinomial and we were factoring $p^2 - 9p - 10$, we would look for two integers that have a product of -10 and a sum of -9. The two integers are -10 and 1, so the polynomial $p^2 - 9p - 10 = (p - 10)(p + 1)$. Now we work on the variable r. Because the first term in the trinomial is p^2r^2, the first term in each binomial must be pr.
$p^2r^2 - 9pr - 10 = (pr - 10)(pr + 1)$.

Quick Check 9
Factor $x^2y^2 + 10xy - 24$.

BUILDING YOUR STUDY STRATEGY

Overcoming Math Anxiety, 2 Mathematical Autobiography One effective tool for understanding your past difficulties in mathematics and how they hinder your ability to learn mathematics today is to write a mathematical autobiography. Write down your successes and failures as well as the reasons you think you succeeded or failed. Go back to your mathematical past as far as you can remember. Write down how friends, relatives, and teachers affected you.

Let your autobiography sit for a few days and then read it over. Read it on an analytical level as if another person had written it, detaching yourself from it personally. Look for patterns, think about strategies to reverse the bad patterns, and continue any good patterns you can find.

Exercises 6.2

 MyMathLab

PRACTICE

WATCH

DOWNLOAD

READ

REVIEW

Vocabulary

1. A polynomial of the form $x^2 + bx + c$ is a second-degree trinomial with a(n) _____ of 1.

2. A(n) _____ trinomial is a trinomial whose two binomial factors are identical.

3. A polynomial is _____ if it cannot be factored.

4. Before attempting to factor a second-degree trinomial, it is wise to factor out any _____.

Factor completely. If the polynomial cannot be factored, write prime.

5. $x^2 - 8x - 20$

6. $x^2 - 2x - 15$

7. $x^2 + 5x - 36$

8. $x^2 - 10x - 39$

9. $x^2 + 12x + 24$

10. $x^2 - 12x + 36$

11. $x^2 + 14x + 48$

12. $x^2 + 14x - 33$

13. $x^2 + 13x - 30$

14. $x^2 - 13x + 30$

15. $x^2 - 5x + 36$

16. $x^2 - 15x + 54$

17. $x^2 - 17x - 60$

18. $x^2 - 17x + 60$

19. $x^2 + 11x - 12$

20. $x^2 + 15x + 56$

21. $x^2 + 14x + 49$

22. $x^2 - 4x - 12$

23. $x^2 + 20x + 91$

24. $x^2 + 14x + 13$

25. $x^2 - 24x + 144$

26. $x^2 + 5x - 14$

27. $x^2 - 13x + 40$

28. $x^2 - 5x - 24$

29. $x^2 - 13x - 30$

30. $x^2 + 18x + 81$

31. $x^2 - 9x + 20$

32. $x^2 - 11x - 28$

33. $x^2 - 16x + 60$

34. $x^2 + 16x + 48$

35. $6x^2 - 54x + 120$

36. $4x^2 - 28x - 72$

37. $5x^2 + 35x - 150$

38. $9x^2 + 126x + 432$

39. $-x^2 + 3x + 70$

40. $-x^2 + 8x - 15$

41. $x^3 + 8x^2 + 16x$

42. $-x^4 + x^3 + 30x^2$

43. $-3x^5 - 6x^4 + 240x^3$

44. $2x^3 - 42x^2 + 196x$

45. $10x^8 + 20x^7 - 990x^6$

46. $35x^4 - 70x^3 + 35x^2$

47. $x^2 + xy - 42y^2$

48. $3x^2 - 36xy - 84y^2$

49. $x^2 - 5xy - 36y^2$

50. $x^2 - xy - 30y^2$

51. $x^2y^2 + 17xy + 72$

52. $x^2y^2 - 9xy + 8$

53. $5x^5 + 50x^4y + 105x^3y^2$

54. $x^2y^2 + 11xy - 60$

Mixed Practice, 55–72

Factor completely using the appropriate technique. If the polynomial cannot be factored, write prime.

55. $x^4 + 9x^3 + 5x + 45$

56. $x^2 - 26x + 169$

57. $x^2 + x + 30$

58. $x^2 - 17x + 42$

59. $x^2 + 22x + 40$

60. $x^2 + 10x$

61. $x^2 + 40x + 400$

62. $x^2 + 4x - 60$

63. $4x^2 + 8x - 96$

64. $x^2 + 16x + 15$

65. $x^4 - 15x^3$

66. $x^2 + 2x - 120$

67. $x^2 - 16x + 63$

68. $x^2 - 7x - 78$

69. $x^2 + 10x - 25$

70. $x^3 - 12x^2 - 6x + 72$

71. $x^2 - 21x - 100$

72. $-x^2 + 17x - 60$

Find the missing value such that the given binomial is a factor of the given polynomial.

73. $x^2 + 10x + ?, x + 2$

74. $x^2 - 16x + ?, x - 7$

75. $x^2 + 11x - ?, x - 4$

76. $x^2 - 7x - ?, x + 17$

Quick Review Exercises

Section 6.2

Multiply.

1. $(2x + 5)(x + 4)$

2. $(3x - 8)(2x - 7)$

3. $(x + 6)(3x - 4)$

4. $(4x - 3)(2x + 9)$

6.3

Factoring Trinomials of the Form $ax^2 + bx + c$, Where $a \neq 1$

OBJECTIVES

1. Factor a trinomial of the form $ax^2 + bx + c$, where $a \neq 1$, by grouping.
2. Factor a trinomial of the form $ax^2 + bx + c$, where $a \neq 1$, by trial and error.

In this section, we continue to learn how to factor second-degree trinomials, focusing on trinomials with a leading coefficient that is not 1. Some examples of this type of trinomial are $2x^2 + 13x + 20$, $8x^2 - 22x - 21$, and $3x^2 - 11x + 8$.

We will examine two methods for factoring this type of trinomial: factoring by grouping and factoring by trial and error. Your instructor may prefer one of these methods to the other or an altogether different method and may ask you to use one method only. However, if you are allowed to use either method, use the one with which you are most comfortable.

Factoring by Grouping

Objective 1 Factor a trinomial of the form $ax^2 + bx + c$, where $a \neq 1$, by grouping. We begin with factoring by grouping. Consider the product $(3x + 2)(2x + 5)$.

$$(3x + 2)(2x + 5) = 6x^2 + 15x + 4x + 10 \quad \text{Distribute.}$$
$$= 6x^2 + 19x + 10 \quad \text{Combine like terms.}$$

Because $(3x + 2)(2x + 5) = 6x^2 + 19x + 10$, we know that $6x^2 + 19x + 10$ can be factored as $(3x + 2)(2x + 5)$. By rewriting the middle term $19x$ as $15x + 4x$, we can factor by grouping. The important skill is being able to determine that $15x + 4x$ is the correct way to rewrite $19x$, instead of $16x + 3x$, $9x + 10x$, $22x - 3x$, or any other two terms whose sum is $19x$.

Factoring $ax^2 + bx + c$, Where $a \neq 1$, by Grouping

1. Multiply $a \cdot c$.
2. Find two integers with a product of $a \cdot c$ and a sum of b.
3. Rewrite the term bx as two terms, using the two integers found in Step 2.
4. Factor the resulting polynomial by grouping.

To factor the polynomial $6x^2 + 19x + 10$ by grouping, we begin by multiplying $6 \cdot 10$, which equals 60. Next, look for two integers with a product of 60 and a sum of 19; those two integers are 15 and 4. We can then rewrite $19x$ as $15x + 4x$. (These terms could be written in the opposite order and would still lead to the correct factoring.) We then factor the polynomial $6x^2 + 15x + 4x + 10$ by grouping.

$$
\begin{aligned}
6x^2 + 19x + 10 &= 6x^2 + 15x + 4x + 10 && \text{Rewrite } 19x \text{ as } 15x + 4x. \\
&= 3x(2x + 5) + 2(2x + 5) && \text{Factor the common factor } 3x \\
& && \text{from the first two terms and} \\
& && \text{the common factor } 2 \text{ from the} \\
& && \text{last two terms.} \\
&= (2x + 5)(3x + 2) && \text{Factor out the common factor} \\
& && 2x + 5.
\end{aligned}
$$

Now we will examine several examples using this technique.

EXAMPLE 1   Factor $2x^2 + 7x + 6$ by grouping.

SOLUTION   We first check to see whether there are any common factors; in this case, there are not. We proceed with factoring by grouping. Because $2 \cdot 6 = 12$, we look for two integers with a product of 12 and a sum of 7, which is the coefficient of the middle term. The integers 3 and 4 meet those criteria, so we rewrite $7x$ as $3x + 4x$.

$$
\begin{aligned}
2x^2 + 7x + 6 &= 2x^2 + 3x + 4x + 6 && \text{Find two integers with a product of} \\
& && \text{12 and a sum of 7. Rewrite } 7x \text{ as} \\
& && 3x + 4x. \\
&= x(2x + 3) + 2(2x + 3) && \text{Factor the common factor } x \text{ from the} \\
& && \text{first two terms and the common fac-} \\
& && \text{tor 2 from the last two terms.} \\
&= (2x + 3)(x + 2) && \text{Factor out the common factor} \\
& && 2x + 3.
\end{aligned}
$$

Quick Check 1

Factor $3x^2 + 13x + 12$ by grouping.

We check that this factoring is correct by multiplying $2x + 3$ by $x + 2$, which should equal $2x^2 + 7x + 6$. The check is left to the reader.

EXAMPLE 2   Factor $5x^2 - 7x + 2$ by grouping.

SOLUTION   We begin by multiplying $5 \cdot 2$ as there are no common factors other than 1. We look for two integers with a product of 10 and a sum of -7. The integers are -5 and -2, so we rewrite $-7x$ as $-5x - 2x$ and then factor by grouping.

$$
\begin{aligned}
5x^2 - 7x + 2 &= 5x^2 - 5x - 2x + 2 && \text{Find two integers with a product of 10} \\
& && \text{and a sum of } -7. \text{ Rewrite } -7x \text{ as} \\
& && -5x - 2x. \\
&= 5x(x - 1) - 2(x - 1) && \text{Factor the common factor } 5x \text{ from the} \\
& && \text{first two terms and the common factor} \\
& && -2 \text{ from the last two terms.} \\
&= (x - 1)(5x - 2) && \text{Factor out the common factor } x - 1.
\end{aligned}
$$

Quick Check 2

Factor $4x^2 - 25x + 36$ by grouping.

EXAMPLE 3   Factor $12x^2 + 11x - 15$ by grouping.

SOLUTION   Because the terms have no common factor other than 1, we begin by multiplying $12(-15)$, which equals -180. We need to find two integers with a product of -180 and a sum of 11. We can start by listing the different factors of 180. Because we know that one of the integers will be positive and one will be negative, we look for two factors in this list that have a difference of 11.

$$1 \cdot 180 \quad 2 \cdot 90 \quad 3 \cdot 60 \quad 4 \cdot 45 \quad 5 \cdot 36 \quad 6 \cdot 30 \quad 9 \cdot 20 \quad 10 \cdot 18 \quad 12 \cdot 15$$

Notice that the pair 9 and 20 has a difference of 11. The two integers are -9 and 20; their product is -180, and their sum is 11. We rewrite $11x$ as $-9x + 20x$ and then factor by grouping.

$$12x^2 + 11x - 15 = 12x^2 - 9x + 20x - 15$$

Find two integers with a product of -180 and a sum of 11. Rewrite $11x$ as $-9x + 20x$.

$$= 3x(4x - 3) + 5(4x - 3)$$

Factor the common factor $3x$ out of the first two terms and the common factor 5 out of the last two terms.

$$= (4x - 3)(3x + 5)$$

Factor out the common factor $4x - 3$.

Quick Check 3

Factor $16x^2 - 38x + 21$ by grouping.

Factoring by Trial and Error

Objective 2 Factor a trinomial of the form $ax^2 + bx + c$, where $a \neq 1$, by trial and error. We now turn our attention to the method of trial and error. We need to factor a trinomial $ax^2 + bx + c$ into the following form:

(Variable Term + Constant)(Variable Term + Constant)

The product of the variable terms will be ax^2, and the product of the constants will equal c. We will use these facts to get started by listing all of the factors of ax^2 and c.

Consider the trinomial $2x^2 + 7x + 6$, which has no common factors other than 1. We begin by listing all of the factors of $2x^2$ and 6.

Factors of $2x^2$: $x \cdot 2x$. Factors of 6: $1 \cdot 6$, $2 \cdot 3$

Because there is only one pair of factors with a product of $2x^2$, we know that if this trinomial is factorable, it will be of the form $(2x + ?)(x + ?)$. We will substitute the different factors of 6 in all possible orders in place of the question marks, satisfying the following products:

$$\overset{2x^2}{\overbrace{(2x + ?)(x + ?)}}_{6}$$

We will keep substituting factors of 6 until the middle term of the product of the two binomials is $7x$. Rather than fully distributing for each trial, we need to look only at the two products shown in the following graphic:

$$(2x + ?)(x + ?)$$

When the sum of these two products is $7x$, we have found the correct factors.

We begin by using the factors 1 and 6, which leads to the binomial factors $(2x + 1)(x + 6)$. Because the middle term for these factors is $13x$, we have not found the correct factors. We then switch the positions of 1 and 6 and try again. However, when we multiply $(2x + 6)(x + 1)$, the middle term equals $8x$, not $7x$. We need to try another pairing, so we try the other factors of 6, which are 2 and 3. When we multiply $(2x + 3)(x + 2)$, the middle term is $7x$, so these are the correct factors.

$$\overset{4x}{\overbrace{(2x + 3)(x + 2)}}_{3x}$$

Therefore, $2x^2 + 7x + 6 = (2x + 3)(x + 2)$.

EXAMPLE 4   Factor $10x^2 + 13x - 3$ by trial and error.

SOLUTION   There are no common factors other than 1, so we begin by listing the factors of $10x^2$ and -3.

$$\text{Factors of } 10x^2: \quad x \cdot 10x, \quad 2x \cdot 5x$$
$$\text{Factors of } -3: \quad -1 \cdot 3, \quad -3 \cdot 1$$

We are looking for two factors that produce the middle term $13x$ when multiplied. We will begin by using x and $10x$ for the variable terms and -1 and 3 for the constants.

Factors	Middle Term
$(x - 1)(10x + 3)$	$-7x$
$(x + 3)(10x - 1)$	$29x$

Neither of these middle terms is equal to $13x$, so we have not found the correct factoring. Also, because neither middle term is the opposite of $13x$, switching the signs of the constants 1 and 3 will not lead to the correct factors either. So $(x + 1)(10x - 3)$ and $(x - 3)(10x + 1)$ are not correct. We switch to the pair $2x$ and $5x$.

Factors	Middle Term
$(2x - 1)(5x + 3)$	x
$(2x + 3)(5x - 1)$	$13x$

The second of these middle terms is the one we are looking for, so $10x^2 + 13x - 3 = (2x + 3)(5x - 1)$.

Now we will try to factor another trinomial by trial and error using a trinomial with terms that have more factors.

Quick Check 4

Factor $2x^2 + x - 28$ by trial and error.

EXAMPLE 5   Factor $12x^2 + 11x - 15$ by trial and error.

SOLUTION   Because there are no common factors to factor out, we begin by listing the factors of $12x^2$ and -15.

$$\text{Factors of } 12x^2: \quad x \cdot 12x, \quad 2x \cdot 6x, \quad 3x \cdot 4x$$
$$\text{Factors of } -15: \quad -1 \cdot 15, \quad -15 \cdot 1, \quad -3 \cdot 5, \quad -5 \cdot 3$$

At first glance, this may seem like it will take a while, but we can shorten the process. For example, we may skip over any pairings resulting in a binomial factor in which both terms have a common factor other than 1, such as $3x - 3$. If the terms of a binomial factor had a common factor other than 1, the original polynomial also would have a common factor, but we know that $12x^2 + 11x - 15$ does not have a common factor that can be factored out.

If the pair of constants -1 and 15 does not produce the desired middle term and does not produce the opposite of the desired middle term, we do not need to use the pair of constants -15 and 1. Instead, we move on to the next pair of constants. Eventually, through trial and error, we find that $12x^2 + 11x - 15 = (3x + 5)(4x - 3)$.

Quick Check 5

Factor $20x^2 + 17x - 24$ by trial and error.

A WORD OF CAUTION If a trinomial has a leading coefficient other than 1, be sure to check whether the three terms have a common factor. If there is a common factor, we may be able to factor a trinomial using the techniques from Section 6.2.

EXAMPLE 6   Factor $8x^2 + 40x + 48$.

SOLUTION   The three terms have a common factor of 8. After we factor out this common factor, the trinomial factor will be $x^2 + 5x + 6$, which is a trinomial with a leading coefficient of 1. We look for two integers with a product of 6 and a sum of 5. Those two integers are 2 and 3.

$$8x^2 + 40x + 48 = 8(x^2 + 5x + 6) \qquad \text{Factor out the common factor 8.}$$
$$= 8(x + 2)(x + 3) \qquad \text{To factor } x^2 + 5x + 6, \text{ we need to find two integers with a product of 6 and a sum of 5. The two integers are 2 and 3.}$$

Quick Check 6

Factor $9x^2 + 27x - 162$.

Factoring out the common factor in the previous example makes factoring the trinomial more manageable. If we were to try factoring by grouping without factoring out the common factor, we would begin by multiplying 8 by 48, which equals 384. We would look for two integers with a product of 384 and a sum of 40, which would be challenging. If we tried to factor by trial and error, we would find that $8x^2$ has two pairs of factors $(x \cdot 8x, 2x \cdot 4x)$ but that 48 has several pairs of factors $(1 \cdot 48, 2 \cdot 24, 3 \cdot 16, 4 \cdot 12, 6 \cdot 8)$. Factoring by trial and error would be tedious at best.

BUILDING YOUR STUDY STRATEGY

Overcoming Math Anxiety, 3 Test Anxiety Many students confuse test anxiety with math anxiety. If you believe you can learn mathematics and you understand the material but you freeze up when taking tests, you may have test anxiety, especially if this is true in your other classes. Many colleges offer seminars or short-term classes about how to reduce test anxiety. Ask your counselor whether such a course would be appropriate for you.

Exercises 6.3

PRACTICE   WATCH   DOWNLOAD   READ   REVIEW

Vocabulary

1. A second-degree trinomial with a leading coefficient not equal to 1 can be written in the form _____.

2. The two techniques for factoring trinomials of the form $ax^2 + bx + c$, where $a \neq 1$, are called _____ and _____.

Factor completely.

3. $5x^2 + 16x + 3$

4. $3x^2 + 16x + 5$

5. $4x^2 + 24x + 35$

6. $4x^2 + 4x - 3$

7. $6x^2 - 19x + 10$

8. $9x^2 + 3x - 20$

9. $14x^2 + 15x - 9$

10. $8x^2 - 34x + 21$

11. $12x^2 + 8x - 15$

12. $12x^2 + 28x - 5$

13. $12x^2 - 25x + 12$

14. $12x^2 + 13x - 35$

15. $2x^2 + 13x + 7$

16. $18x^2 + 93x - 16$

17. $3x^2 + 13x - 10$

18. $4x^2 + 18x - 15$

19. $12x^2 + 11x - 56$

20. $24x^2 + 55x - 24$

21. $16x^2 - 24x + 9$

22. $16x^2 + 66x - 27$

23. $15x^2 - 24x - 12$

24. $15x^2 + 32x - 60$

25. $16x^2 + 24x - 40$

26. $15x^2 + 45x - 150$

27. $16x^2 - 64x + 64$

28. $40x^2 - 100x - 60$

29. $15x^2 - 25x - 560$

30. $-12x^2 - 36x + 120$

Mixed Practice, 31–66

Factor completely using the appropriate technique. If the polynomial cannot be factored, write prime.

31. $x^2 + 14x + 13$

32. $x^2 - 10x - 11$

33. $18x - 9$

34. $3x^2 + 33x + 48$

35. $2x^2 - 7x + 6$

36. $x^2 + 30x + 225$

37. $3x^2 + 2x - 4$

38. $32x^2 - 20x - 25$

39. $x^5 - 6x^4$

40. $x^2 - 8x - 48$

41. $6x^2 - 48x$

42. $x^2 + 15x + 60$

43. $-x^2 - 4x + 77$

44. $2x^2 - 3x - 54$

45. $4x^2 - 7x - 10$

46. $3x^2 - 25x - 18$

47. $x^5 - 7x^3 + 4x^2 - 28$

48. $45x^3 + 30x^2 - 75x - 50$

49. $x^3 + 6x^2 - 15x - 90$

50. $x^2 + 25x + 156$

51. $x^2 - 24x + 144$

52. $x^2 - 3x + 2$

53. $9x^2 - 45x - 54$

54. $3x^3 - 30x^2 - 7x + 70$

55. $-5x^2 + 28x + 12$

56. $x^2 - 6x - 5$

57. $2x^2 - 15x - 27$

58. $x^2 + 8x + 16$

59. $x^2 + 12x - 45$

60. $3x^5 + 6x^4$

61. $-3x^2 - 12x + 96$

62. $x^2 - 17x + 60$

63. $15x^2 + 16x - 15$

64. $18x^2 + 51x + 8$

65. $2x^2 + 9x + 4$

66. $x^2 - 7x - 44$

Writing in Mathematics

Answer in complete sentences.

67. Compare the two factoring methods for trinomials of the form $ax^2 + bx + c$, where $a \neq 1$: factoring by grouping and factoring by trial and error. Which method do you prefer? Explain your reasoning.

68. Explain why it is a good idea to factor out a common factor from a trinomial of the form $ax^2 + bx + c$ before trying other factoring techniques.

Quick Review Exercises

Section 6.3

Multiply.

1. $(x + 8)(x - 8)$

2. $(4x + 3)(4x - 3)$

3. $(x + 8)(x^2 - 8x + 64)$

4. $(2x - 5)(4x^2 + 10x + 25)$

6.4

Factoring Special Binomials

OBJECTIVES

1. Factor a difference of squares.
2. Factor a difference of cubes.
3. Factor a sum of cubes.

Difference of Squares

Objective 1 Factor a difference of squares. Recall the special product $(a + b)(a - b) = a^2 - b^2$ from Section 5.4. The binomial $a^2 - b^2$ is a **difference of**

squares. Based on this special product, a difference of squares factors in the following manner:

Difference of Squares

$$a^2 - b^2 = (a + b)(a - b)$$

To identify a binomial as a difference of squares, we must verify that each term is a perfect square. Variable factors must have exponents that are multiples of 2 such as x^2, y^4, and a^6. Any constant also must be a perfect square. Here are the first ten perfect squares.

$$1^2 = 1 \quad 2^2 = 4 \quad 3^2 = 9 \quad 4^2 = 16 \quad 5^2 = 25$$
$$6^2 = 36 \quad 7^2 = 49 \quad 8^2 = 64 \quad 9^2 = 81 \quad 10^2 = 100$$

EXAMPLE 1 Factor $x^2 - 49$.

SOLUTION This binomial is a difference of squares, as it can be rewritten as $(x)^2 - (7)^2$. Rewriting the binomial in this form helps us use the formula $a^2 - b^2 = (a + b)(a - b)$.

$$x^2 - 49 = (x)^2 - (7)^2 \qquad \text{Rewrite each term as a square.}$$
$$= (x + 7)(x - 7) \qquad \text{Factor using the formula for a difference of squares, } a^2 - b^2 = (a + b)(a - b).$$

We can check our work by multiplying $x + 7$ by $x - 7$, which should equal $x^2 - 49$. The check is left to the reader.

Quick Check 1
Factor $x^2 - 25$.

Although we will continue to write each term as a perfect square, if you can factor a difference of squares without writing each term as a perfect square, do not think that you *must* rewrite each term as a perfect square before proceeding.

EXAMPLE 2 Factor $64a^{10} - 25b^4$.

SOLUTION The first term of this binomial is a square, as 64 is a square and the exponent for the variable factor a is even. The first term can be rewritten as $(8a^5)^2$. In a similar fashion, $25b^4$ can be rewritten as $(5b^2)^2$. This binomial is a difference of squares.

$$64a^{10} - 25b^4 = (8a^5)^2 - (5b^2)^2 \qquad \text{Rewrite each term as a square.}$$
$$= (8a^5 + 5b^2)(8a^5 - 5b^2) \qquad \text{Factor as a difference of squares.}$$

Quick Check 2
Factor $81x^{12} - 100y^{16}$.

This binomial $8x^2 - 81$ is not a difference of squares because the coefficient of the first term (8) is not a square. Because there are no common factors other than 1, this binomial cannot be factored.

EXAMPLE 3 Factor $3x^2 - 108$.

SOLUTION Although this binomial is not a difference of squares (3 and 108 are not squares), the common factor of 3 can be factored out. After we factor out the common factor 3, we have $3x^2 - 108 = 3(x^2 - 36)$. The binomial in parentheses is a difference of squares and can be factored accordingly.

$$3x^2 - 108 = 3(x^2 - 36) \qquad \text{Factor out the common factor 3.}$$
$$= 3[(x)^2 - (6)^2] \qquad \text{Rewrite each term in the binomial factor as a square.}$$
$$= 3(x + 6)(x - 6) \qquad \text{Factor as a difference of squares.}$$

Quick Check 3
Factor $7x^2 - 175$.

If a binomial is a **sum of squares**, it cannot be factored unless the two terms have a common factor. Some examples of a sum of squares are $x^2 + 49$, $4a^2 + 9b^2$, and $64a^{10} + 25b^4$.

> ### Sum of Squares
> A sum of squares, $a^2 + b^2$, cannot be factored.

Occasionally, after you have factored a difference of squares, one or more of the factors may still be factorable. For example, consider the binomial $x^4 - 81$, which factors to be $(x^2 + 9)(x^2 - 9)$. The first factor, $x^2 + 9$, is a sum of squares and cannot be factored. However, the second factor, $x^2 - 9$, is a difference of squares and can be factored further.

EXAMPLE 4   Factor $x^4 - 81$ completely.

SOLUTION   This is a difference of squares, and we factor it accordingly. After we factor the binomial as a difference of squares, one of the binomial factors $(x^2 - 9)$ is a difference of squares and must be factored as well.

$$x^4 - 81 = (x^2)^2 - (9)^2 \qquad \text{Rewrite each term as a perfect square.}$$
$$= (x^2 + 9)(x^2 - 9) \qquad \text{Factor as a difference of squares.}$$
$$= (x^2 + 9)[(x)^2 - (3)^2] \qquad \text{Rewrite each term in the binomial } x^2 - 9 \text{ as a square.}$$
$$= (x^2 + 9)(x + 3)(x - 3) \qquad \text{Factor } x^2 - 9 \text{ as a difference of squares.}$$

Quick Check 4
Factor $x^4 - y^4$.

A WORD OF CAUTION When factoring a difference of squares, check the binomial factor containing a difference to see if it can be factored.

Difference of Cubes

Objective ② **Factor a difference of cubes.**   Another special binomial that can be factored is a **difference of cubes**. In this case, both terms are perfect cubes rather than squares. Here is the formula for factoring a difference of cubes.

> ### Difference of Cubes
> $$a^3 - b^3 = (a - b)(a^2 + ab + b^2)$$

Before proceeding, let's multiply $(a - b)(a^2 + ab + b^2)$ to show that it does equal $a^3 - b^3$.

$$(a - b)(a^2 + ab + b^2) = a \cdot a^2 + a \cdot ab + a \cdot b^2 - b \cdot a^2 \qquad \text{Distribute.}$$
$$- b \cdot ab - b \cdot b^2$$
$$= a^3 + a^2b + ab^2 - a^2b - ab^2 - b^3 \qquad \text{Multiply.}$$
$$= a^3 - b^3 \qquad \text{Combine like terms.}$$

We see that the formula is correct.

For a term to be a cube, its variable factors must have exponents that are multiples of 3, such as x^3, y^6, and z^9. Also, each constant factor must be a perfect cube. Here are the first ten perfect cubes.

$$1^3 = 1 \qquad 2^3 = 8 \qquad 3^3 = 27 \qquad 4^3 = 64 \qquad 5^3 = 125$$
$$6^3 = 216 \qquad 7^3 = 343 \qquad 8^3 = 512 \qquad 9^3 = 729 \qquad 10^3 = 1000$$

We need to memorize the formula for factoring a difference of cubes. Some patterns can help us remember the formula. A difference of cubes, $a^3 - b^3$, has two factors: a binomial $(a - b)$ and a trinomial $(a^2 + ab + b^2)$. The binomial looks just like the difference of cubes without the cubes, including the sign between the terms. The signs between the three terms in the trinomial are addition signs. To find the actual terms in the trinomial factor, the following diagram may be helpful:

$$a^3 - b^3 = (a - b)(a^2 + ab + b^2)$$

1st · 1st   2nd · 2nd

1st · 2nd

EXAMPLE 5   Factor $x^3 - 27$.

SOLUTION   We begin by looking for common factors other than 1 that the two terms share, but there are none. This binomial is not a difference of squares, as the exponent of the variable term is not a multiple of 2 and the constant 27 is not a square. However, the binomial is a difference of cubes. We can rewrite the term x^3 as $(x)^3$, and we can rewrite 27 as $(3)^3$. Rewriting $x^3 - 27$ as $(x)^3 - (3)^3$ will help us identify the terms in the binomial and trinomial factors.

$$x^3 - 27 = (x)^3 - (3)^3$$

    Rewrite each term as a perfect cube.

$$= (x - 3)(x \cdot x + x \cdot 3 + 3 \cdot 3)$$

    Factor as a difference of cubes. The binomial factor is the same as $(x)^3 - (3)^3$ without the cubes. When x is treated as the 1st term in the binomial factor and 3 is treated as the 2nd term, the terms in the trinomial are 1st · 1st + 1st · 2nd + 2nd · 2nd.

$$= (x - 3)(x^2 + 3x + 9)$$

    Simplify each term in the trinomial factor.

Quick Check 5

Factor $x^3 - 125$.

A WORD OF CAUTION A difference of cubes $x^3 - y^3$ cannot be factored as $(x - y)^3$.

EXAMPLE 6   Factor $y^{15} - 64$.

SOLUTION   Although the number 64 is a square, this binomial is not a difference of squares because y^{15} is not a square. For a term to be a square, its variable factors must have exponents that are multiples of 2. This binomial is a difference of cubes. The exponent in the first term is a multiple of 3, and the number 64 is equal to 4^3.

$$y^{15} - 64 = (y^5)^3 - (4)^3$$

    Rewrite each term as a perfect cube.

$$= (y^5 - 4)(y^5 \cdot y^5 + y^5 \cdot 4 + 4 \cdot 4)$$

    Factor as a difference of cubes.

$$= (y^5 - 4)(y^{10} + 4y^5 + 16)$$

    Simplify each term in the trinomial factor.

Quick Check 6

Factor $x^{12} - 8$.

A WORD OF CAUTION When factoring a difference of cubes $a^3 - b^3$, do not attempt to factor the trinomial factor $a^2 + ab + b^2$.

Sum of Cubes

Objective 3 Factor a sum of cubes. Unlike a sum of squares, a **sum of cubes** can be factored. Here is the formula.

> ### Sum of Cubes
> $$a^3 + b^3 = (a + b)(a^2 - ab + b^2)$$

Notice that the terms in the factors are the same as the factors in a *difference* of cubes, with the exception of some of their signs. When a sum of cubes is factored, the binomial factor is a sum rather than a difference. The sign of the middle term in the trinomial is negative rather than positive. The last term in the trinomial factor is positive, just as it was in the formula for a difference of cubes. The diagram shows the differences between the formula for a difference of cubes and a sum of cubes.

$$a^3 - b^3 = (a - b)(a^2 + ab + b^2)$$

$$a^3 + b^3 = (a + b)(a^2 - ab + b^2)$$

EXAMPLE 7 Factor $z^3 + 125$.

SOLUTION   This binomial is a sum of cubes and can be rewritten as $(z)^3 + (5)^3$. Then we can factor the sum of cubes using the formula.

$$
\begin{aligned}
z^3 + 125 &= (z)^3 + (5)^3 & \text{Rewrite each term as a perfect cube.}\\
&= (z + 5)(z \cdot z - z \cdot 5 + 5 \cdot 5) & \text{Factor as a sum of cubes.}\\
&= (z + 5)(z^2 - 5z + 25) & \text{Simplify each term in the trinomial factor.}
\end{aligned}
$$

Quick Check 7

Factor $x^3 + 216$.

A WORD OF CAUTION A sum of cubes $x^3 + y^3$ cannot be factored as $(x + y)^3$.

We finish this section by summarizing the strategies for factoring binomials.

> ### Factoring Binomials
> - Factor out the GCF if there is a common factor other than 1.
> - Determine whether both terms are perfect squares.
>   If the binomial is a sum of squares, it cannot be factored.
>   If the binomial is a difference of squares, factor it by using the formula $a^2 - b^2 = (a + b)(a - b)$. Keep in mind that some of the resulting factors can be differences of squares as well, which need to be factored further.
> - If both terms are not perfect squares, determine whether both are perfect cubes.
>   If the binomial is a difference of cubes, factor using the formula $a^3 - b^3 = (a - b)(a^2 + ab + b^2)$.
>   If the binomial is a sum of cubes, factor using the formula $a^3 + b^3 = (a + b)(a^2 - ab + b^2)$.

BUILDING YOUR STUDY STRATEGY

Overcoming Math Anxiety, 4 Taking the Right Course Many students think they have math anxiety because they constantly feel as though they are in over their heads, when in fact they may not be prepared for their particular class. Taking a course without having the prerequisite skills is not a good idea, and success will be difficult to achieve. Your instructor will be able to advise you about whether you should be taking another course or whether you have the skills to be successful in the course you are currently taking.

Exercises 6.4

PRACTICE WATCH DOWNLOAD READ REVIEW

Vocabulary

1. A binomial of the form $a^2 - b^2$ is a(n) _____ _____.

2. A numerical factor is a(n) _____ if it can be written as n^2 for some integer n.

3. A variable factor is a perfect square if its exponents are _____.

4. A binomial of the form $a^2 + b^2$ is a(n) _____.

5. A binomial of the form $a^3 - b^3$ is a(n) _____.

6. A binomial of the form $a^3 + b^3$ is a(n) _____.

Factor completely. If the polynomial cannot be factored, write prime.

7. $x^2 - 64$
8. $x^2 - 81$
9. $x^2 - 100$
10. $x^2 - 1$
11. $25a^2 - 49$
12. $16a^2 - 9$
13. $x^2 - 20$
14. $x^2 - 27$
15. $a^2 - 16b^2$
16. $m^2 - 9n^2$
17. $25x^2 - 64y^2$
18. $36x^2 - 121y^2$
19. $16 - x^2$
20. $144 - x^2$
21. $4x^2 - 196$

22. $6x^2 - 486$
23. $x^2 + 25$
24. $x^2 + 1$
25. $5x^2 + 20$
26. $4x^2 + 100y^2$
27. $x^4 - 16$
28. $x^4 - 1$
29. $x^4 - 81y^2$
30. $x^8 - 64y^4$
31. $x^3 - 1$
32. $x^3 - y^3$
33. $x^3 - 8$
34. $a^3 - 216$
35. $1000 - y^3$
36. $343 - x^3$
37. $a^3 - 64b^3$
38. $m^3 - 343n^3$
39. $125x^3 - 8y^3$
40. $729x^3 - 1000y^3$
41. $x^3 + y^3$
42. $x^3 + 27$
43. $x^3 + 8$
44. $b^3 + 64$
45. $x^6 + 27$
46. $y^{12} + 125$
47. $64m^3 + n^3$
48. $x^3 + 343y^3$
49. $3x^3 - 375$
50. $7x^3 - 189$
51. $320a^3 + 135b^3$
52. $27a^7b^6 + a^4b^3$

Mixed Practice, 53–88

Factor completely using the appropriate technique.
If the polynomial cannot be factored, write prime.

53. $x^2 - 16x + 64$

54. $3x^3 + 24x^2 + x + 8$

55. $x^2 + 16x + 28$

56. $4x^2 + 4x - 168$

57. $22x^4 - 55x^2$

58. $x^2 - 8x + 33$

59. $6x^2 - 5x - 25$

60. $-18x^2 - 69x + 12$

61. $x^5 - 16x^4 + 60x^3$

62. $x^2 + 18x + 77$

63. $-9x^2 - 225$

64. $25 - x^2$

65. $-6x^2 + 60x - 144$

66. $x^2 - 81x$

67. $x^2 - 10x - 39$

68. $x^2 + 4x - 140$

69. $25x^2 - 36y^8$

70. $x^2 + 3x - 40$

71. $2x^2 + x - 13$

72. $x^3 - 216y^3$

73. $x^2 - 64y^6$

74. $x^3 - 64y^6$

75. $8x^5 - 20x^4 - 52x^2$

76. $20x^2 - 61x + 36$

77. $5x^2 + 45$

78. $60x^2 - 470x + 900$

79. $x^2 + 12x + 35$

80. $343x^3 - 8y^6z^9$

81. $3x^2 - 13x - 38$

82. $2x^2 + 17x + 26$

83. $x^3 + 12x^2 - 6x - 72$

84. $x^2 + 16y^2$

85. $x^3 + 125y^3$

86. $125x^6 - 64y^9$

87. $4x^7 + 12x^6 + 9x^5$

88. $x^3 - 5x^2 + 2x - 10$

Determine which factoring technique is appropriate for the given polynomial.

89. ____ $8x^2 - 26x + 15$ **a.** factor out GCF

90. ____ $9a^2b^9 + 6a^4b^5 - 15a^6b^3$ **b.** factoring by grouping

91. ____ $x^2 + 121$ **c.** trinomial, leading coefficient of 1

92. ____ $x^2 - 3x - 54$ **d.** trinomial, leading coefficient other than 1

93. ____ $125x^3 - 216$ **e.** difference of squares

94. ____ $x^3 + 1331y^3$ **f.** sum of squares

95. ____ $x^3 - 3x^2 - 18x + 54$ **g.** difference of cubes

96. ____ $x^2 - 64$ **h.** sum of cubes

✏️ Writing in Mathematics

Answer in complete sentences.

97. Explain how to identify a binomial as a difference of squares.

98. Explain how to identify a binomial as a difference of cubes or as a sum of cubes.

6.5

Factoring Polynomials: A General Strategy

Objective ① Understand the strategy for factoring a general polynomial. In this section, we will review the different factoring techniques introduced in this chapter and develop a general strategy for factoring any polynomial. Keep in mind that a polynomial must be factored completely, meaning each of its polynomial factors cannot be factored further. For example, if we factored the trinomial $4x^2 + 24x + 32$ to be $(2x + 4)(2x + 8)$, this would not be factored completely because the two terms in each binomial factor have a common factor of 2 that must be factored out as follows:

$$4x^2 + 24x + 32 = (2x + 4)(2x + 8)$$
$$= 2(x + 2) \cdot 2(x + 4)$$
$$= 4(x + 2)(x + 4)$$

If we factor out all common factors as the first step when factoring a polynomial, we can avoid having to factor out common factors at the end of the process. We could have factored out the common factor of 4 from the polynomial $4x^2 + 24x + 32$ at the very beginning. In addition to ensuring that the polynomial has been factored completely, factoring out common factors often makes our work easier and occasionally allows us to factor polynomials that we would not have been able to factor otherwise.

Here is a general strategy for factoring any polynomial.

Factoring Polynomials ──────────────────────

1. Factor out any common factors.
2. Determine the number of terms in the polynomial.
   (a) If there are only *two terms*, check to see if the binomial is one of the special binomials discussed in Section 6.4.
   - Difference of Squares: $a^2 - b^2 = (a + b)(a - b)$
   - Sum of Squares: $a^2 + b^2$ is not factorable.
   - Difference of Cubes: $a^3 - b^3 = (a - b)(a^2 + ab + b^2)$
   - Sum of Cubes: $a^3 + b^3 = (a + b)(a^2 - ab + b^2)$

   (b) If there are *three terms*, try to factor the trinomial using the techniques of Sections 6.2 and 6.3.
   - $x^2 + bx + c = (x + m)(x + n)$: find two integers m and n with a product of c and a sum of b.
   - $ax^2 + bx + c$, where $a \neq 1$: factor either by grouping or by trial and error.

     To use factoring by grouping, refer to objective 1 in Section 6.3.

     To factor by trial and error, refer to objective 2 in Section 6.3.

   (c) If there are *four terms*, try factoring by grouping, discussed in Section 6.1.
3. After the polynomial has been factored, make sure that any factor with two or more terms does not have any common factors other than 1. If there are common factors, factor them out.
4. Check your factoring through multiplication.

We will now factor several polynomials of various forms. Some of the examples will have twists that we did not see in the previous sections. The focus will be on identifying the best technique.

EXAMPLE 1   Factor $-8x^2 - 80x + 192$ completely.

SOLUTION   These three terms have a common factor of -8, and after we factor it out, we have $-8(x^2 + 10x - 24)$. This is a quadratic trinomial with a leading coefficient of 1, so we factor it using the method introduced in Section 6.2.

$$-8x^2 - 80x + 192 = -8(x^2 + 10x - 24) \quad \text{Factor out the GCF } -8.$$
$$= -8(x + 12)(x - 2) \quad \text{Find two integers with a product of } -24 \text{ and a sum of 10. The integers are 12 and } -2.$$

EXAMPLE 2   Factor $343r^9 - 64s^6t^{12}$ completely.

SOLUTION   There are no common factors other than 1, so we begin by noticing that this is a binomial. This is not a difference of squares, as $343r^9$ cannot be rewritten as a perfect square. It is, however, a difference of cubes. All of the variable factors have exponents that are multiples of 3, and the coefficients are perfect cubes.

(Recall the list of the first ten perfect cubes given in Section 6.4: $343 = 7^3$ and $64 = 4^3$.) We begin by rewriting each term as a perfect cube.

$$343r^9 - 64s^6t^{12} = (7r^3)^3 - (4s^2t^4)^3 \quad \text{Rewrite each term as a perfect cube.}$$
$$= (7r^3 - 4s^2t^4)(7r^3 \cdot 7r^3 + 7r^3 \cdot 4s^2t^4 + 4s^2t^4 \cdot 4s^2t^4)$$

Factor as a difference of cubes. (Recall the pattern for the trinomial factor: 1st · 1st + 1st · 2nd + 2nd · 2nd.)

$$= (7r^3 - 4s^2t^4)(49r^6 + 28r^3s^2t^4 + 16s^4t^8)$$

Simplify each term in the trinomial factor.

For a difference or sum of cubes, check that the binomial factor cannot be factored further as one of the special binomials.

▸ **Quick Check 2**
Factor $216x^{12}y^{21} + 125$ completely.

EXAMPLE 3 Factor $2x^3 - 22x^2 - 8x + 88$ completely.

SOLUTION The four terms have a common factor of 2, so we will factor out the GCF. Then we will try to factor by grouping. If we have trouble factoring the polynomial as written, we can rearrange the order of its terms.

$$2x^3 - 22x^2 - 8x + 88 = 2(x^3 - 11x^2 - 4x + 44) \quad \text{Factor out the GCF.}$$
$$= 2[x^2(x - 11) - 4(x - 11)] \quad \text{Factor the common factor } x^2 \text{ from the first two terms and factor the common factor } -4 \text{ from the last two terms.}$$
$$= 2(x - 11)(x^2 - 4) \quad \text{Factor out the common factor } x - 11.$$

Notice that the factor $x^2 - 4$ is a difference of squares and must be factored further.

$$2(x - 11)(x^2 - 4) = 2(x - 11)(x + 2)(x - 2) \quad \text{Factor the difference of squares, } x^2 - 4 = (x + 2)(x - 2)$$

Quick Check 3
Factor $x^4 + 5x^3 - 8x - 40$ completely.

If a binomial is both a difference of squares and a difference of cubes, such as $x^6 - 64$, to factor it completely, we must start by factoring it as a difference of squares. The next example illustrates this.

EXAMPLE 4 Factor $x^6 - 64$ completely.

SOLUTION There are no common factors to factor out, so we begin by factoring this binomial as a difference of squares.

$$x^6 - 64 = (x^3)^2 - (8)^2 \quad \text{Rewrite each term as a perfect square.}$$
$$= (x^3 + 8)(x^3 - 8) \quad \text{Factor as a difference of squares.}$$

Notice that each factor can be factored further. The binomial $x^3 + 8$ is a sum of cubes, and the binomial $x^3 - 8$ is a difference of cubes. We use the fact that $x^3 + 8 = (x + 2)(x^2 - 2x + 4)$ and $x^3 - 8 = (x - 2)(x^2 + 2x + 4)$ to complete the factoring.

$$x^6 - 64 = (x + 2)(x^2 - 2x + 4)(x - 2)(x^2 + 2x + 4)$$

Note what would have occurred if we had first factored $x^6 - 64$ as a difference of cubes.

Quick Check 4
Factor $x^{12} - y^6$ completely.

$$x^6 - 64 = (x^2)^3 - (4)^3 \qquad \text{Rewrite each term as a perfect cube.}$$
$$= (x^2 - 4)(x^4 + 4x^2 + 16) \qquad \text{Factor the difference of cubes.}$$
$$= (x + 2)(x - 2)(x^4 + 4x^2 + 16) \quad \text{Factor the difference of squares.}$$

At this point, we do not know how to factor $x^4 + 4x^2 + 16$, so the technique of Example 4 has factored the binomial $x^6 - 64$ more completely.

EXAMPLE 5 Factor $x^{12} + 1$ completely.

SOLUTION   The two terms do not have a common factor other than 1, so we need to determine whether this binomial matches one of the special forms. The binomial can be rewritten as a sum of cubes, $(x^4)^3 + (1)^3$.

$$x^{12} + 1 = (x^4)^3 + (1)^3 \qquad \text{Rewrite each term as a perfect cube.}$$
$$= (x^4 + 1)(x^8 - x^4 + 1) \quad \text{Factor as a sum of cubes.}$$

Quick Check 5
Factor $x^6 + 64$ completely.

EXAMPLE 6 Factor $15x^5 - 55x^4 + 40x^3$ completely.

SOLUTION   The three terms have a common factor of $5x^3$, so we begin by factoring this out of the trinomial. After we have done this, we can factor the trinomial factor $3x^2 - 11x + 8$ using either of the techniques in Section 6.3. We will factor it by grouping, although you may prefer to use trial and error.

$$15x^5 - 55x^4 + 40x^3 = 5x^3(3x^2 - 11x + 8) \qquad \text{Factor out the common factor } 5x^3.$$

$$= 5x^3(3x^2 - 3x - 8x + 8) \qquad \text{To factor by grouping, we need to find two integers whose product is equal to } 3 \cdot 8 = 24 \text{ and whose sum is } -11. \text{ The two integers are } -3 \text{ and } -8, \text{ so we rewrite the term } -11x \text{ as } -3x - 8x.$$

$$= 5x^3[3x(x - 1) - 8(x - 1)] \qquad \text{Factor the common factor } 3x \text{ from the first two terms and factor the common factor } -8 \text{ from the last two terms.}$$

Quick Check 6
Factor $8x^2 + 42x - 36$ completely.

$$= 5x^3(x - 1)(3x - 8) \qquad \text{Factor out the common factor } x - 1.$$

BUILDING YOUR STUDY STRATEGY

Overcoming Math Anxiety, 5 Study Skills Many students who perform poorly in their math class attribute their performance to math anxiety, when, in reality, poor study skills are to blame. Make sure you are giving your best effort, including

- Working with a study group.
- Reading the text before the material is covered in class.
- Rereading the text after the material is covered in class.
- Completing each homework assignment.
- Making note cards for particularly difficult problems or procedures.
- Getting help if there is a problem you do not understand.
- Asking your instructor questions when you do not understand something.
- Seeing a tutor.

Exercises 6.5

PRACTICE   WATCH   DOWNLOAD   READ   REVIEW

Vocabulary

1. The first step for factoring a trinomial is to factor out _____, if there are any.

2. A binomial of the form $a^2 - b^2$ is a(n) _____.

3. A binomial of the form $a^2 + b^2$ is a(n) _____.

4. A binomial of the form $a^3 - b^3$ is a(n) _____.

5. A binomial of the form $a^3 + b^3$ is a(n) _____.

6. Factoring can be checked by _____ the factors.

Factor completely. If the polynomial cannot be factored, write prime.

7. $x^7 + 18x^5 - 36x$

8. $x^9 - 11x^7 + 37x^4$

9. $84x^2 + 4x - 20$

10. $12x + 20$

11. $a^5b^7 - 3a^4b^6 + 8a^2b^9$

12. $9m^7n^6 + 12m^{10}n^4 + 21m^3n^8$

13. $x^3 + 6x^2 + 5x + 30$

14. $x^3 - 9x^2 + 10x - 90$

15. $x^3 - 7x^2 - 3x + 21$

16. $x^3 + 13x^2 - 11x - 143$

17. $x^2 - 8x - 65$

18. $x^2 - 18x + 45$

19. $x^2 + 13x + 42$

20. $x^2 - 10x + 20$

21. $x^2 + 4x - 165$

22. $x^2 + 13x - 14$

23. $x^2 + 17x - 30$

24. $x^2 - 6x - 280$

25. $x^2 - 23x + 42$

26. $x^2 - 3x - 154$

27. $x^2 + 20x + 100$

28. $x^2 - 14x + 49$

29. $x^2 + 7xy - 60y^2$

30. $x^2 - 12xy + 32y^2$

31. $x^2y^2 + 17xy + 16$

32. $x^2y^2 + 10xy - 11$

33. $4x^2 + 56x + 192$

34. $9x^2 + 54x + 72$

35. $3x^2 - 42x + 135$

36. $4x^2 + 4x - 224$

37. $-10x^2 + 70x + 180$

38. $-6x^2 - 6x + 72$

39. $3x^2 + 10x - 48$

40. $6x^2 - 29x - 5$

41. $21x^2 + 31x + 4$

42. $6x^2 - 13x + 6$

43. $2x^2 + 7x + 14$

44. $6x^2 + 11x - 10$

45. $12x^2 - 41x + 22$

46. $2x^2 - 3x - 12$

47. $9x^2 - 30x + 25$

48. $4x^2 - 28x + 49$

49. $18x^2 - 60x + 42$

50. $6x^2 + 75x + 225$

51. $x^2 - 64$

52. $x^2 - 49$

53. $x^8 - 16y^6$

54. $49x^4 - 81y^{10}$

55. $x^4 - 36x^2$

56. $5x^2 - 125$

57. $x^4 + 81y^2$

58. $16x^{10} + 49y^6$

59. $x^3 - 1000$

60. $x^{21} - 1$

61. $27x^3 - 8y^3$

62. $x^6 - 64y^{15}$

63. $x^3 + 216$

64. $x^{15} + 8$

65. $x^6 + 729y^3$

66. $27x^9 + 125y^{15}$

67. $7x^3 + 189$

68. $3x^3 - 648$

69. $x^3 - 9x^2 - 4x + 36$

70. $x^3 + 5x^2 - 36x - 180$

71. $4x^3 - 28x^2 - x + 7$

72. $9x^3 + 18x^2 - 4x - 8$

73. $x^4 + 16x^3 + x + 16$

74. $x^4 + 7x^3 + 8x + 56$

75. $x^8 - 1$

76. $x^4 - y^4$

77. $x^6 - y^6$

78. $x^6 - 1$

79. $(x + 4)^2 - y^2$

80. $(x - 7)^2 - y^2$

81. $(x^2 - 10x + 25) - y^2$

82. $(x^2 + 16x + 64) - y^2$

83. $x^2 + 6x + 9 - y^2$

84. $x^2 - 20x + 100 - y^2$

Mixed Practice, 85–116

Factor completely. If the polynomial cannot be factored, write prime.

85. $4x^2 + 8x - 5$

86. $x^2 - 100$

87. $x^3 - 6x^2 + 8x - 48$

88. $x^3 + 7x^2 - 9x - 63$

89. $x^2 + 11x - 60$

90. $4x^2 + 28x + 48$

91. $x^2 + 13x - 36$

92. $2x^2 + 17x + 18$

93. $8x^3 + 343$

94. $25x^4 - 49z^2$

95. $x^2 + 21x + 98$

96. $6x^2 + 23x + 15$

97. $16x^4 - 81$

98. $x^2 - 3x - 180$

99. $6x^2 + 78x + 240$

100. $x^4 - 1296$

101. $9x^2 - 121y^6$

102. $x^2 + 15xy - 54y^2$

103. $x^3 + 4x^2 - 25x - 100$

104. $2x^3 - 8x^2 - 3x + 12$

105. $729x^3 - 512y^3$

106. $x^3 + 1331$

107. $x^2y^2 - 15xy + 54$

108. $x^2 - 2x + 48$

109. $3x^2 - 28x - 20$

110. $6x^2 - 35x + 49$

111. $2x^2 + 19x + 25$

112. $8x^2 + 24x + 32$

113. $5x^5 + 20x^3 - 35x^2$

114. $x^2 - 25x + 144$

115. $64x^2 - 169$

116. $27x^3 - 512$

✏ Writing in Mathematics

Answer in complete sentences.

117. *Newsletter* Write a newsletter explaining the following strategies for factoring polynomials. Include a brief example of each.

- Factoring out the GCF
- Factoring by grouping
- Factoring trinomials of the form $x^2 + bx + c$
- Factoring polynomials of the form $ax^2 + bx + c$, where $a \neq 1$, by grouping
- Factoring polynomials of the form $ax^2 + bx + c$, where $a \neq 1$, by trial and error
- Factoring a difference of squares
- Factoring a difference of cubes
- Factoring a sum of cubes

Quick Review Exercises

Section 6.5

Solve.

1. $x - 7 = 0$

2. $x + 3 = 0$

3. $5x - 12 = 0$

4. $2x + 29 = 0$

6.6

Solving Quadratic Equations by Factoring

OBJECTIVES

1. Solve an equation by using the zero-factor property of real numbers.
2. Solve a quadratic equation by factoring.
3. Solve a quadratic equation that is not in standard form.
4. Solve a quadratic equation with coefficients that are fractions.
5. Find a quadratic equation, given its solutions.

Quadratic Equations

A **quadratic equation** is an equation that can be written as $ax^2 + bx + c = 0$, where a, b, and c are real numbers and $a \neq 0$. This form is the **standard form of a quadratic equation**.

We have already learned to solve linear equations ($ax + b = 0$). The difference between these two types of equations is that a quadratic equation has a second-degree term, ax^2. Because of the second-degree term, the techniques used to solve linear equations do not work for quadratic equations.

The Zero-Factor Property of Real Numbers

Objective 1 Solve an equation by using the zero-factor property of real numbers. To solve a quadratic equation, we will use the **zero-factor property of real numbers**.

Zero-Factor Property of Real Numbers

If $a \cdot b = 0$, then $a = 0$ or $b = 0$.

The principle behind this property is that if two or more unknown numbers have a product of zero, then at least one of the numbers must be zero. This property holds true only when the product is equal to 0, not for any other numbers.

EXAMPLE 1 Use the zero-factor property to solve the equation $(x + 3)(x - 7) = 0$.

SOLUTION In this example, the product of two unknown numbers, $x + 3$ and $x - 7$, is equal to 0. The zero-factor property says that either $x + 3 = 0$ or $x - 7 = 0$. Essentially, we have taken an equation that we do not know how to solve, $(x + 3)(x - 7) = 0$, and have rewritten it as two linear equations that we do know how to solve.

$$(x + 3)(x - 7) = 0$$

$x + 3 = 0$	or	$x - 7 = 0$	Set each factor equal to 0.
$x = -3$	or	$x = 7$	Solve each linear equation.

There are two solutions to this equation: -3 and 7. We write these solutions in a solution set as $\{-3, 7\}$.

EXAMPLE 2 Use the zero-factor property to solve the equation $x(3x - 5) = 0$.

SOLUTION Applying the zero-factor property gives us the equations $x = 0$ and $3x - 5 = 0$. The first equation, $x = 0$, is already solved, so we need to solve only the equation $3x - 5 = 0$ to find the second solution.

$$x(3x - 5) = 0$$

$x = 0$	or	$3x - 5 = 0$	Set each factor equal to 0.
$x = 0$	or	$3x = 5$	Solve each linear equation.
$x = 0$	or	$x = \dfrac{5}{3}$	

The solution set for this equation is $\{0, \frac{5}{3}\}$.

Quick Check 1

Use the zero-factor property to solve the equation.

a) $(x - 2)(x + 8) = 0$
b) $x(4x + 9) = 0$

If an equation has the product of more than two factors equal to 0, such as $(x + 4)(x + 1)(x - 2) = 0$, we set each factor equal to 0 and solve. The solution set to this equation is $\{-4, -1, 2\}$.

Solving Quadratic Equations by Factoring

Objective ② **Solve a quadratic equation by factoring.** To solve a quadratic equation, we will use the following procedure:

Solving Quadratic Equations by Factoring

1. Write the equation in standard form: $ax^2 + bx + c = 0$. *We need to collect all of the terms on one side of the equation. It helps to collect all of the terms so that the coefficient of the squared term is positive.*
2. Factor the expression $ax^2 + bx + c$ completely. *If you are struggling with factoring, refer back to Sections 6.1–6.5.*
3. Set each factor equal to 0 and solve the resulting equations. *Each of these equations should be a linear equation.*
4. Finish by checking the solutions. *This is an excellent opportunity to catch mistakes in factoring.*

EXAMPLE 3 Solve $x^2 + 7x - 30 = 0$.

SOLUTION This equation is already in standard form, so we begin by factoring the expression $x^2 + 7x - 30$.

$$x^2 + 7x - 30 = 0$$
$$(x + 10)(x - 3) = 0 \qquad \text{Factor.}$$
$$x + 10 = 0 \qquad \text{or} \qquad x - 3 = 0 \quad \text{Set each factor equal to 0.}$$
$$x = -10 \qquad \text{or} \qquad x = 3 \quad \text{Solve each equation.}$$

The solution set is $\{-10, 3\}$. Now we will check the solutions.

Check ($x = -10$)	**Check ($x = 3$)**
$x^2 + 7x - 30 = 0$	$x^2 + 7x - 30 = 0$
$(-10)^2 + 7(-10) - 30 = 0$	$(3)^2 + 7(3) - 30 = 0$
$100 + 7(-10) - 30 = 0$	$9 + 7(3) - 30 = 0$
$100 - 70 - 30 = 0$	$9 + 21 - 30 = 0$
$0 = 0$	$0 = 0$

The check shows that the solutions are correct.

▸ **Quick Check 2**
Solve $x^2 - x - 20 = 0$.

A WORD OF CAUTION Pay close attention to the instructions to a problem. If you are asked to solve a quadratic equation, do not just factor the quadratic expression and stop. If you are asked to factor a quadratic expression, do not set each factor equal to 0 and solve the resulting equations.

EXAMPLE 4 Solve $3x^2 - 18x - 48 = 0$.

SOLUTION   The equation is in standard form. To factor $3x^2 - 18x - 48$, begin by factoring out the common factor 3.

$$3x^2 - 18x - 48 = 0$$
$$3(x^2 - 6x - 16) = 0 \qquad \text{Factor out the GCF.}$$
$$3(x - 8)(x + 2) = 0 \qquad \text{Factor } x^2 - 6x - 16.$$
$$x - 8 = 0 \quad \text{or} \quad x + 2 = 0 \qquad \text{Set each factor containing a variable}$$
$$\text{equal to 0. You can ignore the numerical}$$
$$\text{factor 3.}$$
$$x = 8 \quad \text{or} \quad x = -2 \quad \text{Solve each equation.}$$

The solution set is $\{-2, 8\}$. The check is left to the reader.

We do not need to set a numerical factor equal to 0 because such an equation will not have a solution. For example, the equation $3 = 0$ has no solution. The zero-factor property says that at least one of the three factors must equal 0; we just know that it cannot be the factor 3 that is equal to 0.

▶ Quick Check 3

Solve $4x^2 + 60x + 224 = 0$.

A WORD OF CAUTION A common numerical factor does not affect the solutions of a quadratic equation.

EXAMPLE 5 Solve $2x^2 - 7x - 15 = 0$.

SOLUTION   When the expression $2x^2 - 7x - 15$ is factored, there is no common factor other than 1 that can be factored out. So the leading coefficient of this trinomial is not 1. We can factor by trial and error or by grouping. We will use factoring by grouping. We look for two integers whose product is equal to $(2)(-15)$, or -30, and whose sum is -7. The two integers are -10 and 3, so we can rewrite the term and then factor by grouping. (Refer to Section 6.3 to review this technique.)

$$2x^2 - 7x - 15 = 0$$
$$2x^2 - 10x + 3x - 15 = 0 \qquad \text{Rewrite } -7x \text{ as } -10x + 3x.$$
$$2x(x - 5) + 3(x - 5) = 0 \qquad \text{Factor the common factor } 2x \text{ from the}$$
$$\text{first two terms and factor the common}$$
$$\text{factor 3 from the last two terms.}$$
$$(x - 5)(2x + 3) = 0 \qquad \text{Factor out the common factor } x - 5.$$
$$x - 5 = 0 \quad \text{or} \quad 2x + 3 = 0 \quad \text{Set each factor equal to 0.}$$
$$x = 5 \quad \text{or} \quad 2x = -3 \quad \text{Solve each equation.}$$
$$x = 5 \quad \text{or} \quad x = -\frac{3}{2}$$

The solution set is $\left\{-\frac{3}{2}, 5\right\}$. The check is left to the reader.

▶ Quick Check 4

Solve $6x^2 - 23x + 7 = 0$.

Objective 3 Solve a quadratic equation that is not in standard form. We now turn our attention to equations that are not already in standard form. In each of the examples that follows, the check of the solutions is left to the reader.

EXAMPLE 6 Solve $x^2 = 49$.

SOLUTION Begin by rewriting this equation in standard form. This can be done by subtracting 49 from each side of the equation. Once this has been done, the expression to be factored is a difference of squares.

$$x^2 = 49$$
$$x^2 - 49 = 0 \qquad \text{Subtract 49.}$$
$$(x + 7)(x - 7) = 0 \qquad \text{Factor.}$$
$$x + 7 = 0 \qquad \text{or} \qquad x - 7 = 0 \quad \text{Set each factor equal to 0.}$$
$$x = -7 \qquad \text{or} \qquad x = 7 \quad \text{Solve each equation.}$$

The solution set is $\{-7, 7\}$.

EXAMPLE 7 Solve $x^2 + 25 = 10x$.

SOLUTION To rewrite this equation in standard form, we need to subtract $10x$ so that all terms will be on the left side of the equation. When we subtract $10x$, we must write the terms in descending order.

$$x^2 + 25 = 10x$$
$$x^2 - 10x + 25 = 0 \qquad \text{Subtract } 10x.$$
$$(x - 5)(x - 5) = 0 \qquad \text{Factor.}$$
$$x - 5 = 0 \qquad \text{or} \qquad x - 5 = 0 \quad \text{Set each factor equal to 0.}$$
$$x = 5 \qquad \text{or} \qquad x = 5 \quad \text{Solve each equation.}$$

Notice that both solutions are identical. In this case, we need to write the repeated solution only once. The solution set is $\{5\}$.

Quick Check 5

Solve $x^2 + 4x = 45$.

Occasionally, we need to simplify one or both sides of an equation to rewrite the equation in standard form. For instance, to solve the equation $x(x + 9) = 10$, we must first multiply x by $x + 9$. You may be wondering why we would want to multiply out the left side because it is already factored. Although it is factored, the product is equal to 10, not 0.

EXAMPLE 8 Solve $x(x + 9) = 10$.

SOLUTION As mentioned, first multiply x by $x + 9$. Then rewrite the equation in standard form.

$$x(x + 9) = 10$$
$$x^2 + 9x = 10 \qquad \text{Multiply.}$$
$$x^2 + 9x - 10 = 0 \qquad \text{Subtract 10.}$$
$$(x + 10)(x - 1) = 0 \qquad \text{Factor.}$$
$$x + 10 = 0 \qquad \text{or} \qquad x - 1 = 0 \quad \text{Set each factor equal to 0.}$$
$$x = -10 \qquad \text{or} \qquad x = 1 \quad \text{Solve each equation.}$$

The solution set is $\{-10, 1\}$.

Quick Check 6

Solve $x(x - 3) = 70$.

A WORD OF CAUTION Make sure the equation you are solving is written as a product equal to 0 before you set each factor equal to 0 and solve.

Objective 4 Solve a quadratic equation with coefficients that are fractions. If an equation contains fractions, clearing those fractions makes it easier to factor the quadratic expression. We can clear the fractions by multiplying both sides of the equation by the LCM of the denominators.

EXAMPLE 9   Solve $\frac{1}{6}x^2 + x + \frac{4}{3} = 0$.

SOLUTION   The LCM for these two denominators is 6, so we can clear the fractions by multiplying both sides of the equation by 6.

$$\frac{1}{6}x^2 + x + \frac{4}{3} = 0$$

$$6 \cdot \left(\frac{1}{6}x^2 + x + \frac{4}{3}\right) = 6 \cdot 0 \qquad \text{Multiply both sides by 6, which is the LCM of the denominators.}$$

$$\overset{1}{6} \cdot \frac{1}{\overset{}{6}}x^2 + 6 \cdot x + \overset{2}{6} \cdot \frac{4}{\overset{}{3}} = 6 \cdot 0 \qquad \text{Distribute and divide out common factors.}$$

$$x^2 + 6x + 8 = 0 \qquad \text{Multiply.}$$

$$(x + 2)(x + 4) = 0 \qquad \text{Factor.}$$

$$x + 2 = 0 \qquad \text{or} \qquad x + 4 = 0 \qquad \text{Set each factor equal to 0.}$$

$$x = -2 \qquad \text{or} \qquad x = -4 \qquad \text{Solve each equation.}$$

The solution set is $\{-4, -2\}$.

Quick Check 7

Solve $\frac{2}{45}x^2 + \frac{4}{15}x - \frac{6}{5} = 0$.

Finding a Quadratic Equation, Given Its Solutions

Objective 5 Find a quadratic equation, given its solutions. If we know the two solutions to a quadratic equation, we can determine an equation with these solutions. The next example illustrates this process.

EXAMPLE 10   Find a quadratic equation in standard form, with integer coefficients, that has the solution set $\{-9, 4\}$.

SOLUTION   We know that $x = -9$ is a solution to the equation. This says that $x + 9$ is a factor of the quadratic expression. Similarly, knowing that $x = 4$ is a solution tells us that $x - 4$ is a factor of the quadratic expression. Multiplying these two factors will give us a quadratic equation with these two solutions.

$$x = -9 \qquad \text{or} \qquad x = 4 \qquad \text{Begin with the solutions.}$$

$$x + 9 = 0 \qquad \text{or} \qquad x - 4 = 0 \qquad \begin{array}{l}\text{Rewrite each equation so the right} \\ \text{side is equal to 0.}\end{array}$$

$$(x + 9)(x - 4) = 0 \qquad \begin{array}{l}\text{Write an equation that has these} \\ \text{two expressions as factors.}\end{array}$$

$$x^2 + 5x - 36 = 0 \qquad \text{Multiply.}$$

A quadratic equation that has the solution set $\{-9, 4\}$ is $x^2 + 5x - 36 = 0$.

Quick Check 8

Find a quadratic equation in standard form, with integer coefficients, that has the solution set $\{-6, 8\}$.

Notice that we say *a* quadratic equation rather than *the* quadratic equation. There are infinitely many quadratic equations with integer coefficients that have this solution set. For example, multiplying both sides of the equation by 2 gives the equation $2x^2 + 10x - 72 = 0$, which has the same solution set.

Exercises 6.6

PRACTICE   WATCH   DOWNLOAD   READ   REVIEW

Vocabulary

1. A(n) _____ is an equation that can be written as $ax^2 + bx + c = 0$, where a, b, and c are real numbers and $a \neq 0$.

2. A quadratic equation is in standard form if it is in the form _____, where $a \neq 0$.

3. The _____ property of real numbers states that if $a \cdot b = 0$, then $a = 0$ or $b = 0$.

4. Once a quadratic expression has been set equal to 0 and factored you set each _____ equal to 0 and solve.

Solve.

5. $(x + 7)(x - 100) = 0$

6. $(x - 2)(x - 10) = 0$

7. $x(x - 12) = 0$

8. $x(x + 5) = 0$

9. $7(x + 8)(x - 6) = 0$

10. $-4(x + 5)(x - 12) = 0$

11. $(x + 7)(3x + 4) = 0$

12. $(x - 3)(5x - 22) = 0$

13. $x^2 - 11x + 18 = 0$

14. $x^2 - 13x + 42 = 0$

15. $x^2 + 15x + 44 = 0$

16. $x^2 + 14x + 48 = 0$

17. $x^2 + 6x - 40 = 0$

18. $x^2 - 3x - 88 = 0$

19. $x^2 - 12x - 45 = 0$

20. $x^2 + 7x - 44 = 0$

21. $x^2 - 16x + 64 = 0$

22. $x^2 + 12x + 36 = 0$

23. $x^2 - 81 = 0$

24. $x^2 - 4 = 0$

25. $x^2 + 7x = 0$

26. $x^2 - 10x = 0$

27. $5x^2 - 22x = 0$

28. $14x^2 + 13x = 0$

29. $3x^2 - 3x - 270 = 0$

30. $4x^2 + 16x - 308 = 0$

31. $-x^2 + 12x - 35 = 0$

32. $-x^2 - 4x + 12 = 0$

33. $3x^2 + 22x - 16 = 0$

34. $2x^2 - 17x + 35 = 0$

35. $27x^2 - 3x - 2 = 0$

36. $6x^2 + 7x - 68 = 0$

37. $x^2 - 2x = 35$

38. $x^2 + 8x = -15$

39. $x^2 = 8x - 16$

40. $x^2 - 13x = 48$

41. $x^2 + 12x = 3x - 18$

42. $x^2 + 11x + 20 = 10x + 76$

43. $x^2 - 3x - 7 = 4x + 11$

44. $2x^2 + 7x - 25 = x^2 + 23x - 40$

45. $x^2 = 9$

46. $x^2 = 25$

47. $x^2 + 11x = 11x + 36$

48. $x^2 - 3x = -3x + 100$

49. $x(x + 4) = 4(x + 16)$

50. $x(x + 7) = (4x + 3) + (3x + 13)$

51. $x(x - 7) = 30$

52. $x(x + 4) = 96$

53. $(x - 5)(x + 6) = -18$

54. $(x + 7)(x + 2) = 84$

55. $(x + 2)(x + 3) = (x + 7)(x - 4)$

56. $(x - 6)(x - 4) = (x + 12)(x - 10)$

57. $\dfrac{1}{6}x^2 - \dfrac{3}{2}x + 3 = 0$

58. $\dfrac{1}{8}x^2 + \dfrac{1}{4}x - 6 = 0$

59. $\dfrac{1}{6}x^2 - \dfrac{5}{4}x - \dfrac{9}{4} = 0$

60. $\dfrac{1}{2}x^2 + \dfrac{11}{12}x + \dfrac{1}{3} = 0$

61. $\dfrac{2}{15}x^2 - \dfrac{7}{10}x + \dfrac{2}{3} = 0$

62. $\dfrac{3}{4}x^2 - \dfrac{3}{4}x - \dfrac{5}{6} = 0$

Find a quadratic equation with integer coefficients that has the given solution set.

63. $\{4, 5\}$

64. $\{-10, 7\}$

65. $\{0, 6\}$

66. $\{4\}$

67. $\{-5, 5\}$

68. $\left\{\dfrac{3}{4}, 6\right\}$

69. $\left\{-\dfrac{2}{5}, \dfrac{1}{2}\right\}$

70. $\left\{-\dfrac{7}{3}, -\dfrac{3}{5}\right\}$

71. Use the fact that $x = \frac{7}{2}$ is a solution to the equation $6x^2 + 7x - 98 = 0$ to find the other solution to the equation.

72. Use the fact that $x = \frac{13}{3}$ is a solution to the equation $3x^2 - 28x + 65 = 0$ to find the other solution to the equation.

For the given quadratic equation, one of its solutions has been provided. Use it to find the other solution.

73. $x^2 + 6x - 667 = 0, x = 23$

74. $x^2 - 78x + 1517 = 0, x = 41$

75. $15x^2 + 11x - 532 = 0, x = -\dfrac{19}{3}$

76. $48x^2 - 154x - 735 = 0, x = \dfrac{35}{6}$.

Writing in Mathematics

Answer in complete sentences.

77. Explain the zero-factor property of real numbers. Describe how this property is used when solving quadratic equations by factoring.

78. Explain why the common factor of 2 has no effect on the solutions of the equation $2(x - 7)(x + 5) = 0$.

79. *Solutions Manual* Write a solutions manual page for the following problem:

$Solve \quad \dfrac{1}{6}x^2 - \dfrac{1}{3}x - 4 = 0.$

Quick Review Exercises

Section 6.6

Evaluate the given function.

1. $f(x) = 3x + 8, f(5)$

2. $f(x) = -10x + 21, f(-8)$

3. $f(x) = -7x - 19, f(2b + 3)$

4. $f(x) = x^2 + 7x - 20, f(6)$

6.7

Quadratic Functions

OBJECTIVES

1 **Evaluate quadratic functions.**
2 **Solve equations involving quadratic functions.**
3 **Solve applied problems involving quadratic functions.**

We first investigated linear functions in Chapter 3. A linear function is a function of the form $f(x) = mx + b$. In this section, we turn our attention to **quadratic functions**.

Quadratic Functions

A quadratic function is a function of the form $f(x) = ax^2 + bx + c$, where $a \neq 0$.

Evaluating Quadratic Functions

Objective 1 **Evaluate quadratic functions.** We begin our investigation of quadratic functions by learning to evaluate these functions for particular values of the variable. For example, if we are asked to find $f(3)$, we are being asked to evaluate the function $f(x)$ at $x = 3$. To do this, we substitute 3 for the variable x and simplify the resulting expression.

EXAMPLE 1 For the function $f(x) = x^2 - 5x - 8$, find $f(-4)$.

SOLUTION Substitute -4 for the variable x and then simplify.

$$
\begin{aligned}
f(-4) &= (-4)^2 - 5(-4) - 8 && \text{Substitute } -4 \text{ for } x. \\
&= 16 - 5(-4) - 8 && \text{Square } -4. \ (-4)(-4) = 16 \\
&= 16 + 20 - 8 && \text{Multiply.} \\
&= 28 && \text{Simplify.}
\end{aligned}
$$

Quick Check 1

For the function
$f(x) = x^2 - 9x + 405$,
find $f(-6)$.

Solving Equations Involving Quadratic Functions

Objective 2 **Solve equations involving quadratic functions.** Now that we have learned to solve quadratic equations, we can solve equations involving quadratic functions. Suppose we were trying to find all values x for which some function $f(x)$ was equal to 0. We replace $f(x)$ with its formula and solve the resulting quadratic equation.

EXAMPLE 2 Let $f(x) = x^2 + 11x - 26$. Find all values x for which $f(x) = 0$.

SOLUTION Begin by replacing the function with its formula; then solve the resulting equation.

$$
\begin{aligned}
f(x) &= 0 \\
x^2 + 11x - 26 &= 0 && \text{Replace } f(x) \text{ with its formula} \\
& && x^2 + 11x - 26. \\
(x + 13)(x - 2) &= 0 && \text{Factor.} \\
x + 13 = 0 \quad &\text{or} \quad x - 2 = 0 && \text{Set each factor equal to 0.} \\
x = -13 \quad &\text{or} \quad x = 2 && \text{Solve each equation.}
\end{aligned}
$$

The two values x for which $f(x) = 0$ are -13 and 2.

▶ Quick Check 2

Let $f(x) = x^2 - 17x + 72$. Find all values x for which $f(x) = 0$.

EXAMPLE 3   Let $f(x) = x^2 - 24$. Find all values x for which $f(x) = 25$.

SOLUTION   After setting the function equal to 25, we need to rewrite the equation in standard form in order to solve it.

$$
\begin{aligned}
f(x) &= 25 \\
x^2 - 24 &= 25 && \text{Replace } f(x) \text{ with its formula.} \\
x^2 - 49 &= 0 && \text{Subtract 25.} \\
(x + 7)(x - 7) &= 0 && \text{Factor.} \\
x + 7 = 0 \quad &\text{or} \quad x - 7 = 0 && \text{Set each factor equal to 0.} \\
x = -7 \quad &\text{or} \quad x = 7 && \text{Solve each equation.}
\end{aligned}
$$

The two values x for which $f(x) = 25$ are -7 and 7.

▶ Quick Check 3

Let $f(x) = x^2 - 6x + 20$. Find all values x for which $f(x) = 92$.

Applications

Objective ③ **Solve applied problems involving quadratic functions.** We conclude the section with an applied problem that requires interpreting the graph of a quadratic function, a U-shaped curve called a **parabola**. Here are some examples. Note that these graphs are not linear.

$f(x) = x^2$

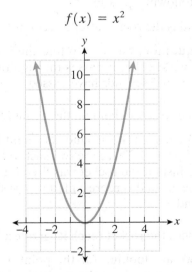

$f(x) = x^2 - 6x + 8$

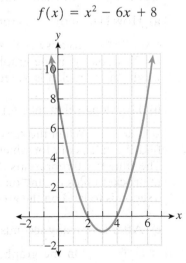

$f(x) = -x^2 + 4x$

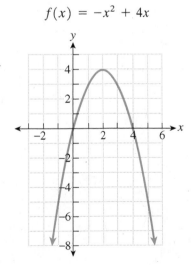

EXAMPLE 4   A rocket is fired into the air from the ground at a speed of 96 feet per second. Its height, in feet, after t seconds is given by the function $h(t) = -16t^2 + 96t$, which is graphed as follows:

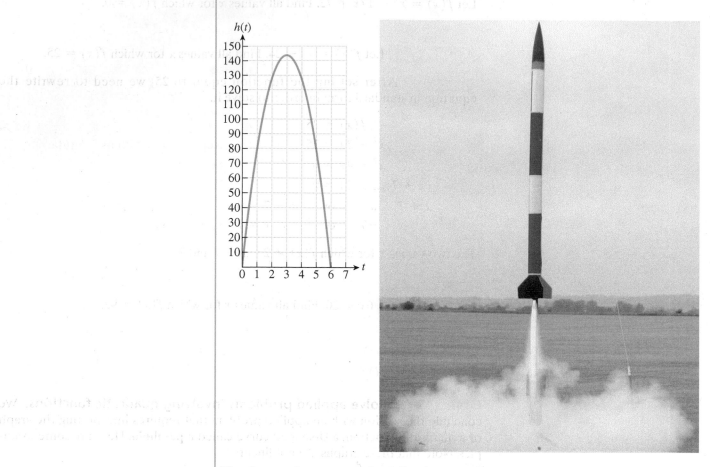

Use the graph to answer the following questions:

a) How high above the ground is the rocket after 5 seconds?

SOLUTION   To answer this question, we need to find the function's value when $t = 5$. Looking at the graph, we see that it passes through the point $(5, 80)$. The height of the rocket is 80 feet after 5 seconds have passed.

b) How long will it take for the rocket to land on the ground?

SOLUTION   When the rocket lands on the ground, its height is 0 feet. We need to find the values of t for which $h(t) = 0$. There are two such values, $t = 0$ and $t = 6$. The time $t = 0$ represents the instant the rocket was fired into the air, so the time the rocket takes to land on the ground is represented by $t = 6$. It takes the rocket 6 seconds to land on the ground.

c) After how many seconds does the rocket reach its greatest height?

SOLUTION   On the graph, we are looking for the point at which the function reaches its highest point. (This point where the parabola changes from rising to falling is called the **vertex** of the parabola.) We see that this point corresponds to a t value of 3, so it reaches its greatest height after 3 seconds.

d) What is the greatest height the rocket reaches?

SOLUTION   From the graph, the best we can say is that the maximum height is between 140 feet and 150 feet. However, because we know the object reaches its greatest height after 3 seconds, we can evaluate the function $h(t) = -16t^2 + 96t$ at $t = 3$.

$$h(t) = -16t^2 + 96t$$
$$h(3) = -16(3)^2 + 96(3) \quad \text{Replace } t \text{ with 3.}$$
$$= -16(9) + 96(3) \quad \text{Square 3.}$$
$$= -144 + 288 \quad \text{Multiply.}$$
$$= 144 \quad \text{Simplify.}$$

The rocket reaches a height of 144 feet.

▶ **Quick Check 4**

A ball is thrown into the air from the top of a building 48 feet above the ground at a speed of 32 feet per second. Its height, in feet, after t seconds is given by the function $h(t) = -16t^2 + 32t + 48$, which is graphed as follows.

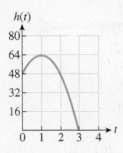

Use the graph to answer the following questions.

a) How high above the ground is the ball after 2 seconds?
b) How long will it take for the ball to land on the ground?
c) After how many seconds does the ball reach its greatest height?
d) What is the greatest height the ball reaches?

BUILDING YOUR STUDY STRATEGY

Overcoming Math Anxiety, 7 Positive Attitude Math anxiety causes many students to think negatively about math. A positive attitude will lead to more success than a negative attitude. Jot down some of the negative thoughts you have about math and your ability to learn and understand mathematics. Write each of these thoughts on a note card; then on the other side of the card, write the opposite statement.

A little confidence will go a long way toward improving your performance in class. Have the confidence to sit in the front row and ask questions during class, knowing that having your questions answered will increase your understanding and your chances for a better grade on the next exam. Finally, each time you experience success, no matter how small, reward yourself.

Exercises 6.7

Vocabulary

1. A(n) _____ is a function that can be expressed as $f(x) = ax^2 + bx + c$, where $a \neq 1$.
2. The graph of a quadratic function is a U-shaped curve called a(n) _____.

Evaluate the given function.

3. $f(x) = x^2 + 8x + 20, f(6)$
4. $f(x) = x^2 + 5x + 40, f(10)$
5. $f(x) = x^2 + 7x - 33, f(-3)$
6. $f(x) = x^2 + 8x + 6, f(-5)$
7. $f(x) = x^2 - 7x + 10, f(5)$
8. $f(x) = x^2 - 10x - 39, f(8)$
9. $g(x) = x^2 + 12x - 45, g(-15)$
10. $g(x) = x^2 - 11x + 22, g(-10)$
11. $g(x) = 3x^2 + 2x - 14, g(7)$
12. $g(x) = 5x^2 - 4x + 8, g(-9)$
13. $f(x) = -2x^2 - 9x + 8, f(-3)$
14. $f(x) = -4x^2 + 16x + 13, f(4)$
15. $h(t) = -16t^2 + 96t + 32, h(4)$
16. $h(t) = -4.9t^2 + 26t + 10, h(2)$
17. $f(x) = x^2 + 4x - 20, f(4a)$
18. $f(x) = x^2 - 3x - 18, f(9a)$
19. $f(x) = x^2 - 7x - 25, f(a + 5)$
20. $f(x) = x^2 + 2x - 17, f(a - 4)$
21. Let $f(x) = x^2 + x - 42$. Find all values x for which $f(x) = 0$.
22. Let $f(x) = x^2 - 7x - 60$. Find all values x for which $f(x) = 0$.
23. Let $f(x) = x^2 - 9x + 20$. Find all values x for which $f(x) = 0$.
24. Let $f(x) = x^2 + 16x + 63$. Find all values x for which $f(x) = 0$.
25. Let $f(x) = x^2 - 23x + 144$. Find all values x for which $f(x) = 18$.
26. Let $f(x) = x^2 + 14x + 14$. Find all values x for which $f(x) = -31$.
27. Let $f(x) = x^2 + 11$. Find all values x for which $f(x) = 60$.
28. Let $f(x) = x^2 + 27$. Find all values x for which $f(x) = 108$.

A **fixed point** for a function $f(x)$ is a value a for which $f(a) = a$. For example, if $f(5) = 5$, $x = 5$ is a fixed point for the function $f(x)$.

Find all fixed points for the following functions by setting the function equal to x and solving the resulting equation for x.

29. $f(x) = x^2 + 7x - 16$
30. $f(x) = x^2 - 5x + 8$
31. $f(x) = x^2 + 14x + 40$
32. $f(x) = x^2 - 9x + 25$

33. A ball is dropped from an airplane flying at an altitude of 400 feet. The ball's height above the ground, in feet, after t seconds is given by the function $h(t) = 400 - 16t^2$, whose graph is shown.

    Use the function and its graph to answer the following questions.

    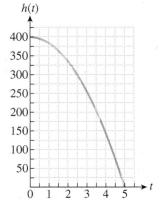

    a) How long will it take for the ball to land on the ground?

    b) How high above the ground is the ball after 2 seconds?

34. A football is kicked up with an initial velocity of 64 feet/second. The football's height above the ground, in feet, after t seconds is given by the function $h(t) = -16t^2 + 64t$, whose graph is shown.

    Use the function and its graph to answer the following questions.

    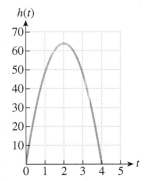

    a) Use the function to determine how high above the ground the football is after 1 second.

b) How long will it take for the football to land on the ground?

c) After how many seconds does the football reach its greatest height?

d) What is the greatest height the football reaches?

35. A man is standing on a cliff 240 feet above a beach. He throws a rock up off the cliff with an initial velocity of 32 feet/second. The rock's height above the beach, in feet, after t seconds is given by the function $h(t) = -16t^2 + 32t + 240$, whose graph is shown.

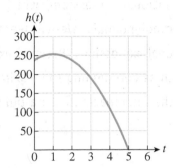

Use the function and its graph to answer the following questions.

a) Use the function to determine how high above the beach the rock is after 3 seconds.

b) How long will it take for the rock to land on the beach?

c) After how many seconds does the rock reach its greatest height above the beach?

d) What is the greatest height above the beach the rock reaches?

36. The average cost in dollars to produce x lawn chairs is given by the function $f(x) = 0.00000016x^2 - 0.0024x + 14.55$, whose graph is shown.

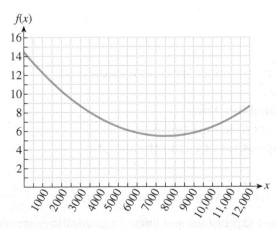

Use the function and its graph to answer the following questions.

a) Use the function to determine the average cost to produce 3000 lawn chairs.

b) What number of lawn chairs corresponds to the lowest average cost of production?

c) What is the lowest average cost that is possible?

37. A teenager starts a company selling personalized coffee mugs. The profit function, in dollars, for producing and selling x mugs is $f(x) = -0.4x^2 + 16x - 70$, whose graph is shown.

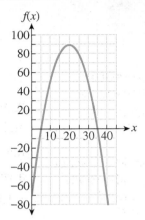

a) What are the start-up costs for the teenager's company?

b) How many mugs must the teenager sell before she breaks even?

c) How many mugs will give the maximum profit?

d) What will the profit be if she sells 25 mugs?

38. A peach farmer must determine how many peaches to thin from his trees. After he thins the peaches, the trees will produce fewer peaches, but they will be larger and of better quality. The expected profit, in dollars, if x percent of the peaches are removed during thinning is given by the function $f(x) = -38x^2 + 2280x + 244,625$, whose graph is shown.

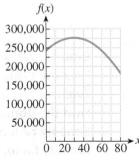

Use the function and its graph to answer the following questions.

a) What will the profit be if the farmer does not thin any peaches?

b) Use the function to determine the profit if 10% of the peaches are thinned.

c) What percent of the peaches must be thinned to produce the maximum profit?

d) What is the maximum potential profit?

Rational Expressions and Equations

In this chapter, we will examine rational expressions, which are fractions whose numerator and denominator are polynomials. We will learn to simplify, add, subtract, multiply, and divide rational expressions. Rational expressions are involved in many applied problems, such as determining the maximum load that a wooden beam can support, finding the illumination from a light source, and solving work-rate problems.

STUDY STRATEGY

Preparing for a Cumulative Exam In this chapter, we will focus on how to prepare for a cumulative exam, such as a final exam. Although some of the strategies are similar to those used to prepare for a chapter test or quiz, there are differences as well.

7.1

Rational Expressions and Functions

OBJECTIVES

1 Evaluate rational expressions.
2 Find the values for which a rational expression is undefined.
3 Evaluate rational functions.
4 Find the domain of a rational function.
5 Simplify rational expressions to lowest terms.
6 Identify factors that are opposites of each other.

A **rational expression** is a quotient of two polynomials, such as $\dfrac{x^2 + 15x + 44}{x^2 - 16}$. A major difference between rational expressions and linear or quadratic expressions is that a rational expression has one or more variables in the denominator. The denominator of a rational expression must not be zero, as division by zero is undefined.

Evaluating Rational Expressions

Objective 1 Evaluate rational expressions. We can evaluate a rational expression for a particular value of the variable just as we evaluated polynomials. We substitute the value for the variable in the expression and then simplify. When simplifying, we evaluate the numerator and denominator separately and then simplify the resulting fraction.

EXAMPLE 1 Evaluate the rational expression $\dfrac{x^2 + 2x - 24}{x^2 - 7x + 12}$ for $x = -5$.

SOLUTION   Begin by substituting -5 for x.

$$\frac{(-5)^2 + 2(-5) - 24}{(-5)^2 - 7(-5) + 12} \qquad \text{Substitute } -5 \text{ for } x.$$

$$= \frac{25 - 10 - 24}{25 + 35 + 12} \qquad \text{Simplify the numerator and denominator separately.}$$

$$= \frac{-9}{72} \qquad \text{Simplify the numerator and denominator.}$$

$$= -\frac{1}{8} \qquad \text{Simplify.}$$

▶ **Quick Check 1**

Evaluate the rational expression $\dfrac{x^2 - 3x - 18}{x^2 - 5x - 6}$ for $x = -4$.

Finding Values for Which a Rational Expression Is Undefined

Objective 2 Find the values for which a rational expression is undefined. Rational expressions are undefined for values of the variable that cause the denominator to equal 0, as division by 0 is undefined. In general, to find the values for which a rational expression is undefined, we set the denominator equal to 0, ignoring the numerator, and solve the resulting equation.

EXAMPLE 2 Find the values for which the rational expression $\dfrac{3}{5x + 4}$ is undefined.

SOLUTION   Begin by setting the denominator, $5x + 4$, equal to 0. Then solve for x.

$$5x + 4 = 0 \qquad \text{Set the denominator equal to 0.}$$
$$5x = -4 \qquad \text{Subtract 4.}$$
$$x = -\frac{4}{5} \qquad \text{Divide by 5.}$$

The expression $\dfrac{3}{5x + 4}$ is undefined for $x = -\dfrac{4}{5}$.

▶ **Quick Check 2**

Find the values for which $\dfrac{3}{2x - 7}$ is undefined.

EXAMPLE 3 Find the values for which $\dfrac{x^2 - 7x + 12}{x^2 + 5x - 36}$ is undefined.

SOLUTION Begin by setting the denominator $x^2 + 5x - 36$ equal to 0, ignoring the numerator. Notice that the resulting equation is quadratic and can be solved by factoring.

$$x^2 + 5x - 36 = 0 \quad \text{Set the denominator equal to 0.}$$
$$(x + 9)(x - 4) = 0 \quad \text{Factor } x^2 + 5x - 36.$$
$$x + 9 = 0 \quad \text{or} \quad x - 4 = 0 \quad \text{Set each factor equal to 0.}$$
$$x = -9 \quad \text{or} \quad x = 4 \quad \text{Solve.}$$

The expression $\dfrac{x^2 - 7x + 12}{x^2 + 5x - 36}$ is undefined when $x = -9$ or $x = 4$.

Quick Check 3

Find the values for which
$\dfrac{x - 4}{x^2 - 8x - 9}$ is undefined.

Rational Functions

A **rational function** $r(x)$ is a function of the form $r(x) = \dfrac{f(x)}{g(x)}$, where $f(x)$ and $g(x)$ are polynomials and $g(x) \neq 0$.

Evaluating Rational Functions

Objective 3 Evaluate rational functions. We begin our investigation of rational functions by learning to evaluate them.

EXAMPLE 4 For $r(x) = \dfrac{x^2 + 13x + 42}{x^2 + 9x + 20}$, find $r(-2)$.

SOLUTION Begin by substituting -2 for x in the function.

$$r(-2) = \frac{(-2)^2 + 13(-2) + 42}{(-2)^2 + 9(-2) + 20} \quad \text{Substitute } -2 \text{ for } x.$$

$$= \frac{4 - 26 + 42}{4 - 18 + 20} \quad \begin{array}{l}\text{Simplify each term in the numerator and} \\ \text{denominator.}\end{array}$$

$$= \frac{20}{6} \quad \text{Simplify the numerator and denominator.}$$

$$= \frac{10}{3} \quad \text{Simplify.}$$

▶ Quick Check 4

For $r(x) = \dfrac{x^2 - 3x - 12}{x^2 + 7x - 15}$, find $r(-6)$.

Finding the Domain of a Rational Function

Objective 4 Find the domain of a rational function. Rational functions differ from linear functions and quadratic functions in that the domain of a rational function is not always the set of real numbers. We have to exclude any value that causes the function to be undefined, namely, any value for which the denominator is equal to 0. Suppose the function $r(x)$ was undefined for $x = 6$. Then the domain of $r(x)$ is the set of all real numbers except 6. This can be expressed in interval notation as $(-\infty, 6) \cup (6, \infty)$, which is the union of the set of all real numbers that are less than 6 with the set of all real numbers that are greater than 6.

EXAMPLE 5 Find the domain of $r(x) = \dfrac{x^2 - 32x + 60}{x^2 - 9x}$.

SOLUTION Begin by setting the denominator equal to 0 and solving for x.

$$
\begin{aligned}
x^2 - 9x &= 0 && \text{Set the denominator equal to 0.} \\
x(x - 9) &= 0 && \text{Factor } x^2 - 9x. \\
x = 0 \quad \text{or} \quad x - 9 &= 0 && \text{Set each factor equal to 0.} \\
x = 0 \quad \text{or} \quad x &= 9 && \text{Solve each equation.}
\end{aligned}
$$

The domain of the function is the set of all real numbers except 0 and 9. In interval notation, this can be written as $(-\infty, 0) \cup (0, 9) \cup (9, \infty)$.

▶ Quick Check 5

Find the domain of $r(x) = \dfrac{x^2 + 11x + 24}{x^2 - 4x - 45}$.

Simplifying Rational Expressions to Lowest Terms

Objective 5 Simplify rational expressions to lowest terms. Rational expressions are often referred to as *algebraic fractions*. As with numerical fractions, we will learn to simplify rational expressions to lowest terms. In later sections, we will learn to add, subtract, multiply, and divide rational expressions.

We simplified a numerical fraction to lowest terms by dividing out factors that were common to the numerator and denominator. For example, consider the fraction $\dfrac{30}{84}$. To simplify this fraction, we could begin by factoring the numerator and denominator.

$$\frac{30}{84} = \frac{2 \cdot 3 \cdot 5}{2 \cdot 2 \cdot 3 \cdot 7}$$

The numerator and denominator have common factors of 2 and 3, which are divided out to simplify the fraction to lowest terms.

$$\frac{\overset{1}{2} \cdot \overset{1}{3} \cdot 5}{\underset{1}{2} \cdot 2 \cdot \underset{1}{3} \cdot 7} = \frac{5}{2 \cdot 7}, \text{ or } \frac{5}{14}$$

┌─ **Simplifying Rational Expressions** ─────────────

To simplify a rational expression to lowest terms, first factor the numerator and denominator completely. Then divide out any common factors in the numerator and denominator.

If P, Q, and R are polynomials, $Q \neq 0$, and $R \neq 0$, then $\dfrac{PR}{QR} = \dfrac{P}{Q}$.

EXAMPLE 6 Simplify the rational expression $\dfrac{10x^3}{8x^5}$. (Assume that $x \neq 0$.)

SOLUTION This rational expression has a numerator and denominator that are monomials. In this case, we can simplify the expression using the properties of exponents developed in Chapter 5.

$$\frac{10x^3}{8x^5} = \frac{\overset{5}{\cancel{10}}x^3}{\underset{4}{\cancel{8}}x^5} \qquad \text{Divide out the common factor 2.}$$

$$= \frac{5x^3}{4x^5} \qquad \text{Simplify.}$$

$$= \frac{5}{4x^2} \qquad \text{Divide the numerator and denominator by } x^3.$$

Quick Check 6

Simplify the rational expression $\dfrac{15x^4}{21x^3}$. (Assume that $x \neq 0$.)

EXAMPLE 7 Simplify $\dfrac{x^2 + 8x - 20}{x^2 - 7x + 10}$. (Assume that the denominator is nonzero.)

SOLUTION The trinomials in the numerator and denominator must be factored before we can simplify this expression. (For a review of factoring techniques, you may refer to Sections 6.1–6.5.)

$$\frac{x^2 + 8x - 20}{x^2 - 7x + 10} = \frac{(x - 2)(x + 10)}{(x - 2)(x - 5)} \qquad \text{Factor the numerator and denominator.}$$

$$= \frac{\overset{1}{\cancel{(x - 2)}}(x + 10)}{\underset{1}{\cancel{(x - 2)}}(x - 5)} \qquad \text{Divide out common factors.}$$

$$= \frac{x + 10}{x - 5} \qquad \text{Simplify.}$$

Quick Check 7

Simplify $\dfrac{x^2 + 10x + 24}{x^2 - 2x - 48}$. (Assume that the denominator is nonzero.)

A WORD OF CAUTION When we are simplifying a rational expression, we must be very careful that we divide out only expressions that are common factors of the numerator and denominator. We cannot *reduce* individual terms in the numerator and denominator as in the following examples.

$$\frac{x + 8}{x - 6} \neq \frac{x + \overset{4}{\cancel{8}}}{x - \underset{3}{\cancel{6}}} \qquad\qquad \frac{x^2 - 25}{x^2 - 36} \neq \frac{\overset{1}{\cancel{x^2}} - 25}{\underset{1}{\cancel{x^2}} - 36}$$

Factor the numerator and denominator completely before attempting to divide out common factors.

EXAMPLE 8 Simplify $\dfrac{x^2 - 8x}{2x^2 - 17x + 8}$. (Assume that the denominator is nonzero.)

SOLUTION The polynomials in the numerator and denominator must be factored before we can simplify this expression. The numerator $x^2 - 8x$ has a common factor of x that must be factored out first.

$$x^2 - 8x = x(x - 8)$$

The denominator $2x^2 - 17x + 8$ is a trinomial with a leading coefficient that is not equal to 1 and can be factored by grouping or by trial-and-error. (For a review of these factoring techniques, you may refer to Section 6.3.)

$$2x^2 - 17x + 8 = (2x - 1)(x - 8)$$

Now we can simplify the rational expression.

$$\frac{x^2 - 8x}{2x^2 - 17x + 8} = \frac{x(x - 8)}{(2x - 1)(x - 8)}$$ Factor the numerator and denominator.

$$= \frac{x(x \overset{1}{\cancel{- 8}})}{(2x - 1)\underset{1}{(\cancel{x - 8})}}$$ Divide out common factors.

$$= \frac{x}{2x - 1}$$ Simplify.

▶ Quick Check 8

Simplify $\dfrac{3x^2 + 16x + 5}{x^2 + 8x + 15}$. (Assume that the denominator is nonzero.)

Identifying Factors in the Numerator and Denominator That Are Opposites

Objective 6 Identify factors that are opposites of each other. Two expressions of the form $a - b$ and $b - a$ are **opposites**. A difference written in the opposite order produces the opposite result. Consider the expressions $a - b$ and $b - a$ when $a = 10$ and $b = 4$. In this case, $a - b = 10 - 4$, or 6, and $b - a = 4 - 10$, or -6. We also can see that $a - b$ and $b - a$ are opposites by noting that their sum, $(a - b) + (b - a)$, is equal to 0.

This is useful to know when simplifying rational expressions. The rational expression $\dfrac{a - b}{b - a}$ simplifies to -1, as any fraction whose numerator is the opposite of its denominator is equal to -1. If a rational expression has a factor in the numerator that is the opposite of a factor in the denominator, these two factors can be divided out to equal -1, as in the next example. We write the -1 in the numerator.

EXAMPLE 9 Simplify $\dfrac{49 - x^2}{x^2 - 12x + 35}$. (Assume that the denominator is nonzero.)

SOLUTION   Begin by factoring the numerator and denominator completely.

$$\frac{49 - x^2}{x^2 - 12x + 35} = \frac{(7 + x)(7 - x)}{(x - 5)(x - 7)}$$ Factor the numerator and denominator.

$$= \frac{(7 + x)\overset{-1}{\cancel{(7 - x)}}}{(x - 5)\underset{1}{\cancel{(x - 7)}}}$$ Divide out the opposite factors.

$$= -\frac{7 + x}{x - 5}$$ Simplify, writing the negative sign in front of the fraction.

Quick Check 9

Simplify $\dfrac{x^2 + 8x - 9}{1 - x^2}$.

(Assume that the denominator

is nonzero.)

A WORD OF CAUTION Two expressions of the form $a + b$ and $b + a$ are not opposites but are equal to each other. Addition in the opposite order produces the same result. When we divide two expressions of the form $a + b$ and $b + a$, the result is 1, not -1.

For example, $\dfrac{x + 2}{2 + x} = 1$.

There is an alternative method for simplifying the expression $\dfrac{49 - x^2}{x^2 - 12x + 35}$ in Example 9. The numerator can be rewritten in standard form as $-x^2 + 49$; then we can factor -1 out of these terms.

$$\frac{49 - x^2}{x^2 - 12x + 35} = \frac{-x^2 + 49}{x^2 - 12x + 35} \qquad \text{Rewrite the numerator in standard form.}$$

$$= \frac{-1(x^2 - 49)}{x^2 - 12x + 35} \qquad \text{Factor } -1 \text{ from the terms in the numerator.}$$

$$= \frac{-1(x + 7)(x - 7)}{(x - 5)(x - 7)} \qquad \text{Factor the numerator and denominator.}$$

$$= \frac{-1(x + 7)\overset{1}{\cancel{(x - 7)}}}{(x - 5)\underset{1}{\cancel{(x - 7)}}} \qquad \text{Divide out common factors.}$$

$$= -\frac{x + 7}{x - 5} \qquad \text{Simplify, writing the negative sign in front of the fraction.}$$

BUILDING YOUR STUDY STRATEGY

Preparing for a Cumulative Review, 1 Study Plan To prepare for a cumulative exam effectively, develop a schedule and study plan. Your schedule should include study time every day, and you should increase the time you spend studying as you get closer to the exam date.

Before you begin to study, find out what material will be covered on the exam by visiting your instructor during office hours. You can find out the topics or chapters that will be emphasized and the format of the exam.

Exercises 7.1

MyMathLab   PRACTICE   WATCH   DOWNLOAD   READ   REVIEW

Vocabulary

1. A(n) _____ is a quotient of two polynomials.

2. Rational expressions are undefined for values of the variable that cause the _____ to equal 0.

3. A(n) _____ $r(x)$ is a function of the form $r(x) = \dfrac{f(x)}{g(x)}$, where $f(x)$ and $g(x)$ are polynomials and $g(x) \neq 0$.

4. The _____ of a rational function excludes all values for which the function is undefined.

5. A rational expression is said to be in _____ if its numerator and denominator do not have any common factors.

6. Two expressions of the form $a - b$ and $b - a$ are _____ .

Evaluate the rational expression for the given value of the variable.

7. $\dfrac{6}{x + 4}$ for $x = 4$

8. $\dfrac{9}{x - 20}$ for $x = 5$

9. $\dfrac{x + 3}{x - 8}$ for $x = -25$

10. $\dfrac{x + 1}{x + 13}$ for $x = -7$

11. $\dfrac{x^2 - 13x - 48}{x^2 - 6x - 12}$ for $x = 3$

12. $\dfrac{x^2 + 5x - 23}{x^2 - 7x + 20}$ for $x = 2$

13. $\dfrac{x^2 - 6x + 15}{x^2 + 14x - 7}$ for $x = -9$

14. $\dfrac{x^2 + 10x - 56}{x - 4}$ for $x = -7$

Find all values of the variable for which the rational expression is undefined.

15. $\dfrac{6}{x - 5}$

16. $\dfrac{x - 2}{x + 6}$

17. $\dfrac{x + 3}{x^2 + x - 56}$

18. $\dfrac{x - 8}{x^2 + 10x + 9}$

19. $\dfrac{x^2 + 7x + 10}{3x^2 + 13x - 10}$

20. $\dfrac{x^2 - 7x + 12}{2x^2 - x - 15}$

21. $\dfrac{6x}{x^2 - 36}$

22. $\dfrac{x - 4}{x^2 - 16x}$

Evaluate the given rational function.

23. $r(x) = \dfrac{20}{x^2 - 5x + 10}, r(-5)$

24. $r(x) = \dfrac{x}{x^2 - 13x - 20}, r(8)$

25. $r(x) = \dfrac{x^2 + 10x + 24}{x^2 - 5x - 66}, r(4)$

26. $r(x) = \dfrac{x^2 - 100}{x^2 + 13x + 30}, r(-3)$

27. $r(x) = \dfrac{x^3 - 7x^2 - 11x + 20}{x^2 + 8x - 20}, r(10)$

28. $r(x) = \dfrac{x^3 + 8x^2 + 17x + 10}{x^3 + 3x^2 - 18x - 40}, r(2)$

Find the domain of the given rational function.

29. $r(x) = \dfrac{x^2 + 18x + 77}{x^2 + 10x}$

30. $r(x) = \dfrac{x^2 - 16x + 60}{x^2 - 9x + 8}$

31. $r(x) = \dfrac{x^2 + 2x - 3}{x^2 - 2x - 15}$

32. $r(x) = \dfrac{x^2 + 7x - 8}{x^2 - 64}$

33. $r(x) = \dfrac{x^2 + 4x - 60}{x^2 + 3x - 18}$

34. $r(x) = \dfrac{x^2 - 13x + 36}{x^2 + 14x + 45}$

Identify the given function as a linear function, a quadratic function, or a rational function.

35. $f(x) = x^2 - 11x + 30$

36. $f(x) = 3x - 8$

37. $f(x) = \dfrac{x^2}{x^3 - 5x^2 + 11x - 35}$

38. $f(x) = \dfrac{x^2 + 3x + 8}{x^2 - 5x - 5}$

39. $f(x) = \dfrac{1}{5}x + \dfrac{4}{9}$

40. $f(x) = -\dfrac{1}{2}x^2 + 3x - \dfrac{1}{7}$

Simplify the given rational expression. (Assume that all denominators are nonzero.)

41. $\dfrac{3x^5}{9x^8}$

42. $\dfrac{10x^7}{12x^{10}}$

43. $\dfrac{x + 5}{x^2 + 11x + 30}$

44. $\dfrac{x^2 - 64}{x - 8}$

45. $\dfrac{x^2 + 11x + 28}{x^2 + 4x - 21}$

46. $\dfrac{x^2 - 7x - 18}{x^2 + 8x + 12}$

47. $\dfrac{x^2 - 4x}{x^2 - 14x + 40}$

48. $\dfrac{x^2 + 10x + 25}{x^2 - 25}$

49. $\dfrac{x^2 - 4x - 45}{x^3 + 125}$

50. $\dfrac{x^2 + 6x - 40}{x^3 + 1000}$

51. $\dfrac{2x^2 + 13x + 6}{2x^2 - 7x - 4}$

52. $\dfrac{4x^2 - 25}{2x^2 - 19x + 35}$

53. $\dfrac{3x^2 - 25x - 50}{x^2 - 3x - 70}$

54. $\dfrac{x^2 + 7x + 12}{4x^2 + 9x - 9}$

55. $\dfrac{3x^2 - 6x - 105}{x^2 - 11x + 28}$

56. $\dfrac{2x^2 + 14x + 20}{5x^2 - 25x - 70}$

Determine whether the two given binomials are or are not opposites.

57. $x + 5$ and $5 + x$

58. $x - 11$ and $11 - x$

59. $14 - x$ and $x - 14$

60. $3x - 2$ and $2x - 3$

61. $2x + 13$ and $-2x - 13$

62. $6x - 7$ and $6x + 7$

Simplify the given rational expression. (Assume that all denominators are nonzero.)

63. $\dfrac{49 - x^2}{x^2 - 12x + 35}$

64. $\dfrac{18 - 2x}{x^2 - 3x - 54}$

65. $\dfrac{8x - x^2}{x^2 - 19x + 88}$

66. $\dfrac{36 - x^2}{x^2 - 12x + 36}$

67. $\dfrac{x^3 - 8}{4 - x^2}$

68. $\dfrac{x^3 - 27}{3 - x}$

Use the given graph of a rational function $r(x)$ to solve the problems that follow.

69.

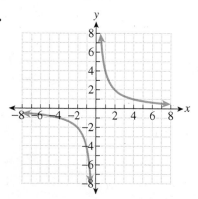

a) Find $r(1)$.   **b)** Find $r(-4)$.

c) Find all values x such that $r(x) = 1$.

70.

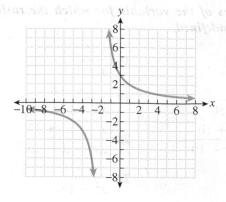

a) Find $r(0)$.

b) Find $r(4)$.

c) Find all values x such that $r(x) = -1$.

Writing in Mathematics

Answer in complete sentences.

71. Explain how to find the values for which a rational expression is undefined.

72. Is the rational expression $\dfrac{(x + 2)(x - 7)}{(x - 5)(x + 2)}$ undefined for the value $x = -2$? Explain your answer

73. Explain how to determine whether two factors are opposites. Use examples.

Quick Review Exercises

Section 7.1

Simplify.

1. $\dfrac{5}{12} + \dfrac{4}{15}$

2. $\dfrac{17}{24} - \dfrac{3}{10}$

3. $\dfrac{14}{45} \cdot \dfrac{165}{308}$

4. $\dfrac{20}{99} \div \dfrac{35}{51}$

7.2

Multiplication and Division of Rational Expressions

OBJECTIVES

1. **Multiply two rational expressions.**
2. **Multiply two rational functions.**
3. **Divide a rational expression by another rational expression.**
4. **Divide a rational function by another rational function.**

Multiplying Rational Expressions

Objective 1 **Multiply two rational expressions.** In this section, we will learn how to multiply and divide rational expressions. Multiplying rational expressions is similar to multiplying numerical fractions. Suppose we need to multiply $\frac{4}{9} \cdot \frac{21}{10}$. Before multiplying, we can divide out factors common to one of the numerators and one of the denominators. For example, the first numerator (4) and the second denominator (10) have a common factor of 2 that can be divided out of each. The second numerator (21) and the first denominator (9) have a common factor of 3 that can be divided out as well.

$$\frac{4}{9} \cdot \frac{21}{10} = \frac{2 \cdot 2}{3 \cdot 3} \cdot \frac{3 \cdot 7}{2 \cdot 5} \qquad \text{Factor each numerator and denominator.}$$

$$= \frac{\overset{1}{2} \cdot 2}{3 \cdot 3} \cdot \frac{\overset{1}{3} \cdot 7}{\underset{1}{2} \cdot 5} \qquad \text{Divide out common factors.}$$

$$= \frac{14}{15} \qquad \text{Multiply remaining factors.}$$

┌─ **Multiplying Rational Expressions** ──────────────────
│
│ $$\frac{A}{B} \cdot \frac{C}{D} = \frac{AC}{BD} \qquad (B \neq 0 \text{ and } D \neq 0)$$
│
└───

To multiply two rational expressions, we will begin by factoring each numerator and denominator completely. After dividing out factors common to a numerator and a denominator, we will express the product of the two rational expressions as a single rational expression, leaving the numerator and denominator in factored form.

EXAMPLE 1 Multiply: $\dfrac{x^2 - 11x + 30}{x^2 + 5x - 24} \cdot \dfrac{x^2 - 9}{x^2 - 2x - 15}$

SOLUTION   Begin by factoring each numerator and denominator. Then divide out common factors.

$$\frac{x^2 - 11x + 30}{x^2 + 5x - 24} \cdot \frac{x^2 - 9}{x^2 - 2x - 15}$$

$$= \frac{(x - 5)(x - 6)}{(x + 8)(x - 3)} \cdot \frac{(x + 3)(x - 3)}{(x - 5)(x + 3)} \qquad \begin{array}{l}\text{Factor the numerators and} \\ \text{denominators completely.}\end{array}$$

$$= \frac{\overset{1}{(x - 5)}(x - 6)}{(x + 8)\underset{1}{(x - 3)}} \cdot \frac{\overset{1}{(x + 3)}\overset{1}{(x - 3)}}{\underset{1}{(x - 5)}\underset{1}{(x + 3)}} \qquad \text{Divide out common factors.}$$

$$= \frac{x - 6}{x + 8} \qquad \text{Simplify.}$$

Quick Check 1

Multiply:
$$\frac{x^2 - 3x - 18}{x^2 - 9x + 20} \cdot \frac{x^2 - 3x - 10}{x^2 + 13x + 30}$$

EXAMPLE 2   Multiply: $\dfrac{x^2 - 10x}{x^2 - 2x - 8} \cdot \dfrac{16 - x^2}{x^2 - 9x - 10}$

SOLUTION   Again, begin by completely factoring both numerators and denominators.

$$\frac{x^2 - 10x}{x^2 - 2x - 8} \cdot \frac{16 - x^2}{x^2 - 9x - 10}$$

$$= \frac{x(x - 10)}{(x + 2)(x - 4)} \cdot \frac{(4 + x)(4 - x)}{(x + 1)(x - 10)} \qquad \text{Factor completely.}$$

$$= \frac{x\cancel{(x - 10)}^{1}}{(x + 2)\cancel{(x - 4)}} \cdot \frac{(4 + x)\cancel{(4 - x)}^{-1}}{(x + 1)\cancel{(x - 10)}_{1}} \qquad \begin{array}{l}\text{Divide out common factors. Notice}\\ \text{that the factors } 4 - x \text{ and } x - 4\\ \text{are opposites.}\end{array}$$

$$= \frac{-x(4 + x)}{(x + 2)(x + 1)} \qquad \text{Multiply remaining factors.}$$

$$= -\frac{x(4 + x)}{(x + 2)(x + 1)} \qquad \begin{array}{l}\text{Write the negative sign in the}\\ \text{numerator in front of the fraction.}\end{array}$$

▶ **Quick Check 2**

Multiply: $\dfrac{36 - x^2}{x^2 + 9x + 14} \cdot \dfrac{x^2 - 7x - 18}{x^2 - 15x + 54}$

Here is a summary of the procedure for multiplying rational expressions.

> **Multiplying Rational Expressions**
> - Completely factor each numerator and each denominator.
> - Divide out factors that are common to a numerator and a denominator, as well as factors in a numerator and denominator that are opposites.
> - Multiply the remaining factors, leaving the numerator and denominator in factored form.

Multiplying Rational Functions

Objective 2 Multiply two rational functions.

EXAMPLE 3   For $f(x) = \dfrac{x^2 - 3x - 18}{x^2 + 8x + 16}$ and $g(x) = \dfrac{x^2 + 3x - 4}{9 - x^2}$, find $f(x) \cdot g(x)$.

SOLUTION   Replace $f(x)$ and $g(x)$ with their formulas and proceed to multiply.

$$f(x) \cdot g(x) = \frac{x^2 - 3x - 18}{x^2 + 8x + 16} \cdot \frac{x^2 + 3x - 4}{9 - x^2} \qquad \begin{array}{l}\text{Replace } f(x) \text{ and } g(x)\\ \text{with their formulas.}\end{array}$$

$$= \frac{(x - 6)(x + 3)}{(x + 4)(x + 4)} \cdot \frac{(x + 4)(x - 1)}{(3 + x)(3 - x)} \qquad \text{Factor completely.}$$

$$= \frac{(x - 6)\cancel{(x + 3)}^{1}}{\cancel{(x + 4)}_{1}(x + 4)} \cdot \frac{\cancel{(x + 4)}^{1}(x - 1)}{\cancel{(3 + x)}_{1}(3 - x)} \qquad \text{Divide out common factors.}$$

$$= \frac{(x - 6)(x - 1)}{(x + 4)(3 - x)} \qquad \text{Multiply remaining factors.}$$

Quick Check 3

For $f(x) = \dfrac{x + 4}{49 - x^2}$ and $g(x) = \dfrac{x^2 - 10x + 21}{x^2 + x - 12}$, find $f(x) \cdot g(x)$.

Dividing a Rational Expression by Another Rational Expression

Objective ③ **Divide a rational expression by another rational expression.**
Dividing a rational expression by another rational expression is similar to dividing a numerical fraction by another numerical fraction. We replace the divisor, which is the rational expression by which we are dividing, with its reciprocal and then multiply.

Dividing Rational Expressions

$$\frac{A}{B} \div \frac{C}{D} = \frac{A}{B} \cdot \frac{D}{C} \qquad (B \neq 0, C \neq 0, \text{ and } D \neq 0)$$

EXAMPLE 4 Divide: $\dfrac{x^2 + 13x + 42}{x^2 + x - 20} \div \dfrac{x^2 + 8x + 12}{x^2 - 4x}$

SOLUTION Begin by inverting the divisor and multiplying. Then factor each numerator and denominator completely.

$$\frac{x^2 + 13x + 42}{x^2 + x - 20} \div \frac{x^2 + 8x + 12}{x^2 - 4x}$$

$$= \frac{x^2 + 13x + 42}{x^2 + x - 20} \cdot \frac{x^2 - 4x}{x^2 + 8x + 12} \qquad \text{Invert the divisor and multiply.}$$

$$= \frac{(x + 6)(x + 7)}{(x + 5)(x - 4)} \cdot \frac{x(x - 4)}{(x + 2)(x + 6)} \qquad \text{Factor completely.}$$

$$= \frac{\overset{1}{\cancel{(x + 6)}}(x + 7)}{(x + 5)\cancel{(x - 4)}} \cdot \frac{x\cancel{(x - 4)}}{(x + 2)\cancel{(x + 6)}} \qquad \text{Divide out common factors.}$$

$$= \frac{x(x + 7)}{(x + 5)(x + 2)} \qquad \text{Multiply remaining factors.}$$

Quick Check 4

Divide:
$$\frac{x^2 - 4}{x^2 - 5x + 4} \div \frac{x^2 - 6x - 16}{x^2 + 3x - 28}$$

EXAMPLE 5 Divide: $\dfrac{x^2 - 14x - 15}{x^2 + 2x - 35} \div \dfrac{x^2 - 1}{5 - x}$

SOLUTION Rewrite the problem as a multiplication problem by inverting the divisor. Then factor each numerator and denominator completely before dividing out common factors. (You may want to factor at the same time you invert the divisor.)

$$\frac{x^2 - 14x - 15}{x^2 + 2x - 35} \div \frac{x^2 - 1}{5 - x}$$

$$= \frac{x^2 - 14x - 15}{x^2 + 2x - 35} \cdot \frac{5 - x}{x^2 - 1} \qquad \text{Invert the divisor and multiply.}$$

$$= \frac{(x - 15)(x + 1)}{(x + 7)(x - 5)} \cdot \frac{5 - x}{(x + 1)(x - 1)} \qquad \text{Factor completely.}$$

$$= \frac{(x - 15)\overset{1}{\cancel{(x + 1)}}}{(x + 7)\cancel{(x - 5)}} \cdot \frac{\overset{-1}{\cancel{5 - x}}}{\cancel{(x + 1)}(x - 1)} \qquad \begin{array}{l}\text{Divide out common factors.}\\ \text{Note that } 5 - x \text{ and } x - 5\\ \text{are opposites.}\end{array}$$

$$= -\frac{x - 15}{(x + 7)(x - 1)} \qquad \text{Multiply remaining factors.}$$

Quick Check 5

Divide:
$$\frac{x^2 - 13x + 36}{x^2 - x - 12} \div \frac{9 - x}{x^2 + 8x + 15}$$

Here is a summary of the procedure for dividing rational expressions.

> **Dividing Rational Expressions**
> - Invert the divisor and change the operation from division to multiplication.
> - Completely factor each numerator and each denominator.
> - Divide out factors that are common to a numerator and a denominator and factors in a numerator and denominator that are opposites.
> - Multiply the remaining factors, leaving the numerator and denominator in factored form.

Dividing Rational Functions

Objective 4 Divide a rational function by another rational function.

EXAMPLE 6 For $f(x) = \dfrac{x^2 - x - 12}{x + 7}$ and $g(x) = x^2 + 3x - 28$, find $f(x) \div g(x)$.

SOLUTION Replace $f(x)$ and $g(x)$ with their formulas and divide. Treat $g(x)$ as a rational function with a denominator of 1. We can see that its reciprocal is $\dfrac{1}{x^2 + 3x - 28}$.

$$
\begin{aligned}
&f(x) \div g(x) \\
&= \frac{x^2 - x - 12}{x + 7} \div x^2 + 3x - 28 && \text{Replace } f(x) \text{ and } g(x) \text{ with their formulas.} \\
&= \frac{x^2 - x - 12}{x + 7} \cdot \frac{1}{x^2 + 3x - 28} && \text{Invert the divisor and multiply.} \\
&= \frac{(x - 4)(x + 3)}{x + 7} \cdot \frac{1}{(x + 7)(x - 4)} && \text{Factor completely.} \\
&= \frac{\overset{1}{\cancel{(x - 4)}}(x + 3)}{x + 7} \cdot \frac{1}{(x + 7)\underset{1}{\cancel{(x - 4)}}} && \text{Divide out common factors.} \\
&= \frac{x + 3}{(x + 7)^2} && \text{Multiply remaining factors.}
\end{aligned}
$$

Quick Check 6

For $f(x) = \dfrac{x^2 - 12x + 36}{x^2 - 11x + 10}$ and $g(x) = x^2 - 8x + 12$, find $f(x) \div g(x)$.

BUILDING YOUR STUDY STRATEGY

Preparing for a Cumulative Exam, 2 Old Quizzes and Tests To prepare for a cumulative exam, begin by reviewing old exams and quizzes. Review and make sure you understand any mistakes you made on them.

Try reworking all of the problems on the exam or quiz. So that you know which topics you need to review and which topics you have under control, you should rework the problems without referring to your notes or textbook. You need to focus on the topics you are struggling with and spend less time on the topics you understand.

Exercises 7.2

Vocabulary

1. To multiply two rational expressions, begin by _____ each numerator and denominator completely.

2. When you are multiplying two rational expressions, _____ out factors common to a numerator and a denominator.

3. When you are multiplying two rational expressions, once the numerator and the denominator do not share any common factors, express the product as a single rational expression, leaving the numerator and denominator in _____ form.

4. When you are dividing by a rational expression, replace the divisor by its _____ and then multiply.

Multiply.

5. $\dfrac{x^2 + 15x + 54}{x^2 + 2x - 15} \cdot \dfrac{x^2 - 25}{x^2 + 4x - 45}$

6. $\dfrac{x^2 + 14x + 49}{x^2 - 10x + 21} \cdot \dfrac{x^2 + 5x - 24}{x^2 - x - 56}$

7. $\dfrac{121 - x^2}{x^2 - 22x + 120} \cdot \dfrac{x^2 - 24x + 140}{x^2 - 18x + 77}$

8. $\dfrac{x^2 - 6x}{x^2 + 2x - 80} \cdot \dfrac{x^2 - 6x - 16}{x^2 - 8x + 12}$

9. $\dfrac{x^2 - 8x - 33}{x^2 - 8x + 16} \cdot \dfrac{2x^2 - 7x - 4}{x^2 + 5x + 6}$

10. $\dfrac{x^2 + 12x + 20}{x^2 - 13x + 40} \cdot \dfrac{x^2 - x - 56}{x^2 + 18x + 80}$

11. $\dfrac{x^2 - 11x}{x^2 + 5x + 4} \cdot \dfrac{x^2 + 10x + 9}{x^2 + 6x}$

12. $\dfrac{x^2 - 6x - 55}{36 - x^2} \cdot \dfrac{x^2 - 4x - 12}{2x^2 + 15x + 25}$

13. $\dfrac{x^3 - 8}{x^2 + x - 42} \cdot \dfrac{x^2 + 9x + 14}{x^2 - 4}$

14. $\dfrac{x^2 + 6x - 55}{x^2 + 6x} \cdot \dfrac{x^3 + 216}{x^2 - 9x + 20}$

15. $\dfrac{9 - x^2}{x^2 - x - 90} \cdot \dfrac{x^2 + 13x + 36}{x^2 + 10x + 21}$

16. $\dfrac{x^2 + 3x - 40}{4x^2 + 29x + 7} \cdot \dfrac{x^2 + 5x - 14}{x^2 + 14x + 48}$

17. $\dfrac{x^2 - 11x + 24}{x^2 - 7x + 12} \cdot \dfrac{x^2 + 4x - 32}{x^2 - 64}$

18. $\dfrac{2x^2 + 24x + 22}{8x^2 + 104x + 320} \cdot \dfrac{x^2 + 3x - 10}{x^2 + 7x + 6}$

19. $\dfrac{2x^2 - x - 36}{x^2 + x - 90} \cdot \dfrac{9x - x^2}{x^2 - 2x - 24}$

20. $\dfrac{x^2 - 3x - 10}{x^2 + 2x} \cdot \dfrac{x^2 + 8x}{x^2 + 3x - 40}$

For the given functions $f(x)$ and $g(x)$, find $f(x) \cdot g(x)$.

21. $f(x) = \dfrac{2}{x - 3}, g(x) = \dfrac{x^2 - 12x + 27}{x^2 - 5x - 36}$

22. $f(x) = \dfrac{x^2 - 9x + 20}{x^2 + x - 2}, g(x) = \dfrac{x^2 + 6x - 16}{x^2 - 25}$

23. $f(x) = \dfrac{x^2 - 13x + 22}{x^2 + 11x - 12}, g(x) = \dfrac{x^2 + 4x - 5}{x^2 - 6x + 8}$

24. $f(x) = x + 7, g(x) = \dfrac{x^2 + 3x - 28}{x^2 + 14x + 49}$

Divide.

25. $\dfrac{x^2 + 3x - 28}{x^2 - 36} \div \dfrac{x^2 - 13x + 36}{x^2 + 11x + 30}$

26. $\dfrac{x^2 - 9x + 8}{x^2 + 6x - 16} \div \dfrac{x^2 + x - 72}{4 - x^2}$

27. $\dfrac{x^2 - 6x + 9}{x^2 - 8x - 9} \div \dfrac{x^2 - 9}{x^2 + 13x + 12}$

28. $\dfrac{x^2 + 5x - 50}{x^2 - 9x + 20} \div \dfrac{x^2 - 4x - 60}{x^2 + 2x - 24}$

29. $\dfrac{2x^2 - 13x + 20}{x^2 + x - 6} \div \dfrac{5x - 2x^2}{x^2 + 14x + 33}$

30. $\dfrac{x^2 - 15x + 56}{x^2 + 11x + 18} \div \dfrac{2x^2 - 15x + 7}{4x^2 - 16x - 48}$

31. $\dfrac{x^2 + 6x - 7}{x^2 + 16x + 55} \div \dfrac{x^2 + 13x + 42}{x^2 + 7x - 44}$

32. $\dfrac{x^2 + 13x + 36}{x^2 - 12x + 32} \div \dfrac{x^2 + 6x - 27}{16 - x^2}$

33. $\dfrac{x^2 - 4x - 5}{x^2 + x - 30} \div \dfrac{x^2 - x - 2}{x^2 + 4x - 12}$

34. $\dfrac{x^2 - 12x + 20}{x^2 + 6x + 5} \div \dfrac{x^2 - 11x + 18}{x^2 - 3x - 40}$

35. $\dfrac{x^2 - 2x - 63}{x^2 - 4x - 21} \div \dfrac{81 - x^2}{x^2 - 7x - 30}$

36. $\dfrac{x^2 - 6x - 27}{x^2 + 3x - 4} \div \dfrac{x^2 - 18x + 81}{2x^2 - 9x + 7}$

37. $\dfrac{x^2 + 10x + 24}{4x^2 - 19x - 5} \div \dfrac{x^2 + 16x + 60}{x^2 + 5x - 50}$

38. $\dfrac{x^2 - 15x + 54}{x^2 - 16x + 48} \div \dfrac{x^2 - 14x + 48}{x^2 - 2x - 8}$

39. $\dfrac{x^2 + 16x + 63}{2x - x^2} \div \dfrac{x^2 + x - 72}{x^2 - 5x + 6}$

40. $\dfrac{x^2 - 12x + 36}{x^2 + 8x + 15} \div \dfrac{6x^2 - x^3}{x^2 + 5x}$

For the given functions $f(x)$ and $g(x)$, find $f(x) \div g(x)$.

41. $f(x) = \dfrac{x^2 + 8x - 9}{x^2 - 10x + 25}, g(x) = x + 9$

42. $f(x) = 2x + 14, g(x) = \dfrac{x^2 + 15x + 56}{x^2 - 10x + 21}$

43. $f(x) = \dfrac{2x^2 - 5x}{x^2 - 1}, g(x) = \dfrac{2x^2 + x - 15}{x^2 - 8x - 9}$

44. $f(x) = \dfrac{x^2 + 4x + 4}{x^2 + 14x + 40}, g(x) = \dfrac{3x^2 + 7x + 2}{5x^2 + 19x - 4}$

Find the missing numerator and denominator.

45. $\dfrac{x^2 - 10x + 16}{x^2 + 4x - 77} \cdot \dfrac{?}{?} = -\dfrac{x^2 - 11x + 24}{x^2 - 5x - 14}$

46. $\dfrac{x^2 + 4x}{x^2 - 81} \cdot \dfrac{?}{?} = \dfrac{x^2 - 6x}{x^2 - 7x - 18}$

47. $\dfrac{x^2 - 10x + 9}{x^2 + 7x} \div \dfrac{?}{?} = \dfrac{x^2 - 13x + 12}{x^2 + 11x + 28}$

48. $\dfrac{x^2 + 12x + 36}{x^2 - 100} \div \dfrac{?}{?} = \dfrac{x^2 - 36}{x^2 + 10x}$

Mixed Practice 49–60

Simplify.

49. $\dfrac{x^2 - 9x - 10}{100 - x^2} \cdot \dfrac{x^2 + 4x - 60}{x^2 - 7x + 6}$

50. $\dfrac{x^2 - x - 12}{81 - x^2} \div \dfrac{x^2 - 3x - 4}{x^2 - 11x + 18}$

51. $\dfrac{3x^2 - 13x - 10}{2x^2 - 17x + 35}$

52. $\dfrac{x^2 - 6x - 27}{x^2 - 9x}$

53. $\dfrac{x^2 - 14x + 24}{x^2 + x - 6} \div \dfrac{x^2 + 2x - 80}{x^2 + 13x + 30}$

54. $\dfrac{x^2 + 9x + 14}{x^2 - 6x + 8} \cdot \dfrac{x^2 + x - 20}{x^2 - x - 6}$

55. $\dfrac{x^2 - 20x + 96}{144 - x^2}$

56. $\dfrac{2x^2 - 9x - 18}{3x^2 - 23x - 8} \div \dfrac{2x^2 + 13x + 15}{x^2 - 3x - 40}$

57. $\dfrac{x^2 + 5x - 84}{x^2 - x - 12} \cdot \dfrac{x^2 + 11x + 24}{2x^2 - 15x + 7}$

58. $\dfrac{x^3 + 27}{x^2 - 7x - 30}$

59. $\dfrac{x^2 + 3x - 54}{x^2 - 2x - 3} \div \dfrac{x^2 + 9x}{x^2 - 7x - 8}$

60. $\dfrac{x^2 + 6x - 16}{x^2 - x - 20} \cdot \dfrac{x^2 + 6x - 55}{x^2 + 17x + 72}$

Writing in Mathematics

Answer in complete sentences.

61. Explain the similarities between dividing numerical fractions and dividing rational expressions. Are there any differences?

Quick Review Exercises

Simplify.

1. $(7x + 8) + (2x - 5)$

2. $(x^2 + 3x - 40) + (x^2 - 9x + 11)$

3. $(8x - 15) - (5x + 27)$

4. $(x^2 - 4x + 6) - (3x^2 - 2x + 35)$

7.3

Addition and Subtraction of Rational Expressions That Have the Same Denominator

OBJECTIVES

1. Add rational expressions that have the same denominator.
2. Subtract rational expressions that have the same denominator.
3. Add or subtract rational expressions that have opposite denominators.

Now that we have learned how to multiply and divide rational expressions, we move on to addition and subtraction. We know from our work with numerical fractions that two fractions must have the same denominator before we can add or subtract them. The same holds true for rational expressions. In this section, we will begin with rational expressions that already have the same denominator. In the next section, we will learn how to add and subtract rational expressions that have different denominators.

Adding Rational Expressions That Have the Same Denominator

Objective 1 Add rational expressions that have the same denominator.
To add fractions that have the same denominator, we add the numerators and place the result over the common denominator. We will follow the same procedure when adding two rational expressions. Of course, we should check that the result is in simplest terms.

> **Adding Rational Expressions That Have the Same Denominator**
>
> $$\frac{A}{C} + \frac{B}{C} = \frac{A + B}{C} \qquad C \neq 0$$

EXAMPLE 1 Add: $\dfrac{7}{x + 3} + \dfrac{5}{x + 3}$

SOLUTION These two fractions have the same denominator, so we add the two numerators and place the result over the common denominator $x + 3$.

$$\frac{7}{x + 3} + \frac{5}{x + 3} = \frac{7 + 5}{x + 3} \qquad \text{Add numerators, placing the sum over the common denominator.}$$

$$= \frac{12}{x + 3} \qquad \text{Simplify the numerator.}$$

Quick Check 1

Add: $\dfrac{9}{2x + 7} + \dfrac{12}{2x + 7}$

The numerator and denominator do not have any common factors, so this is the final result. A common error is to attempt to divide a common factor out of 12 in the numerator and 3 in the denominator, but the number 3 is a term of the denominator, not a factor.

EXAMPLE 2 Add: $\dfrac{6x - 7}{x^2 + 5x + 6} + \dfrac{2x + 23}{x^2 + 5x + 6}$

SOLUTION The two denominators are the same, so we add.

$$\dfrac{6x - 7}{x^2 + 5x + 6} + \dfrac{2x + 23}{x^2 + 5x + 6}$$

$$= \dfrac{(6x - 7) + (2x + 23)}{x^2 + 5x + 6} \qquad \text{Add the numerators.}$$

$$= \dfrac{8x + 16}{x^2 + 5x + 6} \qquad \text{Combine like terms.}$$

$$= \dfrac{8(\overset{1}{\cancel{x + 2}})}{\underset{1}{\cancel{(x + 2)}}(x + 3)} \qquad \begin{array}{l}\text{Factor the numerator and denominator}\\ \text{and divide out the common factor.}\end{array}$$

$$= \dfrac{8}{x + 3} \qquad \text{Simplify.}$$

▶ **Quick Check 2**

Add: $\dfrac{2x + 54}{x^2 + 4x - 32} + \dfrac{3x - 14}{x^2 + 4x - 32}$

EXAMPLE 3 Add: $\dfrac{x^2 - 10x}{x^2 - 5x - 36} + \dfrac{7x - 54}{x^2 - 5x - 36}$

SOLUTION The denominators are the same, so we add the numerators and then simplify.

$$\dfrac{x^2 - 10x}{x^2 - 5x - 36} + \dfrac{7x - 54}{x^2 - 5x - 36}$$

$$= \dfrac{(x^2 - 10x) + (7x - 54)}{x^2 - 5x - 36} \qquad \text{Add numerators.}$$

$$= \dfrac{x^2 - 3x - 54}{x^2 - 5x - 36} \qquad \text{Combine like terms.}$$

$$= \dfrac{(x + 6)(\overset{1}{\cancel{x - 9}})}{(x + 4)\underset{1}{\cancel{(x - 9)}}} \qquad \begin{array}{l}\text{Factor the numerator and denominator}\\ \text{and divide out the common factor.}\end{array}$$

$$= \dfrac{x + 6}{x + 4} \qquad \text{Simplify.}$$

▶ **Quick Check 3**

Add: $\dfrac{x^2 + 6x + 4}{x^2 + 4x - 21} + \dfrac{5x + 24}{x^2 + 4x - 21}$

Subtracting Rational Expressions That Have the Same Denominator

Objective 2 Subtract rational expressions that have the same denominator. Subtracting two rational expressions that have the same denominator is just like adding them except that we subtract the two numerators rather than add them.

Subtracting Rational Expressions That Have the Same Denominator

$$\frac{A}{C} - \frac{B}{C} = \frac{A - B}{C} \qquad C \neq 0$$

EXAMPLE 4   Subtract: $\dfrac{9}{2x + 8} - \dfrac{5}{2x + 8}$

SOLUTION   Because the two fractions have the same denominator, subtract the numerators and place the result over the common denominator.

$$\frac{9}{2x + 8} - \frac{5}{2x + 8} = \frac{4}{2x + 8}$$ Subtract the numerators and place the difference over the denominator.

$$= \frac{\overset{2}{\cancel{4}}}{\underset{1}{\cancel{2}}(x + 4)}$$ Factor the denominator and divide out common factors.

$$= \frac{2}{x + 4}$$ Simplify.

▶ Quick Check 4

Subtract: $\dfrac{25}{6x + 36} - \dfrac{17}{6x + 36}$

EXAMPLE 5   Subtract: $\dfrac{2x^2 - 3x - 9}{7x - x^2} - \dfrac{x^2 + 9x - 44}{7x - x^2}$

SOLUTION   The denominators are the same, so we can subtract these two rational expressions. When the numerator of the second fraction has more than one term, we must remember that we are subtracting the whole numerator, not just the first term. When we subtract the numerators and place the difference over the common denominator, it is a good idea to write each numerator within parentheses. This will remind us to subtract each term in the second numerator.

$$\frac{2x^2 - 3x - 9}{7x - x^2} - \frac{x^2 + 9x - 44}{7x - x^2}$$

$$= \frac{(2x^2 - 3x - 9) - (x^2 + 9x - 44)}{7x - x^2}$$ Subtract the numerators.

$$= \frac{2x^2 - 3x - 9 - x^2 - 9x + 44}{7x - x^2}$$ Change the sign of each term in the second set of parentheses by distributing -1.

$$= \frac{x^2 - 12x + 35}{7x - x^2}$$ Combine like terms.

$$= \frac{\overset{-1}{\cancel{(x - 7)}}(x - 5)}{x\underset{1}{\cancel{(7 - x)}}}$$ Factor the numerator and denominator and divide out the common factor. The -1 results from the fact that $x - 7$ and $7 - x$ are opposites.

$$= -\frac{x - 5}{x}$$ Simplify.

▶ Quick Check 5

Subtract: $\dfrac{3x^2 + 6x - 37}{64 - x^2} - \dfrac{2x^2 + 17x - 61}{64 - x^2}$

A WORD OF CAUTION When subtracting a rational expression that has a numerator containing more than one term, be sure to subtract the *entire* numerator, not just the first term. One way to remember this is by placing the numerators inside parentheses.

Adding or Subtracting Rational Expressions That Have Opposite Denominators

Objective 3 Add or subtract rational expressions that have opposite denominators. Consider the expression $\dfrac{10}{x-2} + \dfrac{3}{2-x}$. Although the two denominators are not the same, they are opposites. We can rewrite the second denominator by factoring out a -1.

$$\dfrac{10}{x-2} + \dfrac{3}{2-x} = \dfrac{10}{x-2} + \dfrac{3}{-1(x-2)} \qquad \text{Factor } -1 \text{ out of the denominator.}$$

$$= \dfrac{10}{x-2} + (-1)\cdot\dfrac{3}{x-2} \qquad \text{Rewrite the second fraction.}$$

$$= \dfrac{10}{x-2} - \dfrac{3}{x-2} \qquad \text{Rewrite as a difference.}$$

$$= \dfrac{7}{x-2} \qquad \text{Subtract.}$$

In general, when adding two rational expressions with opposite denominators, we can rewrite the second denominator as its opposite as long as we change the operation to subtraction.

Similarly, when subtracting two rational expressions with opposite denominators, we can rewrite the second denominator as its opposite by changing the operation to addition.

EXAMPLE 6 Add: $\dfrac{7x}{2x-16} + \dfrac{56}{16-2x}$

SOLUTION The two denominators are opposites, so we may change the second denominator to $2x - 16$ by changing the operation from addition to subtraction.

$$\dfrac{7x}{2x-16} + \dfrac{56}{16-2x}$$

$$= \dfrac{7x}{2x-16} - \dfrac{56}{2x-16} \qquad \begin{array}{l}\text{Rewrite the second denominator as}\\ 2x-16 \text{ by changing the operation}\\ \text{from addition to subtraction.}\end{array}$$

$$= \dfrac{7x-56}{2x-16} \qquad \text{Subtract the numerators.}$$

$$= \dfrac{7\overset{1}{\cancel{(x-8)}}}{2\underset{1}{\cancel{(x-8)}}} \qquad \begin{array}{l}\text{Factor the numerator and denominator}\\ \text{and divide out the common factor.}\end{array}$$

$$= \dfrac{7}{2} \qquad \text{Simplify.}$$

▶ Quick Check 6

Add: $\dfrac{x}{5x-20} + \dfrac{4}{20-5x}$

EXAMPLE 7 Subtract: $\dfrac{x^2 - 4x}{x - 3} - \dfrac{11x - 30}{3 - x}$

SOLUTION These two denominators are opposites, so we begin by rewriting the second rational expression in such a way that the two rational expressions have the same denominator.

$$\frac{x^2 - 4x}{x - 3} - \frac{11x - 30}{3 - x}$$

$$= \frac{x^2 - 4x}{x - 3} + \frac{11x - 30}{x - 3} \qquad \text{Rewrite the second denominator as } x - 3 \text{ by changing the operation from subtraction to addition.}$$

$$= \frac{(x^2 - 4x) + (11x - 30)}{x - 3} \qquad \text{Add the numerators.}$$

$$= \frac{x^2 + 7x - 30}{x - 3} \qquad \text{Combine like terms.}$$

$$= \frac{(x + 10)\cancel{(x - 3)}^{1}}{\cancel{x - 3}_{1}} \qquad \text{Factor the numerator and divide out the common factor.}$$

$$= x + 10 \qquad \text{Simplify.}$$

Quick Check 7
Subtract:
$\dfrac{x^2 - 2x - 11}{x^2 - 16} - \dfrac{7x - 25}{16 - x^2}$

BUILDING YOUR STUDY STRATEGY

Preparing for a Cumulative Exam, 3 Homework and Notes When you are studying a particular topic, look back at your old homework for that topic. If you struggled with a particular type of problem, your homework will reflect that. Your homework should contain some notes about how to do certain problems or how to avoid mistakes.

Your class notes should include examples of the problems in that section of the textbook, as well as pointers from your instructor.

If you have been creating note cards during the semester, they should focus on problems you considered difficult at the time and contain strategies for solving these types of problems.

Exercises 7.3

PRACTICE WATCH DOWNLOAD READ REVIEW

Vocabulary

1. To add fractions that have the same denominator, add the _____ and place the result over the common denominator.

2. To subtract fractions that have the same denominator, _____ the numerators and place the result over the common denominator.

3. When subtracting a rational expression that has a numerator containing more than one term, subtract the entire numerator, not just the _____.

4. When adding two rational expressions that have opposite denominators, you can replace the second denominator with its opposite by changing the addition to _____.

Add.

5. $\dfrac{5}{x + 3} + \dfrac{8}{x + 3}$

6. $\dfrac{9}{x - 6} + \dfrac{7}{x - 6}$

7. $\dfrac{x}{x - 5} + \dfrac{10}{x - 5}$

8. $\dfrac{3x}{4x + 28} + \dfrac{21}{4x + 28}$

9. $\dfrac{x}{x^2 + 5x - 36} + \dfrac{9}{x^2 + 5x - 36}$

10. $\dfrac{2x + 7}{x^2 - 64} + \dfrac{x + 17}{x^2 - 64}$

11. $\dfrac{x^2 - 5x + 9}{x^2 - 8x + 15} + \dfrac{x - 6}{x^2 - 8x + 15}$

12. $\dfrac{x^2 - 13x + 20}{x^2 + 3x - 54} + \dfrac{2x + 10}{x^2 + 3x - 54}$

13. $\dfrac{x^2 + 3x + 11}{x^2 - 2x - 48} + \dfrac{12x + 43}{x^2 - 2x - 48}$

14. $\dfrac{x^2 + 5x + 20}{x^2 - 5x - 14} + \dfrac{5x - 4}{x^2 - 5x - 14}$

15. $\dfrac{x^2 - 16x - 45}{x^2 - 3x - 18} + \dfrac{x^2 - 2x - 27}{x^2 - 3x - 18}$

16. $\dfrac{x^2 - 11x - 34}{x^2 + 16x + 64} + \dfrac{x^2 + 17x - 46}{x^2 + 16x + 64}$

For the given rational functions $f(x)$ and $g(x)$, find $f(x) + g(x)$.

17. $f(x) = \dfrac{3}{x}, g(x) = \dfrac{5}{x}$

18. $f(x) = \dfrac{x}{5x + 30}, g(x) = \dfrac{6}{5x + 30}$

19. $f(x) = \dfrac{x^2 + 3x - 15}{x^2 - 4x - 45}, g(x) = \dfrac{4x + 25}{x^2 - 4x - 45}$

20. $f(x) = \dfrac{2x - 21}{x^2 + 20x + 99}, g(x) = \dfrac{x^2 + 2x - 56}{x^2 + 20x + 99}$

Subtract.

21. $\dfrac{13}{x + 1} - \dfrac{9}{x + 1}$

22. $\dfrac{6}{x - 4} - \dfrac{11}{x - 4}$

23. $\dfrac{x}{x + 7} - \dfrac{7}{x + 7}$

24. $\dfrac{2x}{3x - 15} - \dfrac{10}{3x - 15}$

25. $\dfrac{3x - 7}{x - 8} - \dfrac{x + 9}{x - 8}$

26. $\dfrac{5x - 23}{x - 9} - \dfrac{3x - 5}{x - 9}$

27. $\dfrac{x}{x^2 - 13x + 30} - \dfrac{3}{x^2 - 13x + 30}$

28. $\dfrac{x}{x^2 + 2x - 48} - \dfrac{6}{x^2 + 2x - 48}$

29. $\dfrac{4x - 7}{x^2 - 16} - \dfrac{2x - 15}{x^2 - 16}$

30. $\dfrac{6x + 1}{x^2 - 16x + 63} - \dfrac{3x + 22}{x^2 - 16x + 63}$

31. $\dfrac{x^2 - 2x - 3}{x^2 - x - 72} - \dfrac{5x + 15}{x^2 - x - 72}$

32. $\dfrac{x^2 + 3x + 17}{x^2 - 16} - \dfrac{11x + 1}{x^2 - 16}$

33. $\dfrac{x^2 - 3x + 67}{3x^2 + 17x + 10} - \dfrac{7 - 20x}{3x^2 + 17x + 10}$

34. $\dfrac{5x^2 + 4x}{x^2 - 7x + 6} - \dfrac{x^2 + 5x + 3}{x^2 - 7x + 6}$

35. $\dfrac{(x - 6)(x + 3)}{x^2 - 2x - 15} - \dfrac{9(x - 5)}{x^2 - 2x - 15}$

36. $\dfrac{(2x + 9)(x + 4)}{x^2 - 2x - 24} - \dfrac{(x + 6)(x - 6)}{x^2 - 2x - 24}$

For the given rational functions $f(x)$ and $g(x)$, find $f(x) - g(x)$.

37. $f(x) = \dfrac{12}{x + 8}, g(x) = \dfrac{23}{x + 8}$

38. $f(x) = \dfrac{21}{x - 7}, g(x) = \dfrac{3x}{x - 7}$

39. $f(x) = \dfrac{x^2 + 3x - 5}{x^2 - 11x + 18}, g(x) = \dfrac{8x + 9}{x^2 - 11x + 18}$

40. $f(x) = \dfrac{2x^2 + 10x - 13}{x^2 + 15x + 50}, g(x) = \dfrac{x^2 + 11x + 17}{x^2 + 15x + 50}$

Add or subtract.

41. $\dfrac{2x}{x - 5} + \dfrac{10}{5 - x}$

42. $\dfrac{5x}{2x - 14} + \dfrac{35}{14 - 2x}$

43. $\dfrac{x^2 + 8x}{x - 1} - \dfrac{2x - 11}{1 - x}$

44. $\dfrac{x^2 - 8x - 10}{x - 3} + \dfrac{x - 28}{3 - x}$

45. $\dfrac{x^2 - 3x - 9}{x - 9} + \dfrac{x^2 - 7x + 27}{9 - x}$

46. $\dfrac{3x^2 - 14x - 45}{x - 6} + \dfrac{-2x^2 + 14x + 9}{6 - x}$

Mixed Practice, 47–66

Simplify.

47. $\dfrac{x^2 - 3x + 5}{2x - 20} + \dfrac{4x + 35}{20 - 2x}$

48. $\dfrac{x^2 + 11x + 24}{x^2 - 12x + 32} \cdot \dfrac{x^2 - 4x}{x^3 + 27}$

49. $\dfrac{x^2 - 14x + 49}{x^2 + x - 30} \div \dfrac{3x^2 - 9x - 84}{x^2 - 6x + 5}$

50. $\dfrac{x^2 - 7x - 50}{x - 8} - \dfrac{x^2 + 3x - 46}{8 - x}$

51. $\dfrac{x^2 + 2x - 360}{x^2 + 30x + 200}$

52. $\dfrac{4x^2 - 6x + 3}{x^2 + 17x + 70} - \dfrac{3x^2 - 6x + 52}{x^2 + 17x + 70}$

53. $\dfrac{x^2 - 3x + 45}{x^2 - 81} + \dfrac{x^2 + 29x + 27}{x^2 - 81}$

54. $\dfrac{9x - x^2}{x^2 - 4x - 32} \div \dfrac{x^2 - 16x + 63}{x^2 + 11x + 28}$

55. $\dfrac{121 - x^2}{x^2 - 3x - 4} \cdot \dfrac{x^2 + 4x + 3}{x^2 - 3x - 88}$

56. $\dfrac{10}{5x - 25} + \dfrac{2x}{25 - 5x}$

57. $\dfrac{2x^2 - 15x + 39}{x^2 + 3x - 4} + \dfrac{x^2 - 18x - 9}{x^2 + 3x - 4}$

58. $\dfrac{2x^2 - 3x + 20}{x^2 + 6x - 55} - \dfrac{x^2 + 9x - 15}{x^2 + 6x - 55}$

59. $\dfrac{6x}{3x - 2} - \dfrac{4}{2 - 3x}$

60. $\dfrac{x^2 + 20x + 45}{x^2 + 15x + 56} - \dfrac{3x - 27}{x^2 + 15x + 56}$

61. $\dfrac{5x^2 + 3x - 13}{x^2 - 8x - 9} - \dfrac{4x^2 - 7x - 22}{x^2 - 8x - 9}$

62. $\dfrac{x^2 + 3x - 28}{2x^2 + 15x + 28} \cdot \dfrac{3x^2 + 16x + 16}{x^2 + 17x + 70}$

63. $\dfrac{x^2 + x - 90}{3x^2 + 2x - 16} \div \dfrac{x^2 - 9x}{3x^2 + 17x + 24}$

64. $\dfrac{5x^2 - 4x - 9}{x^2 - 6x - 7}$

65. $\dfrac{2x^2 + 5x + 20}{x^2 + 5x + 6} + \dfrac{3x^2 - 7x - 4}{x^2 + 5x + 6} - \dfrac{4x^2 - 2x + 25}{x^2 + 5x + 6}$

66. $\dfrac{x^2 + 3x - 7}{x^2 - 2x - 8} - \dfrac{x^2 + 5x - 9}{x^2 - 2x - 8} + \dfrac{x^2 - 6x + 14}{x^2 - 2x - 8}$

Find the missing numerator.

67. $\dfrac{?}{x + 6} + \dfrac{18}{x + 6} = 3$

68. $\dfrac{x^2 + 5x}{x - 2} - \dfrac{?}{x - 2} = x + 7$

69. $\dfrac{x^2 + 7x + 17}{(x + 8)(x + 5)} + \dfrac{?}{(x + 8)(x + 5)} = \dfrac{x + 3}{x + 5}$

70. $\dfrac{x^2 - 5x - 24}{(x + 2)(x - 4)} - \dfrac{?}{(x + 2)(x - 4)} = \dfrac{x + 2}{x - 4}$

✏ Writing in Mathematics

Answer in complete sentences.

71. Explain how to determine whether two rational expressions have opposite denominators.

72. Explain why it is a good idea to use parentheses when subtracting a rational expression that has more than one term in the numerator.

7.4

Addition and Subtraction of Rational Expressions That Have Different Denominators

OBJECTIVES

1. Find the least common denominator (LCD) of two or more rational expressions.
2. Add or subtract rational expressions that have different denominators.

The Least Common Denominator of Two or More Rational Expressions

Objective 1 Find the least common denominator (LCD) of two or more rational expressions. If two numerical fractions do not have the same denominator, we cannot add or subtract the fractions until we rewrite them as equivalent fractions with a common denominator. The same holds true for rational expressions that have different denominators. We will begin this section by learning how to find the **least common denominator (LCD)** for two or more rational expressions. Then we will learn how to add or subtract rational expressions that have different denominators.

> **Finding the LCD of Two Rational Expressions**
>
> Begin by completely factoring each denominator; then identify each expression that is a factor of one or both denominators. The LCD is the product of these factors.

If an expression is a repeated factor in one or more of the denominators, we repeat it as a factor in the LCD as well. The exponent used for this factor is the greatest power to which the factor is raised in any one denominator.

EXAMPLE 1   Find the LCD of $\dfrac{7}{24a^3b}$ and $\dfrac{9}{16a}$.

SOLUTION   We begin with the coefficients 24 and 16. The smallest number into which both divide evenly is 48. Moving on to variable factors in the denominator, we see that the variables a and b are factors of one or both denominators. Note that the variable a is raised to the third power in the first denominator; so the LCD must contain a factor of a^3. The LCD is $48a^3b$.

Quick Check 1

Find the LCD of $\dfrac{10}{9r^2s^3}$ and $\dfrac{1}{12rs^6}$.

EXAMPLE 2   Find the LCD of $\dfrac{8}{x^2 - 4x + 3}$ and $\dfrac{9}{x^2 - 9}$.

SOLUTION   Begin by factoring each denominator.

$$\frac{8}{x^2 - 4x + 3} = \frac{8}{(x - 1)(x - 3)} \qquad \frac{9}{x^2 - 9} = \frac{9}{(x + 3)(x - 3)}$$

The factors in the denominators are $x - 1$, $x - 3$, and $x + 3$. Because no expression is repeated as a factor in any one denominator, the LCD is $(x - 1)(x - 3)(x + 3)$.

Quick Check 2

Find the LCD of $\dfrac{10}{x^2 - 13x + 40}$ and $\dfrac{3}{x^2 - 4x - 32}$.

EXAMPLE 3   Find the LCD of $\dfrac{2}{x^2 - 2x - 35}$ and $\dfrac{x}{x^2 + 10x + 25}$.

SOLUTION   Again, begin by factoring each denominator.

$$\frac{2}{x^2 - 2x - 35} = \frac{2}{(x - 7)(x + 5)} \qquad \frac{x}{x^2 + 10x + 25} = \frac{x}{(x + 5)(x + 5)}$$

The two expressions that are factors are $x - 7$ and $x + 5$; the factor $x + 5$ is repeated twice in the second denominator. So the LCD also must have $x + 5$ as a factor twice. The LCD is $(x - 7)(x + 5)(x + 5)$, or $(x - 7)(x + 5)^2$.

Quick Check 3

Find the LCD of $\dfrac{x + 8}{x^2 - 81}$ and $\dfrac{x - 7}{x^2 + 18x + 81}$.

Adding or Subtracting Rational Expressions That Have Different Denominators

Objective 2 Add or subtract rational expressions that have different denominators. To add or subtract two rational expressions that do not have the same denominator, we begin by finding the LCD. We then convert each rational expression to an equivalent rational expression that has the LCD as its denominator. We can then add or subtract as we did in the previous section. As always, we should attempt to simplify the resulting rational expression.

EXAMPLE 4   Add: $\dfrac{2a}{3} + \dfrac{3a}{7}$

SOLUTION   The LCD of these two fractions is 21. We will rewrite each fraction as an equivalent fraction whose denominator is 21. Because $\frac{7}{7} = 1$, multiplying the first fraction by $\frac{7}{7}$ will produce an equivalent fraction whose denominator is 21. In a similar fashion, we multiply the second fraction by $\frac{3}{3}$. Once both fractions have the same denominator, we add the numerators and write the sum above the common denominator.

$$\frac{2a}{3} + \frac{3a}{7} = \frac{2a}{3} \cdot \frac{7}{7} + \frac{3a}{7} \cdot \frac{3}{3} \qquad \text{Multiply the first fraction by } \tfrac{7}{7} \text{ and the second fraction by } \tfrac{3}{3} \text{ to rewrite each fraction with a denominator of 21.}$$

$$= \frac{14a}{21} + \frac{9a}{21} \qquad \text{Multiply numerators and denominators.}$$

$$= \frac{23a}{21} \qquad \text{Add the numerators and place the sum over the common denominator.}$$

EXAMPLE 5   Add: $\dfrac{8}{x + 6} + \dfrac{2}{x - 7}$

SOLUTION   The two denominators are not the same, so we begin by finding the LCD for these two rational expressions. Each denominator has a single factor, and the LCD is the product of these two denominators. The LCD is $(x + 6)(x - 7)$. We will multiply $\dfrac{8}{x + 6}$ by $\dfrac{x - 7}{x - 7}$ to write it as an equivalent fraction whose denominator is the LCD. We need to multiply $\dfrac{2}{x - 7}$ by $\dfrac{x + 6}{x + 6}$ to write it as an equivalent fraction whose denominator is the LCD.

$$\frac{8}{x + 6} + \frac{2}{x - 7}$$

$$= \frac{8}{x + 6} \cdot \frac{x - 7}{x - 7} + \frac{2}{x - 7} \cdot \frac{x + 6}{x + 6} \qquad \text{Multiply to rewrite each expression as an equivalent rational expression that has the LCD as its denominator.}$$

$$= \frac{8x - 56}{(x + 6)(x - 7)} + \frac{2x + 12}{(x - 7)(x + 6)} \qquad \text{Distribute in each numerator, but do not distribute in the denominators.}$$

$$= \frac{(8x - 56) + (2x + 12)}{(x + 6)(x - 7)} \qquad \text{Add the numerators, writing the sum over the common denominator.}$$

$$= \frac{10x - 44}{(x + 6)(x - 7)} \qquad \text{Combine like terms.}$$

$$= \frac{2(5x - 22)}{(x + 6)(x - 7)} \qquad \text{Factor the numerator.}$$

Quick Check 4
Add: $\dfrac{5}{x - 2} + \dfrac{6}{x + 6}$

Because the numerator and denominator do not have any common factors, this rational expression cannot be simplified any further.

A WORD OF CAUTION When we add two rational expressions, we cannot simply add the two numerators and place their sum over the sum of the two denominators.

$$\frac{8}{x+6} + \frac{2}{x-7} \neq \frac{8+2}{(x+6)+(x-7)}$$

We must first find a common denominator and rewrite each rational expression as an equivalent expression whose denominator is equal to the common denominator.

When adding or subtracting rational expressions, we simplify the numerator, but leave the denominator in factored form. After we simplify the numerator, we factor, if possible, and check the denominator for common factors that can be divided out.

EXAMPLE 6 Subtract: $\dfrac{x}{x^2 + 8x + 15} - \dfrac{5}{x^2 + 12x + 35}$

SOLUTION In this example, we must factor each denominator to find the LCD.

$$\frac{x}{x^2 + 8x + 15} - \frac{5}{x^2 + 12x + 35}$$

$$= \frac{x}{(x+3)(x+5)} - \frac{5}{(x+5)(x+7)} \qquad \text{Factor each denominator. The LCD is } (x+3)(x+5)(x+7).$$

$$= \frac{x}{(x+3)(x+5)} \cdot \frac{x+7}{x+7} - \frac{5}{(x+5)(x+7)} \cdot \frac{x+3}{x+3} \qquad \text{Multiply to rewrite each expression as an equivalent rational expression that has the LCD as its denominator.}$$

$$= \frac{x^2 + 7x}{(x+3)(x+5)(x+7)} - \frac{5x + 15}{(x+5)(x+7)(x+3)} \qquad \text{Distribute in each numerator.}$$

$$= \frac{(x^2 + 7x) - (5x + 15)}{(x+3)(x+5)(x+7)} \qquad \text{Subtract the numerators, writing the difference over the LCD.}$$

$$= \frac{x^2 + 7x - 5x - 15}{(x+3)(x+5)(x+7)} \qquad \text{Distribute.}$$

$$= \frac{x^2 + 2x - 15}{(x+3)(x+5)(x+7)} \qquad \text{Combine like terms.}$$

$$= \frac{\overset{1}{\cancel{(x+5)}}(x-3)}{(x+3)\underset{1}{\cancel{(x+5)}}(x+7)} \qquad \text{Factor the numerator and divide out the common factor.}$$

$$= \frac{x-3}{(x+3)(x+7)} \qquad \text{Simplify.}$$

We must be careful to subtract the entire second numerator, not just the first term. In other words, the subtraction must change the sign of each term in the second numerator before we combine like terms. Using parentheses when subtracting the two numerators will help us remember to do this.

▶ Quick Check 5

Add: $\dfrac{x}{x^2 - 6x + 5} + \dfrac{1}{x^2 + 2x - 3}$

EXAMPLE 7 Subtract: $\dfrac{x-6}{x^2-1} - \dfrac{5}{x^2-4x+3}$

SOLUTION   Notice that the first numerator contains a binomial. We must be careful when multiplying to create equivalent rational expressions with the LCD as their denominators. We begin by factoring each denominator to find the LCD.

$$\dfrac{x-6}{x^2-1} - \dfrac{5}{x^2-4x+3}$$

$= \dfrac{x-6}{(x+1)(x-1)} - \dfrac{5}{(x-3)(x-1)}$ Factor each denominator. The LCD is $(x+1)(x-1)(x-3)$.

$= \dfrac{x-6}{(x+1)(x-1)} \cdot \dfrac{x-3}{x-3} - \dfrac{5}{(x-3)(x-1)} \cdot \dfrac{x+1}{x+1}$ Multiply to rewrite each expression as an equivalent rational expression with the LCD as its denominator.

$= \dfrac{x^2-9x+18}{(x+1)(x-1)(x-3)} - \dfrac{5x+5}{(x-3)(x-1)(x+1)}$ Distribute in each numerator.

$= \dfrac{(x^2-9x+18) - (5x+5)}{(x+1)(x-1)(x-3)}$ Subtract the numerators, writing the difference over the LCD.

$= \dfrac{x^2-9x+18-5x-5}{(x+1)(x-1)(x-3)}$ Distribute.

$= \dfrac{x^2-14x+13}{(x+1)(x-1)(x-3)}$ Combine like terms.

$= \dfrac{\overset{1}{\cancel{(x-1)}}(x-13)}{(x+1)\underset{1}{\cancel{(x-1)}}(x-3)}$ Factor the numerator and divide out the common factor.

$= \dfrac{x-13}{(x+1)(x-3)}$ Simplify.

▶ Quick Check 6

Add: $\dfrac{x+5}{x^2+8x+12} + \dfrac{x+9}{x^2-36}$

BUILDING YOUR STUDY STRATEGY

Preparing for a Cumulative Exam, 4 Problems from Your Instructor Some of the most valuable materials for preparing for a cumulative exam are the materials provided by your instructor, such as a review sheet for the final, a practice final, or a list of problems to review from the text. If your instructor believes that these problems are important enough for you to review, they are important enough to appear on the cumulative exam.

Your performance on these problems will show you which topics you understand and which topics require further study.

If you are having difficulty with a certain problem, on a note card, write down the steps to solve that problem. Review your note cards for a short period each day before the exam. This will help you understand how to solve the problem, and it increases your chance of solving a similar problem on the exam.

Exercises 7.4

Vocabulary

1. The _____ of two rational expressions is an expression that is a product of each factor of the two denominators.

2. To add two rational expressions that have different denominators, begin by converting each rational expression to a(n) _____ rational expression that has the LCD as its denominator.

Find the LCD of the given rational expressions.

3. $\dfrac{5}{2a}, \dfrac{1}{3a}$

4. $\dfrac{9}{8x^2}, \dfrac{7}{6x^3}$

5. $\dfrac{6}{x-9}, \dfrac{8}{x+5}$

6. $\dfrac{x}{x-7}, \dfrac{x+2}{2x+3}$

7. $\dfrac{2}{x^2-9}, \dfrac{x+7}{x^2-9x+18}$

8. $\dfrac{x-6}{x^2-3x-28}, \dfrac{x+1}{x^2-x-20}$

9. $\dfrac{3}{x^2+7x+10}, \dfrac{x-1}{x^2+4x+4}$

10. $\dfrac{x-10}{x^2-12x+36}, \dfrac{8}{x^2-36}$

Add or subtract.

11. $\dfrac{3x}{8} + \dfrac{5x}{12}$

12. $\dfrac{8x}{15} - \dfrac{7x}{20}$

13. $\dfrac{9}{5n} - \dfrac{7}{4n}$

14. $\dfrac{7}{10a} + \dfrac{9}{14a}$

15. $\dfrac{10}{m^7 n^2} + \dfrac{13}{m^5 n^3}$

16. $\dfrac{7}{s^4 t^3} - \dfrac{2}{t^8}$

17. $\dfrac{5}{x+2} + \dfrac{3}{x+4}$

18. $\dfrac{7}{x+5} + \dfrac{2}{x-8}$

19. $\dfrac{10}{x+3} - \dfrac{4}{x-3}$

20. $\dfrac{6}{x} - \dfrac{9}{x-4}$

21. $\dfrac{3}{x^2+7x+10} + \dfrac{8}{x^2-x-6}$

22. $\dfrac{10}{x^2-16x+60} + \dfrac{7}{x^2-100}$

23. $\dfrac{1}{x^2-5x-6} - \dfrac{5}{x^2+8x+7}$

24. $\dfrac{3}{x^2-6x-16} - \dfrac{2}{x^2-2x-48}$

25. $\dfrac{5}{x^2-15x+50} + \dfrac{9}{x^2-x-20}$

26. $\dfrac{4}{x^2+12x} - \dfrac{2}{x^2+18x+72}$

27. $\dfrac{3}{x^2-13x+40} - \dfrac{4}{x^2-12x+32}$

28. $\dfrac{2}{x^2+x-6} - \dfrac{4}{x^2-4x-21}$

29. $\dfrac{5}{2x^2+3x-2} + \dfrac{7}{2x^2-9x+4}$

30. $\dfrac{7}{2x^2-15x-27} - \dfrac{3}{2x^2-3x-9}$

31. $\dfrac{x+9}{x^2+8x+15} - \dfrac{2}{x^2+9x+20}$

32. $\dfrac{x-3}{x^2-12x+35} + \dfrac{7}{x^2-3x-10}$

33. $\dfrac{x-3}{x^2-x-20} + \dfrac{6}{x^2-2x-24}$

34. $\dfrac{x-10}{x^2-2x-3} - \dfrac{3}{x^2-9x+18}$

35. $\dfrac{x+14}{x^2+5x-50} - \dfrac{8}{x^2+15x+50}$

36. $\dfrac{x-6}{x^2-16} - \dfrac{2}{x^2+8x+16}$

37. $\dfrac{x-9}{x^2-49} + \dfrac{1}{x^2-7x}$

38. $\dfrac{x+7}{x^2-7x} + \dfrac{2}{x^2-15x+56}$

39. $\dfrac{3}{x^2+11x+28} + \dfrac{x-4}{x^2-x-56}$

40. $\dfrac{2}{x^2+4x-12} + \dfrac{x+3}{x^2-36}$

41. $\dfrac{x+1}{x^2+2x-8} + \dfrac{x+3}{x^2+10x+24}$

42. $\dfrac{x+5}{x^2-8x-9} + \dfrac{x-4}{x^2-4x-5}$

43. $\dfrac{x+9}{2x^2-9x-18} - \dfrac{x-4}{2x^2+17x+21}$

44. $\dfrac{x+2}{x^2+9x+20} - \dfrac{x+8}{x^2+11x+30}$

Mixed Practice 45–60

Simplify.

45. $\dfrac{9}{x^2-11x+28} + \dfrac{3}{x^2-7x+12}$

46. $\dfrac{x-6}{x^2+9x+8} + \dfrac{2}{x^2+4x+3}$

47. $\dfrac{x+10}{x^2+10x+16} + \dfrac{x+7}{x^2+13x+40}$

48. $\dfrac{x^2+11x+24}{x^2-14x+40} \div \dfrac{x^2-5x-24}{100-x^2}$

49. $\dfrac{x^2-2x-24}{x^2+9x+20} \cdot \dfrac{2x^2+x-45}{x^2-7x+6}$

50. $\dfrac{4}{x^2-6x-27} - \dfrac{2}{x^2-12x+27}$

51. $\dfrac{x+2}{x^2+4x-32} - \dfrac{1}{x^2+18x+80}$

52. $\dfrac{x^2+17x+60}{x^2-8x-65}$

53. $\dfrac{3x+17}{x^2-5x} - \dfrac{x^2-15x+18}{5x-x^2}$

54. $\dfrac{x^2+10x+17}{x^2-13x+36} - \dfrac{7x+125}{x^2-13x+36}$

55. $\dfrac{2x^2+19x+42}{36-x^2}$

56. $\dfrac{x-2}{x^2-4x-32} - \dfrac{x+3}{x^2+6x+8}$

57. $\dfrac{3x^2+2x-8}{x^2-9x} \div \dfrac{x^3+8}{x^2-16x+63}$

58. $\dfrac{x^2-15x}{x^2+2x-48} + \dfrac{5x+24}{x^2+2x-48}$

59. $\dfrac{x^2-7x+23}{x^2-81} + \dfrac{12x-67}{81-x^2}$

60. $\dfrac{x^2-7x-18}{x^2-3x-40} \cdot \dfrac{8x-x^2}{x^2-15x+54}$

✏️ Writing in Mathematics

Answer in complete sentences.

61. Explain how to find the LCD of two rational expressions. Use an example to illustrate the process.

62. Here is a student's solution to a problem on an exam. Describe the student's error and provide the correct solution. Assuming that the problem was worth 10 points, how many points would you give to the student for this solution? Explain your reasoning.

$$\frac{5}{(x+3)(x+2)} + \frac{7}{(x+3)(x+6)}$$

$$= \frac{5}{(x+3)(x+2)} \cdot \frac{x+6}{x+6} + \frac{7}{(x+3)(x+6)} \cdot \frac{x+2}{x+2}$$

$$= \frac{5\cancel{(x+6)}^{1} + 7\cancel{(x+2)}^{1}}{(x+3)\cancel{(x+2)}_{1}\cancel{(x+6)}_{1}}$$

$$= \frac{12}{x+3}$$

63. *Solutions Manual* Write a solutions manual page for the following problem:

$$Add: \frac{x+6}{x^2+9x+20} + \frac{4}{x^2+6x+8}$$

OBJECTIVES

1 Simplify complex numerical fractions.
2 Simplify complex fractions containing variables.

Complex Fractions

A **complex fraction** is a fraction or rational expression containing one or more fractions in its numerator or denominator. Here are some examples.

$$\frac{\dfrac{1}{2} + \dfrac{5}{3}}{\dfrac{10}{3} - \dfrac{7}{4}} \qquad \frac{x + 5}{1 - \dfrac{5}{x}} \qquad \frac{\dfrac{1}{2} + \dfrac{1}{x}}{\dfrac{1}{4} - \dfrac{1}{x^2}} \qquad \frac{1 + \dfrac{3}{x} - \dfrac{28}{x^2}}{1 + \dfrac{7}{x}}$$

Objective 1 Simplify complex numerical fractions. To simplify a complex fraction, we must rewrite it so that its numerator and denominator do not contain fractions. We can do this by finding the LCD of all fractions in the complex fraction and then multiplying the numerator and denominator by this LCD. This will clear the fractions in the complex fraction. We finish by simplifying the resulting rational expression, if possible.

We begin with a complex fraction made up of numerical fractions.

EXAMPLE 1 Simplify the complex fraction $\dfrac{1 + \dfrac{4}{3}}{\dfrac{2}{3} + \dfrac{11}{4}}$.

SOLUTION The LCD of the three denominators (3, 3, and 4) is 12; so we begin by multiplying the complex fraction by $\frac{12}{12}$. Notice that when we multiply by $\frac{12}{12}$, we are really multiplying by 1, which does not change the value of the original expression.

$$\frac{1 + \dfrac{4}{3}}{\dfrac{2}{3} + \dfrac{11}{4}} = \frac{12}{12} \cdot \frac{1 + \dfrac{4}{3}}{\dfrac{2}{3} + \dfrac{11}{4}} \qquad \text{Multiply the numerator and denominator by the LCD.}$$

$$= \frac{12 \cdot 1 + \overset{4}{\cancel{12}} \cdot \dfrac{4}{\cancel{3}}}{\overset{4}{\cancel{12}} \cdot \dfrac{2}{\cancel{3}} + \overset{3}{\cancel{12}} \cdot \dfrac{11}{\cancel{4}}} \qquad \text{Distribute and divide out common factors.}$$

$$= \frac{12 + 16}{8 + 33} \qquad \text{Multiply.}$$

$$= \frac{28}{41} \qquad \text{Simplify the numerator and denominator.}$$

There is another method for simplifying complex fractions. We can rewrite the numerator as a single fraction by adding $1 + \frac{4}{3}$, which equals $\frac{7}{3}$.

$$1 + \frac{4}{3} = \frac{3}{3} + \frac{4}{3} = \frac{7}{3}$$

We also can rewrite the denominator as a single fraction by adding $\frac{2}{3} + \frac{11}{4}$, which equals $\frac{41}{12}$.

$$\frac{2}{3} + \frac{11}{4} = \frac{8}{12} + \frac{33}{12} = \frac{41}{12}$$

Once the numerator and denominator are single fractions, we can rewrite $\dfrac{\frac{7}{3}}{\frac{41}{12}}$ as a division problem $\frac{7}{3} \div \frac{41}{12}$ and simplify from there. This method produces the same result of $\frac{28}{41}$.

$$\frac{7}{3} \div \frac{41}{12} = \frac{7}{\underset{1}{3}} \cdot \frac{\overset{4}{12}}{41} = \frac{28}{41}$$

In most of the remaining examples, we will use the LCD method, as the technique is somewhat similar to the technique used to solve rational equations in the next section.

Simplifying Complex Fractions Containing Variables

Objective ② **Simplify complex fractions containing variables.**

EXAMPLE 2 Simplify $\dfrac{1 - \dfrac{9}{x^2}}{1 + \dfrac{3}{x}}$.

SOLUTION   The LCD for the two simple fractions with denominators x and x^2 is x^2; so we will begin by multiplying the complex fraction by $\dfrac{x^2}{x^2}$. Then once we have cleared the fractions, resulting in a rational expression, we simplify the rational expression by factoring and dividing out common factors.

$$\frac{1 - \dfrac{9}{x^2}}{1 + \dfrac{3}{x}} = \frac{x^2}{x^2} \cdot \frac{1 - \dfrac{9}{x^2}}{1 + \dfrac{3}{x}} \qquad \text{Multiply the numerator and denominator by the LCD.}$$

$$= \frac{x^2 \cdot 1 - \overset{1}{x^2} \cdot \dfrac{9}{x^2}}{x^2 \cdot 1 + \overset{x}{x^2} \cdot \dfrac{3}{x}} \qquad \text{Distribute and divide out common factors, clearing the fractions.}$$

$$= \frac{x^2 - 9}{x^2 + 3x} \qquad \text{Multiply.}$$

$$= \frac{\overset{1}{(x + 3)}(x - 3)}{x\underset{1}{(x + 3)}} \qquad \text{Factor the numerator and denominator and divide out the common factor.}$$

$$= \frac{x - 3}{x} \qquad \text{Simplify.}$$

Quick Check 1

Simplify the complex fraction $\dfrac{\dfrac{2}{5} + \dfrac{3}{8}}{\dfrac{1}{4} + \dfrac{7}{10}}$.

Quick Check 2

Simplify $\dfrac{1 + \dfrac{3}{x} - \dfrac{10}{x^2}}{1 - \dfrac{2}{x}}$.

EXAMPLE 3 Simplify $\dfrac{\dfrac{1}{6} + \dfrac{1}{x}}{\dfrac{1}{36} - \dfrac{1}{x^2}}$.

SOLUTION   Begin by multiplying the numerator and denominator by the LCD of all denominators. In this case, the LCD is $36x^2$.

$$\frac{\dfrac{1}{6} + \dfrac{1}{x}}{\dfrac{1}{36} - \dfrac{1}{x^2}} = \frac{36x^2}{36x^2} \cdot \frac{\dfrac{1}{6} + \dfrac{1}{x}}{\dfrac{1}{36} - \dfrac{1}{x^2}}$$ Multiply the numerator and denominator by the LCD.

$$= \frac{\overset{6}{\cancel{36}}x^2 \cdot \dfrac{1}{\cancel{6}} + 36\overset{x}{\cancel{x^2}} \cdot \dfrac{1}{\cancel{x}}}{\overset{1}{\cancel{36}}x^2 \cdot \dfrac{1}{\cancel{36}} - 36\overset{1}{\cancel{x^2}} \cdot \dfrac{1}{\cancel{x^2}}}$$ Distribute and divide out common factors.

$$= \frac{6x^2 + 36x}{x^2 - 36}$$ Multiply.

$$= \frac{6x\cancel{(x + 6)}}{\cancel{(x + 6)}(x - 6)}$$ Factor the numerator and denominator and divide out the common factor.

$$= \frac{6x}{x - 6}$$ Simplify.

Quick Check 3

Simplify $\dfrac{\dfrac{1}{64} - \dfrac{1}{x^2}}{\dfrac{1}{8} - \dfrac{1}{x}}$.

EXAMPLE 4 Simplify $\dfrac{\dfrac{3}{x + 1} - \dfrac{2}{x + 2}}{\dfrac{x}{x + 2} + \dfrac{6}{x + 1}}$.

SOLUTION   The LCD for the four simple fractions is $(x + 1)(x + 2)$.

$$\frac{\dfrac{3}{x + 1} - \dfrac{2}{x + 2}}{\dfrac{x}{x + 2} + \dfrac{6}{x + 1}}$$

$$= \frac{(x + 1)(x + 2)}{(x + 1)(x + 2)} \cdot \frac{\dfrac{3}{x + 1} - \dfrac{2}{x + 2}}{\dfrac{x}{x + 2} + \dfrac{6}{x + 1}}$$ Multiply the numerator and denominator by the LCD.

$$= \frac{\cancel{(x + 1)}(x + 2) \cdot \dfrac{3}{\cancel{x + 1}} - (x + 1)\cancel{(x + 2)} \cdot \dfrac{2}{\cancel{x + 2}}}{(x + 1)\cancel{(x + 2)} \cdot \dfrac{x}{\cancel{x + 2}} + \cancel{(x + 1)}(x + 2) \cdot \dfrac{6}{\cancel{x + 1}}}$$ Distribute and divide out common factors, clearing the fractions.

$$= \frac{3(x + 2) - 2(x + 1)}{x(x + 1) + 6(x + 2)}$$ Multiply.

$$= \frac{3x + 6 - 2x - 2}{x^2 + x + 6x + 12}$$ Distribute.

$$= \frac{x + 4}{x^2 + 7x + 12}$$ Combine like terms.

$$= \frac{\overset{1}{\cancel{x + 4}}}{(x + 3)\cancel{(x + 4)}_{1}}$$ Factor the denominator and divide out the common factor.

$$= \frac{1}{x + 3}$$ Simplify.

Quick Check 4

Simplify $\dfrac{\dfrac{6}{x - 4} + \dfrac{5}{x + 7}}{\dfrac{x + 2}{x - 4}}$.

EXAMPLE 5 Simplify $\dfrac{\dfrac{x^2 + 5x - 14}{x^2 - 9}}{\dfrac{x^2 - 6x + 8}{x^2 + 8x + 15}}$.

SOLUTION   In this case, it will be easier to rewrite the complex fraction as a division problem rather than multiply the numerator and denominator by the LCD. This is the best technique when we have a complex fraction with a single rational expression in its numerator and a single rational expression in its denominator. We have used this method when dividing rational expressions.

$$\frac{\dfrac{x^2 + 5x - 14}{x^2 - 9}}{\dfrac{x^2 - 6x + 8}{x^2 + 8x + 15}}$$

$$= \frac{x^2 + 5x - 14}{x^2 - 9} \div \frac{x^2 - 6x + 8}{x^2 + 8x + 15}$$ Rewrite as a division problem.

$$= \frac{x^2 + 5x - 14}{x^2 - 9} \cdot \frac{x^2 + 8x + 15}{x^2 - 6x + 8}$$ Invert the divisor and multiply.

$$= \frac{(x + 7)(x - 2)}{(x + 3)(x - 3)} \cdot \frac{(x + 3)(x + 5)}{(x - 2)(x - 4)}$$ Factor each numerator and denominator.

$$= \frac{(x + 7)\overset{1}{\cancel{(x - 2)}}}{\underset{1}{\cancel{(x + 3)}}(x - 3)} \cdot \frac{\overset{1}{\cancel{(x + 3)}}(x + 5)}{\underset{1}{\cancel{(x - 2)}}(x - 4)}$$ Divide out common factors.

$$= \frac{(x + 7)(x + 5)}{(x - 3)(x - 4)}$$ Simplify.

Quick Check 5

Simplify $\dfrac{\dfrac{x^2 - 2x - 48}{x^2 + 7x - 30}}{\dfrac{x^2 + 7x + 6}{x^2 - 5x + 6}}$.

BUILDING YOUR STUDY STRATEGY

Preparing for a Cumulative Exam, 5 Cumulative Review Exercises Use your cumulative review exercises to prepare for a cumulative exam. These exercises contain problems representative of the material covered in several previous chapters.

After you have been preparing for a while, try these exercises without referring to your notes, your note cards, or the text. In this way, you can determine which topics require more study. If you made a mistake while solving a problem, make note of the mistake and ways to avoid it in the future. If there are problems that you do not recognize or know how to begin, ask your instructor or a tutor for help.

Exercises 7.5

MyMathLab   PRACTICE   WATCH   DOWNLOAD READ   REVIEW

Vocabulary

1. A(n) _____ is a fraction or rational expression containing one or more fractions in its numerator or denominator.

2. To simplify a complex fraction, multiply the numerator and denominator by the _____ of all fractions in the complex fraction.

Simplify the complex fraction.

3. $\dfrac{\dfrac{2}{5} - \dfrac{1}{4}}{\dfrac{9}{10} + \dfrac{5}{2}}$

4. $\dfrac{\dfrac{3}{7} + \dfrac{2}{3}}{\dfrac{16}{21} - \dfrac{2}{7}}$

5. $\dfrac{2 - \dfrac{3}{8}}{\dfrac{5}{4} + \dfrac{1}{3}}$

6. $\dfrac{\dfrac{5}{6} - 3}{\dfrac{3}{4} + \dfrac{11}{12}}$

7. $\dfrac{x + \dfrac{3}{5}}{x + \dfrac{4}{7}}$

8. $\dfrac{x - \dfrac{2}{9}}{x + \dfrac{5}{4}}$

9. $\dfrac{6 + \dfrac{15}{x}}{x + \dfrac{5}{2}}$

10. $\dfrac{x + \dfrac{3}{7}}{14 + \dfrac{6}{x}}$

11. $\dfrac{14 - \dfrac{4}{x}}{21 - \dfrac{6}{x}}$

12. $\dfrac{10 + \dfrac{8}{x}}{25 + \dfrac{20}{x}}$

13. $\dfrac{3 + \dfrac{15}{x}}{1 - \dfrac{25}{x^2}}$

14. $\dfrac{4 - \dfrac{36}{x^2}}{x + 2 - \dfrac{15}{x}}$

15. $\dfrac{\dfrac{4}{x+3} + \dfrac{2}{x+6}}{\dfrac{x+5}{x+3}}$

16. $\dfrac{\dfrac{10}{x+4} - \dfrac{6}{x-6}}{\dfrac{3x-63}{x-6}}$

17. $\dfrac{\dfrac{12}{x} + \dfrac{3}{x-5}}{\dfrac{x+4}{x} + \dfrac{2}{x-5}}$

18. $\dfrac{\dfrac{8}{x+2} - \dfrac{2}{x-7}}{\dfrac{x+6}{x+2} - \dfrac{4}{x-7}}$

19. $\dfrac{1 + \dfrac{4}{x} - \dfrac{32}{x^2}}{1 + \dfrac{13}{x} + \dfrac{40}{x^2}}$

20. $\dfrac{1 - \dfrac{9}{x} + \dfrac{18}{x^2}}{1 + \dfrac{2}{x} - \dfrac{15}{x^2}}$

21. $\dfrac{\dfrac{8}{x^2} - \dfrac{8}{x} + 2}{\dfrac{4}{x^2} - 1}$

22. $\dfrac{\dfrac{18}{x} - 3}{\dfrac{1}{x} - \dfrac{42}{x^2} + 1}$

23. $\dfrac{\dfrac{x^2 + 14x + 48}{x^2 + 3x - 40}}{\dfrac{x^2 - 3x - 54}{x^2 - 25}}$

24. $\dfrac{\dfrac{x^2 + 13x + 30}{x^2 + 13x - 30}}{\dfrac{x^2 + 5x + 6}{x^2 + 10x - 24}}$

25. $\dfrac{\dfrac{4x^2 - 16x - 9}{8x - x^2}}{\dfrac{4x^2 - 1}{x^2 - x - 56}}$

26. $\dfrac{\dfrac{81 - x^2}{x^2 - 36}}{\dfrac{x^2 - 15x + 54}{3x^2 + 20x + 12}}$

Mixed Practice, 27–52

Simplify the given rational expression using the techniques developed in Sections 7.1–7.5.

27. $\dfrac{x^2 + 4x}{x^2 - x - 42} + \dfrac{x - 6}{x^2 - x - 42}$

28. $\dfrac{x^2 - 14x + 40}{x^2 + 4x + 3} \div \dfrac{x^2 - 6x + 8}{x^2 + 10x + 9}$

29. $\dfrac{x + 3}{x^2 - 2x - 24} + \dfrac{5}{x^2 - 8x + 12}$

30. $\dfrac{6}{x^2 - 2x - 35} - \dfrac{4}{x^2 + 2x - 15}$

31. $\dfrac{x^2 + 7x}{3x^2 - 19x + 20} \div \dfrac{x^2 + 12x + 35}{x^2 - 3x - 10}$

32. $\dfrac{36 - x^2}{x^2 - 12x + 36}$

33. $\dfrac{x + 5}{x^2 - 49} - \dfrac{6}{x^2 - 7x}$

34. $\dfrac{x^2 + 3x - 40}{x^2 + x - 6} \cdot \dfrac{x^2 - 7x - 30}{2x^2 + 17x + 8}$

35. $\dfrac{5x}{x - 2} + \dfrac{10}{2 - x}$

36. $\dfrac{1 - \dfrac{11}{x} + \dfrac{18}{x^2}}{1 - \dfrac{2}{x} - \dfrac{63}{x^2}}$

37. $\dfrac{\dfrac{7}{x + 2} - \dfrac{2}{x - 3}}{\dfrac{x - 5}{x + 2}}$

38. $\dfrac{5x^2 - 12x + 4}{x^3 - 8}$

39. $\dfrac{x^2 - 13x + 14}{x^2 - 6x} - \dfrac{x^2 + 4x - 32}{6x - x^2}$

40. $\dfrac{x^2 + 6x - 16}{x^2 - 4x - 45} \cdot \dfrac{2x^2 + 13x + 15}{x^2 - 4x + 4}$

41. $\dfrac{\dfrac{1}{8} - \dfrac{1}{x}}{\dfrac{1}{x^2} - \dfrac{1}{64}}$

42. $\dfrac{x^2 + 9x}{x - 5} - \dfrac{6x + 50}{5 - x}$

43. $\dfrac{8}{x^2 + 7x + 12} + \dfrac{4}{x^2 + 10x + 24}$

44. $\dfrac{8x}{2x - 5} + \dfrac{20}{5 - 2x}$

45. $\dfrac{x^3 + 64}{x^2 + 14x + 49} \cdot \dfrac{x^2 + 3x - 28}{x^2 - 16}$

46. $\dfrac{10x^2 + 11x + 1}{2x^2 - x - 15} \div \dfrac{x^2 - x - 2}{x^2 - 13x + 30}$

47. $\dfrac{x^2 + 18x + 77}{x^2 - 4x - 32} \cdot \dfrac{x^2 + 6x + 8}{x^2 + 9x + 14}$

48. $\dfrac{x + 3}{x^2 - 2x - 3} + \dfrac{3}{x^2 - 8x + 15}$

49. $\dfrac{x^2 + 7x}{x^2 - 2x - 3} - \dfrac{4x + 18}{x^2 - 2x - 3}$

50. $\dfrac{x + \dfrac{5}{8}}{x - \dfrac{7}{2}}$

51. $\dfrac{x^3 - 1000}{x^2 + 10x - 11} \div \dfrac{3x^2 - 37x + 70}{x^2 + 4x - 5}$

52. $\dfrac{x + 5}{x^2 - 3x + 2} - \dfrac{8}{x^2 - 8x + 12}$

▬▬ Writing in Mathematics

Answer in complete sentences.

53. Explain what a complex fraction is. Compare and contrast complex fractions and the rational expressions found in Section 7.1.

54. One method for simplifying complex fractions is to rewrite the complex fraction as one rational expression divided by another rational expression. When is this the most efficient way to simplify a complex fraction? Give an example.

7.6

Rational Equations

OBJECTIVES

1. Solve rational equations.
2. Solve literal equations containing rational expressions.

Solving Rational Equations

Objective 1 Solve rational equations. In this section, we will learn how to solve **rational equations**, which are equations containing at least one rational expression. The main goal is to rewrite the equation as an equivalent equation that does not contain a rational expression. We then solve the equation using methods developed in earlier chapters.

In Chapter 2, we learned how to solve an equation containing fractions, such as the equation $\frac{1}{4}x - \frac{3}{5} = \frac{9}{10}$. We began by finding the LCD of all fractions and then multiplied both sides of the equation by that LCD to clear the equation of fractions. We will use the same technique in this section. There is a major difference, though, when we solve equations containing a variable in a denominator. Occasionally, we will find a solution that causes one of the rational expressions in the equation to be undefined. If a denominator of a rational expression is equal to 0 when the value of a solution is substituted for the variable, the solution must be omitted and is called an **extraneous solution**. We must check each solution to make sure it is not an extraneous solution.

> ### Solving Rational Equations
> 1. Find the LCD of all denominators in the equation.
> 2. Multiply both sides of the equation by the LCD to clear the equation of fractions.
> 3. Solve the resulting equation.
> 4. Check for extraneous solutions.

EXAMPLE 1 Solve $\dfrac{4}{x} + \dfrac{1}{3} = \dfrac{5}{6}$.

SOLUTION   We begin by finding the LCD of these three fractions, which is $6x$. Then we multiply both sides of the equation by the LCD to clear the equation of fractions. Once we have done this, we can solve the resulting equation.

$$\frac{4}{x} + \frac{1}{3} = \frac{5}{6}$$

$$6x \cdot \left(\frac{4}{x} + \frac{1}{3} \right) = 6x \cdot \frac{5}{6} \qquad \text{Multiply both sides of the equation by the LCD.}$$

$$6x \cdot \frac{4}{x} + 6x \cdot \frac{1}{3} = 6x \cdot \frac{5}{6} \qquad \text{Distribute and divide out common factors.}$$

$$24 + 2x = 5x \qquad \text{Multiply. The resulting equation is linear.}$$

$$24 = 3x \qquad \text{Subtract } 2x \text{ to collect all variable terms on one side of the equation.}$$

$$8 = x \qquad \text{Divide both sides by 3.}$$

Check

$$\frac{4}{(8)} + \frac{1}{3} = \frac{5}{6}$$ Substitute 8 for x.

$$\frac{1}{2} + \frac{1}{3} = \frac{5}{6}$$ Simplify the fraction $\frac{4}{8}$. The LCD of these fractions is 6.

$$\frac{3}{6} + \frac{2}{6} = \frac{5}{6}$$ Write each fraction with a common denominator of 6.

$$\frac{5}{6} = \frac{5}{6}$$ Add.

Because the solution $x = 8$ does not make any rational expression in the original equation undefined, this value is a valid solution. The solution set is $\{8\}$.

Checking for Extraneous Solutions

When checking whether a solution is an extraneous solution, we need only determine whether the solution causes the LCD to equal 0. If the LCD is equal to 0 for this solution, one or more rational expressions are undefined and the solution is an extraneous solution. Also, if the LCD is equal to 0, we have multiplied both sides of the equation by 0. The multiplication property of equality says that we can multiply both sides of an equation by any *nonzero* number without affecting the equality of both sides. In the previous example, the only solution that could possibly be an extraneous solution is $x = 0$ because it is the only value of x for which the LCD is equal to 0.

EXAMPLE 2 Solve $x - 5 - \dfrac{36}{x} = 0$.

SOLUTION The LCD in this example is x. The LCD is equal to 0 only if $x = 0$. If we find that $x = 0$ is a solution, we must omit that solution as an extraneous solution.

$$x - 5 - \frac{36}{x} = 0$$

$$x \cdot \left(x - 5 - \frac{36}{x} \right) = x \cdot 0$$ Multiply each side of the equation by the LCD, x.

$$x \cdot x - x \cdot 5 - \overset{1}{\cancel{x}} \cdot \frac{36}{\underset{1}{\cancel{x}}} = 0$$ Distribute and divide out common factors.

$$x^2 - 5x - 36 = 0$$ Multiply. The resulting equation is quadratic.

$$(x - 9)(x + 4) = 0$$ Factor.

$$x = 9 \quad \text{or} \quad x = -4$$ Set each factor equal to 0 and solve.

You may verify that neither solution causes the LCD to equal 0. The solution set is $\{-4, 9\}$.

A WORD OF CAUTION When we are solving a rational equation, the use of the LCD is completely different than when we are adding or subtracting rational expressions. We use the LCD to clear the denominators of the rational expressions when we are solving a rational equation. When we are adding or subtracting rational expressions, we rewrite each expression as an equivalent expression whose denominator is the LCD.

Quick Check 1

Solve $\dfrac{6}{x} - \dfrac{1}{8} = \dfrac{7}{40}$.

Quick Check 2

Solve $1 = \dfrac{5}{x} + \dfrac{24}{x^2}$.

EXAMPLE 3 Solve $\dfrac{x}{x+2} - 5 = \dfrac{3x+4}{x+2}$.

SOLUTION The LCD is $x + 2$, so we will begin to solve this equation by multiplying both sides of the equation by $x + 2$.

$$\frac{x}{x+2} - 5 = \frac{3x+4}{x+2} \qquad \text{The LCD is } x+2.$$

$$(x+2)\cdot\left(\frac{x}{x+2} - 5\right) = (x+2)\cdot\frac{3x+4}{x+2} \qquad \begin{array}{l}\text{Multiply both sides by the}\\ \text{LCD.}\end{array}$$

$$\overset{1}{\cancel{(x+2)}}\cdot\frac{x}{\underset{1}{\cancel{x+2}}} - (x+2)\cdot 5 = \overset{1}{\cancel{(x+2)}}\cdot\frac{3x+4}{\underset{1}{\cancel{x+2}}} \qquad \begin{array}{l}\text{Distribute and divide out}\\ \text{common factors.}\end{array}$$

$$x - 5x - 10 = 3x + 4 \qquad \begin{array}{l}\text{Multiply. The resulting}\\ \text{equation is linear.}\end{array}$$

$$-4x - 10 = 3x + 4 \qquad \text{Combine like terms.}$$

$$-10 = 7x + 4 \qquad \text{Add } 4x.$$

$$-14 = 7x \qquad \text{Subtract 4.}$$

$$-2 = x \qquad \text{Divide both sides by 7.}$$

The LCD is equal to 0 when $x = -2$, and two rational expressions in the original equation are undefined when $x = -2$. This solution is an extraneous solution, and because there are no other solutions, this equation has no solution. Recall that we write the solution set as $\varnothing$ when there is no solution.

Quick Check 3

Solve $\dfrac{7}{x-4} + 3 = \dfrac{2x-1}{x-4}$.

EXAMPLE 4 Solve $\dfrac{x+9}{x^2+9x+8} = \dfrac{2}{x^2+2x-48}$.

SOLUTION Begin by factoring the denominators to find the LCD.

$$\frac{x+9}{x^2+9x+8} = \frac{2}{x^2+2x-48}$$

$$\frac{x+9}{(x+1)(x+8)} = \frac{2}{(x+8)(x-6)} \qquad \text{The LCD is } (x+1)(x+8)(x-6).$$

$$\overset{1}{\cancel{(x+1)}}\overset{1}{\cancel{(x+8)}}(x-6)\cdot\frac{x+9}{\underset{1}{\cancel{(x+1)}}\underset{1}{\cancel{(x+8)}}}$$

$$= (x+1)\overset{1}{\cancel{(x+8)}}\overset{1}{\cancel{(x-6)}}\cdot\frac{2}{\underset{1}{\cancel{(x+8)}}\underset{1}{\cancel{(x-6)}}} \qquad \begin{array}{l}\text{Multiply by the LCD. Divide}\\ \text{out common factors.}\end{array}$$

$$(x-6)(x+9) = 2(x+1) \qquad \text{Multiply remaining factors.}$$

$$x^2 + 3x - 54 = 2x + 2 \qquad \text{Multiply.}$$

$$x^2 + x - 56 = 0 \qquad \begin{array}{l}\text{Collect all terms on the left side. The}\\ \text{resulting equation is quadratic.}\end{array}$$

$$(x+8)(x-7) = 0 \qquad \text{Factor.}$$

$$x = -8 \quad \text{or} \quad x = 7 \qquad \text{Set each factor equal to 0 and solve.}$$

Quick Check 4

Solve
$\dfrac{x+2}{x^2-3x-54} = \dfrac{2}{x^2-12x+27}$.

The solution $x = -8$ is an extraneous solution because it makes the LCD equal to 0. The reader may verify that the solution $x = 7$ checks. The solution set for this equation is $\{7\}$.

EXAMPLE 5 Solve $\dfrac{x+10}{x^2+4x-5} - \dfrac{1}{x-3} = \dfrac{x-6}{x^2-4x+3}$.

SOLUTION

$$\frac{x+10}{x^2+4x-5} - \frac{1}{x-3} = \frac{x-6}{x^2-4x+3}$$

$$\frac{x+10}{(x+5)(x-1)} - \frac{1}{x-3} = \frac{x-6}{(x-1)(x-3)} \qquad \begin{array}{l}\text{The LCD is}\\ (x+5)(x-1)(x-3).\end{array}$$

$$(x+5)(x-1)(x-3) \cdot \left(\frac{x+10}{(x+5)(x-1)} - \frac{1}{x-3}\right)$$

$$= (x+5)(x-1)(x-3) \cdot \frac{x-6}{(x-1)(x-3)} \qquad \text{Multiply by the LCD.}$$

$$\overset{1}{\cancel{(x+5)}}\overset{1}{\cancel{(x-1)}}(x-3) \cdot \frac{x+10}{\underset{1}{\cancel{(x+5)}}\underset{1}{\cancel{(x-1)}}} - (x+5)(x-1)\overset{1}{\cancel{(x-3)}} \cdot \frac{1}{\underset{1}{\cancel{(x-3)}}}$$

$$= (x+5)\overset{1}{\cancel{(x-1)}}\overset{1}{\cancel{(x-3)}} \cdot \frac{x-6}{\underset{1}{\cancel{(x-1)}}\underset{1}{\cancel{(x-3)}}} \qquad \begin{array}{l}\text{Distribute and divide out}\\ \text{common factors.}\end{array}$$

$$(x-3)(x+10) - (x+5)(x-1) = (x+5)(x-6) \qquad \begin{array}{l}\text{Multiply remaining}\\ \text{factors.}\end{array}$$

$$(x^2+7x-30) - (x^2+4x-5) = x^2-x-30 \qquad \text{Multiply.}$$

$$x^2+7x-30-x^2-4x+5 = x^2-x-30 \qquad \text{Distribute.}$$

$$3x-25 = x^2-x-30 \qquad \text{Combine like terms.}$$

$$0 = x^2-4x-5 \qquad \begin{array}{l}\text{Collect all terms on the right}\\ \text{side. The resulting equation is}\\ \text{quadratic.}\end{array}$$

$$0 = (x+1)(x-5) \qquad \text{Factor.}$$

$$x = -1 \quad \text{or} \quad x = 5 \qquad \begin{array}{l}\text{Set each factor equal to 0 and}\\ \text{solve.}\end{array}$$

Check to verify that neither solution is extraneous. The solution set is $\{-1, 5\}$.

▶ **Quick Check 5**

Solve $\dfrac{x+3}{x^2+x-12} - \dfrac{3}{x^2-2x-3} = \dfrac{x+7}{x^2+5x+4}$.

Literal Equations

Objective 2 Solve literal equations containing rational expressions.
Recall that a literal equation is an equation containing two or more variables and that we solve the equation for one of the variables by isolating that variable on one side of the equation. In this section, we will learn how to solve literal equations containing one or more rational expressions.

EXAMPLE 6 Solve the literal equation $\dfrac{1}{x} + \dfrac{1}{y} = \dfrac{2}{5}$ for x.

SOLUTION   Begin by multiplying by the LCD ($5xy$) to clear the equation of fractions.

$$\frac{1}{x} + \frac{1}{y} = \frac{2}{5}$$

$$5xy \cdot \left(\frac{1}{x} + \frac{1}{y} \right) = 5xy \cdot \frac{2}{5} \qquad \text{Multiply by the LCD, } 5xy.$$

$$5\overset{1}{\cancel{x}}y \cdot \frac{1}{\underset{1}{\cancel{x}}} + 5x\overset{1}{\cancel{y}} \cdot \frac{1}{\underset{1}{\cancel{y}}} = \overset{1}{\cancel{5}}xy \cdot \frac{2}{\underset{1}{\cancel{5}}} \qquad \text{Distribute and divide out common factors.}$$

$$5y + 5x = 2xy \qquad \text{Multiply remaining factors.}$$

Notice that two terms contain the variable for which we are solving. We need to collect both of these terms on the same side of the equation and then factor x out of those terms. This will allow us to divide and isolate x.

$$5y + 5x = 2xy$$

$$5y = 2xy - 5x \qquad \begin{array}{l}\text{Subtract } 5x \text{ to collect all terms with } x \\ \text{on the right side of the equation.}\end{array}$$

$$5y = x(2y - 5) \qquad \text{Factor out the common factor } x.$$

$$\frac{5y}{2y - 5} = \frac{x\overset{1}{\cancel{(2y - 5)}}}{\underset{1}{\cancel{(2y - 5)}}} \qquad \text{Divide both sides by } 2y - 5 \text{ to isolate } x.$$

$$\frac{5y}{2y - 5} = x \qquad \text{Simplify.}$$

$$x = \frac{5y}{2y - 5} \qquad \begin{array}{l}\text{Rewrite with the variable you are solving for} \\ \text{on the left side of the equation.}\end{array}$$

Quick Check 6

Solve the literal equation
$\dfrac{2}{x} + \dfrac{3}{y} = \dfrac{4}{z}$ for x.

As in Chapter 2, we will rewrite the solution so that the variable for which we are solving is on the left side.

EXAMPLE 7 Solve the literal equation $y = \dfrac{2x}{3x - 5}$ for x.

SOLUTION   Begin by multiplying both sides of the equation by $3x - 5$ to clear the equation of fractions.

$$y = \frac{2x}{3x - 5}$$

$$y(3x - 5) = \frac{2x}{\underset{1}{\cancel{3x - 5}}} \cdot \overset{1}{\cancel{(3x - 5)}} \qquad \text{Multiply both sides by } 3x - 5.$$

$$3xy - 5y = 2x \qquad \text{Simplify.}$$

$$3xy - 2x = 5y \qquad \begin{array}{l}\text{Collect all terms containing } x \text{ on the left side} \\ \text{of the equation (subtract } 2x) \text{ and all other} \\ \text{terms on the right side of the equation (add } 5y).\end{array}$$

$$x(3y - 2) = 5y \qquad \begin{array}{l}\text{Factor out the common factor } x \text{ on the} \\ \text{left side of the equation.}\end{array}$$

Quick Check 7

Solve the literal equation
$y = \dfrac{5x}{4x - 3}$ for x.

$$\frac{x\overset{1}{\cancel{(3y - 2)}}}{\underset{1}{\cancel{3y - 2}}} = \frac{5y}{3y - 2} \qquad \text{Divide both sides by } 3y - 2 \text{ to isolate } x.$$

$$x = \frac{5y}{3y - 2} \qquad \text{Simplify.}$$

BUILDING YOUR STUDY STRATEGY

Preparing for a Cumulative Exam, 6 Applied Problems Many students have a difficult time with applied problems on a cumulative exam. Some students are unable to recognize what type of problem an applied problem is, and others cannot recall how to start to solve that type of problem. You will find the following strategy helpful:

- Make a list of the different applied problems you have covered this semester. Create a study sheet for each type of problem.
- Write down an example or two of each type of problem.

Review these study sheets frequently as the exam approaches. This should help you identify the applied problems on the exam as well as remember how to solve them.

Exercises 7.6

Vocabulary

1. A(n) _____ is an equation containing at least one rational expression.

2. To solve a rational equation, begin by multiplying both sides of the equation by the _____ of the denominators in the equation.

3. A(n) _____ of a rational equation is a solution that causes one or more of the rational expressions in the equation to be undefined.

4. A(n) _____ equation is an equation containing two or more variables.

Solve.

5. $\dfrac{x}{9} + \dfrac{11}{18} = \dfrac{7}{6}$

6. $\dfrac{x}{10} + \dfrac{5}{6} = \dfrac{26}{15}$

7. $\dfrac{5}{6} + \dfrac{11}{x} = \dfrac{7}{4}$

8. $\dfrac{1}{8} + \dfrac{13}{x} = \dfrac{2}{3}$

9. $\dfrac{25}{21} - \dfrac{17}{x} = \dfrac{7}{12}$

10. $\dfrac{21}{20} - \dfrac{19}{x} = \dfrac{5}{12}$

11. $x - 5 + \dfrac{12}{x} = 2$

12. $x - \dfrac{25}{x} = 2 + \dfrac{23}{x}$

13. $\dfrac{x}{2} + \dfrac{6}{x} = 4$

14. $\dfrac{x}{3} + 2 - \dfrac{9}{x} = 0$

15. $1 - \dfrac{7}{x} + \dfrac{10}{x^2} = 0$

16. $1 + \dfrac{11}{x} - \dfrac{42}{x^2} = 0$

17. $1 - \dfrac{25}{x^2} = 0$

18. $6 - \dfrac{13}{x} + \dfrac{6}{x^2} = 0$

19. $\dfrac{8x - 3}{x + 7} = \dfrac{2x + 15}{x + 7}$

20. $\dfrac{6x + 13}{x - 1} = \dfrac{4x + 15}{x - 1}$

21. $\dfrac{7x - 11}{5x - 2} = \dfrac{2x - 9}{5x - 2}$

22. $\dfrac{x^2 + 3x}{x + 8} = \dfrac{3x + 64}{x + 8}$

23. $8 + \dfrac{6}{x - 4} = \dfrac{x - 12}{x - 4}$

24. $1 + \dfrac{2x - 7}{x + 3} = \dfrac{4x - 1}{x + 3}$

25. $x + \dfrac{x + 11}{x - 6} = \dfrac{8x - 31}{x - 6}$

26. $x + \dfrac{3x - 10}{x + 1} = \dfrac{9x + 14}{x + 1}$

27. $\dfrac{3}{x-7} = \dfrac{7}{x+5}$

28. $\dfrac{6}{x+4} = \dfrac{9}{2x-3}$

29. $\dfrac{x-3}{x+9} = \dfrac{6}{x+2}$

30. $\dfrac{x-1}{3x-7} = \dfrac{x+1}{2x+7}$

31. $\dfrac{3}{x+2} - \dfrac{1}{x+1} = \dfrac{x+3}{x^2+3x+2}$

32. $\dfrac{2}{x} + \dfrac{3}{x+2} = \dfrac{7x-8}{x^2+2x}$

33. $\dfrac{4}{x+4} + \dfrac{3}{x-4} = \dfrac{24}{x^2-16}$

34. $\dfrac{x}{x+5} + \dfrac{3}{x-7} = \dfrac{36}{x^2-2x-35}$

35. $\dfrac{2}{x^2-x-2} + \dfrac{10}{x^2-2x-3} = \dfrac{x+12}{x^2-x-2}$

36. $\dfrac{20}{x^2+12x+27} - \dfrac{4}{x^2+14x+45} = \dfrac{x+10}{x^2+8x+15}$

37. $\dfrac{x-8}{x-5} + \dfrac{x-9}{x-4} = \dfrac{x+7}{x^2-9x+20}$

38. $\dfrac{x+4}{x^2+5x-14} + \dfrac{2}{x^2+3x-10} = \dfrac{38}{x^2+12x+35}$

39. $\dfrac{x+3}{x^2-4x-12} + \dfrac{x-11}{x^2-2x-24} = \dfrac{x+1}{x^2+6x+8}$

40. $\dfrac{x-2}{x^2+13x+40} + \dfrac{x+5}{x^2+7x-8} = \dfrac{x+3}{x^2+4x-5}$

41. $\dfrac{3x-4}{x^2-10x+21} - \dfrac{x-8}{x^2-18x+77} = \dfrac{x-5}{x^2-14x+33}$

42. $\dfrac{5x+4}{x^2+x-90} - \dfrac{1}{x-9} = \dfrac{3x-2}{x^2-100}$

Mixed Practice, 43–58

43. $1 + \dfrac{13}{x} + \dfrac{42}{x^2} = 0$

44. $3x - 8 = -29$

45. $x^2 - 14x - 120 = 0$

46. $\dfrac{2x}{x+9} = \dfrac{x-2}{x-1}$

47. $2(3x+4) - 19 = 4x - 1$

48. $\dfrac{x}{x+5} + \dfrac{2}{x-9} = \dfrac{28}{x^2-4x-45}$

49. $\dfrac{x}{x+3} + \dfrac{x-4}{x-3} = \dfrac{9x-5}{x^2-9}$

50. $\dfrac{1}{4}x^2 + \dfrac{1}{2}x - 2 = 0$

51. $6x^2 + 29x - 5 = 0$

52. $2 + \dfrac{9}{x} + \dfrac{4}{x^2} = 0$

53. $\dfrac{6}{x+2} = \dfrac{25}{3x+13}$

54. $7 - 5x = 52$

55. $\dfrac{x}{x+6} + \dfrac{3}{x+4} = \dfrac{8}{x^2+10x+24}$

56. $x^2 - 81 = 0$

57. $5x - 17 = 8x + 13$

58. $\dfrac{4}{x^2+4x-5} + \dfrac{x+9}{x^2-1} = \dfrac{41}{x^2+6x+5}$

Solve for the specified variable.

59. $L = \dfrac{A}{W}$ for W

60. $b = \dfrac{2A}{h}$ for A

61. $y = \dfrac{x}{2x+5}$ for x

62. $y = \dfrac{3x-7}{2x}$ for x

63. $y = \dfrac{2x-9}{3x-8}$ for x

64. $y = \dfrac{5x-4}{x-6}$ for x

65. $\dfrac{x}{r} + \dfrac{y}{2r} = 1$ for r

66. $r = \dfrac{d}{t}$ for t

67. $m = \dfrac{y-y_1}{x-x_1}$ for x

68. $\dfrac{1}{R} = \dfrac{1}{R_1} + \dfrac{1}{R_2}$ for R

69. If $x = 9$ is a solution to the equation
$$\dfrac{x-4}{x-1} + \dfrac{7}{x+3} = \dfrac{?}{x^2+2x-3}:$$
a) Find the constant in the missing numerator.
b) Find the other solution to the equation.

70. If $x = 12$ is a solution to the equation
$$\dfrac{x-8}{x-5} + \dfrac{?}{x-2} = \dfrac{7x+19}{x^2-7x+10}:$$
a) Find the constant in the missing numerator.
b) Find the other solution to the equation.

Writing in Mathematics

Answer in complete sentences.

71. Explain how to determine whether a solution is an extraneous solution.

72. You use the LCD when adding two rational expressions, as well as when solving a rational equation. Explain how the LCD is used differently for these two types of problems.

73. *Newsletter* Write a newsletter that explains how to solve rational equations.

CHAPTER 8

A Transition

This chapter provides a transition between beginning algebra and intermediate algebra. We will review concepts covered in the first half of the text and extend these ideas to new topics.

STUDY STRATEGY

Summary of Previous Study Strategies In this chapter, we will summarize the study strategies presented in the first half of the text.

8.1

Linear Equations and Absolute Value Equations

OBJECTIVES

1 Solve linear equations.
2 Solve absolute value equations.

Linear Equations

Objective 1 Solve linear equations. We begin this section by reviewing linear equations and their solutions. Recall the following guidelines for solving linear equations in Chapter 2:

- Simplify each side of the equation. This includes performing any distributive multiplications, clearing all fractions by multiplying each side of the equation by the least common multiple (LCM) of the denominators, and combining like terms.

- Collect all variable terms on one side of the equation and all constant terms on the other side. It is a good idea to collect the variable terms in such a way that the coefficient of the variable term will be positive.

- Divide both sides of the equation by the coefficient of the variable term to find the solution.
- Check your solution and write it in solution set notation.

We will proceed with some examples that are intended as a review.

EXAMPLE 1 Solve $2x - 6 = 10$.

SOLUTION   Begin by isolating the variable term on the left side of the equation.

$$2x - 6 = 10$$
$$2x = 16 \quad \text{Add 6 to both sides to isolate } 2x.$$
$$x = 8 \quad \text{Divide both sides by 2.}$$

Now check this solution.

Check $2x - 6 = 10$

$$2(8) - 6 = 10 \quad \text{Substitute 8 for } x.$$
$$16 - 6 = 10 \quad \text{Multiply.}$$
$$10 = 10 \quad \text{Subtract.}$$

Quick Check 1
Solve $9x + 13 = -14$.

Because both sides simplify to be 10, the solution is valid. The solution set is $\{8\}$.

EXAMPLE 2 Solve $3(2x + 7) - 4x = 5x - 6$.

SOLUTION   Begin by performing the distributive multiplication on the left side of the equation.

$$3(2x + 7) - 4x = 5x - 6$$
$$6x + 21 - 4x = 5x - 6 \quad \text{Distribute 3.}$$
$$2x + 21 = 5x - 6 \quad \text{Combine like terms.}$$
$$27 = 3x \quad \begin{array}{l}\text{Collect variable terms on the right side by} \\ \text{subtracting } 2x \text{ from both sides. Collect constants} \\ \text{on the left side by adding 6 to both sides.}\end{array}$$
$$9 = x \quad \text{Divide both sides by 3.}$$

Quick Check 2

Solve
$3x - 2(4x - 5) = 2x - 11$.

The check is left to the reader. The solution set is $\{9\}$.

EXAMPLE 3 Solve $\dfrac{4}{3}x + \dfrac{5}{6} = \dfrac{9}{4}x - 1$.

SOLUTION   This equation includes fractions. We can clear these fractions by multiplying each side of the equation by the LCM of the denominators, which is 12.

$$\frac{4}{3}x + \frac{5}{6} = \frac{9}{4}x - 1$$
$$12\left(\frac{4}{3}x + \frac{5}{6}\right) = 12\left(\frac{9}{4}x - 1\right) \quad \text{Multiply both sides by 12.}$$
$$\overset{4}{\cancel{12}} \cdot \frac{4}{\cancel{3}}x + \overset{2}{\cancel{12}} \cdot \frac{5}{\cancel{6}} = \overset{3}{\cancel{12}} \cdot \frac{9}{\cancel{4}}x - 12 \cdot 1 \quad \text{Distribute and divide out common factors.}$$
$$16x + 10 = 27x - 12 \quad \text{Multiply.}$$
$$10 = 11x - 12 \quad \text{Subtract } 16x \text{ from both sides.}$$
$$22 = 11x \quad \text{Add 12 to both sides.}$$
$$2 = x \quad \text{Divide both sides by 11.}$$

Quick Check 3

Solve $\dfrac{2}{3}x - \dfrac{1}{5} = \dfrac{1}{2}x + \dfrac{5}{6}$.

The check is left to the reader. The solution set is $\{2\}$.

Equations That Are Identities

In the first three examples of this section, each linear equation had exactly one solution, but recall that this will not always be the case. An equation that is always true regardless of the value substituted for the variable is called an identity. The solution set for an identity is the set of all real numbers, denoted by $\mathbb{R}$.

EXAMPLE 4   Solve $2(2x - 3) + 1 = 4x - 5$.

SOLUTION

$$2(2x - 3) + 1 = 4x - 5$$
$$4x - 6 + 1 = 4x - 5 \quad \text{Distribute 2.}$$
$$4x - 5 = 4x - 5 \quad \text{Combine like terms.}$$
$$-5 = -5 \quad \text{Subtract } 4x \text{ from both sides.}$$

When we subtract $4x$ from each side in an attempt to collect all variable terms on one side of the equation, we eliminate the variable x from the resulting equation. Is the equation $-5 = -5$ a true statement? Yes, and it says that the equation is an identity and that the solution set is the set of all real numbers $\mathbb{R}$.

▶ Quick Check 4

Solve $(2x + 1) - (5 - 3x) = 2(3x - 2) - x$.

Notice that at one point in the previous example, the equation was $4x - 5 = 4x - 5$. If you reach a line where both sides of the equation are identical, the equation is an identity.

Equations That Are Contradictions

Just as some equations are always true regardless of the value chosen for the variable, other equations are never true for any value of the variable. These equations are called contradictions and have no solution. The solution set for these equations is the empty set, or null set, and is denoted $\varnothing$. We can tell that an equation is a contradiction when we are solving it because the variable terms on each side of the equation are eliminated but in this case leave an equation that is false, such as $1 = 2$.

EXAMPLE 5   Solve $4x + 3 = 2(2x + 3) - 1$.

SOLUTION

$$4x + 3 = 2(2x + 3) - 1$$
$$4x + 3 = 4x + 6 - 1 \quad \text{Distribute 2.}$$
$$4x + 3 = 4x + 5 \quad \text{Combine like terms.}$$
$$3 = 5 \quad \text{Subtract } 4x \text{ from both sides.}$$

After we subtract $4x$ from each side of the equation, the resulting equation $3 = 5$ is obviously false. This equation is a contradiction, and its solution set is the empty set $\varnothing$.

▶ Quick Check 5

Solve $5x - 7 = 6(x + 2) - x$.

Absolute Value Equations

Objective 2 Solve absolute value equations. We now introduce equations involving absolute values of linear expressions.

EXAMPLE 6 Solve $|x| = 5$.

SOLUTION Recall that the absolute value of a number x, denoted $|x|$, is a measure of the distance between 0 and that number x on a real number line. In this equation, we are looking for a number x that is 5 units from 0.

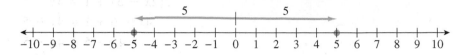

There are two such numbers: 5 and -5. The solution set is $\{-5, 5\}$.

▶ **Quick Check 6**
Solve $|x| = 7$.

The equation in the previous example is an **absolute value equation**. An absolute value equation relates the absolute value of an expression to a constant, such as $|2x - 3| = 7$, or the absolute value of an expression to the absolute value of another expression, such as $|3x - 4| = |2x + 11|$.

Consider the absolute value equation $|2x - 3| = 7$. This equation involves a number, represented by $2x - 3$, whose absolute value is equal to 7. That number must be either 7 or -7. We begin to solve this equation by converting it into the following two equations:

$$2x - 3 = 7 \quad \text{and} \quad 2x - 3 = -7$$

In general, to solve an equation in which the absolute value of an expression is equal to a positive number, we set the expression (without the absolute value bars) equal to that number and to its opposite. Solving those two equations gives the solutions.

Solving Absolute Value Equations

For any expression X and any positive number a, the solutions to the equation

$$|X| = a$$

can be found by solving the two equations

$$X = a \quad \text{and} \quad X = -a.$$

EXAMPLE 7 Solve $|2x - 3| = 7$.

SOLUTION Begin by converting the absolute value equation to two equations that do not involve absolute values.

$$|2x - 3| = 7$$
$$2x - 3 = 7 \quad \text{or} \quad 2x - 3 = -7 \qquad \text{Convert to two linear equations.}$$
$$2x = 10 \quad \text{or} \qquad 2x = -4 \qquad \text{Add 3 to both sides of each equation.}$$
$$x = 5 \quad \text{or} \qquad x = -2 \qquad \text{Divide both sides of each equation by 2.}$$

Check

$x = 5$	$x = -2$
$|2(5) - 3| = 7$	$|2(-2) - 3| = 7$
$|10 - 3| = 7$	$|-4 - 3| = 7$
$|7| = 7$	$|-7| = 7$
$7 = 7$	$7 = 7$

Quick Check 7
Solve $|3x + 8| = 5$.

Because both values check, the solution set is $\{-2, 5\}$.

A WORD OF CAUTION When solving an absolute value equation such as $|2x - 3| = 7$, be sure to rewrite the equation as two equations. Do not simply drop the absolute value bars and solve the resulting equation; if you do, you will miss one of the solutions.

EXAMPLE 8 Solve $3|2x + 7| - 4 = 20$.

SOLUTION We must isolate the absolute value before converting the equation to two linear equations.

$3|2x + 7| - 4 = 20$	
$3|2x + 7| = 24$	Add 4 to both sides.
$|2x + 7| = 8$	Divide both sides by 3.
$2x + 7 = 8$ or $2x + 7 = -8$	Convert to two linear equations.
$2x = 1$ or $2x = -15$	Subtract 7 from both sides of each equation.
$x = \dfrac{1}{2}$ or $x = -\dfrac{15}{2}$	Divide both sides of each equation by 2.

Quick Check 8
Solve
$4|2x - 5| - 9 = 7$.

The solution set is $\left\{-\frac{15}{2}, \frac{1}{2}\right\}$. The check of these solutions is left as an exercise.

A WORD OF CAUTION When solving an absolute value equation, isolate the absolute value before rewriting the equation as two equations without absolute values.

Because the absolute value of a number is a measure of its distance from 0 on the number line, the absolute value of a number cannot be negative. Therefore, an equation that has an absolute value equal to a negative number has no solution. For example, the equation $|x| = -3$ has no solution because there is no number whose absolute value is -3. We write $\varnothing$ for the solution set.

EXAMPLE 9 Solve $|3x - 4| + 8 = 6$.

SOLUTION Begin by isolating the absolute value.

$$|3x - 4| + 8 = 6$$
$$|3x - 4| = -2 \quad \text{Subtract 8 from both sides.}$$

Quick Check 9
Solve $|2x + 3| = -6$.

Because an absolute value cannot equal -2, this equation has no solution. The solution set is $\varnothing$.

A WORD OF CAUTION An equation in which an absolute value is equal to a negative number has no solution. Do not try to rewrite the equation as two equivalent equations.

If two unknown numbers have the same absolute values, either the two numbers are equal or they are opposites. We will use this idea to solve absolute value equations such as $|3x - 4| = |2x + 11|$. If these two absolute values are equal, either the two expressions inside the absolute value bars are equal ($3x - 4 = 2x + 11$) or the first expression is the opposite of the second expression ($3x - 4 = -(2x + 11)$). To find the solution of the original equation, we will solve these two resulting equations.

> ### Solving Absolute Value Equations Involving Two Absolute Values
>
> For any expressions X and Y, the solutions of the equation
>
> $$|X| = |Y|$$
>
> can be found by solving the two equations
>
> $$X = Y \quad \text{and} \quad X = -Y.$$

EXAMPLE 10 Solve $|3x - 4| = |2x + 11|$.

SOLUTION Begin by rewriting this equation as two equations that do not contain absolute values. For the first equation, set $3x - 4$ equal to $2x + 11$; for the second equation, set $3x - 4$ equal to the opposite of $2x + 11$. Finish by solving each equation.

$$3x - 4 = 2x + 11 \quad \text{or} \quad 3x - 4 = -(2x + 11)$$

Now solve each equation separately.

$3x - 4 = 2x + 11$	$3x - 4 = -(2x + 11)$
$x - 4 = 11$ Subtract $2x$ from both sides.	$3x - 4 = -2x - 11$ Distribute.
$x = 15$ Add 4 to both sides.	$5x - 4 = -11$ Add $2x$ to both sides.
	$5x = -7$ Add 4 to both sides.
	$x = -\dfrac{7}{5}$ Divide both sides by 5.

The solution set is $\left\{-\frac{7}{5}, 15\right\}$. The check of these solutions is left to the reader.

Quick Check 10

Solve $|x - 9| = |2x + 13|$.

BUILDING YOUR STUDY STRATEGY

Summary, 1 Study Groups Creating a study group is one of the best ways to learn mathematics and improve your performance on quizzes and exams. When a group of students works together, as long as one student understands the material being covered, there is a good chance that each student in the group will end up understanding the material. Sometimes a concept will be easier for you to understand if one of your peers explains it to you.

You also will find it helpful to have a support group: students who can lean on each other when times are bad. By being supportive of each other, you increase the chances that all of you will learn and be successful in your class.

Exercises 8.1

MyMathLab   Math XL   PRACTICE   WATCH   DOWNLOAD   READ   REVIEW

Vocabulary

1. A(n) _____ is a mathematical statement of equality between two expressions.

2. A(n) _____ of an equation is a value that, when substituted for the variable in the equation, produces a true statement.

3. To clear fractions from an equation, multiply both sides of the equation by the _____ of the denominators.

4. A contradiction is an equation that has ____ solutions.

5. The solution set to a contradiction can be denoted $\varnothing$, which represents _____.

6. An equation that is always true is a(n) _____.

7. For any expression X and any positive number a, to solve the equation $|X| = a$, rewrite the equation as the two equations _____ and _____.

8. The equation $|X| = a$ has no solutions if a is a(n) _____ number.

Solve.

9. $m - 5 = -9$

10. $x + 7 = -3$

11. $5t = -8$

12. $-2b = -28$

13. $7n - 11 = -39$

14. $6n + 32 = 14$

15. $-2x + 9 = 31$

16. $13 - 4x = -43$

17. $9m - 30 = 39$

18. $8m + 35 = -51$

19. $4x + 17 = 2x - 19$

20. $7x + 22 = 10x + 40$

21. $3x - 7 = -x + 15$

22. $-6x + 40 = -3x - 11$

23. $-9r + 22 = 3r + 67$

24. $5r - 41 = 34 - 4r$

25. $2(2x - 4) - 7 = 6x - 11$

26. $5(3 - 2x) + 4x = 3(3x - 1) + 7$

27. $5x - 3(2x - 9) = 4(3x - 8) + 7x$

28. $10 - 6(2x + 1) = 13 - 9x$

29. $2(3x - 1) + 5(x + 4) = 3(x + 7) - (x + 6)$

30. $4(2x + 3) - 3(x + 3) = 2(3x - 2) + (x - 3)$

31. $5x - 3(4x + 1) = 3 + 4(3x + 8)$

32. $3(x + 4) - 4(3x - 10) = 4(2x - 3) + 6(3x + 1)$

33. $\frac{3}{4}t - 6 = \frac{1}{3}t - 1$

34. $\frac{1}{8}n - 7 = -\frac{1}{4}n - 13$

35. $\frac{1}{2}(2x - 7) - \frac{1}{3}x = \frac{4}{3}x - 5$

36. $\frac{2}{3}(x - 6) - \frac{1}{4}x = \frac{3}{8}(8 - x) + \frac{1}{2}x$

37. $2b - 9 = 2b - 9$

38. $4t + 11 = 4t - 11$

39. $3(2n - 1) + 5 = 2(3n + 2)$

40. $5(n - 3) - 3n = 2(n - 7) - 1$

41. $5x - 2(3 - 2x) = 3(3x - 2)$

42. $7x - (3x - 4) = 4x - 4$

43. $|x| = 2$

44. $|x| = 13$

45. $|x + 6| = 13$

46. $|x - 9| = 4$

47. $|3x + 2| = 20$

48. $|2x - 9| = 37$

49. $|x| + 7 = 3$

50. $|x + 7| = 3$

51. $|x + 4| - 12 = 6$

52. $|x - 2| - 8 = 2$

53. $|x - 3| + 7 = 12$

54. $|x + 12| - 10 = 10$

55. $|4x - 11| - 19 = -8$

56. $|7x - 52| + 18 = 14$

57. $2|3x + 2| - 9 = 17$

58. $2|5x - 3| + 7 = 21$

59. $-|x + 3| - 10 = -16$

60. $-3|2x + 1| + 13 = -29$

61. $|4x - 5| = |3x - 23|$

62. $|x - 14| = |3x + 2|$

63. $|x + 12| = |2x - 9|$

64. $|2x + 1| = |x - 19|$

Mixed Practice 65–80

65. $|x + 13| - 12 = -7$

66. $-9x + 10 = -23$

67. $|x - 6| + 14 = 9$

68. $|5x| = |2x - 21|$

69. $25 = 4 - 6x$

70. $3(6x - 1) + 4x = 16(x + 2) - (11 - 3x)$

71. $10x - 17 = 6x - 53$

72. $|4x - 3| + 7 = 16$

73. $\frac{3}{5}x - \frac{1}{2} = \frac{2}{3}x + \frac{3}{4}$

74. $9x - 11 = 13x + 23$

75. $|7x - 11| = |4x + 6|$

76. $\frac{3}{4}x - \frac{2}{3} = \frac{1}{9}x + 7$

77. $|3x + 16| - 4 = 9$

78. $|x + 10| + 7 = 6$

79. $3(4x - 5) + 7x = 5(2x - 9) + 12$

80. $|x - 9| - 10 = -2$

81. Find an absolute value equation whose solution is $\{-2, 2\}$.

82. Find an absolute value equation whose solution is $\{-6, 10\}$.

83. Find an absolute value equation whose solution is $\{-5, 3\}$.

84. Find an absolute value equation whose solution is $\{\frac{1}{2}, \frac{7}{2}\}$.

✏️ Writing in Mathematics

Answer in complete sentences.

85. Explain why the equation $|2x - 7| + 6 = 4$ has no solution.

86. Here is a student's work for solving the equation $|x - 3| = -5$.

$$|x - 3| = -5$$
$$x - 3 = -5 \quad \text{or} \quad x - 3 = 5$$
$$x = -2 \quad \text{or} \quad x = 8$$
$$\{-2, 8\}$$

Explain what the student's error is and how he or she can avoid making a similar error in the future.

Quick Review Exercises

Section 8.1

Evaluate.

1. $f(x) = 3x - 14, f(-6)$

2. $f(x) = x^2 + 17x - 60, f(-5)$

3. $f(x) = \dfrac{x^2 - 6x + 25}{3x + 7}, f(2)$

4. $f(x) = |x - 7| + 3, f(0)$

8.2

Linear Inequalities and Absolute Value Inequalities

OBJECTIVES

1. Graph the solutions of a linear inequality on a number line and express the solutions by using interval notation.
2. Solve linear inequalities.
3. Solve compound linear inequalities.
4. Solve absolute value inequalities.

Linear Inequalities and Their Solutions

Objective 1 Graph the solutions of a linear inequality on a number line and express the solutions by using interval notation. In this section, we will examine solving inequalities. We begin by reviewing linear inequalities and the presentation of their solutions. For example, the solutions of the inequality $x < 4$ are all real numbers that are less than 4. This can be represented on a number line as follows:

This can be expressed in interval notation as $(-\infty, 4)$.

The following table shows the number line and interval notation associated with several types of simple linear inequalities:

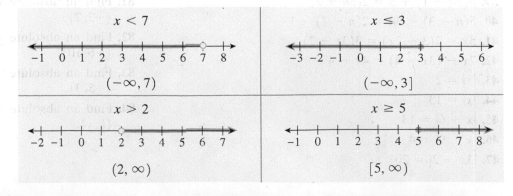

$x < 7$	$x \leq 3$
$(-\infty, 7)$	$(-\infty, 3]$
$x > 2$	$x \geq 5$
$(2, \infty)$	$[5, \infty)$

Recall that we use a closed circle whenever the endpoint is included in the interval ($\leq$ or $\geq$) and an open circle when the endpoint is not included ($<$ or $>$). When expressing the interval in interval notation, we use square brackets when the endpoint is included and parentheses when the endpoint is not included.

Solving Linear Inequalities

Objective **2** **Solve linear inequalities.** Solving a linear inequality is similar to solving a linear equation. The exception is if we multiply or divide both sides of the inequality by a negative number, then the direction of the inequality changes.

EXAMPLE 1 Solve $3x - 5 < -14$.

SOLUTION

$$3x - 5 < -14$$
$$3x < -9 \qquad \text{Add 5 to both sides.}$$
$$x < -3 \qquad \text{Divide both sides by 3.}$$

Here is the number line showing the solution.

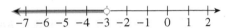

The solution expressed in interval notation is $(-\infty, -3)$.

▶ Quick Check 1
Solve $2x + 5 \leq 9$.

EXAMPLE 2 Solve $5x + 11 \leq 2(2x + 4) - 3$.

SOLUTION

$$5x + 11 \leq 2(2x + 4) - 3$$
$$5x + 11 \leq 4x + 8 - 3 \qquad \text{Distribute 2.}$$
$$5x + 11 \leq 4x + 5 \qquad \text{Combine like terms.}$$
$$x + 11 \leq 5 \qquad \text{Collect variables on the left side by}$$
$$\qquad \qquad \text{subtracting } 4x \text{ from both sides.}$$
$$x \leq -6 \qquad \text{Collect constant terms on the right side by}$$
$$\qquad \qquad \text{subtracting 11 from both sides.}$$

Here is the number line showing the solution.

The solution expressed in interval notation is $(-\infty, -6]$.

▶ Quick Check 2
Solve $3(2x - 1) + 4 \geq 2x - 7$.

EXAMPLE 3 Solve $-2x + 3 > 13$.

SOLUTION

$$-2x + 3 > 13$$
$$-2x > 10 \qquad \text{Subtract 3 from both sides.}$$
$$\frac{-2x}{-2} < \frac{10}{-2} \qquad \text{Divide both sides by } -2.$$
$$\qquad\qquad \text{This changes the direction of the inequality from } > \text{ to } <.$$
$$x < -5 \qquad \text{Simplify.}$$

Here is the number line showing the solution.

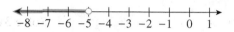

The solution expressed in interval notation is $(-\infty, -5)$.

▶ Quick Check 3
Solve $5 - 2x > -5$.

A WORD OF CAUTION When we multiply or divide both sides of an inequality by a negative number, we must change the direction of the inequality.

Solving Compound Linear Inequalities

Objective 3 Solve compound linear inequalities. A compound inequality is made up of two simple inequalities. For instance, the compound inequality $3 \le x < 7$ represents numbers that are greater than or equal to 3 ($x \ge 3$) and less than 7 ($x < 7$). In set theory, this is referred to as the intersection of these two sets. The intersection of two sets contains the items that are in both sets. The inequality $3 \le x < 7$ can be represented graphically by the following number line:

The interval notation for this interval is $[3, 7)$.

EXAMPLE 4 Solve $-3 < 2x - 1 < 5$.

SOLUTION The goal of solving a compound inequality such as this one is to isolate the variable x between two constants. We will work on all three parts of the inequality at the same time.

$$-3 < 2x - 1 < 5$$
$$-2 < 2x < 6 \qquad \text{Add 1 to each part of the inequality.}$$
$$-1 < x < 3 \qquad \text{Divide each part of the inequality by 2.}$$

Quick Check 4
Solve $-8 \le 3x + 7 \le 1$.

The solution consists of all real numbers greater than -1 and less than 3. Here is the number line showing the solution.

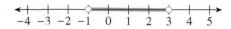

The solution expressed in interval notation is $(-1, 3)$.

Another type of compound inequality involves the word *or*. Consider the compound inequality $x < -2$ *or* $x > 1$. The solutions to this inequality are values that are solutions to either of the two inequalities. In other words, any number that is less than -2 ($x < -2$) *or* is greater than 1 ($x > 1$) is a solution of the compound inequality. Here are the solutions of this compound inequality graphed on a number line.

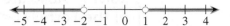

Notice that we have two different intervals that contain solutions. The solution expressed in interval notation is $(-\infty, -2) \cup (1, \infty)$. The symbol $\cup$ represents a union in set theory and combines the two intervals in one solution. The union of two sets is comprised of items that are elements of one set or the other.

EXAMPLE 5   Solve $x + 4 \leq 7$ or $2x - 1 > 11$.

SOLUTION   To solve a compound inequality of this type, first solve each inequality separately. Begin by solving $x + 4 \leq 7$.

$$x + 4 \leq 7$$
$$x \leq 3 \quad \text{Subtract 4 from both sides.}$$

Now solve the other inequality.

$$2x - 1 > 11$$
$$2x > 12 \quad \text{Add 1 to both sides.}$$
$$x > 6 \quad \text{Divide both sides by 2.}$$

Here is a number line showing the solution.

The solution expressed in interval notation is $(-\infty, 3] \cup (6, \infty)$.

▶ Quick Check 5

Solve $x + 3 < -3$ or $2x + 5 > 14$.

Absolute Value Inequalities

Objective ④ **Solve absolute value inequalities.** As in the previous section, we will expand the topic to include absolute values. Consider the inequality $|x| < 4$. Any real number in the following interval has an absolute value less than 4:

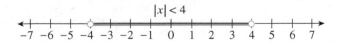

This can be expressed as the compound inequality $-4 < x < 4$. Using this idea, whenever we have an absolute value of an expression that is less than a positive number, we begin by "trapping" the expression between that positive number and its opposite, in this case, $-4 < x < 4$. We then proceed to solve the resulting compound inequality. Here are the solutions displayed on a number line.

Solving Absolute Value Inequalities of the Form $|X| < a$ or $|X| \leq a$

For any expression X and any nonnegative number a, the solutions of the inequality $|X| < a$ can be found by solving the compound inequality

$$-a < X < a.$$

(If $a = 0$, this inequality has no solutions.)

Similarly, for any expression X and any nonnegative number a, the solutions of the inequality $|X| \leq a$ can be found by solving the compound inequality

$$-a \leq X \leq a.$$

(If $a = 0$, solve the equation $X = a$.)

EXAMPLE 6 Solve $|x - 4| < 2$.

SOLUTION   The first step is to "trap" $x - 4$ between -2 and 2.

$$|x - 4| < 2$$
$$-2 < x - 4 < 2 \quad \text{"Trap" } x - 4 \text{ between } -2 \text{ and } 2.$$
$$2 < x < 6 \quad \text{Add 4 to each part of the inequality.}$$

Here is the number line showing the solution.

Quick Check 6
Solve $|x + 3| \leq 1$.

The solution expressed in interval notation is $(2, 6)$.

As with equations involving absolute values, we must isolate the absolute value before we rewrite the inequality as a compound inequality.

EXAMPLE 7 Solve $|3x + 7| - 5 \leq 4$.

SOLUTION

$$|3x + 7| - 5 \leq 4$$
$$|3x + 7| \leq 9 \quad \text{Add 5 to both sides.}$$
$$-9 \leq 3x + 7 \leq 9 \quad \text{Rewrite as a compound inequality.}$$
$$-16 \leq 3x \leq 2 \quad \text{Subtract 7 from each part of the inequality.}$$
$$-\frac{16}{3} \leq x \leq \frac{2}{3} \quad \text{Divide each part of the inequality by 3.}$$

Quick Check 7
Solve $|2x - 1| + 4 < 9$.

Here is the number line showing the solution.

The solution expressed in interval notation is $\left[-\frac{16}{3}, \frac{2}{3} \right]$.

A WORD OF CAUTION When solving an absolute value inequality, we must isolate the absolute value before we rewrite the inequality as a compound inequality.

If we have an inequality in which an absolute value is less than a negative number, such as $|x| < -2$, or less than 0, such as $|x| < 0$, this inequality has no solution. Because an absolute value is always 0 or greater, it can never be *less than* a negative number or zero.

EXAMPLE 8   Solve $|4x + 3| + 7 < 5$.

SOLUTION

$$|4x + 3| + 7 < 5$$
$$|4x + 3| < -2 \quad \text{Subtract 7 from both sides.}$$

Because an absolute value cannot be less than a negative number, this inequality has no solution: $\varnothing$.

A WORD OF CAUTION An inequality in which an absolute value is less than a negative number has no solution. Do not try to rewrite the inequality as a compound inequality.

Consider the inequality $|x| > 4$. Notice that we now have the absolute value of x *greater than* 4 rather than *less than* 4. Inequalities with an absolute value *greater* than a positive number must be approached in a different manner than absolute value inequalities with an absolute value *less* than a positive number. We cannot "trap" the expression between two constants. Solutions of the inequality $|x| > 4$ are in one of two categories. First, any positive number greater than 4 will have an absolute value greater than 4 as well. Second, any negative number less than -4 also will have an absolute value greater than 4. The following number line shows where the solutions of this inequality can be found:

This can be expressed symbolically as $x < -4$ or $x > 4$.

> ### Solving Absolute Value Inequalities
> ### of the Form $|X| > a$ or $|X| \geq a$
>
> For any expression X and any nonnegative number a, the solutions of the inequality $|X| > a$ can be found by solving the compound inequality
>
> $$X < -a \quad \text{or} \quad X > a.$$
>
> Similarly, for any expression X and any nonnegative number a, the solutions of the inequality $|X| \geq a$ can be found by solving the compound inequality
>
> $$X \leq -a \quad \text{or} \quad X \geq a.$$

EXAMPLE 9   Solve $|x + 3| > 2$.

SOLUTION   Begin by converting this inequality to the compound inequality $x + 3 < -2$ or $x + 3 > 2$. Then solve each inequality.

$$|x + 3| > 2$$
$$x + 3 < -2 \quad \text{or} \quad x + 3 > 2 \quad \text{Rewrite as a compound inequality.}$$
$$x < -5 \quad \text{or} \quad x > -1 \quad \text{Subtract 3 from both sides to solve}$$
$$\text{each inequality.}$$

Quick Check 8

Solve $|x + 1| - 3 < -8$.

Here is the number line showing the solution.

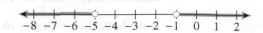

The solution expressed in interval notation is $(-\infty, -5) \cup (-1, \infty)$.

▶ Quick Check 9

Solve $|x - 2| > 4$.

Whether we are solving an absolute value equation or an absolute value inequality, the first step is to isolate the absolute value. The following table shows the correct step to take when *comparing an absolute value with a nonnegative number*:

	Example	What to Do
"Equal To"	$\lvert 2x + 9 \rvert = 5$	$2x + 9 = 5$ or $2x + 9 = -5$
"Less Than" **or** **"Less Than or Equal To"**	$\lvert x - 4 \rvert < 3$ or $\lvert x - 4 \rvert \leq 3$	$-3 < x - 4 < 3$ or $-3 \leq x - 4 \leq 3$
"Greater Than" **or** **"Greater Than or Equal To"**	$\lvert 3x + 5 \rvert > 7$ or $\lvert 3x + 5 \rvert \geq 7$	$3x + 5 < -7$ or $3x + 5 > 7$ or $3x + 5 \leq -7$ or $3x + 5 \geq 7$

EXAMPLE 10 Solve $|4x - 9| - 3 \geq 5$.

SOLUTION Begin by isolating the absolute value.

$$|4x - 9| - 3 \geq 5$$
$$|4x - 9| \geq 8 \quad \text{Add 3 to both sides.}$$

Because this inequality involves an absolute value that is *greater than* or equal to 8, we will rewrite this absolute value inequality as two linear inequalities.

$$4x - 9 \leq -8 \quad \text{or} \quad 4x - 9 \geq 8 \quad \text{Convert to two linear inequalities.}$$
$$4x \leq 1 \quad \text{or} \quad 4x \geq 17 \quad \text{Add 9 to both sides of each inequality.}$$
$$x \leq \frac{1}{4} \quad \text{or} \quad x \geq \frac{17}{4} \quad \text{Divide both sides of each inequality by 4.}$$

Here is the number line showing the solution.

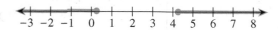

The solution expressed in interval notation is $\left(-\infty, \frac{1}{4}\right] \cup \left[\frac{17}{4}, \infty\right)$.

▶ Quick Check 10

Solve $|2x + 7| + 5 > 10$.

Consider the inequality $|x| > -2$. Because the absolute value of any number must be 0 or greater, $|x|$ must be greater than -2 for any real number x. The solution set is the set of all real numbers $\mathbb{R}$.

EXAMPLE 11   Solve $|3x + 5| - 3 > -4$.

SOLUTION   Begin by isolating the absolute value.

$$|3x + 5| - 3 > -4$$
$$|3x + 5| > -1 \quad \text{Add 3 to both sides to isolate the absolute value.}$$

This inequality must always be true, so the solution is the set of all real numbers $\mathbb{R}$. Here is the number line showing the solution.

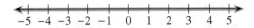

The interval notation associated with the set of real numbers is $(-\infty, \infty)$.

▶ Quick Check 11

Solve $|7x - 13| \geq -1$.

The following table summarizes the solutions for an equation or inequality that *compares an absolute value with a negative number*:

Equation or Inequality	Example	Solution
Equal to a negative number	$|x + 3| = -2$	$\varnothing$
Less than a negative number	$|2x - 1| < -4$	$\varnothing$
Greater than a negative number	$|3x + 4| > -3$	All real numbers: $\mathbb{R}$

BUILDING YOUR STUDY STRATEGY

Summary, 2 Using Your Textbook and Other Resources Your textbook is a valuable resource when used properly. Read a section the night before your instructor covers it to familiarize yourself with the material. This way, you can prepare questions to ask your instructor in class. After a section is covered in class, reread the section.

As you reread a section, use the textbook to create note cards to help you memorize new terms or procedures. After you read through an example, attempt the Quick Check exercise that follows to reinforce the concept presented in the example. As you work through the homework exercises, refer back to the examples found in that section if you need assistance.

In each section, the feature titled A Word of Caution points out common mistakes that students make and offers advice for avoiding those mistakes.

Your instructor is a valuable resource for answering questions and providing advice. Take advantage of your instructor's office hours in addition to your time in class. The tutorial center is another valuable resource.

Finally, the online supplement to this textbook at MyMathLab.com can be helpful. At this site, you will find video clips, tutorial exercises, and more.

Exercises 8.2

PRACTICE   WATCH   DOWNLOAD   READ   REVIEW

Vocabulary

1. A(n) _____ is an inequality containing linear expressions.

2. When graphing an inequality, use a(n) _____ circle to indicate an endpoint that is not included as a solution.

3. You can express the solutions of an inequality on a number line and by using _____ notation.

4. When solving a linear inequality, you must change the direction of the inequality whenever you multiply or divide both sides of the inequality by a(n) _____ number.

5. An inequality that is composed of two or more individual inequalities is called a(n) _____ inequality.

6. Before rewriting an absolute value inequality as a compound inequality, you must _____ the absolute value.

Solve the inequality. Graph your solution on a number line and write your solution in interval notation.

7. $x - 6 \leq 2$

8. $x - 5 > 4$

9. $3x + 2 \geq -10$

10. $2x + 5 > 9$

11. $-3x + 2 < 17$

12. $-4x - 9 \geq 3$

13. $\frac{2}{3}x - \frac{5}{6} > -2$

14. $\frac{3}{5}x - \frac{1}{3} < \frac{2}{5}$

15. $5(2x + 1) - 7x \leq 4x - 13$

16. $2x - 5(x - 3) < x + 9$

17. $5 \leq x - 3 \leq 11$

18. $-2 < x + 5 < 4$

19. $-10 \leq 7x + 4 \leq 53$

20. $7 < 6x - 5 < 49$

21. $-9 < 2x + 5 < -4$

22. $-8 \leq 3x + 7 \leq 28$

23. $-6 < \frac{3}{5}x + \frac{2}{5} < -2$

24. $\frac{7}{4} \leq \frac{1}{2}x - \frac{3}{8} \leq \frac{5}{2}$

25. $x + 6 < 8$ or $x - 3 > 5$

26. $x - 4 \leq -7$ or $x - 8 \geq -1$

27. $3x + 4 \leq -17$ or $2x - 9 \geq 9$

28. $\frac{2}{3}x - 2 < -4$ or $x + \frac{5}{3} > \frac{17}{2}$

29. $3x - 11 > 5x - 3$ or $2x + 31 < 6x + 7$

30. $2x + 17 \geq 7x - 13$ or $4x - 5 \leq 5x - 13$

31. $|x + 2| < 3$

32. $|2x - 9| < 7$

33. $|x - 5| + 7 \leq 13$

34. $|x + 2| - 6 \leq 1$

35. $|4x + 9| - 8 \leq -3$

36. $|7x + 14| + 9 < 6$

37. $|3x - 1| + 5 < 9$

38. $|6x - 5| - 2 \leq 11$

39. $2|2x + 10| + 19 \leq 11$

40. $3|x - 9| - 5 < 4$

41. $|x - 4| > 1$

42. $|2x + 6| > 4$

43. $|x + 6| + 5 \geq 8$

44. $|x - 2| - 3 \geq 2$

45. $|5x + 4| \geq -6$

46. $|8x - 21| + 7 \geq 10$

47. $|4x - 17| - 5 > 6$

48. $|x + 4| + 4 > 2$

49. $2|2x + 3| + 5 > 19$

50. $4|x + 5| - 11 > 17$

Mixed Practice, 51–64

Solve the inequality. Graph your solution on a number line and write your solution in interval notation

51. $|x + 4| \leq 6$

52. $|x + 10| > 4$

53. $-3x + 10 \geq 34$ or $6x - 9 \geq 33$

54. $-9 < 4x - 1 < 25$

55. $|x - 5| + 9 > 4$

56. $|x - 5| - 6 < -2$

57. $2x + 7 \geq -9$

58. $4x - 9 < 2x - 27$ or $5x + 11 > x - 13$

59. $|x - 9| + 8 \leq 3$

60. $-3x + 17 > -4$

61. $|2x + 5| - 9 \geq 4$

62. $|2x - 1| - 7 < 10$

63. $17 \leq 5x - 3 < 37$

64. $|4x - 3| + 6 > 11$

65. Find an absolute value inequality whose solution is $(-2, 2)$.

66. Find an absolute value inequality whose solution is $[-2, 6]$.

67. Find an absolute value inequality whose solution is $(-\infty, 1) \cup (9, \infty)$.

68. Find an absolute value inequality whose solution is $(-\infty, -4] \cup [-1, \infty)$.

Writing in Mathematics

Answer in complete sentences.

69. Explain why the inequality $|x + 5| < -3$ has no solutions, while every real number is a solution to the inequality $|x + 5| > -3$.

70. Explain why the inequality $|x| - 7 < -4$ has solutions, but the inequality $|x - 7| < -4$ does not.

71. *Solutions Manual* Write a solutions manual page for the following problem.
Solve. $|2x - 3| + 8 \leq 15$

8.3

Graphing Linear Equations and Linear Functions; Graphing Absolute Value Functions

OBJECTIVES

1. **Graph linear equations by using *x*- and *y*-intercepts.**
2. **Graph linear equations by using the slope and *y*-intercept.**
3. **Graph linear functions.**
4. **Graph absolute value functions by plotting points.**

In Chapter 3, we learned how to graph linear equations in two variables, such as $4x - y = 8$ and $y = -\frac{2}{3}x + 2$. We will begin this section with a brief review of how to graph this type of equation.

Graphing Linear Equations in Two Variables Using the *x*- and *y*-Intercepts

Objective 1 Graph linear equations by using *x*- and *y*-intercepts. We developed two techniques for graphing linear equations. The first involved finding the *x*- and *y*-intercepts of the line and then using these points to graph the line. Recall that the x-intercept of a line is the point where the line intersects the x-axis. To find the x-intercept, we substitute 0 for y in the equation and solve for x. The y-intercept is the point where the line crosses the y-axis, and we can find it by substituting 0 for x in the equation and solving for y.

EXAMPLE 1 Find any intercepts and graph $4x - y = 8$.

SOLUTION Find the x-intercept by substituting 0 for y and solving for x.

$$4x - 0 = 8 \quad \text{Substitute 0 for } y.$$
$$4x = 8 \quad \text{Simplify.}$$
$$x = 2 \quad \text{Divide both sides by 4.}$$

The x-intercept is at $(2, 0)$. To find the y-intercept, substitute 0 for x and solve for y.

$$4(0) - y = 8 \quad \text{Substitute 0 for } x.$$
$$-y = 8 \quad \text{Simplify.}$$
$$y = -8 \quad \text{Divide both sides by } -1.$$

The y-intercept is at $(0, -8)$.

It is helpful to find a third point before graphing the line to serve as a check for the other two points. If the three points do not lie on a straight line, at least one of the points is incorrect. To find a third point, we may select any value to substitute for x and solve for y. In this example, we will use 1 for x, but we could use any value we choose.

$$4(1) - y = 8 \quad \text{Substitute 1 for } x.$$
$$4 - y = 8 \quad \text{Multiply.}$$
$$-y = 4 \quad \text{Subtract 4 from both sides.}$$
$$y = -4 \quad \text{Divide both sides by } -1.$$

This tells us that the point $(1, -4)$ lies on the line. Here is a graph showing the line, as well as the three points we have found.

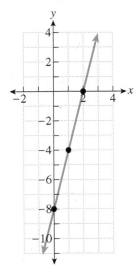

Quick Check 1

Find any intercepts and graph $5x + 2y = -10$.

Graphing a Linear Equation Using Its Slope and y-Intercept

Objective 2 Graph linear equations by using the slope and y-intercept.
A linear equation is in slope–intercept form if it is in the form $y = mx + b$. The constant m that is multiplied by x is the slope of the line, and the constant b represents the y-coordinate of the y-intercept. For example, for the equation $y = -\frac{2}{3}x + 2$, the slope of the line is $-\frac{2}{3}$ and the y-intercept is $(0, 2)$. Recall that slope is a measure of how quickly the line rises or falls as it moves to the right. A line whose slope is 4 moves up four units for every one unit it moves to the right, while a line whose slope is $-\frac{2}{3}$ moves down two units for every three units it moves to the right.

If an equation is in slope–intercept form, it provides the information needed to graph the line. We begin by placing the y-intercept on the graph. From that point, we use the slope of the line to locate other points on the graph.

Quick Check 2

Graph $y = \frac{7}{2}x - 4$.

EXAMPLE 2 Graph $y = 2x + 4$.

SOLUTION Because this equation is in slope–intercept form, we know that the y-intercept is $(0, 4)$, and we plot this point on the graph. The slope of this line is 2; so we can find another point on the line by starting at the y-intercept, $(0, 4)$, and moving two units up and one unit to the right. This tells us that the point $(1, 6)$ also is on the line. We could continue to find more points on the line using the same procedure (up two and to the right one). A graph of the line is shown to the right.

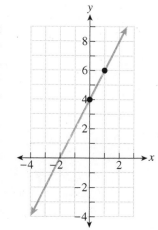

Graphing Linear Equations

- Equations in standard form ($Ax + By = C$) are often easier to graph by finding and plotting the x- and y-intercepts.
- Equations in slope–intercept form ($y = mx + b$) are often easier to graph by plotting the y-intercept and using the slope to find other points.

Linear Functions and Their Graphs

Objective 3 Graph linear functions. A linear function is a function of the form $f(x) = mx + b$. Recall that the notation $f(x)$, read "f of x," stands for the function f evaluated at x. For example, consider the linear function $f(x) = 3x - 8$. If we wanted to evaluate $f(6)$, we would substitute 6 for x in the function and simplify.

$$f(6) = 3(6) - 8 \quad \text{Substitute 6 for } x.$$
$$= 18 - 8 \quad \text{Multiply.}$$
$$= 10 \quad \text{Subtract.}$$

Graphing a linear function $f(x) = mx + b$ is identical to graphing a linear equation $y = mx + b$. We plot points of the form $(x, f(x))$, beginning with the y-intercept. We then use the slope of the line to find other points on the line.

EXAMPLE 3 Graph $f(x) = -\frac{3}{2}x + 6$.

SOLUTION The y-intercept of this graph is at $(0, 6)$, so we begin by placing that point on the graph. The slope of this line is $-\frac{3}{2}$; so beginning at the y-intercept, we move three units down and two units to the right. This tells us that the point $(2, 3)$ is on the graph.

Quick Check 3

Graph the linear function $f(x) = -x + 6$.

Absolute Value Functions

Objective 4 Graph absolute value functions by plotting points. We will now graph our first nonlinear function: the **absolute value function** $f(x) = |x|$. We will begin to graph this function by creating the following table of function values for various values of x:

x	$f(x) = |x|$	$(x, f(x))$
-2	$f(-2) = |-2| = 2$	$(-2, 2)$
-1	$f(-1) = |-1| = 1$	$(-1, 1)$
0	$f(0) = |0| = 0$	$(0, 0)$
1	$f(1) = |1| = 1$	$(1, 1)$
2	$f(2) = |2| = 2$	$(2, 2)$

Here is the graph. Notice that the graph is not a straight line; instead, it is V-shaped. *The most important point for graphing an absolute value function is the point of the V, where the graph changes from falling to rising.* The turning point is the origin for this particular function.

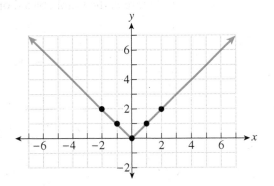

To graph an absolute value function, we find the x-coordinate of the turning point, select two values to the left and right of this value, and create a table of values. Choosing values for x that are to the left and to the right of the turning point is crucial. Suppose we had chosen only positive values for x when graphing $f(x) = |x|$. All of our points would have been on the straight line located to the right of the origin, and our graph would have been a straight line rather than a V shape.

The turning point occurs at the value of x that makes the expression inside the absolute value bars equal to 0. This is because the minimum output of an absolute value occurs when we take the absolute value of 0.

Graphing an Absolute Value Function

- Determine the value of x for which the expression inside the absolute value bars is equal to 0.
- In addition to this value, select two values that are less than this value and two that are greater.
- Create a table of function values for these values of x.
- Place the points $(x, f(x))$ on the graph and draw the V-shaped graph that passes through these points.

EXAMPLE 4 Graph $f(x) = |x + 3| - 2$.

SOLUTION For an absolute value function, begin by finding the value of x that makes the expression inside the absolute value bars equal to 0.

$$x + 3 = 0 \quad \text{Set } x + 3 \text{ equal to } 0.$$
$$x = -3 \quad \text{Subtract 3 from both sides.}$$

Now select two values that are less than -3, such as -5 and -4, and two values that are greater than -3, such as -2 and -1. Next, create a table of values.

x	$f(x) = |x + 3| - 2$	$(x, f(x))$
-5	$f(-5) = |-5 + 3| - 2 = 2 - 2 = 0$	$(-5, 0)$
-4	$f(-4) = |-4 + 3| - 2 = 1 - 2 = -1$	$(-4, -1)$
-3	$f(-3) = |-3 + 3| - 2 = 0 - 2 = -2$	$(-3, -2)$
-2	$f(-2) = |-2 + 3| - 2 = 1 - 2 = -1$	$(-2, -1)$
-1	$f(-1) = |-1 + 3| - 2 = 2 - 2 = 0$	$(-1, 0)$

Here is the graph, based on the points from the table.

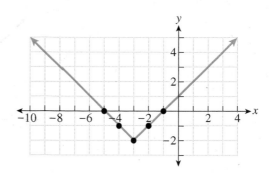

Quick Check 4

Graph the function
$f(x) = |x + 1| + 3$.

Using Your Calculator You can graph absolute value functions using the TI-84. (Recall that to access the absolute value function on the TI-84, you press the [MATH] key; you will find the absolute value function under the **NUM** menu.) To enter the equation of the function from Example 4, $f(x) = |x + 3| - 2$, press the [Y=] key. Enter $|x + 3| - 2$ next to Y_1. Then press the key labeled [GRAPH] to graph the function.

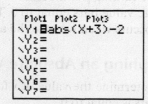

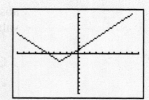

Finding the Domain and Range of an Absolute Value Function

Recall that the domain of a function is the set of all possible input values for the function and the range of a function is the set of all possible output values for the function. From the graph of a function, the domain can be read from left to right and the range can be read from bottom to top. Let's look at the graph of $f(x) = |x|$ again.

Notice that the graph extends to negative infinity on the left and to infinity on the right. Its domain is the set of real numbers $\mathbb{R}$, which is expressed in interval notation as $(-\infty, \infty)$. The lowest value of this function is 0, but it has no upper bound. The range of this function is $[0, \infty)$.

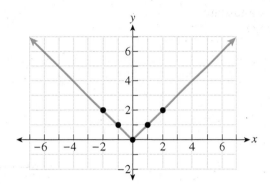

Let's reexamine the graph of $f(x) = |x + 3| - 2$. The domain of this function is also the set of real numbers. What is the range? The lowest function value for this function is -2, so the range is $[-2, \infty)$.

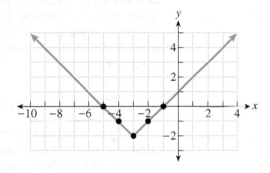

EXAMPLE 5 Graph the function $f(x) = |x - 1| + 4$ and find the domain and range of the function.

SOLUTION We begin by finding the x-coordinate of the turning point of the graph. To do this, we set the expression inside the absolute value bars equal to 0 and solve for x.

$$x - 1 = 0 \quad \text{Set } x - 1 \text{ equal to 0.}$$
$$x = 1 \quad \text{Add 1 to both sides.}$$

Now we can create a table of values using two values for x that are less than 1 and two that are greater than 1.

x	$f(x) = \lvert x - 1\rvert + 4$	$(x, f(x))$
-1	$f(-1) = \lvert -1 - 1\rvert + 4 = 6$	$(-1, 6)$
0	$f(0) = \lvert 0 - 1\rvert + 4 = 5$	$(0, 5)$
1	$f(1) = \lvert 1 - 1\rvert + 4 = 4$	$(1, 4)$
2	$f(2) = \lvert 2 - 1\rvert + 4 = 5$	$(2, 5)$
3	$f(3) = \lvert 3 - 1\rvert + 4 = 6$	$(3, 6)$

Graph the function
$f(x) = |x - 5| - 4$ and state
the domain and range.

Below is the graph. From this graph, we can see that the domain is the set of all real numbers and the range is $[4, \infty)$.

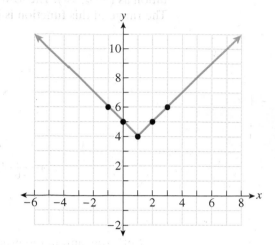

A WORD OF CAUTION When we graph an absolute value function, if we choose values for x wisely, the graph will display a series of points that forms a V. If all of our points appear to lie on a straight line, we have chosen values for x that are all on one side of the point where the graph changes from decreasing to increasing or we have made some mistakes when evaluating the function. In either case, we should go back and check our work.

EXAMPLE 6   Graph $f(x) = -|x| + 2$ and state the domain and range.

SOLUTION   Notice that this absolute value function is slightly different from the first few we graphed. A negative sign is in front of the absolute value bars, which will have a significant impact on how the graph looks. However, we will use the same approach to graphing this function as the previous absolute value functions. We begin by finding the x-coordinate of the turning point by setting the expression inside the absolute value bars equal to 0. In this case, $x = 0$ is the x-coordinate of the turning point. Now we can create a table of values using two values for x that are less than 0 and two that are greater than 0.

Graph the function
$f(x) = -|x - 4| - 5$ and state
the domain and range.

x	$f(x) = -\lvert x \rvert + 2$	$(x, f(x))$
-2	$f(-2) = -\lvert -2 \rvert + 2 = -2 + 2 = 0$	$(-2, 0)$
-1	$f(-1) = -\lvert -1 \rvert + 2 = -1 + 2 = 1$	$(-1, 1)$
0	$f(0) = -\lvert 0 \rvert + 2 = 0 + 2 = 2$	$(0, 2)$
1	$f(1) = -\lvert 1 \rvert + 2 = -1 + 2 = 1$	$(1, 1)$
2	$f(2) = -\lvert 2 \rvert + 2 = -2 + 2 = 0$	$(2, 0)$

The graph is to the right. From this graph, we can see that the domain is the set of all real numbers. This time the function has a maximum value of 2 with no lower bound; so the range is $(-\infty, 2]$.

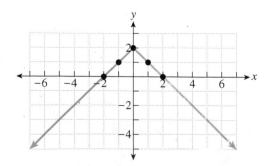

EXAMPLE 7   Find the absolute value function for the graph.

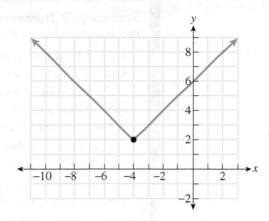

SOLUTION   To find the function, let's focus on the turning point of this graph, which is $(-4, 2)$. Because the x-coordinate is -4, the expression $x + 4$ must be inside the absolute value bars. The y-coordinate of the turning point is 2, which tells us that 2 is added to the absolute value. The function is of the form $f(x) = a|x + 4| + 2$, where a is a real number. To determine the value of a, we need to use the coordinates of another point on the graph, such as the y-intercept $(0, 6)$. This point tells us that $f(0) = 6$. We will use this fact to find a.

$$f(0) = 6$$
$$a|0 + 4| + 2 = 6 \quad \text{Substitute 0 for } x \text{ in the function } f(x).$$
$$4a + 2 = 6 \quad \text{Simplify the absolute value.}$$
$$4a = 4 \quad \text{Subtract 2 from both sides.}$$
$$a = 1 \quad \text{Divide both sides by 4.}$$

Substituting 1 for a, we find that the function is $f(x) = |x + 4| + 2$.

▶ Quick Check 7

Find the absolute value function for the graph.

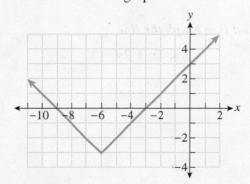

Exercises 8.3

PRACTICE   WATCH   DOWNLOAD   READ   REVIEW

Vocabulary

1. A(n) _____ is a function of the form $f(x) = |x|$.

2. The graph of an absolute value function is _____-shaped.

3. Find $f(0)$ to find the _____ of a function.

4. Set $f(x) = 0$ to find the _____ of a function.

Find the intercepts and then graph the line.

5. $4x + 3y = -24$ **6.** $3x + 2y = 12$

7. $2x - 5y = 10$ **8.** $-4x + 6y = -12$

9. $\dfrac{2}{9}x + \dfrac{1}{3}y = 2$

10. $\dfrac{1}{6}x - \dfrac{1}{3}y = -\dfrac{2}{3}$

11. $8x - 3y = 12$ **12.** $7x + 10y = 35$

13. $y = -3x + 4$ **14.** $y = -\frac{1}{5}x + 2$ **20.** $y = -\frac{5}{2}x + 5$ **21.** $y = 4x$

22. $y = -\frac{1}{3}x$

Graph the line using the slope and y-intercept.

15. $y = 3x + 2$ **16.** $y = 2x - 7$

Graph the linear function.

23. $f(x) = x + 7$ **24.** $f(x) = x - 3$

17. $y = -4x + 8$ **18.** $y = -5x - 3$

25. $f(x) = 4x - 5$ **26.** $f(x) = 2x + 3$

19. $y = \frac{2}{3}x - 6$

27. $f(x) = -5x + 8$ **28.** $f(x) = -3x - 6$ **34.** $f(x) = |x + 6|$

35. $f(x) = |x| + 3$

29. $f(x) = \dfrac{3}{4}x - 6$ **30.** $f(x) = -\dfrac{5}{3}x + 2$

36. $f(x) = |x| - 4$

31. $f(x) = 2$ **32.** $f(x) = -7$

37. $f(x) = |x + 3| - 4$

Graph the absolute value function. State the domain and range of the function.

33. $f(x) = |x - 7|$

38. $f(x) = |x + 1| + 2$

39. $f(x) = |x - 6| + 3$

44. $f(x) = |3x + 12|$

45. $f(x) = |4x + 8| - 5$

40. $f(x) = |x - 2| - 5$

41. $f(x) = |x + 4| - 2$

46. $f(x) = |5x - 10| - 6$ **47.** $f(x) = 2|x - 1| + 3$

42. $f(x) = |x - 1| + 6$

48. $f(x) = 3|x + 5| - 7$

43. $f(x) = |2x - 6|$

49. $f(x) = -|x + 6|$

53. $f(x) = -3|x + 2| + 9$ **54.** $f(x) = -4|x - 4| - 1$

50. $f(x) = -|x| + 6$

Find the intercepts of the absolute value function.

55. $f(x) = |x - 3| - 7$
56. $f(x) = |x + 4| - 2$
57. $f(x) = |x| - 6$
58. $f(x) = |x + 5|$
59. $f(x) = |x + 2| + 4$

51. $f(x) = -|x - 3| - 4$

60. $f(x) = |x - 1| + 8$
61. $f(x) = -|x - 4| + 3$
62. $f(x) = -|x + 7| + 9$

Find the absolute value function on the graph.

63.

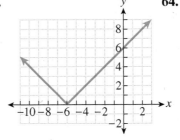

64.

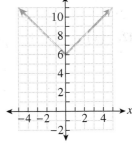

52. $f(x) = -|x + 8| + 5$

65.

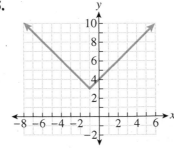

66.

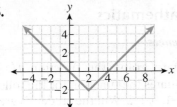

67.

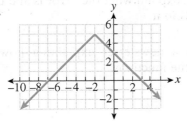

68.

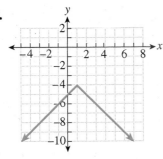

73. $f(x) = x + 3$

74. $f(x) = |x| + 3$

75. $f(x) = |x + 4|$

76. $f(x) = \dfrac{5}{2}x - 6$

77. $f(x) = |x + 2| - 7$

Mixed Practice, 69–80

Graph the function.

69. $f(x) = -\dfrac{3}{2}x + 7$

70. $f(x) = 2x - 5$

78. $f(x) = 7$

71. $f(x) = |x - 3| - 2$

72. $f(x) = |x + 5| + 4$

79. $f(x) = \dfrac{3}{7}x$

80. $f(x) = -|x - 2| + 4$

Answer in complete sentences.

81. A student is trying to graph the function $f(x) = |x - 5| + 1$ and evaluates the function for the following values of x: $-2, -1, 0, 1, 2$. Will the student's graph be correct? If not, explain what the error is and how the student can avoid it.

82. *Newsletter* Write a newsletter explaining how to graph absolute value functions.

8.4

Review of Factoring; Quadratic Equations and Rational Equations

OBJECTIVES

1. Factor polynomials.
2. Solve quadratic equations.
3. Solve rational equations.

Factoring Polynomials

Objective 1 Factor polynomials. A polynomial is factored when it has been written as a product of two or more expressions; these expressions are the factors.

Factoring Out the Greatest Common Factor (GCF)

Every time we attempt to factor a polynomial, we should begin by attempting to factor out the greatest common factor (GCF) of all of the terms.

> **EXAMPLE 1** Factor $12x^5 - 3x^4 + 15x^2$.
>
> SOLUTION   The largest number that divides into these three coefficients is 3. The variable x is a factor of all three terms. For the GCF, we use the largest power of x that is a factor of all of the terms, which is x^2. The GCF of these three terms is $3x^2$. We finish by factoring the GCF out of each term.
>
> $$12x^5 - 3x^4 + 15x^2 = 3x^2(4x^3 - x^2 + 5)$$
>
> Recall that we can check the factoring through multiplication. The reader can verify that $3x^2(4x^3 - x^2 + 5)$ equals $12x^5 - 3x^4 + 15x^2$.

Quick Check 1
Factor $36x^6 + 60x^5 - 12x^3$.

General Factoring Strategy

The first step in factoring any polynomial is to factor the GCF out of all terms. Once the GCF has been factored out, we must check to see if the resulting polynomial can be factored further. (In the previous example, the polynomial $4x^3 - x^2 + 5$ could not be factored further.)

Once we have dealt with the GCF, the factoring strategy is generally determined by the number of terms in the polynomial. Here is a summary from Chapter 6.

1. Factor out any common factors.
2. Determine the number of terms in the polynomial.
   a. If there are *four terms*, try factoring by grouping, discussed in Section 6.1.
   b. If there are *three terms*, try factoring the trinomial using the techniques of Sections 6.2 and 6.3.
      - $x^2 + bx + c = (x + m)(x + n)$: Find two integers m and n whose product is c and whose sum is b.
      - $ax^2 + bx + c$ ($a \neq 1$): We have two methods for factoring this type of trinomial: by grouping or by trial and error. To use factoring by grouping, refer to Objective 1 in Section 6.3. To factor by trial and error, refer to Objective 2 in Section 6.3.
   c. If there are only *two terms*, check to see if the binomial is one of the special binomials discussed in Section 6.4.
      - Difference of Squares: $a^2 - b^2 = (a + b)(a - b)$
      - Sum of Squares: $a^2 + b^2$ is not factorable.
      - Difference of Cubes: $a^3 - b^3 = (a - b)(a^2 + ab + b^2)$
      - Sum of Cubes: $a^3 + b^3 = (a + b)(a^2 - ab + b^2)$
3. After the polynomial has been factored, make sure any factor with two or more terms does not have any common factors other than 1. If there are common factors, factor them out.
4. Check your factoring through multiplication.

Factoring by Grouping

An important factoring technique is factoring by grouping. This technique is often used when a polynomial has four or more terms. To factor a polynomial by grouping, we split the terms of the polynomial into two groups. We then factor out a common factor of each group. At this point, if the two groups share a common factor, this common factor can be factored out of each group, leaving the polynomial in factored form.

EXAMPLE 2   Factor $x^3 - 6x^2 - 10x + 60$.

SOLUTION   There are no factors (other than 1) that are common to all four terms, so we proceed to factor by grouping. We will consider $x^3 - 6x^2$ to be the first group and $-10x + 60$ to be the second group.

$$x^3 - 6x^2 - 10x + 60 = x^2(x - 6) - 10(x - 6) \qquad \text{Factor } x^2 \text{ out of the first two terms and } -10 \text{ out of the last two terms.}$$

$$= (x - 6)(x^2 - 10) \qquad \text{Factor out the common factor } x - 6.$$

Recall that we can check the factoring by multiplying these two binomials. Their product should equal the original polynomial.

Quick Check 2
Factor $x^3 - 8x^2 + 4x - 32$.

Factoring Trinomials

We will now discuss factoring quadratic trinomials of the form $x^2 + bx + c$, where b and c are integers. To factor such a polynomial, we look for two integers m and n whose product is c (that is, $m \cdot n = c$) and whose sum is b (that is, $m + n = b$). If we can find two integers that satisfy these conditions, the polynomial factors to be $(x + m)(x + n)$.

When the constant term c of the trinomial is positive, this tells us that the two integers we are looking for have the same sign. The sign of b tells us what the sign of each integer will be. When the constant term is negative, we are looking for one positive integer and one negative integer. The sign of the integer with the largest absolute value is the same as the sign of b.

EXAMPLE 3 Factor $x^2 + 8x + 15$.

SOLUTION Because the three terms do not contain a common factor other than 1, begin by looking for two integers whose product is 15 and whose sum is 8. The integers that satisfy the conditions are 3 and 5, so $x^2 + 8x + 15$ can be factored as $(x + 3)(x + 5)$.

$$x^2 + 8x + 15 = (x + 3)(x + 5)$$

EXAMPLE 4 Factor $x^2 - 10x + 16$.

SOLUTION We cannot factor out a common factor, so we look for the integers with a product of 16 and a sum of -10. The two integers are -2 and -8.

$$x^2 - 10x + 16 = (x - 2)(x - 8)$$

Quick Check 3

Factor.

a) $x^2 + 11x + 28$
b) $x^2 - 13x + 30$

EXAMPLE 5 Factor $3x^2 - 15x - 42$.

SOLUTION We begin by factoring out the common factor 3. This gives us $3(x^2 - 5x - 14)$. We then factor the trinomial factor by finding two integers with a product of -14 and a sum of -5. Again, because the product must be negative, we are looking for one negative integer and one positive integer. In this case, the integers are -7 and 2.

$$3x^2 - 15x - 42 = 3(x^2 - 5x - 14) \quad \text{Factor out 3.}$$
$$= 3(x - 7)(x + 2) \quad \text{Factor the trinomial.}$$

▶ **Quick Check 4**

Factor $2x^2 - 14x - 36$.

EXAMPLE 6 Factor $-x^2 - 6x + 55$.

SOLUTION When the coefficient of the leading term is negative, we begin by factoring a negative common factor from all of the terms. In this case, we will factor out -1 and then factor the resulting trinomial.

$$-x^2 - 6x + 55 = -(x^2 + 6x - 55) \quad \text{Factor out } -1$$
$$= -(x + 11)(x - 5) \quad \text{Factor the trinomial.}$$

Quick Check 5

Factor $-x^2 + 17x - 70$.

If the leading coefficient of a quadratic trinomial is not equal to 1 and that coefficient cannot be factored out as a common factor, we must use a different technique to factor the polynomial. We will use factoring by grouping to factor polynomials of the form $ax^2 + bx + c$ $(a \neq 1)$. (You also can use the method of trial and error, as presented in Section 6.3.)

We begin by multiplying a by c, then find two integers m and n whose product is equal to $a \cdot c$ and whose sum is b. Once we find these two integers, we rewrite the polynomial as $ax^2 + mx + nx + c$ and factor by grouping.

EXAMPLE 7 Factor $2x^2 - 3x - 20$.

SOLUTION We cannot factor out any common factors, so we begin by multiplying $2(-20)$, which equals -40. Next, we look for two integers whose product is -40 and whose sum is -3. The two integers are -8 and 5; so we will replace the term $-3x$ in the original polynomial by $-8x + 5x$ and then factor by grouping.

$$2x^2 - 3x - 20 = 2x^2 - 8x + 5x - 20 \qquad \text{Rewrite } -3x \text{ as } -8x + 5x.$$
$$= 2x(x - 4) + 5(x - 4) \qquad \text{Factor the common factor } 2x$$
$$\text{from the first two terms and}$$
$$\text{the common factor } 5 \text{ from the}$$
$$\text{last two terms.}$$
$$= (x - 4)(2x + 5) \qquad \text{Factor out the common factor}$$
$$x - 4.$$

Quick Check 6
Factor $6x^2 - 7x - 20$.

Factoring a Difference of Squares

A binomial of the form $a^2 - b^2$ is called a difference of squares, and it can be factored using the following formula:

$$a^2 - b^2 = (a + b)(a - b)$$

EXAMPLE 8 Factor $4x^2 - 25$.

SOLUTION We cannot factor any common factors out of this binomial, so we check to see whether it is a difference of squares. The binomial can be rewritten as $(2x)^2 - (5)^2$, so this is a difference of squares and can be factored using the formula.

$$4x^2 - 25 = (2x)^2 - (5)^2 \qquad \text{Rewrite as the difference of two}$$
$$\text{squares.}$$
$$= (2x + 5)(2x - 5) \qquad \text{Factor using the formula}$$
$$a^2 - b^2 = (a + b)(a - b).$$

Quick Check 7
Factor $9x^2 - 100$.

Sum of Squares

A binomial that is a sum of squares $(a^2 + b^2)$ cannot be factored.

Factoring a Difference or a Sum of Cubes

A binomial that is a difference of cubes $(a^3 - b^3)$ or a sum of cubes $(a^3 + b^3)$ can be factored using the following formulas:

Difference of Cubes: $a^3 - b^3 = (a - b)(a^2 + ab + b^2)$
Sum of Cubes: $a^3 + b^3 = (a + b)(a^2 - ab + b^2)$

EXAMPLE 9 Factor $8x^3 - 125$.

SOLUTION This binomial is a difference of cubes: $8x^3 = (2x)^3$ and $125 = 5^3$.

$$8x^3 - 125 = (2x)^3 - (5)^3 \qquad \text{Rewrite each term as}$$
$$\text{a perfect cube.}$$
$$= (2x - 5)(2x \cdot 2x + 2x \cdot 5 + 5 \cdot 5) \qquad \text{Factor as a difference}$$
$$\text{of cubes.}$$
$$= (2x - 5)(4x^2 + 10x + 25) \qquad \text{Simplify each term in}$$
$$\text{the trinomial factor.}$$

Quick Check 8
Factor $27x^3 - 64y^3$.

Recall from Chapter 6 that the major difference between factoring a difference of cubes and factoring a sum of cubes is keeping track of the signs.

Solving Quadratic Equations

Objective ② **Solve quadratic equations.** We now review the solution of quadratic equations by factoring. A quadratic equation is an equation that can be written in the form $ax^2 + bx + c = 0$, where a, b, and c are real numbers and $a \neq 0$. Recall the following guidelines for solving quadratic equations:

- Simplify each side of the equation. This includes performing any distributive multiplications, clearing all fractions by multiplying each side of the equation by the LCD, and combining like terms.
- Collect all terms on one side of the equation, leaving 0 on the other side. It is a good idea to move all terms to one side in such a way that the coefficient of the second-degree term is positive.
- Factor the quadratic expression.
- Set each factor equal to 0 and solve each equation.

The principle behind this procedure is the zero-factor property, which says that if two unknown numbers have a product of zero, at least one of these factors must be equal to zero.

EXAMPLE 10   Solve $x^2 + 7x = 30 - 6x$.

SOLUTION   We begin to solve this equation by collecting all terms on the left side of the equation.

$$x^2 + 7x = 30 - 6x$$
$$x^2 + 13x - 30 = 0 \qquad \text{Add } 6x \text{ and subtract } 30 \text{ (on both sides)}.$$
$$(x + 15)(x - 2) = 0 \qquad \text{Factor}.$$
$$x + 15 = 0 \quad \text{or} \quad x - 2 = 0 \quad \text{Set each factor equal to } 0.$$
$$x = -15 \quad \text{or} \quad x = 2 \quad \text{Solve}.$$

◀ The solution set is $\{-15, 2\}$.

Quick Check 9

Solve $x(x + 3) = 7x + 32$.

EXAMPLE 11   Solve $\frac{1}{2}x^2 - \frac{1}{4}x = 2x^2 - 3$.

SOLUTION   We begin to solve this equation by clearing all fractions. We do this by multiplying each side of the equation by 4, which is the least common denominator (LCD).

$$\frac{1}{2}x^2 - \frac{1}{4}x = 2x^2 - 3$$

$$4 \cdot \left(\frac{1}{2}x^2 - \frac{1}{4}x \right) = 4 \cdot (2x^2 - 3) \qquad \text{Multiply both sides by 4}.$$

$$\overset{2}{\cancel{4}} \cdot \frac{1}{\cancel{2}}x^2 - \overset{1}{\cancel{4}} \cdot \frac{1}{\cancel{4}}x = 4 \cdot 2x^2 - 4 \cdot 3 \qquad \begin{array}{l}\text{Distribute and divide out common} \\ \text{factors}.\end{array}$$

$$2x^2 - x = 8x^2 - 12 \qquad \text{Simplify}.$$

$$0 = 6x^2 + x - 12 \qquad \begin{array}{l}\text{Collect all terms on the right side.} \\ \text{Subtract } 2x^2 \text{ and add } x \text{ (on both sides)}.\end{array}$$

$$0 = (3x - 4)(2x + 3) \qquad \text{Factor}.$$

$$3x - 4 = 0 \quad \text{or} \quad 2x + 3 = 0 \qquad \text{Set each factor equal to } 0.$$

$$x = \frac{4}{3} \quad \text{or} \quad x = -\frac{3}{2} \qquad \text{Solve}.$$

Quick Check 10

Solve $\frac{1}{5}x^2 - \frac{1}{10}x - 1 = 0$.

◀ The solution set is $\left\{ -\frac{3}{2}, \frac{4}{3} \right\}$.

Solving Rational Equations

Objective 3 Solve rational equations. We have learned to solve rational equations, which are equations that contain one or more rational expressions. An example of such an equation is $\dfrac{2x}{x-2} - \dfrac{5}{x+1} = 3$. A first step in solving a rational equation is to multiply each side of the equation by the LCD. Then we proceed to solve the resulting equation. We must check that a solution does not cause a denominator to be 0. Such solutions are called extraneous solutions and are omitted from the solution set.

To find the LCD for two or more rational expressions:

• Completely factor each denominator.
• Identify each factor that is a factor of at least one denominator. The LCD is equal to the product of these factors.
• If an expression is a repeated factor of one or more of the denominators, repeat it as a factor in the LCD as well. The exponent used for this factor is equal to the greatest power to which the factor is raised in any one denominator.

EXAMPLE 12 Solve $\dfrac{1}{x+3} + \dfrac{1}{x} = \dfrac{9}{x(x+3)}$.

SOLUTION The LCD for these rational expressions is $x(x+3)$. We see that the values 0 and -3 for x cause the LCD to be equal to 0 and therefore cannot be solutions of this equation.

$$\frac{1}{x+3} + \frac{1}{x} = \frac{9}{x(x+3)}$$

$$x(x+3)\left(\frac{1}{x+3} + \frac{1}{x}\right) = x(x+3)\left(\frac{9}{x(x+3)}\right) \quad \text{Multiply both sides by the LCD.}$$

$$x(x+3) \cdot \frac{1}{x+3} + x(x+3) \cdot \frac{1}{x} = x(x+3) \cdot \frac{9}{x(x+3)} \quad \begin{array}{l}\text{Distribute and divide}\\ \text{out common factors.}\end{array}$$

$$x + x + 3 = 9 \qquad \text{Simplify.}$$
$$2x + 3 = 9 \qquad \text{Combine like terms.}$$
$$2x = 6 \qquad \begin{array}{l}\text{Subtract 3 from}\\ \text{both sides.}\end{array}$$
$$x = 3 \qquad \begin{array}{l}\text{Divide both sides}\\ \text{by 2.}\end{array}$$

◀ This value does not cause a denominator to equal 0. The solution set is {3}.

Quick Check 11

Solve $\dfrac{x}{x-4} - \dfrac{8}{x-3} = 1$.

EXAMPLE 13 Solve $\dfrac{1}{x-5} + \dfrac{1}{x+5} = \dfrac{10}{x^2-25}$.

SOLUTION Factor each denominator to find the LCD.

$$\frac{1}{x-5} + \frac{1}{x+5} = \frac{10}{x^2-25}$$

$$\frac{1}{x-5} + \frac{1}{x+5} = \frac{10}{(x+5)(x-5)} \quad \begin{array}{l}\text{Factor. The LCD is}\\ (x+5)(x-5).\end{array}$$

$$(x+5)(x-5)\left(\frac{1}{x-5} + \frac{1}{x+5}\right) = \frac{10}{(x+5)(x-5)} \cdot (x+5)(x-5)$$

$$\begin{array}{l}\text{Multiply both sides by}\\ \text{the LCD.}\end{array}$$

$$(x + 5)(x - 5) \cdot \frac{1}{x - 5} + (x + 5)(x - 5) \cdot \frac{1}{x + 5}$$

$$= \frac{10}{(x + 5)(x - 5)} \cdot (x + 5)(x - 5) \qquad \text{Distribute and divide out common factors.}$$

$$x + 5 + x - 5 = 10 \qquad\qquad \text{Simplify}$$

$$2x = 10 \qquad\qquad\qquad \text{Combine like terms.}$$

$$x = 5 \qquad\qquad\qquad\quad \text{Divide both sides by 2.}$$

This solution must be omitted, as $x = 5$ causes a denominator to be equal to 0. Therefore, this equation has no solution and its solution set is $\varnothing$.

▶ **Quick Check 12**

Solve $\dfrac{x}{x + 3} + \dfrac{1}{x + 2} = \dfrac{7x}{x^2 + 5x + 6}$.

BUILDING YOUR STUDY STRATEGY

Summary, 4 Test-Taking Strategies: Preparation   Through careful preparation and effective test-taking strategies, you can maximize your grade on a math exam. Here is a summary of some test-taking strategies.

• Write down important facts as soon as you get your test.
• Quickly read through the test.
• Begin by solving easier problems first.
• Review your test as thoroughly as possible before turning it in.

When preparing for a cumulative exam,

• Begin preparing early.
• Review your old exams, quizzes, and homework.
• Use review materials from your instructor and the cumulative review exercises in the text.
• Continue to meet regularly with your study group.

Exercises 8.4

PRACTICE   WATCH   DOWNLOAD   READ   REVIEW

Vocabulary

1. A polynomial has been _____ when it is represented as the product of two or more polynomials.

2. The process of factoring a polynomial by first breaking the polynomial into two sets of terms is called factoring by _____.

3. Before attempting to factor a second-degree trinomial, it is wise to factor out any _____.

4. A binomial of the form $a^2 - b^2$ is a(n) _____.

5. A binomial of the form $a^3 - b^3$ is a(n) _____.

6. A binomial of the form $a^3 + b^3$ is a(n) _____.

7. The _____ property of real numbers states that if $a \cdot b = 0$, then $a = 0$ or $b = 0$.

8. Once a quadratic expression has been set equal to 0 and factored, you set each _____ equal to 0 and solve.

Factor completely.

9. $36x^8 - 16x^4 + 50x^3$

10. $9a^4 + 24a^3 - 3$

11. $20a^3b - 28a^2b^4 - 16a^5b^2$

12. $15x^3y^2z^4 - 5xy^6z^{10} + 40x^6y - 25x^4y^4z^4$

13. $n^3 + 4n^2 + 5n + 20$

14. $x^3 - 9x^2 + 2x - 18$

15. $x^3 + 7x^2 - 3x - 21$

16. $2t^3 - 16t^2 - 10t + 80$

17. $x^2 - 13x + 40$

18. $n^2 + 3n - 54$

19. $2x^2 - 8x - 64$

20. $x^2 - 6x - 16$

21. $a^2 + 13ab + 36b^2$

22. $m^2n^2 - 11mn + 28$

23. $4x^2 - 20x - 56$

24. $3x^2 - 33x + 90$

25. $2x^2 + x - 36$

26. $3x^2 + 11x - 20$

27. $6x^2 + 25x + 24$

28. $12x^2 - 23x + 10$

29. $x^2 - 36$

30. $x^2 - 81$

31. $16b^2 - 9$

32. $2a^2 - 98$

33. $x^2 + 16$

34. $x^2 + 81$

35. $x^3 - 8$

36. $x^3 + 64$

37. $27x^3 + 125$

38. $8x^3 - 343y^3$

39. $x^4 - 81$

40. $625n^4 - 1$

41. $x^3 - 7x^2 - 9x + 63$

42. $2x^3 + 5x^2 - 98x - 245$

43. $n^4 + 4n^3 + 8n + 32$

44. $x^4 - 9x^3 - x + 9$

Solve.

45. $x^2 + 3x - 4 = 0$

46. $x^2 - 7x - 30 = 0$

47. $t^2 + 17t + 72 = 0$

48. $3a^2 - 18a + 24 = 0$

49. $x^2 - 2x - 48 = 0$

50. $x^2 + 12x + 36 = 0$

51. $4x^2 - 44x + 72 = 0$

52. $x^2 + 6x - 55 = 0$

53. $2x^2 + 7x + 6 = 0$

54. $4x^2 + 4x - 35 = 0$

55. $x^2 - 25 = 0$ **56.** $x^2 - 121 = 0$

57. $9x^2 - 4 = 0$ **58.** $4x^2 - 81 = 0$

59. $x^2 - 25x = 0$ **60.** $x^2 - 16x = 0$

61. $x^2 + 4x = 21$ **62.** $x^2 = 11x - 18$

63. $x^2 + 11x = 4x - 6$

64. $x^2 + x + 5 = 9x - 7$

65. $\dfrac{4}{3}x^2 + \dfrac{14}{3}x + 2 = 0$

66. $\dfrac{1}{15}x^2 + \dfrac{3}{5}x + \dfrac{4}{3} = 0$

Solve.

67. $\left|x^2 - 13x\right| = 30$

68. $\left|x^2 + 5x\right| = 6$

69. $\left|x^2 + 10x\right| = 24$

70. $\left|x^2 + 8x + 6\right| = 6$

Find a quadratic equation with integer coefficients whose solution set is given.

71. $\{-9, 4\}$ **72.** $\{-3, 0\}$

73. $\left\{\dfrac{1}{3}, 5\right\}$ **74.** $\left\{-\dfrac{2}{3}, \dfrac{5}{2}\right\}$

75. $\{-12, 12\}$ **76.** $\{-7\}$

Solve.

77. $\dfrac{8}{x} = \dfrac{7}{x - 2}$ **78.** $\dfrac{5}{x - 6} = \dfrac{3}{x + 12}$

79. $x - 3 = \dfrac{10}{x}$ **80.** $x + \dfrac{4}{x} = 5$

81. $\dfrac{x^2 - 23}{x - 3} + 7 = 0$ **82.** $x + \dfrac{6x - 17}{x - 5} = -3$

83. $\dfrac{x + 1}{x + 2} = \dfrac{6}{x + 6}$ **84.** $\dfrac{x - 1}{x + 9} = \dfrac{4}{x - 3}$

85. $\dfrac{x}{x - 3} + \dfrac{4}{x + 5} = \dfrac{8x}{(x - 3)(x + 5)}$

86. $\dfrac{x + 2}{x + 4} + \dfrac{3}{x + 7} = \dfrac{6}{(x + 4)(x + 7)}$

87. $\dfrac{x-4}{x-1} + \dfrac{4}{x+1} = \dfrac{x+17}{x^2-1}$

88. $\dfrac{x}{x^2+13x+40} + \dfrac{3}{x^2+2x-15} = \dfrac{4}{x^2+5x-24}$

89. $\dfrac{3}{x-1} + \dfrac{7}{x+2} = \dfrac{9}{x^2+x-2}$

90. $\dfrac{3}{x+1} + \dfrac{1}{x-5} = \dfrac{2x-4}{x^2-4x-5}$

Solve.

91. $\left|\dfrac{2x-15}{x}\right| = 3$

92. $\left|\dfrac{3x+1}{2x-5}\right| = 4$

93. $\left|\dfrac{x^2+5x-48}{x}\right| = 3$

94. $\left|\dfrac{x^2+9x-20}{x}\right| = 10$

✏️ Writing in Mathematics

Answer in complete sentences.

95. What is an extraneous solution of a rational equation? Why do you omit them from the solution set? Explain your answer.

8.5

Systems of Equations (Two Equations in Two Unknowns and Three Equations in Three Unknowns)

OBJECTIVES

1. Solve systems of two linear equations in two unknowns.
2. Determine whether an ordered triple is a solution of a system of three equations in three unknowns.
3. Solve systems of three linear equations in three unknowns.
4. Solve applied problems by using a system of three linear equations in three unknowns.

Systems of Two Linear Equations in Two Unknowns

Objective 1 Solve systems of two linear equations in two unknowns. We begin this section by reviewing how to solve a system of two linear equations in two variables. A solution of a system of two linear equations is an ordered pair that satisfies both equations simultaneously. In Chapter 4, we learned two techniques for solving a system of linear equations: by substitution and by addition.

The graph of each equation in a system of linear equations is a line, and if these two lines cross at exactly one point, this ordered pair is the only solution of the system. In this case, the system is said to be independent.

Independent System

The figure shows the graphs of $y = 2x + 5$ and $y = -x - 1$. These two lines intersect at the ordered pair $(-2, 1)$, and this point of intersection is the solution to this independent system of equations.

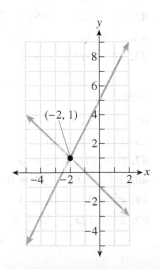

Inconsistent System

If the two lines associated with a system of equations are parallel lines, the system has no solution and is said to be inconsistent.

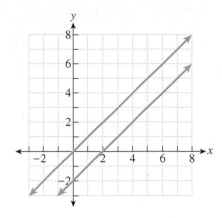

Dependent System

If the two lines associated with a system of equations are the same line, the system is said to be a dependent system. For example, consider the system
$$\begin{aligned} x + y &= 5 \\ 2x + 2y &= 10 \end{aligned}.$$

The figure shows the graph associated with this system. Each ordered pair that is on the line is a solution. We write the solution in the form $(x, 5 - x)$ by solving one of the equations for y in terms of x.

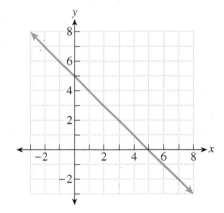

The Substitution Method

Now we turn our attention to solving a system of equations by substitution. This technique requires us to solve one of the equations for one of the variables in terms of the other variable. The expression that we find is then *substituted* for that variable in the other equation, giving us one equation with one variable. After solving that equation, we substitute this value into the expression we originally substituted to solve for the other variable.

EXAMPLE 1 Solve by substitution. $\begin{aligned} x + 3y &= 1 \\ 3x - 2y &= 14 \end{aligned}$

SOLUTION   If there is a variable with a coefficient of 1, it is a good idea to solve the equation for that variable. (Using this strategy will help us avoid the use of fractions.) Solving the first equation for x gives us $x = 1 - 3y$. The expression $1 - 3y$ is then substituted into the equation $3x - 2y = 14$ for x.

$$
\begin{aligned}
3x - 2y &= 14 \\
3(1 - 3y) - 2y &= 14 &&\text{Substitute } 1 - 3y \text{ for } x. \\
3 - 9y - 2y &= 14 &&\text{Distribute.} \\
3 - 11y &= 14 &&\text{Combine like terms.} \\
-11y &= 11 &&\text{Subtract 3 from both sides.} \\
y &= -1 &&\text{Divide both sides by } -11.
\end{aligned}
$$

This value is then substituted for y into the equation $x = 1 - 3y$.

$$x = 1 - 3(-1) \quad \text{Substitute } -1 \text{ for } y.$$
$$x = 1 + 3 \quad \text{Multiply.}$$
$$x = 4 \quad \text{Add.}$$

The ordered pair solution is $(4, -1)$.

▶ Quick Check 1

Solve by substitution.
$$2x - 5y = -24$$
$$4x + y = -4$$

The Addition Method

Another technique for solving a system of equations is solving by addition. We multiply one or both equations by a constant in such a way that one of the variables has opposite coefficients in the two equations. When we add the two equations, this variable is eliminated, resulting in an equation that contains only one variable. We finish finding the solution just as we did when solving by substitution.

EXAMPLE 2   Solve. $\begin{aligned} 4x + 5y &= 13 \\ 2x + 7y &= 11 \end{aligned}$

SOLUTION   If we multiply the second equation by -2, the coefficient for the x term will be -4, which is the opposite of the coefficient of the x term in the first equation. (Recall that there will be times when we must multiply each equation by a different constant to eliminate one variable.)

$$
\begin{array}{lll}
4x + 5y = 13 & & 4x + 5y = 13 \\
2x + 7y = 11 & \xrightarrow{\text{Multiply by } -2} & -4x - 14y = -22
\end{array}
$$

$$
\begin{array}{l}
4x + 5y = 13 \\
\underline{-4x - 14y = -22} \quad \text{Add.} \\
 -9y = -9 \\
 y = 1 \quad \text{Divide both sides by } -9.
\end{array}
$$

We now substitute 1 for y into either original equation to find x.

$$
\begin{aligned}
4x + 5y &= 13 \\
4x + 5(1) &= 13 \quad \text{Substitute 1 for } y. \\
4x + 5 &= 13 \quad \text{Multiply.} \\
4x &= 8 \quad \text{Subtract 5 from both sides.} \\
x &= 2 \quad \text{Divide both sides by 4.}
\end{aligned}
$$

The solution is $(2, 1)$.

▶ Quick Check 2

Solve by addition.
$$3x + 2y = 13$$
$$5x - 3y = 9$$

Applications of Systems of Two Linear Equations in Two Unknowns

We can use a system of two linear equations in two unknowns to solve many applied problems, including perimeter problems, mixture problems, and interest problems. Refer to Section 4.4 to review these topics in more detail. Here is an example of a mixture problem.

EXAMPLE 3 A chemist has one solution that is 16% sodium and a second solution that is 28% sodium. She wants to combine these solutions to make 90 milliliters of a solution that is 20% sodium. How many milliliters of each original solution does she need to use?

SOLUTION: The two unknowns are the volume of the 16% sodium solution and the volume of the 28% sodium solution that need to be mixed together. We will use x and y to represent those quantities. To determine the volume of sodium contributed by each solution as well as the volume of sodium in the mixture, we multiply the volume of the solution by the concentration of sodium in the solution. The following table summarizes the information:

Solution	Volume of Solution	% Concentration of Sodium	Volume of Sodium
16%	x	0.16	$0.16x$
28%	y	0.28	$0.28y$
Mixture (20%)	90	0.20	18

The first equation in the system comes from the fact that the volume of the two solutions must equal 90 milliliters. As an equation, this can be represented by $x + y = 90$. (This equation can be found in the table in the column labeled "Volume of Solution.") The second equation comes from the total volume of sodium, in the column labeled "Volume of Sodium." We know that the total volume of sodium is 18 milliliters (20% of the 90 milliliters in the mixture is sodium); so the second equation in the system is $0.16x + 0.28y = 18$. Here is the system we must solve.

$$x + y = 90$$
$$0.16x + 0.28y = 18$$

We begin by clearing the second equation of decimals. This can be done by multiplying both sides of the second equation by 100.

$$x + y = 90 \qquad\qquad x + y = 90$$
$$0.16x + 0.28y = 18 \xrightarrow{\text{Multiply by 100.}} 16x + 28y = 1800$$

To solve this system of equations, we can use the addition method. If we multiply the first equation by -16, the variable terms containing x are opposites.

$$x + y = 90 \xrightarrow{\text{Multiply by } -16.} -16x - 16y = -1440$$
$$16x + 28y = 1800 \qquad\qquad 16x + 28y = 1800$$

$$
\begin{aligned}
-16x - 16y &= -1440 \\
\underline{16x + 28y} &= \underline{1800} \quad \text{Add to eliminate } x. \\
12y &= 360 \\
y &= 30 \qquad \text{Divide both sides by 12.}
\end{aligned}
$$

We know that the chemist must use 30 milliliters of the solution that is 28% sodium. To determine how much of the 16% sodium solution she must use, we substitute 30 for y in the equation $x + y = 90$.

$$x + (30) = 90 \quad \text{Substitute 30 for } y.$$
$$x = 60 \quad \text{Subtract 30.}$$

She must use 60 milliliters of the 16% sodium solution and 30 milliliters of the 28% sodium solution.

▶ Quick Check 3

A chemist has one solution that is 60% acid and a second solution that is 50% acid. He wants to combine the solutions to make a new solution that is 52% acid. If the chemist needs to make 400 milliliters of this new solution, how many milliliters of the two solutions should he mix?

Solutions of a System of Three Equations in Three Unknowns

Objective ② Determine whether an ordered triple is a solution of a system of three equations in three unknowns. We now turn our attention to systems of three equations in three unknowns. Each of the three equations will be of the form $ax + by + cz = d$, where a, b, c, and d are real numbers. If there is a unique solution of such a system, it will be an **ordered triple** (x, y, z).

EXAMPLE 4 Is $(3, 2, 4)$ a solution of the following system of equations?

$$\begin{aligned} 2x - 3y + z &= 4 \\ x + 2y - z &= 3 \\ 2x - y - 2z &= -4 \end{aligned}$$

SOLUTION   To determine whether the ordered triple is a solution of the system of equations, we will substitute 3 for x, 2 for y, and 4 for z in each equation. If each equation is true for these three values, the ordered triple is a solution of the system of equations.

$2x - 3y + z = 4$	$x + 2y - z = 3$	$2x - y - 2z = -4$
$2(3) - 3(2) + (4) = 4$	$(3) + 2(2) - (4) = 3$	$2(3) - (2) - 2(4) = -4$
$6 - 6 + 4 = 4$	$3 + 4 - 4 = 3$	$6 - 2 - 8 = -4$
$4 = 4$	$3 = 3$	$-4 = -4$

Because the ordered triple makes each equation in the system true, the ordered triple $(3, 2, 4)$ is a solution of the system of equations.

Quick Check 4

Is $(4, -2, 5)$ a solution of the following system of equations?

$$\begin{aligned} x - 2y - z &= 3 \\ 3x + 2y + 2z &= 26 \\ 5x - 3y - 4z &= 6 \end{aligned}$$

Solving a System of Three Linear Equations in Three Unknowns

Objective ③ Solve systems of three linear equations in three unknowns. The graph of a linear equation with three variables is a two-dimensional **plane**.

For a system of three linear equations in three unknowns, if the planes associated with the equations intersect at a single point, this ordered triple (x, y, z) is the solution of the system of equations.

Some systems of three equations in three unknowns have no solution. Such a system is called an inconsistent system. When we try to solve an inconsistent system, we obtain an equation that is a contradiction, such as $0 = 1$. Graphically, the following systems are inconsistent, as the three planes do not have a point in common:

Some systems of three equations in three unknowns have infinitely many solutions. Such a system is called a dependent system of equations. In solving a dependent system of equations, we will obtain an equation that is an identity, such as $0 = 0$. Graphically, if at least two of the planes are identical or if the intersection of the three planes is a line, the system is a dependent system.

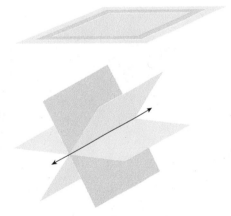

Because graphing equations in three dimensions is beyond the scope of this text, we will focus on solving systems of three linear equations in three unknowns algebraically.

Solving a System of Three Linear Equations in Three Unknowns

- Select two of the equations and use the addition method to eliminate one of the variables.
- Select a different pair of equations and use the addition method to eliminate the same variable, leaving two equations in two unknowns.
- Solve the system of two equations for the two unknowns.
- Substitute these two values in any of the original three equations and solve for the unknown variable.

We will now apply this technique to the system of equations from the previous example.

EXAMPLE 5 Solve the system.

$$2x - 3y + z = 4 \quad (\text{Eq. 1})$$
$$x + 2y - z = 3 \quad (\text{Eq. 2})$$
$$2x - y - 2z = -4 \quad (\text{Eq. 3})$$

SOLUTION Notice that the three equations have been labeled. This will help us keep track of the equations as we solve the system. We must choose a variable to eliminate first, and in this example, it will be z. We may begin by adding Equations 1 and 2 together, as the coefficients of the z-terms are opposites.

$$\begin{array}{ll} 2x - 3y + z = 4 & (\text{Eq. 1}) \\ \underline{x + 2y - z = 3} & (\text{Eq. 2}) \\ 3x - y \quad\;\; = 7 & (\text{Eq. 4}) \end{array}$$

We need to select a different pair of equations and eliminate z. By multiplying Equation 1 by 2 and adding the product to Equation 3, we can eliminate z once again.

$$\begin{array}{ll} 4x - 6y + 2z = 8 & (2 \cdot \text{Eq. 1}) \\ \underline{2x - y - 2z = -4} & (\text{Eq. 3}) \\ 6x - 7y \quad\quad = 4 & (\text{Eq. 5}) \end{array}$$

We now work to solve the system of equations formed by Equations 4 and 5, which is a system of two equations in two unknowns. We will solve this system using the addition method as well, although we could choose the substitution method if it was convenient. We will eliminate the variable y by multiplying Equation 4 by -7.

$$\begin{array}{ll} 3x - y = 7 & (\text{Eq. 4}) \\ 6x - 7y = 4 & (\text{Eq. 5}) \end{array} \xrightarrow{\text{Multiply by } -7.} \begin{array}{l} -21x + 7y = -49 \\ \underline{6x - 7y = \;\;\; 4} \\ -15x \quad\quad\; = -45 \quad \text{Add.} \\ \quad\quad x \quad\quad = 3 \quad \text{Divide both} \\ \quad\quad\quad\quad\quad\quad\quad\quad\quad \text{sides by } -15. \end{array}$$

We now substitute 3 for x in either of the equations that contained only two variables. We will use Equation 4.

$$\begin{array}{ll} 3x - y = 7 & \\ 3(3) - y = 7 & \text{Substitute 3 for } x \text{ in Equation 4.} \\ 9 - y = 7 & \text{Multiply.} \\ -y = -2 & \text{Subtract 9 from both sides.} \\ y = 2 & \text{Divide both sides by } -1. \end{array}$$

To find z, we will substitute 3 for x and 2 for y in any of the original equations that contained three variables. We will use Equation 1.

$$\begin{array}{ll} 2x - 3y + z = 4 & \\ 2(3) - 3(2) + z = 4 & \text{Substitute 3 for } x \text{ and 2 for } y \text{ in Equation 1.} \\ 6 - 6 + z = 4 & \text{Multiply.} \\ 0 + z = 4 & \text{Combine like terms.} \\ z = 4 & \end{array}$$

The solution of this system is the ordered triple (3, 2, 4).

Quick Check 5

Solve the system.

$$\begin{array}{l} x + y + z = 0 \\ 2x - y + 3z = -9 \\ -3x + 2y - 4z = 13 \end{array}$$

EXAMPLE 6 Solve the system.

$$3x + 2y + 2z = 7 \quad \text{(Eq. 1)}$$
$$4x + 4y - 3z = -17 \quad \text{(Eq. 2)}$$
$$-x - 6y + 4z = 13 \quad \text{(Eq. 3)}$$

SOLUTION   In this example, we will eliminate x first. It is a good idea to choose x because the coefficient of the x-term in Equation 3 can easily be multiplied to become the opposite of the coefficients of the x-terms in Equations 1 and 2. We begin by multiplying Equation 3 by 3 and adding it to Equation 1.

$$\begin{array}{rl} 3x + 2y + 2z = 7 & \text{(Eq. 1)} \\ \underline{-3x - 18y + 12z = 39} & (3 \cdot \text{Eq. 3}) \\ -16y + 14z = 46 & \text{(Eq. 4)} \end{array}$$

We need to select a different pair of equations and eliminate x. By multiplying Equation 3 by 4 and adding it to Equation 2, we can eliminate x once again.

$$\begin{array}{rl} 4x + 4y - 3z = -17 & \text{(Eq. 2)} \\ \underline{-4x - 24y + 16z = 52} & (4 \cdot \text{Eq. 3}) \\ -20y + 13z = 35 & \text{(Eq. 5)} \end{array}$$

We now solve the system of equations formed by Equations 4 and 5. We will use the addition method to eliminate the variable y. To determine what to multiply each equation by, we should find the LCM of 16 and 20, which is 80. If we multiply Equation 4 by 5, the coefficient of the y-term will be -80. If we multiply Equation 5 by -4, the coefficient of the y-term will be 80. This will make the coefficients of the y-terms opposites, allowing us to add the equations together and eliminate y.

$$-16y + 14z = 46 \quad \text{(Eq. 4)} \xrightarrow{\text{Multiply by 5.}} -80y + 70z = 230$$
$$-20y + 13z = 35 \quad \text{(Eq. 5)} \xrightarrow{\text{Multiply by } -4.} 80y - 52z = -140$$

$$\begin{array}{rl} -80y + 70z = 230 & \\ \underline{80y - 52z = -140} & \\ 18z = 90 & \text{Add.} \\ z = 5 & \text{Divide both sides by 18.} \end{array}$$

We now substitute 5 for z in either of the equations that contained only two variables. We will use Equation 4.

$$\begin{array}{rl} -16y + 14z = 46 & \\ -16y + 14(5) = 46 & \text{Substitute 5 for } z \text{ in Equation 4.} \\ -16y + 70 = 46 & \text{Multiply.} \\ -16y = -24 & \text{Subtract 70 from both sides.} \\ y = \dfrac{3}{2} & \text{Divide both sides by } -16 \text{ and simplify.} \end{array}$$

To find x, we will substitute 5 for z and $\frac{3}{2}$ for y in any of the original equations that contained three variables. We will use Equation 1.

$$\begin{array}{rl} 3x + 2y + 2z = 7 & \\ 3x + 2\left(\dfrac{3}{2}\right) + 2(5) = 7 & \text{Substitute } \frac{3}{2} \text{ for } y \text{ and 5 for } z \text{ in Equation 1.} \\ 3x + 3 + 10 = 7 & \text{Multiply.} \end{array}$$

$$3x + 13 = 7 \quad \text{Combine like terms.}$$
$$3x = -6 \quad \text{Subtract 13 from both sides.}$$
$$x = -2 \quad \text{Divide both sides by 3.}$$

The solution of this system is the ordered triple $\left(-2, \frac{3}{2}, 5\right)$.

Quick Check 6
Solve the system.
$$2x + y - z = -8$$
$$-4x - 3y + 3z = 25$$
$$6x + 5y + 4z = 3$$

Applications of Systems of Three Linear Equations in Three Unknowns

Objective 4 Solve applied problems by using a system of three linear equations in three unknowns. We finish the section with an application involving a system of three equations in three unknowns.

EXAMPLE 7   A baseball team has three prices for admission to their games. Adults are charged $7, senior citizens are charged $5, and children are charged $4. At last night's game, 1000 people were in attendance, generating $5600 in receipts. If we know that 300 more children than senior citizens were at the game, find how many adult tickets, senior citizen tickets, and child tickets were sold.

SOLUTION   There are three unknowns in this problem: the number of adult tickets sold, the number of senior citizen tickets sold, and the number of child tickets sold. We will let a, s, and c represent these three quantities, respectively. Here is a table of the unknowns.

> ### *Unknowns*
> Number of adult tickets sold: a
> Number of senior citizen tickets sold: s
> Number of child tickets sold: c

Solving a problem with three unknowns requires that we establish a system of three equations. Because we know that 1000 people were at last night's game, the first equation in the system is $a + s + c = 1000$.

We also know that the revenue from all of the tickets was $5600, which will lead to the second equation. The amount received from the adult tickets was $7a$ (a tickets at $7 each). In the same way, the amount received from senior citizen tickets was $5s$ and the amount received from child tickets was $4c$. The second equation in the system is $7a + 5s + 4c = 5600$.

The third equation comes from knowing that 300 more children than senior citizens were at the game. In other words, the number of children at the game was equal to the number of senior citizens plus 300. The third equation is $c = s + 300$, which can be rewritten as $-s + c = 300$.

Here is the system with which we will be working.

$$a + s + c = 1000 \quad (\text{Eq. 1})$$
$$7a + 5s + 4c = 5600 \quad (\text{Eq. 2})$$
$$-s + c = 300 \quad (\text{Eq. 3})$$

Because Equation 3 has only two variables, we will use the addition method to combine Equations 1 and 2, eliminating the variable a. We begin by multiplying Equation 1 by -7 and adding it to Equation 2.

$$\begin{array}{ll} -7a - 7s - 7c = -7000 & (-7 \cdot \text{Eq. 1}) \\ 7a + 5s + 4c = 5600 & (\text{Eq. 2}) \\ \hline -2s - 3c = -1400 & (\text{Eq. 4}) \end{array}$$

We now have two equations that contain only the two variables s and c. We can solve the system of equations formed by Equations 3 and 4. We will use the addition method to eliminate the variable c by multiplying Equation 3 by 3 and adding it to Equation 4.

$$-s + c = 300 \xrightarrow{\text{Multiply by 3.}} -3s + 3c = 900$$
$$-2s - 3c = -1400 \qquad\qquad\qquad -2s - 3c = -1400$$

$$
\begin{array}{rcl}
-3s + 3c &=& 900 \\
-2s - 3c &=& -1400 \\
\hline
-5s &=& -500 \quad \text{Add.} \\
s &=& 100 \quad \text{Divide both sides by } -5.
\end{array}
$$

There were 100 senior citizens at the game. To find the number of children at the game, we will substitute 100 for s in Equation 3.

$$
\begin{array}{rl}
-s + c = 300 & \\
-100 + c = 300 & \text{Substitute 100 for } s \text{ in Equation 3.} \\
c = 400 & \text{Add 100 to both sides.}
\end{array}
$$

There were 400 children at the game. (Because we knew that 300 more children than senior citizens were at the game, we could have just added 300 to 100.) To find the number of adults at the game, we will substitute 100 for s and 400 for c in Equation 1.

$$
\begin{array}{rl}
a + s + c = 1000 & \\
a + (100) + (400) = 1000 & \text{Substitute 100 for } s \text{ and 400 for } c \text{ in Equation 1.} \\
a = 500 & \text{Solve for } a.
\end{array}
$$

There were 500 adults, 100 senior citizens, and 400 children at last night's game. The reader can verify that the total revenue for 500 adults, 100 senior citizens, and 400 children is $5600.

▶ Quick Check 7

Gilbert looks in his wallet and finds $1, $5, and $10 bills totaling $111. There are 30 bills in all, and Gilbert has 4 more $5 bills than he has $10 bills. How many bills of each type does Gilbert have in his wallet?

BUILDING YOUR STUDY STRATEGY

Summary, 5 Math Anxiety Math anxiety can hinder your success in a mathematics class, but you can overcome it. The first step is to understand what has caused your anxiety. Relaxation techniques can help you overcome the physical symptoms of math anxiety. Developing a positive attitude and confidence in your abilities will help as well.

Poor performance on math exams can be caused by other factors, such as test anxiety, improper placement, and poor study skills. If you freeze when taking exams in other classes and do poorly on them even when you understand the material, you may have test anxiety. An academic counselor or learning resource specialist can help.

Exercises 8.5

MyMathLab

PRACTICE   WATCH   DOWNLOAD   READ   REVIEW

Vocabulary

1. A(n) _____ consists of two or more linear equations.

2. An ordered pair (x, y) is a solution to a system of two linear equations if _____ _____.

3. A system of two linear equations is a(n) _____ system if it has exactly one solution.

4. A system of two linear equations is a(n) _____ system if it has no solution.

5. A system of two linear equations is a(n) _____ system if it has infinitely many solutions.

6. To solve a system of equations by substitution, begin by solving one of the equations for one of the _____.

7. The solution of a system of three equations in three unknowns is a(n) _____.

8. To solve a system of three equations in three unknowns, begin by eliminating one of the variables to create a system of _____ equations in _____ unknowns.

Solve by addition or substitution.

9. $y = 2x - 16$
   $3x + 2y = 17$

10. $y = 3x - 7$
    $4x + 5y = 136$

11. $2x - 7y = 41$
    $x = 4y + 23$

12. $-5x + 3y = -54$
    $x = 5y + 2$

13. $y = \frac{2}{3}x + 11$
    $4x - 3y = -45$

14. $x = \frac{5}{2}y - 1$
    $4x + 9y = 72$

15. $y = 3x + 7$
    $6x - 2y = -14$

16. $x = 5 - 2y$
    $4x + 8y = -20$

17. $2x - 3y = 10$
    $4x - 2y = 28$

18. $x + 2y = -12$
    $3x - 4y = 26$

19. $x - 4y = 7$
    $3x + 2y = 14$

20. $5x + y = -2$
    $3x - 7y = -43$

21. $4x + 3y = -28$
    $3x - 2y = -4$

22. $-5x + 4y = 22$
    $2x + 5y = 11$

23. $6x - 4y = 11$
    $9x - 6y = 17$

24. $4x + y = 13$
    $12x + 3y = 39$

25. $\frac{3}{4}x + \frac{1}{3}y = 1$
    $\frac{2}{5}x - \frac{1}{4}y = \frac{31}{10}$

26. $\frac{1}{6}x + \frac{1}{2}y = -3$
    $\frac{2}{3}x - \frac{3}{4}y = \frac{7}{4}$

Solve using a system of two equations in two unknowns.

27. The length of a rectangle is 3 inches more than twice its width. If the perimeter of the rectangle is 54 inches, find its length and width.

28. The length of a rectangle is 4 feet less than 3 times its width. If the perimeter of the rectangle is 96 feet, find its length and width.

29. A jar contains 65 coins; some are dimes, and the rest are quarters. If the coins have a value of $13.10, how many of each type of coin are in the jar?

30. A bouquet with 12 carnations and 5 roses costs $54, while a bouquet with 6 carnations and 4 roses costs $36. What is the cost of a single carnation? What is the cost of a single rose?

31. Faustino deposited a total of $7500 in two bank accounts. One of the accounts paid 6% annual interest, while the other paid 3% annual interest. If Faustino earned $387 in interest during the first year, how much did he deposit in each account?

32. Hasinah invested $6000 in two mutual funds. During the first year, one fund increased in value by 13% and the other increased in value by 5%. If Hasinah earned a profit of $660 during the first year, how much did he invest in each fund?

33. A chemist has two solutions: one is 15% acid, and the other is 30% acid. How much of each solution should she mix to create 60 milliliters of a solution that is 25% acid?

34. A chemist has two solutions: one is 20% acid, and the other is 60% acid. How much of each solution should he mix to produce 120 milliliters of a solution that is 28% acid?

Is the ordered triple a solution to the given system of equations?

35. $(3, 2, 6)$

$$x + y + z = 11$$
$$x - y + 2z = 17$$
$$4x - 3y - 2z = -6$$

36. $(2, -4, -1)$

$$x + y - z = -1$$
$$5x + 2y + 2z = 0$$
$$\frac{1}{2}x + 2y - 6z = -1$$

37. $(-5, 2, 0)$

$$x + 2y + 3z = -1$$
$$3x - y - 6z = -17$$
$$4x - 3y + z = -26$$

38. $(1, -1, -6)$

$$x - y - z = 8$$
$$5x + 7y + z = -8$$
$$-2x + 5y - 4z = 21$$

Solve.

39.
$$x + 2y + 3z = 23$$
$$-2x + 3y + z = 17$$
$$-3x + 5y - 4z = 12$$

40.
$$4x - y + 6z = 25$$
$$2x + 3y + 4z = 49$$
$$5x + 2y - 3z = 8$$

41.
$$x + y + z = 2$$
$$2x + 3y - z = 5$$
$$7x + 4y + 2z = 25$$

42.
$$x + y - z = -13$$
$$3x + 2y + 3z = 6$$
$$4x + 9y + 12z = 45$$

43.
$$3x + 2y + 5z = -8$$
$$9x - 4y + 6z = -38$$
$$-6x - 6y + 7z = -62$$

44.
$$4x + 3y + 2z = 19$$
$$2x + 5y - 4z = 18$$
$$-8x + y + 6z = 29$$

45.
$$2x + 3y + z = 5$$
$$-2x - y + 4z = 60$$
$$x + 2y - 8z = -30$$

46.
$$x - y - z = 16$$
$$2x + 3y + 2z = -5$$
$$4x + 5y + 4z = -5$$

47.
$$2x - 3y - z = -6$$
$$-3x + 2y + 4z = 24$$
$$5x - 4y + 3z = -18$$

48.
$$x + 4y + 2z = -3$$
$$2x - 3y - z = 19$$
$$4x + 9y + 5z = 3$$

49.
$$4x + 2y + z = -5$$
$$2x - y - 6z = 0$$
$$-8x + 6y + 3z = -30$$

50.
$$x + 3y - 6z = 8$$
$$3x + 4y - 2z = 9$$
$$5x + 6y - 12z = 22$$

51.
$$\frac{1}{2}x + \frac{1}{3}y + z = 3$$
$$\frac{2}{3}x - 4y - 3z = 13$$
$$3x + 4y + 5z = 11$$

52.
$$\frac{3}{4}x - \frac{5}{2}y - \frac{1}{3}z = -14$$
$$x + \frac{3}{4}y + \frac{7}{2}z = -26$$
$$2x - 3y - 4z = -4$$

53.
$$x + 2y + z = 8$$
$$3x + 4y + 2z = 9$$
$$3x - 4y = -37$$

54.
$$2x + 3y - z = 10$$
$$-x + 4y + 2z = 200$$
$$5x + 2y = 88$$

Solve using a system of three equations in three unknowns.

55. Jonah opens his wallet and finds that all of the bills are $1 bills, $5 bills, or $10 bills. There are 35 bills in his wallet. There are four more $5 bills than $1 bills. If the total amount of bills is $246, how many $10 bills does Jonah have?

56. A cash register has no $1 bills in it. All of the bills are $5 bills, $10 bills, or $20 bills. There are a total of 37 bills in the cash register, and the total value of these bills is $310. If the number of $10 bills in the register is twice the number of $20 bills, how many $5 bills are in the register?

57. A campus club held a bake sale as a fund-raiser, selling coffee, muffins, and bacon-and-egg sandwiches. The club members charged $1 for a cup of coffee, $2 for a muffin, and $3 for a bacon-and-egg sandwich. They sold a total of 50 items, raising $85 dollars. If the club members sold five more muffins than cups of coffee, how many bacon-and-egg sandwiches did they sell?

58. A grocery store was supporting a local charity by asking shoppers to donate $1, $5, or $20 at the checkout. A total of 110 shoppers donated $430. The amount of money raised from $5 donations was $50 higher than the amount of money raised from $20 donations. How many shoppers donated $20?

59. Abraham is 8 years older than Belen. The sum of Belen's age and Celeste's age is three years more than twice Abraham's age. If the sum of their three ages is 138, how old are Abraham, Belen, and Celeste?

60. The total of Dharma's, Eugenio's, and Fern's final exam scores is 271. If Dharma's score is added to Eugenio's score, the sum is 11 points less than twice Fern's score. If Eugenio's score is 5 points higher than Dharma's score, what is each student's final exam score?

61. The measures of the three angles in a triangle must total 180°. The measure of angle A is 20° less than the measure of angle C. The measure of angle C is twice the measure of angle B. Find the measure of each angle.

62. The measures of the three angles in a triangle must total 180°. The measure of angle A is 15° more than the measure of angle B. The measure of angle B is 15° greater than four times the measure of angle C. Find the measure of each angle.

63. Recall the introduction to problems about interest in Section 4.4. Mary invested a total of $40,000 in three different bank accounts. One account pays an annual interest rate of 3%, the second account pays 5% annual interest, and the third account pays 6% annual interest. In one year, Mary earned a total of $1960 in interest from these three accounts. If Mary invested $8000 more in the account that pays 5% interest than she did in the account that pays 6% interest, find the amount she invested in each account.

64. Hua-Ling invested a total of $10,000 in three bank accounts. The accounts paid 4%, 5%, and 6% annual interest. In the first year, Hua-Ling earned $545 in interest. If she invested $1000 more at 5% than she invested at 4%, how much did she invest in each account?

65. Pilar invested a total of $8000 in three mutual funds. During the first year, the first fund increased in value by 2%, the second fund increased by 10%, and the third fund increased by 25%. In the first year, she earned a profit of $550. If Pilar invested $1000 less in the fund that increased by 25% than she invested in the fund that increased by 10%, how much did she invest in each fund?

66. Lev invested a total of $5000 in three stocks. During the first year, the first stock increased in value by 8%, the second stock increased by 6%, and the third stock increased by 1%. In the first year, he earned a profit of $310. If Lev invested the same amount in the stock that increased by 6% as he invested in the stock that increased by 1%, how much did he invest in each stock?

67. Salim invested a total of $25,000 in three stocks. During the first year, the first stock increased in value by 5% and the second stock increased by 7%, but the third stock decreased by 40%. In the first year, he lost $1330. If Salim invested the same amount in the stock that increased by 7% as he did in the stock that decreased by 40%, how much did he invest in each stock?

68. Dennis invested a total of $100,000 in three different mutual funds. After one year, the first fund showed a profit of 8%, the second fund showed a loss of 5%, and the third fund showed a profit of 2%. Dennis invested $10,000 more in the fund that lost 5% than he invested in the fund that made a 2% profit. In the first year, Dennis made a profit of $2900 from the three funds. How much did he invest in each fund?

69. A chemist wants to mix three different solutions to create 100 milliliters of a solution that is 13.5% alcohol. Solution A is 10% alcohol, solution B is 15% alcohol, and solution C is 30% alcohol. The amount of solution A that is used must be twice the amount of solution B that is used. How many milliliters of each solution should the chemist combine?

70. A chemist wants to mix three different solutions to create 50 milliliters of a solution that is 28% alcohol. Solution A is 20% alcohol, solution B is 30% alcohol, and solution C is 50% alcohol. The amount of solution A that is used must be 20 milliliters more than the amount of solution B that is used. How many milliliters of each solution should the chemist combine?

━━━ Writing in Mathematics

Answer in complete sentences.

71. Write a word problem that has the following solution: There were 40 children, 200 adults, and 60 senior citizens in attendance. Your problem must lead to a system of three equations in three unknowns. Explain how you created your problem.

72. Write a word problem for the following system of equations.

$$x + y + z = 350{,}000$$
$$0.05x + 0.07y - 0.04z = 17{,}000$$
$$y = 2x$$

Explain how you created your problem.

Radical Expressions and Equations

In this chapter, we will investigate radical expressions and equations and their applications. Among the applications is the method for finding the distance between any two objects and a way to determine the speed a car was traveling by measuring the skid marks left by its tires.

STUDY STRATEGY

Note Taking If you have poor note-taking skills, you will not learn as much during the class period as you might if your skills were better. In this chapter, we will focus on how to take notes in a math class. We will discuss how to be more efficient when taking notes, what material to include in your notes, and how to rework your notes.

9.1

Square Roots; Radical Notation

OBJECTIVES

1. Find the square root of a number.
2. Simplify the square root of a variable expression.
3. Approximate the square root of a number by using a calculator.
4. Find *n*th roots.
5. Multiply radical expressions.
6. Divide radical expressions.
7. Evaluate radical functions.
8. Find the domain of a radical function.

Square Roots

Consider the equation $x^2 = 36$. There are two solutions to this equation: $x = 6$ and $x = -6$.

┌─ **Square Root** ─────────────────────────────────────┐
│ A number a is a **square root** of a number b if $a^2 = b$. │
└──┘

The numbers 6 and -6 are square roots of 36 because $6^2 = 36$ and $(-6)^2 = 36$. The number 6 is the positive square root of 36, while the number -6 is the negative square root of 36.

Objective ① **Find the square root of a number.**

┌─ **Principal Square Root** ──────────────────────────────┐
│ The **principal square root** of b, denoted $\sqrt{b}$, for $b > 0$, is the positive number │
│ a such that $a^2 = b$. │
└──┘

The expression $\sqrt{b}$ is called a **radical expression**. The sign $\sqrt{}$ is called a **radical sign**, while the expression contained inside the radical sign is called the **radicand**.

EXAMPLE 1 Simplify $\sqrt{25}$.

SOLUTION   We are looking for a positive number a such that $a^2 = 25$. The number is 5, so $\sqrt{25} = 5$.

EXAMPLE 2 Simplify $\sqrt{\dfrac{1}{9}}$.

SOLUTION   Because $\left(\dfrac{1}{3}\right)^2 = \dfrac{1}{3} \cdot \dfrac{1}{3} = \dfrac{1}{9}$, $\sqrt{\dfrac{1}{9}} = \dfrac{1}{3}$.

EXAMPLE 3 Simplify $-\sqrt{49}$.

SOLUTION   In this example, we are looking for the negative square root of 49, which is -7. So $-\sqrt{49} = -7$. We can find the principal square root of 49 first and then make it negative.

Quick Check 1

Simplify.

a) $\sqrt{49}$ **b)** $\sqrt{\dfrac{4}{25}}$

c) $-\sqrt{36}$

The principal square root of a negative number, such as $\sqrt{-49}$, is not a real number because there is no real number a such that $a^2 = -49$. We will learn in Section 9.6 that $\sqrt{-49}$ is called an *imaginary* number.

Square Roots of Variable Expressions

Objective ② **Simplify the square root of a variable expression.** Now we turn our attention to simplifying radical expressions containing variables, such as $\sqrt{x^6}$.

┌─ **Simplifying** $\sqrt{a^2}$ ────────────────────────────┐
│ For any real number a, $\sqrt{a^2} = |a|$. │
└──┘

You may be wondering why the absolute value bars are necessary. For any nonnegative number a, $\sqrt{a^2} = a$. For example, $\sqrt{8^2} = 8$. The absolute value bars are necessary in order to include negative values of a. Suppose $a = -10$. Then

$\sqrt{a^2} = \sqrt{(-10)^2}$, which is equal to $\sqrt{100}$, or 10. So $\sqrt{a^2}$ equals the opposite of a. In either case, the principal square root of a^2 will be a nonnegative number.

$$\sqrt{a^2} = \begin{cases} a & \text{if } a \geq 0 \\ -a & \text{if } a < 0 \end{cases}$$

The absolute value bars address both cases. We must use absolute values when dealing with variables because we do not know whether the variable is negative.

EXAMPLE 4 Simplify $\sqrt{x^6}$.

SOLUTION   We begin by rewriting the radicand as a square. Note that $x^6 = (x^3)^2$.

$$\sqrt{x^6} = \sqrt{(x^3)^2} \quad \text{Rewrite the radicand as a square.}$$
$$= |x^3| \quad \text{Simplify.}$$

Because we do not know whether x is negative, the absolute value bars are necessary.

EXAMPLE 5 Simplify $\sqrt{64y^{10}}$.

SOLUTION   Again, we rewrite the radicand as a square.

$$\sqrt{64y^{10}} = \sqrt{(8y^5)^2} \quad \text{Rewrite the radicand as a square.}$$
$$= |8y^5| \quad \text{Simplify.}$$

Because we know that 8 is a positive number, we can remove it from the absolute value bars. This allows us to write the expression as $8|y^5|$.

▸ Quick Check 2
Simplify.
a) $\sqrt{a^{14}}$ b) $\sqrt{25b^{22}}$

EXAMPLE 6 Simplify $\sqrt{36x^4}$.

SOLUTION   We rewrite the radicand as a square.

$$\sqrt{36x^4} = \sqrt{(6x^2)^2} \quad \text{Rewrite the radicand as a square.}$$
$$= |6x^2| \quad \text{Simplify.}$$

Because we know that 6 is a positive number, it can be removed from the absolute value bars. Because x^2 cannot be negative either, it may be removed from the absolute value bars as well.

$$\sqrt{36x^4} = 6x^2$$

Quick Check 3

Simplify $\sqrt{64x^{24}}$.

> From this point on, we will assume that all variable factors in a radicand represent nonnegative real numbers. This eliminates the need to use absolute value bars when simplifying radical expressions whose radicand contains variables.

Approximating Square Roots Using a Calculator

Objective 3 Approximate the square root of a number by using a calculator. Consider the expression $\sqrt{12}$. There is no positive integer that is the square root of 12. In such a case, we can use a calculator to approximate the radical expression. All calculators have a function for calculating square roots. Rounding to the nearest thousandth, we see that $\sqrt{12} \approx 3.464$. The symbol $\approx$ is read as *is approximately equal to;* so the principal square root of 12 is approximately equal to 3.464. If we square 3.464, it is equal to 11.999296, which is very close to 12.

EXAMPLE 7 Approximate $\sqrt{42}$ to the nearest thousandth using a calculator.

SOLUTION Because $6^2 = 36$ and $7^2 = 49$, we know that $\sqrt{42}$ must be a number between 6 and 7.

$$\sqrt{42} \approx 6.481$$

▶ **Quick Check 4**

Approximate $\sqrt{109}$ to the nearest thousandth using a calculator.

Using Your Calculator We can approximate square roots by using the TI-84.

```
√(42)
          6.480740698
```

*n*th Roots

Objective 4 **Find *n*th roots.** Now we move on to discuss roots other than square roots.

┌─ **Principal *n*th Root** ─────────────────────────────────────

For any positive integer $n > 1$ and any number b, if $a^n = b$ and both a and b have the same sign, a is the **principal *n*th root** of b, denoted $a = \sqrt[n]{b}$. The number n is called the **index** of the radical.

└──

A square root has an index of 2, and the radical is written without the index. If the index is 3, this is called a **cube root**. If n is even, the principal *n*th root is a nonnegative number, but if n is odd, the principal *n*th root has the same sign as the radicand. As with square roots, an even root of a negative number is not a real number. For example, $\sqrt[6]{-64}$ is not a real number. However, an odd root of a negative number, such as $\sqrt[3]{-64}$, is a negative real number.

EXAMPLE 8 Simplify $\sqrt[3]{125}$.

SOLUTION Look for a number that, when cubed, is equal to 125. Because $125 = 5^3$, $\sqrt[3]{125} = \sqrt[3]{(5)^3} = 5$.

EXAMPLE 9 Simplify $\sqrt[4]{81}$.

SOLUTION In this example, we are looking for a number that when raised to the fourth power is equal to 81. (We can use a factor tree to factor 81.) Because $81 = 3^4$, $\sqrt[4]{81} = \sqrt[4]{(3)^4} = 3$.

Using Your Calculator   Find the function for calculating nth roots on the TI-84 by pressing the [MATH] key and selecting option 5 under the MATH menu.

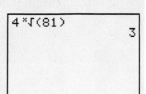

Press the index for the radical, the nth root function, and then the radicand inside a set of parentheses. Here is the screen shot of the calculation of $\sqrt[4]{81}$.

Quick Check 5

Simplify.

a) $\sqrt[3]{27}$ **b)** $\sqrt[4]{256}$
c) $\sqrt[3]{-343}$

EXAMPLE 10   Simplify $\sqrt[5]{-32}$.

SOLUTION   Notice that the radicand is negative. So we are looking for a negative number that when raised to the fifth power is equal to -32. (If the index were even, this expression would not be a real number.) Because $(-2)^5 = -32$, $\sqrt[5]{-32} = \sqrt[5]{(-2)^5} = -2$.

For any nonnegative number x, $\sqrt[n]{x^n} = x$.

EXAMPLE 11   Simplify $\sqrt[4]{x^{20}}$. (Assume that x is nonnegative.)

SOLUTION   We begin by rewriting the radicand as an expression raised to the fourth power. We can rewrite x^{20} as $(x^5)^4$.

$$\sqrt[4]{x^{20}} = \sqrt[4]{(x^5)^4} \quad \text{Rewrite the radicand as an expression raised to the fourth power.}$$
$$= x^5 \quad \text{Simplify.}$$

▶ **Quick Check 6**

Simplify $\sqrt[6]{x^{42}}$. (Assume that x is nonnegative.)

EXAMPLE 12   Simplify $\sqrt[3]{64a^3b^9c^{21}}$. (Assume that $a, b,$ and c are nonnegative.)

SOLUTION   We begin by rewriting the radicand as a cube. We can rewrite $64a^3b^9c^{21}$ as $(4ab^3c^7)^3$.

$$\sqrt[3]{64a^3b^9c^{21}} = \sqrt[3]{(4ab^3c^7)^3} \quad \text{Rewrite the radicand as a cube.}$$
$$= 4ab^3c^7 \quad \text{Simplify.}$$

Quick Check 7

Simplify $\sqrt[5]{-243x^{35}y^{40}}$. (Assume that x and y are nonnegative.)

EXAMPLE 13   Simplify $\sqrt{x^2 - 8x + 16}$. (Assume that $x \geq 4$.)

SOLUTION   This is a square root, so we must begin by rewriting the radicand as a square. If we factor the radicand, we see that it can be expressed as $(x - 4)(x - 4)$, or $(x - 4)^2$.

$$\sqrt{x^2 - 8x + 16} = \sqrt{(x - 4)^2} \quad \text{Rewrite the radicand as a square.}$$
$$= x - 4 \quad \text{Simplify. (Because } x \geq 4, x - 4 \text{ is nonnegative.)}$$

Quick Check 8

Simplify $\sqrt{x^2 + 10x + 25}$. (Assume that $x \geq -5$.)

Multiplying Radical Expressions

Objective 5 Multiply radical expressions. We know that $\sqrt{9} \cdot \sqrt{100} = 3 \cdot 10$, or 30. We also know that $\sqrt{9 \cdot 100} = \sqrt{900}$, or 30. In this case, we see that $\sqrt{9} \cdot \sqrt{100} = \sqrt{9 \cdot 100}$. If two radical expressions with nonnegative radicands have the same index, we can multiply the two expressions by multiplying the two radicands and writing the product inside the same radical.

> **Product Rule for Radicals**
>
> For any root n, if $\sqrt[n]{a}$ and $\sqrt[n]{b}$ are real numbers, then $\sqrt[n]{a} \cdot \sqrt[n]{b} = \sqrt[n]{ab}$.

For example, the product of $\sqrt{2}$ and $\sqrt{8}$ is $\sqrt{16}$, which simplifies to equal 4.

Quick Check 9

Multiply $\sqrt{6b^5} \cdot \sqrt{150b^3}$.
(Assume that b is nonnegative.)

EXAMPLE 14 Multiply $\sqrt{45n} \cdot \sqrt{5n}$. (Assume that n is nonnegative.)

SOLUTION   Because both radicals are square roots, we can multiply the radicands.

$$\sqrt{45n} \cdot \sqrt{5n} = \sqrt{225n^2} \quad \text{Multiply the radicands.}$$
$$= 15n \quad \text{Simplify the square root.}$$

EXAMPLE 15 Multiply $7\sqrt{2} \cdot 9\sqrt{2}$.

SOLUTION   We multiply the factors in front of the radicals by each other and multiply the radicands by each other.

$$7\sqrt{2} \cdot 9\sqrt{2} = 63\sqrt{4} \quad \begin{array}{l}\text{Multiply the factors in front of the radicals } (7 \cdot 9).\\ \text{Multiply the radicands.}\end{array}$$
$$= 63 \cdot 2 \quad \text{Simplify the square root.}$$
$$= 126 \quad \text{Multiply.}$$

Quick Check 10

Multiply $3\sqrt{6} \cdot 8\sqrt{6}$.

Dividing Radical Expressions

Objective 6 Divide radical expressions. We can rewrite the quotient of two radical expressions that have the same index as the quotient of the two radicands inside the same radical.

> **Quotient Rule for Radicals**
>
> For any root n, if $\sqrt[n]{a}$ and $\sqrt[n]{b}$ are real numbers and $b \neq 0$, then $\dfrac{\sqrt[n]{a}}{\sqrt[n]{b}} = \sqrt[n]{\dfrac{a}{b}}$.

EXAMPLE 16 Simplify $\dfrac{\sqrt{108}}{\sqrt{3}}$.

SOLUTION   Because both radicals are square roots, we begin by dividing the radicands. We write the quotient of the radicands under a single square root.

$$\frac{\sqrt{108}}{\sqrt{3}} = \sqrt{\frac{108}{3}} \quad \text{Rewrite as the square root of the quotient of the radicands.}$$
$$= \sqrt{36} \quad \text{Divide.}$$
$$= 6 \quad \text{Simplify the square root.}$$

EXAMPLE 17 Simplify $\dfrac{\sqrt[3]{40b^7}}{\sqrt[3]{5b^4}}$. (Assume that b is nonnegative.)

SOLUTION Because the index of both radicals is the same, begin by dividing the radicands.

$$\frac{\sqrt[3]{40b^7}}{\sqrt[3]{5b^4}} = \sqrt[3]{\frac{40b^7}{5b^4}} \quad \text{Divide the radicands.}$$

$$= \sqrt[3]{8b^3} \quad \text{Simplify the radicand.}$$

$$= 2b \quad \text{Simplify the radical.}$$

Quick Check 11

Simplify.

a) $\dfrac{\sqrt{350}}{\sqrt{14}}$ **b)** $\dfrac{\sqrt[5]{2916a^{18}}}{\sqrt[5]{12a^3}}$

(Assume that a is nonnegative.)

Radical Functions

Objective 7 Evaluate radical functions. A **radical function** is a function that involves radicals, such as $f(x) = \sqrt{x-4} + 3$.

EXAMPLE 18 For the radical function $f(x) = \sqrt{x+5} - 2$, find $f(-1)$.

SOLUTION To evaluate this function, substitute -1 for x and simplify.

$$f(-1) = \sqrt{(-1)+5} - 2 \quad \text{Substitute } -1 \text{ for } x.$$

$$= \sqrt{4} - 2 \quad \text{Simplify the radicand.}$$

$$= 2 - 2 \quad \text{Take the square root of 4.}$$

$$= 0 \quad \text{Subtract.}$$

Quick Check 12

For the radical function $f(x) = \sqrt{3x+13} + 33$, find $f(-3)$.

Finding the Domain of Radical Functions

Objective 8 Find the domain of a radical function. Radical functions involving even roots are different from many of the functions we have seen to this point in that their domain is restricted. To find the domain of a radical function involving an even root, we need to find the values of the variable that make the radicand nonnegative. In other words, set the radicand greater than or equal to zero and solve. The domain of a radical function involving odd roots is the set of all real numbers. Remember that square roots are considered to be even roots with an index of 2.

EXAMPLE 19 Find the domain of the radical function $f(x) = \sqrt{x-9} + 7$. Express your answer in interval notation.

SOLUTION Because the radical has an even index, we begin by setting the radicand $(x - 9)$ greater than or equal to zero. We solve this inequality to find the domain.

$$x - 9 \geq 0 \quad \text{Set the radicand greater than or equal to 0.}$$

$$x \geq 9 \quad \text{Add 9.}$$

The domain of the function is $[9, \infty)$.

Quick Check 13

Find the domain of the radical function $f(x) = \sqrt[6]{x+18} - 30$. Express your answer in interval notation.

EXAMPLE 20 Find the domain of the radical function $f(x) = \sqrt[5]{14x - 9} + 21$. Express your answer in interval notation.

SOLUTION Because this radical function involves an odd root, its domain is the set of all real numbers $\mathbb{R}$. This can be expressed in interval notation as $(-\infty, \infty)$.

▶ Quick Check 14

Find the domain of the radical function $f(x) = \sqrt[3]{16x - 409} + 38$. Express your answer in interval notation.

BUILDING YOUR STUDY STRATEGY

Note Taking, 1 Choosing a Seat One important yet frequently overlooked aspect of effective note taking is choosing an appropriate seat in class. You must sit where you can clearly see the board, preferably in the center of the room. Try not to sit behind anyone who will obstruct your vision.

Location also impacts your ability to hear your instructor clearly. You will find that your instructor speaks toward the middle of the classroom; so finding a seat toward the center of the classroom should ensure that you hear everything your instructor says. Try not to sit close to students who talk to each other during class; their discussions may distract you from what your instructor is saying.

In summary, try to choose your classroom seat the same way you choose a seat at a movie theater. Make sure you can see and hear everything.

Exercises 9.1

MyMathLab *Powered by CourseCompass™ and MathXL*

PRACTICE WATCH DOWNLOAD READ REVIEW

Vocabulary

1. A number a is a(n) _____ of a number b if $a^2 = b$.

2. The _____ square root of b, denoted $\sqrt{b}$, for $b > 0$, is the positive number a such that $a^2 = b$.

3. For any positive integer $n > 1$ and any number b, if $a^n = b$ and both a and b have the same sign, a is the principal _____ of b, denoted $a = \sqrt[n]{b}$.

4. For the expression $a = \sqrt[n]{b}$, n is called the _____ of the radical.

5. The expression contained inside a radical is called the _____.

6. A radical with an index of 3 is also known as a(n) _____ root.

7. A(n) _____ is a function that involves radicals.

8. The domain of a radical function involving an even root consists of values of the variable for which the radicand is _____.

Simplify the radical expression. Indicate if the expression is not a real number.

9. $\sqrt{36}$

10. $\sqrt{64}$

11. $\sqrt{4}$

12. $\sqrt{100}$

13. $\sqrt{\dfrac{1}{81}}$

14. $\sqrt{\dfrac{1}{49}}$

15. $\sqrt{\dfrac{25}{36}}$

16. $\sqrt{\dfrac{121}{4}}$

17. $\sqrt{-16}$

18. $\sqrt{-36}$

19. $-\sqrt{49}$

20. $-\sqrt{81}$

Simplify the radical expression. Where appropriate, include absolute values.

21. $\sqrt{a^{14}}$

22. $\sqrt{b^{10}}$

23. $\sqrt{x^{34}}$

24. $\sqrt{x^{42}}$

25. $\sqrt{9x^6}$

26. $\sqrt{16x^2}$

27. $\sqrt{\dfrac{1}{49}x^4}$

28. $\sqrt{\dfrac{1}{100}x^{24}}$

29. $\sqrt{a^{18}b^{22}}$

30. $\sqrt{m^6n^{22}}$

31. $\sqrt{x^8y^{10}z^{14}}$

32. $\sqrt{x^{20}y^{16}z^{26}}$

Find the missing number or expression. Assume that all variables represent nonnegative real numbers.

33. $\sqrt{?} = 9$

34. $\sqrt{?} = 16$

35. $\sqrt{?} = 3x$

36. $\sqrt{?} = 5a^3$

Approximate to the nearest thousandth using a calculator.

37. $\sqrt{55}$

38. $\sqrt{98}$

39. $\sqrt{326}$

40. $\sqrt{409}$

41. $\sqrt{0.53}$

42. $\sqrt{0.06}$

Simplify the radical expression. Assume that all variables represent nonnegative real numbers.

43. $\sqrt[3]{125}$

44. $\sqrt[3]{-64}$

45. $\sqrt[5]{-243}$

46. $\sqrt[4]{1296}$

47. $\sqrt[4]{x^{20}}$

48. $\sqrt[7]{x^{56}}$

49. $\sqrt[6]{a^{42}b^{24}}$

50. $\sqrt[3]{m^{33}n^{27}}$

51. $\sqrt[3]{343m^{21}}$

52. $\sqrt[3]{216n^{42}}$

53. $\sqrt[4]{81x^{12}y^{20}}$

54. $\sqrt[6]{64s^{36}t^{54}}$

55. $\sqrt{x^2 + 6x + 9}, x \geq -3$

56. $\sqrt{x^2 + 12x + 36}, x \geq -6$

Simplify. Assume that all variables represent nonnegative real numbers.

57. $\sqrt{27} \cdot \sqrt{3}$

58. $\sqrt{8} \cdot \sqrt{8}$

59. $\sqrt{10} \cdot \sqrt{90}$

60. $\sqrt{2} \cdot \sqrt{72}$

61. $\sqrt{a^9} \cdot \sqrt{a^{17}}$

62. $\sqrt{b^{15}} \cdot \sqrt{b}$

63. $\sqrt{x^{19}} \cdot \sqrt{x^{19}}$

64. $\sqrt{x^{13}} \cdot \sqrt{x^{13}}$

65. $\dfrac{\sqrt{180}}{\sqrt{5}}$

66. $\dfrac{\sqrt{63}}{\sqrt{7}}$

67. $\dfrac{\sqrt{800}}{\sqrt{8}}$

68. $\dfrac{\sqrt{1872}}{\sqrt{13}}$

69. $\dfrac{\sqrt{x^{23}}}{\sqrt{x^5}}$

70. $\dfrac{\sqrt{x^{31}}}{\sqrt{x^{27}}}$

71. $\dfrac{\sqrt{a^{13}}}{\sqrt{a}}$

72. $\dfrac{\sqrt{a^{21}}}{\sqrt{a^7}}$

73. $\sqrt[3]{6} \cdot \sqrt[3]{36}$

74. $\sqrt[3]{12} \cdot \sqrt[3]{18}$

75. $\sqrt[4]{48} \cdot \sqrt[4]{27}$

76. $\sqrt[5]{16} \cdot \sqrt[5]{64}$

77. $\sqrt[4]{x^7} \cdot \sqrt[4]{x^{13}}$

78. $\sqrt[3]{x^{10}} \cdot \sqrt[3]{x^{41}}$

79. $\sqrt[5]{a^{11}b^8} \cdot \sqrt[5]{a^4b^2}$

80. $\sqrt[6]{m^{15}n^8} \cdot \sqrt[6]{m^9n^{28}}$

81. $\dfrac{\sqrt[4]{324}}{\sqrt[4]{4}}$

82. $\dfrac{\sqrt[3]{875}}{\sqrt[3]{7}}$

83. $\dfrac{\sqrt[5]{x^{32}}}{\sqrt[5]{x^7}}$

84. $\dfrac{\sqrt[4]{x^{29}}}{\sqrt[4]{x^{17}}}$

85. $7\sqrt{6} \cdot 8\sqrt{6}$

86. $9\sqrt{5} \cdot 4\sqrt{5}$

87. $5\sqrt{12} \cdot 10\sqrt{27}$

88. $11\sqrt{8} \cdot 2\sqrt{50}$

89. $9\sqrt{x} \cdot 12\sqrt{x}$

90. $15\sqrt{x} \cdot 8\sqrt{x}$

Find the missing number.

91. $\sqrt{20} \cdot \sqrt{?} = 10$

92. $\sqrt{21} \cdot \sqrt{?} = 42$

93. $\dfrac{\sqrt{?}}{\sqrt{8}} = 7$

94. $\dfrac{\sqrt{?}}{\sqrt{6}} = 6$

Evaluate the radical function. Round to the nearest thousandth if necessary.

95. $f(x) = \sqrt{x - 5}$; find $f(21)$.

96. $f(x) = \sqrt{3x + 4}$; find $f(20)$.

97. $f(x) = \sqrt{2x + 19} - 2$; find $f(3)$.

98. $f(x) = \sqrt{4x - 11} - 10$; find $f(5)$.

99. $f(x) = \sqrt{2x + 9} + 7$; find $f(10)$.

100. $f(x) = \sqrt{5x - 4} - 13$; find $f(16)$.

101. $f(x) = \sqrt[3]{x^2 + 7x + 81}$; find $f(4)$.

102. $f(x) = \sqrt[4]{x^2 + 4x - 36}$; find $f(9)$.

Find the domain of the radical function. Express your answer in interval notation.

103. $f(x) = \sqrt{x - 4} + 11$

104. $f(x) = \sqrt{2x + 9} - 20$

105. $f(x) = \sqrt[4]{3x - 8} - 17$

106. $f(x) = \sqrt[6]{4x} - 34$

107. $f(x) = \sqrt{13 - 2x} + 5$

108. $f(x) = \sqrt{8 - x} - 2$

109. $f(x) = \sqrt[3]{15x - 42} + 6$

110. $f(x) = \sqrt[5]{10x + 115} - 45$

✏ Writing in Mathematics

Answer in complete sentences.

111. Which of the following are real numbers, and which are not real numbers: $-\sqrt{64}$, $\sqrt{-64}$, $-\sqrt[3]{64}$, $\sqrt[3]{-64}$? Explain your reasoning.

112. Explain how to find the domain of a radical function. Use examples.

9.2

Rational Exponents

OBJECTIVES

1. Simplify expressions containing exponents of the form $1/n$.
2. Simplify expressions containing exponents of the form m/n.
3. Simplify expressions containing rational exponents.
4. Simplify expressions containing negative rational exponents.
5. Use rational exponents to simplify radical expressions.

Rational Exponents of the Form $1/n$

Objective 1 Simplify expressions containing exponents of the form $1/n$.
We have used exponents to represent repeated multiplication. For example, x^n says that the base x is a factor n times.

$$x^3 = x \cdot x \cdot x$$
$$x^6 = x \cdot x \cdot x \cdot x \cdot x \cdot x$$

We run into a problem with this definition when we encounter an expression with a fractional exponent, such as $x^{1/2}$. Saying that the base x is a factor $\frac{1}{2}$ times does not make any sense. Using the properties of exponents introduced in Chapter 5, we know that $x^{1/2} \cdot x^{1/2} = x^{1/2+1/2}$, or x. If we multiply $x^{1/2}$ by itself, the result is x. The same is true when we multiply $\sqrt{x}$ by itself, suggesting that $x^{1/2} = \sqrt{x}$.

> For any integer $n > 1$, we define $a^{1/n}$ to be the nth root of a, or $\sqrt[n]{a}$.

EXAMPLE 1 Rewrite $81^{1/4}$ as a radical expression and simplify if possible.

SOLUTION

$$81^{1/4} = \sqrt[4]{81}$$ Rewrite as a radical expression. An exponent of 1/4 is equivalent to a fourth root.

$$= \sqrt[4]{3^4}$$ Rewrite the radicand as a number to the fourth power.

$$= 3$$ Simplify.

EXAMPLE 2 Rewrite $(-125x^6)^{1/3}$ as a radical expression and simplify if possible.

SOLUTION

$$(-125x^6)^{1/3} = \sqrt[3]{(-5x^2)^3}$$ Rewrite as a radical expression. Rewrite the radicand as a cube.

$$= -5x^2$$ Simplify. Keep in mind that an odd root of a negative number is negative.

▶ Quick Check 1

Rewrite as a radical expression and simplify if possible.

a) $36^{1/2}$ **b)** $(-32x^{15})^{1/5}$

Quick Check 2

Rewrite $(x^{32}y^4z^{24})^{1/4}$ as a radical expression and simplify if possible. (Assume that all variables represent nonnegative values.)

EXAMPLE 3 Rewrite $(a^{10}b^5c^{20})^{1/5}$ as a radical expression and simplify if possible.

SOLUTION

$$(a^{10}b^5c^{20})^{1/5} = \sqrt[5]{a^{10}b^5c^{20}}$$ Rewrite as a radical expression.

$$= \sqrt[5]{(a^2bc^4)^5}$$ Rewrite the radicand.

$$= a^2bc^4$$ Simplify.

For any negative number x and even integer n, $x^{1/n}$ is not a real number. For example, $(-64)^{1/6}$ is not a real number because $(-64)^{1/6} = \sqrt[6]{-64}$ and an even root of a negative number is not a real number.

EXAMPLE 4 Rewrite $\sqrt[7]{x}$ by using rational exponents.

SOLUTION

$$\sqrt[7]{x} = x^{1/7} \quad \text{Rewrite using the definition } \sqrt[n]{x} = x^{1/n}.$$

Quick Check 3
Rewrite $\sqrt[9]{a}$ using rational exponents.

Rational Exponents of the Form m/n

Objective 2 Simplify expressions containing exponents of the form m/n.
We now turn our attention to rational exponents of the form m/n for any integers m and $n > 1$. The expression $a^{m/n}$ can be rewritten as $(a^{1/n})^m$, which is equivalent to $(\sqrt[n]{a})^m$.

> For any integers m and n, $n > 1$, we define $a^{m/n}$ to be $(\sqrt[n]{a})^m$. This is also equivalent to $\sqrt[n]{a^m}$. The denominator in the exponent, n, is the root we are taking. The numerator in the exponent, m, is the power to which we raise this radical.
>
>
> power ⟶ ⟵ root
> $a^{m/n}$

When simplifying an expression of the form $a^{m/n}$, take the nth root of a first if $\sqrt[n]{a}$ can be simplified. Otherwise, raise a to the m power and then attempt to simplify $\sqrt[n]{a^m}$.

EXAMPLE 5 Rewrite $(243x^{10})^{3/5}$ as a radical expression and simplify if possible.

SOLUTION

$$
\begin{aligned}
(243x^{10})^{3/5} &= \left(\sqrt[5]{243x^{10}}\right)^3 && \text{Rewrite as a radical expression.} \\
&= \left(\sqrt[5]{(3x^2)^5}\right)^3 && \text{Rewrite the radicand.} \\
&= (3x^2)^3 && \text{Simplify the radical.} \\
&= 27x^6 && \text{Raise } 3x^2 \text{ to the third power.}
\end{aligned}
$$

▶ **Quick Check 4**
Rewrite $(4096x^{18})^{5/6}$ as a radical expression and simplify if possible. (Assume that x is nonnegative.)

EXAMPLE 6 Rewrite $\sqrt[5]{x^3}$ by using rational exponents.

SOLUTION

$$\sqrt[5]{x^3} = x^{3/5} \quad \text{Rewrite using the definition } \sqrt[n]{x^m} = x^{m/n}.$$

▶ **Quick Check 5**
Rewrite $\sqrt[12]{x^5}$ by using rational exponents. (Assume that x is nonnegative.)

Simplifying Expressions Containing Rational Exponents

Objective ③ **Simplify expressions containing rational exponents.** The properties of exponents developed in Chapter 5 for integer exponents are true for fractional exponents as well. Here is a summary of those properties.

Properties of Exponents

For any bases x and y:

1. $x^m \cdot x^n = x^{m+n}$
2. $(x^m)^n = x^{m \cdot n}$
3. $(xy)^n = x^n y^n$
4. $\dfrac{x^m}{x^n} = x^{m-n} \ (x \neq 0)$

5. $x^0 = 1 \ (x \neq 0)$
6. $\left(\dfrac{x}{y}\right)^n = \dfrac{x^n}{y^n} \ (y \neq 0)$
7. $x^{-n} = \dfrac{1}{x^n} \ (x \neq 0)$

EXAMPLE 7 Simplify the expression $x^{4/3} \cdot x^{5/6}$. (Assume that x is nonnegative.)

SOLUTION When multiplying two expressions with the same base, add the exponents and keep the base.

$$x^{4/3} \cdot x^{5/6} = x^{\frac{4}{3}+\frac{5}{6}} \quad \text{Add the exponents; keep the base.}$$
$$= x^{\frac{8}{6}+\frac{5}{6}} \quad \text{Rewrite the fractions with a common denominator.}$$
$$= x^{13/6} \quad \text{Add.}$$

▸ **Quick Check 6**

Simplify the expression $x^{5/8} \cdot x^{7/12}$. (Assume that x is nonnegative.)

EXAMPLE 8 Simplify the expression $(x^{3/4})^{2/5}$. (Assume that x is nonnegative.)

SOLUTION When raising an exponential expression to another power, multiply the exponents and keep the base.

$$(x^{3/4})^{2/5} = x^{\frac{3}{4} \cdot \frac{2}{5}} \quad \text{Multiply the exponents; keep the base.}$$
$$= x^{3/10} \quad \text{Multiply.}$$

Quick Check 7

Simplify the expression $(x^{7/10})^{4/9}$. (Assume that x is nonnegative.)

EXAMPLE 9 Simplify the expression $\left(\dfrac{b^4}{c^2 d^6}\right)^{3/2}$, where $c \neq 0, d \neq 0$. (Assume that all variables represent nonnegative values.)

SOLUTION Begin by raising each factor to the $\frac{3}{2}$ power.

$$\left(\frac{b^4}{c^2 d^6}\right)^{3/2} = \frac{b^{4 \cdot \frac{3}{2}}}{c^{2 \cdot \frac{3}{2}} d^{6 \cdot \frac{3}{2}}} \quad \text{Raise each factor to the } \tfrac{3}{2} \text{ power.}$$

$$= \frac{b^6}{c^3 d^9} \quad \text{Multiply exponents.}$$

▸ **Quick Check 8**

Simplify the expression $\left(\dfrac{x^9}{y^3 z^{12}}\right)^{5/3}$, where $y \neq 0, z \neq 0$.

Simplifying Expressions Containing Negative Rational Exponents

Objective 4 Simplify expressions containing negative rational exponents.

EXAMPLE 10   Simplify the expression $64^{-5/6}$.

SOLUTION   Begin by rewriting the expression with a positive exponent.

$$64^{-5/6} = \frac{1}{64^{5/6}} \qquad \text{Rewrite the expression with a positive exponent.}$$

$$= \frac{1}{(\sqrt[6]{64})^5} \qquad \text{Rewrite in radical notation.}$$

$$= \frac{1}{2^5} \qquad \text{Simplify the radical.}$$

$$= \frac{1}{32} \qquad \text{Raise 2 to the fifth power.}$$

Quick Check 9

Simplify the expression $81^{-3/2}$.

Using Rational Exponents to Simplify Radical Expressions

Objective 5 Use rational exponents to simplify radical expressions. In the previous section, we learned that we may multiply two radicals if they have the same index. In other words, $\sqrt[n]{a} \cdot \sqrt[n]{b} = \sqrt[n]{ab}$ if $\sqrt[n]{a}$ and $\sqrt[n]{b}$ are real numbers. If the two indices are not the same, we can use fractional exponents to multiply the radicals.

EXAMPLE 11   Simplify the expression $\sqrt{a} \cdot \sqrt[5]{a}$. (Assume that a is nonnegative.) Express your answer in radical notation.

SOLUTION   Begin by rewriting the radicals using fractional exponents.

$$\sqrt{a} \cdot \sqrt[5]{a} = a^{1/2} \cdot a^{1/5} \qquad \text{Rewrite both radicals using fractional exponents.}$$

$$= a^{\frac{1}{2} + \frac{1}{5}} \qquad \text{Add the exponents, keeping the base.}$$

$$= a^{\frac{5}{10} + \frac{2}{10}} \qquad \text{Rewrite each fraction with a common denominator.}$$

$$= a^{7/10} \qquad \text{Add.}$$

$$= \sqrt[10]{a^7} \qquad \text{Rewrite in radical notation.}$$

Quick Check 10

Simplify the expression $\sqrt[3]{x} \cdot \sqrt[4]{x}$. (Assume that x is nonnegative.) Express your answer in radical notation.

BUILDING YOUR STUDY STRATEGY

Note Taking, 2 Note-Taking Speed "I'm a slow writer. There's no way I can take down all of the notes in time." This is a common concern for students. Try to focus on writing down enough information so that you will understand the material later, rather than thinking you must copy every word your instructor writes or speaks. Then rewrite your notes, filling in any blanks or adding explanations, as soon as possible after class.

During class, try to use abbreviations whenever possible. Write your notes using phrases rather than complete sentences.

With your instructor's approval, you may want to record a lecture. After class, you can use the recording to help fill in holes in your notes.

If you are falling behind in your note taking, leave space in your notes. Afterward ask a classmate if you can borrow his or her notes to get the information you missed.

Exercises 9.2

PRACTICE WATCH DOWNLOAD READ REVIEW

Vocabulary

1. For any integer $n > 1$, $a^{1/n} = $ _____.
2. For any integers m and n, $n > 1$, $a^{m/n} = $ _____
   _____.
3. An exponent of the form m/n is said to be a(n) _____ exponent.
4. For the expression $x^{m/n}$, m represents the _____ to which x is raised and n represents the _____ that is being taken.

Rewrite each radical expression using rational exponents.

5. $\sqrt[4]{x}$
6. $\sqrt[5]{a}$
7. $\sqrt{7}$
8. $\sqrt[3]{10}$
9. $9\sqrt[4]{d}$
10. $\sqrt[4]{9d}$

Rewrite as a radical expression and simplify if possible. Assume that all variables represent nonnegative real numbers.

11. $64^{1/2}$
12. $25^{1/2}$
13. $(-343)^{1/3}$
14. $(-1024)^{1/5}$
15. $(x^{30})^{1/5}$
16. $(a^{28})^{1/4}$
17. $(64a^{33}b^{21})^{1/3}$
18. $(32x^{35}y^{40})^{1/5}$
19. $(-243x^{55}y^{25}z^5)^{1/5}$
20. $(-125a^{24}b^3c^{27})^{1/3}$

Rewrite each radical expression using rational exponents. Assume that all variables represent nonnegative real numbers.

21. $(\sqrt[5]{x})^3$
22. $(\sqrt[4]{x})^7$
23. $(\sqrt[9]{y})^8$
24. $(\sqrt[12]{a})^{17}$
25. $(\sqrt[3]{3x^2})^7$
26. $(\sqrt[9]{2x^4})^2$
27. $(\sqrt[8]{10x^4y^5})^3$
28. $(\sqrt[5]{a^6b^7c^8})^4$

Rewrite as a radical expression and simplify if possible. Assume that all variables represent nonnegative real numbers.

29. $25^{3/2}$
30. $16^{3/4}$
31. $32^{2/5}$
32. $1000^{7/3}$
33. $(x^{12})^{2/3}$
34. $(x^{20})^{6/5}$
35. $(256a^8b^{24})^{3/4}$
36. $(4x^{16}y^{32}z^{64})^{5/2}$
37. $(-125x^9y^{15}z^3)^{4/3}$
38. $(256a^4b^8c^{20})^{7/4}$

Simplify the expression. Assume that all variables represent nonnegative real numbers.

39. $x^{7/10} \cdot x^{1/10}$
40. $x^{3/4} \cdot x^{11/4}$
41. $x^{4/3} \cdot x^{1/2}$
42. $x^{10/7} \cdot x^{1/14}$
43. $a^{5/3} \cdot a^{3/4} \cdot a^{1/6}$
44. $m^{4/5} \cdot m^{5/2} \cdot m^{7/10}$
45. $x^{1/3}y^{3/4} \cdot x^{1/6}y^{1/6}$
46. $x^{3/8}y^{1/3} \cdot x^{7/10}y^{1/4}$

47. $(x^{3/4})^{2/7}$
48. $(x^{5/6})^{9/20}$
49. $(a^{3/5})^{3/5}$
50. $(b^{2/7})^{7/2}$
51. $(x^{5/12})^4$
52. $(x^{12})^{7/6}$
53. $\dfrac{x^{4/5}}{x^{3/10}} \ (x \neq 0)$
54. $\dfrac{x^{7/6}}{x^{11/12}} \ (x \neq 0)$
55. $\dfrac{x^{5/8}}{x^{1/3}} \ (x \neq 0)$
56. $\dfrac{x^{9/10}}{x^{21/40}} \ (x \neq 0)$
57. $(x^{5/4})^0 \ (x \neq 0)$
58. $(x^{2/9})^0 \ (x \neq 0)$
59. $32^{-1/5}$
60. $125^{-1/3}$
61. $27^{-4/3}$
62. $100^{-3/2}$
63. $216^{-4/3} \cdot 216^{-1/3}$
64. $16^{-3/4} \cdot 16^{-7/4}$
65. $\dfrac{125^{2/3}}{125^{7/3}}$
66. $\dfrac{16^{3/4}}{16^{9/4}}$
67. $\dfrac{216^{7/3}}{216^{8/3}}$
68. $\dfrac{4^{3/2}}{4^5}$

Simplify each expression. Assume that all variables represent nonnegative real numbers. Express your answer in radical notation.

69. $\sqrt[4]{x} \cdot \sqrt[5]{x}$
70. $\sqrt[9]{x} \cdot \sqrt[18]{x}$
71. $\sqrt[12]{a} \cdot \sqrt[4]{a}$
72. $\sqrt[3]{b} \cdot \sqrt[8]{b}$
73. $\dfrac{\sqrt[4]{m}}{\sqrt[12]{m}} \ (m \neq 0)$
74. $\dfrac{\sqrt{n}}{\sqrt[3]{n}} \ (n \neq 0)$
75. $\dfrac{\sqrt[30]{x}}{\sqrt[5]{x}} \ (x \neq 0)$
76. $\dfrac{\sqrt[10]{x}}{\sqrt[5]{x}} \ (x \neq 0)$

Writing in Mathematics

Answer in complete sentences.

77. Is $-16^{1/2}$ a real number? Explain your answer.

78. Is $16^{-1/2}$ a real number? Explain your answer.

9.3

Simplifying, Adding, and Subtracting Radical Expressions

OBJECTIVES

1. Simplify radical expressions by using the product property.
2. Add or subtract radical expressions containing like radicals.
3. Simplify radical expressions before adding or subtracting.

Simplifying Radical Expressions Using the Product Property

Objective 1 Simplify radical expressions by using the product property.
A radical expression is considered simplified if the radicand contains no factors with exponents greater than or equal to the index of the radical. For example, $\sqrt[3]{x^5}$ is not simplified because an exponent inside the radical is greater than the index of the radical. The goal for simplifying radical expressions is to remove as many factors as possible from the radicand. We will use the product property for radical expressions to help us with this.

We could rewrite $\sqrt[3]{x^5}$ as $\sqrt[3]{x^3 \cdot x^2}$, then rewrite this radical expression as the product of two radicals. Using the product property for radicals, $\sqrt[n]{a} \cdot \sqrt[n]{b} = \sqrt[n]{ab}$, we know that $\sqrt[3]{x^3 \cdot x^2} = \sqrt[3]{x^3} \cdot \sqrt[3]{x^2}$. The reason for rewriting $\sqrt[3]{x^5}$ as $\sqrt[3]{x^3} \cdot \sqrt[3]{x^2}$ is that the radical $\sqrt[3]{x^3}$ equals x.

$$
\begin{aligned}
\sqrt[3]{x^5} &= \sqrt[3]{x^3 \cdot x^2} \\
&= \sqrt[3]{x^3} \cdot \sqrt[3]{x^2} \\
&= x\sqrt[3]{x^2}
\end{aligned}
$$

Now the radicand contains no factors with an exponent that is greater than or equal to the index 3 and is simplified.

Simplifying Radical Expressions

- Completely factor any numerical factors in the radicand.
- Rewrite each factor as a product of two factors. The exponent for the first factor should be the largest multiple of the radical's index that is less than or equal to the factor's original exponent.
- Use the product property to remove factors from the radicand.

EXAMPLE 1 Simplify $\sqrt[4]{a^{23}}$. (Assume that a is nonnegative.)

SOLUTION   We begin by rewriting a^{23} as a product of two factors. The largest multiple of the index (4) that is less than or equal to the exponent for this factor (23) is 20; so we will rewrite a^{23} as $a^{20} \cdot a^3$.

$$
\begin{aligned}
\sqrt[4]{a^{23}} &= \sqrt[4]{a^{20} \cdot a^3} && \text{Rewrite } a^{23} \text{ as the product of two factors.} \\
&= \sqrt[4]{a^{20}} \cdot \sqrt[4]{a^3} && \text{Use the product property of radicals to rewrite the radical as the product of two radicals.} \\
&= a^5\sqrt[4]{a^3} && \text{Simplify the radical.}
\end{aligned}
$$

▶ Quick Check 1

Simplify $\sqrt[5]{x^{17}}$. (Assume that x is nonnegative.)

EXAMPLE 2 Simplify $\sqrt{x^{11}y^{10}z^5}$. (Assume that all variables represent nonnegative values.)

SOLUTION Again, we begin by rewriting factors as a product of two factors. In this example, the exponent of the factor y is a multiple of the index 2. We do not need to rewrite this factor as the product of two factors.

$$\sqrt{x^{11}y^{10}z^5} = \sqrt{(x^{10} \cdot x)y^{10}(z^4 \cdot z)} \qquad \text{Rewrite factors.}$$
$$= \sqrt{x^{10}y^{10}z^4} \cdot \sqrt{xz} \qquad \text{Rewrite as the product of two radicals.}$$
$$= x^5y^5z^2\sqrt{xz} \qquad \text{Simplify the radical.}$$

▶ **Quick Check 2**

Simplify $\sqrt{a^8b^{15}c^7d}$. (Assume that all variables represent nonnegative values.)

EXAMPLE 3 Simplify $\sqrt{24}$.

SOLUTION Begin by rewriting 24 using its prime factorization ($2^3 \cdot 3$).

$$\sqrt{24} = \sqrt{2^3 \cdot 3} \qquad \text{Factor 24.}$$
$$= \sqrt{(2^2 \cdot 2) \cdot 3} \qquad \text{Rewrite } 2^3 \text{ as } 2^2 \cdot 2.$$
$$= \sqrt{2^2} \cdot \sqrt{2 \cdot 3} \qquad \text{Rewrite as the product of two radicals.}$$
$$= 2\sqrt{6} \qquad \text{Simplify.}$$

We could have used a different tactic to simplify this square root. The largest factor of 24 that is a perfect square is 4; so we could begin by rewriting 24 as $4 \cdot 6$. Because we know that the square root of 4 is 2, we could factor 4 out of the radicand and write it as 2 in front of the radical.

$$\sqrt{24} = \sqrt{4 \cdot 6}$$
$$= 2\sqrt{6}$$

▶ **Quick Check 3**

Simplify $\sqrt{90}$.

EXAMPLE 4 Simplify $\sqrt[3]{324}$.

SOLUTION Begin by factoring 324 to be $2^2 \cdot 3^4$.

$$\sqrt[3]{324} = \sqrt[3]{2^2 \cdot 3^4} \qquad \text{Factor 324.}$$
$$= \sqrt[3]{2^2 \cdot (3^3 \cdot 3)} \qquad \text{Rewrite } 3^4 \text{ as } 3^3 \cdot 3.$$
$$= \sqrt[3]{3^3} \cdot \sqrt[3]{2^2 \cdot 3} \qquad \text{Rewrite as the product of two radicals.}$$
$$= 3\sqrt[3]{12} \qquad \text{Simplify.}$$

Quick Check 4

Simplify $\sqrt[3]{280}$.

There is an alternative approach for simplifying radical expressions. Suppose we were trying to simplify $\sqrt[5]{a^{48}}$. Using the previous method, we would arrive at the answer $a^9\sqrt[5]{a^3}$.

$$\sqrt[5]{a^{48}} = \sqrt[5]{a^{45} \cdot a^3} \qquad \text{Rewrite } a^{48} \text{ as } a^{45} \cdot a^3 \text{ because 45 is the highest multiple of 5 that is less than or equal to 48.}$$
$$= \sqrt[5]{a^{45}} \cdot \sqrt[5]{a^3} \qquad \text{Rewrite as the product of two radicals.}$$
$$= a^9\sqrt[5]{a^3} \qquad \text{Simplify.}$$

We know that for every five times a is repeated as a factor in the radicand, we can take a^5 out of the radicand and write it as a in front of the radical. We need to determine how many groups of five can be removed from the radicand, using division. If we divide the exponent 48 by the index 5, the quotient is 9 with a remainder of 3. When we divide the exponent of a factor in the radicand by the index of the radical, the quotient tells us the exponent of the factor removed from the radicand and the remainder tells us the exponent of the factor remaining in the radicand.

An Alternative Approach for Simplifying $\sqrt[n]{x^p}$

- Divide p by n: $\frac{p}{n} = q + \frac{r}{n}$
- The quotient q tells us how many times x will be a factor in front of the radical.
- The remainder r tells us how many times x will remain as a factor in the radicand.

$$\sqrt[n]{x^p} = x^q \sqrt[n]{x^r}$$

EXAMPLE 5 Simplify $\sqrt[6]{a^{31}b^{18}c^5d^{53}}$. (Assume that all variables represent non-negative values.)

SOLUTION We will work with one factor at a time, beginning with a. The index, 6, divides into the exponent, 31, five times with a remainder of one. This tells us we can write a^5 as a factor in front of the radical and can write a^1, or a, in the radicand.

$$\sqrt[6]{a^{31}b^{18}c^5d^{53}} = a^5\sqrt[6]{ab^{18}c^5d^{53}}$$

For the factor b, $18 \div 6 = 3$ with a remainder of 0. We will write b^3 as a factor in front of the radical, and because the remainder is 0, we will not write b as a factor in the radicand. For the factor c, the index does not divide into 5, so c^5 remains as a factor in the radicand. Finally, for the factor d, $53 \div 6 = 8$ with a remainder of 5. We will write d^8 as a factor in front of the radical and d^5 as a factor in the radicand.

$$\sqrt[6]{a^{31}b^{18}c^5d^{53}} = a^5b^3d^8\sqrt[6]{ac^5d^5}$$

▶ Quick Check 5

Simplify $\sqrt[5]{x^{33}y^6z^{50}w^{18}}$.

Adding and Subtracting Radical Expressions Containing Like Radicals

Objective 2 **Add and subtract radical expressions containing like radicals.**

Like Radicals

Two radical expressions are called **like radicals** if they have the same index and the same radicand.

The radical expressions $5\sqrt[3]{4x}$ and $9\sqrt[3]{4x}$ are like radicals because they have the same index (3) and the same radicand ($4x$). Here are some examples of radical expressions that are not like radicals.

$\sqrt{5}$ and $\sqrt[3]{5}$ The two radicals have different indices.

$\sqrt[4]{7x^2y^3}$ and $\sqrt[4]{7x^3y^2}$ The two radicands are different.

We can add and subtract radical expressions by combining like radicals similar to the way we combine like terms. We add or subtract the coefficients in front of the like radicals.

$$6\sqrt{2} + 3\sqrt{2} = 9\sqrt{2}$$

EXAMPLE 6 Simplify $12\sqrt{13} + \sqrt{3} + \sqrt{3} - 6\sqrt{13}$.

SOLUTION There are two pairs of like radicals in this example. There are two radical expressions containing $\sqrt{13}$ and two radical expressions containing $\sqrt{3}$.

$$
\begin{aligned}
12\sqrt{13} &+ \sqrt{3} + \sqrt{3} - 6\sqrt{13} \\
&= 6\sqrt{13} + \sqrt{3} + \sqrt{3} && \text{Subtract } 12\sqrt{13} - 6\sqrt{13}. \\
&= 6\sqrt{13} + 2\sqrt{3} && \text{Add } \sqrt{3} + \sqrt{3}.
\end{aligned}
$$

▶ Quick Check 6
Simplify $9\sqrt{10} - 13\sqrt{5} + 6\sqrt{10} + 8\sqrt{5}$.

EXAMPLE 7 Simplify $18\sqrt[5]{x^3y^2} - 2\sqrt[5]{x^2y^3} - 8\sqrt[5]{x^3y^2}$.

SOLUTION Of the three terms, only the first and third contain like radicals.

$$18\sqrt[5]{x^3y^2} - 2\sqrt[5]{x^2y^3} - 8\sqrt[5]{x^3y^2} = 10\sqrt[5]{x^3y^2} - 2\sqrt[5]{x^2y^3}$$

Subtract $18\sqrt[5]{x^3y^2} - 8\sqrt[5]{x^3y^2}$.

▶ Quick Check 7
Simplify $16\sqrt[5]{a^4b^3} - 11\sqrt[5]{a^4b^3} - 5\sqrt[5]{a^4b^3}$.

Objective 3 Simplify radical expressions before adding or subtracting.
Are the expressions $\sqrt{24}$ and $\sqrt{54}$ like radicals? We must simplify each radical completely before we can determine whether the two expressions are like radicals. In this case, $\sqrt{24} = 2\sqrt{6}$ and $\sqrt{54} = 3\sqrt{6}$; so $\sqrt{24}$ and $\sqrt{54}$ are like radicals.

EXAMPLE 8 Simplify $\sqrt{12} + \sqrt{3}$.

SOLUTION We begin by simplifying each radical completely. Because 12 can be written as $4 \cdot 3$, $\sqrt{12}$ can be simplified to $2\sqrt{3}$. We also could use the prime factorization of 12 $(2^2 \cdot 3)$ to simplify $\sqrt{12}$.

$$
\begin{aligned}
\sqrt{12} + \sqrt{3} &= \sqrt{4 \cdot 3} + \sqrt{3} && \text{Factor 12.} \\
&= 2\sqrt{3} + \sqrt{3} && \text{Simplify } \sqrt{4 \cdot 3}. \\
&= 3\sqrt{3} && \text{Add.}
\end{aligned}
$$

Quick Check 8
Simplify $\sqrt{63} + \sqrt{7}$.

EXAMPLE 9 Simplify $\sqrt{45} - \sqrt{80} - \sqrt{20}$.

SOLUTION In this example, we must simplify all three radicals before proceeding.

$$
\begin{aligned}
\sqrt{45} - \sqrt{80} - \sqrt{20} &= \sqrt{9 \cdot 5} - \sqrt{16 \cdot 5} - \sqrt{4 \cdot 5} && \text{Factor each radicand.} \\
&= 3\sqrt{5} - 4\sqrt{5} - 2\sqrt{5} && \text{Simplify each radical.} \\
&= -3\sqrt{5} && \text{Combine like radicals.}
\end{aligned}
$$

▶ Quick Check 9
Simplify $\sqrt{18} - \sqrt{32} + \sqrt{98}$.

BUILDING YOUR STUDY STRATEGY

Note Taking, 3 Things to Include What belongs in your notes? Begin by including anything your instructor writes on the board. Instructors give verbal cues when they want you to include something in your notes. Your instructor may pause to give you enough time to finish writing in your notebook or may repeat the phrase to make sure you accurately write down the statement in your notes.

Some instructors warn the class that a particular topic, problem, or step is difficult. When you hear this, your instructor is telling you to take the best notes you can because you will need them later.

Exercises 9.3

 MyMathLab

 PRACTICE WATCH DOWNLOAD READ · REVIEW

Vocabulary

1. Two radical expressions are called _____ if they have the same index and the same radicand.
2. To add radical expressions with like radicals, add the _____ of the radicals and place the sum in front of the like radical.

Simplify.

3. $\sqrt{12}$
4. $\sqrt{18}$
5. $\sqrt{45}$
6. $\sqrt{252}$
7. $\sqrt{432}$
8. $\sqrt{448}$
9. $\sqrt[3]{192}$
10. $\sqrt[3]{800}$
11. $\sqrt[3]{1296}$
12. $\sqrt[3]{2187}$
13. $\sqrt[4]{1200}$
14. $\sqrt[5]{448}$

Simplify the radical expression. Assume that all variables represent nonnegative real numbers.

15. $\sqrt{x^9}$
16. $\sqrt{a^{15}}$
17. $\sqrt[3]{m^{13}}$
18. $\sqrt[3]{x^{40}}$
19. $\sqrt[5]{x^{74}}$
20. $\sqrt[4]{b^{82}}$
21. $\sqrt{x^{15}y^{12}}$
22. $\sqrt{a^{23}b^3}$
23. $\sqrt{xy^7}$
24. $\sqrt{x^{20}y^{11}}$
25. $\sqrt{x^{33}y^{17}z^{16}}$
26. $\sqrt{r^{19}s^{18}t^{28}}$
27. $\sqrt[3]{x^{13}y^{11}z}$
28. $\sqrt[3]{x^{27}y^{24}z^{32}}$
29. $\sqrt[4]{a^{14}b^{35}c^9}$
30. $\sqrt[5]{a^{33}b^5c^{24}}$
31. $\sqrt{27x^{11}y^{12}}$
32. $\sqrt{150x^{14}y^5}$
33. $\sqrt[4]{162x^{23}y^6z^{16}}$
34. $\sqrt[3]{250x^{11}y^{25}z^3}$

Add or subtract. Assume that all variables represent nonnegative real numbers.

35. $10\sqrt{5} + 17\sqrt{5}$
36. $8\sqrt{11} - 19\sqrt{11}$
37. $9\sqrt[3]{4} - 15\sqrt[3]{4}$
38. $14\sqrt[3]{20} + 6\sqrt[3]{20}$
39. $10\sqrt{15} - 3\sqrt{15} + 8\sqrt{15}$
40. $7\sqrt{6} - 19\sqrt{6} - 32\sqrt{6}$
41. $10\sqrt{7} - 3\sqrt{3} - 18\sqrt{3} - 5\sqrt{7}$
42. $9\sqrt{10} + \sqrt{17} - 3\sqrt{17} + 8\sqrt{10}$
43. $(8\sqrt{2} - 4\sqrt{3}) - (6\sqrt{2} + 9\sqrt{3})$
44. $(2\sqrt{5} + 7\sqrt{6}) - (11\sqrt{6} - 13\sqrt{5})$
45. $5\sqrt{x} - 7\sqrt{x}$
46. $13\sqrt{y} + 12\sqrt{y}$
47. $3\sqrt[5]{a} + 8\sqrt[5]{a}$
48. $11\sqrt[4]{x} - 2\sqrt[4]{x}$
49. $16\sqrt{x} - 9\sqrt{x} + 15\sqrt{x}$
50. $-24\sqrt{x} - 17\sqrt{x} + 3\sqrt{x}$
51. $4\sqrt{x} - 11\sqrt{y} - 6\sqrt{y} + \sqrt{x}$
52. $-2\sqrt{a} + 9\sqrt{b} - 18\sqrt{a} - 5\sqrt{b}$
53. $8\sqrt[3]{x} + 7\sqrt[4]{x} - 10\sqrt[4]{x} + 13\sqrt[3]{x}$
54. $\sqrt[4]{ab^3} + 12\sqrt[4]{a^2b^3} + 23\sqrt[4]{ab^3} - 25\sqrt[4]{a^2b^3}$
55. $\sqrt{50} + \sqrt{128}$
56. $\sqrt{48} - \sqrt{300}$
57. $7\sqrt{24} - 9\sqrt{150}$
58. $8\sqrt{320} + 13\sqrt{125}$
59. $10\sqrt{3} + 2\sqrt{27} + 5\sqrt{108}$
60. $3\sqrt{98} - 6\sqrt{200} - 14\sqrt{2}$

61. $6\sqrt[4]{2} + 7\sqrt[4]{1250} - 2\sqrt[4]{162}$

62. $3\sqrt[3]{3} - 5\sqrt[3]{24} - 8\sqrt[3]{192}$

63. $20\sqrt{12} - 9\sqrt{18} - 13\sqrt{147} - 8\sqrt{72}$

64. $6\sqrt{50} + 7\sqrt{180} - 10\sqrt{162} + 15\sqrt{405}$

Find the missing radical expression.

65. $(8\sqrt{3} + 7\sqrt{2}) + (?) = 15\sqrt{3} - 4\sqrt{2}$

66. $(3\sqrt{200} - 6\sqrt{108}) + (?) = 19\sqrt{2} - 50\sqrt{3}$

67. $(3\sqrt{50} - \sqrt{405}) - (?) = 3\sqrt{98} - 13\sqrt{20}$

68. $(4\sqrt{224} - 2\sqrt{360}) - (?) = \sqrt{640} + 4\sqrt{350}$

Writing in Mathematics

Answer in complete sentences.

69. Explain how to simplify $\sqrt{360}$.

70. Explain how to determine whether radical expressions are like radicals.

9.4

Multiplying and Dividing Radical Expressions

OBJECTIVES

1. Multiply radical expressions.
2. Use the distributive property to multiply radical expressions.
3. Multiply radical expressions that have two or more terms.
4. Multiply radical expressions that are conjugates.
5. Rationalize a denominator that has one term.
6. Rationalize a denominator that has two terms.

Multiplying Two Radical Expressions

Objective 1 Multiply radical expressions. In Section 9.1, we learned how to multiply one radical by another as well as how to divide one radical by another.

> **Multiplying Radicals with the Same Index**
>
> For any positive integer $n > 1$, if $\sqrt[n]{x}$ and $\sqrt[n]{y}$ are real numbers, then
>
> $$\sqrt[n]{x} \cdot \sqrt[n]{y} = \sqrt[n]{xy} \quad \text{and} \quad \frac{\sqrt[n]{x}}{\sqrt[n]{y}} = \sqrt[n]{\frac{x}{y}}.$$

In this section, we will build on that knowledge and learn how to multiply and divide expressions containing two or more radicals. We will begin with a review of multiplying radicals.

EXAMPLE 1 Multiply $\sqrt{18} \cdot \sqrt{8}$.

SOLUTION   Because the index of each radical is the same and neither radicand is a perfect square, we begin by multiplying the two radicands.

$$\sqrt{18} \cdot \sqrt{8} = \sqrt{144} \quad \text{Multiply the radicands.}$$
$$= 12 \quad \text{Simplify the radical.}$$

EXAMPLE 2 Multiply $\sqrt[3]{a^{13}b^7c^2} \cdot \sqrt[3]{a^{10}b^8c^{17}}$.

SOLUTION Because powers in each radical are greater than the index of that radical, we could simplify each radical first. However, then we would have to multiply and simplify the radical again. A more efficient approach is to multiply first and then simplify only once.

$$\sqrt[3]{a^{13}b^7c^2} \cdot \sqrt[3]{a^{10}b^8c^{17}} = \sqrt[3]{a^{23}b^{15}c^{19}}$$ Multiply the radicands by adding the exponents for each factor.

$$= a^7b^5c^6\sqrt[3]{a^2c}$$ Simplify the radical. For each factor, take out as many groups of 3 as possible.

EXAMPLE 3 Multiply $9\sqrt{6} \cdot 7\sqrt{10}$.

SOLUTION Because the index is the same for each radical, we can multiply the radicands together. The factors in front of each radical, 9 and 7, will be multiplied by each other as well. After multiplying, we finish by simplifying the radical completely.

$$9\sqrt{6} \cdot 7\sqrt{10} = 63\sqrt{60}$$ Multiply factors in front of the radicals and multiply the radicands.

$$= 63\sqrt{2^2 \cdot 3 \cdot 5}$$ Factor the radicand.

$$= 63 \cdot 2\sqrt{3 \cdot 5}$$ Simplify the radical.

$$= 126\sqrt{15}$$ Multiply.

Quick Check 1

Multiply.

a) $\sqrt{45} \cdot \sqrt{80}$

b) $\sqrt[3]{x^4y^2z} \cdot \sqrt[3]{x^8yz^4}$

c) $4\sqrt{8} \cdot 9\sqrt{6}$

It is important to note that whenever we multiply the square root of an expression by the square root of the same expression, the product is equal to the expression itself as long as the expression is nonnegative.

┌ Multiplying a Square Root by Itself ──────────

For any nonnegative x,

$$\sqrt{x} \cdot \sqrt{x} = x.$$

Using the Distributive Property with Radical Expressions

Objective 2 **Use the distributive property to multiply radical expressions.** Now we will use the distributive property to multiply radical expressions.

EXAMPLE 4 Multiply $\sqrt{5}(\sqrt{10} - \sqrt{5})$.

SOLUTION Begin by distributing $\sqrt{5}$ to each term in the parentheses; then multiply the radicals as in the previous examples.

$$\sqrt{5}(\sqrt{10} - \sqrt{5}) = \sqrt{5} \cdot \sqrt{10} - \sqrt{5} \cdot \sqrt{5}$$ Distribute $\sqrt{5}$.

$$= \sqrt{50} - 5$$ Multiply. Recall that $\sqrt{5} \cdot \sqrt{5} = 5$.

$$= 5\sqrt{2} - 5$$ Simplify the radical.

▸ **Quick Check 2**

Multiply $\sqrt{12}(\sqrt{3} + \sqrt{15})$.

EXAMPLE 5 Multiply $\sqrt[4]{x^{11}y^6}(\sqrt[4]{x^5y^{19}} + \sqrt[4]{x^{11}y^2})$. (Assume that x and y are nonnegative.)

SOLUTION We begin by using the distributive property. Because each radical has an index of 4, we can then multiply the radicals.

$$\sqrt[4]{x^{11}y^6}(\sqrt[4]{x^5y^{19}} + \sqrt[4]{x^{11}y^2}) = \sqrt[4]{x^{11}y^6} \cdot \sqrt[4]{x^5y^{19}} + \sqrt[4]{x^{11}y^6} \cdot \sqrt[4]{x^{11}y^2}$$

Distribute $\sqrt[4]{x^{11}y^6}$.

$$= \sqrt[4]{x^{16}y^{25}} + \sqrt[4]{x^{22}y^8}$$

Multiply by adding exponents for each factor.

$$= x^4y^6\sqrt[4]{y} + x^5y^2\sqrt[4]{x^2}$$

Simplify each radical.

Because the radicals are not like radicals, we cannot simplify this expression any further.

▸ Quick Check 3

Multiply $\sqrt{x^9y^6}(\sqrt{x^3y^6} - \sqrt{x^8y^7})$. (Assume that x and y are nonnegative.)

Multiplying Radical Expressions That Have at Least Two Terms

Objective ③ **Multiply radical expressions that have two or more terms.**

EXAMPLE 6 Multiply $(8\sqrt{6} + \sqrt{2})(3\sqrt{12} - 4\sqrt{3})$.

SOLUTION We begin by multiplying each term in the first set of parentheses by each term in the second set of parentheses using the distributive property. Because there are two terms in each set of parentheses we can use the FOIL technique. Multiply factors outside a radical by factors outside a radical and multiply radicands by radicands.

$$(8\sqrt{6} + \sqrt{2})(3\sqrt{12} - 4\sqrt{3})$$
$$= 8 \cdot 3\sqrt{6 \cdot 12} - 8 \cdot 4\sqrt{6 \cdot 3} + 3\sqrt{2 \cdot 12} - 4\sqrt{2 \cdot 3} \quad \text{Distribute.}$$
$$= 24\sqrt{72} - 32\sqrt{18} + 3\sqrt{24} - 4\sqrt{6} \quad \text{Multiply.}$$
$$= 24 \cdot 6\sqrt{2} - 32 \cdot 3\sqrt{2} + 3 \cdot 2\sqrt{6} - 4\sqrt{6} \quad \text{Simplify each radical.}$$
$$= 144\sqrt{2} - 96\sqrt{2} + 6\sqrt{6} - 4\sqrt{6} \quad \text{Multiply.}$$
$$= 48\sqrt{2} + 2\sqrt{6} \quad \text{Combine like radicals.}$$

EXAMPLE 7 Multiply $(\sqrt{5} + \sqrt{6})^2$.

SOLUTION To square any binomial, multiply it by itself.

$$(\sqrt{5} + \sqrt{6})^2 = (\sqrt{5} + \sqrt{6})(\sqrt{5} + \sqrt{6}) \quad \text{Rewrite as } (5 + \sqrt{6})(5 + \sqrt{6}).$$
$$= \sqrt{5} \cdot \sqrt{5} + \sqrt{5} \cdot \sqrt{6} + \sqrt{6} \cdot \sqrt{5} + \sqrt{6} \cdot \sqrt{6} \quad \text{Distribute.}$$
$$= 5 + \sqrt{30} + \sqrt{30} + 6 \quad \text{Multiply.}$$
$$= 11 + 2\sqrt{30} \quad \text{Combine like terms.}$$

▸ Quick Check 4

Multiply. **a)** $(5\sqrt{3} + 4\sqrt{2})(7\sqrt{3} - 6\sqrt{2})$ **b)** $(\sqrt{7} - \sqrt{10})^2$

A WORD OF CAUTION Whenever we square a binomial, such as $(\sqrt{5} + \sqrt{6})^2$, we must multiply the binomial by itself. We cannot simply square each term.

$$(a + b)^2 \neq a^2 + b^2$$

Multiplying Conjugates

Objective 4 Multiply radical expressions that are conjugates. The expressions $\sqrt{13} + \sqrt{5}$ and $\sqrt{13} - \sqrt{5}$ are called **conjugates**. Two expressions are conjugates if they are of the form $x + y$ and $x - y$. Notice that the two terms are the same, with the exception of the sign of the second term.

The multiplication of two conjugates follows a pattern. Let's look at the product $(\sqrt{x} + \sqrt{y})(\sqrt{x} - \sqrt{y})$.

$$(\sqrt{x} + \sqrt{y})(\sqrt{x} - \sqrt{y}) = x - \sqrt{xy} + \sqrt{xy} - y \quad \text{Distribute. Note that}$$
$$\sqrt{x} \cdot \sqrt{x} = x \text{ and}$$
$$\sqrt{y} \cdot \sqrt{y} = y.$$
$$= x - y \quad \text{Combine the two opposite}$$
$$\text{terms } -\sqrt{xy} \text{ and } \sqrt{xy}.$$

Whenever we multiply conjugates, the two middle terms will be opposites of each other; therefore, their sum is 0. We can multiply the first term in the first set of parentheses by the first term in the second set of parentheses, multiply the second term in the first set of parentheses by the second term in the second set of parentheses, and then place a minus sign between the two products.

Multiplication of Two Conjugates

$$\overset{a^2}{\overbrace{(a + b)(a - b)}} = a^2 - b^2$$
$$\underset{b^2}{\underbrace{}}$$

EXAMPLE 8 Multiply $(\sqrt{17} + \sqrt{23})(\sqrt{17} - \sqrt{23})$.

SOLUTION These two expressions are conjugates, so we multiply them accordingly.

$$(\sqrt{17} + \sqrt{23})(\sqrt{17} - \sqrt{23}) = (\sqrt{17})^2 - (\sqrt{23})^2 \quad \text{Multiply using the rule for}$$
$$\text{multiplying conjugates.}$$
$$= 17 - 23 \quad \text{Square each square root.}$$
$$= -6 \quad \text{Subtract.}$$

EXAMPLE 9 Multiply $(2\sqrt{6} - 8\sqrt{5})(2\sqrt{6} + 8\sqrt{5})$.

SOLUTION When we multiply two conjugates, we must remember to multiply the factors in front of the radicals by each other and to multiply the radicands by each other.

$$(2\sqrt{6} - 8\sqrt{5})(2\sqrt{6} + 8\sqrt{5}) = 2\sqrt{6} \cdot 2\sqrt{6} - 8\sqrt{5} \cdot 8\sqrt{5} \quad \text{Multiply the}$$
$$\text{conjugates.}$$
$$= 4 \cdot 6 - 64 \cdot 5 \quad \text{Multiply.}$$
$$= 24 - 320 \quad \text{Multiply.}$$
$$= -296 \quad \text{Subtract.}$$

▶ Quick Check 5

Multiply. **a)** $(\sqrt{38} - \sqrt{29})(\sqrt{38} + \sqrt{29})$ **b)** $(8\sqrt{11} - 5\sqrt{7})(8\sqrt{11} + 5\sqrt{7})$

Rationalizing the Denominator

Objective 5 Rationalize a denominator that has one term. Earlier in this chapter, we introduced a criterion for determining whether a radical was simplified. We stated that for a radical to be simplified, its index must be greater than any power in the radical. We now add two other rules.

- There can be no fractions in a radicand.
- There can be no radicals in the denominator of a fraction.

For example, we would not consider the following expressions to be simplified: $\sqrt{\frac{3}{10}}$, $\frac{9}{\sqrt{2}}$, $\frac{6}{\sqrt{4} - \sqrt{3}}$, and $\frac{\sqrt{6} + \sqrt{12}}{\sqrt{3} - 8}$. The process of rewriting an expression without a radical in its denominator is called **rationalizing the denominator**.

The rational expression $\frac{\sqrt{16}}{\sqrt{49}}$ is not simplified, as there is a radical in the denominator. However, we know that $\sqrt{49} = 7$; so we can simplify the denominator in such a way that it no longer contains a radical.

$$\frac{\sqrt{16}}{\sqrt{49}} = \frac{4}{7} \quad \text{Simplify the numerator and denominator.}$$

The radical expression $\sqrt{\frac{75}{3}}$ is not simplified, as there is a fraction inside the radical. We can simplify $\frac{75}{3}$ to be 25, rewriting the radical without a fraction inside.

$$\sqrt{\frac{75}{3}} = \sqrt{25} = 5 \quad \text{Simplify the fraction, then } \sqrt{25}.$$

Suppose we needed to simplify $\frac{\sqrt{15}}{\sqrt{2}}$. We cannot simplify $\sqrt{2}$, and the fraction itself cannot be simplified. In such a case, we will multiply both the numerator and denominator by an expression that will allow us to rewrite the denominator without a radical. Then we simplify.

EXAMPLE 10   Rationalize the denominator: $\frac{\sqrt{15}}{\sqrt{2}}$

SOLUTION   If we multiply the denominator by $\sqrt{2}$, the denominator will equal 2 and will be rationalized.

$$\frac{\sqrt{15}}{\sqrt{2}} = \frac{\sqrt{15}}{\sqrt{2}} \cdot \frac{\sqrt{2}}{\sqrt{2}} \quad \text{Multiply by } \frac{\sqrt{2}}{\sqrt{2}}, \text{ which makes the denominator equal}$$

$$\text{to 2. Multiplying by } \frac{\sqrt{2}}{\sqrt{2}} \text{ is equivalent to multiplying by 1.}$$

$$= \frac{\sqrt{30}}{2} \quad \text{Multiply.}$$

Because $\sqrt{30}$ cannot be simplified, this expression cannot be simplified further.

Quick Check 6

Rationalize the denominator.

$$\frac{\sqrt{70}}{\sqrt{3}}$$

EXAMPLE 11   Rationalize the denominator: $\frac{11}{\sqrt{12}}$

SOLUTION   At first glance, we might think that multiplying the numerator and denominator by $\sqrt{12}$ is the correct way to proceed. However, if we multiply the numerator and denominator by $\sqrt{3}$, the radicand in the denominator will be 36, which is a perfect square.

$$\frac{11}{\sqrt{12}} = \frac{11}{\sqrt{12}} \cdot \frac{\sqrt{3}}{\sqrt{3}}$$ Multiply by $\frac{\sqrt{3}}{\sqrt{3}}$ to make the radicand in the denominator a perfect square.

$$= \frac{11\sqrt{3}}{\sqrt{36}}$$ Multiply.

$$= \frac{11\sqrt{3}}{6}$$ Simplify the radical in the denominator.

Multiplying by $\frac{\sqrt{12}}{\sqrt{12}}$ also would be valid, but the subsequent process of simplifying would be difficult. One way to determine the best expression by which to multiply is to completely factor the radicand in the denominator. In this example, $12 = 2^2 \cdot 3$. The factor 2 is already a perfect square, but the factor 3 is not. Multiplying by $\sqrt{3}$ makes the factor 3 a perfect square as well.

Quick Check 7

Rationalize the denominator:

$$\frac{2}{\sqrt{20}}$$

EXAMPLE 12   Rationalize the denominator. $\sqrt{\dfrac{5a^3b^{14}c^6}{80a^9b^7c^{11}}}$ (Assume that all variables represent nonnegative values.)

SOLUTION   Notice that the numerator and denominator have common factors. We begin by simplifying the fraction to lowest terms.

$$\sqrt{\frac{5a^3b^{14}c^6}{80a^9b^7c^{11}}} = \sqrt{\frac{b^7}{16a^6c^5}}$$ Divide out common factors and simplify.

$$= \frac{\sqrt{b^7}}{\sqrt{16a^6c^5}}$$ Rewrite as the quotient of two square roots. Notice that the factors 16 and a^6 are already perfect squares, but c^5 is not.

$$= \frac{\sqrt{b^7}}{\sqrt{16a^6c^5}} \cdot \frac{\sqrt{c}}{\sqrt{c}}$$ Multiply by $\frac{\sqrt{c}}{\sqrt{c}}$.

$$= \frac{\sqrt{b^7c}}{\sqrt{16a^6c^6}}$$ Multiply.

$$= \frac{b^3\sqrt{bc}}{4a^3c^3}$$ Simplify both radicals.

Quick Check 8

Rationalize the denominator. $\sqrt{\dfrac{12x^2y^8z^5}{75x^5y^3z^{15}}}$ (Assume that all variables represent nonnegative values.)

Rationalizing a Denominator That Has Two Terms

Objective 6 Rationalize a denominator that has two terms. In the previous examples, each denominator had only one term. If a denominator is a binomial that contains one or two square roots, we rationalize the denominator by multiplying the numerator and denominator by the conjugate of the denominator. For example, consider the expression $\dfrac{6}{\sqrt{11} + \sqrt{7}}$. We know from earlier in this section that multiplying $\sqrt{11} + \sqrt{7}$ by its conjugate $\sqrt{11} - \sqrt{7}$ produces a product that does not contain a radical.

EXAMPLE 13 Rationalize the denominator: $\dfrac{6}{\sqrt{11} + \sqrt{7}}$

SOLUTION Because this denominator is a binomial, we multiply the numerator and denominator by the conjugate of the denominator.

$$\dfrac{6}{\sqrt{11} + \sqrt{7}} = \dfrac{6}{\sqrt{11} + \sqrt{7}} \cdot \dfrac{\sqrt{11} - \sqrt{7}}{\sqrt{11} - \sqrt{7}}$$ Multiply the numerator and denominator by the conjugate of the denominator ($\sqrt{11} - \sqrt{7}$).

$$= \dfrac{6\sqrt{11} - 6\sqrt{7}}{\sqrt{11} \cdot \sqrt{11} - \sqrt{7} \cdot \sqrt{7}}$$ Distribute in the numerator. Multiply conjugates in the denominator.

$$= \dfrac{6\sqrt{11} - 6\sqrt{7}}{11 - 7}$$ $\sqrt{11} \cdot \sqrt{11} = 11, \sqrt{7} \cdot \sqrt{7} = 7$

$$= \dfrac{6\sqrt{11} - 6\sqrt{7}}{4}$$ Subtract.

$$= \dfrac{6(\sqrt{11} - \sqrt{7})}{4}$$ Factor the numerator.

$$= \dfrac{\overset{3}{\cancel{6}}(\sqrt{11} - \sqrt{7})}{\underset{2}{\cancel{4}}}$$ Divide out the common factor 2.

$$= \dfrac{3(\sqrt{11} - \sqrt{7})}{2}$$ Simplify.

▶ **Quick Check 9**

Rationalize the denominator: $\dfrac{\sqrt{15}}{\sqrt{5} + \sqrt{3}}$

EXAMPLE 14 Rationalize the denominator: $\dfrac{4\sqrt{3} - 3\sqrt{5}}{2\sqrt{3} - \sqrt{5}}$

SOLUTION Because the denominator is a binomial, we begin by multiplying the numerator and denominator by the conjugate of the denominator, which is $2\sqrt{3} + \sqrt{5}$.

$$\dfrac{4\sqrt{3} - 3\sqrt{5}}{2\sqrt{3} - \sqrt{5}} = \dfrac{4\sqrt{3} - 3\sqrt{5}}{2\sqrt{3} - \sqrt{5}} \cdot \dfrac{2\sqrt{3} + \sqrt{5}}{2\sqrt{3} + \sqrt{5}}$$ Multiply the numerator and denominator by the conjugate of the denominator.

$$= \dfrac{4\sqrt{3} \cdot 2\sqrt{3} + 4\sqrt{3} \cdot \sqrt{5} - 3\sqrt{5} \cdot 2\sqrt{3} - 3\sqrt{5} \cdot \sqrt{5}}{2\sqrt{3} \cdot 2\sqrt{3} - \sqrt{5} \cdot \sqrt{5}}$$ Multiply numerators and denominators.

$$= \dfrac{8 \cdot 3 + 4\sqrt{15} - 6\sqrt{15} - 3 \cdot 5}{4 \cdot 3 - 5}$$ Simplify each product.

$$= \dfrac{24 + 4\sqrt{15} - 6\sqrt{15} - 15}{12 - 5}$$ Multiply.

$$= \dfrac{9 - 2\sqrt{15}}{7}$$ Combine like terms and like radicals.

▶ **Quick Check 10**

Rationalize the denominator: $\dfrac{2\sqrt{6} - 7\sqrt{2}}{2\sqrt{6} + 3\sqrt{2}}$

BUILDING YOUR STUDY STRATEGY

Note Taking, 4 Being an Active Learner Some students fall into the trap of taking notes mechanically without thinking about the material. In a math class, there can be no learning without thinking. Try to be an active learner while taking notes. Do your best to understand each statement you write in your notes.

When your instructor writes a problem on the board, try to solve it yourself in your notes. When you have finished solving the problem, compare your solution to your instructor's solution. If you make a mistake or your solution is different from your instructor's solution, you can make editor's notes on your solution.

Exercises 9.4

MyMathLab

 PRACTICE   WATCH   DOWNLOAD   READ   REVIEW

Vocabulary

1. For any nonnegative x, $\sqrt{x} \cdot \sqrt{x} =$ _____.

2. Two expressions of the form $x + y$ and _____ are called conjugates.

3. The process of rewriting an expression without a radical in its denominator is called _____ the denominator.

4. To rationalize a denominator containing two terms and at least one square root, multiply the numerator and denominator by the _____ of the denominator.

Multiply. Assume that all variables represent nonnegative real numbers.

5. $\sqrt{12} \cdot \sqrt{75}$

6. $\sqrt{98} \cdot \sqrt{8}$

7. $4\sqrt{27} \cdot 6\sqrt{3}$

8. $8\sqrt{125} \cdot 2\sqrt{20}$

9. $7\sqrt{32} \cdot 5\sqrt{6}$

10. $9\sqrt{30} \cdot 4\sqrt{15}$

11. $6\sqrt[3]{24} \cdot 2\sqrt[3]{18}$

12. $5\sqrt[3]{36} \cdot 9\sqrt[3]{30}$

13. $\sqrt{x^{17}} \cdot \sqrt{x^5}$

14. $\sqrt{x^{33}} \cdot \sqrt{x^{13}}$

15. $\sqrt{6a^7b^6} \cdot \sqrt{10a^5b^9}$

16. $\sqrt{21a^{10}b^3} \cdot \sqrt{14a^9b^9}$

17. $\sqrt[4]{x^{15}y^{10}z^5} \cdot \sqrt[4]{x^9y^2z^{18}}$

18. $\sqrt[3]{x^{10}y^{14}z^{17}} \cdot \sqrt[3]{x^6y^{19}z^8}$

Multiply. Assume that all variables represent nonnegative real numbers.

19. $\sqrt{2}(\sqrt{8} - \sqrt{6})$

20. $\sqrt{6}(\sqrt{2} + \sqrt{3})$

21. $\sqrt{98}(\sqrt{18} + \sqrt{10})$

22. $\sqrt{15}(\sqrt{30} - \sqrt{35})$

23. $6\sqrt{3}(9\sqrt{6} - 4\sqrt{15})$

24. $17\sqrt{10}(8\sqrt{2} + 3\sqrt{5})$

25. $\sqrt{m^5n^9}(\sqrt{m^3n^4} + \sqrt{m^8n^7})$

26. $\sqrt{xy^{11}}(\sqrt{x^7y^3} - \sqrt{x^{39}y^{15}})$

27. $\sqrt[3]{a^7b^{10}c^{13}}(\sqrt[3]{a^{11}b^{35}} + \sqrt[3]{a^{23}c^8})$

28. $\sqrt[3]{x^4y^7z^{10}}(\sqrt[3]{x^8y^{16}z^{24}} - \sqrt[3]{x^{16}y^{12}z^2})$

Multiply.

29. $(\sqrt{2} + \sqrt{5})(\sqrt{2} - \sqrt{3})$

30. $(\sqrt{3} + \sqrt{8})(\sqrt{6} - \sqrt{2})$

31. $(7\sqrt{2} + 4\sqrt{3})(5\sqrt{2} - \sqrt{3})$

32. $(8\sqrt{5} - 3\sqrt{2})(2\sqrt{5} - 4\sqrt{2})$

33. $(2\sqrt{7} - 7\sqrt{3})(2\sqrt{7} - 6\sqrt{3})$

34. $(\sqrt{6} + 2\sqrt{11})(9\sqrt{6} + \sqrt{11})$

35. $(6\sqrt{3} + 4\sqrt{5})(3\sqrt{5} - 2\sqrt{3})$

36. $(2\sqrt{2} - 9\sqrt{7})(8\sqrt{7} - 5\sqrt{2})$

37. $(4\sqrt{5} - 3\sqrt{2})^2$

38. $(6 + 7\sqrt{3})^2$

Multiply the conjugates.

39. $(\sqrt{7} - \sqrt{10})(\sqrt{7} + \sqrt{10})$

40. $(\sqrt{26} + \sqrt{3})(\sqrt{26} - \sqrt{3})$

41. $(9\sqrt{6} + 3\sqrt{8})(9\sqrt{6} - 3\sqrt{8})$

42. $(5\sqrt{18} - 2\sqrt{24})(5\sqrt{18} + 2\sqrt{24})$

43. $(8 - 11\sqrt{2})(8 + 11\sqrt{2})$

44. $(4\sqrt{3} + 15)(4\sqrt{3} - 15)$

Simplify. Assume that all variables represent nonnegative real numbers.

45. $\sqrt{\dfrac{12}{x^4y^6}}$

46. $\sqrt{\dfrac{b^7}{a^{10}c^2}}$

47. $\sqrt{\dfrac{126}{7}}$

48. $\sqrt{\dfrac{100}{5}}$

49. $\sqrt{\dfrac{135}{20}}$

50. $\sqrt{\dfrac{14}{18}}$

Rationalize the denominator and simplify. Assume that all variables represent nonnegative real numbers.

51. $\dfrac{\sqrt{8}}{\sqrt{3}}$

52. $\dfrac{\sqrt{24}}{\sqrt{7}}$

53. $\dfrac{1}{\sqrt{2}}$

54. $\dfrac{5}{\sqrt{5}}$

55. $\sqrt{\dfrac{27}{11a^7}}$

56. $\sqrt{\dfrac{80}{3n^{10}}}$

57. $\sqrt[3]{\dfrac{s^8}{2r^2t}}$

58. $\sqrt[3]{\dfrac{2x^{10}}{7y^{16}z^{22}}}$

59. $\dfrac{14}{\sqrt{12}}$

60. $\dfrac{15}{\sqrt{50}}$

61. $\dfrac{8}{\sqrt{18a}}$

62. $\dfrac{6}{\sqrt{20b^5}}$

63. $\dfrac{x^4z^8}{\sqrt{x^3y^5z^{10}}}$

64. $\dfrac{xy^2z^9}{\sqrt{x^5y^6z^7}}$

Rationalize the denominator and simplify.

65. $\dfrac{9}{\sqrt{13}-\sqrt{7}}$

66. $\dfrac{10}{\sqrt{20}+\sqrt{2}}$

67. $\dfrac{4\sqrt{3}}{\sqrt{3}+\sqrt{11}}$

68. $\dfrac{5\sqrt{5}}{\sqrt{15}-\sqrt{5}}$

69. $\dfrac{6\sqrt{3}}{\sqrt{13}-3}$

70. $\dfrac{8\sqrt{2}}{4-\sqrt{6}}$

71. $\dfrac{5\sqrt{5}-3\sqrt{3}}{4\sqrt{5}+2\sqrt{3}}$

72. $\dfrac{9\sqrt{3}+4\sqrt{2}}{5\sqrt{3}-4\sqrt{2}}$

73. $\dfrac{7\sqrt{11}+2\sqrt{2}}{4\sqrt{11}-5\sqrt{2}}$

74. $\dfrac{2\sqrt{5}+\sqrt{7}}{4\sqrt{5}-\sqrt{7}}$

75. $\dfrac{4\sqrt{2}-\sqrt{3}}{2\sqrt{2}-3\sqrt{3}}$

76. $\dfrac{2\sqrt{3}-9\sqrt{5}}{6\sqrt{3}-4\sqrt{5}}$

Mixed Practice, 77–98

Simplify. Assume that all variables represent nonnegative real numbers.

77. $\sqrt{\dfrac{90}{98}}$

78. $\sqrt{10x^5}\cdot\sqrt{18x^9}$

79. $(8\sqrt{7}+5\sqrt{5})^2$

80. $\dfrac{28}{\sqrt{32}}$

81. $\sqrt[3]{25a^8bc^7}\cdot\sqrt[3]{25ab^5c^7}$

82. $\sqrt[3]{\dfrac{2x^4y^{13}}{54x^{10}y^2}}$

83. $\dfrac{10\sqrt{5}-7\sqrt{7}}{\sqrt{5}+\sqrt{7}}$

84. $\sqrt{162x^9y^8z^{15}}$

85. $\sqrt[3]{1080}$

86. $\sqrt{60}(7\sqrt{3}-2\sqrt{15})$

87. $(3\sqrt{10}-7\sqrt{2})(4\sqrt{10}+9\sqrt{5})$

88. $\dfrac{8\sqrt{2}}{\sqrt{10}}$

89. $-\sqrt{7x^9}(2\sqrt{14x}-\sqrt{7x^{13}})$

90. $(9\sqrt{7}-8\sqrt{8})(9\sqrt{7}+8\sqrt{8})$

91. $\sqrt[4]{a^{17}b^{34}c^{44}}$

92. $\sqrt{1008}$

93. $\sqrt{\dfrac{a^5b^8}{12c^9}}$

94. $\dfrac{13\sqrt{5}+6}{10-7\sqrt{5}}$

95. $\dfrac{10x^2}{\sqrt[3]{36x^8}}$

96. $(20\sqrt{3}-7\sqrt{10})(8\sqrt{3}+15\sqrt{2})$

97. $(18\sqrt{7}-\sqrt{11})(18\sqrt{7}+\sqrt{11})$

98. $(4\sqrt{14}-3\sqrt{7})^2$

99. Develop a general formula for the product $(\sqrt{a}+\sqrt{b})^2$.

100. Develop a general formula for the product $(a\sqrt{b}+c\sqrt{d})^2$.

⟶ **Writing in Mathematics**

Answer in complete sentences.

101. Explain how to determine whether two radical expressions are conjugates.

102. *Solutions Manual* Write a solutions manual page for the following problem.

Simplify $(5\sqrt{2} + 4\sqrt{3})(8\sqrt{2} - 3\sqrt{3})$.

Quick Review Exercises

Section 9.4

Find the prime factorization of the given number.

1. 144

2. 1400

3. 1024

4. 29,106

9.5

Radical Equations and Applications of Radical Equations

OBJECTIVES

1. Solve radical equations.
2. Solve equations containing radical functions.
3. Solve equations containing rational exponents.
4. Solve equations in which a radical is equal to a variable expression.
5. Solve equations containing two radicals.
6. Solve applied problems involving a pendulum and its period.
7. Solve other applied problems involving radicals.

Solving Radical Equations

Objective 1 Solve radical equations. A **radical equation** is an equation containing one or more radicals. Here are some examples of radical equations.

$$\sqrt{x} = 9 \qquad \sqrt[3]{2x - 5} = 3 \qquad x + \sqrt{x} = 20$$

$$\sqrt[4]{3x - 8} = \sqrt[4]{2x + 11} \qquad \sqrt{x - 4} + \sqrt{x + 8} = 6$$

In this section, we will learn how to solve radical equations. We will find a way to convert a radical equation to an equivalent equation that we already know how to solve.

┌─ **Raising Equal Numbers to the Same Power** ─────────────────┐
│ If two numbers a and b are equal, then for any n, $a^n = b^n$. │
└──┘

If we raise two equal numbers to the same power, they remain equal to each other. We will use this fact to solve radical equations.

┌─ **Solving Radical Equations** ──────────────────────────────
- Isolate a radical term containing the variable on one side of the equation.
- Raise both sides of the equation to the nth power, where n is the index of the radical. *For any nonnegative number x and any integer $n > 1$, $(\sqrt[n]{x})^n = x$.*
- If the resulting equation does not contain a radical, solve the equation. If the resulting equation does contain a radical, begin the process again by isolating the radical on one side of the equation.
- Check the solution(s).

It is crucial that we check all solutions when solving a radical equation, as raising both sides of an equation to an even power can introduce **extraneous solutions**. When raising both sides of an equation to an nth power, it is possible to arrive at an extraneous solution—a solution that does not satisfy the original equation. In solving a radical equation, all solutions must be checked.

EXAMPLE 1   Solve $\sqrt{x - 5} = 3$.

SOLUTION   Because the radical $\sqrt{x - 5}$ is already isolated on the left side of the equation, we begin by squaring both sides of the equation.

$$\sqrt{x - 5} = 3$$
$$(\sqrt{x - 5})^2 = 3^2 \quad \text{Square both sides.}$$
$$x - 5 = 9 \quad \text{Simplify.}$$
$$x = 14 \quad \text{Add 5 to both sides.}$$

We need to check this solution using the original equation.

$$\sqrt{14 - 5} = 3 \quad \text{Substitute 14 for } x.$$
$$\sqrt{9} = 3 \quad \text{Subtract.}$$
$$3 = 3 \quad \text{Simplify the square root.}$$

The solution $x = 14$ checks, so the solution set is $\{14\}$.

EXAMPLE 2   Solve $\sqrt[3]{6x + 4} + 7 = 11$.

SOLUTION   In this example, begin by isolating the radical.

$$\sqrt[3]{6x + 4} + 7 = 11$$
$$\sqrt[3]{6x + 4} = 4 \quad \text{Subtract 7 from both sides to isolate the radical.}$$
$$(\sqrt[3]{6x + 4})^3 = 4^3 \quad \text{Raise both sides of the equation to the third power.}$$
$$6x + 4 = 64 \quad \text{Simplify.}$$
$$6x = 60 \quad \text{Subtract 4 from both sides.}$$
$$x = 10 \quad \text{Divide both sides by 6.}$$

Now check the solution using the original equation.

$$\sqrt[3]{6(10) + 4} + 7 = 11 \quad \text{Substitute 10 for } x.$$
$$\sqrt[3]{64} + 7 = 11 \quad \text{Simplify the radicand}$$
$$4 + 7 = 11 \quad \text{Simplify the cube root.}$$
$$11 = 11 \quad \text{Add. The solution checks.}$$

The solution set is $\{10\}$. Because we raised both sides of the equation to an odd power, we did not introduce any extraneous solutions.

Quick Check 1

Solve.

a) $\sqrt{x + 2} = 7$
b) $\sqrt[3]{x + 9} + 10 = 6$

EXAMPLE 3   Solve $\sqrt{x} + 8 = 5$.

SOLUTION   Begin by isolating $\sqrt{x}$ on the left side of the equation.

$$\sqrt{x} + 8 = 5$$
$$\sqrt{x} = -3 \quad \text{Subtract 8 from both sides to isolate the square root.}$$
$$(\sqrt{x})^2 = (-3)^2 \quad \text{Square both sides of the equation.}$$
$$x = 9 \quad \text{Simplify.}$$

Now check this solution using the original equation.

$$\sqrt{9} + 8 = 5 \qquad \text{Substitute 9 for } x.$$
$$3 + 8 = 5 \qquad \text{Simplify the square root. The principal square root of 9 is 3,}$$
$$\text{not } -3.$$
$$11 = 5 \qquad \text{Add.}$$

This solution does not check, so it is an extraneous solution. The equation has no solution; the solution set is $\varnothing$.

▶ **Quick Check 2**
Solve $\sqrt{2x - 9} - 8 = -11$.

If we obtain an equation in which an even root is equal to a negative number, such as $\sqrt{x} = -3$, this equation will not have any solutions. This is because the principal even root of a number, if it exists, cannot be negative.

Solving Equations Involving Radical Functions

Objective 2 Solve equations containing radical functions.

EXAMPLE 4 For $f(x) = \sqrt{x^2 + 5x + 11} - 2$, find all values for which $f(x) = 3$.

SOLUTION   Begin by setting the function equal to 3.

$$f(x) = 3$$
$$\sqrt{x^2 + 5x + 11} - 2 = 3 \qquad \text{Replace } f(x) \text{ with its formula.}$$
$$\sqrt{x^2 + 5x + 11} = 5 \qquad \text{Add 2 to both sides to isolate the radical.}$$
$$(\sqrt{x^2 + 5x + 11})^2 = 5^2 \qquad \text{Square both sides.}$$
$$x^2 + 5x + 11 = 25 \qquad \text{Simplify.}$$
$$x^2 + 5x - 14 = 0 \qquad \text{The equation is quadratic, so collect all terms on the left side of the equation.}$$
$$(x + 7)(x - 2) = 0 \qquad \text{Factor.}$$
$$x + 7 = 0 \quad \text{or} \quad x - 2 = 0 \qquad \text{Set each factor equal to 0.}$$
$$x = -7 \quad \text{or} \quad x = 2 \qquad \text{Solve.}$$

It is left to the reader to verify that neither solution is an extraneous solution: $f(-7) = 3$ and $f(2) = 3$.

▶ **Quick Check 3**
For $f(x) = \sqrt{3x - 8} + 4$, find all values x for which $f(x) = 9$.

Solving Equations with Rational Exponents

Objective 3 Solve equations containing rational exponents. The next examples involve equations containing fractional exponents. Recall that $x^{1/n} = \sqrt[n]{x}$.

EXAMPLE 5 Solve $x^{1/3} + 7 = -3$.

SOLUTION   Begin by rewriting $x^{1/3}$ as $\sqrt[3]{x}$.

$$x^{1/3} + 7 = -3$$
$$\sqrt[3]{x} + 7 = -3 \qquad \text{Rewrite } x^{1/3} \text{ as } \sqrt[3]{x} \text{ using radical notation.}$$
$$\sqrt[3]{x} = -10 \qquad \text{Subtract 7 to isolate the radical.}$$
$$(\sqrt[3]{x})^3 = (-10)^3 \qquad \text{Raise both sides to the third power.}$$
$$x = -1000 \qquad \text{Simplify.}$$

It is left to the reader to verify that the solution is not an extraneous solution. The solution set is $\{-1000\}$.

EXAMPLE 6 Solve $(1 - 5x)^{1/2} - 3 = 3$.

SOLUTION   Begin by rewriting the equation using a radical.

$$(1 - 5x)^{1/2} - 3 = 3$$
$$\sqrt{1 - 5x} - 3 = 3 \qquad \text{Rewrite using radical notation.}$$
$$\sqrt{1 - 5x} = 6 \qquad \text{Add 3 to isolate the radical.}$$
$$(\sqrt{1 - 5x})^2 = 6^2 \qquad \text{Square both sides.}$$
$$1 - 5x = 36 \qquad \text{Simplify.}$$
$$-5x = 35 \qquad \text{Subtract 1 from both sides.}$$
$$x = -7 \qquad \text{Divide both sides by } -5.$$

It is left to the reader to verify that the solution is not an extraneous solution. The solution set is $\{-7\}$.

Quick Check 4

Solve.

a) $x^{1/2} - 10 = -7$
b) $(x + 4)^{1/3} + 8 = 2$

Solving Equations in Which a Radical Is Equal to a Variable Expression

Objective ④ Solve equations in which a radical is equal to a variable expression. After we isolated the radical in all of the previous examples, the resulting equation had a radical expression equal to a constant. In the next example, we will learn how to solve equations that result in a radical equal to a variable expression.

EXAMPLE 7 Solve $\sqrt{6x + 16} = x$.

SOLUTION   Because the radical is already isolated, we begin by squaring both sides. This will result in a quadratic equation, which we solve by collecting all terms on one side of the equation and factoring.

$$\sqrt{6x + 16} = x$$
$$(\sqrt{6x + 16})^2 = x^2 \qquad\qquad \text{Square both sides.}$$
$$6x + 16 = x^2 \qquad\qquad \text{Simplify.}$$
$$0 = x^2 - 6x - 16 \qquad\qquad \text{Collect all terms on the right side of the equation by subtracting } 6x \text{ and } 16 \text{ from both sides.}$$
$$0 = (x - 8)(x + 2) \qquad\qquad \text{Factor.}$$
$$x = 8 \quad \text{or} \quad x = -2 \qquad \text{Set each factor equal to 0 and solve.}$$

Now we check both solutions.

$x = 8$	$x = -2$
$\sqrt{6(8) + 16} = 8$	$\sqrt{6(-2) + 16} = -2$
$\sqrt{48 + 16} = 8$	$\sqrt{-12 + 16} = -2$
$\sqrt{64} = 8$	$\sqrt{4} = -2$
$8 = 8$	$2 = -2$
True	False

Quick Check 5

Solve $\sqrt{12x - 20} = x$.

The solution $x = -2$ is an extraneous solution. The solution set is $\{8\}$.

EXAMPLE 8   Solve $\sqrt{x} + 6 = x$.

SOLUTION   Begin by isolating the radical.

$\sqrt{x} + 6 = x$

$\qquad \sqrt{x} = x - 6$ Subtract 6 from both sides to isolate the radical.

$(\sqrt{x})^2 = (x - 6)^2$ Square both sides.

$\qquad x = (x - 6)(x - 6)$ Square the binomial by multiplying it by itself.

$\qquad x = x^2 - 12x + 36$ Multiply. The resulting equation is quadratic.

$\qquad 0 = x^2 - 13x + 36$ Subtract x to collect all terms on the right side of the equation.

$\qquad 0 = (x - 4)(x - 9)$ Factor.

$\quad x = 4 \quad \text{or} \quad x = 9$ Set each factor equal to 0 and solve.

Now check both solutions.

$x = 4$	$x = 9$
$\sqrt{4} + 6 = 4$	$\sqrt{9} + 6 = 9$
$2 + 6 = 4$	$3 + 6 = 9$
$8 = 4$	$9 = 9$
False	True

Quick Check 6

Solve $\sqrt{2x} + 4 = x$.

The solution $x = 4$ is an extraneous solution. The solution set is $\{9\}$.

Solving Radical Equations Containing Two Radicals

Objective 5 Solve equations containing two radicals.

EXAMPLE 9   Solve $\sqrt[5]{6x + 5} = \sqrt[5]{4x - 3}$.

SOLUTION   We raise both sides to the fifth power. Because both radicals have the same index, this will result in an equation that does not contain a radical.

$\sqrt[5]{6x + 5} = \sqrt[5]{4x - 3}$

$(\sqrt[5]{6x + 5})^5 = (\sqrt[5]{4x - 3})^5$ Raise both sides to the fifth power.

$\qquad 6x + 5 = 4x - 3$ Simplify.

$$2x + 5 = -3 \qquad \text{Subtract } 4x \text{ from both sides.}$$
$$2x = -8 \qquad \text{Subtract 5 from both sides.}$$
$$x = -4 \qquad \text{Divide both sides by 2.}$$

It is left to the reader to verify that the solution is not an extraneous solution. This solution checks, and the solution set is $\{-4\}$.

Occasionally, equations containing two square roots will still contain a square root after we have squared both sides. This will require us to square both sides a second time.

Quick Check 7

Solve $\sqrt[3]{5x - 11} = \sqrt[3]{7x + 33}$.

EXAMPLE 10 Solve $\sqrt{x + 6} - \sqrt{x - 1} = 1$.

SOLUTION   We must begin by isolating one of the two radicals on the left side of the equation. We will isolate $\sqrt{x + 6}$, as it is positive.

$$\sqrt{x + 6} - \sqrt{x - 1} = 1$$
$$\sqrt{x + 6} = 1 + \sqrt{x - 1} \qquad \text{Add } \sqrt{x - 1} \text{ to isolate the radical } \sqrt{x + 6} \text{ on the left side.}$$
$$(\sqrt{x + 6})^2 = (1 + \sqrt{x - 1})^2 \qquad \text{Square both sides.}$$
$$x + 6 = (1 + \sqrt{x - 1})(1 + \sqrt{x - 1}) \qquad \text{Square the binomial on the right side by multiplying it by itself.}$$
$$x + 6 = 1 \cdot 1 + 1 \cdot \sqrt{x - 1} + 1 \cdot \sqrt{x - 1} + \sqrt{x - 1} \cdot \sqrt{x - 1} \qquad \text{Distribute.}$$
$$x + 6 = 1 + 2\sqrt{x - 1} + x - 1 \qquad \text{Simplify.}$$
$$x + 6 = 2\sqrt{x - 1} + x \qquad \text{Combine like terms.}$$
$$6 = 2\sqrt{x - 1} \qquad \text{Subtract } x \text{ from both sides isolate the to radical.}$$
$$3 = \sqrt{x - 1} \qquad \text{Divide both sides by 2.}$$
$$3^2 = (\sqrt{x - 1})^2 \qquad \text{Square both sides}$$
$$9 = x - 1 \qquad \text{Simplify.}$$
$$10 = x \qquad \text{Add 1 to both sides.}$$

Quick Check 8

Solve: $\sqrt{x + 3} - \sqrt{x - 2} = 1$.

It is left to the reader to verify that the solution is not an extraneous solution. The solution set is $\{10\}$.

A Pendulum and Its Period

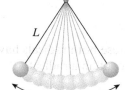

Objective 6 Solve applied problems involving a pendulum and its period. The **period** of a pendulum is the amount of time it takes to swing from one extreme to the other and back again. The period T of a pendulum in seconds can be found by the formula $T = 2\pi\sqrt{\dfrac{L}{32}}$, where L is the length of the pendulum in feet.

EXAMPLE 11   A pendulum has a length of 3 feet. Find its period, rounded to the nearest hundredth of a second.

SOLUTION   Substitute 3 for L in the formula and simplify to find the period T.

$$T = 2\pi\sqrt{\frac{L}{32}}$$

$$T = 2\pi\sqrt{\frac{3}{32}} \quad \text{Substitute 3 for } L.$$

$$T \approx 1.92 \qquad \text{Approximate using a calculator.}$$

The period of a pendulum that is 3 feet long is approximately 1.92 seconds.

Quick Check 9

A pendulum has a length of 6 feet. Find its period, rounded to the nearest hundredth of a second.

EXAMPLE 12   If a pendulum has a period of 1 second, find its length in feet. Round to the nearest hundredth of a foot.

SOLUTION   In this example, substitute 1 for T and solve for L. To solve this equation for L, isolate the radical and square both sides.

$$T = 2\pi\sqrt{\frac{L}{32}}$$

$$1 = 2\pi\sqrt{\frac{L}{32}} \qquad \text{Substitute 1 for } T.$$

$$\frac{1}{2\pi} = \sqrt{\frac{L}{32}} \qquad \text{Divide both sides by } 2\pi \text{ to isolate the radical.}$$

$$\left(\frac{1}{2\pi}\right)^2 = \left(\sqrt{\frac{L}{32}}\right)^2 \qquad \text{Square both sides.}$$

$$\frac{1}{4\pi^2} = \frac{L}{32} \qquad \text{Simplify.}$$

$$\overset{8}{\cancel{32}} \cdot \frac{1}{4\pi^2} = \overset{1}{\cancel{32}} \cdot \frac{L}{\underset{1}{\cancel{32}}} \qquad \text{Multiply both sides by 32 and simplify to isolate } L.$$

$$\frac{8}{\pi^2} = L \qquad \text{Simplify.}$$

$$L \approx 0.81 \qquad \text{Approximate using a calculator.}$$

The length of the pendulum is approximately 0.81 foot.

▶ **Quick Check 10**

If a pendulum has a period of 3 seconds, find its length in feet. Round to the nearest hundredth of a foot.

Other Applications Involving Radicals

Objective 7 **Solve other applied problems involving radicals.**

EXAMPLE 13   A vehicle made 150 feet of skid marks on the asphalt before crashing. The speed, s, in miles per hour, the vehicle was traveling when it started skidding can be approximated by the formula $s = \sqrt{30df}$, where d represents the length of the skid marks in feet and f represents the drag factor of the road. If the drag factor for asphalt is 0.75, find the speed the car was traveling. Round to the nearest mile per hour.

SOLUTION   Begin by substituting 150 for d and 0.75 for f.

$$s = \sqrt{30df}$$
$$s = \sqrt{30(150)(0.75)} \quad \text{Substitute 150 for } d \text{ and 0.75 for } f.$$
$$s = \sqrt{3375} \quad \text{Simplify the radicand.}$$
$$s \approx 58 \quad \text{Approximate using a calculator.}$$

The car was traveling approximately 58 miles per hour when it started skidding.

▶ **Quick Check 11**

A vehicle made 215 feet of skid marks on the asphalt before crashing. The speed, s, the vehicle was traveling in miles per hour when it started skidding can be approximated by the formula $s = \sqrt{30df}$, where d represents the length of the skid marks in feet and f represents the drag factor of the road. If the drag factor for asphalt is 0.75, find the speed the car was traveling when it started skidding. Round to the nearest mile per hour.

BUILDING YOUR STUDY STRATEGY

Note Taking, 5 Formatting Your Notes A good note-taking system takes advantage of the margins for specific tasks. You can use the left margin as a place to write down key words or to denote important material. You can then use the right margin to clarify steps in problems or to take down advice from your instructor.

Exercises 9.5

MyMathLab    PRACTICE   WATCH   DOWNLOAD   READ   REVIEW

Vocabulary

1. A(n) _____ equation is an equation containing one or more radicals.

2. If two numbers a and b are equal, then for any n, $a^n = $ _____.

3. To solve a radical equation, first _____ one radical containing the variable on one side of the equation.

4. A(n) _____ solution is a solution to the equation that results when we raise a given equation to a power but is not a solution to the original equation.

5. An object suspended from a support so that it swings freely back and forth under the influence of gravity is called a(n) _____.

6. The _____ of a pendulum is the amount of time it takes the pendulum to swing from one extreme to the other and back again.

Solve. Check for extraneous solutions.

7. $\sqrt{x + 3} = 10$

8. $\sqrt{x - 6} = 8$

9. $\sqrt[3]{2x + 9} = 5$

10. $\sqrt[4]{4x - 3} = 3$

11. $\sqrt{5x + 17} = -6$

12. $\sqrt[3]{x - 8} = -4$

13. $\sqrt{x + 5} - 7 = -2$

14. $\sqrt{3x - 8} + 11 = 4$

15. $\sqrt[3]{2x + 7} + 3 = 6$

16. $\sqrt[4]{5x - 4} + 12 = 16$

17. $\sqrt{x^2 + 5x - 1} - 2 = 5$

18. $\sqrt{x^2 + x - 4} + 6 = 10$

19. For the function $f(x) = \sqrt{3x + 9}$, find all values x for which $f(x) = 12$.

20. For the function $f(x) = \sqrt{x - 8} + 7$, find all values x for which $f(x) = 13$.

21. For the function $f(x) = \sqrt[3]{5x - 1} + 5$, find all values x for which $f(x) = 9$.

22. For the function $f(x) = \sqrt[4]{2x - 3} - 7$, find all values x for which $f(x) = -4$.

23. For the function $f(x) = \sqrt{x^2 - 5x + 2} + 10$, find all values x for which $f(x) = 14$.

24. For the function $f(x) = \sqrt{x^2 + 8x + 40} - 3$, find all values x for which $f(x) = 2$.

Solve. Check for extraneous solutions.

25. $x^{1/2} + 8 = 10$

26. $x^{1/3} - 11 = -20$

27. $(x + 10)^{1/2} - 4 = 3$

28. $(2x - 35)^{1/2} + 6 = 17$

29. $(5x + 6)^{1/3} - 8 = -2$

30. $(x^2 - 10x + 49)^{1/2} + 2 = 7$

31. $x = \sqrt{2x + 48}$

32. $\sqrt{3x + 10} = x$

33. $\sqrt{4x + 13} = x - 2$

34. $x + 9 = \sqrt{6x + 46}$

35. $\sqrt{2x - 5} + 4 = x$

36. $\sqrt{3x + 13} - 3 = x$

37. $x = \sqrt{49 - 8x} + 7$

38. $x = \sqrt{2x + 9} - 5$

39. $2x - 3 = \sqrt{30 - 7x}$

40. $3x + 5 = \sqrt{27x + 27}$

41. $3x = 1 + \sqrt{4x^2 + x + 7}$

42. $x = \sqrt{54 + 5x - x^2} - 3$

43. $\sqrt{4x - 15} = \sqrt{3x + 11}$

44. $\sqrt[3]{6x + 7} = \sqrt[3]{x - 5}$

45. $\sqrt[4]{x^2 - 8x + 4} = \sqrt[4]{3x - 14}$

46. $\sqrt{5x^2 + 3x - 11} = \sqrt{4x^2 - 6x - 25}$

47. $\sqrt{x + 4} = \sqrt{x - 1} + 1$

48. $\sqrt{x + 14} - \sqrt{x - 10} = 2$

49. $\sqrt{2x + 3} = 1 + \sqrt{x + 1}$

50. $\sqrt{2x + 11} = 2 + \sqrt{x + 2}$

51. $\sqrt{2x + 12} = 1 + \sqrt{x + 5}$

52. $\sqrt{3x - 2} + \sqrt{x + 3} = 3$

53. $\sqrt{3x + 1} - \sqrt{x + 4} = 1$

54. $\sqrt{3x + 3} - \sqrt{2x - 3} = 2$

For Exercises 55–60, use the formula $T = 2\pi\sqrt{\dfrac{L}{32}}$.

55. A pendulum has a length of 5 feet. Find its period, rounded to the nearest hundredth of a second.

56. A pendulum has a length of 2.2 feet. Find its period, rounded to the nearest hundredth of a second.

57. A pendulum has a length of 1.8 feet. Find its period, rounded to the nearest hundredth of a second.

58. A pendulum has a length of 3.5 feet. Find its period, rounded to the nearest hundredth of a second.

59. If a pendulum has a period of 1.8 seconds, find its length in feet. Round to the nearest tenth of a foot.

60. If a pendulum has a period of 3.5 seconds, find its length in feet. Round to the nearest tenth of a foot.

Skid-mark analysis is one way to estimate the speed a car was traveling prior to an accident. The speed, s, the vehicle was traveling in miles per hour can be approximated by the formula $s = \sqrt{30df}$, where d represents the length of the skid marks in feet and f represents the drag factor of the road.

61. A vehicle involved in an accident made 70 feet of skid marks on the asphalt before crashing. If the drag factor for asphalt is 0.75, find the speed the car was traveling when it started skidding. Round to the nearest mile per hour.

62. A vehicle involved in an accident made 240 feet of skid marks on the asphalt before crashing. If the drag factor for asphalt is 0.75, find the speed the car was traveling when it started skidding. Round to the nearest mile per hour.

63. A vehicle involved in an accident made 185 feet of skid marks on a concrete road before crashing. If the drag factor for concrete is 0.95, find the speed the car was traveling when it started skidding. Round to the nearest mile per hour.

64. A vehicle involved in an accident made 60 feet of skid marks on a concrete road before crashing. If the drag factor for concrete is 0.95, find the speed the car was traveling when it started skidding. Round to the nearest mile per hour.

Body Surface Area (BSA), a measure of the surface area of a human body, is involved in many medical applications including chemotherapy dosing. The BSA, in square meters, can be approximated using the Mosteller formula $BSA = \sqrt{\dfrac{hw}{3600}}$, *where h is the person's height in centimeters and w is the person's weight in kilograms. Find the BSA of a person with the given measurements. Round to the nearest hundredth of a square meter.*

65. Adult male—height: 177 centimeters; weight: 89 kilograms

66. Adult female—height: 163 centimeters; weight: 75 kilograms

67. 12-year-old female—height: 151 centimeters; weight: 50 kilograms

68. 16-year-old male—height: 171 centimeters; weight: 70 kilograms

69. If a person whose height is 190 centimeters has a BSA of 1.9 square meters, find the person's weight to the nearest kilogram.

70. If a person whose height is 155 centimeters has a BSA of 1.6 square meters, find the person's weight to the nearest kilogram.

A water tank has a hole at the bottom, and the rate r at which water flows out of the hole in gallons per minute can be found by the formula $r = 19.8\sqrt{d}$, *where d represents the depth of the water in the tank, in feet.*

71. Find the rate of water flow if the depth of water in the tank is 49 feet.

72. Find the rate of water flow if the depth of water in the tank is 9 feet.

73. Find the rate of water flow if the depth of water in the tank is 13 feet. Round to the nearest tenth of a gallon per minute.

74. Find the rate of water flow if the depth of water in the tank is 22 feet. Round to the nearest tenth of a gallon per minute.

75. If water is flowing out of the tank at a rate of 30 gallons per minute, find the depth of water in the tank. Round to the nearest tenth of a foot.

76. If water is flowing out of the tank at a rate of 100 gallons per minute, find the depth of water in the tank. Round to the nearest tenth of a foot.

The sight distance d, in miles, to the horizon can be approximated using the formula $d = \sqrt{1.5h}$, *where h is the eyelevel of the person, in feet. Round all answers to the nearest tenth of a mile.*

77. A kayaker is paddling in the ocean when he sees the shore on the horizon. If the kayaker's eyelevel is 2 feet above the water, how far does he have to paddle to reach the shore?

78. Jon is climbing a rock wall on a cruise ship when he sees an island on the horizon. If his eyelevel is 150 feet above the water, how far from the island is the cruise ship?

79. The crow's nest of a tall ship is a perch on the main mast that puts an observer at an eyelevel 100 feet above the water. If the observer sees the base of another ship on the horizon, how far away is the other ship?

80. While on a cruise, Jean watches the sun set on the horizon. If Jean's eyelevel is 35 feet above the water, what is the distance to the horizon?

✏ Writing in Mathematics

Answer in complete sentences.

81. Write a real-world word problem that involves estimating the speed a car was traveling when it started skidding, based on the length of its skid marks. Solve your problem, explaining each step of the process.

82. What is an extraneous solution to an equation? Explain how to determine that a solution to a radical equation is actually an extraneous solution.

83. *Newsletter* Write a newsletter that explains how to solve a radical equation.

9.6 The Complex Numbers

OBJECTIVES

1. Rewrite square roots of negative numbers as imaginary numbers.
2. Add and subtract complex numbers.
3. Multiply imaginary numbers.
4. Multiply complex numbers.
5. Divide by a complex number.
6. Divide by an imaginary number.
7. Simplify expressions containing powers of *i*.

Imaginary Numbers

Objective 1 Rewrite square roots of negative numbers as imaginary numbers. Section 9.1 stated that the square root of a negative number, such as $\sqrt{-1}$ and $\sqrt{-25}$, is not a real number. This is because no real number equals a negative number when it is squared. The square root of a negative number is an **imaginary number**.

We define the **imaginary unit** i to be a number that is equal to $\sqrt{-1}$. The number i has the property that $i^2 = -1$.

Imaginary Unit i

$$i = \sqrt{-1}$$
$$i^2 = -1$$

All imaginary numbers can be expressed in terms of i because $\sqrt{-1}$ is a factor of every imaginary number.

EXAMPLE 1 Express $\sqrt{-25}$ in terms of i.

SOLUTION Whenever we have a square root with a negative radicand, we begin by factoring out i. Then we simplify the resulting square root.

$$\begin{aligned}
\sqrt{-25} &= \sqrt{25(-1)} && \text{Rewrite } -25 \text{ as } 25(-1). \\
&= \sqrt{25} \cdot \sqrt{-1} && \text{Rewrite as the product of two square roots.} \\
&= \sqrt{25}\,i && \text{Rewrite } \sqrt{-1} \text{ as } i. \\
&= 5i && \text{Simplify the square root.}
\end{aligned}$$

As you become more experienced at working with imaginary numbers, you may want to combine a few of the previous steps into one step.

EXAMPLE 2 Express $\sqrt{-40}$ in terms of i.

SOLUTION

$$\begin{aligned}
\sqrt{-40} &= \sqrt{40} \cdot \sqrt{-1} && \text{Rewrite as the product of two square roots.} \\
&= 2\sqrt{10} \cdot i && \text{Simplify the square root. Rewrite } \sqrt{-1} \text{ as } i. \\
&= 2i\sqrt{10} && \text{Rewrite with } i \text{ in front of the radical.}
\end{aligned}$$

A WORD OF CAUTION After rewriting the square root of a negative number, such as $\sqrt{-40}$, as an imaginary number, be sure that i does not appear in the radicand. Instead, i should be written in front of the radical.

EXAMPLE 3 Express $-\sqrt{-12}$ in terms of i.

SOLUTION Notice that in this example, a negative sign is in front of the square root as well as in the radicand. We simplify the square root first, making the result negative.

$$\begin{aligned}
-\sqrt{-12} &= -\sqrt{12} \cdot \sqrt{-1} && \text{Rewrite as the product of two square roots.} \\
&= -2i\sqrt{3} && \text{Simplify the square root. Rewrite } \sqrt{-1} \text{ as } i.
\end{aligned}$$

Quick Check 1

Express in terms of i.

a) $\sqrt{-36}$
b) $\sqrt{-63}$
c) $-\sqrt{-54}$

Complex Numbers

The set of imaginary numbers and the set of real numbers are subsets of the set of **complex numbers**.

> ### Complex Numbers
>
> A **complex number** is a number of the form $a + bi$, where a and b are real numbers.

Real numbers are complex numbers for which $b = 0$: the real number 7 can be written as $7 + 0i$. Imaginary numbers are complex numbers for which $a = 0$ but $b \neq 0$: the imaginary number $3i$ can be written as $0 + 3i$. We often associate the word *complex* with something that is difficult, but here *complex* refers to the fact that these numbers are made up of two parts.

> ### Real and Imaginary Parts of a Complex Number
>
> For the complex number $a + bi$, the number a is the **real part** and the number b is the **imaginary part**.

Addition and Subtraction of Complex Numbers

Objective ② Add and subtract complex numbers. We now focus on operations involving complex numbers. We add two complex numbers by adding the two real parts and adding the two imaginary parts. We can follow a similar technique for subtraction.

EXAMPLE 4 Simplify $(6 + 5i) + (7 - 2i)$.

SOLUTION Begin by removing the parentheses; then combine the two real parts and the two imaginary parts of these complex numbers.

$$(6 + 5i) + (7 - 2i) = 6 + 5i + 7 - 2i \quad \text{Remove parentheses.}$$
$$= 13 + 3i \quad \text{Combine the two real parts.}$$
$$\text{Combine the two imaginary parts.}$$

Notice that the process of adding these two complex numbers is similar to simplifying the expression $(6 + 5x) + (7 - 2x)$.

EXAMPLE 5 Simplify $(-2 + 9i) - (8 - 5i)$.

SOLUTION We must distribute the negative sign to both parts of the second complex number, just as we distributed negative signs when we subtracted variable expressions.

$$(-2 + 9i) - (8 - 5i) = -2 + 9i - 8 + 5i \quad \text{Distribute.}$$
$$= -10 + 14i \quad \text{Combine the two real parts and}$$
$$\text{combine the two imaginary parts.}$$

▸ **Quick Check 2**

Simplify.

a) $(3 + 12i) + (-8 + 15i)$
b) $(14 - 6i) - (3 + 22i)$

Multiplying Imaginary Numbers

Objective 3 Multiply imaginary numbers. Before learning to multiply two complex numbers, we will discuss the multiplication of two imaginary numbers. Suppose we wanted to multiply $6i$ by $9i$. Just as $6x \cdot 9x = 54x^2$, the product $6i \cdot 9i$ is equal to $54i^2$. However, recall that $i^2 = -1$. So this product is $54(-1)$, or -54. When multiplying two imaginary numbers, we substitute -1 for i^2.

EXAMPLE 6 Multiply $8i \cdot 13i$.

SOLUTION

$$
\begin{aligned}
8i \cdot 13i &= 104i^2 && \text{Multiply.} \\
&= 104(-1) && \text{Rewrite } i^2 \text{ as } -1. \\
&= -104 && \text{Multiply.}
\end{aligned}
$$

Quick Check 3

Multiply $4i \cdot 15i$.

EXAMPLE 7 Multiply $\sqrt{-24} \cdot \sqrt{-45}$.

SOLUTION Although it may be tempting to multiply -24 by -45 and combine the two square roots, we cannot do this. The property $\sqrt{x} \cdot \sqrt{y} = \sqrt{xy}$ holds true only if x or y is nonnegative. We must rewrite each square root as an imaginary number before multiplying.

$$
\begin{aligned}
\sqrt{-24} \cdot \sqrt{-45} &= i\sqrt{24} \cdot i\sqrt{45} && \text{Rewrite each radical as an imaginary number.} \\
&= i\sqrt{2^3 \cdot 3} \cdot i\sqrt{3^2 \cdot 5} && \text{Factor each radicand.} \\
&= i^2\sqrt{2^3 \cdot 3^3 \cdot 5} && \text{Multiply the two radicands.} \\
&= 2 \cdot 3 \cdot i^2\sqrt{2 \cdot 3 \cdot 5} && \text{Simplify the square root.} \\
&= -6\sqrt{30} && \text{Rewrite } i^2 \text{ as } -1 \text{ and simplify.}
\end{aligned}
$$

When we multiply $\sqrt{24}$ by $\sqrt{45}$, our work will be easier if we factor 24 and 45 before multiplying, rather than trying to simplify $\sqrt{1080}$.

Quick Check 4

Multiply $\sqrt{-5} \cdot \sqrt{-120}$.

Multiplying Complex Numbers

Objective 4 Multiply complex numbers. We multiply two complex numbers by using the distributive property. Often, a product of two complex numbers will contain a term with i^2, and we will rewrite i^2 as -1.

EXAMPLE 8 Multiply $3i(4 - 5i)$.

SOLUTION Begin by multiplying $3i$ by both terms in the parentheses.

$$
\begin{aligned}
3i(4 - 5i) &= 3i \cdot 4 - 3i \cdot 5i && \text{Distribute.} \\
&= 12i - 15i^2 && \text{Multiply.} \\
&= 12i + 15 && \text{Rewrite } i^2 \text{ as } -1 \text{ and simplify.} \\
&= 15 + 12i && \text{Rewrite in the form } a + bi.
\end{aligned}
$$

Quick Check 5

Multiply $-6i(7 + 8i)$.

EXAMPLE 9 Multiply $(9 + i)(2 + 7i)$.

SOLUTION In this example, we must multiply each term in the first set of parentheses by each term in the second set.

$$
\begin{aligned}
(9 + i)(2 + 7i) &= 9 \cdot 2 + 9 \cdot 7i + i \cdot 2 + i \cdot 7i && \text{Distribute (FOIL).} \\
&= 18 + 63i + 2i + 7i^2 && \text{Multiply.} \\
&= 18 + 65i - 7 && \text{Add } 63i + 2i. \text{ Rewrite } i^2 \text{ as} \\
& && -1 \text{ and simplify.} \\
&= 11 + 65i && \text{Combine like terms.}
\end{aligned}
$$

Quick Check 6
Multiply $(3 - 2i)(8 + i)$.

EXAMPLE 10 Multiply $(7 + 2i)^2$.

SOLUTION Recall that we square a binomial by multiplying it by itself.

$$
\begin{aligned}
(7 + 2i)^2 &= (7 + 2i)(7 + 2i) && \text{Multiply } 7 + 2i \text{ by itself.} \\
&= 7 \cdot 7 + 7 \cdot 2i + 2i \cdot 7 + 2i \cdot 2i && \text{Distribute.} \\
&= 49 + 14i + 14i + 4i^2 && \text{Multiply.} \\
&= 49 + 28i - 4 && \text{Add } 14i + 14i. \text{ Rewrite } i^2 \\
& && \text{as } -1 \text{ and simplify.} \\
&= 45 + 28i && \text{Combine like terms.}
\end{aligned}
$$

Quick Check 7
Multiply $(9 - 4i)^2$.

EXAMPLE 11 Multiply $(5 + 6i)(5 - 6i)$.

SOLUTION

$$
\begin{aligned}
(5 + 6i)(5 - 6i) &= 5 \cdot 5 - 5 \cdot 6i + 6i \cdot 5 - 6i \cdot 6i && \text{Distribute.} \\
&= 25 - 30i + 30i - 36i^2 && \text{Multiply.} \\
&= 25 - 36i^2 && \text{Combine like terms.} \\
&= 25 + 36 && \text{Rewrite } i^2 \text{ as } -1 \text{ and} \\
& && \text{simplify.} \\
&= 61 && \text{Add.}
\end{aligned}
$$

Quick Check 8
Multiply $(7 + 4i)(7 - 4i)$.

In the previous example, the two complex numbers that were multiplied were conjugates. Their product was a real number that did not have an imaginary part. Two complex numbers of the form $a + bi$ and $a - bi$ are conjugates, and their product will always be equal to $a^2 + b^2$.

$$
\begin{aligned}
(a + bi)(a - bi) &= a^2 - abi + abi - b^2i^2 && \text{Distribute.} \\
&= a^2 - b^2i^2 && \text{Combine like terms.} \\
&= a^2 + b^2 && \text{Rewrite } i^2 \text{ as } -1 \text{ and simplify.}
\end{aligned}
$$

EXAMPLE 12 Multiply $(10 - 3i)(10 + 3i)$.

SOLUTION We will use the fact that $(a + bi)(a - bi) = a^2 + b^2$ for two complex numbers that are conjugates.

$$
\begin{aligned}
(10 - 3i)(10 + 3i) &= 10^2 + 3^2 && \text{The product equals } a^2 + b^2. \\
&= 100 + 9 && \text{Square 10 and 3.} \\
&= 109 && \text{Add.}
\end{aligned}
$$

▶ **Quick Check 9**
Multiply $(11 - 4i)(11 + 4i)$.

Dividing by a Complex Number

Objective 5 Divide by a complex number. Because the imaginary number i is a square root ($\sqrt{-1}$), a simplified expression cannot contain i in its denominator. In a procedure similar to rationalizing a denominator (Section 9.4), we will use conjugates to rewrite the expression without i in the denominator.

EXAMPLE 13 Simplify $\dfrac{2}{3 + i}$.

SOLUTION Begin by multiplying the numerator and denominator by the conjugate of the denominator, which is $3 - i$.

$$\frac{2}{3 + i} = \frac{2}{3 + i} \cdot \frac{3 - i}{3 - i} \qquad \text{Multiply the numerator and denominator by the conjugate of the denominator.}$$

$$= \frac{6 - 2i}{3^2 + 1^2} \qquad \text{Multiply the numerators and denominators.}$$

$$= \frac{6 - 2i}{10} \qquad \text{Simplify the denominator.}$$

$$= \frac{\overset{1}{2}(3 - i)}{\underset{5}{10}} \qquad \text{Factor the numerator. Divide out factors common to the numerator and denominator.}$$

$$= \frac{3 - i}{5} \qquad \text{Simplify.}$$

$$= \frac{3}{5} - \frac{1}{5}i \qquad \text{Rewrite in the form } a + bi.$$

Quick Check 10

Simplify $\dfrac{15}{8 + 6i}$.

EXAMPLE 14 Simplify $\dfrac{1 + 6i}{2 + 5i}$.

SOLUTION In this example, the numerator has two terms and we must multiply using the distributive property.

$$\frac{1 + 6i}{2 + 5i} = \frac{1 + 6i}{2 + 5i} \cdot \frac{2 - 5i}{2 - 5i} \qquad \text{Multiply the numerator and denominator by the conjugate of the denominator.}$$

$$= \frac{2 - 5i + 12i - 30i^2}{2^2 + 5^2} \qquad \text{Multiply.}$$

$$= \frac{2 + 7i - 30i^2}{4 + 25} \qquad \text{Combine like terms in the numerator. Square 2 and 5 in the denominator.}$$

$$= \frac{2 + 7i + 30}{29} \qquad \text{Rewrite } i^2 \text{ as } -1 \text{ and simplify. Simplify the denominator.}$$

$$= \frac{32 + 7i}{29} \qquad \text{Combine like terms.}$$

$$= \frac{32}{29} + \frac{7}{29}i \qquad \text{Rewrite in the form } a + bi.$$

Quick Check 11

Simplify $\dfrac{9 + 2i}{7 - 3i}$.

Note that the expression $\dfrac{1 + 6i}{2 + 5i}$ is equivalent to $(1 + 6i) \div (2 + 5i)$. If we are asked to divide a complex number by another complex number, we begin by rewriting the expression as a fraction and then proceed as in the previous example.

Dividing by an Imaginary Number

Objective 6 Divide by an imaginary number. When a denominator is an imaginary number, we multiply the numerator and denominator by i to rewrite the fraction without i in the denominator.

EXAMPLE 15 Simplify $\dfrac{5 + 2i}{3i}$.

SOLUTION   Because the denominator is an imaginary number, we begin by multiplying the fraction by $\frac{i}{i}$.

$$\frac{5 + 2i}{3i} = \frac{5 + 2i}{3i} \cdot \frac{i}{i} \qquad \text{Multiply the numerator and denominator by } i.$$

$$= \frac{5i + 2i^2}{3i^2} \qquad \text{Multiply.}$$

$$= \frac{5i - 2}{-3} \qquad \text{Rewrite } i^2 \text{ as } -1 \text{ and simplify.}$$

$$= -\frac{5i - 2}{3} \qquad \text{Factor } -1 \text{ out of the denominator.}$$

$$= \frac{-5i + 2}{3} \qquad \text{Distribute.}$$

$$= \frac{2}{3} - \frac{5}{3}i \qquad \text{Rewrite in } a - bi \text{ form.}$$

Quick Check 12

Simplify $\dfrac{15 - 8i}{12i}$.

Powers of i

Objective 7 Simplify expressions containing powers of i. Occasionally, i may be raised to a power greater than 2. We finish this section by learning to simplify such expressions. The expression i^3 can be rewritten as $i^2 \cdot i$, which is equivalent to $-1 \cdot i$, or $-i$. The expression i^4 can be rewritten as $i^2 \cdot i^2$, which is equivalent to $-1(-1)$, or 1. The following table shows the first four positive powers of i:

$$
\begin{array}{cccc}
i & i^2 & i^3 & i^4 \\
\downarrow & \downarrow & \downarrow & \downarrow \\
i & -1 & -i & 1
\end{array}
$$

We can use the fact that $i^4 = 1$ to simplify greater powers of i.

$$i^5 = i^4 \cdot i = 1 \cdot i = i \qquad\qquad i^6 = i^4 \cdot i^2 = 1(-1) = -1$$
$$i^7 = i^4 \cdot i^3 = 1 \cdot i^3 = 1(-i) = -i \qquad i^8 = i^4 \cdot i^4 = 1 \cdot 1 = 1$$

We can now see a pattern.

$$
\begin{array}{cccccccc}
i & i^2 & i^3 & i^4 & i^5 & i^6 & i^7 & i^8 \\
\downarrow & \downarrow & \downarrow & \downarrow & \downarrow & \downarrow & \downarrow & \downarrow \\
i & -1 & -i & 1 & i & -1 & -i & 1
\end{array}
$$

In general, to simplify i^n, where n is a whole number, we divide n by 4. If the remainder is equal to r, $i^n = i^r$.

Remainder	0	1	2	3
i^n	1	i	-1	$-i$

EXAMPLE 16 Simplify i^{27}.

SOLUTION If we divide the exponent 27 by 4, the remainder is 3. So $i^{27} = i^3 = -i$.

Quick Check 13
Simplify i^{30}.

BUILDING YOUR STUDY STRATEGY

Note Taking, 6 Rewriting Your Notes A good strategy is to rewrite your notes as soon as possible after class. The simple task of rewriting your notes serves as a review of the material that was covered in class. If you rewrite your notes while the material is still fresh in your mind, you have a better chance of being able to read what you have written.

As you rework your notes, take the time to supplement them. Replace a brief definition with the full definition from the text. Add notes to clarify what you wrote down in class.

Finally, consider creating a page in your notes that contains the problems (without solutions) your instructor solved during class. When you begin to review for the exam, this list of problems will be a good review sheet.

Exercises 9.6

MyMathLab

PRACTICE WATCH DOWNLOAD READ REVIEW

Vocabulary

1. The square root of a negative number is a(n) _____ number.

2. The imaginary unit i is a number that is equal to _____ .

3. The number i has the property that $i^2 = $ _____ .

4. A(n) _____ number is a number of the form $a + bi$, where a and b are real numbers.

5. For the complex number $a + bi$, the number a is the _____ part.

6. For the complex number $a + bi$, the number b is the _____ part.

Express in terms of i.

7. $\sqrt{-4}$

8. $\sqrt{-16}$

9. $\sqrt{-81}$

10. $\sqrt{-100}$

11. $-\sqrt{-169}$

12. $-\sqrt{-225}$

13. $\sqrt{-50}$

14. $\sqrt{-18}$

15. $-\sqrt{-252}$

16. $\sqrt{-243}$

Add or subtract the complex numbers.

17. $(8 + 9i) + (3 + 5i)$

18. $(13 + 11i) - (6 + 2i)$

19. $(6 - 7i) - (2 + 10i)$

20. $(1 + 6i) + (5 - 12i)$

21. $(-3 + 8i) + (3 - 4i)$

22. $(5 - 9i) + (5 + 9i)$

23. $(12 + 13i) - (12 - 13i)$

24. $(14 - i) - (21 + 11i)$

25. $(1 - 12i) - (8 + 8i) + (5 - 4i)$

26. $(-9 + 2i) - (5 + 6i) - (10 - 20i)$

Find the missing complex number.

27. $(4 - 7i) + ? = 10 + 2i$

28. $(11 + 10i) + ? = 20 - 3i$

29. $(3 + 4i) - ? = 1 - 5i$

30. $? - (-9 + 7i) = -15 - 3i$

Multiply.

31. $7i \cdot 14i$

32. $3i \cdot 8i$

33. $-4i \cdot 5i$

34. $i(-9i)$

35. $\sqrt{-49} \cdot \sqrt{-64}$

36. $\sqrt{-25} \cdot \sqrt{-25}$

37. $\sqrt{-12} \cdot \sqrt{-18}$

38. $\sqrt{-28} \cdot \sqrt{-7}$

39. $\sqrt{-20} \cdot \sqrt{-45}$

40. $\sqrt{-27} \cdot \sqrt{-50}$

Multiply. Write your answer in a + bi form.

41. $7i(8 + 5i)$

42. $3i(10 - 9i)$

43. $-6i(9 + 4i)$

44. $-5i(11 - 14i)$

45. $(7 + 2i)(5 + i)$

46. $(9 + 8i)(1 + 4i)$

47. $(3 - 5i)(4 + 10i)$

48. $(5 - 7i)(4 - i)$

49. $(6 + 7i)^2$

50. $(10 + 4i)^2$

51. $(1 - 5i)^2$

52. $(3 - 8i)^2$

Multiply the conjugates using the fact that $(a + bi)(a - bi) = a^2 + b^2.$

53. $(5 + 2i)(5 - 2i)$

54. $(7 + 4i)(7 - 4i)$

55. $(12 - 8i)(12 + 8i)$

56. $(6 - i)(6 + i)$

57. $(5 + 6i)(5 - 6i)$

58. $(11 + 3i)(11 - 3i)$

Simplify by rationalizing the denominator. Write your answer in a + bi form.

59. $\dfrac{6}{5 + i}$

60. $\dfrac{20}{4 - 3i}$

61. $\dfrac{25i}{9 - 7i}$

62. $\dfrac{10i}{6 + 7i}$

63. $\dfrac{4 + 7i}{7 - 2i}$

64. $\dfrac{9 - 5i}{2 - 3i}$

65. $\dfrac{1 + 6i}{7 + 6i}$

66. $\dfrac{5 - 4i}{5 + 4i}$

Simplify by rationalizing the denominator. Write your answer in a + bi form.

67. $\dfrac{8}{i}$

68. $\dfrac{5}{6i}$

69. $\dfrac{5 - 7i}{3i}$

70. $\dfrac{3 + 10i}{5i}$

71. $\dfrac{6 + i}{-4i}$

72. $\dfrac{2 - 9i}{-8i}$

Divide. Write your answer in a + bi form.

73. $(7 + 3i) \div 2i$

74. $(2 - 13i) \div 6i$

75. $(8 - 7i) \div (1 + 3i)$

76. $(5 + 8i) \div (5 - 11i)$

Find the missing complex number.

77. $(4 + i)(?) = 4 + 35i$

78. $(7 - 5i)(?) = 31 - i$

79. $\dfrac{?}{1 + 9i} = 4 - 3i$

80. $\dfrac{?}{10 - 3i} = 6 - 4i$

Simplify.

81. i^{45}

82. i^{72}

83. i^{42}

84. i^{99}

85. $\dfrac{i^{37}}{i^{15}}$

86. $i^{26} \cdot i^{31}$

87. $i^{21} + i^{53}$

88. $i^{66} - i^{80}$

Mixed Practice, 89–114

Simplify. Write your answer in a + bi form when appropriate.

89. $(7 + 2i)(6 - 3i)$

90. $(4 - 6i)(4 + 6i)$

91. $\dfrac{9 + 4i}{5i}$

92. $8i(17 - 3i)$

93. $-9i(12 + 5i)$

94. $(18 - 13i) - (8 - 5i)$

95. $12i \div (4 - 2i)$

96. $\dfrac{10 - 9i}{5 - i}$

97. $(2 - 5i)(2 + 5i)$

98. $(14 - 11i) + (-23 + 6i)$

99. $\sqrt{-24} \cdot \sqrt{-27}$

100. $(6 - 4i) \div (8i)$

101. $\dfrac{15i}{9 - 2i}$

102. $(16 - 9i)^2$

103. $\sqrt{-252}$

104. $(11 + 4i)(6 - 13i)$

105. $(9 - 3i)^2$

106. $7i \cdot 12i$

107. $(8 - 11i) + (15 + 21i)$

108. i^{207}

109. $-14i \cdot 9i$

110. $\sqrt{-20} \cdot \sqrt{-15}$

111. i^{323}

112. $\dfrac{7 - 6i}{-2i}$

113. $(30 - 17i) - (54 - 33i)$

114. $\sqrt{-2673}$

▬▬ Writing in Mathematics

Answer in complete sentences.

115. Explain how adding two complex numbers is similar to adding two variable expressions.

CHAPTER 10

Quadratic Equations

In this chapter, we will learn how to apply techniques other than factoring to solve quadratic equations. *Quadratic equations* are equations that can be written in the form $ax^2 + bx + c = 0$, where $a \neq 0$. One important goal of this chapter is to determine which technique will provide the most efficient solution to a particular equation. We also will apply these techniques to new application problems that previously could not be solved because they produce equations that are not factorable. In this chapter, we also will examine the graphs of quadratic equations and functions. The graph of a quadratic equation is called a parabola and is U-shaped. The techniques used to graph linear equations also will be applied in graphing quadratic equations, along with some new techniques. The chapter ends by examining inequalities that involve quadratic and rational expressions.

STUDY STRATEGY

Time Management When asked why they are having difficulties in a particular class, some students claim that they do not have enough time. However, many of these students have enough time but lack the time management skills to make the most of their time. In this chapter, we will discuss effective time management strategies, focusing on how to make more efficient use of available time.

10.1

Solving Quadratic Equations by Extracting Square Roots; Completing the Square

OBJECTIVES

1. Solve quadratic equations by factoring.
2. Solve quadratic equations by extracting square roots.
3. Solve quadratic equations by extracting square roots involving a linear expression that is squared.
4. Solve applied problems by extracting square roots.
5. Solve quadratic equations by completing the square.
6. Find a quadratic equation, given its solutions.

Solving Quadratic Equations by Factoring

Objective 1 Solve quadratic equations by factoring. In Chapter 6, we learned how to solve quadratic equations through the use of factoring. We begin this section with a review of this technique. We start by simplifying both sides of the equation completely. This includes any distributing that must be done and combining like terms when possible. After that, we need to collect all of the terms on one side of the equation with 0 on the other side of the equation. Recall that it is a good idea to move the terms to the side of the equation that will produce a positive second-degree term. After the equation contains an expression equal to 0, we need to factor the expression. Finally, we set each factor equal to 0 and solve the resulting equation.

EXAMPLE 1 Solve $x^2 - 7x = -10$.

SOLUTION

$$x^2 - 7x = -10$$
$$x^2 - 7x + 10 = 0 \qquad \text{Add 10 to collect all terms on the left side.}$$
$$(x - 2)(x - 5) = 0 \qquad \text{Factor.}$$
$$x - 2 = 0 \quad \text{or} \quad x - 5 = 0 \qquad \text{Set each factor equal to 0.}$$
$$x = 2 \quad \text{or} \quad x = 5 \qquad \text{Solve the resulting equations.}$$

The solution set is $\{2, 5\}$.

EXAMPLE 2 Solve $x^2 = 49$.

SOLUTION

$$x^2 = 49$$
$$x^2 - 49 = 0 \qquad \text{Collect all terms on the left side.}$$
$$(x + 7)(x - 7) = 0 \qquad \text{Factor (difference of squares).}$$
$$x + 7 = 0 \quad \text{or} \quad x - 7 = 0 \qquad \text{Set each factor equal to 0.}$$
$$x = -7 \quad \text{or} \quad x = 7 \qquad \text{Solve the resulting equations.}$$

The solution set is $\{-7, 7\}$.

Quick Check 1

Solve.

a) $x^2 = 2x + 15$
b) $x^2 = 121$

Solving Quadratic Equations by Extracting Square Roots

Objective 2 Solve quadratic equations by extracting square roots. In the preceding example, we tried to find a number x that, when squared, equals 49. The principal square root of 49 is 7, which gives us one of the two solutions. In an equation where we have a squared term equal to a constant, we can take the square root of both sides of the equation to find the solution as long as we take both the positive and negative square root of the constant. The symbol $\pm$ is used to represent the positive and negative square root and is read as *plus or minus*. For example, $x = \pm 7$ means $x = 7$ or $x = -7$. This technique for solving quadratic equations is called **extracting square roots**.

> **Extracting Square Roots**
>
> 1. Isolate the squared term.
> 2. Take the square root of each side. (Remember to take both the *positive* and *negative* ($\pm$) square root of the constant.)
> 3. Simplify the square root.
> 4. Solve by isolating the variable.

Now we will use extracting square roots to solve an equation that we would not have been able to solve by factoring.

EXAMPLE 3 Solve $x^2 - 50 = 0$.

SOLUTION The expression $x^2 - 50$ cannot be factored because 50 is not a perfect square. We proceed to solve this equation by extracting square roots.

$$x^2 - 50 = 0$$
$$x^2 = 50 \qquad \text{Add 50 to both sides to isolate } x^2.$$
$$\sqrt{x^2} = \pm\sqrt{50} \qquad \text{Take the square root of each side.}$$
$$x = \pm 5\sqrt{2} \qquad \text{Simplify the square root. } \sqrt{50} = \sqrt{25 \cdot 2} = 5\sqrt{2}$$

The solution set is $\{-5\sqrt{2}, 5\sqrt{2}\}$. Using a calculator, we find that the solutions are approximately ± 7.07.

A WORD OF CAUTION When taking the square root of both sides of an equation, do not forget to use the symbol $\pm$ on the side of the equation containing the constant.

This technique also can be used to find complex solutions to equations, as well as real solutions.

EXAMPLE 4 Solve $x^2 = -16$.

SOLUTION   If we had added the 16 to the left side of the equation, the resulting equation would have been $x^2 + 16 = 0$. The expression $x^2 + 16$ is not factorable. (Recall that the sum of 2 squares is not factorable.) The only way to find a solution would be to take the square roots of both sides of the original equation. We proceed to solve this equation by extracting square roots.

$$x^2 = -16$$
$$\sqrt{x^2} = \pm\sqrt{-16} \qquad \text{Take the square root of each side.}$$
$$x = \pm 4i \qquad \text{Simplify the square root.}$$

The solution set is $\{-4i, 4i\}$. Note that these two solutions are not real numbers.

Quick Check 2

Solve.

a) $x^2 = 28$
b) $x^2 + 32 = 0$

Objective 3 Solve quadratic equations by extracting square roots involving a linear expression that is squared. Extracting square roots is an excellent technique for solving quadratic equations whenever the equation is made up of a squared term and a constant term. Consider the equation $(2x - 7)^2 = 25$. To use factoring to solve this equation, we would have to square $2x - 7$, collect all terms on the left side of the equation by subtracting 25, and hope that the resulting expression could be factored. Extracting square roots is a more efficient way to solve this equation.

EXAMPLE 5 Solve $(2x - 7)^2 = 25$.

SOLUTION

$$(2x - 7)^2 = 25$$
$$\sqrt{(2x - 7)^2} = \pm\sqrt{25}$$ Take the square root of each side.
$$2x - 7 = \pm 5$$ Simplify the square root. Note that the square root of $(2x - 7)^2$ is $2x - 7$.
$$2x = 7 \pm 5$$ Add 7.
$$x = \frac{7 \pm 5}{2}$$ Divide by 2.

$\frac{7 + 5}{2} = 6$ and $\frac{7 - 5}{2} = 1$, so the solution set is $\{1, 6\}$.

EXAMPLE 6 Solve $(3x + 4)^2 + 35 = 15$.

SOLUTION

$$(3x + 4)^2 + 35 = 15$$
$$(3x + 4)^2 = -20$$ Subtract 35 to isolate the squared term.
$$\sqrt{(3x + 4)^2} = \pm\sqrt{-20}$$ Take the square root of each side.
$$3x + 4 = \pm 2i\sqrt{5}$$ Simplify the square root.
$$3x = -4 \pm 2i\sqrt{5}$$ Subtract 4.
$$x = \frac{-4 \pm 2i\sqrt{5}}{3}$$ Divide both sides by 3.

Because we cannot simplify the numerator in this case, these are the solutions. The solution set is $\left\{\dfrac{-4 - 2i\sqrt{5}}{3}, \dfrac{-4 + 2i\sqrt{5}}{3}\right\}$.

▶ Quick Check 3
Solve.

a) $(3x + 1)^2 = 100$ **b)** $2(2x - 3)^2 + 17 = -1$

Solving Applied Problems by Extracting Square Roots

Objective 4 Solve applied problems by extracting square roots. Problems involving the area of a geometric figure often lead to quadratic equations, as area is measured in square units. Here are two useful area formulas that can lead to quadratic equations that can be solved by extracting square roots.

Figure	Square	Circle
	s	r
Area	$A = s^2$	$A = \pi r^2$

EXAMPLE 7   A square has an area of 40 square centimeters. Find the length of its side, rounded to the nearest tenth of a centimeter.

SOLUTION   In this problem, the unknown quantity is the length of the side of the square, while we know that the area is 40 cm². We will let x represent the length of the side. Because the area of a square is equal to its side squared, the equation we need to solve is $x^2 = 40$.

$$x^2 = 40$$
$$\sqrt{x^2} = \pm\sqrt{40} \quad \text{Take the square root of each side.}$$
$$x = \pm 2\sqrt{10} \quad \text{Simplify the square roots.}$$

Because x represents the length of the side of the square, it must be positive. We may omit the solution $x = -2\sqrt{10}$. The solution is $x = 2\sqrt{10}$ cm. Rounding this to the nearest tenth, we know that the length of the side of the square is 6.3 cm.

Quick Check 4

A square has an area of 150 square inches. Find the length of its side, rounded to the nearest tenth of an inch.

EXAMPLE 8   A circle has an area of 100 square feet. Find the radius of the circle, rounded to the nearest tenth of a foot.

SOLUTION   In this problem, the unknown quantity is the radius of the circle and we will let r represent the radius. Because the area of a circle is given by the formula $A = \pi r^2$, the equation we need to solve is $\pi r^2 = 100$.

$$\pi r^2 = 100$$

$$\frac{\overset{1}{\cancel{\pi}} r^2}{\underset{1}{\cancel{\pi}}} = \frac{100}{\pi} \quad \text{Divide both sides by } \pi.$$

$$\sqrt{r^2} = \pm\sqrt{\frac{100}{\pi}} \quad \text{Take the square root of each side.}$$

$$r = \pm\sqrt{\frac{100}{\pi}} \quad \text{Simplify.}$$

Again, we may omit the negative solution. The solution is $r = \sqrt{\frac{100}{\pi}}$ ft. Rounding this to the nearest tenth, the radius is 5.6 feet.

Quick Check 5

A circle has an area of 20 square centimeters. Find the radius of the circle, rounded to the nearest tenth of a centimeter.

Solving Quadratic Equations by Completing the Square

Objective 5 Solve quadratic equations by completing the square. We can solve any quadratic equation by converting it to an equation with a squared term equal to a constant. Rewriting the equation in this form allows us to solve it by extracting square roots. We will now examine a procedure for doing this called **completing the square**. This procedure is used for an equation such as $x^2 - 6x - 16 = 0$, which has both a second-degree term (x^2) and a first-degree term $(-6x)$.

The first step is to isolate the variable terms on one side of the equation with the constant term on the other side. This can be done by adding 16 to both sides of the equation. The resulting equation is $x^2 - 6x = 16$.

The next step is to add a number to both sides of the equation that makes the side of the equation containing the variable terms a perfect square trinomial. To do this, we take half of the coefficient of the first-degree term, which in this case is -6, and square it.

$$\left(\frac{-6}{2}\right)^2 = (-3)^2 = 9$$

After adding 9 to both sides of the equation, we obtain the equation $x^2 - 6x + 9 = 25$. The expression on the left side of the equation, $x^2 - 6x + 9$, is a perfect square trinomial and can be factored as $(x - 3)^2$. The resulting equation, $(x - 3)^2 = 25$, is in the correct form for extracting square roots. (This equation will be solved completely in the next example.)

Here is the procedure for solving a quadratic equation by completing the square, provided the coefficient of the squared term is 1.

> ## Completing the Square
>
> 1. Isolate all variable terms on one side of the equation, with the constant term on the other side of the equation.
> 2. Identify the coefficient of the first-degree term. Take half of that number, square it, and add that to both sides of the equation.
> 3. Factor the resulting perfect square trinomial.
> 4. Take the square root of each side of the equation. Be sure to include $\pm$ on the side where the constant is.
> 5. Solve the resulting equation.

In the following example, we will complete the solution of $x^2 - 6x - 16 = 0$ by completing the square.

EXAMPLE 9 Solve $x^2 - 6x - 16 = 0$ by completing the square.

SOLUTION

$$x^2 - 6x - 16 = 0$$
$$x^2 - 6x = 16 \qquad \text{Add 16.}$$
$$x^2 - 6x + 9 = 16 + 9 \quad \left(\tfrac{-6}{2}\right)^2 = (-3)^2 = 9$$
$$\qquad\qquad\qquad\qquad \text{Add 9 to complete the square.}$$
$$(x - 3)^2 = 25 \qquad \text{Simplify. Factor the left side.}$$
$$\sqrt{(x - 3)^2} = \pm\sqrt{25} \quad \text{Take the square root of each side.}$$
$$x - 3 = \pm 5 \qquad \text{Simplify the square root.}$$
$$x = 3 \pm 5 \qquad \text{Add 3.}$$

$3 + 5 = 8$ and $3 - 5 = -2$, so the solution set is $\{-2, 8\}$.

Note that the equation in the previous example could have been solved with less work by factoring $x^2 - 6x - 16$. Use factoring whenever possible because it is often the quickest and most direct way to find the solutions.

EXAMPLE 10 Solve $x^2 + 8x + 20 = 0$ by completing the square.

SOLUTION

$$x^2 + 8x + 20 = 0$$
$$x^2 + 8x = -20 \qquad \text{Subtract 20.}$$
$$x^2 + 8x + 16 = -20 + 16 \quad \text{Half of 8 is 4, which equals 16 when}$$
$$\qquad\qquad\qquad\qquad\text{squared: } \left(\tfrac{8}{2}\right)^2 = (4)^2 = 16. \text{ Add 16.}$$
$$x^2 + 8x + 16 = -4 \qquad \text{Simplify.}$$
$$(x + 4)^2 = -4 \qquad \text{Factor the left side.}$$

$$\sqrt{(x+4)^2} = \pm\sqrt{-4} \qquad \text{Take the square root of each side.}$$
$$x + 4 = \pm 2i \qquad \text{Simplify the square root.}$$
$$x = -4 \pm 2i \qquad \text{Subtract 4.}$$

Quick Check 6

Solve by completing the square.

a) $x^2 + 8x + 12 = 0$
b) $x^2 - 6x + 10 = 0$

The solution set is $\{-4 - 2i, -4 + 2i\}$.

Note that the expression $x^2 + 8x + 20$ does not factor; so completing the square is the only technique we have for solving this equation. In the first two examples of completing the square, the coefficient of the first-degree term was an even integer. If this is not the case, we must use fractions to complete the square.

EXAMPLE 11 Solve $x^2 - 5x - 5 = 0$ by completing the square.

SOLUTION The expression $x^2 - 5x - 5$ does not factor, so we proceed with completing the square.

$$x^2 - 5x - 5 = 0$$
$$x^2 - 5x = 5 \qquad \text{Add 5.}$$
$$x^2 - 5x + \frac{25}{4} = 5 + \frac{25}{4} \qquad \text{Half of } -5 \text{ is } -\frac{5}{2}, \text{ which equals } \frac{25}{4} \text{ when squared: } \left(-\frac{5}{2}\right)^2 = \frac{25}{4}. \text{ Add } \frac{25}{4}.$$
$$x^2 - 5x + \frac{25}{4} = \frac{45}{4} \qquad \text{Add 5 and } \frac{25}{4} \text{ by rewriting 5 as a fraction whose denominator is 4: } 5 + \frac{25}{4} = \frac{20}{4} + \frac{25}{4}.$$
$$\left(x - \frac{5}{2}\right)^2 = \frac{45}{4} \qquad \text{Factor.}$$
$$\sqrt{\left(x - \frac{5}{2}\right)^2} = \pm\sqrt{\frac{45}{4}} \qquad \text{Take the square root of each side.}$$
$$x - \frac{5}{2} = \pm\frac{3\sqrt{5}}{2} \qquad \text{Simplify the square root.}$$
$$x = \frac{5}{2} \pm \frac{3\sqrt{5}}{2} \qquad \text{Add } \frac{5}{2}.$$

The solution set is $\left\{\dfrac{5 - 3\sqrt{5}}{2}, \dfrac{5 + 3\sqrt{5}}{2}\right\}$.

Quick Check 7

Solve $x^2 + 7x - 18 = 0$ by completing the square.

In the previous example, half of b was a fraction, causing us to add a fraction to both sides of the equation. In this case, factoring the resulting trinomial can be difficult. Keep this fact in mind: when adding $\left(\dfrac{b}{2}\right)^2$, or $\dfrac{b^2}{4}$, to both sides while completing the square, the trinomial will factor to be of the form $\left(x + \dfrac{b}{2}\right)^2$. This fact can be verified by simplifying $\left(x + \dfrac{b}{2}\right)^2$ and seeing that it is equal to $x^2 + bx + \dfrac{b^2}{4}$.

$$\left(x + \frac{b}{2}\right)^2 = \left(x + \frac{b}{2}\right)\left(x + \frac{b}{2}\right) \qquad \text{Rewrite as a product.}$$
$$= x^2 + \frac{b}{2}x + \frac{b}{2}x + \frac{b^2}{4} \qquad \text{Multiply.}$$
$$= x^2 + bx + \frac{b^2}{4} \qquad \text{Combine like terms.}$$

A WORD OF CAUTION To solve a quadratic equation by completing the square, we must be sure that the leading coefficient is positive 1. If the leading coefficient is not equal to 1, we divide both sides of the equation by the leading coefficient.

EXAMPLE 12   Solve $2x^2 - 9x + 5 = 0$ by completing the square.

SOLUTION   The leading coefficient is 2, so we begin by dividing each term on both sides of the equation by 2. We can then solve this equation by completing the square.

$$2x^2 - 9x + 5 = 0$$

$$x^2 - \frac{9}{2}x + \frac{5}{2} = 0 \qquad \text{Divide both sides of the equation by 2 so that the leading coefficient is equal to 1.}$$

$$x^2 - \frac{9}{2}x = -\frac{5}{2} \qquad \text{Subtract } \frac{5}{2}.$$

$$x^2 - \frac{9}{2}x + \frac{81}{16} = -\frac{5}{2} + \frac{81}{16} \qquad \text{Half of } -\frac{9}{2} \text{ is } -\frac{9}{4}. \left(-\frac{9}{4}\right)^2 = \frac{81}{16}. \text{ Add } \frac{81}{16} \text{ to both sides of the equation.}$$

$$x^2 - \frac{9}{2}x + \frac{81}{16} = \frac{41}{16} \qquad \text{Simplify: } -\frac{5}{2} + \frac{81}{16} = -\frac{40}{16} + \frac{81}{16}.$$

$$\left(x - \frac{9}{4}\right)^2 = \frac{41}{16} \qquad \text{Factor. In completing the square with } x^2 - bx, \text{ the expression on the left side will factor to be of the form } \left(x - \frac{b}{2}\right)^2.$$

$$\sqrt{\left(x - \frac{9}{4}\right)^2} = \pm\sqrt{\frac{41}{16}} \qquad \text{Take the square root of each side.}$$

$$x - \frac{9}{4} = \pm\frac{\sqrt{41}}{4} \qquad \text{Simplify each square root.}$$

$$x = \frac{9 \pm \sqrt{41}}{4} \qquad \text{Add } \frac{9}{4}.$$

The solution set is $\left\{\dfrac{9 - \sqrt{41}}{4}, \dfrac{9 + \sqrt{41}}{4}\right\}$.

Quick Check 8

Solve $2x^2 - 32x + 92 = 0$ by completing the square.

Finding a Quadratic Equation, Given Its Solutions

Objective 6 Find a quadratic equation, given its solutions.

EXAMPLE 13   Find a quadratic equation in standard form, with integer coefficients, that has the solution set $\left\{-6, \frac{1}{2}\right\}$.

SOLUTION   We know that $x = -6$ is a solution to the equation. This tells us that $x + 6$ is a factor of the quadratic expression. Similarly, knowing that $x = \frac{1}{2}$ is a solution tells us that $2x - 1$ is a factor of the quadratic expression.

$$x = \frac{1}{2}$$

$$2 \cdot x = \frac{1}{\cancel{2}} \cdot \cancel{2} \qquad \text{Multiply both sides by 2 to clear the fractions.}$$

$$2x = 1 \qquad \text{Simplify.}$$

$$2x - 1 = 0 \qquad \text{Subtract 1.}$$

Multiplying these two factors will give us a quadratic equation with these two solutions.

$$x = -6 \quad \text{or} \quad x = \frac{1}{2} \qquad \text{Begin with the solutions.}$$

$$x + 6 = 0 \quad \text{or} \quad 2x - 1 = 0 \qquad \text{Rewrite each equation so that the right side is equal to 0.}$$

$$(x + 6)(2x - 1) = 0 \qquad \text{Write an equation that has these two expressions as factors.}$$

$$2x^2 - x + 12x - 6 = 0 \qquad \text{Multiply.}$$

$$2x^2 + 11x - 6 = 0 \qquad \text{Simplify.}$$

A quadratic equation that has the solution set $\left\{-6, \frac{1}{2}\right\}$ is $2x^2 + 11x - 6 = 0$.

Notice that we say *a* quadratic equation rather than *the* quadratic equation. There are infinitely many quadratic equations with integer coefficients that have this solution set. For example, multiplying both sides of the equation by 3 gives us the equation $6x^2 + 33x - 18 = 0$, which has the same solution set.

Quick Check 9

Find a quadratic equation in standard form, with integer coefficients, that has the solution set $\left\{\frac{5}{3}, -2\right\}$.

EXAMPLE 14 Find a quadratic equation in standard form, with integer coefficients, that has the solution set $\{-6i, 6i\}$.

SOLUTION   We know that $x = -6i$ is a solution to the equation. This tells us that $x + 6i$ is a factor of the quadratic expression. Similarly, knowing that $x = 6i$ is a solution tells us that $x - 6i$ is a factor of the quadratic expression. Multiplying these two factors will give us a quadratic equation with these two solutions.

$$x = -6i \quad \text{or} \quad x = 6i \qquad \text{Begin with the solutions.}$$

$$x + 6i = 0 \quad \text{or} \quad x - 6i = 0 \qquad \text{Rewrite each equation so that the right side is equal to 0.}$$

$$(x + 6i)(x - 6i) = 0 \qquad \text{Write an equation with one side having these two expressions as factors.}$$

$$x^2 - 6i\,x + 6i\,x - 36i^2 = 0 \qquad \text{Multiply.}$$

$$x^2 + 36 = 0 \qquad \text{Simplify. Recall that } i^2 = -1.$$

A quadratic equation that has the solution set $\{-6i, 6i\}$ is $x^2 + 36 = 0$.

Quick Check 10

Find a quadratic equation in standard form, with integer coefficients, that has the solution set $\{-10i, 10i\}$.

BUILDING YOUR STUDY STRATEGY

Time Management, 1 Keeping Track The first step in achieving effective time management is keeping track of your time over a one-week period. Write down the times you spend on school, work, and leisure activities. This will give you a good idea of how much extra time you have to devote to studying, as well as how much time you devote to other activities.

Once you have made needed changes to your current schedule, try to set aside more time for studying math. You should be studying between two and four hours per week for each hour you spend in class. Try to schedule some time each day rather than cramming all of your studying into the weekend.

Exercises 10.1 MyMathLab

PRACTICE

WATCH

DOWNLOAD

READ

REVIEW

Vocabulary

1. The method of solving an equation by taking the square root of both sides is called solving by _____.

2. To solve an equation by extracting square roots, first isolate the expression that is _____.

3. The method of solving an equation by rewriting the variable expression as a square of a binomial is called solving by _____.

4. To solve the equation $x^2 + bx = c$ by completing the square, first add _____ to both sides of the equation.

Solve by factoring.

5. $x^2 - 3x - 10 = 0$

6. $x^2 + 9x + 14 = 0$

7. $x^2 + 7x = 0$

8. $x^2 - 4x = 0$

9. $3x^2 - 13x + 4 = 0$

10. $2x^2 - 21x + 27 = 0$

11. $x^2 - 2x = 24$

12. $x^2 - 45 = -4x$

13. $x^2 - 9 = 0$

14. $x^2 - 25 = 0$

15. $x^2 - 4x = 7x + 26$

16. $x^2 + 8x + 13 = 5x + 41$

Solve by extracting square roots.

17. $x^2 = 64$

18. $x^2 = 81$

19. $x^2 - 24 = 0$

20. $x^2 - 27 = 0$

21. $x^2 = -72$

22. $x^2 = -25$

23. $x^2 + 52 = 32$

24. $x^2 - 17 = 63$

25. $(x - 7)^2 = 18$

26. $(x + 3)^2 = 100$

27. $(x + 6)^2 = -49$

28. $(x - 1)^2 = -60$

29. $(x + 5)^2 + 33 = 15$

30. $(x + 3)^2 - 11 = 38$

31. $2(x - 9)^2 - 17 = 83$

32. $3(x + 1)^2 + 11 = 83$

33. $\left(x - \dfrac{2}{5} \right)^2 = \dfrac{49}{25}$

34. $\left(x + \dfrac{3}{4} \right)^2 = -\dfrac{25}{16}$

Fill in the missing term that makes the expression a perfect square trinomial. Factor the resulting expression.

35. $x^2 + 12x +$ ____

36. $x^2 - 2x +$ ____

37. $x^2 - 5x +$ ____

38. $x^2 + 13x +$ ____

39. $x^2 - 8x +$ ____

40. $x^2 + 18x +$ ____

41. $x^2 + \dfrac{3}{4}x +$ ____

42. $x^2 - \dfrac{7}{3}x +$ ____

For Exercises 43–50, approximate to the nearest tenth when necessary.

43. The area of a square is 81 square meters. Find the length of a side of the square.

44. The area of a square is 144 square feet. Find the length of a side of the square.

45. The area of a square is 128 square inches. Find the length of a side of the square.

46. The area of a square is 200 square centimeters. Find the length of a side of the square.

47. The area of a circle is 24 square inches. Find the radius of the circle.

48. The area of a circle is 60 square centimeters. Find the radius of the circle.

49. The area of a circle is 250 square meters. Find the radius of the circle.

50. The area of a circle is 48 square feet. Find the radius of the circle.

Solve by completing the square.

51. $x^2 - 2x - 63 = 0$ 52. $x^2 + 10x - 39 = 0$

53. $x^2 + 6x - 11 = 0$

54. $x^2 - 8x - 17 = 0$

55. $x^2 - 4x = -12$

56. $x^2 + 12x = -48$

57. $x^2 - 14x + 30 = 0$

58. $x^2 + 20x + 125 = 0$

59. $x^2 + 8x + 44 = 0$

60. $x^2 + 26x - 84 = 0$

61. $x^2 - 16 = -6x$

62. $x^2 - 48 = 2x$

63. $x^2 - 3x - 54 = 0$

64. $x^2 + 9x + 20 = 0$

65. $x^2 + 7x - 10 = 0$

66. $x^2 - 5x - 8 = 0$

67. $x^2 - 9x + 36 = 0$

68. $x^2 + 11x + 37 = 0$

69. $x^2 + \dfrac{5}{2}x + 1 = 0$

70. $x^2 - \dfrac{23}{6}x + \dfrac{7}{2} = 0$

71. $2x^2 - 2x - 144 = 0$

72. $4x^2 - 56x + 172 = 0$

73. $2x^2 - 9x + 4 = 0$

74. $3x^2 - 13x - 30 = 0$

75. $2x^2 - 6x + 5 = 0$

76. $4x^2 - 20x + 29 = 0$

Find a quadratic equation with integer coefficients that has the following solution set.

77. $\{-5, 2\}$

78. $\{-4, -3\}$

79. $\{6, 8\}$

80. $\{0, 5\}$

81. $\left\{-2, \dfrac{3}{4}\right\}$

82. $\left\{\dfrac{1}{2}, \dfrac{11}{4}\right\}$

83. $\{-3, 3\}$

84. $\{-6, 6\}$

85. $\{-5i, 5i\}$

86. $\{-i, i\}$

Mixed Practice, 87–114

Solve by any method (factoring, extracting square roots, or completing the square).

87. $x^2 + 13x + 30 = 0$

88. $x^2 + 12 = 0$

89. $x^2 + 6x - 17 = 0$

90. $(x - 5)^2 = 1$

91. $x^2 - 6x - 7 = 0$

92. $x^2 - 8x = 0$

93. $2x^2 - 15x + 25 = 0$

94. $x^2 - 6x = -10$

95. $(x - 4)^2 - 11 = 16$

96. $x^2 - 5x - 36 = 0$

97. $x^2 - 4x = 20$

98. $x^2 + 85 = 18x$

99. $x^2 - 5x - 6 = 0$

100. $(2x + 8)^2 - 5 = 11$

101. $x^2 - 8x + 19 = 0$

102. $x^2 - 20x + 91 = 0$

103. $3(x + 3)^2 + 13 = -11$

104. $x^2 - 9 = 0$

105. $x^2 + 3x + 9 = 0$

106. $x^2 - 2x + 50 = 0$

107. $x^2 + 16x = 0$

108. $6x^2 + 13x + 6 = 0$

109. $x(x + 5) - 7(x + 5) = 0$

110. $(4x - 3)(4x - 3) = 25$

111. $-16x^2 + 64x + 80 = 0$

112. $\left(x + \dfrac{b}{2a}\right)^2 = \dfrac{b^2 - 4ac}{4a^2}$, where a, b, and c are constants and $a \neq 0$.

113. $\dfrac{2}{3}x^2 + \dfrac{8}{3}x - \dfrac{10}{3} = 0$

114. $x^2 - 10x + 11 = 0$

Writing in Mathematics

Answer in complete sentences.

115. Explain why you use the symbol $\pm$ when taking the square root of each side of an equation.

10.2

The Quadratic Formula

The Quadratic Formula

Objective 1 Derive the quadratic formula. Completing the square to solve a quadratic equation can be tedious. As an alternative, in this section, we will develop and use the **quadratic formula**, which is a numerical formula that gives the solution(s) of *any* quadratic equation.

We derive the quadratic formula by solving the general equation $ax^2 + bx + c = 0$ (where a, b, and c are real numbers and $a \neq 0$) by completing the square. Recall that the coefficient of the second-degree term must be equal to 1; so the first step is to divide both sides of the equation $ax^2 + bx + c = 0$ by a.

$$ax^2 + bx + c = 0$$

$$x^2 + \frac{b}{a}x + \frac{c}{a} = 0 \qquad \text{Divide both sides by } a.$$

$$x^2 + \frac{b}{a}x = -\frac{c}{a} \qquad \text{Subtract the constant term } \frac{c}{a}.$$

$$x^2 + \frac{b}{a}x + \frac{b^2}{4a^2} = -\frac{c}{a} + \frac{b^2}{4a^2} \qquad \text{Half of } \frac{b}{a} \text{ is } \frac{b}{2a}. \left(\frac{b}{2a}\right)^2 = \frac{b^2}{4a^2}. \text{ Add } \frac{b^2}{4a^2} \text{ to both sides of the equation.}$$

$$x^2 + \frac{b}{a}x + \frac{b^2}{4a^2} = \frac{b^2 - 4ac}{4a^2} \qquad \text{Simplify the right side of the equation as a single fraction by rewriting } -\frac{c}{a} \text{ as } -\frac{4ac}{4a^2}.$$

$$\left(x + \frac{b}{2a}\right)^2 = \frac{b^2 - 4ac}{4a^2} \qquad \text{Factor the left side of the equation.}$$

$$\sqrt{\left(x + \frac{b}{2a}\right)^2} = \pm\sqrt{\frac{b^2 - 4ac}{4a^2}} \qquad \text{Take the square root of both sides.}$$

$$x + \frac{b}{2a} = \pm\frac{\sqrt{b^2 - 4ac}}{\sqrt{4a^2}} \qquad \text{Simplify the square root on the left side. Rewrite the right side as the quotient of two square roots.}$$

$$x + \frac{b}{2a} = \pm\frac{\sqrt{b^2 - 4ac}}{2a} \qquad \text{Simplify the square root in the denominator.}$$

$$x = -\frac{b}{2a} \pm \frac{\sqrt{b^2 - 4ac}}{2a} \qquad \text{Subtract } \frac{b}{2a}.$$

$$x = \frac{-b \pm \sqrt{b^2 - 4ac}}{2a} \qquad \text{Rewrite as a single fraction.}$$

The Quadratic Formula

For a general quadratic equation $ax^2 + bx + c = 0$ (where a, b, and c are real numbers and $a \neq 0$), the quadratic formula tells us that the solutions of this equation are given by

$$x = \frac{-b \pm \sqrt{b^2 - 4ac}}{2a}.$$

If we can identify the coefficients a, b, and c in a quadratic equation, we can find the solutions of the equation by substituting these values for a, b, and c in the quadratic formula.

Identifying the Coefficients to Be Used in the Quadratic Formula

Objective 2 Identify the coefficients a, b, and c of a quadratic equation.
The first step in using the quadratic formula is to identify the coefficients a, b, and c. We can do this only after the equation is in standard form: $ax^2 + bx + c = 0$.

EXAMPLE 1 For the quadratic equation, identify a, b, and c.

a) $x^2 - 6x + 8 = 0$

SOLUTION $a = 1$, $b = -6$, and $c = 8$. Be sure to include the negative sign when identifying coefficients that are negative.

b) $3x^2 - 5x = 7$

SOLUTION Before identifying the coefficients, we must convert this equation to standard form: $3x^2 - 5x - 7 = 0$. So $a = 3$, $b = -5$, and $c = -7$.

c) $x^2 + 8 = 0$

SOLUTION In this example, we do not see a first-degree term. In this case, $b = 0$. The coefficients that we do see tell us that $a = 1$ and $c = 8$.

Quick Check 1

For the given quadratic equation, identify a, b, and c.

a) $x^2 + 11x - 13 = 0$
b) $5x^2 - 11 = 9x$
c) $x^2 = 30$

Solving Quadratic Equations by the Quadratic Formula

Objective 3 Solve quadratic equations by using the quadratic formula.
Now we will solve several equations using the quadratic formula.

EXAMPLE 2 Solve $x^2 - 6x + 8 = 0$.

SOLUTION We can use the quadratic formula with $a = 1$, $b = -6$, and $c = 8$.

$$x = \frac{-b \pm \sqrt{b^2 - 4ac}}{2a}$$

$$x = \frac{6 \pm \sqrt{(-6)^2 - 4(1)(8)}}{2(1)}$$ Substitute 1 for a, -6 for b, and 8 for c. When you use the formula, think of the $-b$ in the numerator as the "opposite of b." The opposite of -6 is 6.

$$x = \frac{6 \pm \sqrt{36 - 32}}{2}$$ Simplify each term in the radicand.

$$x = \frac{6 \pm \sqrt{4}}{2}$$ Subtract.

$$x = \frac{6 \pm 2}{2}$$ Simplify the square root.

$\dfrac{6 + 2}{2} = 4$ and $\dfrac{6 - 2}{2} = 2$; so the solution set is $\{2, 4\}$.

Note that the equation in the previous example could have been solved more quickly by factoring $x^2 - 6x + 8$ to be $(x - 4)(x - 2)$ and then solving. Use factoring whenever possible, treating the quadratic formula as an alternative.

EXAMPLE 3 Solve $3x^2 + 8x = -3$.

SOLUTION   To solve this equation, we must rewrite the equation in standard form by collecting all terms on the left side of the equation. In other words, we will rewrite the equation as $3x^2 + 8x + 3 = 0$.

If an equation does not quickly factor, we should proceed directly to the quadratic formula rather than try to factor an expression that may not be factorable. Here $a = 3$, $b = 8$, and $c = 3$.

$$x = \frac{-8 \pm \sqrt{(8)^2 - 4(3)(3)}}{2(3)}$$ Substitute 3 for a, 8 for b, and 3 for c in the quadratic formula.

$$x = \frac{-8 \pm \sqrt{28}}{6}$$ Simplify the radicand.

$$x = \frac{-8 \pm 2\sqrt{7}}{6}$$ Simplify the square root.

$$x = \frac{\overset{1}{2}(-4 \pm \sqrt{7})}{\underset{3}{6}}$$ Factor the numerator and divide out the common factor.

$$x = \frac{-4 \pm \sqrt{7}}{3}$$ Simplify.

The solution set is $\left\{ \dfrac{-4 - \sqrt{7}}{3}, \dfrac{-4 + \sqrt{7}}{3} \right\}$. These solutions are approximately -2.22 and -0.45, respectively.

Using Your Calculator Here is the screen that shows how to approximate $\dfrac{-4 + \sqrt{7}}{3}$ and $\dfrac{-4 - \sqrt{7}}{3}$.

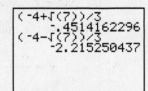

```
(-4+√(7))/3
          -.4514162296
(-4-√(7))/3
          -2.215250437
```

▶ Quick Check 2

Solve by using the quadratic formula.

a) $x^2 + 7x - 30 = 0$

b) $7x^2 + 21x = -9$

EXAMPLE 4 Solve $x^2 - 4x = -5$.

SOLUTION We begin by rewriting the equation in standard form: $x^2 - 4x + 5 = 0$. The quadratic expression in this equation does not factor, so we use the quadratic formula with $a = 1$, $b = -4$, and $c = 5$.

$$x = \frac{4 \pm \sqrt{(-4)^2 - 4(1)(5)}}{2(1)}$$ Substitute 1 for a, -4 for b, and 5 for c in the quadratic formula.

$$x = \frac{4 \pm \sqrt{-4}}{2}$$ Simplify the radicand.

$$x = \frac{4 \pm 2i}{2}$$ Simplify the square root. Be sure to include i, as you are taking the square root of a negative number.

$$x = \frac{\overset{1}{\cancel{2}}(2 \pm i)}{\underset{1}{\cancel{2}}}$$ Factor the numerator and divide out the common factor.

$$x = 2 \pm i$$ Simplify.

Quick Check 3

Solve $x^2 - 7x = -19$.

The solution set is $\{2 - i, 2 + i\}$.

If an equation has coefficients that are fractions, multiply each side of the equation by the LCD to clear the equation of fractions. If we can solve the equation by factoring, it will be easier to factor without the fractions. If we cannot solve by factoring, the quadratic formula will be easier to simplify using integers rather than fractions.

EXAMPLE 5 Solve $\frac{1}{2}x^2 - x + \frac{1}{3} = 0$.

SOLUTION The first step is to clear the fractions by multiplying each side of the equation by the LCD, which in this example is 6.

$$6 \cdot \left(\frac{1}{2}x^2 - x + \frac{1}{3}\right) = 6 \cdot 0$$ Multiply both sides of the equation by the LCD.

$$3x^2 - 6x + 2 = 0$$ Distribute and simplify.

Now use the quadratic formula with $a = 3$, $b = -6$, and $c = 2$.

$$x = \frac{6 \pm \sqrt{(-6)^2 - 4(3)(2)}}{2(3)}$$ Substitute 3 for a, -6 for b, and 2 for c in the quadratic formula.

$$x = \frac{6 \pm \sqrt{12}}{6}$$ Simplify the radicand.

$$x = \frac{6 \pm 2\sqrt{3}}{6}$$ Simplify the square root.

$$x = \frac{\overset{1}{\cancel{2}}(3 \pm \sqrt{3})}{\underset{3}{\cancel{6}}}$$ Factor the numerator and divide out common factors.

Quick Check 4

Solve $\frac{1}{4}x^2 + \frac{1}{3}x + \frac{1}{2} = 0$.

$$x = \frac{3 \pm \sqrt{3}}{3}$$ Simplify.

The solution set is $\left\{\dfrac{3 - \sqrt{3}}{3}, \dfrac{3 + \sqrt{3}}{3}\right\}$. These solutions are approximately 0.42 and 1.58, respectively.

In addition to clearing any fractions, make sure the coefficient a of the second-degree term is positive. If this term is negative, you can collect all terms on the other side of the equation or multiply each side of the equation by negative 1.

EXAMPLE 6 Solve $-2x^2 + 11x + 6 = 0$.

SOLUTION We begin by rewriting the equation so that a is positive because factoring a quadratic expression is more convenient when the leading coefficient is positive. Also, we may find that simplifying the quadratic formula is easier when the leading coefficient a is positive.

$0 = 2x^2 - 11x - 6$ Collect all terms on the right side of the equation.

When the leading coefficient is not 1, factoring often is difficult or time-consuming—if the expression is factorable at all. In such a situation, go directly to the quadratic formula. In this example, we can use the quadratic formula with $a = 2$, $b = -11$, and $c = -6$.

$$x = \frac{11 \pm \sqrt{(-11)^2 - 4(2)(-6)}}{2(2)}$$ Substitute 2 for a, -11 for b, and -6 for c in the quadratic formula.

$$x = \frac{11 \pm \sqrt{169}}{4}$$ Simplify the radicand.

$$x = \frac{11 \pm 13}{4}$$ Simplify the square root.

$\frac{11 + 13}{4} = 6$ and $\frac{11 - 13}{4} = -\frac{1}{2}$, so the solution set is $\left\{-\frac{1}{2}, 6\right\}$.

▶ **Quick Check 5**

Solve $-6x^2 - 7x + 20 = 0$.

Although the quadratic formula can be used to solve *any* quadratic equation, it does not always provide the most efficient way to solve a particular equation. We should check to see whether factoring or extracting square roots can be used before we use the quadratic formula.

General Strategy for Solving Quadratic Equations

- If the equation has one squared term that contains a variable and all other terms are constant terms, solve the equation by extracting square roots.
  Examples: $x^2 - 52 = 0$ $(x - 7)^2 - 15 = 33$
- If the equation is of the form $x^2 + bx + c = 0$ or $ax^2 + bx + c = 0$ and you can quickly factor the trinomial, solve the equation by factoring.
  Examples: $x^2 - 7x + 12 = 0$ $2x^2 - 5x + 2 = 0$
- If you have an equation of the form $x^2 + bx + c = 0$ in which the trinomial cannot be factored and the coefficient b is even, consider solving the equation by completing the square. If b is odd, as in $x^2 + 5x + 7 = 0$, or if the leading coefficient is not equal to 1, as in $2x^2 - 9x + 11 = 0$, using the quadratic formula is often more efficient than completing the square.
  Examples: $x^2 - 4x + 8 = 0$ $x^2 + 16x - 3 = 0$
- In all other cases, use the quadratic formula.

Using the Discriminant to Determine the Number and Type of Solutions of a Quadratic Equation

Objective 4 Use the discriminant to determine the number and type of solutions of a quadratic equation. In the quadratic formula, the expression $b^2 - 4ac$ is called the **discriminant**. The discriminant can provide some information about the solutions. If the discriminant is negative ($b^2 - 4ac < 0$), the equation has two nonreal complex solutions. This is because we take the square root of a negative number in the quadratic formula. If the discriminant is zero, $b^2 - 4ac = 0$, the equation has one real solution. In this case, the quadratic formula simplifies to be $x = \dfrac{-b \pm \sqrt{0}}{2a}$, or simply $x = \dfrac{-b}{2a}$. If the discriminant is positive, $b^2 - 4ac > 0$, the equation has two real solutions. The square root of a positive discriminant is a real number; so the quadratic formula produces two real solutions. The following chart summarizes what the discriminant tells us about the number and type of solutions of an equation:

Solutions of a Quadratic Equation Based on the Discriminant

$b^2 - 4ac$	Number and Type of Solutions
Negative	Two Nonreal Complex Solutions
Zero	One Real Solution
Positive	Two Real Solutions

When working on an applied problem, we need to know if the corresponding equation has no real solutions. (It also will be important to know this when we are graphing quadratic equations, which is covered later in this chapter.)

EXAMPLE 7 For the quadratic equation, use the discriminant to determine the number and type of solutions.

a) $x^2 - 6x - 16 = 0$

SOLUTION

$(-6)^2 - 4(1)(-16) = 100$ Substitute 1 for a, -6 for b, and -16 for c.

Because the discriminant is positive, this equation has two real solutions.

b) $x^2 + 36 = 0$

SOLUTION

$(0)^2 - 4(1)(36) = -144$ Substitute 1 for a, 0 for b, and 36 for c.

The discriminant is negative. This equation has two nonreal complex solutions.

c) $x^2 + 10x + 25 = 0$

SOLUTION

$(10)^2 - 4(1)(25) = 0$ Substitute 1 for a, 10 for b, and 25 for c.

Because the discriminant equals 0, this equation has one real solution.

Quick Check 6

For each given quadratic equation, use the discriminant to determine the number and type of solutions.

a) $x^2 + 18x - 63 = 0$
b) $x^2 + 5x + 42 = 0$
c) $x^2 - 20x + 100 = 0$

Using the Discriminant to Determine Whether a Quadratic Expression Is Factorable

Objective 5 Use the discriminant to determine whether a quadratic expression is factorable. The discriminant also can be used to tell us whether a quadratic expression is factorable. If the discriminant is equal to 0 or a positive number that is a perfect square (1, 4, 9, and so on), the expression is factorable.

EXAMPLE 8 For the quadratic expression, use the discriminant to determine whether the expression can be factored.

a) $x^2 - 6x - 27$

SOLUTION

$$(-6)^2 - 4(1)(-27) = 144 \quad \text{Substitute 1 for } a, -6 \text{ for } b, \text{ and } -27 \text{ for } c.$$

The discriminant is a perfect square ($\sqrt{144} = 12$), so the expression can be factored.

$$x^2 - 6x - 27 = (x - 9)(x + 3)$$

b) $2x^2 + 7x + 4$

SOLUTION

$$(7)^2 - 4(2)(4) = 17 \quad \text{Substitute 2 for } a, 7 \text{ for } b, \text{ and 4 for } c.$$

The discriminant is not a perfect square, so the expression is not factorable.

▶ Quick Check 7

For each given quadratic expression, use the discriminant to determine whether the expression can be factored.

a) $x^2 + 14x + 12$
b) $5x^2 - 36x - 32$

Projectile Motion Problems

Objective 6 Solve projectile motion problems. An application that leads to a quadratic equation involves the height, in feet, of an object propelled into the air after t seconds. Recall that the height, in feet, of a projectile after t seconds can be found by the function $h(t) = -16t^2 + v_0 t + s$, where v_0 is the initial velocity of the projectile and s is the initial height.

Height of a Projectile

$$h(t) = -16t^2 + v_0 t + s$$
t: Time (seconds)
v_0: Initial velocity (feet/second)
s: Initial height (feet)

EXAMPLE 9 A rock is thrown at a speed of 48 feet/second from ground level. How long will it take until the rock lands on the ground?

SOLUTION The initial velocity of the rock is 48 feet per second, so $v_0 = 48$. Because the rock is thrown from ground level, the initial height is 0 feet. The function for the height of the rock after t seconds is $h(t) = -16t^2 + 48t$.

The rock's height when it lands on the ground is 0 feet, so we set the function equal to 0 and solve for the time t in seconds.

$-16t^2 + 48t = 0$	Set the function equal to 0.
$0 = 16t^2 - 48t$	Collect all terms on the right side of the equation so that the leading coefficient is positive.
$0 = 16t(t - 3)$	Factor out the GCF (16t).
$16t = 0$ or $t - 3 = 0$	Set each variable factor equal to 0.
$t = 0$ or $t = 3$	Solve each equation.

The time of 0 seconds corresponds to the precise moment the rock was thrown and does not represent the time required to land on the ground. The solution is 3 seconds.

▶ Quick Check 8

A rock is thrown upward at an initial velocity of 80 feet per second from ground level. After how many seconds will the rock land on the ground?

EXAMPLE 10 A golf ball is launched by a slingshot at an initial velocity of 88 feet per second from a platform that is 95 feet high. When will the golf ball be at a height of 175 feet? (Round to the nearest hundredth of a second.)

SOLUTION   The initial velocity of the golf ball is 88 feet per second, so $v_0 = 88$. Because the golf ball was launched from a platform 95 feet high, the initial height $s = 95$. The function for the height of the golf ball after t seconds is $h(t) = -16t^2 + 88t + 95$.

To find when the golf ball is at a height of 175 feet, we set the function equal to 175 and solve for the time t in seconds.

$-16t^2 + 88t + 95 = 175$	Set the function equal to 175.
$0 = 16t^2 - 88t + 80$	Collect all terms on the right side of the equation.
$0 = 8(2t^2 - 11t + 10)$	Factor out the GCF (8).
$0 = 2t^2 - 11t + 10$	Divide both sides by 8.

This trinomial does not factor, so we will use the quadratic formula with $a = 2$, $b = -11$, and $c = 10$ to solve the equation.

$$t = \frac{11 \pm \sqrt{(-11)^2 - 4(2)(10)}}{2(2)} \quad \text{Substitute 2 for } a, -11 \text{ for } b, \text{ and 10 for } c.$$

$$t = \frac{11 \pm \sqrt{41}}{4} \quad \text{Simplify the radicand and the denominator.}$$

We use a calculator to approximate these solutions.

$$\frac{11 + \sqrt{41}}{4} \approx 4.35 \qquad \frac{11 - \sqrt{41}}{4} \approx 1.15$$

The golf ball is at a height of 175 feet after approximately 1.15 seconds and again after approximately 4.35 seconds.

▶ Quick Check 9

A projectile is launched at an initial velocity of 36 feet per second from the top of a building 40 feet high. When will the projectile be at a height of 50 feet? (Round to the nearest hundredth of a second.)

EXAMPLE 11 If a projectile is launched upward at a speed of 96 feet per second from a platform 7 feet above the ground, will it ever reach a height of 160 feet? If so, when will it be at this height?

SOLUTION The function for the height of the projectile after t seconds is $h(t) = -16t^2 + 96t + 7$. We begin by setting the function equal to 160 and solving for t.

$$-16t^2 + 96t + 7 = 160 \quad \text{Set the function equal to 160.}$$
$$0 = 16t^2 - 96t + 153 \quad \text{Collect all terms on the right side.}$$

The trinomial does not have any common factors other than 1, so we will use the quadratic formula with $a = 16$, $b = -96$, and $c = 153$ to solve this equation.

$$t = \frac{96 \pm \sqrt{(-96)^2 - 4(16)(153)}}{2(16)} \quad \text{Substitute 16 for } a, -96 \text{ for } b, \text{ and 153 for } c.$$

$$t = \frac{96 \pm \sqrt{-576}}{32} \quad \text{Simplify the radicand and the denominator.}$$

Because the discriminant is negative, this equation has no real-number solutions. The projectile does not reach a height of 160 feet.

A WORD OF CAUTION When the quadratic formula is used to solve an applied problem, a negative discriminant indicates that there are no real solutions to this problem.

Quick Check 10

A projectile is launched at an initial velocity of 36 feet per second from the top of a building 40 feet high. Will the projectile ever reach a height of 80 feet? If so, when will it be at this height?

BUILDING YOUR STUDY STRATEGY

Time Management 2, Study after Class The best time to study new material is as soon as possible after class. Look for a block of time close to your class period. You can study the new material on campus if necessary. Try to study each day at the same time. Begin each study session by reworking your notes; then move on to attempting the homework exercises.

If possible, establish a second study period during the day to use for review purposes. This second study period should take place later in the day and can be used to review homework or notes or to read ahead for the next class period.

Exercises 10.2

PRACTICE   WATCH   DOWNLOAD   READ   REVIEW

Vocabulary

1. The _____ formula is a formula for calculating the solutions of a quadratic equation.

2. In the quadratic formula, the expression $b^2 - 4ac$ is called the _____.

3. If the discriminant is negative, the quadratic equation has _____ real solutions.

4. If the discriminant is zero, the quadratic equation has _____ unique real solution.

5. If the discriminant is positive, the quadratic equation has _____ real solutions.

6. If the discriminant is 0 or a positive perfect square, the quadratic expression in the equation is _____.

Solve by using the quadratic formula.

7. $x^2 - 5x - 36 = 0$

8. $x^2 + 4x - 45 = 0$

9. $x^2 - 4x + 2 = 0$

10. $x^2 + 10x + 13 = 0$

11. $x^2 + x + 7 = 0$

12. $x^2 - 3x + 18 = 0$

13. $x^2 + 12 = 0$

14. $x^2 + 12x = 0$

15. $x^2 + 7x + 11 = 0$

16. $x^2 + 8x + 21 = 0$

17. $x^2 - 3x - 88 = 0$

$10 = 0$

$12 = 0$

$8 = 0$

21. $x^2 - 4x = -32$

22. $x^2 + 6x = 8$

23. $x^2 - 3x = 9$

24. $x^2 = 7x$

25. $-4 = 19x - 5x^2$

26. $4x - x^2 = 3$

27. $x^2 - 6x + 9 = 0$

28. $x^2 + 10x + 25 = 0$

29. $x^2 - 24 = 0$

30. $x^2 + 49 = 0$

31. $x(x - 4) + 3x = 20$

32. $(2x + 1)(x - 3) = -9$

33. $x^2 - \frac{1}{5}x + \frac{3}{4} = 0$

34. $\frac{2}{3}x^2 - \frac{3}{5}x + \frac{1}{4} = 0$

35. $-x^2 + 7x - 12 = 0$

36. $-2x^2 + 15x = 8$

For each of the following quadratic equations, use the discriminant to determine the number and type of solutions.

37. $x^2 + 12x - 30 = 0$

38. $x^2 - 9x + 21 = 0$

39. $2x^2 - 3x + 5 = 0$

40. $25x^2 - 20x + 4 = 0$

41. $x^2 + \frac{2}{5}x + \frac{5}{6} = 0$

42. $x^2 - 5x - 9 = 0$

43. $9x^2 - 12x + 4 = 0$

44. $x^2 - \frac{2}{3}x + \frac{1}{9} = 0$

Use the discriminant to determine whether each of the given quadratic expressions is factorable. If the expression can be factored, write factorable. Otherwise, write prime.

45. $x^2 + 12x - 35$

46. $x^2 + 30x + 221$

47. $x^2 + 52x + 667$

48. $x^2 - 88x + 1886$

49. $35x^2 - 116x + 65$

50. $2x^2 + 13x - 25$

51. $5x^2 - 16x - 18$

52. $32x^2 + 76x - 33$

Mixed Practice, 53–88

Solve each of the following quadratic equations using the most efficient technique (factoring, extracting square roots, completing the square, or using the quadratic formula).

53. $x^2 - 5x - 15 = 0$

54. $x^2 - 68 = 0$

55. $3x^2 + 2x - 1 = 0$

56. $x^2 - 20x + 91 = 0$

57. $(5x - 4)^2 = 36$

58. $7x(8x - 3) + 4(8x - 3) = 0$

59. $2x^2 + 8x = -9$

60. $x^2 + 179x = 0$

61. $x^2 + 324 = 0$

62. $x^2 + \frac{3}{5}x - \frac{1}{12} = 0$

63. $6x^2 - 29x + 28 = 0$

64. $x^2 + 8x - 9 = 0$

65. $3(2x + 1)^2 - 7 = 23$

66. $5x^2 + 11x - 9 = 0$

67. $x^2 - 9x - 21 = 0$

68. $4x^2 - 25 = 0$

69. $16x^2 - 24x + 9 = 0$

70. $x^2 - 15x + 50 = 0$

71. $x^2 + x + 20 = 0$

72. $x^2 + 13x + 36 = 0$

73. $x^2 - 4x - 2 = 0$

74. $3x^2 - 2x - 16 = 0$

75. $x^2 - 6x + 10 = 0$

76. $(x - 8)^2 + 13 = 134$

77. $\frac{3}{4}x^2 + \frac{2}{3}x - \frac{1}{2} = 0$

78. $x^2 + 3x - 18 = 0$

79. $2x(3x + 7) - 5(3x + 7) = 0$

80. $(2x + 3)^2 - 10 = 71$

81. $2(2x - 9)^2 + 13 = 77$

82. $x^2 + x - 72 = 0$

83. $x^2 + 3x - 4 = 0$

84. $x^2 + 10x + 21 = 0$

85. $x^2 - 10x + 18 = 0$

86. $x^2 + 2x + 4 = 0$

87. $x^2 - 16x + 63 = 0$

88. $4x^2 - 12x - 11 = 0$

For Exercises 89–102, use the function $h(t) = -16t^2 + v_0 t + s.$

89. An object is launched upward from the ground at an initial speed of 128 feet per second. How long will it take until the object lands on the ground?

90. An object is launched upward at an initial speed of 48 feet per second from a platform 160 feet above the ground. How long will it take until it lands on the ground?

91. Ubaldo Jimenez is standing on a cliff above a beach. He throws a rock upward at a speed of 70 feet per second from a height 90 feet above the beach. How long will it take until the rock lands on the beach? Round to the nearest tenth of a second.

92. Jan is standing on the roof of a building. She launches a water balloon upward at an initial speed of 44 feet per second from a height of 20 feet. How long will it take until the balloon lands on the ground? Round to the nearest tenth of a second.

93. An object is launched upward at an initial velocity of 80 feet per second from ground level. At what time(s) is the object 64 feet above the ground?

94. An object is launched upward at an initial speed of 112 feet per second from ground level. At what time(s) is the object 160 feet above the ground?

95. An object is launched upward at an initial velocity of 120 feet per second from the top of a building 50 feet high. At what time(s) is the object 195 feet above the ground? Round to the nearest tenth of a second.

96. An object is launched upward at an initial velocity 116 feet per second from a cliff 300 feet above beach. At what time(s) is the object 350 feet above the ground? Round to the nearest tenth of a second.

A rock is thrown upward at the given velocity from a height of 5 feet above the ground. Does the rock reach a height of 30 feet above the ground? If it does, state how long the rock takes to reach the height of 30 feet. (Round to the nearest tenth of a second.) If it does not, explain.

97. 16 feet per second

98. 48 feet per second

99. 42 feet per second

100. 30 feet per second

101. A projectile is launched straight up from the ground. If it takes 6 seconds for the projectile to land on the ground, find the original velocity of the projectile.

102. A projectile is launched straight up from the ground. If it takes 7.5 seconds for the projectile to land on the ground, find the original velocity of the projectile.

Writing in Mathematics

Answer in complete sentences.

103. Explain how the discriminant tells whether an equation has two real solutions, one real solution, or two nonreal complex solutions.

10.3

Equations That Are Quadratic in Form

OBJECTIVES

1. Solve equations by making a *u*-substitution.
2. Solve radical equations.
3. Solve rational equations.
4. Solve work-rate problems.

In this section, we will learn how to solve several types of equations that are **quadratic in form**. For example, $x^4 - 13x^2 + 36 = 0$ is not a quadratic equation, but if we rewrite it as $(x^2)^2 - 13(x^2) + 36 = 0$, we can see that it looks like a quadratic equation.

Solving Equations by Making a u-Substitution

Objective 1 Solve equations by making a u-substitution. One approach to solving equations that are quadratic in form is to use a **u-substitution**. We substitute the variable u for an expression such as x^2 so that the resulting equation is a quadratic equation in u. In other words, the equation can be rewritten in the form $au^2 + bu + c = 0$. We can then solve this quadratic equation applying the methods presented in Sections 10.1 and 10.2 (factoring, extracting square roots, completing the square, and using the quadratic formula). After solving this equation for u, we replace u with the expression it previously substituted for and then solve the resulting equations for the original variable.

EXAMPLE 1 Solve $x^4 - 13x^2 + 36 = 0$.

SOLUTION   Let $u = x^2$. We can then replace x^2 in the original equation with u, and we can replace x^4 with u^2. The resulting equation will be $u^2 - 13u + 36 = 0$, which is quadratic.

$$x^4 - 13x^2 + 36 = 0$$
$$u^2 - 13u + 36 = 0 \qquad \text{Substitute } u \text{ for } x^2.$$
$$(u - 4)(u - 9) = 0 \qquad \text{Factor.}$$
$$u - 4 = 0 \quad \text{or} \quad u - 9 = 0 \qquad \text{Set each factor equal to 0.}$$
$$u = 4 \quad \text{or} \quad u = 9 \qquad \text{Solve.}$$

Now we replace u with x^2 and solve the resulting equations for x.

$$u = 4 \qquad \text{or} \quad u = 9$$
$$x^2 = 4 \qquad \text{or} \quad x^2 = 9 \qquad \text{Substitute } x^2 \text{ for } u.$$
$$\sqrt{x^2} = \pm\sqrt{4} \quad \text{or} \quad \sqrt{x^2} = \pm\sqrt{9} \qquad \text{Solve by taking the square roots of both sides of the equation.}$$
$$x = \pm 2 \qquad \text{or} \quad x = \pm 3 \qquad \text{Simplify the square root.}$$

The solution set is $\{-2, 2, -3, 3\}$.

Quick Check 1

Solve $x^4 - x^2 - 12 = 0$.

A WORD OF CAUTION When solving an equation by using a u-substitution, *do not stop after solving for u.* You must solve for the variable in the original equation.

The challenge is determining when a u-substitution will be helpful and determining what to let u represent. Look for an equation in which the variable part of the first term is the square of the variable part of a second term; in other words, its exponent is twice the exponent of the second term. Then let u represent the variable part with the smaller exponent.

EXAMPLE 2 Find the u-substitution that will convert the equation to a quadratic equation.

a) $x - 7\sqrt{x} - 30 = 0$

SOLUTION   Let $u = \sqrt{x}$. This allows us to replace $\sqrt{x}$ with u and x with u^2, because $u^2 = (\sqrt{x})^2 = x$. The resulting equation is $u^2 - 7u - 30 = 0$, which is quadratic.

b) $x^{2/3} + 9x^{1/3} + 8 = 0$

SOLUTION   Let $u = x^{1/3}$. We can then replace $x^{2/3}$ with u^2, because $(x^{1/3})^2 = x^{2/3}$. The resulting equation is $u^2 + 9u + 8 = 0$.

c) $(x^2 + 6x)^2 + 13(x^2 + 6x) + 40 = 0$

SOLUTION   Let $u = x^2 + 6x$ as this is the expression that is being squared. The resulting equation is $u^2 + 13u + 40 = 0$.

▶ Quick Check 2

Find the u-substitution that will convert the given equation to a quadratic equation.

a) $x + 11\sqrt{x} - 26 = 0$
b) $2x^{2/3} - 17x^{1/3} + 8 = 0$
c) $(x^2 - 4x)^2 - 9(x^2 - 4x) - 36 = 0$

EXAMPLE 3   Solve $x + 3\sqrt{x} - 10 = 0$.

SOLUTION   Let $u = \sqrt{x}$. The resulting equation is $u^2 + 3u - 10 = 0$, which is a quadratic equation solvable by factoring. If we could not use factoring, we would have to use the quadratic formula to solve for u.

$$x + 3\sqrt{x} - 10 = 0$$
$$u^2 + 3u - 10 = 0 \qquad \text{Replace } \sqrt{x} \text{ with } u.$$
$$(u - 2)(u + 5) = 0 \qquad \text{Factor.}$$
$$u - 2 = 0 \quad \text{or} \quad u + 5 = 0 \qquad \text{Set each factor equal to 0.}$$
$$u = 2 \quad \text{or} \quad u = -5 \qquad \text{Solve for } u.$$
$$\sqrt{x} = 2 \quad \text{or} \quad \sqrt{x} = -5 \qquad \text{Replace } u \text{ with } \sqrt{x}.$$
$$(\sqrt{x})^2 = 2^2 \quad \text{or} \quad (\sqrt{x})^2 = (-5)^2 \qquad \text{Square both sides of the equation.}$$
$$x = 4 \quad \text{or} \quad x = 25 \qquad \text{Simplify.}$$

Recall that any time we square each side of an equation, we must check for extraneous roots.

Check $(x = 25)$

$$(25) + 3\sqrt{(25)} - 10 = 0 \qquad \text{Substitute 25 for } x \text{ in the original equation.}$$
$$25 + 3 \cdot 5 - 10 = 0 \qquad \text{Simplify the square root.}$$
$$30 = 0 \qquad \text{Simplify.}$$

So $x = 25$ is not a solution of the equation. We could have seen this before squaring each side of the equation $\sqrt{x} = -5$. The square root of x cannot be negative, so the equation $\sqrt{x} = -5$ cannot have a solution. The check whether $x = 4$ is actually a solution is left to the reader. The solution set is $\{4\}$.

A WORD OF CAUTION   Whenever we square both sides of an equation, such as in the previous example, we must check the solutions for extraneous roots.

EXAMPLE 4   Solve $x^{2/3} - 6x^{1/3} - 7 = 0$.

SOLUTION   Let $u = x^{1/3}$. The resulting equation is $u^2 - 6u - 7 = 0$, which can be solved by factoring.

$$x^{2/3} - 6x^{1/3} - 7 = 0$$
$$u^2 - 6u - 7 = 0 \qquad \text{Replace } x^{1/3} \text{ with } u.$$
$$(u - 7)(u + 1) = 0 \qquad \text{Factor.}$$

$$u - 7 = 0 \quad \text{or} \quad u + 1 = 0 \qquad \text{Set each factor equal to 0.}$$
$$u = 7 \quad \text{or} \quad u = -1 \qquad \text{Solve for } u.$$
$$x^{1/3} = 7 \quad \text{or} \quad x^{1/3} = -1 \qquad \text{Replace } u \text{ with } x^{1/3}.$$
$$(x^{1/3})^3 = 7^3 \quad \text{or} \quad (x^{1/3})^3 = (-1)^3 \qquad \text{Raise each side to the third power.}$$
$$x = 343 \quad \text{or} \quad x = -1 \qquad \text{Simplify.}$$

The solution set is $\{-1, 343\}$.

Quick Check 3

Solve.

a) $x - 6x^{1/2} + 5 = 0$
b) $x^{2/3} - 4x^{1/3} + 3 = 0$

Solving Radical Equations

Objective 2 Solve radical equations. Some equations that contain square roots cannot be solved by a u-substitution. When this happens, we will use the techniques developed in Section 9.5. We begin by isolating the radical; then we proceed to square both sides of the equation. This can lead to an equation that is quadratic.

EXAMPLE 5 Solve $\sqrt{x + 7} + 5 = x$.

SOLUTION We begin by isolating the radical so that we may square each side of the equation.

$$\sqrt{x + 7} + 5 = x$$
$$\sqrt{x + 7} = x - 5 \qquad \text{Subtract 5 to isolate the radical.}$$
$$(\sqrt{x + 7})^2 = (x - 5)^2 \qquad \text{Square both sides.}$$
$$x + 7 = (x - 5)(x - 5) \qquad \text{Square the binomial by multiplying it by itself.}$$
$$x + 7 = x^2 - 10x + 25 \qquad \text{Multiply.}$$
$$0 = x^2 - 11x + 18 \qquad \text{Subtract } x \text{ and 7 to collect all terms on the right side of the equation.}$$
$$0 = (x - 2)(x - 9) \qquad \text{Factor.}$$
$$x - 2 = 0 \quad \text{or} \quad x - 9 = 0 \qquad \text{Set each factor equal to 0.}$$
$$x = 2 \quad \text{or} \quad x = 9 \qquad \text{Solve.}$$

Because we have squared each side of the equation, we must check for extraneous roots.

$x = 2$	$x = 9$
$\sqrt{(2) + 7} + 5 = (2)$	$\sqrt{(9) + 7} + 5 = (9)$
$\sqrt{9} + 5 = 2$	$\sqrt{16} + 5 = 9$
$3 + 5 = 2$	$4 + 5 = 9$
$8 = 2$	$9 = 9$
False	True

The solution $x = 2$ is an extraneous solution and must be omitted. The solution set is $\{9\}$.

Quick Check 4

Solve $x + 7 = \sqrt{x + 9}$.

Solving Rational Equations

Objective 3 Solve rational equations. Solving rational equations, which were covered in Chapter 7, often requires that we solve a quadratic equation. We begin to solve a rational equation by finding the LCD and multiplying each side of the equation by it to clear the equation of fractions. The resulting equation could be quadratic, as demonstrated in the next example. Once we solve the resulting equation, any solution that causes a denominator in the original equation to be equal to 0 must be omitted.

EXAMPLE 6 Solve $\dfrac{x}{x-4} + \dfrac{2}{x+3} = \dfrac{6}{x^2-x-12}$.

SOLUTION   We begin by factoring the denominators to find the LCD. The LCD is $(x-4)(x+3)$, and solutions of $x=4$ and $x=-3$ must be omitted because either would result in a denominator of 0.

$$\frac{x}{x-4} + \frac{2}{x+3} = \frac{6}{x^2-x-12}$$

$$\frac{x}{x-4} + \frac{2}{x+3} = \frac{6}{(x-4)(x+3)} \qquad \text{The LCD is } (x-4)(x+3).$$

$$(x-4)(x+3) \cdot \left(\frac{x}{x-4} + \frac{2}{x+3} \right) = (x-4)(x+3) \cdot \frac{6}{(x-4)(x+3)}$$

Multiply by the LCD.

$$\overset{1}{\cancel{(x-4)}}(x+3) \cdot \frac{x}{\underset{1}{\cancel{(x-4)}}} + (x-4)\overset{1}{\cancel{(x+3)}} \cdot \frac{2}{\underset{1}{\cancel{(x+3)}}}$$

$$= \overset{1}{\cancel{(x-4)}}\,\overset{1}{\cancel{(x+3)}} \cdot \frac{6}{\underset{1}{\cancel{(x-4)}}\,\underset{1}{\cancel{(x+3)}}} \qquad \begin{array}{l} \text{Distribute and divide} \\ \text{out common factors.} \end{array}$$

$$\begin{array}{ll} x(x+3) + 2(x-4) = 6 & \text{Multiply remaining factors.} \\ x^2 + 3x + 2x - 8 = 6 & \text{Multiply.} \\ x^2 + 5x - 8 = 6 & \text{Combine like terms.} \\ x^2 + 5x - 14 = 0 & \begin{array}{l}\text{Collect all terms on the} \\ \text{left side by subtracting 6.}\end{array} \\ (x+7)(x-2) = 0 & \text{Factor.} \\ x+7 = 0 \quad \text{or} \quad x-2 = 0 & \text{Set each factor equal to 0.} \\ x = -7 \quad \text{or} \quad x = 2 & \text{Solve.} \end{array}$$

Because neither solution causes a denominator to equal 0, we do not need to omit either solution. The solution set is $\{-7, 2\}$.

Quick Check 5

Solve $\dfrac{2}{x+1} + \dfrac{1}{x-1} = 1$.

Solving Work-Rate Problems

Objective 4 Solve work-rate problems. The last example of the section is a work-rate problem. Work-rate problems involve rational equations and were introduced in Chapter 7.

EXAMPLE 7   A water tower has two drainpipes attached to it. Alone, the smaller pipe takes 15 minutes longer than the larger pipe to empty the tower. If both drainpipes are used together, the tower can be drained in 30 minutes. How long does it take the small pipe alone to drain the tower? (Round your answer to the nearest tenth of a minute.)

SOLUTION   If we let t represent the amount of time it takes for the larger pipe to drain the tower, then the time required for the small pipe to drain the tower can be represented by $t + 15$. Recall that the work-rate is the reciprocal of the time required to complete the entire job. So the work-rate for the smaller pipe is $\frac{1}{t+15}$ and the work-rate for the large pipe is $\frac{1}{t}$. To determine the portion of the job completed by each pipe when both are working, we multiply the work-rate for each pipe by the amount of time it takes for the two pipes together to drain the tower. Here is a table showing the important information.

Pipe	Time to Complete the Job Alone	Work-Rate	Time Working	Portion of the Job Completed
Smaller	$t + 15$ minutes	$\dfrac{1}{t + 15}$	30	$\dfrac{30}{t + 15}$
Larger	t minutes	$\dfrac{1}{t}$	30	$\dfrac{30}{t}$

After adding the portion of the tower drained by the smaller pipe in 30 minutes to the portion of the tower drained by the larger pipe, the sum will equal 1, which represents finishing the entire job. The equation is $\frac{30}{t+15} + \frac{30}{t} = 1$.

$$\frac{30}{t + 15} + \frac{30}{t} = 1 \qquad \text{The LCD is } t(t + 15).$$

$$t(t + 15) \cdot \left(\frac{30}{t + 15} + \frac{30}{t} \right) = t(t + 15) \cdot 1 \qquad \text{Multiply both sides by the LCD}$$

$$t(t + 15) \cdot \frac{30}{(t+15)} + t(t + 15) \cdot \frac{30}{t} = t(t + 15) \cdot 1 \qquad \text{Distribute and divide out common factors.}$$

$$30t + 30(t + 15) = t(t + 15) \qquad \text{Multiply remaining factors.}$$

$$30t + 30t + 450 = t^2 + 15t \qquad \text{Multiply. The resulting equation is quadratic.}$$

$$60t + 450 = t^2 + 15t \qquad \text{Combine like terms.}$$

$$0 = t^2 - 45t - 450 \qquad \text{Collect all terms on the right side of the equation.}$$

The quadratic expression does not factor, so we will use the quadratic formula.

$$t = \frac{45 \pm \sqrt{(-45)^2 - 4(1)(-450)}}{2(1)} \qquad \text{Substitute 1 for } a, -45 \text{ for } b, \text{ and } -450 \text{ for } c.$$

$$t = \frac{45 \pm \sqrt{3825}}{2} \qquad \text{Simplify the radicand.}$$

At this point, we must use a calculator to approximate the solutions for t.

$$\frac{45 + \sqrt{3825}}{2} \approx 53.4 \qquad \frac{45 - \sqrt{3825}}{2} \approx -8.4$$

We omit the negative solution, so $t \approx 53.4$. The amount of time required by the small pipe is represented by $t + 15$; so it takes the small pipe approximately 53.4 + 15, or 68.4, minutes to drain the tank.

Quick Check 6

Working alone, Gabe can clean the gymnasium floor in 50 minutes less time than it takes Rob. If both janitors work together, it takes them 45 minutes to clean the gymnasium floor. How long does it take Gabe, working alone, to clean the gymnasium floor? (Round your answer to the nearest tenth of a minute.)

BUILDING YOUR STUDY STRATEGY

Time Management, 3 When to Study When should you study math? Try to schedule your math study sessions for the time of day you are at your sharpest. For example, if you feel most alert in the mornings, reserve as much time as possible in the mornings to study math. If you get tired while studying late at night, change your study schedule so that you can study math when you are more alert and focused.

Exercises 10.3

PRACTICE   WATCH   DOWNLOAD   READ   REVIEW

Vocabulary

1. Replacing a variable expression with the variable u to rewrite an equation as a quadratic equation is called solving by _____.

2. Whenever both sides of an equation are squared, it is necessary to check for _____ solutions.

Solve by making a u-substitution.

3. $x^4 - 5x^2 + 4 = 0$

4. $x^4 + 5x^2 - 36 = 0$

5. $x^4 - 6x^2 + 9 = 0$

6. $x^4 + 12x^2 + 32 = 0$

7. $x^4 + 7x^2 - 18 = 0$

8. $x^4 + x^2 - 2 = 0$

9. $x^4 - 13x^2 + 36 = 0$

10. $x^4 + 8x^2 + 16 = 0$

11. $x - 13\sqrt{x} + 36 = 0$

12. $x - 10\sqrt{x} + 21 = 0$

13. $x + 2\sqrt{x} - 48 = 0$

14. $x - 5\sqrt{x} - 24 = 0$

15. $x + 9\sqrt{x} + 20 = 0$

16. $x + 11\sqrt{x} + 18 = 0$

17. $x - 8x^{1/2} + 7 = 0$

18. $x + 4x^{1/2} - 21 = 0$

19. $x + 9x^{1/2} + 18 = 0$

20. $x - 11x^{1/2} + 30 = 0$

21. $x - 2x^{1/2} - 80 = 0$

22. $x + 10x^{1/2} + 25 = 0$

23. $x^{2/3} - 5x^{1/3} + 6 = 0$

24. $x^{2/3} + 3x^{1/3} - 4 = 0$

25. $x^{2/3} + 5x^{1/3} - 6 = 0$

26. $x^{2/3} - 12x^{1/3} + 20 = 0$

27. $x^{2/3} + 9x^{1/3} + 20 = 0$

28. $x^{2/3} - 4x^{1/3} - 45 = 0$

29. $(x - 3)^2 + 5(x - 3) + 4 = 0$

30. $(x + 7)^2 + 2(x + 7) - 24 = 0$

31. $(2x - 9)^2 - 6(2x - 9) - 27 = 0$

32. $(4x + 2)^2 - 4(4x + 2) - 60 = 0$

Solve.

33. $\sqrt{x^2 + 6x} = 4$

34. $\sqrt{x^2 - 8x} = 3$

35. $\sqrt{3x - 6} = x - 2$

36. $\sqrt{4x + 52} = x + 5$

37. $\sqrt{x + 15} - x = 3$

38. $\sqrt{3x^2 + 8x + 5} - 5 = 2x$

39. $\sqrt{x - 1} + 2 = \sqrt{2x + 5}$

40. $\sqrt{2x + 3} - \sqrt{x - 2} = 2$

Solve.

41. $x = \dfrac{40}{x + 6}$

42. $x - 9 = \dfrac{52}{x}$

43. $1 + \dfrac{7}{x} - \dfrac{60}{x^2} = 0$

44. $1 - \dfrac{19}{x} + \dfrac{90}{x^2} = 0$

45. $\dfrac{1}{x} + \dfrac{7}{x + 2} = \dfrac{10}{x(x + 2)}$

46. $\dfrac{4}{x + 3} + \dfrac{1}{x - 5} = \dfrac{3}{x^2 - 2x - 15}$

47. $\dfrac{2}{x + 3} + \dfrac{x + 7}{x + 1} = \dfrac{9}{4}$

48. $\dfrac{x}{x + 7} - \dfrac{4}{x + 2} = \dfrac{7}{x^2 + 9x + 14}$

49. One small pipe takes twice as long to fill a tank as a larger pipe does. If the two pipes together take 40 minutes to fill the tank, how long does it take each pipe individually to fill the tank?

50. Rob takes 5 hours longer than Genevieve to paint a room. If they work together, they can paint a room in 6 hours. How long does it take Rob to paint a room by himself?

akes 1 hour longer than a large hose to
he two hoses are used at the same time,
tank in 3 hours. How long does it take
using the smaller hose alone? Round
to the nearest tenth of an hour.

52. A water tank has two drainpipes attached to it. The larger pipe can drain the tank in 2 hours less than the smaller pipe can. If both pipes are being used, they can drain the tank in 5 hours. How long does it take the smaller pipe alone to drain the tank? Round to the nearest tenth of an hour.

53. A new printer can print a set of newsletters in 15 minutes less than an older printer can. If both printers work simultaneously, they can print the set of newsletters in 40 minutes. How long does it take the older printer alone to print the set of newsletters? Round to the nearest tenth of a minute.

54. It takes Alison 10 minutes more than it takes Elaine to stain a cedar fence. If they work together, the two of them can stain a cedar fence in 25 minutes. How long does it take Alison to stain a cedar fence? Round to the nearest tenth of a minute.

Mixed Practice, 55–78

Solve using the technique of your choice.

55. $x^2 - 8x - 13 = 0$

56. $(7x - 11)^2 - 6(7x - 11) = 0$

57. $x - 2\sqrt{x} - 48 = 0$

58. $x^2 + 15x + 54 = 0$

59. $(3x - 2)^2 = 32$

60. $x^{2/3} + 3x^{1/3} - 4 = 0$

61. $x^2 - 5x + 14 = 0$

62. $x^4 - 5x^2 - 36 = 0$

63. $x^2 - 6x - 91 = 0$

64. $(2x + 15)^2 = 18$

65. $\dfrac{x + 1}{x + 3} + \dfrac{7}{x + 4} = \dfrac{5}{x^2 + 7x + 12}$

66. $3x^2 + x - 8 = 0$

67. $\sqrt{3x - 2} = x - 2$

68. $x + \sqrt{x} - 12 = 0$

69. $(5x + 3)^2 + 2(5x + 3) - 15 = 0$

70. $x = \sqrt{6x - 27} + 3$

71. $(x + 8)^2 = -144$

72. $\dfrac{x + 3}{x - 4} + \dfrac{9}{x + 2} = \dfrac{2}{x^2 - 2x - 8}$

73. $x^4 - 3x^2 - 4 = 0$

74. $x^2 + 13x + 50 = 0$

75. $x^{2/3} + 12x^{1/3} + 35 = 0$

76. $x^2 - 15x + 56 = 0$

77. $x^2 + 10x + 25 = 0$

78. $(x + 4)^2 = -108$

Writing in Mathematics

Answer in complete sentences.

79. Suppose you are solving an equation that is quadratic in form by using the substitution $u = x^2$. Once you have solved the equation for u, explain how you would solve for x.

80. Suppose you are solving an equation that is quadratic in form by using the substitution $u = \sqrt{x}$. Once you have solved the equation for u, explain how you would solve for x.

Quick Review Exercises

Section 10.3

Solve.

1. $(x - 3)^2 = 49$

2. $x^2 - 9x - 36 = 0$

3. $x^2 - 6x - 13 = 0$

4. $x^2 + 11x + 40 = 0$

10.4

Graphing Quadratic Equations

OBJECTIVES

1 Graph quadratic equations in standard form.
2 Graph parabolas that open downward.
3 Graph quadratic equations of the form $y = a(x - h)^2 + k$.

Graphing Quadratic Equations in Standard Form

Objective 1 **Graph quadratic equations in standard form.** The graphs of quadratic equations are not lines like the graphs of linear equations or V-shaped like the graphs of absolute value equations. The graphs of quadratic equations are U-shaped and are called **parabolas**. Let's consider the graph of the most basic quadratic equation: $y = x^2$. We will first create a table of ordered pairs to represent points on the graph.

x	$y = x^2$
-2	4
-1	1
0	0
1	1
2	4

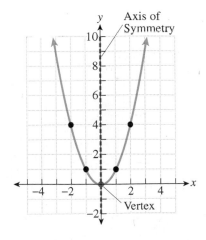

The figure at the right shows these points and the graph of $y = x^2$. Notice that the shape, called a parabola, is not a straight line, but is U-shaped.

The point where the graph changes from decreasing to increasing is called the **vertex.** In the figure, the vertex is located at the bottom of the parabola. Notice that if we draw a vertical line through the vertex of the parabola, the left and right sides become mirror images. The graph of an equation is said to be **symmetric** if we can fold the graph along a line and the two sides of the graph coincide; in other words, a graph is symmetric if one side of the graph is a mirror image of the other side. A parabola is always symmetric, and we call the vertical line through the vertex the **axis of symmetry**. For this parabola, the equation of the axis of symmetry is $x = 0$.

We graph parabolas by plotting points, and the choice of our points is very important. We look for the y-intercept, the x-intercept(s) if there are any, and the vertex. We also use the axis of symmetry to help us find "mirror" points that are symmetric to points we have already graphed.

As before, we find the y-intercept by substituting 0 for x and solving for y. We will see that the y-intercept of a quadratic equation in standard form ($y = ax^2 + bx + c$) is always the point $(0, c)$. We find the x-intercepts, if there are any, by substituting 0 for y and solving for x. This equation will be quadratic, and we solve it using previous techniques.

A parabola opens upward if $a > 0$, and the vertex will be at the lowest point of the parabola. A parabola opens downward if $a < 0$, and the vertex will be at the highest point of the parabola. Parabolas that open downward will be covered later in this section. To learn how to find the coordinates of the vertex, we begin by completing the square for the equation $y = ax^2 + bx + c$.

$$y = ax^2 + bx + c$$

$$y - c = a\left(x^2 + \frac{b}{a}x\right)$$ Subtract c from both sides. Factor a from the two terms containing x.

$$y - c + \frac{b^2}{4a} = a\left(x^2 + \frac{b}{a}x + \frac{b^2}{4a^2}\right)$$ Half of $\frac{b}{a}$ is $\frac{b}{2a}$. Add $\left(\frac{b}{2a}\right)^2$, or $\frac{b^2}{4a^2}$, to the terms inside the parentheses. Because there is a factor in front of the parentheses, add $a \cdot \frac{b^2}{4a^2}$, or $\frac{b^2}{4a}$, to the left side.

$$y = a\left(x + \frac{b}{2a}\right)^2 + \frac{4ac - b^2}{4a}$$ Factor the trinomial inside the parentheses. Solve for y and collect all terms on the right side of the equation.

Note: $c - \dfrac{b^2}{4a} = \dfrac{4ac - b^2}{4a}$

Because a squared expression cannot be negative, the minimum value of y occurs when $x + \dfrac{b}{2a} = 0$, or in other words, when $x = \dfrac{-b}{2a}$.

If the equation is in standard form, $y = ax^2 + bx + c$, we can find the x-coordinate of the vertex using the formula $x = \dfrac{-b}{2a}$. We then find the y-coordinate of the vertex by substituting this value for x in the original equation.

Strategy for Graphing Quadratic Equations in Standard Form ($y = ax^2 + bx + c$)

- **Find the vertex.**

  Use the formula $x = \dfrac{-b}{2a}$ to find the x-coordinate of the vertex. Substitute this value for x in the original equation to find the y-coordinate.

- **Find the y-intercept.**

  Substitute 0 for x to find the y-coordinate of the y-intercept. The y-intercept is $(0, c)$.

- **Find the x-intercept(s) if there are any.**

  Substitute 0 for y in the original equation and solve for x if possible. If you cannot solve the equation by factoring, use the quadratic formula.

- **Use the axis of symmetry to add additional points to the graph.**

  The axis of symmetry is a vertical line extending upward from the vertex. It can be used to find the point on the parabola that is symmetric to the y-intercept.

EXAMPLE 1   Graph $y = x^2 + 6x + 8$.

SOLUTION   We begin by finding the vertex using the formula $x = \dfrac{-b}{2a}$ to find its x-coordinate.

$$x = \frac{-6}{2(1)} = -3$$ Substitute 1 for a and 6 for b in $x = \dfrac{-b}{2a}$.

Now we substitute this value for x in the original equation and solve for y.

$$y = (-3)^2 + 6(-3) + 8$$ Substitute -3 for x.
$$y = -1$$ Simplify.

The vertex is at $(-3, -1)$.

Because the equation is in standard form, the y-intercept is the point $(0,$ this case, the y-intercept is $(0, 8)$. (Alternatively, we could substitute 0 for x a solve for y.)

To find the x-intercepts, we substitute 0 for y and attempt to solve for x.

$0 = x^2 + 6x + 8$ Substitute 0 for y in the original equation.

$0 = (x + 2)(x + 4)$ Factor the trinomial.

$x = -2$ or $x = -4$ Set each factor equal to 0 and solve.

The x-intercepts are $(-2, 0)$ and $(-4, 0)$.

On the left is a sketch showing the vertex, y-intercept, x-intercepts, and axis of symmetry. The y-intercept is three units to the right of the axis of symmetry; so there is a mirror point with the same y-coordinate located three units to the left of this axis. The completed graph of the parabola is shown below.

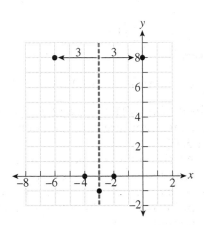 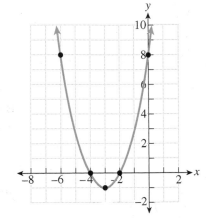

Quick Check 1

Graph $y = x^2 - 8x + 7$.

Using Your Calculator You can use the TI–84 to graph parabolas. To graph $y = x^2 + 6x + 8$, begin by tapping the [Y=] key and keying $x^2 + 6x + 8$ next to Y_1 as shown in the screen shot on the left.

To graph the parabola, tap the [GRAPH] key. On the right is the screen you should see in the standard viewing window.

 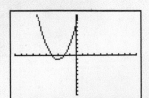

EXAMPLE 2   Graph $y = x^2 - 4x - 7$.

SOLUTION   Again, we begin by finding the vertex using the formula $x = \dfrac{-b}{2a}$.

$$x = \frac{-(-4)}{2(1)} = 2 \quad \text{Substitute 1 for } a \text{ and } -4 \text{ for } b.$$

We substitute 2 for x in the original equation to find the y-coordinate of the vertex.

$$y = (2)^2 - 4(2) - 7 \quad \text{Substitute 2 for } x.$$
$$y = -11 \quad\quad\quad\quad \text{Simplify.}$$

The vertex is at $(2, -11)$.

Because this equation is in standard form, we see that the y-intercept is $(0, -7)$. Now we find the x-intercepts by substituting 0 for y and solving the equation for x.

$$0 = x^2 - 4x - 7 \quad \text{Substitute 0 for } y.$$

Because we cannot factor this expression, we use the quadratic formula to find the x-intercepts.

$$x = \frac{-(-4) \pm \sqrt{(-4)^2 - 4(1)(-7)}}{2(1)} \quad \text{Substitute 1 for } a, -4 \text{ for } b, \text{ and } -7 \text{ for } c.$$

$$x = \frac{4 \pm \sqrt{44}}{2} \quad \text{Simplify the radicand and denominator.}$$

$$x = \frac{4 \pm 2\sqrt{11}}{2} \quad \text{Simplify the square root.}$$

$$x = \frac{\overset{1}{\cancel{2}}(2 \pm \sqrt{11})}{\underset{1}{\cancel{2}}} \quad \begin{array}{l}\text{Divide out common} \\ \text{factors.}\end{array}$$

$$x = 2 \pm \sqrt{11} \quad \text{Simplify.}$$

Because $2 + \sqrt{11} \approx 5.3$ and $2 - \sqrt{11} \approx -1.3$, the x-intercepts are approximately $(5.3, 0)$ and $(-1.3, 0)$.

At the right is a sketch of the parabola showing the vertex, y-intercept, x-intercepts, and axis of symmetry $(x = 2)$. Also shown is the point $(4, -7)$, which is symmetric to the y-intercept.

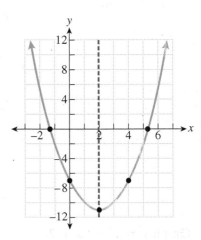

Quick Check 2

Graph $y = x^2 + 6x - 9$.

Occasionally, a parabola will not have any x-intercepts. In this case, we will have a negative discriminant $(b^2 - 4ac)$ when using the quadratic formula. If the vertex is above the x-axis, the parabola does not have x-intercepts. If the vertex is on the x-axis, the vertex is the only x-intercept of the parabola.

EXAMPLE 3 Graph $y = x^2 - 2x + 2$.

SOLUTION The x-coordinate of the vertex is found using the formula $x = \dfrac{-b}{2a}$.

$$x = \frac{-(-2)}{2(1)} = 1 \quad \text{Substitute 1 for } a \text{ and } -2 \text{ for } b.$$

Now we substitute 1 for x in the original equation and solve for y.

$$y = (1)^2 - 2(1) + 2 \quad \text{Substitute 1 for } x.$$
$$y = 1 \quad \text{Simplify.}$$

The vertex is at $(1, 1)$.

Because the equation is in standard form, we see that the y-intercept is $(0, 2)$.

If we plot these two points on the graph, we see that there cannot be any x-intercepts. The vertex is above the x-axis, and the parabola moves only in an upward direction from there. Therefore, this parabola does not have any x-intercepts.

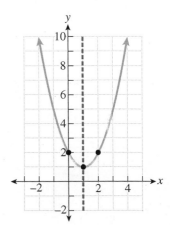

If we overlooked the visual evidence and chose to use the quadratic for to find the x-intercepts, we would have ended up with $x = \dfrac{2 \pm \sqrt{-4}}{2}$. Because t. discriminant is negative, the equation does not have any real solutions and the parabola does not have any x-intercepts.

The graph shows the axis of symmetry ($x = 1$) and a third point, $(2, 2)$, that is symmetric to the y-intercept.

A WORD OF CAUTION If a parabola that opens upward has its vertex above the x-axis, there are no x-intercepts.

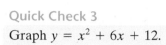
Quick Check 3
Graph $y = x^2 + 6x + 12$.

Graphing Parabolas That Open Downward

Objective 2 Graph parabolas that open downward. Some parabolas open downward rather than upward. The way to determine which way a parabola will open is by writing the equation in standard form: $y = ax^2 + bx + c$. If a is positive, as it was in the previous examples, the parabola will open upward. If a is negative, the parabola will open downward. For instance, the graph of $y = -3x^2 + 5x - 7$ would open downward because the coefficient of the second-degree term is negative. The following example shows how to graph a parabola that opens downward.

EXAMPLE 4 Graph $y = -x^2 + 4x + 12$.

SOLUTION   Begin by finding the x-coordinate of the vertex.

$$x = \frac{-4}{2(-1)} = 2 \quad \text{Substitute } -1 \text{ for } a \text{ and } 4 \text{ for } b.$$

Now substitute 2 for x in the original equation to find the y-coordinate.

$$y = -(2)^2 + 4(2) + 12 \quad \text{Substitute 2 for } x.$$
$$y = 16 \quad \text{Simplify.}$$

The vertex is at $(2, 16)$.

Because this equation is already in standard form, the y-intercept is $(0, 12)$.

If we plot the vertex and the y-intercept on the graph, we will see that there must be two x-intercepts. The vertex is above the x-axis, and the parabola opens downward; so the graph must cross the x-axis. To find the x-intercepts, we substitute 0 for y in the original equation and solve for x.

$$0 = -x^2 + 4x + 12 \quad \text{Substitute 0 for } y.$$
$$x^2 - 4x - 12 = 0 \quad \text{Collect all terms on the left side of the equation}$$
$$\text{so that the coefficient of the squared term is positive.}$$

$(x - 6)(x + 2) = 0$ Factor.

$x = 6$ or $x = -2$ Set each factor equal to 0 and solve.

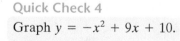
Quick Check 4
Graph $y = -x^2 + 9x + 10$.

The x-intercepts are $(6, 0)$ and $(-2, 0)$.

At the right is the graph, showing the axis of symmetry ($x = 2$) and the point $(4, 12)$ that is symmetric to the y-intercept.

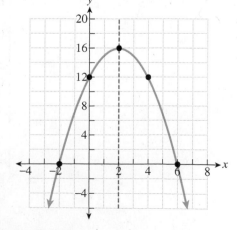

0 Quadratic Equations

EXAMPLE 5 Graph $y = -\frac{1}{2}x^2 - 2x + 4$.

SOLUTION This parabola will open downward because the second-degree term has a negative coefficient. Begin by finding the x-coordinate of the vertex.

$$x = \frac{-(-2)}{2\left(-\frac{1}{2}\right)} = -2 \quad \text{Substitute } -\frac{1}{2} \text{ for } a \text{ and } -2 \text{ for } b.$$

Now substitute -2 for x in the original equation to find the y-coordinate.

$$y = -\frac{1}{2}(-2)^2 - 2(-2) + 4 \quad \text{Substitute } -2 \text{ for } x.$$

$$y = -2 + 4 + 4 \qquad\qquad\quad \text{Simplify each term.}$$

$$y = 6 \qquad\qquad\qquad\qquad \text{Simplify.}$$

The vertex is at $(-2, 6)$.

The equation is in general form, so the y-intercept is $(0, 4)$.

Because the vertex is above the x-axis and the parabola opens downward, the graph must have two x-intercepts. To find the x-intercepts, substitute 0 for y in the original equation and solve for x.

$$0 = -\frac{1}{2}x^2 - 2x + 4 \quad \text{Substitute 0 for } y.$$

$$\frac{1}{2}x^2 + 2x - 4 = 0 \qquad \begin{array}{l}\text{Collect all terms on the left side of the}\\\text{equation so that the coefficient of the}\\\text{squared term is positive.}\end{array}$$

$$2\left(\frac{1}{2}x^2 + 2x - 4\right) = 2 \cdot 0 \quad \begin{array}{l}\text{Multiply both sides of the equation by the}\\\text{LCD (2) to clear the equation of fractions.}\end{array}$$

$$x^2 + 4x - 8 = 0 \qquad \text{Distribute and simplify.}$$

Because we cannot factor this expression, we must use the quadratic formula to find the x-intercepts.

$$x = \frac{-4 \pm \sqrt{(4)^2 - 4(1)(-8)}}{2(1)} \quad \text{Substitute 1 for } a, 4 \text{ for } b, \text{ and } -8 \text{ for } c.$$

$$x = \frac{-4 \pm \sqrt{48}}{2} \qquad\qquad \text{Simplify the radicand and denominator.}$$

$$x = \frac{-4 \pm 4\sqrt{3}}{2} \qquad\qquad \text{Simplify the square root.}$$

$$x = -2 \pm 2\sqrt{3} \qquad\qquad \text{Simplify.}$$

Quick Check 5

Graph $y = -\frac{1}{4}x^2 - \frac{5}{2}x - 4$.

Because $-2 + 2\sqrt{3} \approx 1.5$ and $-2 - 2\sqrt{3} \approx -5.5$, the x-intercepts are approximately $(1.5, 0)$ and $(-5.5, 0)$.

To the right is the graph, showing the axis of symmetry $(x = -2)$ and the point $(-4, 4)$ that is symmetric to the y-intercept.

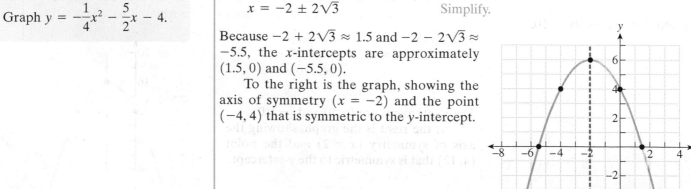

A WORD OF CAUTION If a parabola that opens downward has its vertex belo
x-axis, it has no *x*-intercepts.

Graphing Quadratic Equations of the Form $y = a(x - h)^2 + k$

Objective 3 Graph quadratic equations of the form $y = a(x - h)^2 + k$.
Now that we have covered graphing quadratic equations in standard form, we turn
our attention to graphing equations of the form $y = a(x - h)^2 + k$. One of the differences between graphing equations of this form is in the way we find the vertex.

Graphing Equations of the Form $y = a(x - h)^2 + k$

The graph of the quadratic equation $y = a(x - h)^2 + k$ is a parabola with vertex (h, k) and axis of symmetry $x = h$. The parabola opens upward if a is positive and opens downward if a is negative.

If $a > 0$, the expression $a(x - h)^2 + k$ achieves its minimum value k when $x = h$;
so the vertex of $y = a(x - h)^2 + k$ is the point (h, k). Recall that $(x - h)^2$ is nonnegative and has its minimum value when $x - h = 0$, or $x = h$. In this case,
$a(x - h)^2$ is equal to 0 and $a(x - h)^2 + k = k$. A similar argument holds true for
(h, k) being the vertex of $y = a(x - h)^2 + k$ in the case of $a < 0$.

EXAMPLE 6 Find the vertex and axis of symmetry for the parabola.

a) $y = (x - 4)^2 + 3$

SOLUTION   This equation is in the form $y = a(x - h)^2 + k$. The axis of symmetry is $x = 4$ and the vertex is $(4, 3)$.

b) $y = -(x + 1)^2 - 4$

SOLUTION   This parabola opens downward, but that does not affect how we find
the axis of symmetry or the vertex. The axis of symmetry is $x = -1$, and the vertex
is $(-1, -4)$.

Quick Check 6

Find the vertex and axis of
symmetry for the parabola.

a) $y = (x + 2)^2 - 8$
b) $y = -2(x - 8)^2 + 7$

EXAMPLE 7 Graph $y = (x + 4)^2 - 9$.

SOLUTION   This parabola opens upward, and the vertex is $(-4, -9)$. Next, we find
the *y*-intercept.

$$y = (0 + 4)^2 - 9 \quad \text{Substitute 0 for } x.$$
$$y = 7 \quad \text{Simplify.}$$

The *y*-intercept is $(0, 7)$. Because the parabola opens upward and the vertex is
below the *x*-axis, the parabola has two *x*-intercepts. We find the coordinates of
the *x*-intercepts by substituting 0 for *y* and solving for *x* by extracting square
roots.

$$0 = (x + 4)^2 - 9 \quad \text{Substitute 0 for } y.$$
$$9 = (x + 4)^2 \quad \text{Add 9 to isolate } (x + 4)^2.$$
$$\pm\sqrt{9} = \sqrt{(x + 4)^2} \quad \text{Take the square root of each side.}$$
$$\pm 3 = x + 4 \quad \text{Simplify each square root.}$$
$$-4 \pm 3 = x \quad \text{Subtract 4 to isolate } x.$$

The x-coordinates of the x-intercepts are $-4 + 3 = -1$ and $-4 - 3 = -7$. The x-intercepts are $(-1, 0)$ and $(-7, 0)$. The axis of symmetry is $x = -4$, and the point $(-8, 7)$ is symmetric to the y-intercept.

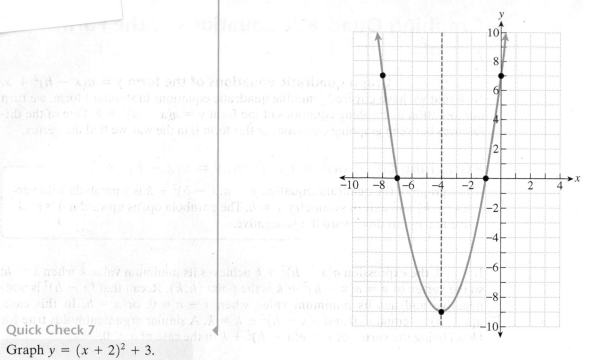

Quick Check 7

Graph $y = (x + 2)^2 + 3$.

EXAMPLE 8 Graph $y = -(x - 2)^2 - 1$.

SOLUTION This parabola opens downward, and the vertex is $(2, -1)$.
Next, we find the y-intercept by substituting 0 for x.

$$y = -(0 - 2)^2 - 1 \quad \text{Substitute 0 for } x.$$
$$y = -4 - 1 \quad \text{Simplify.}$$
$$y = -5 \quad \text{Simplify.}$$

The y-intercept is $(0, -5)$.
Because the parabola opens downward and the vertex is below the x-axis, the parabola does not have any x-intercepts.
The axis of symmetry is $x = 2$, and the point $(4, -5)$ is symmetric to the y-intercept.

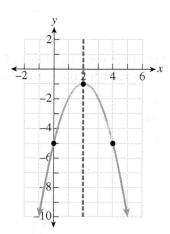

Quick Check 8

Graph $y = -(x + 1)^2 + 4$.

BUILDING YOUR STUDY STRATEGY

Time Management, 4 Setting Goals One way to get the most from a study session is to establish a set of goals to accomplish for each session. Setting goals will encourage you to work quickly and efficiently. Many students set a goal of studying for a certain amount of time, but time alone is not a worthy goal. Create a to-do list each time you start a study session, and you will find that you have a greater chance of reaching your goals.

Exercises 10.4 *MyMathLab*

PRACTICE   WATCH   DOWNLOAD   READ   REVIEW

Vocabulary

1. The graph of a quadratic equation is a U-shaped graph called a(n) _____.

2. A parabola opens upward if the leading coefficient is _____.

3. A parabola opens downward if the leading coefficient is _____.

4. The turning point of a parabola is called its _____.

5. To find the _____ of a parabola, substitute 0 for x and solve for y.

6. To find the _____ of a parabola, substitute 0 for y and solve for x.

Find the vertex of the parabola as well as the equation of the axis of symmetry associated with each of the following quadratic equations.

7. $y = x^2 + 8x - 22$

8. $y = x^2 - 6x - 45$

9. $y = x^2 - 7x + 10$

10. $y = x^2 + 9x + 40$

11. $y = -x^2 + 12x + 62$

12. $y = -x^2 - 4x + 17$

13. $y = 2x^2 + 8x - 19$

14. $y = 3x^2 + 6x + 16$

15. $y = -4x^2 + 24x - 11$

16. $y = -2x^2 - 20x + 175$

17. $y = x^2 + \frac{3}{2}x + 8$

18. $y = \frac{1}{4}x^2 + 6x - 32$

19. $y = x^2 + 10x$

20. $y = x^2 + 10$

21. $y = (x - 7)^2 + 12$

22. $y = (x + 2)^2 + 9$

23. $y = (x + 1)^2 - 5$

24. $y = (x - 6)^2 - 13$

25. $y = -(x - 9)^2 - 7$

26. $y = -(x + 4)^2 - 6$

Find the x- and y-intercepts of the parabola associated with the given quadratic equations. If necessary, round to the nearest tenth. If the parabola does not have any x-intercepts, state no x-intercepts.

27. $y = x^2 + 3x - 40$

28. $y = x^2 - 11x + 28$

29. $y = x^2 - 5x + 3$

30. $y = x^2 + 6x - 9$

31. $y = x^2 + 5x + 15$

32. $y = x^2 - 2x + 6$

33. $y = 2x^2 + 6x - 15$

34. $y = 2x^2 + 5x - 42$

35. $y = -x^2 - 5x + 6$

36. $y = -x^2 + 8x - 12$

37. $y = -x^2 + 6x + 20$

38. $y = -x^2 - 10x + 32$

39. $y = -x^2 + 7x - 15$

40. $y = -x^2 + 8x - 22$

41. $y = x^2 - 8x + 16$

42. $y = x^2 + 12x$

43. $y = (x - 7)^2 - 9$

44. $y = (x + 2)^2 - 6$

45. $y = (x + 5)^2 + 4$

46. $y = (x + 9)^2 - 4$

47. $y = -(x - 1)^2 + 12$

48. $y = -(x - 8)^2 - 1$

Graph the given parabolas. Label the vertex and all intercepts.

49. $y = x^2 - 2x - 3$

50. $y = x^2 + x - 6$

51. $y = x^2 - 5x$

52. $y = x^2 + 6x + 9$

59. $y = -\dfrac{1}{2}x^2 + 3x - 3$

53. $y = x^2 - 2x - 1$

54. $y = \dfrac{1}{2}x^2 - 2x + \dfrac{3}{2}$

60. $y = -x^2 + 4x - 1$

55. $y = x^2 - 6x + 10$

56. $y = x^2 + 6x + 10$

61. $y = -x^2 + 3x - 4$

62. $y = -x^2 - 2x - 3$

57. $y = -x^2 + 4x - 4$

58. $y = -x^2 - 4x + 5$

63. $y = (x - 3)^2 - 4$

64. $y = (x + 1)^2 - 9$

65. $y = -(x - 2)^2 + 1$ **66.** $y = -(x + 3)^2 + 9$ **70.** $y = (x - 2)^2 + 3$

Writing in Mathematics

Answer in complete sentences.

67. $y = (x - 4)^2 - 2$

71. Explain how to determine that a parabola does not have any x-intercepts.

72. *Newsletter* Write a newsletter explaining how to graph an equation of the form $y = ax^2 + bx + c$.

68. $y = -(x + 1)^2 + 3$ **69.** $y = -(x - 2)^2 - 4$

10.5

Applications Using Quadratic Equations

OBJECTIVES

1 Solve applied geometric problems.
2 Solve problems by using the Pythagorean theorem.
3 Solve applied problems by using the Pythagorean theorem.

In this section, we will learn how to solve applied problems resulting in quadratic equations.

Solving Applied Geometric Problems

Objective 1 Solve applied geometric problems. Problems involving the area of a geometric figure often lead to quadratic equations, as area is measured in square units. Here are some useful area formulas.

Figure	Rectangle	Triangle
Dimensions	Length l, Width w	Base b, Height h
Area	$A = l \cdot w$	$A = \frac{1}{2}bh$

EXAMPLE 1 The height of a triangle is 5 centimeters less than its base. The area is 18 square centimeters. Find the base and the height of the triangle.

SOLUTION In this problem, the unknown quantities are the base and the height, while we know that the area is 18 square centimeters. Because the height is given in terms of the base, a wise choice is to represent the base of the triangle as x. Because the height is 5 centimeters less than the base, it can be represented by $x - 5$. This information is summarized in the following table:

Unknowns	Known	
Base: x	Area: 18 cm^2	
Height: $x - 5$		

Because the area of a triangle is given by the formula $A = \frac{1}{2}bh$, the equation we need to solve is $\frac{1}{2}x(x - 5) = 18$.

$$\frac{1}{2}x(x - 5) = 18$$

$$\overset{1}{\cancel{2}} \cdot \frac{1}{\underset{1}{\cancel{2}}}x(x - 5) = 2 \cdot 18 \qquad \text{Multiply both sides by 2.}$$

$$x^2 - 5x = 36 \qquad \text{Simplify each side of the equation.}$$

$$x^2 - 5x - 36 = 0 \qquad \text{Rewrite in standard form.}$$

$$(x - 9)(x + 4) = 0 \qquad \text{Factor.}$$

$$x - 9 = 0 \quad \text{or} \quad x + 4 = 0 \quad \text{Set each factor equal to 0.}$$

$$x = 9 \quad \text{or} \quad x = -4 \quad \text{Solve.}$$

Look back at the table of unknowns. If $x = -4$, the base is -4 centimeters and the height is -9 centimeters, which is not possible. The solutions derived from $x = -4$ are omitted. If $x = 9$, the base is 9 centimeters, while the height is $9 - 5 = 4$ centimeters.

$$\text{Base: } x = 9$$
$$\text{Height: } x - 5 = 9 - 5 = 4$$

Now put the answer in a complete sentence with the proper units. The base of the triangle is 9 centimeters, and the height is 4 centimeters.

▶ Quick Check 1

The base of a triangle is 2 inches longer than three times its height. If the area of the triangle is 60 square inches, find the base and height of the triangle.

EXAMPLE 2 The length of a rectangle is 7 inches less than twice its width. The area of the rectangle is 240 square inches. Find the length and the width of the rectangle, rounded to the nearest tenth of an inch.

SOLUTION In this problem, the unknown quantities are the length and the width, while we know that the area is 240 square inches. Because the length is given in terms of the width, a wise choice is to represent the width of the rectangle as x. Because the length is 7 inches less than twice the width, it can be represented by $2x - 7$. This information is summarized in the following table:

Unknowns	*Known*	
Length: $2x - 7$	Area: 240 in.^{2}	x
Width: x		$2x - 7$

Because the area of a rectangle is equal to its length times its width, the equation we need to solve is $x(2x - 7) = 240$.

$$x(2x - 7) = 240$$
$$2x^2 - 7x = 240 \quad \text{Distribute.}$$
$$2x^2 - 7x - 240 = 0 \quad \text{Rewrite in standard form.}$$

This trinomial does not factor, so we will use the quadratic formula with $a = 2$, $b = -7$, and $c = -240$ to solve the equation.

$$x = \frac{-(-7) \pm \sqrt{(-7)^2 - 4(2)(-240)}}{2(2)} \quad \begin{array}{l} \text{Substitute 2 for } a, -7 \text{ for } b, \text{and} \\ -240 \text{ for } c. \end{array}$$

$$x = \frac{7 \pm \sqrt{1969}}{4} \quad \begin{array}{l} \text{Simplify the radicand and} \\ \text{the denominator.} \end{array}$$

We use a calculator to approximate these solutions.

$$\frac{7 + \sqrt{1969}}{4} \approx 12.8 \qquad \frac{7 - \sqrt{1969}}{4} \approx -9.3$$

We may omit the negative solution, as both the length and width of the rectangle would be negative. If $x \approx 12.8$, the width is approximately 12.8 inches, while the length is approximately $2(12.8) - 7 = 18.6$ inches.

$$\text{Width: } x \approx 12.8$$
$$\text{Length: } 2x - 7 \approx 2(12.8) - 7 = 18.6$$

The width of the rectangle is approximately 12.8 inches, and the length is approximately 18.6 inches.

Quick Check 2

The length of a rectangle is 8 inches more than its width. The area of the rectangle is 350 square inches. Find the length and the width of the rectangle, rounded to the nearest tenth of an inch.

Solving Problems by Using the Pythagorean Theorem

Objective 2 Solve problems by using the Pythagorean theorem. Other applications of geometry that lead to quadratic equations involve the Pythagorean theorem, which is an equation that relates the lengths of the three sides of a right triangle.

The side opposing the right angle is called the **hypotenuse** and is labeled c in the figure at the top of the next page. The other two sides that form the right angle are called the **legs** of the triangle and are labeled a and b. (It makes no difference which is a and which is b.)

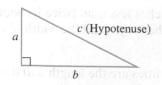

Pythagorean Theorem

For any right triangle whose hypotenuse has length c and whose legs have lengths a and b, respectively,

$$a^2 + b^2 = c^2.$$

EXAMPLE 3 A right triangle has a hypotenuse that measures 18 inches, and one of its legs is 6 inches long. Find the length of the other leg, to the nearest tenth of an inch.

SOLUTION In this problem, the length of one of the legs is unknown. We can label the unknown leg as either a or b.

Unknowns	Known
a	b: 6 in.
	Hypotenuse (c): 18 in.

$a^2 + 6^2 = 18^2$	Substitute 6 for b and 18 for c in $a^2 + b^2 = c^2$.
$a^2 + 36 = 324$	Square 6 and 18.
$a^2 = 288$	Subtract 36.
$\sqrt{a^2} = \pm\sqrt{288}$	Solve by extracting square roots.
$a = \pm 12\sqrt{2}$	Simplify the square root.

Because the length of a leg must be a positive number, we are concerned only with $12\sqrt{2}$, which rounds to 17.0 inches. The length of the other leg is approximately 17.0 inches.

Quick Check 3

One leg of a right triangle measures 5 inches, while the hypotenuse measures 11 inches. Find, to the nearest hundredth of an inch, the length of the other leg of the triangle.

Applications of the Pythagorean Theorem

Objective 3 Solve applied problems by using the Pythagorean theorem.
Now we turn our attention to solving applied problems using the Pythagorean theorem. In these problems, we begin by drawing a picture of the situation. We must be able to identify a right triangle in the figure in order to apply the Pythagorean theorem.

EXAMPLE 4 A 5-foot ladder is leaning against a wall. If the bottom of the ladder is 3 feet from the base of the wall, how high up the wall is the top of the ladder?

SOLUTION The ladder, the wall, and the ground form a right triangle, with the ladder being the hypotenuse. In this problem, the height of the wall, which is the length of one of the legs in the right triangle, is unknown.

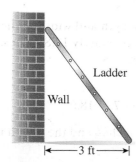

Unknowns	Known
a	b: 3 ft
	Hypotenuse (c): 5 ft

Quick Check 4

An 8-foot ladder is leaning against a wall. If the bottom of the ladder is 2 feet from the base of the wall, how high up the wall is the top of the ladder? (Round to the nearest tenth of a foot.)

$a^2 + 3^2 = 5^2$	Substitute 3 for b and 5 for c in $a^2 + b^2 = c^2$.
$a^2 + 9 = 25$	Square 3 and 5.
$a^2 = 16$	Subtract 9.
$\sqrt{a^2} = \pm\sqrt{16}$	Solve by extracting square roots.
$a = \pm 4$	Simplify the square root.

Again, the negative solution does not make sense in this problem. The ladder is resting at a point on the wall that is 4 feet above the ground.

EXAMPLE 5 The Modesto airport is located 120 miles north and 50 miles west of the Visalia airport. If a plane flies directly from Visalia to Modesto, how many miles is the flight?

SOLUTION The directions of north and west form a 90-degree angle, so the picture shows a right triangle whose hypotenuse (the direct distance from Visalia to Modesto) is unknown.

Unknowns	Known
Hypotenuse c	a: 120 mi
	b: 50 mi

$$120^2 + 50^2 = c^2 \quad \text{Substitute 120 for } a \text{ and 50 for } b \text{ in } a^2 + b^2 = c^2.$$
$$14{,}400 + 2500 = c^2 \quad \text{Square 120 and 50.}$$
$$16{,}900 = c^2 \quad \text{Simplify.}$$
$$\pm\sqrt{16{,}900} = \sqrt{c^2} \quad \text{Solve by extracting square roots.}$$
$$\pm 130 = c \quad \text{Simplify the square root.}$$

The negative solution does not make sense in this problem. The direct distance from the Visalia airport to the Modesto airport is 130 miles.

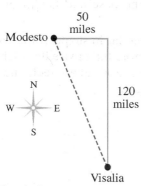

Quick Check 5

Cassie's backyard is in the shape of a rectangle whose dimensions are 70 feet by 240 feet. She needs a hose that will extend from one corner of her yard to the corner that is diagonally opposite to it. How long does the hose have to be?

BUILDING YOUR STUDY STRATEGY

Time Management, 5 Studying Difficult Subjects First and Taking Brief Breaks If you have more than one subject to study, as most students do, the order in which you study the subjects is important. A good idea is to arrange your study schedule so that you study the most difficult subject first, while you are most alert.

Another suggestion to keep your mental energy at its highest while you are studying is to take brief ten-minute study breaks. One study break per hour will help keep you from feeling fatigued.

Exercises 10.5

PRACTICE   WATCH   DOWNLOAD   READ   REVIEW

Vocabulary

1. State the formula for the area of a triangle.

   _____

2. In a right triangle, the side opposite the right angle is called the _____.

3. In a right triangle, the sides adjacent to the right angle are called _____.

4. The _____ theorem states that for any right triangle whose hypotenuse has length c and whose two legs have lengths a and b, respectively, $a^2 + b^2 = c^2$.

For all problems, approximate to the nearest tenth when necessary.

5. The length of a rectangle is 5 inches more than its width. If the area of the rectangle is 66 square inches, find its length and width.

6. The width of a rectangle is 6 feet less than its length. If the area of the rectangle is 112 square feet, find its length and width.

7. The length of a rectangle is twice its width. If the area of the rectangle is 120 square meters, find its length and width.

8. The length of a rectangle is 3 inches more than twice its width. If the area of the rectangle is 75 square inches, find its length and width.

9. The width of a rectangle is 13 feet less than twice its length. If the area of the rectangle is 68 square feet, find its length and width.

10. The length of a rectangle is 7 meters more than four times its width. If the area of the rectangle is 650 square meters, find its length and width.

11. The base of a triangle is 5 inches more than its height. If the area of the triangle is 42 square inches, find the base and height of the triangle.

12. The height of a triangle is 1 foot less than three times its base. If the area of the triangle is 22 square feet, find the base and height of the triangle.

13. The height of a triangle is 1 inch more than twice its base. If the area of the triangle is 15 square inches, find the base and height of the triangle.

14. The height of a triangle is 7 inches less than its base. If the area of the triangle is 32 square inches, find the base and height of the triangle.

15. A rectangular photograph has an area of 80 square inches. If the width of the photograph is 2 inches less than its height, find the dimensions of the photograph.

16. The area of a rectangular patio is 700 square feet. If the length of the patio is 5 feet less than twice its width, find the dimensions of the patio.

17. The length of a rectangular rug is 10 inches less than twice its width. If the area of the rug is 2160 square inches, find its dimensions.

18. The width of a rectangular room is 14 meters less than twice its length. If the area of the room is 125 square meters, find its dimensions.

19. The width of a rectangular table is 16 inches less than its length. If the area of the table is 540 square inches, find its dimensions.

20. Steve has a rectangular lawn, and the length of the lawn is 25 feet more than its width. If the area of the lawn is 7000 square feet, find its dimensions.

21. Tina made a quilt that was 8 inches taller than it was wide. She then sewed a 4-inch border around the entire quilt. If the area of the quilt and its border is 1920 square inches, find the dimensions of the quilt without the border.

22. The length of a rectangular swimming pool is 2 meters more than twice its width. The pool is surrounded by a concrete deck that is 2 meters wide. If the area of the surface of the pool and deck is 180 square meters, find the dimensions of the pool.

23. A kite is in the shape of a triangle. The base of the kite is twice its height. If the area of the kite is 256 square inches, find the base and height of the kite.

24. A hang glider is triangular in shape. If the base of the hang glider is 2 feet more than twice its height and the area of the hang glider is 30 square feet, find the hang glider's base and height.

25. The sail on a sailboat is shaped like a triangle, with an area of 46 square feet. The height of the sail is 8 feet more than the base of the sail. Find the base and height of the sail.

26. A kite is in the shape of a triangle and is made with 250 square inches of material. The base of the kite is 20 inches longer than the height of the kite. Find the base and the height of the kite.

27. The two legs of a right triangle are 10 inches and 16 inches. Find the hypotenuse of the triangle.

28. The two legs of a right triangle are 7 centimeters and 12 centimeters. Find the hypotenuse of the triangle.

29. A right triangle with a hypotenuse of 15 feet has a leg that measures 9 feet. Find the length of the other leg.

30. A right triangle with a hypotenuse of 25 inches has a leg that measures 24 inches. Find the length of the other leg.

31. A right triangle with a leg that measures 12 meters has a hypotenuse of 24 meters. Find the length of the other leg.

32. A right triangle with a leg that measures 8 feet has a hypotenuse of 23 feet. Find the length of the other leg.

33. Patti drove 80 miles to the west and then drove 60 miles south. How far is she from her starting location?

34. Victor flew to a city that was 700 miles north and 2400 miles east of his starting point. How far did he fly to reach this city?

35. George is casting a shadow on the ground. If George is 2 feet shorter than the length of the shadow on the ground and the tip of the shadow is 10 feet from the top of George's head, how tall is George?

36. A 15-foot ladder is leaning against the wall. If the distance between the base of the ladder and the wall is 3 feet less than the height of the top of the ladder on the wall, how high up the wall does the ladder reach?

37. A guy wire 40 feet long runs from the top of a pole to a spot on the ground. If the height of the pole is 5 feet more than the distance from the base of the pole to the spot where the guy wire is anchored, how tall is the pole?

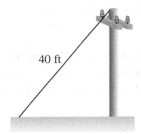

40 ft

38. A 12-foot ramp leads to a doorway. If the distance between the ground and the doorway is 8 feet less than the horizontal distance covered by the ramp, how high above the ground is the doorway?

39. A rectangular computer screen is 13 inches wide and 10 inches high. Find the length of its diagonal.

40. The bases on a baseball diamond form a square whose side is 90 feet. How far is it from home plate to second base?

41. The length of a rectangular quilt is 1 foot more than its width. If the diagonal of the quilt is 6.5 feet, find the length and width of the quilt.

42. The diagonal of a rectangular table is 9 feet, and the length of the table is 5 feet more than its width. Find the length and width of the table.

Use the following fact about right triangles for Exercises 43–46: The legs of a right triangle represent the base and height of that triangle.

43. The height of a right triangle is 3 feet less than the base of the triangle. The area of the triangle is 54 square feet.

  a) Use the information to find the base and height of the triangle.

  b) Find the hypotenuse of the triangle.

44. The base of a right triangle is 4 feet less than twice the height of the triangle. The area of the triangle is 24 square feet.

  a) Use the information to find the base and height of the triangle.

  b) Use the information to find the hypotenuse of the triangle.

45. A road sign indicating falling rocks is in the shape of an equilateral triangle, with each side measuring 80 centimeters.

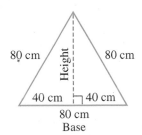

80 cm   Height   80 cm

40 cm   40 cm

80 cm
Base

  a) Use the Pythagorean theorem to find the height of the triangle. Round to the nearest tenth of a centimeter.

  b) Find the area of the sign.

46. A farmer fenced in a corral in the shape of an equilateral triangle, with each side measuring 30 feet.

  a) Use the Pythagorean theorem to find the height of the triangle. Round to the nearest tenth of a foot.

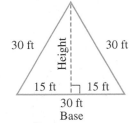

30 ft   Height   30 ft

15 ft   15 ft

30 ft
Base

  b) Find the area of the corral.

✏️ Writing in Mathematics

Answer in complete sentences.

47. Write a word problem whose solution is *The length of the rectangle is 14 feet, and the width is 9 feet.* The problem must lead to a quadratic equation.

48. Write a word problem associated with the equation $60^2 + b^2 = 90^2$. Explain how you created the problem. Solve your problem, explaining each step.

10.6

Quadratic and Rational Inequalities

OBJECTIVES

1 Solve quadratic inequalities.
2 Solve rational inequalities.
3 Solve inequalities involving functions.
4 Solve applied problems involving inequalities.

Quadratic Inequalities

Objective 1 Solve quadratic inequalities. In this section, we will expand our knowledge of inequalities to include two different types of inequalities: quadratic inequalities and rational inequalities.

> **Quadratic Inequalities**
>
> A **quadratic inequality** is an inequality that can be rewritten as $ax^2 + bx + c < 0$, $ax^2 + bx + c \leq 0$, $ax^2 + bx + c > 0$, or $ax^2 + bx + c \geq 0$.

The first step to solving a quadratic inequality is to find its **zeros**, which are values of x for which $ax^2 + bx + c = 0$. For example, to find the zeros for the inequality $x^2 + 9x - 22 > 0$, we set $x^2 + 9x - 22$ equal to 0 and solve for x.

$$x^2 + 9x - 22 = 0 \quad \text{Set the quadratic expression equal to 0.}$$
$$(x + 11)(x - 2) = 0 \quad \text{Factor.}$$
$$x = -11 \quad \text{or} \quad x = 2 \quad \text{Set each factor equal to 0 and solve.}$$

The zeros for this inequality are -11 and 2.

The zeros of an inequality divide the number line into intervals and often act as boundary points. In any particular interval created by the zeros of an inequality, each real number in the interval is a solution of the inequality or each real number in the interval is not a solution of the inequality. By picking one value in each interval and testing it, we can determine which intervals contain solutions and which do not.

When solving a strict inequality involving the symbol $<$ or $>$, the zeros are not included in the solutions of the inequality and we place an open circle on each zero on the number line. When solving a weak inequality involving the symbol $\leq$ or $\geq$, the zeros are included in the solutions of the inequality and we place a closed circle on each zero.

EXAMPLE 1 Solve $x^2 + x - 20 \leq 0$.

SOLUTION We begin by finding the zeros.

$$x^2 + x - 20 = 0 \quad \text{Set the quadratic expression equal to 0.}$$
$$(x + 5)(x - 4) = 0 \quad \text{Factor.}$$
$$x = -5 \quad \text{or} \quad x = 4 \quad \text{Set each factor equal to 0 and solve.}$$

The zeros for this inequality are -5 and 4. We plot these zeros on a number line and create boundaries between the three intervals, which have been labeled I, II, and III in the figure that follows. The zeros are included as solutions, and we place closed circles on the number line at $x = -5$ and $x = 4$.

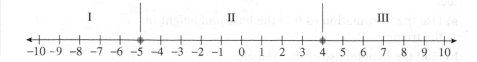

I   II   III

Now we choose a value from each of the three intervals we have created to be the test points. A **test point** is a value of the variable x that we use to evaluate the expression in the inequality, allowing us to determine which intervals contain solutions of the inequality. We will use $x = -6$, $x = 0$, and $x = 5$. Because we are looking for intervals where $x^2 + x - 20 \leq 0$, the solution will be made up of the intervals whose test points produce a negative result when substituted into the expression $x^2 + x - 20$.

Test Point (x)	-6	0	5
$x^2 + x - 20$	$(-6)^2 + (-6) - 20$ $= 36 - 6 - 20$ $= 10$	$(0)^2 + (0) - 20$ $= 0 + 0 - 20$ $= -20$	$(5)^2 + (5) - 20$ $= 25 + 5 - 20$ $= 10$

The only test point for which the expression $x^2 + x - 20$ is negative is $x = 0$, which is in interval II; so the interval $[-5, 4]$ is the solution of this inequality.

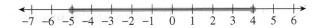

When the expression with which we are working can be factored, we can use a sign chart to determine which intervals are solutions to the inequality. A **sign chart** is a chart that can be used to determine whether an expression is positive or negative for certain intervals of real numbers. A sign chart focuses on whether a factor is positive or negative for each interval, by the use of a test point. If we know the sign of each factor, we can easily find the sign of the product, allowing us to solve the inequality. The initial sign chart should look like the following:

Test Point	$x + 5$	$x - 4$	$(x + 5)(x - 4)$
-6			
0			
5			

We fill in the first row by determining the sign of each factor when $x = -6$. Because $-6 + 5$ is negative, we put a negative sign in the first row underneath $x + 5$. In the same way, $x - 4$ is negative when $x = -6$; so we put another negative sign in the first row underneath $x - 4$. The product of two negative factors is positive; so we put a positive sign in the first row under $(x + 5)(x - 4)$. Here is the sign chart after it has been completed.

Test Point	$x + 5$	$x - 4$	$(x + 5)(x - 4)$
-6	$-$	$-$	$+$
0	$+$	$-$	$-$
5	$+$	$+$	$+$

Notice that the product is negative in the interval containing the test point $x = 0$. Therefore, the solution is the interval $[-5, 4]$.

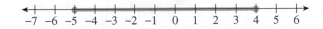

Quick Check 1

Solve $x^2 - 14x + 48 \leq 0$.

If the quadratic expression does not factor, we cannot use a sign chart. In that case, we will find the zeros of the expression by using the quadratic formula. We will then substitute the values for the test points directly into the quadratic expression.

EXAMPLE 2 Solve $x^2 + 6x + 4 > 0$.

SOLUTION We find the zeros by solving the equation $x^2 + 6x + 4 = 0$. Because $x^2 + 6x + 4$ does not factor, we will use the quadratic formula to solve the equation.

$$x = \frac{-6 \pm \sqrt{6^2 - 4(1)(4)}}{2(1)}$$ Substitute 1 for a, 6 for b, and 4 for c.

$$x = \frac{-6 \pm \sqrt{20}}{2}$$ Simplify the radicand.

$$x = \frac{-6 \pm 2\sqrt{5}}{2}$$ Simplify the square root.

$$x = \frac{\overset{1}{2}(-3 \pm \sqrt{5})}{\underset{1}{2}}$$ Divide out common factors.

$$x = -3 \pm \sqrt{5}$$ Simplify.

The zeros for this inequality are $-3 - \sqrt{5}$ and $-3 + \sqrt{5}$. We need an approximate value for each zero to determine where each zero belongs on the number line. These two zeros are approximately equal to -0.8 and -5.2. The zeros are not included as solutions, so we place open circles at the zeros.

We will use $x = -6$, $x = -1$, and $x = 0$ as test points. We are looking for intervals where the expression $x^2 + 6x + 4$ is greater than 0, and our solution will be made up of the intervals whose test points produce a positive result when substituted into $x^2 + 6x + 4$.

Test Point	$x^2 + 6x + 4$	Sign
-6	$(-6)^2 + 6(-6) + 4 = 4$	$+$
-1	$(-1)^2 + 6(-1) + 4 = -1$	$-$
0	$(0)^2 + 6(0) + 4 = 4$	$+$

Notice that the product is positive in the intervals containing the test points $x = -6$ and $x = 0$. Here is the solution.

In interval notation, we can express this solution as $(-\infty, -3 - \sqrt{5}) \cup (-3 + \sqrt{5}, \infty)$. (Notice that we used the exact values in the solution, not the approximate values.)

▶ **Quick Check 2**

Solve $x^2 + 3x - 15 \geq 0$.

If the expression in the inequality has no zeros, every real number is a solution of the inequality or the inequality has no solutions at all.

EXAMPLE 3 Solve $x^2 - 5x + 7 \le 0$.

SOLUTION   We begin by looking for the zeros of $x^2 - 5x + 7$. Because this expression does not factor, we will use the quadratic formula.

$$x = \frac{-(-5) \pm \sqrt{(-5)^2 - 4(1)(7)}}{2(1)} \qquad \text{Substitute 1 for } a, -5 \text{ for } b, \text{ and 7 for } c.$$

$$x = \frac{5 \pm \sqrt{-3}}{2} \qquad \text{Simplify the radicand and denominator.}$$

The discriminant is negative, so this expression has no real zeros. In this case, we can pick any real number and use it as the only test point. When $x = 0$, we can see that $x^2 - 5x + 7$ is equal to 7, which is not less than or equal to 0. This inequality has no solution.

▸ Quick Check 3
Solve $x^2 - 5x + 20 > 0$.

Rational Inequalities

Objective ② **Solve rational inequalities.**

> ⌐ Rational Inequalities ───────────────────────────
> A **rational inequality** is an inequality that involves a rational expression, such as
> $$\frac{x + 2}{x - 4} < 0.$$

There are two differences between solving a rational inequality and solving a quadratic inequality. The first difference is that the zeros of the numerator and the denominator are used to divide the real number line into intervals. The second difference is that the zeros from the denominator are never included in the solution, even when the inequality is a weak inequality involving $\le$ or $\ge$. This is because if a value causes a denominator to equal 0, the rational expression is undefined for that value.

EXAMPLE 4 Solve $\dfrac{(x + 3)(x + 5)}{x - 1} \ge 0$.

SOLUTION   Begin by finding the zeros of the numerator.

$$(x + 3)(x + 5) = 0 \qquad \text{Set the numerator equal to 0.}$$
$$x = -3 \quad \text{or} \quad x = -5 \quad \text{Set each factor equal to 0 and solve.}$$

The zeros of the numerator are -3 and -5. Now find the zeros of the denominator.

$$x - 1 = 0 \quad \text{Set the denominator equal to 0.}$$
$$x = 1 \quad \text{Solve.}$$

The zero of the denominator is 1. Here are all of the zeros on a single number line, dividing the number line into four intervals.

Keep in mind that the value $x = 1$ cannot be included in any solution, as it is a zero of the denominator. We will use the values $x = -6, x = -4, x = 0,$ and $x = 2$ as test points. Because the numerator factors and the denominator is a linear expression, we can use a sign chart. We are looking for intervals where the expression is positive.

Test Point	$x + 3$	$x + 5$	$x - 1$	$\dfrac{(x + 3)(x + 5)}{x - 1}$
-6	$-$	$-$	$-$	$-$
-4	$-$	$+$	$-$	$+$
0	$+$	$+$	$-$	$-$
2	$+$	$+$	$+$	$+$

The intervals containing $x = -4$ and $x = 2$ are solutions of this inequality, as represented on the following number line:

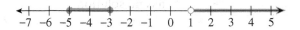

This can be represented in interval notation as $[-5, -3] \cup (1, \infty)$.

▶ Quick Check 4

Solve $\dfrac{(x + 2)(x - 6)}{(x - 8)(x + 7)} \leq 0.$

A WORD OF CAUTION When we solve a rational inequality, the zeros of the denominator are excluded as solutions because the rational expression is undefined for those values.

EXAMPLE 5 Solve $\dfrac{x^2 - 4x - 12}{x^2 - 9} < 0.$

SOLUTION   Begin by finding the zeros of the numerator.

$$x^2 - 4x - 12 = 0 \qquad \text{Set the numerator equal to 0.}$$
$$(x - 6)(x + 2) = 0 \qquad \text{Factor.}$$
$$x - 6 = 0 \quad \text{or} \quad x + 2 = 0 \quad \text{Set each factor equal to 0.}$$
$$x = 6 \quad \text{or} \quad x = -2 \qquad \text{Solve.}$$

The zeros of the numerator are 6 and -2. Now find the zeros of the denominator.

$$x^2 - 9 = 0 \qquad \text{Set the denominator equal to 0.}$$
$$(x + 3)(x - 3) = 0 \qquad \text{Factor.}$$
$$x + 3 = 0 \quad \text{or} \quad x - 3 = 0 \quad \text{Set each factor equal to 0.}$$
$$x = -3 \quad \text{or} \quad x = 3 \qquad \text{Solve.}$$

The zeros of the denominator are -3 and 3. Here are all of the zeros on a single number line, dividing the number line into five intervals.

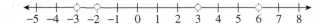

In this example, none of the zeros can be included in any solution, as the inequality was strictly less than 0 and not less than or equal to 0. We will use the values $x = -4$, $x = -2.5$, $x = 0$, $x = 4$, and $x = 7$ as test points. Here is the sign chart; keep in mind that we are looking for intervals in which this expression is negative.

Test Point	$x - 6$	$x + 2$	$x + 3$	$x - 3$	$\dfrac{(x - 6)(x + 2)}{(x + 3)(x - 3)}$
-4	$-$	$-$	$-$	$-$	$+$
-2.5	$-$	$-$	$+$	$-$	$-$
0	$-$	$+$	$+$	$-$	$+$
4	$-$	$+$	$+$	$+$	$-$
7	$+$	$+$	$+$	$+$	$+$

The intervals containing $x = -2.5$ and $x = 4$ are solutions of this inequality, as represented on the following number line:

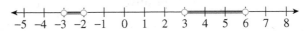

This can be represented in interval notation as $(-3, -2) \cup (3, 6)$.

▶ **Quick Check 5**

Solve $\dfrac{x^2 - 6x}{x^2 + 5x + 4} > 0$.

When solving rational inequalities, if the inequality contains expressions on both sides, we must rewrite the inequality in such a way that there is a single rational expression on one side of the inequality and 0 on the other side. We then solve the inequality the same way we solved the previous examples.

EXAMPLE 6 Solve $\dfrac{x^2 + 4x + 9}{x + 6} \geq 2$.

SOLUTION Begin by subtracting 2 from both sides of the inequality; then combine the left side of the inequality as a single rational expression.

$$\frac{x^2 + 4x + 9}{x + 6} \geq 2$$

$$\frac{x^2 + 4x + 9}{x + 6} - 2 \geq 0 \quad \text{Subtract 2 from both sides.}$$

$$\frac{x^2 + 4x + 9}{x + 6} - 2 \cdot \frac{x + 6}{x + 6} \geq 0 \quad \text{Multiply 2 by } \frac{x + 6}{x + 6} \text{ so that both expressions have the same denominator.}$$

$$\frac{x^2 + 4x + 9 - 2x - 12}{x + 6} \geq 0 \quad \text{Distribute and combine numerators.}$$

$$\frac{x^2 + 2x - 3}{x + 6} \geq 0 \quad \text{Simplify the numerator.}$$

Now find the zeros of the numerator.

$$x^2 + 2x - 3 = 0 \quad \text{Set the numerator equal to 0.}$$

$$(x - 1)(x + 3) = 0 \quad \text{Factor.}$$

$$x - 1 = 0 \quad \text{or} \quad x + 3 = 0 \quad \text{Set each factor equal to 0.}$$

$$x = 1 \quad \text{or} \quad x = -3 \quad \text{Solve.}$$

The zeros of the numerator are 1 and -3. Now find the zeros of the denominator.

$$x + 6 = 0 \quad \text{Set the denominator equal to 0.}$$

$$x = -6 \quad \text{Solve.}$$

The only zero of the denominator is −6. Here are all of the zeros on a single number line, dividing the number line into four intervals.

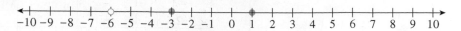

In this example, the zeros from the numerator are included as solutions, while the zeros from the denominator are excluded as solutions. We will use the values $x = -7$, $x = -4$, $x = 0$, and $x = 2$ as test points. Here is the sign chart; keep in mind that we are looking for intervals in which the expression $\dfrac{(x + 3)(x - 1)}{x + 6}$ is positive.

Test Point	$x + 3$	$x - 1$	$x + 6$	$\dfrac{(x + 3)(x - 1)}{x + 6}$
−7	−	−	−	−
−4	−	−	+	+
0	+	−	+	−
2	+	+	+	+

The intervals containing $x = -4$ and $x = 2$ are solutions to this inequality, as represented on the following number line:

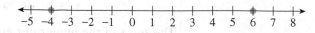

This can be represented in interval notation as $(-6, -3] \cup [1, \infty)$.

Quick Check 6

Solve $\dfrac{x^2 - 17}{x - 3} < 4$.

Solving Inequalities Involving Functions

Objective 3 Solve inequalities involving functions. We move on to examining inequalities involving functions.

EXAMPLE 7 Given $f(x) = x^2 - 2x - 16$, find all values x for which $f(x) \leq 8$.

SOLUTION   We begin by setting the function less than or equal to 8.

$$f(x) \leq 8$$
$$x^2 - 2x - 16 \leq 8 \quad \text{Set the function less than or equal to 8}$$
$$x^2 - 2x - 24 \leq 0 \quad \text{Subtract 8 to write the inequality in standard form.}$$

We now find the zeros for this inequality.

$$x^2 - 2x - 24 = 0 \qquad \text{Set the quadratic expression equal to 0.}$$
$$(x - 6)(x + 4) = 0 \qquad \text{Factor.}$$
$$x - 6 = 0 \quad \text{or} \quad x + 4 = 0 \quad \text{Set each factor equal to 0.}$$
$$x = 6 \quad \text{or} \quad x = -4 \qquad \text{Solve.}$$

The zeros for this inequality are 6 and −4.

We will use $x = -5$, $x = 0$, and $x = 7$ as our test points. Our solution will be made up of the intervals whose test points produce a negative result when substituted into the expression $x^2 - 2x - 24$. Here is the sign chart after it has been completed.

Test Point	$x - 6$	$x + 4$	$(x - 6)(x + 4)$
-5	$-$	$-$	$+$
0	$-$	$+$	$-$
7	$+$	$+$	$+$

The product is negative in the interval containing the test point $x = 0$. Here is our solution represented on a number line.

Quick Check 7

Given $f(x) = x^2 + 10x + 35$, find all values x for which $f(x) < 14$.

In interval notation, the solution is expressed as $[-4, 6]$.

Solving Applied Problems Involving Inequalities

Objective 4 Solve applied problems involving inequalities.

EXAMPLE 8 A projectile with an initial velocity of 96 feet per second is fired from the roof of a building 72 feet tall. The height of the projectile, in feet, after t seconds is given by the function $h(t) = -16t^2 + 96t + 72$. During what period of time is the projectile at least 200 feet above the ground?

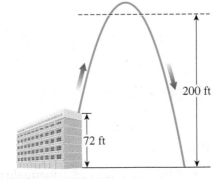

SOLUTION   To find the time interval that the projectile is at least 200 feet above the ground, we must solve the inequality $h(t) \geq 200$.

$$h(t) \geq 200$$

$-16t^2 + 96t + 72 \geq 200$ Replace $h(t)$ with $-16t^2 + 96t + 72$.

$-16t^2 + 96t - 128 \geq 0$ Subtract 200 to rewrite the inequality in standard form.

$16t^2 - 96t + 128 \leq 0$ Multiply both sides of the inequality by -1. Change the direction of the inequality.

Now we find the zeros of the inequality.

$$16t^2 - 96t + 128 = 0$$

$16(t^2 - 6t + 8) = 0$ Factor out the common factor 16.

$16(t - 2)(t - 4) = 0$ Factor the trinomial.

$t = 2$ or $t = 4$ Set each variable factor equal to 0 and solve.

The zeros of the inequality are $t = 2$ and $t = 4$.

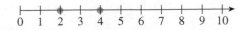

We will use $t = 1$, $t = 3$, and $t = 5$ as test points. (Note that t must be greater than or equal to 0 because it represents the amount of time since the projectile was fired.) In this case, we will substitute the values for the test points in the function

$h(t)$. If the function's output for one of the test points is 200 or higher, each point in the interval containing the test point is a solution to the inequality $h(t) \geq 200$.

$t = 1$	$t = 3$	$t = 5$
$h(1) = -16(1)^2 + 96(1) + 72$	$h(3) = -16(3)^2 + 96(3) + 72$	$h(5) = -16(5)^2 + 96(5) + 72$
$= -16(1) + 96 + 72$	$= -16(9) + 288 + 72$	$= -16(25) + 480 + 72$
$= -16 + 96 + 72$	$= -144 + 288 + 72$	$= -400 + 480 + 72$
$= 152$	$= 216$	$= 152$

The inequality $h(t) \geq 200$ is true only in the interval containing the test point $t = 3$; so the projectile's height is at least 200 feet from 2 seconds after launch until 4 seconds after launch.

Quick Check 8

A projectile with an initial velocity of 272 feet per second is fired from ground level. The height of the projectile, in feet, after t seconds is given by the function $h(t) = -16t^2 + 272t$. During what period of time is the projectile at least 960 feet above the ground?

Exercises 10.6

 MyMathLab

 PRACTICE   WATCH   DOWNLOAD   READ   REVIEW

Vocabulary

1. A(n) _____ inequality is an inequality involving a quadratic expression.
2. The _____ of a quadratic inequality in standard form are values of the variable for which the quadratic expression is equal to 0.
3. The zeros of a(n) _____ inequality are not included in the solutions of that inequality.
4. The zeros from the _____ of a rational inequality are never included as a solution.

Solve each quadratic inequality. Express your solution on a number line and using interval notation.

5. $(x - 5)(x - 1) < 0$

6. $(x + 3)(x - 2) > 0$

7. $-2(x - 6)(x + 3) \leq 0$

8. $x(x - 4) > 0$

9. $x^2 - 4x - 21 < 0$

10. $x^2 + 9x + 18 \leq 0$

11. $x^2 - 10x + 16 \geq 0$

12. $x^2 + 3x - 54 > 0$

13. $x^2 - 25 \leq 0$

14. $x^2 - 4x \geq 0$

15. $x^2 + 6x + 3 > 0$

16. $x^2 - 5x - 11 < 0$

17. $3x^2 - 5x - 1 \geq 0$

18. $2x^2 + 7x + 4 \leq 0$

19. $x^2 + 3x + 5 > 0$

20. $x^2 + 7x + 14 > 0$

21. $x^2 - 2x + 24 < 0$

22. $x^2 + x + 8 < 0$

23. $x^2 - x \geq 56$

24. $x^2 - 8x \leq 20$

25. $-x^2 + 10x - 5 > 0$

26. $-x^2 + 6x + 1 < 0$

Solve each polynomial inequality. Express your solution on a number line and using interval notation.

27. $(x - 1)(x + 2)(x - 4) \geq 0$

28. $(x + 8)(x - 5)(x - 2) \leq 0$

29. $(x - 7)^2(x + 5)(x + 9) \leq 0$

30. $(x - 10)^3(x + 4)^2(x - 4) \geq 0$

Solve each rational inequality. Express your solution on a number line and using interval notation.

31. $\dfrac{x - 3}{x + 4} < 0$

32. $\dfrac{x + 8}{x - 6} > 0$

33. $\dfrac{(x + 2)(x - 2)}{x + 1} \leq 0$

34. $\dfrac{(x + 7)(x - 4)}{(x - 5)(x + 10)} < 0$

35. $\dfrac{x - 4}{x^2 + 9x + 18} < 0$

36. $\dfrac{x^2 + 11x + 24}{x + 5} > 0$

37. $\dfrac{x^2 + x - 20}{x^2 - 4} \geq 0$

38. $\dfrac{x^2 - 7x - 8}{x^2 - 4x - 21} \leq 0$

39. $\dfrac{x^2 - 2x - 48}{x^2 + 13x + 36} \leq 0$

40. $\dfrac{x^2 + 11x + 30}{x^2 + 3x - 28} \geq 0$

41. $\dfrac{x^2 - 4x + 3}{x^2 + 4x - 32} < 0$

42. $\dfrac{x^2 - 81}{x^2 - 15x + 54} \leq 0$

43. $\dfrac{4x - 7}{x - 4} > 3$

44. $\dfrac{6x + 18}{x + 2} \leq 5$

45. $\dfrac{x^2 + 9x + 12}{x + 3} \geq 2$

46. $\dfrac{x^2 - 3x - 46}{x - 7} < 4$

47. $\dfrac{x^2 + 3x + 10}{x - 2} \leq x$

48. $\dfrac{x^2 + 7x + 21}{x + 4} \geq x$

49. A projectile with an initial velocity of 64 feet per second is fired upward from the roof of a building 27 feet tall. The height of the projectile, in feet, after t seconds is given by the function $h(t) = -16t^2 + 64t + 27$. For what length of time is the projectile at least 75 feet above the ground?

50. A projectile with an initial velocity of 208 feet per second is fired upward from the roof of a building 98 feet tall. The height of the projectile, in feet, after t seconds is given by the function $h(t) = -16t^2 + 208t + 98$. For what length of time is the projectile at least 450 feet above the ground?

51. A projectile with an initial velocity of 32 feet per second is fired upward from ground level. The height of the projectile, in feet, after t seconds is given by the function $h(t) = -16t^2 + 32t$. For what length of time is the projectile at least 12 feet above the ground?

52. A projectile with an initial velocity of 48 feet per second is fired upward from ground level. The height of the projectile, in feet, after t seconds is given by the function $h(t) = -16t^2 + 48t$. For what length of time is the projectile at least 20 feet above the ground?

53. A projectile with an initial velocity of 125 feet per second is fired upward from the roof of a building 48 feet tall.

a) List the function $h(t)$ that gives the height of the projectile in feet after t seconds.

b) For what time interval is the projectile at least 200 feet above the ground?

54. A projectile with an initial velocity of 150 feet per second is fired upward from the roof of a building 80 feet tall.

a) List the function $h(t)$ that gives the height of the projectile in feet after t seconds.

b) For what time interval is the projectile at least 300 feet above the ground?

55. Given $f(x) = x^2 - 8x + 12$, find all values x for which $f(x) \leq 0$.

56. Given $f(x) = x^2 + 13x - 5$, find all values x for which $f(x) \geq 0$.

57. Given $f(x) = x^2 - 5x + 13$, find all values x for which $f(x) \geq 7$.

58. Given $f(x) = x^2 + 4x - 31$, find all values x for which $f(x) < 14$.

59. Given $f(x) = \dfrac{x + 9}{x - 6}$, find all values x for which $f(x) \leq 0$.

60. Given $f(x) = \dfrac{x^2 - 17x + 70}{x^2 + 2x - 48}$, find all values x for which $f(x) < 0$.

61. Given $f(x) = \dfrac{x^2 - 8x - 33}{x^2 + 13x + 42}$, find all values x for which $f(x) > 0$.

62. Given $f(x) = \dfrac{x^2 + 14x + 24}{x^2 + 6x + 5}$, find all values x for which $f(x) \geq 0$.

Find each quadratic inequality whose solution is given.

63.

64.

65.

66.

Find each rational inequality whose solution is given.

67.

68.

Writing in Mathematics

Answer in complete sentences.

71. *Solutions Manual* Write a solutions manual page for the following problem.

$$Solve \ \frac{x^2 - 6x - 16}{x^2 - 16} \geq 0.$$

69.

70.

Functions

In this chapter, we will continue to explore functions. In addition to linear and quadratic functions, we will examine new functions such as the square root function and the cubic function. We also will cover the algebra of functions, learning ways to create a new function from two or more existing functions. We will finish the chapter by discussing inverse functions.

STUDY STRATEGY

Study Environment It is very important to study in the proper environment. This chapter will focus on how to create an environment that allows you to get the most out of your study sessions. We will discuss where to study and what the conditions should be in that location.

11.1

Review of Functions

OBJECTIVES

1　Review of functions, domain, and range.
2　Represent a function as a set of ordered pairs.
3　Use the vertical-line test to determine whether a graph represents a function.
4　Use function notation.
5　Evaluate functions.
6　Interpret graphs of functions.

Functions; Domain and Range

Objective 1 Review of functions, domain, and range. Suppose a college charges its students a $50 registration fee in addition to an enrollment fee of $26 per unit. A student who signs up for 12 units would be charged $312 for the classes (12 units times $26 per unit) plus the $50 registration fee, or a total of $362. The amount a student pays depends on the number of units the student takes. We say that the amount a student pays is a function of the number of units in which the student is enrolled. In general, if a student is taking x units, the student's fees can be found using the formula $50 + 26x$.

Recall from Chapter 3 that a **function** is a relation that takes an input value and assigns a particular output value to it. In the previous example, the input value is the number of units the student is taking and the output value is the total fees for that student. For a relation to define a function, each input value must be assigned one and only one output value. In terms of the previous example, this means that students who are taking the same number of units pay the same amount of money. It is not possible for two students to each take 12 units but pay a different amount.

As we first saw in Chapter 3, the set of input values for a function is called the **domain** of the function. The domain for the previous example is the set of units in which a student can be enrolled. The possible values in the domain would be the set $\{1, 2, 3, \dots\}$. The set of output values for a function is called the **range** of the function. Here is a table showing possible values in the range of this function.

Domain (Units)	1	2	3	...	x
Range (Fees, $)	$50 + 26(1) = 76$	$50 + 26(2) = 102$	$50 + 26(3) = 128$	...	$50 + 26x$

If there is no maximum number of units that a student can take, this table would continue indefinitely.

Although many of our functions will be given by a formula, many functions will not. For instance, consider the set of students enrolled in your math class. If we asked each student in your class to tell us the month of his or her birthday, a function would exist in which the input value is a student and the output value is the month of the student's birthday. The domain of this function is the set of students in your math class, and the range is the set of months from January through December.

EXAMPLE 1 The World Cup is a soccer tournament that is held every four years. Here are the winners of the World Cup for the years 1930–2010. (The tournament was not held in 1942 or 1946 due to World War II.)

Year	Winner	Year	Winner
1930	Uruguay	1978	Argentina
1934	Italy	1982	Italy
1938	Italy	1986	Argentina
1950	Uruguay	1990	West Germany
1954	West Germany	1994	Brazil
1958	Brazil	1998	France
1962	Brazil	2002	Brazil
1966	England	2006	Italy
1970	Brazil	2010	Spain
1974	West Germany		

a) Does a function exist for which the input value is the year of the tournament and the output value is the winner of that tournament?

SOLUTION   Because each year listed has only one winner, this correspondence is a function. This is true even though some teams, such as Italy, have won more than once. By the definition of a function, each input value must be associated with one and only one output value. It is possible for more than one input value to be associated with the same output value.

The domain of this function is the set of years in which the World Cup has been held, and the range of this function is the set of teams that have won the World Cup.

b) Does a function exist for which the input value is the winner of a tournament and the output value is the year the country won the tournament?

SOLUTION   No, this correspondence is not a function, as one input value could be associated with more than one output value. For instance, the input value Italy is associated with the years 1934, 1938, 1982, and 2006.

▶ **Quick Check 1**

Here are the names and ages of the five members of a study group.

Name	Tiffany	Tyler	Teresa	Tim	Tina
Age	19	22	19	20	24

a) Does a function exist for which the input value is the name of a member of the study group and the output value is the age of that person?

b) Does a function exist for which the input value is the age of a member of the study group and the output value is the name of the person?

Ordered-Pair Notation

Objective 2 Represent a function as a set of ordered pairs. Functions can be expressed as a set of ordered pairs. The first coordinate of each ordered pair will be the input value of the function, and the second coordinate will be the corresponding output value. A set of ordered pairs represents a function if none of the first coordinates are repeated.

EXAMPLE 2   Determine whether the set of ordered pairs is a function. If it is a function, state its domain and range.

$$\{(-3, 9), (-2, 4), (-1, 1), (0, 0), (1, 1), (2, 4), (3, 9)\}$$

SOLUTION   This set of ordered pairs is a function because no first coordinate is repeated. Notice that three pairs of ordered pairs share the same second coordinate. This does not violate the definition of a function. Although each possible input value of a function can be associated with only one output value, a particular output value of a function can be associated with several different input values.

The domain of this function is the set $\{-3, -2, -1, 0, 1, 2, 3\}$.
The range is $\{0, 1, 4, 9\}$.

▶ Quick Check 2

Determine whether the set of ordered pairs is a function. If it is a function, state its domain and range.

$$\{(16, -3), (13, -2), (10, -1), (7, 0), (10, 1)\}$$

Vertical-Line Test

Objective 3 Use the vertical-line test to determine whether a graph represents a function. Although we have examined only sets of ordered pairs that have a **finite,** or limited, number of ordered pairs, the graph of an equation may represent a function as well. The graph of an equation represents an **infinite,** or unlimited, number of ordered pairs. If there are two ordered pairs on the graph of an equation that share the same x-coordinate but they have different y-coordinates, the graph does not represent a function.

EXAMPLE 3   Determine whether the graph below represents a function.

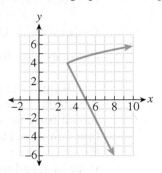

SOLUTION   This graph does not represent a function because there are points on the graph that have the same *x*-coordinates but different *y*-coordinates. For example, the points $(6, 5)$ and $(6, -2)$ have the same *x*-coordinate but different *y*-coordinates. This means that one input value is associated with more than one output value, violating the definition of a function.

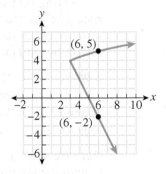

To determine whether a graph represents a function, we will apply the **vertical-line test.**

The Vertical-Line Test

If a vertical line can be drawn that intersects a graph at more than one point, the graph does not represent a function.

The graph from the previous example fails the vertical-line test because a vertical line can be drawn that falls through both $(6, 5)$ and $(6, -2)$; so the graph does not represent a function.

EXAMPLE 4   Use the vertical-line test to determine whether the graph below represents a function.

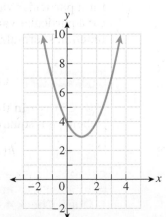

Quick Check 3

Use the vertical-line test to determine whether the following graph represents a function.

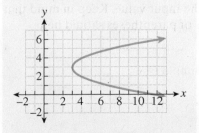

SOLUTION   We cannot draw a vertical line that intersects this graph at more than one point. This graph passes the vertical-line test, so it does represent a function.

Function Notation

Objective 4 Use function notation.

Consider the following graph of the equation $y = 2x + 5$.

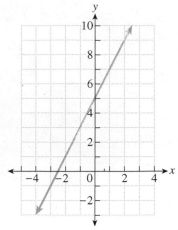

Because the graph passes the vertical-line test, the graph represents a function. The equation is solved for y in terms of x, and we say that y is a function of x. The input of this function is x, and the output is y. The value of y depends on the value of x, and we say that y is the **dependent variable** in the equation. Typically, the equation will be solved for the dependent variable in terms of the other variable. The other variable in an equation is called the **independent variable.** In this equation, the variable x is the independent variable.

Saying that y is a function of x can be expressed symbolically as $y = f(x)$. We read $f(x)$ as "f of x." The letter f is the name of the function, and x represents the input value of the function. The input variable is always the independent variable. The notation $f(x)$ represents the output value of a function f for the input value x.

A WORD OF CAUTION The notation $f(x)$ represents the *output* of function f for the input value x. It does not indicate the product of f and x. We often use the letter f for the name of a function, but we may choose any letter, such as g, h, or F or even a Greek letter such as ϕ (phi).

Because $y = 2x + 5$ is a function, we also can write it as $f(x) = 2x + 5$. When an equation contains $f(x)$ instead of y, the equation is expressed in **function notation.**

$f(x) = 2x + 5$	$f(x) = 2x + 5$	$f(x) = 2x + 5$
⇑	⇑	⇑
The variable inside the parentheses is the input variable for the function.	$f(x)$ is the output value of the function f when the input value is x.	The expression on the right side of the equation is the formula for this function.

Evaluating Functions

Objective 5 Evaluate functions.

Finding the output value of a function $f(x)$ for a particular value of x is called **evaluating** the function. To evaluate a function for a particular value of the variable, we substitute that value for the variable in the function's formula, then simplify the resulting expression.

EXAMPLE 5 Let $h(x) = x^2 + 7x - 30$. Find $h(-8)$.

SOLUTION In this example, we need to square the input value. Keep in mind that when -8 is squared, the result is positive. The use of parentheses should help.

$$h(-8) = (-8)^2 + 7(-8) - 30 \quad \text{Substitute } -8 \text{ for } x.$$
$$= -22 \quad \text{Simplify.}$$

▶ Quick Check 4

Let $f(x) = x^2 - 3x - 20$. Find $f(-5)$.

EXAMPLE 6 Let $f(x) = 7x - 5$. Find $f(3a + 2)$.

SOLUTION   In this example, we are substituting a variable expression, $3a + 2$, for the input variable x rather than substituting a constant as in previous examples.

$$\begin{aligned} f(3a + 2) &= 7(3a + 2) - 5 && \text{Substitute } 3a + 2 \text{ for } x. \\ &= 21a + 14 - 5 && \text{Multiply.} \\ &= 21a + 9 && \text{Combine like terms.} \end{aligned}$$

▶ Quick Check 5

Let $f(x) = -4x + 21$. Find $f(3m - 9)$.

Interpreting Graphs

Objective 6 **Interpret graphs of functions.** The ability to read and interpret a graph is a valuable skill because the graph of a function reveals important information about the function itself. To begin, we can determine the domain and range of a function from its graph. Recall that the domain of a function is the set of all possible input values for that function. This can be read from left to right along the x-axis on a graph. The range of a function is the set of all possible output values for the function, and this can be read vertically from the bottom to the top of the graph along the y-axis. The following graph of a function $f(x)$ will help us understand these concepts.

The graph begins at the point $(5, 2)$ and extends upward to the right. We can express the domain of the function in interval notation as $[5, \infty)$, as the set of possible input values begins at $x = 5$ and continues without bound. The range of the function is $[2, \infty)$, as the lowest function value is 2, and the values of the function increase without bound from there.

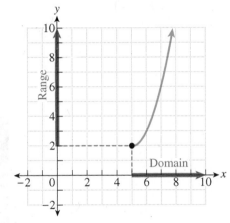

Consider the graph of $f(x)$ shown here. This graph extends indefinitely to the left and to the right, so the domain of the function $f(x)$ is the set of all real numbers $\mathbb{R}$. For the range, this function has a minimum value of -6, as the point $(-2, -6)$ is the lowest point on the graph. The function increases without limit, so the range of the function $f(x)$ is $[-6, \infty)$.

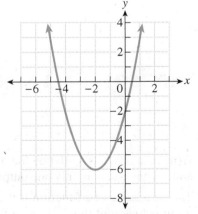

We can use the graph of a function to evaluate the function for a particular input value even when we do not know the formula for the function.

Suppose we wanted to use the graph of a function $f(x)$ to evaluate the function when $x = 6$, or in other words, find $f(6)$. The point on the graph that has an x-coordinate of 6 is the point $(6, 5)$. Because the y-coordinate is 5, we know that $f(6) = 5$.

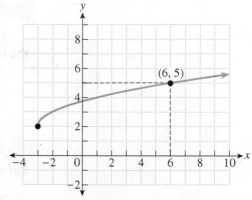

We also can use the graph of a function to determine which input value(s) produce a particular output value.

Suppose we wanted to use the graph of a function $f(x)$ to determine the values of x for which the function $f(x) = -7$. We are looking for a point or points on the graph that have a y-coordinate of -7. There are two such points on this graph: $(-4, -7)$ and $(-6, -7)$. $f(x) = -7$ when $x = -4$ and when $x = -6$.

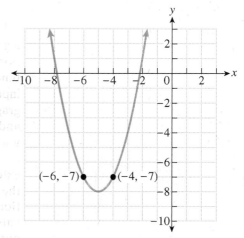

BUILDING YOUR STUDY STRATEGY

Study Environment, 1 Location When you are choosing a place to study, select one that is free from distractions. For example, if you study in a room that has a television on, you will find yourself repeatedly glancing up at the television. This steals time and attention from the task at hand. Working in a room that has people entering and exiting can be distracting as well.

Exercises 11.1   MyMathLab

PRACTICE   WATCH   DOWNLOAD   READ   REVIEW

Vocabulary

1. A(n) _____ is a relation that takes one input value and assigns one and only one output value to it.

2. The _____ of a function is the set of all possible input values, and the _____ of a function is the set of all possible output values.

3. Substituting a value for the function's variable and simplifying the resulting expression is called _____ the function.

4. The _____ is a method that determines whether a graph represents a function.

5. Does a function exist for which the input value is a college graduate and the output value is the starting salary for that graduate's first job? Explain.

6. Does a function exist for which the input value is a woman and the output value is the number of children the woman has? Explain.

7. Does a function exist for which the input value is a person and the output value is the number of jobs the person has held in his or her lifetime? Explain.

8. Does a function exist for which the input value is an orchestra and the output value is the number of players in that orchestra? Explain.

9. Does a function exist for which the input value is a temperature in degrees Fahrenheit and the output value is a city that had that temperature as its high temperature last Tuesday? Explain.

10. Does a function exist for which the input value is the price per share of a stock and the output value is the name of the stock? Explain.

Determine whether the set of ordered pairs is a function. If it is a function, state its domain and range.

11. {(1960, Kennedy), (1964, Johnson), (1968, Nixon), (1972, Nixon), (1976, Carter), (1980, Reagan), (1984, Reagan)}

12. {(2003, Marlins), (2004, Red Sox), (2005, White Sox), (2006, Cardinals), (2007, Red Sox)}

13. {(5, −5), (3, −3), (1, −1), (−1, 1), (−3, 3), (−5, 5)}

14. {(−2, 8), (−1, 6), (0, 4), (1, 2), (2, 0), (3, −2), (4, −4), (5, −6), (6, −8)}

15. {(−6, 5), (−3, 5), (0, 5), (3, 5), (6, 5)}

16. {(9, −3), (4, −2), (1, −1), (0, 0), (1, 1), (4, 2), (9, 3)}

Use the vertical-line test to determine whether the graph represents a function.

17.
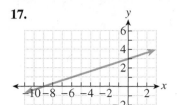

18.
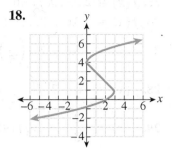

19.
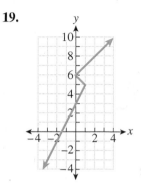

20.
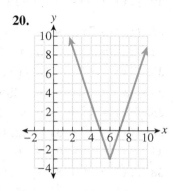

21.
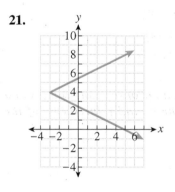

22.
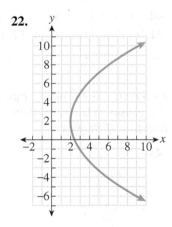

23.
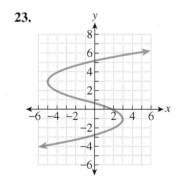

24.
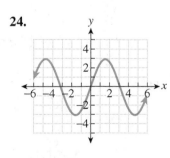

Evaluate the given function.

25. $f(x) = 2x - 9, f(-6)$
26. $f(x) = -3x + 8, f(-17)$
27. $f(x) = -5x - 2, f\left(\dfrac{3}{5}\right)$
28. $f(x) = 4x - 3, f\left(-\dfrac{7}{2}\right)$
29. $f(x) = -\dfrac{2}{3}x + 10, f(9)$
30. $f(x) = \dfrac{9}{4}x - 8, f(-16)$
31. $f(x) = 7x - 4, f(a + 6)$
32. $f(x) = 3x - 20, f(b - 8)$
33. $f(x) = -2x - 17, f(5n + 2)$
34. $f(x) = -4x + 11, f(3m - 10)$
35. $f(x) = x^2 + 7x - 8, f(5)$
36. $f(x) = x^2 - 3x - 12, f(6)$
37. $f(x) = x^2 - 9x + 16, f(-7)$
38. $f(x) = x^2 + 8x - 23, f(-4)$
39. $f(x) = (x + 6)^2 + 37, f(3)$
40. $f(x) = (x - 4)^2 - 60, f(-9)$
41. $f(x) = |3x - 2| + 17, f(-4)$
42. $f(x) = |4x + 19| - 21, f(-8)$

Determine the domain and range of the function $f(x)$ on the graph. Also determine the x- and y-intercepts of the function if they exist.

43.

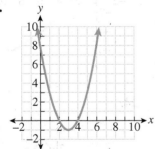

44.

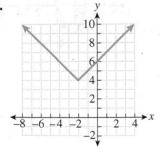

45.

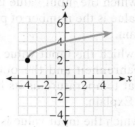

46.

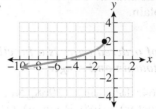

Use the graph of the function $f(x)$ to find the indicated function value.

47. $f(-3)$

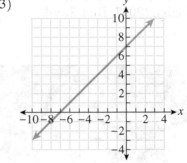

48. $f(4)$

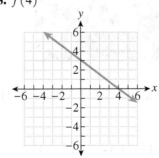

49. $f(-2)$

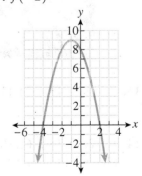

50. $f(4)$

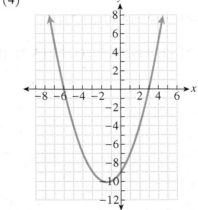

Use the graph of the function f(x) to determine which values of x satisfy the given equation.

51. $f(x) = -4$

52. $f(x) = -2$

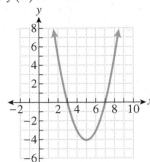

53. $f(x) = -9$

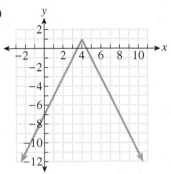

54. $f(x) = -4$

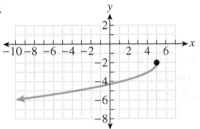

Draw a graph of a function f(x) that meets the given conditions.

55. $f(1) = 2, f(3) = 7, f(5) = 4$, and $f(8) = 6$

56. $f(-5) = -4, f(-2) = 1, f(0) = 3, f(2) = -4$, and $f(5) = -1$

57. Domain: $(-\infty, \infty)$; range: $[-4, \infty), f(1) = -3$

58. Domain: $[-2, \infty)$, range: $[3, \infty), f(2) = 5$

Writing in Mathematics

Answer in complete sentences.

59. If a vertical line can be drawn that intersects a graph at two points, explain why this graph does not represent a function.

60. Explain how to find the domain and range of a function from its graph.

61. Given the graph of a function $f(x)$, explain how to find all values x for which $f(x) = 2$. Use an example to illustrate the process.

62. Given the graph of a function $f(x)$, explain how to find $f(2)$. Use an example to illustrate the process.

Quick Review Exercises

Section 11.1

Graph. Label all intercepts.

1. $y = 3x - 9$

2. $4x - 3y = -24$

3. $y = x^2 - 8x + 7$

4. $y = -(x - 4)^2 + 1$

11.2

Linear Functions

OBJECTIVES

1. **Graph linear functions.**
2. **Determine a linear function from its graph.**
3. **Determine a linear function from data.**
4. **Solve applied problems involving linear profit functions.**

As discussed in Chapter 3, a linear function is a function that can be written in the form $f(x) = mx + b$, where m and b are real numbers.

Graphing Linear Functions

Objective 1 Graph linear functions. Recall that the graph of a linear function is a line and that the two characteristics that determine the graph of a line are its y-intercept and its slope. To graph a linear function, $f(x) = mx + b$, we begin by putting the y-intercept, which is the point $(0, b)$, on the graph. Next, we use the slope m of the line to find additional points on the graph.

EXAMPLE 1 Graph $f(x) = -\frac{2}{3}x + 4$.

SOLUTION We begin by plotting the y-intercept $(0, 4)$ on the graph.

The slope of this line is $m = -\frac{2}{3}$. Beginning at the y-intercept, we can find a second point on the line by moving two units down and three units to the right, which is at the point $(3, 2)$.

Quick Check 1
Graph $f(x) = \frac{3}{4}x - 6$.

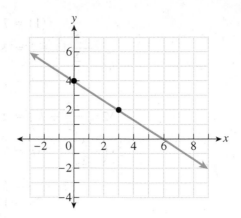

Some functions do not have an x-intercept. One example is a **constant function** of the form $f(x) = b$. The graph of this function is a horizontal line that has a y-intercept at the point $(0, b)$. The reason this type of function is called a constant function is that its output value remains the same, or stays constant, regardless of the input value x.

EXAMPLE 2   Graph $f(x) = 2$.

SOLUTION   The graph of this constant function is a horizontal line with a y-intercept at $(0, 2)$.

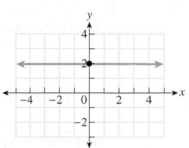

Quick Check 2
Graph $f(x) = -5$.

Finding a Linear Function for a Given Situation

Objective 2 Determine a linear function from its graph. We can determine the linear function $f(x) = mx + b$ from its graph if we can find the coordinates of at least two points that lie on its graph. We begin by finding m. If the line passes through the points (x_1, y_1) and (x_2, y_2), we can find the slope of the line using the formula $m = \dfrac{y_2 - y_1}{x_2 - x_1}$.

Consider the line passing through the points $(1, 7)$ and $(3, 4)$, as shown in the graph at the right. We can substitute 1 for x_1, 7 for y_1, 3 for x_2, and 4 for y_2 in the formula $m = \dfrac{y_2 - y_1}{x_2 - x_1}$ to find m.

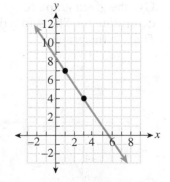

$$m = \frac{4 - 7}{3 - 1} \qquad \text{Substitute into } m = \frac{y_2 - y_1}{x_2 - x_1}.$$

$$m = -\frac{3}{2} \qquad \text{Simplify the numerator and denominator.}$$

Now that we have found the slope, we know that the function is of the form $f(x) = -\frac{3}{2}x + b$. We turn our attention to finding b. We choose one of the points on the line, substitute its coordinates in the function, and solve for b. Because the point $(1, 7)$ is on the graph of the function, we know that $f(1) = 7$.

$$f(1) = 7$$

$$-\frac{3}{2}(1) + b = 7 \qquad \text{Substitute 1 for } x \text{ in the function } f(x).$$

$$-\frac{3}{2} + b = 7 \qquad \text{Multiply.}$$

$$2 \cdot \left(-\frac{3}{2} + b\right) = 2 \cdot 7 \qquad \text{Multiply both sides of the equation by 2 to clear the equation of fractions.}$$

$$\overset{1}{\cancel{2}} \cdot \left(-\frac{3}{\underset{1}{\cancel{2}}}\right) + 2 \cdot b = 2 \cdot 7 \qquad \text{Distribute and divide out common factors.}$$

$$-3 + 2b = 14 \qquad \text{Simplify.}$$

$$2b = 17 \qquad \text{Add 3 to both sides to isolate the term containing } b.$$

$$b = \frac{17}{2} \qquad \text{Divide both sides by 2.}$$

Replacing b with $\frac{17}{2}$, we find that the function is $f(x) = -\frac{3}{2}x + \frac{17}{2}$.

To Determine a Linear Function from Its Graph

1. Determine the coordinates of two points (x_1, y_1) and (x_2, y_2) on the line.
2. Find the slope m of the line using the formula $m = \dfrac{y_2 - y_1}{x_2 - x_1}$.
3. Substitute the value found for m in the formula for a linear function, $f(x) = mx + b$. Then set $f(x_1) = y_1$, or $f(x_2) = y_2$, and solve for b.
4. Substitute the value for b in the formula $f(x) = mx + b$.

EXAMPLE 3 Use the given graph to determine the linear function $f(x)$ on the graph.

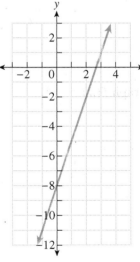

SOLUTION   We begin by determining the coordinates of any two points on the line. This line passes through the points $(2, -2)$ and $(3, 1)$. Now we find the slope m of the line.

$$m = \frac{1 - (-2)}{3 - 2} \qquad \text{Substitute into } m = \frac{y_2 - y_1}{x_2 - x_1}.$$

$$m = 3 \qquad \text{Simplify.}$$

The function is of the form $f(x) = 3x + b$. Because the point $(3, 1)$ is on the graph of the function, we know that $f(3) = 1$. We can use this fact to find b.

Quick Check 3

Use the given graph to determine the linear function $f(x)$ on the graph.

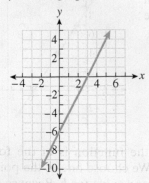

$$f(3) = 1$$

$$3(3) + b = 1 \qquad \text{Substitute 3 for } x \text{ in the function } f(x).$$

$$9 + b = 1 \qquad \text{Multiply.}$$

$$b = -8 \qquad \text{Subtract 9 from both sides to isolate } b.$$

Replacing b with -8, we find that the function is $f(x) = 3x - 8$.

Finding a Linear Function from Data

Objective 3 Determine a linear function from data.

EXAMPLE 4 The freezing point of water is 0°C on the Celsius scale and 32°F on the Fahrenheit scale. The boiling point of water is 100°C on the Celsius scale and 212°F on the Fahrenheit scale. Find a linear function $F(x) = mx + b$ whose input is a Celsius temperature and whose output is the corresponding Fahrenheit temperature.

SOLUTION Because a Celsius temperature of 0°C corresponds to a Fahrenheit temperature of 32°F, we know that $F(0) = 32$. In a similar fashion, we know that $F(100) = 212$. We can find the slope of this linear function by using $(0, 32)$ for (x_1, y_1) and $(100, 212)$ for (x_2, y_2).

$$m = \frac{212 - 32}{100 - 0} \quad \text{Substitute.}$$

$$m = \frac{9}{5} \qquad\qquad \text{Simplify the fraction to lowest terms.}$$

The function is of the form $F(x) = \frac{9}{5}x + b$. We will now use the fact that $F(0) = 32$ to find b.

$$F(0) = 32$$

$$\frac{9}{5}(0) + b = 32 \quad \text{Substitute 0 for } x \text{ in the function } F(x).$$

$$b = 32 \quad \text{Simplify.}$$

The function that converts a Celsius temperature x to its corresponding Fahrenheit temperature is $F(x) = \frac{9}{5}x + 32$.

Quick Check 4

Mary held her wedding reception at a country club. There were 150 guests at the reception, and Mary was charged $3500. Juliet held her wedding reception at the same country club and was charged $2100 for 80 guests. Find a linear function $f(x) = mx + b$ whose input is the number of guests at a reception and whose output is the corresponding charge by the country club.

Applications of Linear Functions

Objective 4 Solve applied problems involving linear profit functions.
A specific business application that can involve linear functions is determining the cost to manufacture x units of a product. Functions also can be used to determine the revenue that will be generated by selling those x units as well as the profit that will result from their sale.

Suppose a company is manufacturing items. Such a company has fixed costs (rent, utilities, and so on.) as well as variable costs that depend on the number of items manufactured (materials, payroll, and so on.). The **cost function** $C(x)$ is equal to the fixed costs plus the variable costs associated with producing x items. The **revenue function** $R(x)$ tells us how much money will be earned by selling these x items. The revenue function is equal to the product of the selling price of each item and the number of those particular items sold. Finally, the **profit function** $P(x)$ is equal to the difference of the revenue function and the cost function; that is, $P(x) = R(x) - C(x)$ because profit is how much revenue is left over after costs are paid.

EXAMPLE 5 A student club decides to sell burgers on campus to raise money. The club must pay the college a $25 fee to reserve space for a booth. In addition, it must spend another $40 for condiments and paper goods. The club determines that it will cost $0.55 for ingredients to make each burger, and it plans to sell the burgers for $3 each.

a) Find the cost function $C(x)$, the revenue function $R(x)$, and the profit function $P(x)$.

SOLUTION   The cost function is equal to the fixed costs plus the cost to make x burgers. The fixed costs are $65 ($25 for booth space and $40 for condiments and paper goods). Each burger costs $0.55 for ingredients, so it costs $0.55x$ for the ingredients in x burgers. The cost function is $C(x) = 65 + 0.55x$.

Because each burger is sold for $3, the revenue function for selling x burgers is $R(x) = 3x$. The profit function is equal to the difference of the revenue function and the cost function, $P(x) = R(x) - C(x)$. In this example, $P(x) = 3x - (65 + 0.55x)$, which simplifies to $P(x) = 2.45x - 65$.

b) How much profit will be generated if the club makes and sells 50 burgers?

SOLUTION   To determine the profit, evaluate the profit function $P(x) = 2.45x - 65$ when $x = 50$.

$$P(50) = 2.45(50) - 65 \quad \text{Substitute 50 for } x.$$
$$= 57.5 \quad\quad\quad\quad \text{Simplify.}$$

Making and selling 50 burgers will generate a profit of $57.50.

c) How many burgers does the club need to make and sell to break even?

SOLUTION   The club breaks even when the profit is 0.

$$P(x) = 0 \quad\quad\quad \text{Set } P(x) \text{ equal to 0.}$$
$$2.45x - 65 = 0 \quad\quad \text{Replace } P(x) \text{ with its formula.}$$
$$2.45x = 65 \quad\quad \text{Add 65 to both sides.}$$
$$x \approx 26.5 \quad\quad \text{Divide both sides by 2.45.}$$

Because the club cannot break even until it sells 26.5 burgers, it needs to make and sell 27 burgers to reach this point.

d) If the goal of the club is to raise $500, how many burgers does it need to make and sell?

SOLUTION   Begin by setting the profit function equal to $500 and solving for x.

$$P(x) = 500 \quad\quad\quad \text{Set } P(x) \text{ equal to 500.}$$
$$2.45x - 65 = 500 \quad\quad \text{Replace } P(x) \text{ with its formula.}$$
$$2.45x = 565 \quad\quad \text{Add 65 to both sides.}$$
$$x \approx 230.6 \quad\quad \text{Divide both sides by 2.45.}$$

This solution needs to be a whole number, as the club cannot make 230.6 burgers. Making and selling only 230 burgers would result in a profit of only $2.45(230) - 65$, or $498.50. The club needs to make and sell 231 burgers to raise at least $500.

▶ **Quick Check 5**

Ross decides to sell calendars that feature the pictures of 12 renowned mathematicians. To do this, he must pay $50 for a business license. Each calendar costs Ross $1.25 to produce, and he plans to sell them for $9.95 each.

a) Find the cost function $C(x)$, the revenue function $R(x)$, and the profit function $P(x)$.

b) How many calendars will Ross have to produce and sell to make a $1000 profit?

Exercises 11.2

PRACTICE   WATCH   DOWNLOAD   READ   REVIEW

Vocabulary

1. A(n) _____ function is a function of the form $f(x) = mx + b$.

2. The _____ function describes how much must be spent to produce x items.

3. The _____ function describes how much money is earned from selling x items.

4. The _____ function is equal to the difference between the revenue function and the cost function.

9. $f(x) = 2x + 4$

10. $f(x) = 3x - 9$

Graph each function.

5. $f(x) = x - 7$

6. $f(x) = x + 4$

11. $f(x) = -3x + 3$

12. $f(x) = -4x - 8$

7. $f(x) = -x + 3$

8. $f(x) = -x - 5$

13. $g(x) = 4x - 6$

14. $g(x) = -6x + 4$

15. $f(x) = \dfrac{2}{3}x - 4$

20. $f(x) = -\dfrac{5}{8}x$

16. $f(x) = -\dfrac{1}{5}x - 1$

21. $f(x) = 7$

17. $f(x) = -\dfrac{3}{4}x + 6$

22. $f(x) = -2$

18. $f(x) = \dfrac{2}{5}x - 2$

Use the graph to determine the linear function $f(x)$ on the graph.

23.

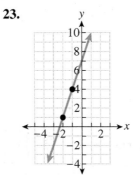

24.

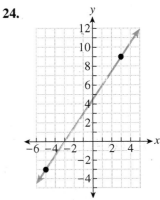

19. $f(x) = \dfrac{3}{7}x$

25.

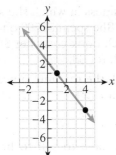

26.

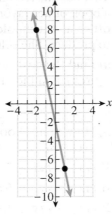

27.

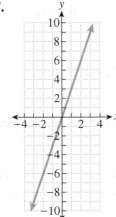

28.

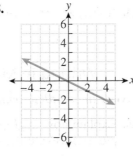

29.

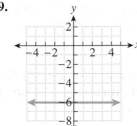

30.

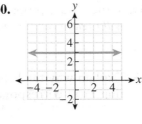

31. John's telephone plan charges him a connection fee for each call, in addition to charging him per minute. A 10-minute phone call costs a total of $0.69, while a 30-minute phone call costs $1.29.

a) Find a linear function $f(x) = mx + b$ whose input is the length of a call in minutes and whose output is the corresponding charge for that call.

b) In your own words, explain what the slope and y-intercept of this function represent.

c) Use the function from part a to determine the cost of a phone call that lasts 44 minutes.

32. A community college charges each of its students a registration fee. Students also pay a tuition fee for each academic unit they take. Last semester Amadou took 12 units and paid a total of $855, while Jia Li took 15 units and paid a total of $1050.

a) Find a linear function $f(x) = mx + b$ whose input is the number of units taken by a student and whose output is the total fees paid.

b) In your own words, explain what the slope and y-intercept of this function represent.

c) Use the function from part a to determine the total fees paid by a student taking 18 units.

33. A car rental company charges a base fee for each car rented, in addition to a fee for each mile driven. If a person drives a car for 100 miles, the total charge is $35. If a person drives a car for 150 miles, the total charge is $42.50.

a) Find a linear function $f(x) = mx + b$ whose input is the number of miles driven and whose output is the corresponding total charge for renting the car.

b) In your own words, explain what the slope and y-intercept of this function represent.

c) Use the function from part a to determine the cost of renting a car and driving it 260 miles.

34. A certain county charges a flat fine for speeding, in addition to a fee for each mile per hour a driver goes over the speed limit. A driver who was going 63 mph in a 55 mph zone was fined $159, while another driver who was traveling 58 mph in a 40 mph zone was fined $249.

a) Find a linear function $f(x) = mx + b$ whose input is the number of miles per hour over the speed limit that a person was driving and whose output is the fine that must be paid.

b) Use the function from part a to determine the fine for a person who was driving 56 mph in a 45 mph zone.

35. An elementary school booster club is wrapping gifts at a local mall as a fund-raiser. In addition to paying $50 to rent space for the day, the booster club also had to spend $75 on materials. It decides to charge $4 to wrap each gift.

a) Find the cost function $C(x)$, the revenue function $R(x)$, and the profit function $P(x)$.

b) How much profit will be generated if the booster club wraps 75 gifts?

36. Members of a sorority have set up a car wash to raise money for a scholarship fund. They paid a gas station $20 to use the parking lot and water. They also paid $10 for soap and buckets. They are charging $5 per car.

a) Find the cost function $C(x)$, the revenue function $R(x)$, and the profit function $P(x)$.

b) How much profit will be generated if they wash 185 cars?

37. The art club at a community college is selling burgers at lunchtime as a fund-raiser. The club spent $12 for condiments and supplies. The cost for the meat and bun for each burger is $0.40, and the club is charging $3 for each burger.

   a) Find the cost function $C(x)$, the revenue function $R(x)$, and the profit function $P(x)$.

   b) How much profit will be generated if the art club sells 60 burgers?

38. A student has started a business selling her home-made fruit jams at a local farmer's market. She spent $25 to rent a space at the market. Each jar of jam costs her $3.25 to make, and she sells each jar for $6.

   a) Find the cost function $C(x)$, the revenue function $R(x)$, and the profit function $P(x)$.

   b) How much profit will be generated if she sells 30 jars of jam?

39. Marge has started a business selling gift baskets out of her home. She spent $1200 remodeling her home to accommodate the business. Each basket costs her $7.50 to make, and she sells them for $29.95 each. Customers pay all shipping fees.

   a) Find the cost function $C(x)$, the revenue function $R(x)$, and the profit function $P(x)$.

   b) How many gift baskets will she have to make and sell to generate a profit of at least $10,000?

40. Tina has started an online business in which she sells a book of her favorite recipes. She spent $1500 on her office and technology, and each book costs her $0.50 to produce. She sells each book for $8.

   a) Find the cost function $C(x)$, the revenue function $R(x)$, and the profit function $P(x)$.

   b) How many books will she have to sell to break even?

41. If $f(x) = mx + 7$ and $f(5) = 22$, find m.
42. If $f(x) = mx - 6$ and $f(8) = 34$, find m.
43. If $f(x) = mx - 13$ and $f(-6) = -25$, find m.

44. If $f(x) = mx + 24$ and $f(-9) = 51$, find m.

Writing in Mathematics

Answer in complete sentences.

45. Explain how to graph a linear function. Use an example to illustrate the process.

46. Explain how to determine a linear function $f(x)$ from its graph, provided that you know the coordinates of two points on the graph. Use an example to illustrate the process.

47. Write a word problem whose solution is *The company will break even if it makes and sells 2385 items*.

48. Explain why the break-even point for a profit function $P(x)$ corresponds to the function's x-intercept.

11.3

Quadratic Functions

OBJECTIVES

1. Graph quadratic functions of the form $f(x) = a(x - h)^2 + k$ by shifting.
2. Find the maximum or minimum value of a quadratic function.
3. Solve applied maximum–minimum problems.
4. Simplify difference quotients for quadratic functions.

Objective 1 Graph quadratic functions of the form $f(x) = a(x - h)^2 + k$ by shifting. Before we learn to graph a quadratic function of the form $f(x) = a(x - h)^2 + k$ by shifting, let's recall a few facts from Chapter 10 about this type of function.

Graph of $f(x) = a(x - h)^2 + k$

- The graph is a U-shaped parabola.
- The parabola opens upward if $a > 0$, and it opens downward if $a < 0$.
- The vertex, or turning point, of the parabola is the point (h, k).
- The axis of symmetry is $x = h$.
- The y-coordinate of the y-intercept of the parabola is equal to $f(0)$.
- If the parabola has any x-intercepts, they can be found by setting $f(x) = 0$ and solving for x.
- The domain of a quadratic function is the set of all real numbers: $(-\infty, \infty)$. The range can be determined from the graph.

The basic quadratic function $f(x) = x^2$ has its vertex at the origin. Here is its graph.

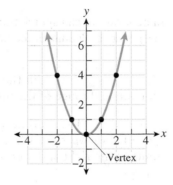

x	$f(x)$
-2	4
-1	1
0	0
1	1
2	4

Other quadratic functions can be graphed by **shifting** or **translating** this basic graph.

Vertical Translations

The function $f(x) = x^2 + k$ can be graphed by shifting the parabola $f(x) = x^2$ vertically by k units. The vertex moves from $(0, 0)$ to $(0, k)$.

$$f(x) = x^2 + 3$$
Shift the basic parabola three units upward.

$$f(x) = x^2 - 2$$
Shift the basic parabola two units downward.

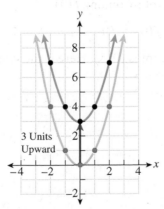

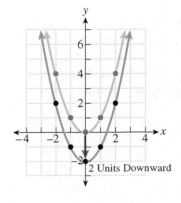

Horizontal Translations

The function $f(x) = (x - h)^2$ can be graphed by shifting the parabola $f(x) = x^2$ horizontally by h units. The vertex moves from $(0, 0)$ to $(h, 0)$.

$$f(x) = (x - 1)^2$$
*Shift the basic parabola
one unit to the right.*

$$f(x) = (x + 4)^2$$
*Shift the basic parabola
four units to the left.*

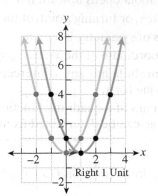

Right 1 Unit

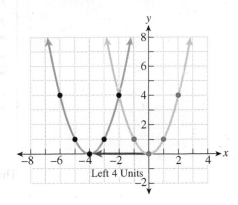

Left 4 Units

In general, we can sketch the graph of $f(x) = (x - h)^2 + k$ by shifting the graph of $f(x) = x^2$ by h units in the horizontal direction and by k units in the vertical direction.

EXAMPLE 1 Sketch the graph of $f(x) = (x - 3)^2 - 4$ by shifting. State the domain and range of the function.

SOLUTION The vertex of this parabola is $(3, -4)$, so we shift the basic parabola three units to the right and four units down.

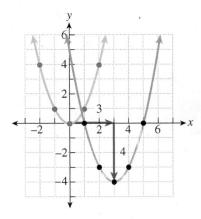

We can add more detail to the graph by adding its intercepts. Notice that by shifting, we already know that the x-intercepts are $(1, 0)$ and $(5, 0)$. We can determine the y-intercept by finding $f(0)$.

$$f(0) = (0 - 3)^2 - 4 = 5 \quad \text{Substitute 0 for } x \text{ and simplify.}$$

The y-intercept is $(0, 5)$. Here is the graph, including all intercepts.

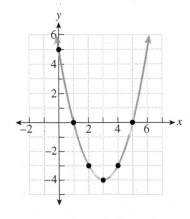

Quick Check 1

Sketch the graph of $f(x) = (x + 2)^2 - 1$ by shifting. State the domain and range of the function.

The domain of the function is $(-\infty, \infty)$. By looking at the graph, we see that the lowest value of this function is -4. So the range of the function is $[-4, \infty)$.

EXAMPLE 2 Sketch the graph of $f(x) = (x + 2)^2 + 5$ by shifting. State the domain and range of the function.

SOLUTION   The vertex of this parabola is $(-2, 5)$, so we shift the basic parabola two units to the left and five units up.

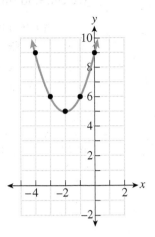

We can determine that the y-intercept is $(0, 9)$ by finding $f(0)$.

$$f(0) = (0 + 2)^2 + 5 = 4 + 5 = 9$$

Quick Check 2

Sketch the graph of $f(x) = (x - 1)^2 + 4$ by shifting. State the domain and range of the function.

Also, because the vertex is above the x-axis and the parabola opens upward, there are no x-intercepts. The domain of the function is $(-\infty, \infty)$. The lowest value of this function is 5, so the range of the function is $[5, \infty)$.

We know that the graph of $f(x) = a(x - h)^2 + k$ opens downward when $a < 0$. To sketch the graph of a parabola in this situation, we begin by rotating the graph of $f(x) = x^2$ about the x-axis as shown. Following this rotation, we can shift the graph horizontally and/or vertically, depending on the values of h and k.

$$f(x) = x^2 \qquad\qquad\qquad f(x) = -x^2$$

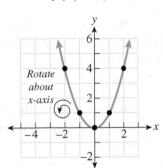
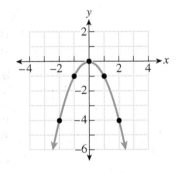

EXAMPLE 3 Sketch the graph of $f(x) = -(x + 1)^2 + 3$ by shifting. State the domain and range of the function.

SOLUTION   Because $a < 0$, we know that this parabola opens downward. We begin by rotating the parabola $f(x) = x^2$ about the x-axis. The vertex of this parabola is $(-1, 3)$, so we now shift the parabola one unit to the left and three units up.

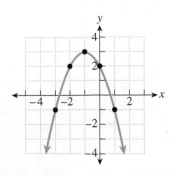

We can add more detail to the graph by adding the *x*- and *y*-intercepts. To find the *y*-intercept, find $f(0)$.

$$f(0) = -(0 + 1)^2 + 3 = -1 + 3 = 2$$

We can find the *x*-intercepts by setting the function equal to 0 and solving for *x*.

$-(x + 1)^2 + 3 = 0$	Set the function equal to 0.
$-(x + 1)^2 = -3$	Subtract 3 from both sides.
$(x + 1)^2 = 3$	Divide both sides by -1.
$\sqrt{(x + 1)^2} = \pm\sqrt{3}$	Take the square root of each side.
$x = -1 \pm \sqrt{3}$	Simplify and solve for *x* by subtracting 1.

$-1 + \sqrt{3} \approx 0.7$ and $-1 - \sqrt{3} \approx -2.7$, so the *x*-intercepts can be plotted at $(0.7, 0)$ and $(-2.7, 0)$. Here is the graph, including all intercepts.

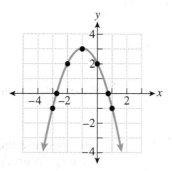

The domain of the function is $(-\infty, \infty)$. The highest value of this function is 3, so the range of the function is $(-\infty, 3]$.

EXAMPLE 4   State the rotation, horizontal shift, and vertical shift used to graph the given function.

a) $f(x) = (x - 9)^2 + 17$

SOLUTION   Because $a > 0$, there is no rotation about the *x*-axis. The vertex for this parabola is $(9, 17)$. The horizontal shift is 9 units to the right, and the vertical shift is 17 units up.

b) $f(x) = (x + 12)^2 - 5$

SOLUTION   Because $a > 0$, there is no rotation about the *x*-axis. The vertex for this parabola is $(-12, -5)$. The horizontal shift is 12 units to the left, and the vertical shift is 5 units down.

c) $f(x) = -(x + 8)^2 + 21$

SOLUTION   Because $a < 0$, there is a rotation about the *x*-axis. The vertex for the rotated parabola is $(-8, 21)$. The horizontal shift is 8 units to the left, and the vertical shift is 21 units up.

Minimum and Maximum Values of Quadratic Functions

Objective 2 **Find the maximum or minimum value of a quadratic function.**

Maximum and Minimum Values of a Function

The smallest possible output of a function is called the **minimum value** of the function. The greatest possible output of a function is called the **maximum value** of the function.

Each parabola that opens upward has a minimum value at its vertex. It has no maximum value.

To find the minimum value of a quadratic function whose graph is a parabola that opens upward, we need to find the y-coordinate of its vertex. For example, we can see that the following parabola does not go below the line $y = -4$, which is the y-coordinate of the vertex. The minimum value of this parabola is -4.

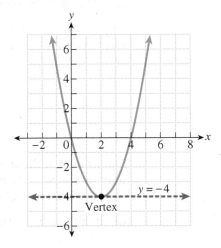

Recall that for quadratic functions of the form $f(x) = ax^2 + bx + c$, we can find the x-coordinate of the vertex using the formula $x = -\dfrac{b}{2a}$. To find the y-coordinate of the vertex, we evaluate the function for this value of x. If $a > 0$, this y-coordinate will be the minimum value of the function.

For quadratic functions of the form $f(x) = a(x - h)^2 + k$, the vertex is (h, k). If $a > 0$, the minimum value of the function is k.

EXAMPLE 5 Find the minimum value of the function $f(x) = 3x^2 - 12x + 17$.

SOLUTION Because the graph of this function is a parabola that opens upward $(a > 0)$, the function has a minimum value at its vertex. To find the vertex, we begin by finding the x-coordinate using the formula $x = \dfrac{-b}{2a}$.

$$x = \frac{-(-12)}{2(3)} = 2 \quad \text{Substitute 3 for } a \text{ and } -12 \text{ for } b \text{ and simplify.}$$

The minimum value of this function occurs when $x = 2$. To find the minimum value, we evaluate the function when $x = 2$.

$$f(2) = 3(2)^2 - 12(2) + 17 \quad \text{Substitute 2 for } x.$$
$$= 5 \quad \text{Simplify.}$$

The minimum value for this function is 5.

Do all quadratic functions have a minimum value? No, if the graph of a quadratic function is a parabola that opens downward, the function does not have a minimum value. Such a function does have a maximum value, which can be found at the vertex.

EXAMPLE 6 Find the maximum or minimum value of the function $f(x) = -3(x + 2)^2 - 5$.

SOLUTION Because this parabola will open downward, the function has a maximum value at its vertex. The vertex of this function is $(-2, -5)$. The maximum value of the function is -5, which occurs when $x = -2$.

Quick Check 5

Find the maximum or minimum value of a quadratic function.

a) $f(x) = -x^2 + 10x - 35$
b) $f(x) = 5(x - 2)^2 + 47$

Applied Maximum–Minimum Problems

Objective 3 Solve applied maximum–minimum problems.

EXAMPLE 7 What is the maximum product of two numbers whose sum is 40?

SOLUTION There are two unknown numbers in this problem. If we let x represent the first number, we can represent the second number with $40 - x$.

> **Unknowns**
> First number: x
> Second number: $40 - x$

The product of these two numbers is given by the function $f(x) = x(40 - x)$. This function simplifies to be $f(x) = -x^2 + 40x$. Because this function is quadratic and its graph is a parabola that opens downward ($a < 0$), its maximum value can be found at the vertex. The maximum product occurs when $x = \dfrac{-b}{2a}$.

$$x = \frac{-40}{2(-1)} = 20 \quad \text{Substitute } -1 \text{ for } a \text{ and } 40 \text{ for } b \text{ and simplify.}$$

The maximum product occurs when $x = 20$.

> First number: $x = 20$
> Second number: $40 - x = 40 - 20 = 20$

The two numbers whose sum is 40 that have the greatest product are 20 and 20. The maximum product is 400.

▶ Quick Check 6

What is the maximum product of two numbers whose sum is 62?

EXAMPLE 8 A farmer wants to fence off a rectangular pen for some pigs. If he has 120 feet of fencing, what dimensions would give the pen the largest possible area?

SOLUTION There are two unknowns in this problem: the length and the width of the rectangle.

Suppose we let x represent the length of the rectangle. Because the perimeter is equal to 120 feet, the total length of the remaining two sides is $120 - 2x$. Therefore, each remaining side is $\dfrac{120 - 2x}{2}$, or $60 - x$.

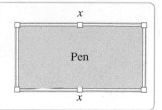

Pen

The width of a rectangle is equal to the difference of half the perimeter and the length, $W = \frac{P}{2} - L$. To verify this, solve the formula for the perimeter of a rectangle, $P = 2L + 2W$, for W.

> **Unknowns**
> Length: x
> Width: $60 - x$

The area of a rectangle is equal to its length times its width. The area of this pen is given by the function $A(x) = x(60 - x) = -x^2 + 60x$. Because this function is quadratic and its graph is a parabola that opens downward ($a < 0$), its maximum value can be found at the vertex. The maximum area occurs when $x = \dfrac{-b}{2a}$.

$$x = \frac{-60}{2(-1)} = 30 \quad \text{Substitute } -1 \text{ for } a \text{ and } 60 \text{ for } b \text{ and simplify.}$$

The maximum area occurs when $x = 30$.

> Length: $x = 30$
> Width: $60 - x = 60 - 30 = 30$

The maximum area occurs when both the length and the width are 30 feet. The maximum area that can be enclosed is 900 square feet.

▶ Quick Check 7

What is the largest possible rectangular area that can be fenced in with 264 meters of fencing?

Difference Quotients

Objective ④ **Simplify difference quotients for quadratic functions.**

> The **difference quotient** $\dfrac{f(x + h) - f(x)}{h}$ is used to determine the rate of change for a function $f(x)$ at a particular value of x.

We will now learn how to simplify this difference quotient for quadratic functions.

EXAMPLE 9 For the function $f(x) = x^2 - 8x + 14$, simplify the difference quotient $\dfrac{f(x + h) - f(x)}{h}$.

SOLUTION We begin to simplify the difference quotient by simplifying $f(x + h)$.

$$
\begin{aligned}
f(x + h) &= (x + h)^2 - 8(x + h) + 14 && \text{Substitute } x + h \text{ for } x. \\
&= (x + h)(x + h) - 8(x + h) + 14 && \text{Square } x + h \text{ by} \\
&&& \text{multiplying it by itself.} \\
&= x^2 + xh + xh + h^2 - 8(x + h) + 14 && \text{Multiply using the} \\
&&& \text{distributive property.} \\
&= x^2 + 2xh + h^2 - 8(x + h) + 14 && \text{Combine like terms.} \\
&= x^2 + 2xh + h^2 - 8x - 8h + 14 && \text{Distribute.}
\end{aligned}
$$

There are no like terms to combine, so we can substitute into the difference quotient.

$$
\begin{aligned}
\frac{f(x + h) - f(x)}{h} &= \frac{(x^2 + 2xh + h^2 - 8x - 8h + 14) - (x^2 - 8x + 14)}{h} \\
&&& \hspace{-4cm}\text{Substitute for } f(x + h) \text{ and } f(x). \\
&= \frac{x^2 + 2xh + h^2 - 8x - 8h + 14 - x^2 + 8x - 14}{h} \\
&&& \hspace{-4cm}\text{Simplify the numerator by removing} \\
&&& \hspace{-4cm}\text{parentheses.} \\
&= \frac{2xh + h^2 - 8h}{h} && \hspace{-3cm}\text{Combine like terms.} \\
&= \frac{\overset{1}{\cancel{h}}(2x + h - 8)}{\underset{1}{\cancel{h}}} && \hspace{-3cm}\text{Divide out common factors.} \\
&= 2x + h - 8 && \hspace{-3cm}\text{Simplify.}
\end{aligned}
$$

$$
\frac{f(x + h) - f(x)}{h} = 2x + h - 8 \quad \text{for} \quad f(x) = x^2 - 8x + 14
$$

▶ **Quick Check 8**

For the function $f(x) = x^2 + 3x + 317$, simplify the difference quotient $\dfrac{f(x + h) - f(x)}{h}$.

BUILDING YOUR STUDY STRATEGY

Study Environment, 3 Work space When you sit down to study, you need a space large enough to accommodate all of your materials. Make sure you can fit your textbook, notes, homework notebook, study cards, calculator, ruler, and other supplies on your desk or table. Anything you might use should be within easy reach. If your work space is disorganized and cluttered, you will waste time searching for something you need and shuffling through your materials.

Vocabulary

1. The graph of a quadratic equation is a U-shaped graph called a(n) _____.
2. The turning point of a parabola is called its _____.
3. To find the _____ of a parabola, substitute 0 for x and solve for y.
4. To find the _____ of a parabola, substitute 0 for y and solve for x.
5. To graph the function $f(x) = (x - h)^2$, apply a(n) _____ shift of h units.
6. To graph the function $f(x) = x^2 + k$, apply a(n) _____ shift of k units.
7. A quadratic function whose graph opens upward has a(n) _____ value at its vertex.
8. A quadratic function whose graph opens downward has a(n) _____ value at its vertex.

Without actually graphing the function, state the shift(s) that are applied to the graph of $f(x) = x^2$ to graph the given function. If the graph of $f(x) = x^2$ must be rotated about the x-axis, state this first.

9. $f(x) = (x + 6)^2$
10. $f(x) = (x - 8)^2$
11. $f(x) = x^2 + 9$
12. $f(x) = x^2 - 11$
13. $f(x) = (x - 5)^2 - 9$
14. $f(x) = (x + 12)^2 + 30$
15. $f(x) = (x + 10)^2 - 40$
16. $f(x) = (x - 4)^2 + 49$
17. $f(x) = -(x - 2)^2 + 13$

18. $f(x) = -(x + 7)^2 - 16$

Graph the function by shifting. Label the vertex, y-intercept, and any x-intercepts. (Round x-intercepts to the nearest tenth.) State the domain and range of the function.

19. $f(x) = x^2 + 7$

20. $f(x) = x^2 - 4$

21. $f(x) = (x - 3)^2$

22. $f(x) = (x + 2)^2$

23. $f(x) = (x - 4)^2 - 1$

24. $f(x) = (x - 3)^2 - 9$

25. $f(x) = (x - 1)^2 - 4$

26. $f(x) = (x - 2)^2 - 1$

27. $f(x) = (x + 3)^2 - 5$

33. $f(x) = -(x + 4)^2 + 9$

28. $f(x) = (x + 4)^2 - 3$

34. $f(x) = -(x - 1)^2 + 4$

29. $f(x) = (x + 1)^2 - 8$ **30.** $f(x) = (x + 2)^2 - 6$

35. $f(x) = -(x - 3)^2 + 7$

36. $f(x) = -(x + 1)^2 + 8$

31. $f(x) = (x - 2)^2 + 4$ **32.** $f(x) = (x - 3)^2 + 2$

37. $f(x) = -(x + 2)^2 - 3$

38. $f(x) = -(x + 3)^2 - 5$

Determine whether the given quadratic function has a maximum value or a minimum value. Then find that maximum or minimum value.

39. $f(x) = x^2 - 8x + 20$

40. $f(x) = x^2 - 6x - 35$

41. $f(x) = -x^2 + 4x - 30$

42. $f(x) = -x^2 + 14x - 76$

43. $f(x) = (x - 7)^2 + 18$

44. $f(x) = (x + 3)^2 - 19$

45. $f(x) = -(x + 16)^2 - 33$

46. $f(x) = -(x - 14)^2 + 47$

47. $f(x) = 7(x - 4)^2 + 46$

48. $f(x) = -8(x + 11)^2 - 50$

49. $f(x) = 3x^2 - 20x + 121$

50. $f(x) = -2x^2 - 14x + 207$

51. A girl throws a rock upward with an initial velocity of 32 feet/second. The height of the rock (in feet) after t seconds is given by the function $h(t) = -16t^2 + 32t + 5$. What is the maximum height the rock reaches?

52. A pilot flying at a height of 5000 feet determines that she must eject from the plane. The ejection seat launches with an initial velocity of 144 feet/second. The height of the pilot (in feet) t seconds after ejection is given by the function $h(t) = -16t^2 + 144t + 5000$. What is the maximum height the pilot reaches?

53. At the start of a college football game, a referee tosses a coin to determine which team will receive the opening kickoff. The height of the coin (in meters) after t seconds is given by the function $h(t) = -4.9t^2 + 2.1t + 1.5$. What is the maximum height the coin reaches?

54. If an astronaut on the moon throws a rock upward with an initial velocity of 78 feet per second, the height of the rock (in feet) after t seconds is given by the function $h(t) = -2.6t^2 + 78t + 5$. What is the maximum height the rock reaches?

55. What is the maximum product of two numbers whose sum is 24?

56. What is the maximum product of two numbers whose sum is 100?

57. A farmer has 300 feet of fencing to make a rectangular corral. What dimensions will result in the maximum area? What is the maximum area possible?

58. Emeril wants to fence off a rectangular herb garden adjacent to his house, using the house to form the fourth side of the rectangle as shown.

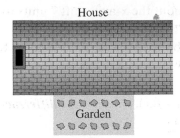

House

Garden

If Emeril has 80 feet of fencing, what dimensions of the herb garden will produce the maximum area? What is the maximum possible area?

59. A company produces small frying pans. The average cost to produce each pan in dollars is given by the function $f(x) = 0.000625x^2 - 0.0875x + 6.5$, where x is the number of pans produced (in thousands). For what number of pans is the average cost per pan minimized? What is the minimum average cost per pan that is possible?

60. A company produces radios. The average cost to produce each radio in dollars is given by the function $f(x) = 0.009x^2 - 0.432x + 9.3$, where x is the number of radios produced (in thousands). For what number of radios is the average cost per radio minimized? What is the minimum cost per radio that is possible?

61. A minor league baseball team is considering raising ticket prices for the upcoming season. If it raises ticket prices by x dollars, the expected revenue function per game is $r(x) = -250(x - 3)^2 + 37,750$. (This takes into account lower attendance that will be caused by higher prices.) What increase in ticket prices will produce the maximum revenue for the baseball team? What is the maximum revenue that is possible?

62. A movie theater is considering lowering ticket prices. If it lowers ticket prices by x dollars, the expected revenue function per week is $r(x) = -500(x - 2.5)^2 + 28,025$. What decrease in ticket prices will produce the maximum revenue for the theater? What is the maximum revenue that is possible?

Determine a quadratic function that results when applying the given shifts to the graph of $f(x) = x^2$.

63. Shift six units to the right.

64. Shift four units up.

65. Shift 3 units to the left and 11 units down.

66. Shift two units to the right and five units down.

67. Rotate about the x-axis, shift 7 units to the right and 13 units up.

68. Rotate about the x-axis, shift 9 units to the left and 22 units down.

For the function $f(x)$, simplify the difference quotient
$$\frac{f(x + h) - f(x)}{h}.$$

69. $f(x) = x^2 - 4$

70. $f(x) = x^2 - 10x$

71. $f(x) = x^2 - 9x + 17$

72. $f(x) = x^2 + 8x + 45$

73. $f(x) = 3x^2 - 11x + 49$

74. $f(x) = -x^2 - 16x + 105$

Writing in Mathematics

Answer in complete sentences.

75. Explain how to determine that a parabola does not have any x-intercepts.

76. Explain how to determine whether a quadratic function has a minimum value or a maximum value. Explain how to find the minimum or maximum value of a quadratic function. Use an example to illustrate the process.

77. *Newsletter* Write a newsletter explaining how to graph a function of the form $f(x) = (x - h)^2 + k$.

11.4

Other Functions and Their Graphs

OBJECTIVES

1 Graph absolute value functions by shifting.

2 Graph square-root functions.

3 Graph cubic functions.

4 Determine a function from its graph.

In this section, we will learn how to graph absolute value functions by shifting. We first learned how to graph these functions by plotting points in Section 8.3. We will then move on to learn how to graph square root functions and cubic functions.

Objective 1 Graph absolute value functions by shifting. Recall from Section 8.3 that the graph of an absolute value function $f(x) = a|x - h| + k$ is V-shaped. Here is the graph of the basic absolute function $f(x) = |x|$.

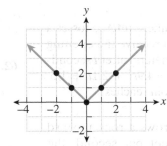

x	$f(x)$
-2	2
-1	1
0	0
1	1
2	2

To sketch the graph of the function $f(x) = |x - h| + k$, we shift the graph of $f(x) = |x|$ by h units horizontally and by k units vertically. The tip of the V, the point where the function changes from decreasing to increasing, should be located at (h, k).

We can add details such as x- and y-intercepts to the graph. To determine the y-coordinate of the y-intercept, we find $f(0)$. To find the x-intercepts, if any exist, we set the function equal to 0 and solve for x.

The domain of an absolute value function is the set of all real numbers: $(-\infty, \infty)$. The range of the function can be determined by examining the graph.

EXAMPLE 1 Sketch the graph of $f(x) = |x - 3| + 4$ by shifting. State the domain and range of the function.

SOLUTION   In this example, $h = 3$ and $k = 4$. We need to shift the graph of $f(x) = |x|$ by three units to the right and by four units up.

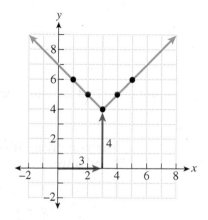

We can add more detail to the graph by adding its intercepts. Notice that by shifting, we already know that there are no x-intercepts. We can determine the y-intercept by finding $f(0)$.

$$f(0) = |0 - 3| + 4 = 7 \quad \text{Substitute 0 for } x \text{ and simplify.}$$

The y-intercept is $(0, 7)$. Here is the graph, including all intercepts.

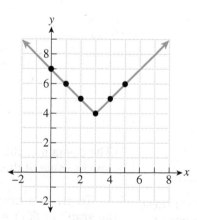

Quick Check 1

Sketch the graph of $f(x) = |x + 1| + 5$ by shifting. State the domain and range of the function.

The domain of the function is $(-\infty, \infty)$. By looking at the graph, we see that the lowest value of this function is 4; so the range of the function is $[4, \infty)$.

EXAMPLE 2 Sketch the graph of $f(x) = |x + 2| - 5$ by shifting. State the domain and range of the function.

SOLUTION In this example, $h = -2$ and $k = -5$. We need to shift the graph of $f(x) = |x|$ by two units to the left and by five units down.

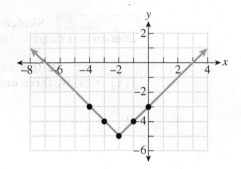

To find the y-intercept, we need to find $f(0)$.

$$f(0) = |0 + 2| - 5 = 2 - 5 = -3$$

The y-intercept is $(0, -3)$. To find the x-intercepts, we set the function equal to 0 and solve.

$$
\begin{array}{lll}
|x + 2| - 5 = 0 & & \text{Set the function equal to 0.} \\
|x + 2| = 5 & & \text{Isolate the absolute value.} \\
x + 2 = 5 \quad \text{or} \quad x + 2 = -5 & & \text{Rewrite as two linear equations.} \\
x = 3 \quad \text{or} \qquad x = -7 & & \text{Solve each equation by subtracting 2.}
\end{array}
$$

The x-intercepts are $(3, 0)$ and $(-7, 0)$. Here is the graph, including all intercepts.

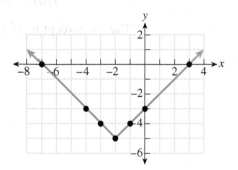

The domain of the function is $(-\infty, \infty)$. By looking at the graph, we see that the lowest value of this function is -5; so the range of the function is $[-5, \infty)$.

Quick Check 2

Sketch the graph of $f(x) = |x - 4| - 2$ by shifting. State the domain and range of the function.

To graph a function of the form $f(x) = -|x - h| + k$, we begin by rotating the graph of $f(x) = |x|$ about the x-axis. (Recall that the negative sign in front of the absolute value indicates that the graph opens downward.) We finish by applying any horizontal or vertical shifts that are necessary.

EXAMPLE 3 Sketch the graph of $f(x) = -|x - 4| - 1$ by shifting. State the domain and range of the function.

SOLUTION In this example, $h = 4$ and $k = -1$. After rotating the graph of $f(x) = |x|$ about the x-axis, we need to shift this rotated graph by four units to the right and by one unit down.

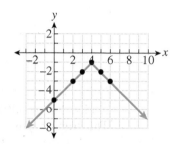

Notice that by shifting, we already know that there are no x-intercepts. We can determine the y-intercept by finding $f(0)$.

$$f(0) = -|0 - 4| - 1 = -4 - 1 = -5 \quad \text{Substitute 0 for } x \text{ and simplify.}$$

The y-intercept is $(0, -5)$. Here is the graph, including all intercepts.

The domain of the function is $(-\infty, \infty)$. By looking at the graph, we see that the greatest value of this function is -1; so the range of the function is $(-\infty, -1]$.

Quick Check 3

Sketch the graph of $f(x) = -|x - 2| - 3$ by shifting. State the domain and range of the function.

Graphing Square-Root Functions

Objective 2 Graph square-root functions. Now we will learn to graph the **square-root function.** The basic square-root function is the function $f(x) = \sqrt{x}$. Recall that the square root of a negative number is an imaginary number, so the radicand must be nonnegative. We begin to graph this function by selecting values for x and evaluating the function for these values. It is a good idea to choose values of x that are perfect squares, such as 0, 1, and 4.

x	$f(x) = \sqrt{x}$	$(x, f(x))$
0	$f(0) = \sqrt{0} = 0$	$(0, 0)$
1	$f(1) = \sqrt{1} = 1$	$(1, 1)$
4	$f(4) = \sqrt{4} = 2$	$(4, 2)$

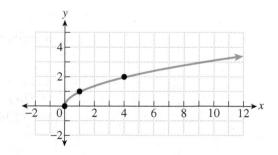

The domain of this function, which is read from left to right along the x-axis on this graph, is $[0, \infty)$. The range of this function, which is read from bottom to top along the y-axis, is also $[0, \infty)$.

We now turn our attention to graphing square-root functions of the form $f(x) = a\sqrt{x - h} + k$.

To sketch the graph of the function $f(x) = \sqrt{x - h} + k$, we shift the graph of $f(x) = \sqrt{x}$ by h units horizontally and by k units vertically. The graph of the function should begin at the point (h, k).

As with the absolute value function, we can add details such as x- and y-intercepts to the graph. To determine the y-coordinate of the y-intercept, we find $f(0)$. To find the x-intercepts, if any exist, we set the function equal to 0 and solve for x.

The domain of the function $f(x) = \sqrt{x - h} + k$ is $[h, \infty)$, and the range is $[k, \infty)$. Both the domain and range can be determined from the graph of the function.

EXAMPLE 4 Sketch the graph of $f(x) = \sqrt{x - 5} + 3$ by shifting. State the domain and range of the function.

SOLUTION In this example, $h = 5$ and $k = 3$. We need to shift the graph of $f(x) = \sqrt{x}$ by five units to the right and by three units up.

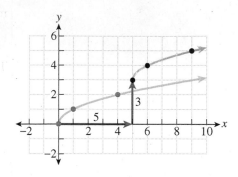

Notice that by shifting, we already know that there are no x-intercepts or y-intercepts. The graph begins at $(5, 3)$ and moves only up and to the right from there.

The domain of the function is $[5, \infty)$, and the range is $[3, \infty)$.

Quick Check 4

Sketch the graph of $f(x) = \sqrt{x - 2} + 6$ by shifting. State the domain and range of the function.

Using Your Calculator You can graph square-root functions using the TI-84. To enter the function from Example 4, $f(x) = \sqrt{x - 5} + 3$, tap the [Y=] key. Enter $\sqrt{x - 5} + 3$ next to Y_1. Use parentheses to separate the radicand from the rest of the expression. Tap the key labeled [GRAPH] to graph the function in the standard window.

 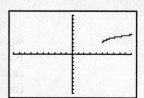

EXAMPLE 5 Sketch the graph of $f(x) = \sqrt{x + 2} - 3$ by shifting. State the domain and range of the function.

SOLUTION In this example, $h = -2$ and $k = -3$. We need to shift the graph of $f(x) = \sqrt{x}$ by two units to the left and by three units down.

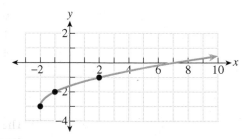

We can add more detail to the graph by plotting the x- and y-intercepts. To find the y-intercept of this function, we evaluate $f(0)$.

$$f(0) = \sqrt{0 + 2} - 3 \qquad \text{Substitute 0 for } x.$$
$$= \sqrt{2} - 3 \qquad \text{Simplify the radicand.}$$
$$\approx -1.6 \qquad \text{Approximate using a calculator.}$$

The y-intercept is located approximately at $(0, -1.6)$. To find the x-intercept, we set the function equal to 0 and solve for x.

$$\sqrt{x + 2} - 3 = 0 \quad \text{Set the function equal to 0.}$$
$$\sqrt{x + 2} = 3 \quad \text{Add 3 to isolate the square root.}$$
$$(\sqrt{x + 2})^2 = 3^2 \quad \text{Square both sides.}$$
$$x + 2 = 9 \quad \text{Simplify each side.}$$
$$x = 7 \quad \text{Subtract 2.}$$

The x-intercept is at $(7, 0)$. Here is the graph, including all intercepts.

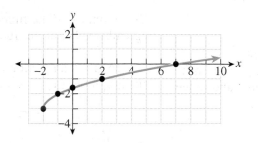

Quick Check 5

Sketch the graph of $f(x) = \sqrt{x + 1} - 2$ by shifting. State the domain and range of the function.

The domain of this function is $[-2, \infty)$, and the range is $[-3, \infty)$.

To graph a function of the form $f(x) = -\sqrt{x - h} + k$, we begin by rotating the graph of $f(x) = \sqrt{x}$ about the x-axis.

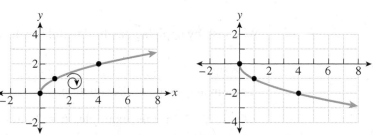

x	$-\sqrt{x}$
0	0
1	-1
4	-2

We finish by applying any horizontal or vertical shifts that are necessary.

EXAMPLE 6   Sketch the graph of $f(x) = -\sqrt{x + 7} + 1$ by shifting. State the domain and range of the function.

SOLUTION   In this example, $h = -7$ and $k = 1$. After rotating the graph of $f(x) = \sqrt{x}$ about the x-axis, we need to shift the rotated graph by seven units to the left and by one unit up.

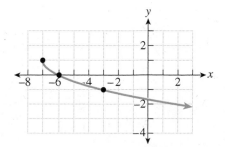

Notice that by shifting, we already know that the x-intercept is $(-6, 0)$. We can determine the y-intercept by finding $f(0)$.

$$f(0) = -\sqrt{0 + 7} + 1 = -\sqrt{7} + 1 \approx -1.6 \quad \text{Substitute 0 for x and simplify.}$$

The y-intercept is approximately $(0, -1.6)$. Here is the graph, including all intercepts.

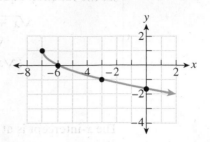

Quick Check 6

Sketch the graph of $f(x) = -\sqrt{x + 1} - 5$ by shifting. State the domain and range of the function.

The domain of the function is $[-7, \infty)$. By looking at the graph, we see that the greatest value of this function is 1; so the range of the function is $(-\infty, 1]$.

To graph a function of the form $f(x) = \sqrt{-(x - h)} + k$, we begin by rotating the graph of $f(x) = \sqrt{x}$ about the y-axis.

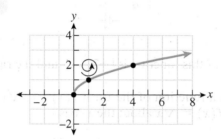 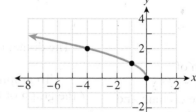

We finish by applying any horizontal or vertical shifts that are necessary.

EXAMPLE 7   Sketch the graph of $f(x) = \sqrt{-(x - 3)} + 6$ by shifting. State the domain and range of the function.

SOLUTION   In this example, $h = 3$ and $k = 6$. After rotating the graph of $f(x) = \sqrt{x}$ about the y-axis, we need to shift the rotated graph by three units to the right and by six units up.

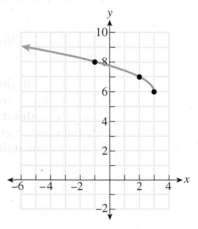

Notice that by shifting, we already know that there are no x-intercepts. We can determine the y-intercept by finding $f(0)$.

$$f(0) = \sqrt{-(0 - 3)} + 6 = \sqrt{3} + 6 \approx 7.7 \quad \text{Substitute 0 for } x \text{ and simplify.}$$

The y-intercept is approximately $(0, 7.7)$. Here is the graph, including the y-intercept.

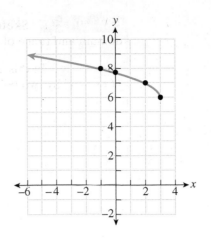

From the graph, we see that the domain of the function is $(-\infty, 3]$ and the range is $[6, \infty)$.

▶ Quick Check 7

Sketch the graph of $f(x) = \sqrt{-(x+4)} - 2$ by shifting. State the domain and range of the function.

Graphing Cubic Functions

Objective ③ **Graph cubic functions.** The other function we will investigate in this section is the **cubic function.** The basic cubic function is the function $f(x) = x^3$. Here is a table of function values for values of x from -2 to 2.

x	$f(x) = x^3$	$(x, f(x))$
-2	$f(-2) = (-2)^3 = -8$	$(-2, -8)$
-1	$f(-1) = (-1)^3 = -1$	$(-1, -1)$
0	$f(0) = 0^3 = 0$	$(0, 0)$
1	$f(1) = 1^3 = 1$	$(1, 1)$
2	$f(2) = 2^3 = 8$	$(2, 8)$

We plot these points and draw a smooth curve through them. The graph at the left extends forever to the left and to the right; so the domain is the set of all real numbers $\mathbb{R}$, which can be expressed as $(-\infty, \infty)$. The graph also extends forever upward and downward; so the range of this function is also $(-\infty, \infty)$. This is true for all cubic functions.

To sketch the graph of the function $f(x) = (x - h)^3 + k$, we shift the graph of $f(x) = x^3$ by h units horizontally and by k units vertically.

EXAMPLE 8 Sketch the graph of $f(x) = (x + 2)^3 - 1$ by shifting. State the domain and range of the function.

SOLUTION   In this example, $h = -2$ and $k = -1$. We need to shift the graph of $f(x) = x^3$ by two units to the left and by one unit down.

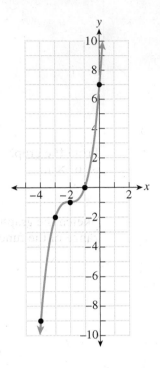

Quick Check 8

Sketch the graph of $f(x) = (x - 1)^3 + 1$ by shifting. State the domain and range of the function.

◀ The domain of the function is $(-\infty, \infty)$, and the range is $(-\infty, \infty)$.

To graph a function of the form $f(x) = -(x - h)^3 + k$, we begin by rotating the graph of $f(x) = x^3$ about the x-axis.

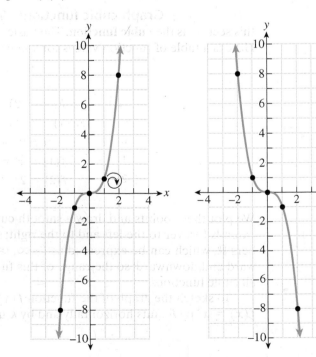

x	$-x^3$
-2	8
-1	1
0	0
1	-1
2	-8

We finish by applying any horizontal or vertical shifts that are necessary.

EXAMPLE 9 Sketch the graph of $f(x) = -(x - 1)^3 + 4$ by shifting. State the domain and range of the function.

SOLUTION In this example, $h = 1$ and $k = 4$. After rotating the graph of $f(x) = x^3$ about the x-axis, we need to shift the rotated graph by one unit to the right and by four units up.

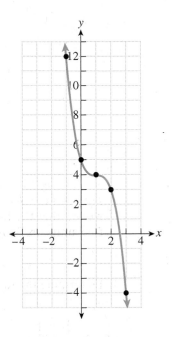

Quick Check 9

Sketch the graph of $f(x) = -(x + 3)^3$ by shifting. State the domain and range of the function.

The domain of the function is $(-\infty, \infty)$, and the range is $(-\infty, \infty)$.

Determining a Function from Its Graph

Objective ④ **Determine a function from its graph.**

EXAMPLE 10 Determine the function $f(x) = \sqrt{x - h} + k$ that has been graphed.

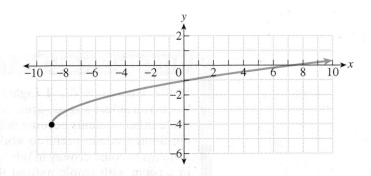

SOLUTION The graph of this function tells us that $f(x)$ is a square-root function. To find the function, let's focus on the point where this graph begins, which is at $(-9, -4)$. The function $f(x) = \sqrt{x}$ has been shifted by nine units to the left and by four units down, so $h = -9$ and $k = -4$. The function is $f(x) = \sqrt{x + 9} - 4$.

EXAMPLE 11 Determine the function $f(x) = (x - h)^3 + k$ that has been graphed.

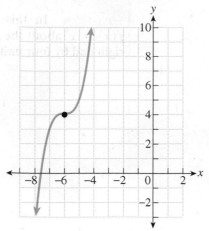

SOLUTION From the graph, we see that $f(x)$ is a function of the form $f(x) = (x - h)^3 + k$. Focusing on the point where the graph flattens out, $(-6, 4)$, we see that the function $f(x) = x^3$ has been shifted by six units to the left and by four units up. So $h = -6$ and $k = -4$, and the function is $f(x) = (x + 6)^3 + 4$.

▶ **Quick Check 10**

Determine the function $f(x)$ that has been graphed.

a)

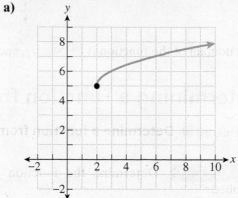

b)

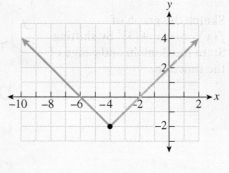

BUILDING YOUR STUDY STRATEGY

Study Environment, 4 Lighting Lighting is an important consideration when you select a study area. Some students prefer a bright, well-lit room, while other students become fidgety and uncomfortable in this type of lighting. Some students prefer to work in a room with soft, warm light, while other students become drowsy in this type of lighting. Some students prefer to work in a room with ample natural light. Whatever your preference, make sure there is enough light so that you can see clearly without straining your eyes. Working with insufficient light will make your eyes tired, which will make you tired as well.

Exercises 11.4 *MyMathLab*

PRACTICE   WATCH   DOWNLOAD   READ   REVIEW

Vocabulary

1. To find the domain of a square root function, set the _____ greater than or equal to 0 and solve.

2. The domain and range of any cubic function are the set of _____.

Graph the given absolute value function and state its domain and range.

3. $f(x) = |x - 2| + 6$

4. $f(x) = |x - 4| - 3$

5. $f(x) = |x + 1| - 5$

6. $f(x) = |x + 3| - 2$

7. $f(x) = -|x + 6| + 3$

8. $f(x) = -|x + 2| - 1$

9. $f(x) = -|x - 7| - 2$

10. $f(x) = -|x - 5| + 4$

Graph each given square-root function and state its domain and range.

11. $f(x) = \sqrt{x + 2}$

12. $f(x) = \sqrt{x} - 3$

13. $f(x) = \sqrt{x + 4} + 6$

14. $f(x) = \sqrt{x + 1} - 7$

20. $f(x) = \sqrt{-(x + 2)} + 4$

15. $f(x) = \sqrt{x - 5} - 2$

Graph the given cubic function and state its domain and range.

21. $f(x) = x^3 - 1$ **22.** $f(x) = (x + 1)^3$

16. $f(x) = \sqrt{x - 9} - 10$

17. $f(x) = -\sqrt{x - 2} + 3$

23. $f(x) = (x + 4)^3 + 1$ **24.** $f(x) = (x - 2)^3 - 4$

18. $f(x) = -\sqrt{x + 5} - 4$

19. $f(x) = \sqrt{-(x - 3)} + 1$

25. $f(x) = (x + 2)^3 + 7$ **26.** $(x + 1)^3 - 10$

31.
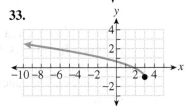

32.
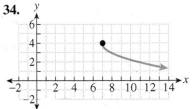

33.

27. $f(x) = -(x - 1)^3 + 4$ **28.** $f(x) = -(x + 2)^3 - 5$

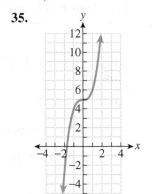

34.

Determine the function f(x) that has been graphed.

29.

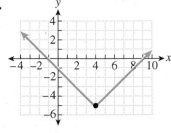

35.   **36.**
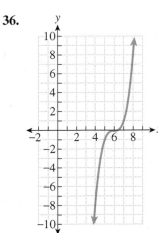

30.
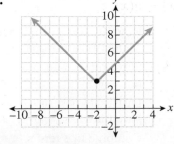

▬▬ Writing in Mathematics

Answer in complete sentences.

37. Explain the similarities in and differences between graphing a quadratic function and graphing a square-root function.

38. Explain why both the domain and the range of a cubic function are the set of real numbers.

11.5

The Algebra of Functions

1. Find the sum, difference, product, and quotient functions for two functions $f(x)$ and $g(x)$.
2. Solve applications involving the sum function or the difference function.
3. Find the composite function of two functions $f(x)$ and $g(x)$.
4. Find the domain of a composite function $(f \circ g)(x)$.

In this section, we will examine several ways to combine two or more functions into a single function. Just as we use addition, subtraction, multiplication, and division to combine two numbers, we can use these operations to combine functions as well.

The Sum Function and the Difference Function

Objective 1 Find the sum, difference, product, and quotient functions for two functions $f(x)$ and $g(x)$. The function that results when two functions $f(x)$ and $g(x)$ are added together is called the **sum function** and is denoted by $(f + g)(x)$. The function $(f - g)(x)$ is the difference of the two functions $f(x)$ and $g(x)$.

The Sum Function —————————————

For any two functions $f(x)$ and $g(x)$, $(f + g)(x) = f(x) + g(x)$.

The Difference Function ————————————

For any two functions $f(x)$ and $g(x)$, $(f - g)(x) = f(x) - g(x)$.

EXAMPLE 1 If $f(x) = x^2 + 3x - 10$ and $g(x) = 3x^2 - 5x - 9$, find the following:

a) $(f + g)(x)$

SOLUTION   Begin by rewriting $(f + g)(x)$ as $f(x) + g(x)$.

$$(f + g)(x) = f(x) + g(x) \qquad \text{Rewrite as the sum of the two functions}$$
$$= (x^2 + 3x - 10) + (3x^2 - 5x - 9) \qquad \text{Substitute for each function.}$$
$$= x^2 + 3x - 10 + 3x^2 - 5x - 9 \qquad \text{Remove parentheses.}$$
$$= 4x^2 - 2x - 19 \qquad \text{Combine like terms.}$$

b) $(f - g)(x)$

SOLUTION   Begin by rewriting $(f - g)(x)$ as $f(x) - g(x)$.

$$(f - g)(x) = f(x) - g(x) \qquad \text{Rewrite as the difference of the two functions.}$$
$$= (x^2 + 3x - 10) - (3x^2 - 5x - 9) \qquad \text{Substitute for each function.}$$
$$= x^2 + 3x - 10 - 3x^2 + 5x + 9 \qquad \text{Distribute to remove parentheses.}$$
$$= -2x^2 + 8x - 1 \qquad \text{Combine like terms.}$$

c) $(f + g)(-3)$

SOLUTION   Because we have already found that $(f + g)(x) = 4x^2 - 2x - 19$, we can substitute -3 for x in this function.

$$(f + g)(x) = 4x^2 - 2x - 19$$
$$(f + g)(-3) = 4(-3)^2 - 2(-3) - 19 \quad \text{Substitute } -3 \text{ for } x.$$
$$= 23 \qquad\qquad\qquad\qquad \text{Simplify.}$$

$(f + g)(-3) = 23$. An alternative method to find $(f + g)(-3)$ is to substitute -3 for x in the functions $f(x)$ and $g(x)$ and then add the results. The reader can verify that $f(-3) = -10$ and $g(-3) = 33$; so $(f + g)(-3) = -10 + 33 = 23$.

> **Quick Check 1**
>
> If $f(x) = x^2 - 9x + 20$ and $g(x) = 3x - 44$, find the given function.
>
> **a)** $(f + g)(x)$
> **b)** $(f - g)(x)$
> **c)** $(f + g)(7)$
> **d)** $(f - g)(-2)$

The Product Function and the Quotient Function

The function $(f \cdot g)(x)$ is the product of the two functions $f(x)$ and $g(x)$. The function $\left(\dfrac{f}{g}\right)(x)$ is the quotient of the two functions $f(x)$ and $g(x)$.

> **The Product Function**
>
> For any two functions $f(x)$ and $g(x)$, $(f \cdot g)(x) = f(x) \cdot g(x)$.

> **The Quotient Function**
>
> For any two functions $f(x)$ and $g(x)$, $\left(\dfrac{f}{g}\right)(x) = \dfrac{f(x)}{g(x)}, g(x) \neq 0$.

EXAMPLE 2   If $f(x) = x - 5$ and $g(x) = x^2 + 6x + 8$, find $(f \cdot g)(x)$.

SOLUTION   Begin by writing $(f \cdot g)(x)$ as $f(x) \cdot g(x)$.

$$(f \cdot g)(x) = f(x) \cdot g(x) \qquad\qquad \text{Rewrite as the product of the two functions.}$$
$$= (x - 5)(x^2 + 6x + 8) \qquad \text{Substitute for each function.}$$
$$= x^3 + 6x^2 + 8x - 5x^2 - 30x - 40 \quad \text{Multiply using the distributive property.}$$
$$= x^3 + x^2 - 22x - 40 \qquad\qquad \text{Combine like terms.}$$

> **Quick Check 2**
>
> If $f(x) = 3x + 4$ and $g(x) = 4x - 7$, find $(f \cdot g)(x)$.

EXAMPLE 3   If $f(x) = x^2 - 3x - 40$ and $g(x) = x^2 - 25$, find $\left(\dfrac{f}{g}\right)(x)$ and list any restrictions on its domain.

SOLUTION   Begin by writing $\left(\dfrac{f}{g}\right)(x)$ as $\dfrac{f(x)}{g(x)}$. Then simplify the resulting rational expression, if possible, using the techniques in Section 7.1.

$$\left(\frac{f}{g}\right)(x) = \frac{f(x)}{g(x)}$$ Rewrite as the quotient of the two functions.

$$= \frac{x^2 - 3x - 40}{x^2 - 25}$$ Substitute for each function.

$$= \frac{(x - 8)(x + 5)}{(x + 5)(x - 5)}$$ Factor the numerator and denominator.

$$= \frac{(x - 8)\overset{1}{\cancel{(x + 5)}}}{\underset{1}{\cancel{(x + 5)}}(x - 5)}$$ Divide out common factors.

$$= \frac{x - 8}{x - 5}$$ Simplify.

Recall that any value x for which the denominator of a rational expression, such as $\left(\frac{f}{g}\right)(x)$, is equal to 0 is not in the domain of the function. In this case, $x \neq -5, 5$.

▶ **Quick Check 3**

If $f(x) = x^2 + 3x - 18$ and $g(x) = x^2 + 13x + 42$, find $\left(\frac{f}{g}\right)(x)$ and list any restrictions on its domain.

Applications

Objective ② **Solve applications involving the sum function or the difference function.**

EXAMPLE 4   The number of public elementary and secondary schools in the United States in a particular year can be approximated by the function $f(x) = 950x + 82{,}977$, where x represents the number of years after 1990. The number of private elementary and secondary schools in the United States in a particular year can be approximated by the function $g(x) = 188x + 25{,}941$, where again x represents the number of years after 1990. (*Source:* U.S. Department of Education, National Center for Education Statistics)

a) Find $(f + g)(x)$. In your own words, explain what this function represents.

SOLUTION

$$(f + g)(x) = f(x) + g(x)$$ Rewrite as the sum of the two functions.

$$= (950x + 82{,}977) + (188x + 25{,}941)$$ Substitute for each function.

$$= 950x + 82{,}977 + 188x + 25{,}941$$ Remove parentheses.

$$= 1138x + 108{,}918$$ Combine like terms.

$(f + g)(x) = 1138x + 108{,}918$. This function gives the combined number of public and private elementary and secondary schools x years after 1990.

b) Find $(f + g)(19)$. In your own words, explain what this number represents.

SOLUTION

$$(f + g)(x) = 1138x + 108{,}918$$
$$(f + g)(19) = 1138(19) + 108{,}918 \quad \text{Substitute 19 for } x.$$
$$= 130{,}540 \quad\quad\quad\quad\quad \text{Simplify.}$$

This number tells us that there will be a total of approximately 130,540 public and private elementary and secondary schools in 2009, which is 19 years after 1990.

▶ Quick Check 4

The number of students enrolled at a public college in the United States in a particular year can be approximated by the function $f(x) = 111{,}916x + 9{,}528{,}000$, where x represents the number of years after 1990. The number of students enrolled at a private college in the United States in a particular year can be approximated by the function $g(x) = 43{,}973x + 2{,}591{,}000$, where again x represents the number of years after 1990. (*Source:* U.S. Department of Education, National Center for Education Statistics)

a) Find $(f + g)(x)$. In your own words, explain what this function represents.
b) Find $(f - g)(x)$. In your own words, explain what this function represents.

Composition of Functions

Objective ③ **Find the composite function of two functions $f(x)$ and $g(x)$.**
Another way to combine two functions is to use the output of one function as the input for the other function. When this is done, it is called the **composition** of the two functions. For example, consider the functions $f(x) = x + 5$ and $g(x) = 2x + 1$. If we evaluated the function $g(x)$ when $x = 7$, the output will be 15.

$$g(7) = 2(7) + 1 \quad \text{Substitute 7 for } x.$$
$$= 15 \quad\quad\quad \text{Simplify.}$$

We can visualize this with a picture of a function "machine." The machine takes an input of 7 and creates an output of 15.

$$7 \longrightarrow \boxed{g(x) = 2x + 1} \longrightarrow 15$$

Now if we evaluate the function $f(x)$ when $x = 15$, this is a composition of the two functions. The output of function $g(x)$ is the input of the function $f(x)$.

$$f(15) = 15 + 5 \quad \text{Substitute 15 for } x.$$
$$= 20 \quad\quad\quad \text{Add.}$$

The function $f(x)$ takes an input of 15 and creates an output of 20.

$$7 \longrightarrow \boxed{g(x) = 2x + 1} \longrightarrow 15 \longrightarrow \boxed{f(x) = x + 5} \longrightarrow 20$$

Symbolically, this can be represented as $f(g(7)) = 20$.

Composite Function

For any two functions $f(x)$ and $g(x)$, the **composite function** $(f \circ g)(x)$ is defined as $(f \circ g)(x) = f(g(x))$ and read "f of g of x."
The symbol $\circ$ is used to denote the **composition of two functions.**

Suppose that $f(x) = 3x - 5$ and $g(x) = 4x + 9$ and that we want to find $(f \circ g)(5)$. We rewrite $(f \circ g)(5)$ as $f(g(5))$ and begin by evaluating $g(5)$.

$$g(5) = 4(5) + 9 \quad \text{Substitute 5 for } x.$$
$$= 29 \qquad\quad \text{Simplify.}$$

Now we evaluate $f(29)$.

$$
\begin{aligned}
(f \circ g)(5) &= f(g(5)) \\
&= f(29) && \text{Substitute 29 for } g(5). \\
&= 3(29) - 5 && \text{Substitute 29 for } x \text{ in the function } f(x). \\
&= 82 && \text{Simplify.}
\end{aligned}
$$

$$5 \longrightarrow \boxed{g(x) = 4x + 9} \longrightarrow 29 \longrightarrow \boxed{f(x) = 3x - 5} \longrightarrow 82$$

Again, suppose that $f(x) = 3x - 5$ and $g(x) = 4x + 9$ and that we want to find the composite function $(f \circ g)(x)$. We begin by rewriting $(f \circ g)(x)$ as $f(g(x))$; then we replace $g(x)$ with the expression $4x + 9$.

$$
\begin{aligned}
(f \circ g)(x) &= f(g(x)) \\
&= f(4x + 9) && \text{Replace } g(x) \text{ with } 4x + 9. \\
&= 3(4x + 9) - 5 && \text{Substitute } 4x + 9 \text{ for } x \text{ in the function } f(x). \\
&= 12x + 27 - 5 && \text{Distribute.} \\
&= 12x + 22 && \text{Combine like terms.}
\end{aligned}
$$

Notice that if we evaluate this composite function for $x = 5$, the output will be $12(5) + 22$, or 82. This is the same result we obtained by first evaluating $g(5)$ and then evaluating $f(x)$ for this value.

EXAMPLE 5 Given that $f(x) = 2x + 11$ and $g(x) = 3x - 10$, find $(f \circ g)(x)$.

SOLUTION When finding a composite function, it is crucial to substitute the correct expression into the correct function. A safe way to ensure this is by rewriting $(f \circ g)(x)$ as $f(g(x))$ and then replacing the "inner" function with the appropriate expression. In this example, we will replace $g(x)$ with $3x - 10$. Then we will evaluate the "outer" function for this expression.

$$
\begin{aligned}
(f \circ g)(x) &= f(g(x)) \\
&= f(3x - 10) && \text{Replace } g(x) \text{ with } 3x - 10. \\
&= 2(3x - 10) + 11 && \text{Substitute } 3x - 10 \text{ for } x \text{ in the function } f(x). \\
&= 6x - 20 + 11 && \text{Distribute.} \\
&= 6x - 9 && \text{Combine like terms.}
\end{aligned}
$$

Quick Check 5

Given that $f(x) = 4x - 9$ and $g(x) = 2x + 7$, find $(f \circ g)(x)$.

EXAMPLE 6 Given that $f(x) = 5x - 6$ and $g(x) = x^2 + 2x - 8$, find the given composite functions.

a) $(f \circ g)(x)$

SOLUTION

$$
\begin{aligned}
(f \circ g)(x) &= f(g(x)) \\
&= f(x^2 + 2x - 8) && \text{Replace } g(x) \text{ with } x^2 + 2x - 8.
\end{aligned}
$$

$$= 5(x^2 + 2x - 8) - 6 \quad \text{Substitute } x^2 + 2x - 8 \text{ for } x \text{ in the function } f(x).$$
$$= 5x^2 + 10x - 40 - 6 \quad \text{Distribute.}$$
$$= 5x^2 + 10x - 46 \quad \text{Combine like terms.}$$

b) $(g \circ f)(x)$

SOLUTION   In this example, the outer function $g(x)$ is a quadratic function.

$$(g \circ f)(x) = g(f(x))$$
$$= g(5x - 6) \qquad\qquad \text{Replace } f(x) \text{ with } 5x - 6.$$
$$= (5x - 6)^2 + 2(5x - 6) - 8 \qquad \text{Substitute } 5x - 6 \text{ for } x \text{ in the function } g(x).$$
$$= (5x - 6)(5x - 6) + 2(5x - 6) - 8 \qquad \text{Square the binomial } 5x - 6 \text{ by multiplying it by itself.}$$
$$= 25x^2 - 30x - 30x + 36 + 10x - 12 - 8 \qquad \text{Multiply } (5x - 6)(5x - 6) \text{ and } 2(5x - 6).$$
$$= 25x^2 - 50x + 16 \qquad \text{Combine like terms.}$$

Quick Check 6

Given that $f(x) = x + 3$ and $g(x) = x^2 - 3x - 28$, find the given composite functions.

a) $(f \circ g)(x)$
b) $(g \circ f)(x)$

The Domain of a Composite Function

Objective 4 Find the domain of a composite function $(f \circ g)(x)$. The domain of a composite function $(f \circ g)(x)$ is the set of all input values x in the domain of $g(x)$ whose output from $g(x)$ is in the domain of $f(x)$. In all of the previous examples, the domain was the set of all real numbers $\mathbb{R}$, as none of the functions had any restrictions on their domains.

EXAMPLE 7   Given that $f(x) = \dfrac{x + 9}{2x - 1}$ and $g(x) = 6x + 15$, find $(f \circ g)(x)$ and state its domain.

SOLUTION   Because $g(x)$ is a linear function, there are no restrictions on its domain. Once we find the composite function $(f \circ g)(x)$, we will find the domain of that function.

$$(f \circ g)(x) = f(g(x))$$
$$= f(6x + 15) \qquad \text{Replace } g(x) \text{ with } 6x + 15.$$
$$= \frac{(6x + 15) + 9}{2(6x + 15) - 1} \qquad \text{Substitute } 6x + 15 \text{ for } x \text{ in the function } f(x).$$
$$= \frac{6x + 15 + 9}{12x + 30 - 1} \qquad \text{Distribute.}$$
$$= \frac{6x + 24}{12x + 29} \qquad \text{Combine like terms.}$$

So $(f \circ g)(x) = \frac{6x + 24}{12x + 29}$. The composite function is a rational function, and we find the restrictions on the domain by setting the denominator equal to 0 and solving.

$$12x + 29 = 0 \qquad \text{Set the denominator equal to 0.}$$
$$12x = -29 \qquad \text{Subtract 29.}$$
$$x = -\frac{29}{12} \qquad \text{Divide by 12.}$$

The domain of this composite function $(f \circ g)(x)$ is the set of all real numbers except $-\frac{29}{12}$.

Quick Check 7

Given that $f(x) = \dfrac{2x + 5}{x + 7}$ and $g(x) = x - 4$, find $(f \circ g)(x)$ and state its domain.

BUILDING YOUR STUDY STRATEGY

Study Environment, 5 Being Comfortable It is important that you are comfortable while studying, without being too comfortable. If the room is too warm, you may get tired. If the room is too cold, you may be distracted by thinking about how cold you are. If your chair is not comfortable, you may fidget and lose your concentration. If your chair is too comfortable, you may get sleepy. You may have the same problem if you eat a large meal before sitting down to study. In conclusion, choose a situation where you will be comfortable but not too comfortable.

Exercises 11.5

PRACTICE   WATCH   DOWNLOAD   READ   REVIEW

Vocabulary

1. For two functions $f(x)$ and $g(x)$, the function denoted by $(f + g)(x)$ is called the _____ function.

2. For two functions $f(x)$ and $g(x)$, the difference function is denoted by _____.

3. For two functions $f(x)$ and $g(x)$, the product function is denoted by _____.

4. For two functions $f(x)$ and $g(x)$, the function denoted by $\left(\dfrac{f}{g}\right)(x)$ is called the _____ function.

5. When the output of one function is used as the input for another function, this is called the _____ of the two functions.

6. For any two functions $f(x)$ and $g(x)$, the _____ function $(f \circ g)(x)$ is defined as $(f \circ g)(x) = f(g(x))$.

For the given functions $f(x)$ and $g(x)$, find
a) $(f + g)(x)$ b) $(f + g)(8)$ c) $(f + g)(-3)$

7. $f(x) = 4x + 11, g(x) = 3x - 17$

8. $f(x) = 2x - 13, g(x) = -7x + 6$

9. $f(x) = 5x + 8, g(x) = x^2 - x - 19$

10. $f(x) = x^2 - 7x + 12, g(x) = x^2 + 4x - 32$

For the given functions $f(x)$ and $g(x)$, find
a) $(f - g)(x)$ b) $(f - g)(6)$ c) $(f - g)(-5)$

11. $f(x) = 6x - 11, g(x) = -2x - 5$

12. $f(x) = 8x - 13, g(x) = 8x + 13$

13. $f(x) = 10x + 37, g(x) = x^2 - 5x - 12$

14. $f(x) = x^2 + 7x + 100, g(x) = -x^2 + 12x - 25$

For the given functions $f(x)$ and $g(x)$, find
a) $(f \cdot g)(x)$ b) $(f \cdot g)(5)$ c) $(f \cdot g)(-3)$

15. $f(x) = 2x - 3, g(x) = x + 4$

16. $f(x) = 3x + 7, g(x) = 4x - 1$

17. $f(x) = x - 6, g(x) = x^2 + 3x - 4$

18. $f(x) = 2x - 5, g(x) = x^2 - 5x + 8$

For the given functions $f(x)$ and $g(x)$, find

a) $\left(\dfrac{f}{g}\right)(x)$ *b)* $\left(\dfrac{f}{g}\right)(7)$ *c)* $\left(\dfrac{f}{g}\right)(-2)$

19. $f(x) = 3x + 1, g(x) = x + 7$

20. $f(x) = 6x - 22, g(x) = x^2 + 11x + 10$

21. $f(x) = x^2 - 9, g(x) = x^2 + 7x + 12$

22. $f(x) = x^2 + 10x + 16, g(x) = x^2 - x - 72$

Let $f(x) = 2x + 9$ and $g(x) = 5x - 1$. Find the following.

23. $(f + g)(8)$ **24.** $(f + g)(-2)$

25. $(f - g)(-4)$ **26.** $(f - g)(5)$

27. $(f \cdot g)(10)$ **28.** $(f \cdot g)(-3)$

29. $\left(\dfrac{f}{g}\right)(-2)$ **30.** $\left(\dfrac{f}{g}\right)(0)$

Let $f(x) = 5x - 9$ and $g(x) = 2x - 17$. Find the following and simplify completely.

31. $(f + g)(x)$ **32.** $(f - g)(x)$

33. $(f \cdot g)(x)$

34. $\left(\dfrac{f}{g}\right)(x)$

Let $f(x) = x - 10$ and $g(x) = x^2 - 8x - 20$. Find the following and simplify completely.

35. $(f - g)(x)$

36. $(f + g)(x)$

37. $\left(\dfrac{f}{g}\right)(x)$

38. $(f \cdot g)(x)$

39. The number of male doctors, in thousands, in the United States in a particular year can be approximated by the function $f(x) = 10.4x + 398$, where x represents the number of years after 1980. The number of female doctors, in thousands, in the United States in a particular year can be approximated by the function $g(x) = 9.1x + 49$, where again x represents the number of years after 1980. (*Source:* American Medical Association)

a) Find $(f + g)(x)$. In your own words, explain what this function represents.

b) Find $(f + g)(40)$. In your own words, explain what this number represents.

40. The number of male inmates who are HIV positive in the United States in a particular year can be approximated by the function $f(x) = 223x + 20{,}969$, where x represents the number of years after 1995. The number of female inmates who are HIV positive in the United States in a particular year can be approximated by the function $g(x) = 83x + 2102$, where again x represents the number of years after 1995. (*Source:* U.S. Department of Justice, Bureau of Justice Statistics)

a) Find $(f + g)(x)$. In your own words, explain what this function represents.

b) Find $(f + g)(27)$. In your own words, explain what this number represents.

41. The number of master's degrees, in thousands, earned by females in the United States in a particular year can be approximated by the function $f(x) = 9.2x + 181.8$, where x represents the number of years after 1990. The number of master's degrees, in thousands, earned by males in the United States in a particular year can be approximated by the function $g(x) = 3.4x + 160.9$, where again x represents the number of years after 1990. (*Source:* U.S. Department of Education, National Center for Education Statistics)

a) Find $(f - g)(x)$. In your own words, explain what this function represents.

b) Find $(f - g)(30)$. In your own words, explain what this number represents.

42. The amount of money, in billions of dollars, spent on health care that was covered by insurance in the United States in a particular year can be approximated by the function $f(x) = x^2 + 11x + 244$, where x represents the number of years after 1990. The amount of money, in billions of dollars, spent on health care that was paid out of pocket in the United States in a particular year can be approximated by the function $g(x) = 6x + 129$, where again x represents the number of years after 1990. (*Source:* U.S. Centers for Medicare and Medicaid Services)

a) Find $(f - g)(x)$. In your own words, explain what this function represents.

b) Find $(f - g)(40)$. In your own words, explain what this number represents.

Let $f(x) = 4x + 7$ and $g(x) = x - 3$. Find the following.

43. $(f \circ g)(5)$ 44. $(f \circ g)(-2)$
45. $(g \circ f)(-1)$ 46. $(g \circ f)(10)$

For the given functions $f(x)$ and $g(x)$, find
a) $(f \circ g)(x)$ b) $(f \circ g)(5)$

47. $f(x) = 3x + 2, g(x) = x^2 + 5x - 6$

48. $f(x) = 2x - 7, g(x) = x^2 - 8x + 10$

49. $f(x) = x^2 - 7x + 12, g(x) = x + 8$

50. $f(x) = x^2 + 9x - 22, g(x) = 4x - 3$

For the given functions $f(x)$ and $g(x)$, find
a) $(f \circ g)(x)$ b) $(g \circ f)(x)$

51. $f(x) = 3x + 5, g(x) = 2x + 4$

52. $f(x) = 5x - 9, g(x) = -x + 6$

53. $f(x) = x + 4, g(x) = x^2 + 3x - 40$

54. $f(x) = x^2 - 7x - 18, g(x) = x - 9$

For the given functions $f(x)$ and $g(x)$, find $(f \circ g)(x)$ and state its domain.

55. $f(x) = \dfrac{5x}{x + 7}, g(x) = 2x + 13$

56. $f(x) = \dfrac{2x - 3}{3x + 5}, g(x) = x + 8$

57. $f(x) = \sqrt{2x - 10}, g(x) = x + 11$

58. $f(x) = \sqrt{x - 2}, g(x) = 3x + 14$

For the given function $f(x)$, find $(f \circ f)(x)$.

59. $f(x) = 3x - 10$
60. $f(x) = -5x + 18$
61. $f(x) = x^2 + 6x + 12$

62. $f(x) = x^2 - 2x - 15$

For the given functions $f(x)$ and $g(x)$, find a value of x for which $(f \circ g)(x) = (g \circ f)(x)$.

63. $f(x) = x^2 + 4x + 3, g(x) = x + 5$
64. $f(x) = x^2 + 6x - 9, g(x) = x - 3$
65. $f(x) = x + 7, g(x) = x^2 - 25$
66. $f(x) = x - 4, g(x) = 2x^2 + 15x + 18$

For the given function $g(x)$, find a function $f(x)$ such that $(f \circ g)(x) = x$.

67. $g(x) = x + 8$
68. $g(x) = -5x$
69. $g(x) = 3x + 8$

70. $g(x) = 4x - 17$

Writing in Mathematics

Answer in complete sentences.

71. In general, is $(f + g)(x)$ equal to $(g + f)(x)$? If your answer is yes, explain why. If your answer is no, give an example that shows why, in general, they are not equal.

72. In general, is $(f - g)(x)$ equal to $(g - f)(x)$? If your answer is yes, explain why. If your answer is no, give an example that shows why, in general, they are not equal.

11.6

Inverse Functions

OBJECTIVES

1 Determine whether a function is one-to-one.
2 Use the horizontal-line test to determine whether a function is one-to-one.
3 Understand inverse functions.
4 Determine whether two functions are inverse functions.
5 Find the inverse of a one-to-one function.
6 Find the inverse of a function from its graph.

One-to-One Functions

Objective 1 **Determine whether a function is one-to-one.** Recall that for any function $f(x)$, each value in the domain corresponds to only one value in the range.

> **One-to-One Function**
>
> If every element in the range of a function $f(x)$ has at most one value in the domain that corresponds to it, the function $f(x)$ is called a **one-to-one function.**

In other words, if $f(x)$ is different for each input value x in the domain, $f(x)$ is a one-to-one function.

Suppose for some function $f(x)$, both $f(-1)$ and $f(3)$ are equal to 2. This function is not a one-to-one function because one output value is associated with two different input values. However, the function shown in the following table is a one-to-one function, because each function value corresponds to only one input value.

x	0	1	4	9	16
$f(x)$	0	1	2	3	4

A function whose input is a person's name and whose output is that person's birthday is not a one-to-one function because several people (input) can have the same birthday (output). A function whose input is a person's name and whose output is that person's Social Security number is a one-to-one function because no two people can have the same Social Security number.

EXAMPLE 1 Determine whether the function represented by the set of ordered pairs $\{(-7, -5), (-5, -2), (-2, 4), (3, 3), (6, -7)\}$ is a one-to-one function.

SOLUTION   Because each x-value corresponds to only one y-value and each y-value corresponds to only one x-value, the function is one-to-one.

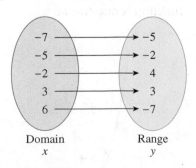

Domain   Range
x y

▶ Quick Check 1

Determine whether the function represented by the set of ordered pairs $\{(-4, -9), (-2, -7), (1, -6), (2, -7), (6, -11)\}$ is a one-to-one function.

Horizontal-Line Test

Objective 2 Use the horizontal-line test to determine whether a function is one-to-one. We can determine whether a function is one-to-one by applying the **horizontal-line test** to its graph.

> ┌─ **Horizontal-Line Test** ──────────────────
> If a horizontal line can intersect the graph of a function at more than one point, the function is not one-to-one.

Consider the graph of a quadratic function shown. We can draw a horizontal line that intersects the function at two points, as indicated. The coordinates of these two points are $(-2, 6)$ and $(2, 6)$. This shows that two different input values, -2 and 2, correspond to the same output value (6). Therefore, the function is not one-to-one.

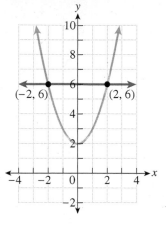

The linear function graphed is a one-to-one function. No horizontal line crosses the graph of this function at more than one point, so the function passes the horizontal-line test.

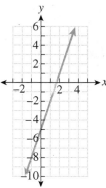

Quick Check 2

Determine whether the function is one-to-one.

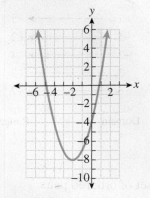

EXAMPLE 2 Use the horizontal-line test to determine whether the function is one-to-one.

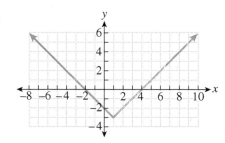

SOLUTION We can draw a horizontal line that crosses the graph of this absolute value function at more than one point, as shown here. This function fails the horizontal-line test and is not one-to-one.

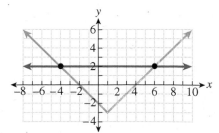

Inverse Functions

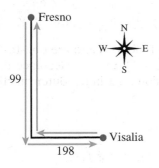

Objective 3 Understand inverse functions. Anne commutes to work from Visalia to Fresno each day. She starts by taking Highway 198 west and then takes Highway 99 north. How does she return home each day? She begins by taking Highway 99 south and then takes Highway 198 east. Her trips are depicted in the map at the left.

The second route takes Anne back to the starting point. The two routes have an **inverse** relationship. In this section, we will be examining **inverse functions.**

The inverse of a one-to-one function "undoes" what the function does. For example, if a function $f(x)$ takes an input value of 3 and produces an output value of 7, its inverse function takes an input value of 7 and produces an output value of 3.

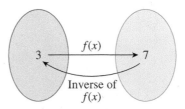

We see that the ordered pair $(3, 7)$ is in the function $f(x)$ and that the ordered pair $(7, 3)$ is in the inverse function of $f(x)$. The inputs of a function are the outputs of its inverse function, and the outputs of a function are the inputs of its inverse function. In general, if (a, b) is in a function, (b, a) is in the inverse of that function.

Verifying That Two Functions Are Inverses

Objective 4 Determine whether two functions are inverse functions. We can determine whether two functions are inverse functions algebraically by finding their composite functions.

> **Inverse Functions**
>
> Two one-to-one functions $f(x)$ and $g(x)$ are inverse functions if $(f \circ g)(x) = x$ and $(g \circ f)(x) = x$.

If $f(x)$ and $g(x)$ are inverse functions, each function "undoes" the actions of the other function.

The function g takes an input value x and produces an output value $g(x)$.

The function f takes this value and produces an output value of x.

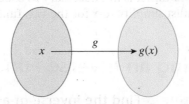

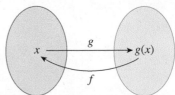

So $f(g(x)) = x$, or in other words, $(f \circ g)(x) = x$. In a similar fashion, we could show that $(g \circ f)(x) = x$ as well.

EXAMPLE 3 Determine whether the following two functions are inverse functions:
$$f(x) = 5x - 2, g(x) = \frac{x + 2}{5}$$

SOLUTION Both of these functions are linear functions and are one-to-one. We will determine whether $(f \circ g)(x) = x$ and $(g \circ f)(x) = x$. (Replace the inner function with its formula, substitute that expression for x in the outer function, and simplify.)

$(f \circ g)(x) = x$	$(g \circ f)(x) = x$
$(f \circ g)(x) = f(g(x))$	$(g \circ f)(x) = g(f(x))$
$\quad = f\left(\frac{x + 2}{5}\right)$	$\quad = g(5x - 2)$
$\quad = 5\left(\frac{x + 2}{5}\right) - 2$	$\quad = \frac{(5x - 2) + 2}{5}$
$\quad = \overset{1}{\cancel{5}}\left(\frac{x + 2}{\underset{1}{\cancel{5}}}\right) - 2$	$\quad = \frac{5x - 2 + 2}{5}$
$\quad = x + 2 - 2$	$\quad = \frac{5x}{5}$
$\quad = x$	$\quad = \frac{\overset{1}{\cancel{5}}x}{\underset{1}{\cancel{5}}}$
	$\quad = x$

◄ Because $(f \circ g)(x) = x$ and $(g \circ f)(x) = x$, these two functions are inverses.

Quick Check 3

Determine whether the following two functions are inverse functions:

$$f(x) = \frac{x - 7}{4}, g(x) = 4x + 7$$

EXAMPLE 4 Determine whether the following two functions are inverse functions:
$$f(x) = \frac{1}{4}x - \frac{3}{4}, g(x) = 3x + 4$$

SOLUTION These two functions are linear and one-to-one. We begin by determining whether $(f \circ g)(x) = x$.

$$\begin{aligned}
(f \circ g)(x) &= f(g(x)) \\
&= f(3x + 4) && \text{Replace } g(x) \text{ with } 3x + 4. \\
&= \frac{1}{4}(3x + 4) - \frac{3}{4} && \text{Substitute } 3x + 4 \text{ for } x \text{ in the function } f(x). \\
&= \frac{3}{4}x + 1 - \frac{3}{4} && \text{Distribute.} \\
&= \frac{3}{4}x + \frac{1}{4} && \text{Combine like terms.}
\end{aligned}$$

$(f \circ g)(x) \neq x$. These two functions are not inverses.

Note that it is not necessary to check $(g \circ f)(x)$ because both composite functions must simplify to x for the two functions to be inverse functions.

Quick Check 4

Determine whether the following two functions are inverse functions:

$$f(x) = \frac{1}{3}x + 4,$$
$$g(x) = 3x - 12$$

Finding an Inverse Function

Objective 5 Find the inverse of a one-to-one function. We use the notation $f^{-1}(x)$ to denote the inverse of a function $f(x)$. We read $f^{-1}(x)$ as f *inverse of* x.

A WORD OF CAUTION When a superscript of -1 is written after the name of a function, the -1 is not an exponent; it is used to denote the inverse of a function. In other words, $f^{-1}(x)$ is not the same as $\frac{1}{f(x)}$.

Here is a procedure that can be used to find the inverse of a one-to-one function $f(x)$.

Finding $f^{-1}(x)$

1. **Determine whether $f(x)$ is one-to-one.** We can use the horizontal-line test to determine this. If $f(x)$ is not one-to-one, it does not have an inverse function.
2. **Replace $f(x)$ with y.**
3. **Interchange x and y.** We interchange these two variables because we know that the input of $f(x)$ must be the output of $f^{-1}(x)$ and the output of $f(x)$ must be the input of $f^{-1}(x)$.
4. **Solve the resulting equation for y.** This allows us to express the inverse function as a function of x.
5. **Replace y with $f^{-1}(x)$.**

EXAMPLE 5 Find $f^{-1}(x)$ for the function $f(x) = 5x - 3$.

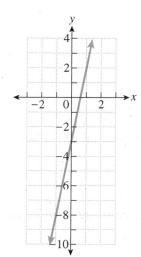

SOLUTION   We begin by determining whether the function is one-to-one. Because the function is a linear function, it is one-to-one. Shown at the left is the graph of $f(x)$. The function clearly passes the horizontal-line test.
   We begin to find $f^{-1}(x)$ by replacing $f(x)$ with y.

$$f(x) = 5x - 3$$
$$y = 5x - 3 \quad \text{Replace } f(x) \text{ with } y.$$
$$x = 5y - 3 \quad \text{Interchange } x \text{ and } y.$$
$$x + 3 = 5y \quad \text{Add 3 to isolate the term containing } y.$$
$$\frac{x + 3}{5} = y \quad \text{Divide both sides by 5 to isolate } y.$$
$$f^{-1}(x) = \frac{x + 3}{5} \quad \text{Replace } y \text{ with } f^{-1}(x). \text{ It is customary to write } f^{-1}(x) \text{ on the left side.}$$

The inverse of $f(x) = 5x - 3$ is $f^{-1}(x) = \dfrac{x + 3}{5}$, which could be written as $f^{-1}(x) = \dfrac{1}{5}x + \dfrac{3}{5}$.

Quick Check 5

Find $f^{-1}(x)$ for the function $f(x) = \frac{1}{2}x + 10$.

EXAMPLE 6 Find $f^{-1}(x)$ for the function $f(x) = \dfrac{8}{x + 1}$ and state the restrictions on its domain.

SOLUTION   In this example, $f(x)$ is a rational function. We have not yet learned to graph rational functions, but the graph of $f(x)$, which has been generated by technology, is shown at the right. (We could use a graphing calculator or software to generate this graph.) The function passes the horizontal-line test.

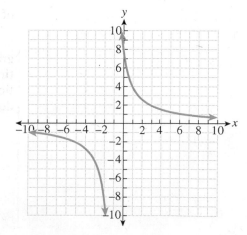

Begin to find $f^{-1}(x)$ by replacing $f(x)$ with y.

$$f(x) = \frac{8}{x + 1}$$

$$y = \frac{8}{x + 1}$$ Replace $f(x)$ with y.

$$x = \frac{8}{y + 1}$$ Interchange x and y.

$$x(y + 1) = \frac{8}{\cancel{y + 1}} \cdot (\cancel{y + 1})$$ Multiply both sides by $y + 1$ to clear the equation of fractions.

$$x(y + 1) = 8$$ Simplify.

$$xy + x = 8$$ Multiply.

$$xy = 8 - x$$ Subtract x from both sides to isolate the term containing y.

$$y = \frac{8 - x}{x}$$ Divide both sides by x to isolate y.

$$f^{-1}(x) = \frac{8 - x}{x}$$ Replace y with $f^{-1}(x)$.

The inverse of $f(x) = \dfrac{8}{x + 1}$ is $f^{-1}(x) = \dfrac{8 - x}{x}$.

Note that the domain of this inverse function is the set of all real numbers except 0, because the denominator of the function is equal to 0 when $x = 0$. This makes the inverse function undefined when $x = 0$.

▶ Quick Check 6

Find $f^{-1}(x)$ for the function $f(x) = \dfrac{3 + 5x}{x}$ and state the restrictions on its domain.

Recall that the output values of a one-to-one function are the input values of its inverse function. So the range of a one-to-one function $f(x)$ is the domain of its inverse function $f^{-1}(x)$. Occasionally, if the range of a one-to-one function $f(x)$ is not the set of real numbers, we must restrict the domain of $f^{-1}(x)$ accordingly. This is illustrated in the next example.

EXAMPLE 7   Find $f^{-1}(x)$ for the function $f(x) = \sqrt{x + 4} - 2$. State the domain of $f^{-1}(x)$.

SOLUTION   Begin by showing that the function is one-to-one. Following is the graph of $f(x)$. (For help on graphing square-root functions, refer back to Section 11.4.) The function passes the horizontal-line test, so it is a one-to-one function that has an inverse function. The range of $f(x)$ is $[-2, \infty)$, and this is the domain of its inverse function $f^{-1}(x)$.

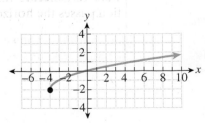

Begin to find $f^{-1}(x)$ by replacing $f(x)$ with y.

$$f(x) = \sqrt{x + 4} - 2$$

$y = \sqrt{x + 4} - 2$ Replace $f(x)$ with y.

$x = \sqrt{y + 4} - 2$ Interchange x and y.

$x + 2 = \sqrt{y + 4}$ Add 2 to both sides to isolate the radical.

$(x + 2)^2 = \left(\sqrt{y + 4}\right)^2$ Square both sides.

$(x + 2)(x + 2) = y + 4$ Square $x + 2$ by multiplying it by itself.

$x^2 + 4x + 4 = y + 4$ Multiply $(x + 2)(x + 2)$.

$x^2 + 4x = y$ Subtract 4 from both sides to isolate y.

$f^{-1}(x) = x^2 + 4x$ Replace y with $f^{-1}(x)$.

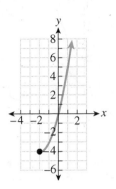

The inverse of $f(x) = \sqrt{x + 4} - 2$ is $f^{-1}(x) = x^2 + 4x$. The domain of $f^{-1}(x)$ is $[-2, \infty)$.

At the left is the graph of $f^{-1}(x)$. Notice that the graph does pass the horizontal-line test with this restricted domain. If we did not restrict this domain, the graph of $f^{-1}(x)$ would be a parabola and the function would not be one-to-one.

Quick Check 7

Find $f^{-1}(x)$ for the function $f(x) = \sqrt{x - 9} + 8$. State the domain of $f^{-1}(x)$.

Finding an Inverse Function from a Graph

Objective 6 Find the inverse of a function from its graph. We know that if $f(x)$ is a one-to-one function and $f(a) = b$, $f^{-1}(b) = a$. This tells us that if the point (a, b) is on the graph of $f(x)$, the point (b, a) is on the graph of $f^{-1}(x)$.

EXAMPLE 8   If the function is one-to-one, find its inverse.

$$\{(-2, -3), (-1, -2), (0, 1), (1, 5), (2, 13)\}$$

SOLUTION   Because each value of x corresponds to only one value of y and each value of y corresponds to only one value of x, this is a one-to-one function.

To find the inverse function, we interchange each x-coordinate and y-coordinate. The inverse function is $\{(-3, -2), (-2, -1), (1, 0), (5, 1), (13, 2)\}$.

EXAMPLE 9   For the given graph of a one-to-one function $f(x)$, graph its inverse function $f^{-1}(x)$.

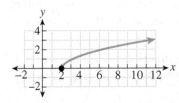

SOLUTION   We begin by identifying the coordinates of some points that are on the graph of this function. We will use the points $(2, 0)$, $(3, 1)$, and $(6, 2)$.

By interchanging each x-coordinate with its corresponding y-coordinate, we know that the points $(0, 2)$, $(1, 3)$, and $(2, 6)$ are on the graph of $f^{-1}(x)$. We finish by drawing a graph that passes through these points. Shown at the right is the graph of $f^{-1}(x)$.

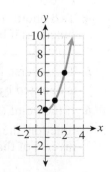

Quick Check 8

For the given graph of a one-to-one function $f(x)$, graph its inverse function $f^{-1}(x)$.

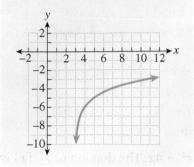

Here are the graphs of $f(x)$ and $f^{-1}(x)$ from the previous example on the same set of axes, along with the line $y = x$. Notice that the two functions look somewhat similar; in fact, they are mirror images of each other. For any one-to-one function $f(x)$ and its inverse function $f^{-1}(x)$, their graphs are symmetric to each other about the line $y = x$. If we fold the graph along the line $y = x$, the graphs of $f(x)$ and $f^{-1}(x)$ will lie on top of each other.

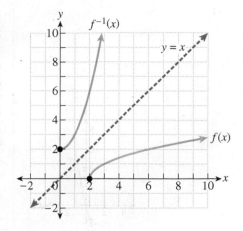

BUILDING YOUR STUDY STRATEGY

Study Environment, 6 Distractions Under ideal circumstances, you should do some of your studying on campus and some at home. The best time for studying new material is as soon as possible after class. Because studying new material takes more concentration, find a location with few distractions. Most campus libraries have an area designated as a silent study area.

While studying at home, stay away from the computer, phone, and television. These devices will steal time away from you, without your even realizing it.

Exercises 11.6 MyMathLab

Vocabulary

1. If $f(x)$ is different for each input value x in its domain, $f(x)$ is a(n) _____ function.

2. If a(n) _____ can intersect the graph of a function at more than one point, the function is not one-to-one.

3. If $f(x)$ is a one-to-one function such that $f(a) = b$, its _____ function $f^{-1}(x)$ is a function for which $f^{-1}(b) = a$.

4. Two one-to-one functions $f(x)$ and $g(x)$ are inverse functions if both $(f \circ g)(x)$ and $(g \circ f)(x)$ are equal to ____.

5. The inverse function of a one-to-one function $f(x)$ is denoted by _____.

6. If the point (a, b) is on the graph of a one-to-one function, the point _____ is on the graph of the inverse of that function.

Determine whether the function $f(x)$ is a one-to-one function.

7.

x	−3	0	3	6	9
f(x)	−8	−2	4	10	16

8.

x	−5	−1	1	4	10
f(x)	9	5	3	0	−6

9.

x	−4	−2	0	2	4
f(x)	16	4	0	4	16

10.

x	−3	−2	−1	0	1
f(x)	3	2	1	0	1

Determine whether the function represented by the set of ordered pairs is a one-to-one function.

11. $\{(-9, -3), (-4, 0), (1, 1), (5, -2), (10, -3)\}$

12. $\{(1, 4), (3, 8), (5, 12), (7, 8), (9, 4)\}$

13. $\{(-8, -4), (-5, 3), (-1, 0), (4, 3), (9, 10)\}$

14. $\{(0, 1), (1, 2), (2, 4), (3, 8), (4, 16)\}$

15. Is the function whose input is a person and whose output is that person's mother a one-to-one function? Explain your answer in your own words.

16. Is the function whose input is a student and whose output is that student's favorite math teacher a one-to-one function? Explain your answer in your own words.

17. Is the function whose input is a state and whose output is that state's governor a one-to-one function? Explain your answer in your own words.

18. Is the function whose input is a licensed driver and whose output is that driver's license number a one-to-one function? Explain your answer in your own words.

Use the horizontal-line test to determine whether the function is one-to-one.

19.

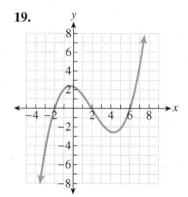

20.

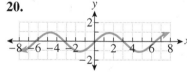

21.

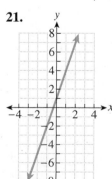

22.

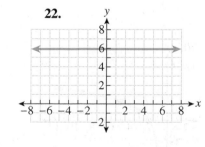

23.

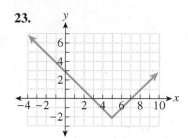

24.

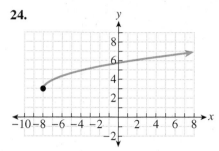

Determine whether the functions $f(x)$ and $g(x)$ are inverse functions by showing that $(f \circ g)(x) = x$ and $(g \circ f)(x) = x$.

25. $f(x) = x + 5, g(x) = 5 + x$

26. $f(x) = x + 8, g(x) = x - 8$

27. $f(x) = 4x, g(x) = \dfrac{x}{4}$

28. $f(x) = 7x, g(x) = -7x$

29. $f(x) = 3x - 4, g(x) = \dfrac{x + 4}{3}$

30. $f(x) = 2x + 5, g(x) = \dfrac{1}{2}x - 5$

31. $f(x) = -x + 13, g(x) = x - 13$

32. $f(x) = 8x + 32, g(x) = \dfrac{1}{8}x - 4$

For the given function $f(x)$, find $f^{-1}(x)$.

33. $f(x) = x + 9$

34. $f(x) = x - 4$

35. $f(x) = \dfrac{x}{3}$

36. $f(x) = -8x$

37. $f(x) = 3x + 14$

38. $f(x) = 2x - 11$

39. $f(x) = 7x - 6$

40. $f(x) = -5x + 16$

41. $f(x) = -\dfrac{3}{4}x + 6$

42. $f(x) = \dfrac{2}{3}x - 10$

43. $f(x) = mx$

44. $f(x) = mx + b$

45. $f(x) = \dfrac{1}{x} + 3$

46. $f(x) = \dfrac{1}{x} - 5$

47. $f(x) = \dfrac{1}{x + 3}$

48. $f(x) = \dfrac{1}{x - 5}$

49. $f(x) = \dfrac{5 - 6x}{x}$

50. $f(x) = \dfrac{1 + 10x}{x}$

51. $f(x) = \dfrac{8 + 4x}{3x}$

52. $f(x) = \dfrac{2x}{7x - 10}$

For the given function f(x), find $f^{-1}(x)$. State the domain of $f^{-1}(x)$.

53. $f(x) = \sqrt{x}$
54. $f(x) = \sqrt{x - 4}$
55. $f(x) = \sqrt{x} - 7$
56. $f(x) = \sqrt{x - 6} - 2$

57. $f(x) = \sqrt{x - 8} + 3$

58. $f(x) = \sqrt{x + 11} + 5$

59. $f(x) = x^2 - 9 \ (x \geq 0)$
60. $f(x) = (x + 6)^2 + 5 \ (x \geq -6)$

61. $f(x) = x^2 - 6x + 8 \ (x \geq 3)$ (*Hint:* Try completing the square.)

62. $f(x) = x^2 + 4x - 12 \ (x \geq -2)$ (*Hint:* Try completing the square.)

If the function represented by the set of ordered pairs is one-to-one, find its inverse.

63. $\{(-5, -17), (-1, -9), (1, -5), (4, 1), (7, 7)\}$

64. $\{(-2, -1), (0, 5), (1, 8), (4, 17), (7, 26)\}$

65. $\{(-2, 21), (-1, 17), (0, 13), (1, 9), (2, 13)\}$

66. $\{(-10, 4), (-9, 5), (-6, 6), (-1, 7), (6, 8)\}$

For the given graph of a one-to-one function f(x), graph its inverse function $f^{-1}(x)$ without finding a formula for f(x) or $f^{-1}(x)$.

67.

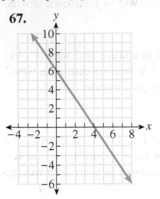

68.

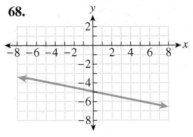

69.

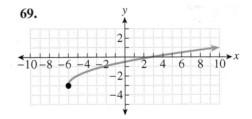

70.

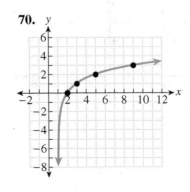

Graph a one-to-one function f(x) that meets the given criteria.

71. $f(x)$ is a linear function, $f(4) = 9$, and $f^{-1}(5) = -2$.

72. $f(x)$ is a linear function, $f^{-1}(5) = -7$, and $f^{-1}(-6) = 8$.

73. $f(x)$ is a quadratic function, the domain of $f(x)$ is restricted to $[3, \infty)$, $f(3) = -1$, $f(4) = 0$, $f^{-1}(3) = 5$, and $f^{-1}(8) = 6$.

74. $f(x)$ is a quadratic function, the domain of $f(x)$ is restricted to $[1, \infty)$, $f^{-1}(-8) = 1$, $f^{-1}(-2) = 3$, and $f^{-1}(8) = 5$.

Writing in Mathematics

Answer in complete sentences.

75. Explain how the horizontal-line test shows whether a function is or is not one-to-one.

76. Explain how to find the inverse function of a one-to-one function $f(x)$. Use an example to illustrate the process.

77. *Solutions Manual* Write a solutions manual page for the following problem.

For the one-to-one function $f(x) = \dfrac{3 + 2x}{4x}$, *find* $f^{-1}(x)$.

Using Matrices to Solve Systems of Equations

Matrix

A **matrix** is a rectangular array of numbers, such as $\begin{bmatrix} 1 & 5 & 7 & 20 \\ 0 & 4 & -3 & 5 \\ 0 & 0 & 6 & 6 \end{bmatrix}$. The numbers in a matrix are called **elements**. A matrix is often described by the number of **rows** and **columns** it contains. The matrix in this example is a three by four, or 3×4, matrix. (The plural form of matrix is **matrices**.) We refer to the first row of a matrix as R_1, the second row as R_2, and so on.

We can use matrices to solve systems of equations in a manner that is similar to using the addition method. For example, to solve the system of equations $\begin{aligned} 2x - 5y &= -9 \\ 4x + 3y &= -5 \end{aligned}$, we begin by creating the **augmented matrix** $\begin{bmatrix} 2 & -5 & | & -9 \\ 4 & 3 & | & -5 \end{bmatrix}$. The first column of the matrix contains the coefficients of the variable x from the two equations. The second column contains the coefficients of the variable y. The dashed vertical line separates these coefficients from the constants in each equation.

We will use **row operations** to convert a matrix to a form in which we can easily solve the system of equations.

Row Operations

1. Any two rows of a matrix can be interchanged.
2. The elements in any row can be multiplied by any nonzero number.
3. The elements in any row can be changed by adding a nonzero multiple of another row's elements to them.

To solve a system of two equations in two unknowns, our goal is to transform the augmented matrix associated with that system to one of the form $\begin{bmatrix} a & b & | & c \\ 0 & d & | & e \end{bmatrix}$. This matrix corresponds to the system of equations $\begin{aligned} ax + by &= c \\ dy &= e \end{aligned}$. We can then easily solve the second equation for y and substitute that value in the first equation to solve for x. So the goal is to transform the matrix into one whose first element in the second row is 0.

EXAMPLE 1 Solve $\begin{aligned} 2x - 5y &= -9 \\ 4x + 3y &= -5 \end{aligned}$.

SOLUTION The augmented matrix associated with this system is $\begin{bmatrix} 2 & -5 & | & -9 \\ 4 & 3 & | & -5 \end{bmatrix}$.

We can change the first element in row 2 to 0 by adding -2 times the first row to the second row.

$$\begin{bmatrix} 2 & -5 & | & -9 \\ 4 & 3 & | & -5 \end{bmatrix}$$

$$\begin{bmatrix} 2 & -5 & | & -9 \\ 0 & 13 & | & 13 \end{bmatrix} \quad \text{Multiply } R_1 \text{ by } -2 \text{ and add to } R_2.$$

The second row of this matrix is equivalent to the equation $13y = 13$, which can be solved by dividing both sides of the equation by 13. The solution of this equation is $y = 1$.

The first row of this matrix is equivalent to the equation $2x - 5y = -9$. If we substitute 1 for y, we can solve this equation for x.

$$\begin{aligned} 2x - 5(1) &= -9 \\ 2x - 5 &= -9 \\ 2x &= -4 \\ x &= -2 \end{aligned}$$

The solution of the system of equations is $(-2, 1)$.

EXAMPLE 2 Solve $\begin{aligned} 3x + 4y &= 6 \\ 2x - y &= -7 \end{aligned}$.

SOLUTION The augmented matrix associated with this system is $\begin{bmatrix} 3 & 4 & | & 6 \\ 2 & -1 & | & -7 \end{bmatrix}$.

We begin by multiplying row 2 by 3 so that the first element in row 2 is a multiple of the first element in row 1.

$$\begin{bmatrix} 3 & 4 & | & 6 \\ 2 & -1 & | & -7 \end{bmatrix}$$

$$\begin{bmatrix} 3 & 4 & | & 6 \\ 6 & -3 & | & -21 \end{bmatrix} \quad \text{Multiply } R_2 \text{ by 3.}$$

$$\begin{bmatrix} 3 & 4 & | & 6 \\ 0 & -11 & | & -33 \end{bmatrix} \quad \text{Multiply } R_1 \text{ by } -2 \text{ and add to } R_2.$$

This matrix is equivalent to the system of equations $\begin{array}{l} 3x + 4y = 6 \\ -11y = -33 \end{array}$. We solve the second equation for y.

$$-11y = -33$$
$$y = 3 \qquad \text{Divide both sides by } -11.$$

Substitute 3 for y in the equation $3x + 4y = 6$ and solve for x.

$$3x + 4(3) = 6$$
$$3x + 12 = 6$$
$$3x = -6$$
$$x = -2$$

◀ The solution of the system of equations is $(-2, 3)$.

To solve a system of three equations in three unknowns, we begin by setting up a 3×4 augmented matrix. Using row operations, our goal is to transform the matrix to one of the form $\begin{bmatrix} a & b & c & | & d \\ 0 & e & f & | & g \\ 0 & 0 & h & | & i \end{bmatrix}$.

EXAMPLE 3 Solve the system $\begin{array}{l} x + y + z = 1 \\ 2x - 3y + 4z = 29 \\ -x - 2y + 3z = 8 \end{array}$.

SOLUTION The augmented matrix associated with this system is

$\begin{bmatrix} 1 & 1 & 1 & | & 1 \\ 2 & -3 & 4 & | & 29 \\ -1 & -2 & 3 & | & 8 \end{bmatrix}$. We begin by changing the first element in row 2 and row 3 to 0.

$$\begin{bmatrix} 1 & 1 & 1 & | & 1 \\ 2 & -3 & 4 & | & 29 \\ -1 & -2 & 3 & | & 8 \end{bmatrix}$$

$$\begin{bmatrix} 1 & 1 & 1 & | & 1 \\ 0 & -5 & 2 & | & 27 \\ 0 & -1 & 4 & | & 9 \end{bmatrix} \quad \text{Multiply } R_1 \text{ by } -2 \text{ and add to } R_2. \text{ Add } R_1 \text{ to } R_3.$$

Now we need to change the second element of row 3 to a 0. We begin to do that by changing that element to a multiple of the second element of row 2.

$$\begin{bmatrix} 1 & 1 & 1 & | & 1 \\ 0 & -5 & 2 & | & 27 \\ 0 & 5 & -20 & | & -45 \end{bmatrix} \quad \text{Multiply } R_3 \text{ by } -5.$$

$$\begin{bmatrix} 1 & 1 & 1 & | & 1 \\ 0 & -5 & 2 & | & 27 \\ 0 & 0 & -18 & | & -18 \end{bmatrix} \quad \text{Add } R_2 \text{ to } R_3.$$

The last row is equivalent to the equation $-18z = -18$, whose solution is $z = 1$. We substitute this value for z in the equation that is equivalent to row 2, $-5y + 2z = 27$.

$$-5y + 2(1) = 27$$
$$-5y + 2 = 27$$
$$-5y = 25$$
$$y = -5$$

Now we substitute -5 for y and 1 for z in the equation that is equivalent to row 1, $x + y + z = 1$.

$$x + (-5) + (1) = 1$$
$$x - 4 = 1$$
$$x = 5$$

The solution of this system is $(5, -5, 1)$.

Exercises A-2

Solve the system of equations by using matrices.

1. $2x + 3y = 13$
$5x - 4y = -2$

2. $3x - 2y = 16$
$7x + 5y = 18$

3. $-4x + 9y = 75$
$3x - 7y = -58$

4. $x + 2y = -23$
$6x + y = -39$

5. $11x + 7y = 42$
$19x - 13y = -78$

6. $15x + 8y = 9$

$-10x + 9y = -6$

7. $x + 3y + 2z = 11$
$3x - 2y - z = 4$
$-2x + 4y + 3z = 5$

8. $x - y + z = 1$
$4x + 3y + 2z = 10$
$4x - 2y - 5z = 31$

9. $x + y + z = 3$
$2x + 3y + 4z = 16$
$3x - y + 4z = 23$

10. $x + y + z = 2$
$-2x - 3y + 8z = -26$
$5x - 4y - 9z = 20$

11. $3x + 7y - 8z = 60$
$5x - 4y + 7z = -44$
$-4x + y + 10z = -36$

12. $6x + y + 3z = -40$

$-5x + \dfrac{3}{2}y - z = 20$

$\dfrac{9}{2}x + \dfrac{1}{5}y + \dfrac{3}{4}z = 19$

INDEX OF APPLICATIONS

INDEX